VIRTUTEM FORMA DECORAT

Emblem of Leonardo, on back of *Ginevra de
Benci* panel – Vienna, Liechtenstein Gallery

LEONARDO DA VINCI

REYNAL & COMPANY, NEW YORK

Neptune – Drawing by Leonardo – Windsor, Royal Collection

F O R E W O R D

This memorial edition arose out of the great Leonardo Exposition held in Milan just before the last war. Although the little Tuscan town of Vinci, near Empoli, is listed as Leonardo's birthplace, Milan, the capital of Lombardy, has long considered him as its greatest master. His tremendous work as artist, scientist, and engineer is indissolubly linked with that city. It was an outstanding feature of the Milan exposition that it gave broad scope to the display of aspects of the many-sided pioneering genius of Leonardo that were less known, notably his scientific activity.

Medieval castle in village of Vinci Fiorentino

Scholars from all over the world have contributed toward bringing out the universal character of this profound and constructive spirit. The authors of the sections of this work have labored to assemble the documents that show how deeply Leonardo penetrated into the most varied fields of human knowledge. Just as interesting as the artist who was equally a genius in painting, sculpture, and architecture, was the farsighted city planner, the imaginative inventor, the designer of artillery and hydraulic engineer, the forerunner in the domain of aerodynamic flight. Never before had Leonardo's all-embracing grasp of life and his insight into nature and its laws, wherever he encountered them, been presented so manifestly.

Shortly before Italy entered the war the exposition was closed. The materials that had been assembled were scattered to the four winds. The reconstructed machines, the models prepared according to Leonardo's drawings, and the thousands of photographic reproductions that were to have constituted the nucleus of a museum of the sciences that had been planned for Milan, either found their way abroad or were packed into a warehouse to decay.

Church of Santa Lucia, in which Leonardo was baptized

The only net result of the enormous outlay represented in the exposition was the documentation of the present work, with its numerous illustrations and treatments of individual topics, in which the authors of the several sections have brought together and set forth the results of scholarly research. They lend to Leonardo's creative power a rare efficacy and evidence, and transmit to our time a vivid picture of one of the most important creative personalities not only of the Italian Renaissance but in all the range of human culture.

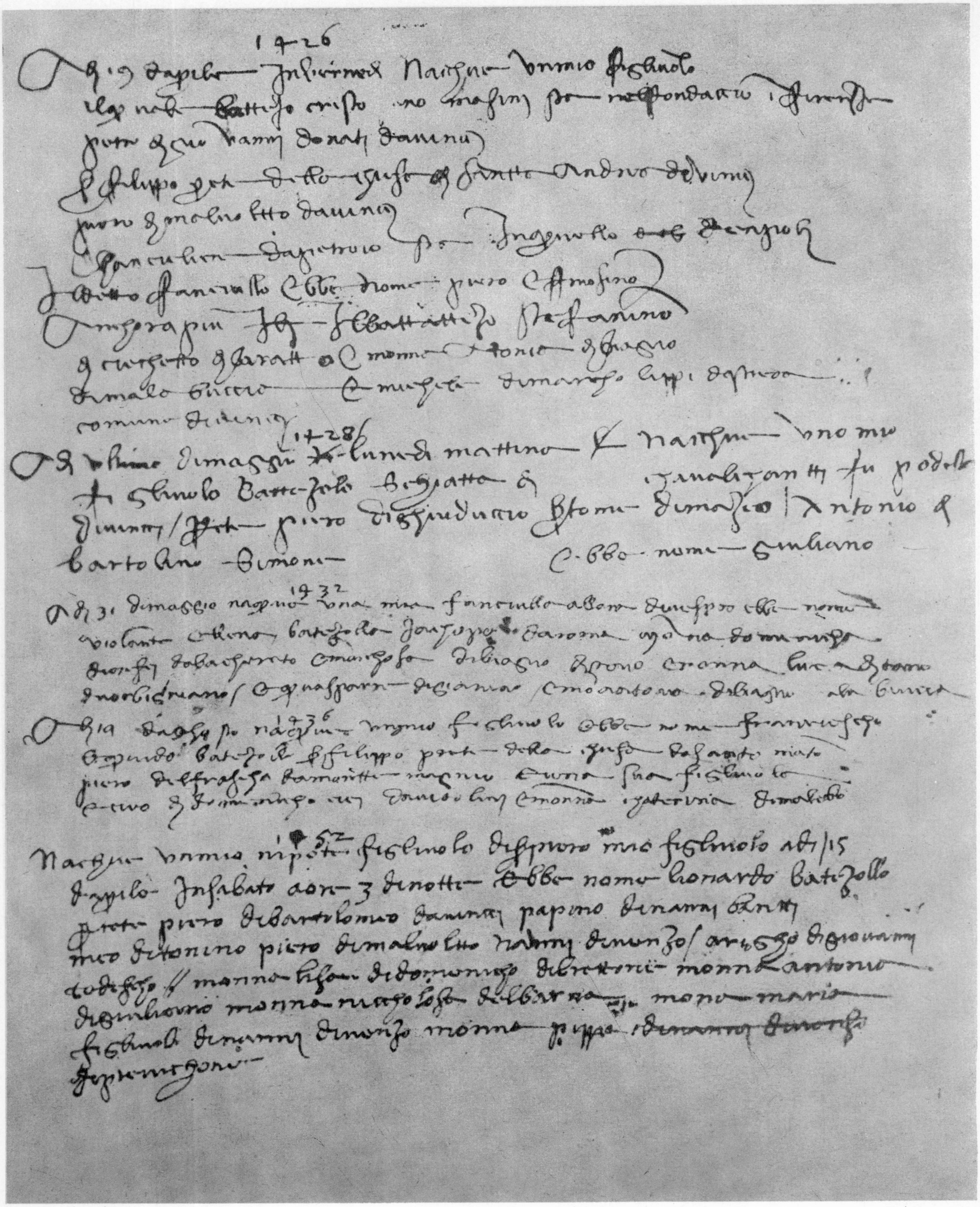

1426

1428

1432

1436

1452

The Notary's certification P. 389, last paragraph, which is still preserved in the Archives in Florence and which records the birth of Leonardo

THE BIRTH OF LEONARDO

Emil Möller, the accurate inquirer into all the circumstances of the life and fertile labors of Da Vinci, marked the occasion of the Leonardo Exposition with some anticipations of the fruits of the researches he had carried on for years with exemplary patience, in the firm belief that the publication of documentary data on the birth of the great master would be of use to students and admirers of our country's history.

As we know, it had not been possible to determine the exact date on which Leonardo was born; the most reasonable and best-supported conclusions could only give limits, and widely varying ones at that, within which the event must have taken place. Ignoring the indirect hints given by chroniclers or biographers who lived only a little later than Leonardo, and hence could be given greater credence, and trying to harmonize the somewhat contradictory evidence contained in the tax reports for the family of Ser Piero da Vinci for the years 1457 and 1469-1470, Smiraglia Scognamiglio succeeded, by careful collation, in fixing the date of the artist's birth as most probably 1452. The first report refers to a "Lionardo, son of Ser Piero, illegitimate, born to him and Chaterina, at present Donna da Cartabriga di Piero del Vacha da Vinci, five years old," while the second speaks of "Lionardo, son of Ser Piero, illegitimate, seventeen years old." Later, however, the accurate Gerolamo Calvi observed that these data were anything but contradictory, in view of the shifts in dates that could arise out of the differences according to whether the chronology used was in conformity with the Florentine style or the common style, and in view also of the natural tendency to round out the numbers of years in documents made out according to the testimony of the interested parties.

A medieval house in Vinci Fiorentino

This uncertainty, which the most acute historical criticism had proved unable to solve, has now been eliminated by the discovery of a note in which Antonio, the father of Ser Piero da Vinci, set down the event of the birth and baptism of little Leonardo in 1452, thereby following, even at the advanced age of eighty, his custom of writing down the most noteworthy events occurring in the family. Professor Möller gives the text of the document as follows:

"A grandson of mine was born, son of Ser Piero my son, on April 15, Saturday at three o'clock in the night. His name was Lionardo. He was baptized by Priest Piero di Bartolomeo da Vinci, Papino di Nanni Banti, Meo di Tonino, Piero di Malvolto, Nanni di Venzo, Arrigo di Giovanni, German. Monna Lisa di Domenico di Brettone, Monna Antonia di Giuliano, Monna Niccolosa del Barna, Monna Maria, daughter of Nanni di Venzo, Monna Pippa ["di Nanni di Venzo" crossed out] di Previcone."

Certainly, we could not ask for more precise details as to this event, of so little importance in and of itself, but so full of moment for the history of human genius. We have learned not only the day but even the hour in which Leonardo saw the light, which, according to the calendar of those times, was 22:30. The customs of the time would have required the boy to be baptized the Sunday after Easter in the Church of Santa Croce, to which he was escorted by a small group of the family and others chosen from the notables of the village of Vinci.

Möller, basing himself on these and other archival data, believes that the birthplace of our hero was not the Villa di Anchiano, as Uzielli affirmed, but a house under the south side of the cliff of the castle of Vinci, toward the east; but at all events, those who live on the hills so closely connected with the Florentine essence of Leonardo's genius are proud to be associated with him in fame and affection.

Church of Santissima Annunziata in Vinci

Leonardo da Vinci – Self-portrait (red chalk) – Turin, Royal Library

8

THE PORTRAIT OF LEONARDO

The figures of Leonardo's drawings and paintings are unforgettable in their vitality and physical grace. The multitude whose anxious faces are turned to the Virgin in the *Adoration of the Magi*, the apostles in the *Last Supper* gesticulating in protest against Christ's betrayal, the combatants at Anghiari whose martial struggles reverberate from his drawings, as well as those figures, the Madonnas, or the Christ of the *Last Supper*, whose inner life as victors over falsehood is expressed in every trait—may not the source of their beauty lie in the physical grace of Leonardo himself? In the notes that were collected to form the *Treatise on Painting* there appear frequent references to the relationship between the artist and his creations, between his mental make-up, so to speak, and his work. Is it not possible that the ideal of human beauty pursued by Leonardo should have had its origin not only in his ability to observe reality and reconstitute it in his thought, but also in his consciousness of the symmetry of his own members and of their capacities, and of the service they rendered him as models? Is it not likely that his knowledge of the human figure, whose anatomy he expounded visually with an unrivalled depth of expression, was associated with his awareness of his own body, whose every motion, every impulse, was under his control?

At the end of our search for the original model of that perfect beauty of limb which harbors so much spiritual force stands the figure of Leonardo himself. From the verbal and pictorial testimony of his contemporaries and from his own drawings and notes relating to himself, we can imagine him a splendid figure of a man, majestic in physique and in the expressiveness of the face with its limpid eyes, whose intent and profound gaze had the clarity and sweetness vouchsafed only to those with great keenness of vision. Even after a long beard hid his resolute chin, the fine features remained evident. None of the writers who has spoken of him has given us such a precise portrait as that which Tommaso da Celano has left of St. Francis, a description which would have enabled us to reconstruct his actual appearance. But in the comments left by those who were near enough to him to be familiar with his habits, and in the echoes of the lively tradition that very soon formed itself about him, may be found proof of such winning physical beauty as to justify the attraction, the affection, and perhaps even the antipathies he aroused.

Vasari's picture of Leonardo came by way of the living voice of "a handsome and courteous old man"—from "that Francesco de' Melzi, Milanese gentleman, who in the time of Leonardo was a lovely boy," [1] and from Florentine artists who had known the son of Ser Piero da Vinci. Vasari recalls the "physical beauty never adequately praised," the "more than infinite grace in every action," the "great strength conjoined with dexterity, the spirit and courage, always regal and magnanimous." His biography of Leonardo begins thus: "Truly heaven sometimes sends us those who represent not only humanity but also divinity itself, so that, observing these models, we can draw nearer in spirit and excellence of intellect to the sublimities of heaven."

Leonardo – Presumed self-portrait in *Adoration of the Magi* – Florence, Uffizi Gallery

---

[1] G. Vasari, *Vite de' più eccellenti architetti, pittori, e scultori italiani.* 1st ed., Florence, 1550; 2d ed., Florence, 1568. See also *Vita di Leonardo da Vinci, pittore e scultore fiorentino*, ed. G. Poggi, Florence, 1919.

LEONARDO
VINCI

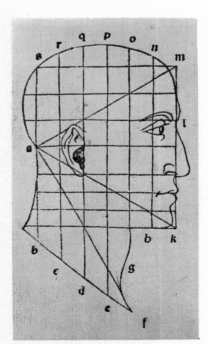

Left: Head of Verrocchio's *David*, for which Leonardo possibly served as model – Florence, Museo Nazionale

Right: Leonardo – Presumed self-portrait – Milan, Ambrosiana

Presumed portrait of Leonardo in Luca Pacioli's *Trattato de divina proportione*, Venice, 1509

Writing perhaps ten years before Vasari, the "Anonimo Gaddiano" [2] similarly observes: "He was so rare and universal that one might say that nature, so miraculous was her creation, had wished to endow him not only with beauty of body, which he had in great degree, but also with the command of many rare virtues." From the same source comes the further comment: "He was beautiful in person, well proportioned, graceful, and of fine appearance. He wore his red *pitocco* [3] short to the knee, whereas the custom at that time was to wear garments long. Reaching to the middle of his breast he had a fine beard, curling and well shaped." Paolo Giovio's *Frammenti*, published by Tiraboschi in the *Storia della letteratura italiana*, and his biography of Leonardo preserved in manuscript form in the Torre Rezzonico Library, repeat the praises of Leonardo's beauty: "He was of a most affable, cultivated, liberal disposition, with a charming countenance, and since he was a wonderful inventor and arbiter of theatrical delights in an elegant style, and could sing skillfully to the lyre, he was the delight of all princes."

In the *Idea del tempio della pittura*,[4] in that curious chapter in which he speaks of the "seven parts or kinds of design," Lomazzo gives to each kind a symbolic governor, placed above the temple's roof. "To Da Vinci," he says, "I have given the lion, for the reason that just as this animal is more noble than all the others, so much more noble is the style of this famous painter, for as the lion conquers all other animals, so does he conquer those who set themselves to gaze at his things and wish to imitate them. He knew all the fine arts, and possessed the ability to mingle the one and the other, as one sees from many books written by him and illustrated with his left hand. He had long hair, and eyebrows and beard so long that he appeared one of learning's true nobility, as was in former times the Druid Hermes [5] or the ancient Prometheus, and was dear to many princes, but especially to François de Valois, the first king of France, who, when the artist was dying, held him in his arms—a truly glorious death, since it happened in the hands of such a king."

An account of the death of Leonardo in the arms of Francis I, as Lomazzo describes it, is also given by Vasari, but modern scholars reject the story. His comparison of Leonardo's majesty to

---

[2] Codex Magliabechiano, XVII, 17. Florence, Biblioteca Nazionale.
[3] A short coat (translator's note).
[4] G. P. Lomazzo, *Idea del tempio della pittura*, Milan, G. Pontio, 1590, p. 8.
[5] Probably Hermes Trismegistus (translator's note).

that of an antique philosopher is paralleled in verses by the Neoplatonist Giovanni di Francesco Nesi, who knew the artist in Florence around 1501:

Leonardo, self-portrait – Amsterdam, Geemente Museum

> In carbon vidi già con arte intera
> Imago veneranda del mio Vinci
> Che in Delo e in Creta e Samo me' non era,
>
> Tal che se col pennel ritrahi di quinci
> Qualcunche tu ti sia che di colore
> Pinga non però lei superi et vinci
>
> Perchè più degna et di maggior valore
> Fa l'arte quella, in cui par che s'infonda
> Quanto in sè cape il suo primo valore.[6]

Jean Lemaire de Belges, in his poem, *La plainte du désiré* (1509), follows his eulogy of Louis XII with praises of the king's protégé, *"Léonard, qui a grâces supernes."*

Comments on Leonardo's attractive physical aspect are supplemented by others dwelling on his kindly ways. Vasari records that the Duke of Milan, "hearing Leonardo's marvellous discourses, became so enamored of his qualities that it appeared incredible." Referring to the period of the artist's youth he says: "With his reasoning he conquered and with his arguments he confounded every strong intellect," and adds: "He was so pleasing in conversation that he drew to himself people's very hearts."

Drawing by Leonardo – Presumed self-portrait – London, British Museum

Benvenuto Cellini, in the first of the *Discorsi sopra l'arte*, reports something said by that same king of France, Francis I, with respect to Leonardo's capacity for winning over his listeners. Recalling his discovery in Paris, around 1542, of "a book written in ink, copied from one by the great Leonardo da Vinci," Cellini thinks to add some recollections of the great Tuscan who had preceded him to France: "This book was of great excellence, and beautifully made, with the marvellous genius of the said Leonardo (no greater man than he, I believe, has been born into the world), concerning the three great arts of sculpture, painting, and architecture. And because he abounded in great genius, and had some knowledge of Latin and Greek literature, King Francis, being deeply fascinated by his virtues, took such pleasure in hearing him converse that few were the days in the year when he could bear to be separated from him; which was the cause of his not being able to carry out the remarkable studies over which he took such infinite pains. I must not fail to repeat the words spoken of him by the King, who said to me in the presence of the Cardinal of Ferrara, the Cardinal of Lorraine, and the King of Navarre, that he believed no other man had been born into the world who knew as much as Leonardo—not so much speaking of sculpture, painting, and architecture, as saying that he was a very great philosopher."

Of Leonardo's way of life, of those very things that might give us the clearest insight into his personality, we know little. Vasari records his gentlemanly habits, saying that "he always had servants, and horses as well as all other animals, which he delighted in and which he trained with great patience and love." The trait must have seemed most praiseworthy to Vasari, for he adds: "Because of which nature so much wished to favor him that wherever he turned his thoughts, mind, and spirit, he showed such sublimity in everything that for perfection in quickness, vivacity, goodness, grace, and charm, no one has ever equalled him." Further proof of Leonardo's love of animals appears in a letter written January 6, 1515, by the Florentine traveller Andrea Corsali: "The Gujrati eat nothing that contains blood, nor is it permitted among them to harm any living thing— as is the way also of our Leonardo Vinci." [7] Vasari's account points to yet other qualities: "With the splendor of his beautiful countenance he brightened every sorrowing spirit, and with words he could persuade others away from hardened prejudices. With his strength he restrained violence, and with his right hand could bend one of the iron rings set in a wall, or a horseshoe, as though it were of lead. He liberally welcomed and gave hospitality to every friend, rich or poor, provided he had talent and virtue. In every action he ornamented and did honor to even the barest and most wretched room." Lomazzo records in the *Idea del tempio della pittura* that "Leonardo always seemed to tremble when he began to paint."

Portrait of Leonardo seated on bank of Loire – Windsor, Royal Collection

---

[6] "In a charcoal drawing, I saw with complete art depicted/ The venerable image of my Vinci/ Than which there was no better in Delos, Crete, or Samos,/ So much so that though thou may'st portray with brush hereafter/ Whoever thou may'st be, painting with color/ Never wilt thou surpass or vanquish him in skill./ For more to be esteemed and of greater value/ Does art render that which is infused/ Through and through with his supreme worth."

[7] See G. B. Ramusio, *Primo volume delle navigazioni et viaggi*, Venice, 1550, fol. 194 v.

LEONARDVS DAVINCI

Left: Portrait of Leonardo – Florence, Uffizi Gallery (See note on this painting, facing p. 16)

Right: Portrait of Leonardo by unknown painter – Florence, Uffizi Gallery

The comments of those who knew Leonardo are confirmed in his manuscripts by the frequent admonitions he gives as precepts for living. The virtues stressed—patience, forgiveness, and manly acceptance of toil—indicate the harmony that existed between his features and his moral qualities.

It is conceivable that Leonardo also derived from his own person that canon for the proportions of the human body which he established for the adult male standing with feet together. For this he took the measure of the lip as equal to a twelfth part of the height of the face, or to a fourteenth part of that of the head, and contained one hundred and twelve times in the total height of the figure, which, expressed metrically, corresponds to the median stature of 168 centimeters.[8]

Does this give us one actual item of physical description? If so, the Vitruvian canon may possibly be regarded as offering a valuable basis for a reconstruction of Leonardo's figure. The drawing of a head, with its proportions indicated, which appears in Luca Pacioli's *Trattato de divina proportione* (Venice, 1509, fol. 17 r) corresponds with various drawings of Leonardo's.

Aristotle with the features of Leonardo – Bronze by a Lombard master of sixteenth century – Museum, Brunswick

Our image of Leonardo centers in the red chalk drawing preserved in the Royal Library in Turin. On the basis of this drawing Uzielli[9] made a study of Leonardo's appearance, which was further discussed by Müntz.[10] Luca Beltrami contributed further comparisons at the time of the fourth centenary of the death of da Vinci.[11] In February of 1926 Emil Möller published an article in *Belvedere* entitled *Wie sah Leonardo aus?*—a study in which all the material relating to Leonardo was given renewed attention. As one of the essays written in honor of Julius Schlosser in 1928, Leo Planiscig[12] published a series of comparisons between the profile portrait of Leonardo, attributed to Ambrogio de Predis, in the Ambrosiana in Milan, and a group of marble and bronze reliefs depicting Aristotle. The image of Leonardo has thus appeared differently to each new investigator, re-forming

---

[8] G. Favaro, *Il canone di Leonardo sulle proporzioni del corpo umano*, Istituto Anatomico della Regia Università di Padova, 1917. *Misure e proporzioni del corpo umano secondo Leonardo*, Venice, 1918. "Le proporzioni del corpo umano in un codice anonimo del Quattrocento postillato da Leonardo," in *Reale Accademia d'Italia*, Rome, 1934, Vol. XII.

[9] A. Uzielli, *Ricerche intorno a Leonardo da Vinci*, Ser. II, Rome, Salviucci, 1884, p. 463-466.

[10] E. Müntz, "*Les portraits de Léonard de Vinci*," in *L'Encyclopédie*, Oct. 15, 1894, p. 445-448. *Léonard de Vinci*, Paris, Hachette, 1899, p. 486-493.

[11] L. Beltrami, "The Face of Leonardo," in *Emporium*, Jan., 1919, and in *Per il centenario della morte di Leonardo da Vinci*, Bergamo, 1919, p. 75-95.

[12] L. Planiscig, *Leonardos Porträte und Aristoteles*, Vienna, Amalthea Verlag, 1928.

itself in the light of new discoveries and comparisons of various kinds. Over the course of time many figures have come to be considered as reflecting his person: Verrocchio's statue of David; the figure of Plato in Raphael's *School of Athens*; the recurrent figure of an old man in Luini's frescoes at Saronno depicting the marriage of the Virgin and Jesus disputing in the Temple. An image of Leonardo has thus been reconstructed in which, except for a few realistic details, the elements have been frankly idealized. The impression that predominates is of course that of the venerable sage whose portrait is transmitted to us in the words of Lomazzo.

Posterity has dwelt upon an image of Leonardo haloed with the majesty of old age, but the youth and the man in his prime may perhaps be rediscovered in the painter's own works. In the *Adoration of the Magi* (on which Leonardo worked between 1481 and 1482), at the right, is the figure of youth standing aloof from the group that turns toward the Virgin. Recently Gerolamo Calvi [13] has raised the possibility that this may be a self-portrait. The figure under the lightly accented draperies is slim, and the head with its long hair shows fine and very regular features, keen and deep-set eyes. If this image is accepted as representing Leonardo, it would seem not at all strange that the same youthful figure should have served as the model for the bronze statue of David, whose fine-drawn lineaments under the elegant hand of Verrocchio take on the subtle grace of an attitude surprised in a living being. The sculptor may well have harmonized the elements he took from his model, characterizing the energy of adolescent limbs by a realistic enlargement of the joints, and accentuating the sinuosity of the lips to give them that semblance of breathing vitality. The face has the same characteristic that occur in the portrait of the aged Leonardo—regular features and broad cheekbones, the great square in which the eyes are inscribed, the tenuously delineated oval outline terminating in the pronounced chin, and the lengthened lips with their undulant modelling—as indestructible marks of an eloquent physiognomy.

In a slight sketch of a head in the Uffizi may be seen certain parallels to the figure in the *Adoration of the Magi*. Bode [14] believes this drawing to be related to the St. Leonardo of the *Resurrection* altarpiece in Berlin, which with incredible rashness he seeks to attribute to Leonardo himself. Müller-Walde suggests that Leonardo served as the model for the Archangel Michael in the painting of Tobias and the three archangels [15] by an anonymous Tuscan whom Berenson [16] has identified as Francesco Botticini. The manuscript of Florenzio's *Trattato di musica* in the Trivulziana, illuminated by the miniaturist Attavanti, bears a border figure of a bearded man raising a lute which may possibly be an image of Leonardo. Framed by flowing locks, with a long beard in which the mustaches mingle, the head recalls figures of the Deity in paintings by Bergognone, though the effect of the craggy forhead is lost. Attempts have been made to see Leonardo and his musician friend Atalante Migliorotti in analogous figures in the Vatican Library's Breviary of Matthias Corvinus. It has also been suggested that Botticelli portrayed the young Leonardo standing beside Savonarola and Lorenzo de' Medici in the Uffizi *Adoration of the Magi*.

These and other conjectures, actuated by the untrustworthy play of chance resemblances, are not entirely convincing even to those who indulge an almost sentimental desire to find the physiognomic type corresponding with Leonardo's extraordinary spiritual character. An element of greater plausibility enters when such conjectures dwell on some of the male heads drawn by Leonardo himself.

First among these is the head crowned with thorns in the Academy of Fine Arts in Venice. There is nothing to indicate whether or not the drawing, assuming that its traditional attribution to Leonardo may be upheld, served in connection with a painting. However, in a mediocre painting in the Castello Sforzesco there appears a figure of Christ between two tormentors which may relate to the Venice drawing. The forceful, sorrowing head, that of a forty-year-old man, might easily be seen as representing a phase of the artist's life between that depicted in the youth of the *Adoration of the Magi* and that reflected in the old man in the Turin Royal Library. Confirmation of the iconographic value of the work seems to be offered by two other drawings. One was noted by Ravaisson-Mollien in his edition of Ms. I [17] of the Institut de France (fol. 136 v.), and a shrewd sense of caricature vibrates in the few essential lines that compose it. The other (Cod. Atl., fol. 315 v.-*b*) presents the same cast of features as the Venice drawing, although their flabbiness reveals a pupil's hand.

To these three portraits may be added another group comprising a number of drawings in which Leonardo seems to have made use of his own head for a study in proportion. Most important of these is a drawing in the gallery of the Venice Academy. Reproduced in almost all Leonardo stud-

[13] G. Calvi, *Vita di Leonardo*, Brescia, Morcelliana, 1936, p. 44.

[14] W. Bode, *Studien uber Leonardo da Vinci*, C. Grotsch, 1921, p. 86.

[15] P. Müller-Walde, *Leonardo da Vinci*, Munich, 1889, p. 3.

[16] B. Berenson, *Italian Pictures of the Renaissance: A List of the Principal Artists and Their Works, with an Index of Places*, Oxford, Clarendon Press, 1932, p. 107.

[17] *Les manuscrits de Léonard de Vinci... de la Bibliothèque de l'Institut de France*, ed. and catalogued by Charles Ravaisson-Mollien, Paris, Quantin, 1881.

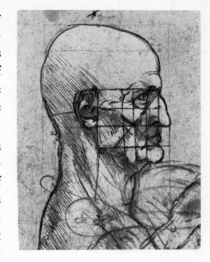

Drawing by Leonardo – Venice, Academy

Profile of Leonardo taken from Venice drawing

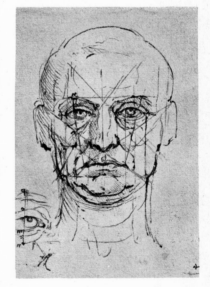

Proportions of human face – Self-portrait by Da Vinci – Turin, Royal Collection

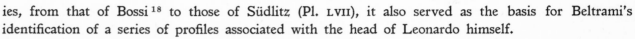

From 1568 edition of Vasari's *Life*

ies, from that of Bossi[18] to those of Südlitz (Pl. LVII), it also served as the basis for Beltrami's identification of a series of profiles associated with the head of Leonardo himself.

Similar in type is a profile in the Windsor collection (no. 12499),[19] which Müntz calls "idealized,"[20] but which should perhaps be considered a caricature. The drawings numbered 12466, 12476 r. and 12485 r. appear related to it. These drawings give the impression of studies made for a further purpose, and the subject of one of them reappears in the *Last Supper* as the apostle Thaddeus, whose figure conforms with those of the entire group of drawings. The face in the ruined fresco is characterized by a high forehead, soft beard, and flowing hair. It is also distinguished by an intensity that suggests a correspondence with more than the character of the apostle alone: Thaddeus' manner of expressing himself in profound and measured judgments might well be imagined as close to that of the artist himself. The visual resemblance becomes still more striking in copies of the *Last Supper*.

Again, we may possibly have Leonardo's image in two profile drawings, one in the Ambrosiana, the other in Windsor Castle. As already recognized by Beltrami, the first is undoubtedly a copy of the second, which for its part certainly is not from Leonardo's own hand. However, both show the artist at about fifty, with an intent face in which the characteristics of the Turin portrait are antirely recognizable. The portrait that Paolo Giovio had in his possession when Leonardo was still alive, known to us through an inferior copy in the Uffizi,[21] must certainly have been related to these two.

The same type appears in the profile view of a terra-cotta bust, probably by Giovan Francesco Rustici, in the Castello Sforzesco, placed there by Mr. Gregor Aharon. Also best seen in connection with this group are two profile drawings of Leonardo wearing a travelling cap (Windsor, no. 12441). The lined and venerable face suggests that the portrait was made when he made the trip from Rome to northern Italy, or at the time of his journey to France.

To his stay in France is justly assigned the Turin drawing, the only iconographic document offering a reliable point of reference, for which further confirmation may be found in a ruined panel in the Cherbourg Museum, offering a disciple's representation of his master.

The noble beauty of the Turin drawing, firm and sure in its technique, harmonizes with the majesty of the face: it corresponds in almost every way with the image of Leonardo that has come down to us in a unanimously accepted tradition. That this is how Leonardo looked in the last decade of his life is confirmed by a likeness of him seen together with that of Jean Perréal in a drawing in Ms. 14363 in the Bibliothèque Nationale, dating probably from 1509.[22] The same venerable figure appears in a sketch in the Windsor collection, probably executed by one of the master's pupils, in which an old man is seen pensively seated on what is taken to be the bank of the Loire. Michelangelo himself contributed to establishing the tradition of Leonardo's majesty with a drawing now in the British Museum,[23] in which Leonardo, dressed in a great robe, holds up a skull as though giving instruction on its parts, and it seems quite possible that Raphael may have drawn the inspiration for his figure of Plato from this aspect of Leonardo.

[18] B. Bossi, *Del Cenacolo di Leonardo da Vinci*, Milan, 1810.
[19] K. Clark, *A Catalogue of the Drawings of Leonardo da Vinci in the Collection of His Majesty the King at Windsor Castle*, Cambridge, 1935.
[20] E. Müntz, *Le musée de portraits de Paul Jove*, Paris, Imprimerie Nationale, 1900, p. 90-91.
[21] L. Rovelli, *L'opera storica e artistica di Paolo Giovio: Il museo dei ritratti*, Como, 1928.
[22] L. Dorez, "Léonard de Vinci et Jean Perréal: Conjectures," in *Léonard de Vinci*, articles collected by M. Miguon, Rome, for publications of *Nouvelle Revue d'Italie*, 1919, p. 67-86.
[23] K. Frey, *Die Handzeichnungen des Michelangelo Buonarroti*, 1909, no. 41.

Portrait of Leonardo – Etching by D. Cunego – Milan, Da Vinci Collection, Castello Sforzesco

14

Above, left: Figure of Plato, from cartoon for Raphael's *School of Athens*, supposedly representation of Leonardo – Milan, Ambrosiana. –– Center: "The weary hand" – Left hand of Leonardo – Cod. Atl., fol. 238 v-*b*. — Right: Presumed portrait of Leonardo, possibly self-portrait – Cherbourg, Museum. — Below, left: Presumed portrait of Leonardo – Marble bas-relief by sixteenth-century Lombard master – Milan, Castello Sforzesco. — Right: Portrait of Leonardo – Terra cotta by sixteenth-century Tuscan master – New York, Aharon Collection.

15

The long series of representations in which we see Leonardo in the guise of a philosopher—the image he most clearly presented to his immediate posterity—begins with Lombard painting. In the frescoes of the Sanctuary of Saronno, and in the background of a painting in Prince Borromeo's collection, Bernardino Luini represents him with the white beard, deep-set eyes, and wrinkled skin of the Turin drawing. Similar figures of aged men may be seen in the works of Bergognone. An anonymous painter, perhaps Spanish, gives the features of Leonardo to St. Joseph in a *Holy Family* in Florence owned by Delfino Cinelli. Vasari uses the same image of an old man with white hair and beard in his fresco over the fireplace of the Sala di Leone X in the Palazzo Vecchio in Florence. Leonardo is here represented in right profile together with Michelangelo and with Giuliano and Lorenzo de' Medici.[24] The likeness is quite similar to that in the portrait which must have been in Giovio's collection, and which was certainly known to Vasari. In the frontispiece of the 1568 edition of Vasari's life of Leonardo, the profile has a hardness which accentuates the mass of the hair and beard, the sunken hollow of the eyes, and the flare of the nostrils. This portrait was later echoed in the engravings for the *Opus chronographicum* of Peter Opmer, printed in Antwerp in 1611, in Isaac Bullart's *Académie des sciences et des arts*, printed in Amsterdam in 1682, and in several medallions. Of these last, only one is noteworthy—that executed in 1669 in connection with the publication of the *Treatise on Painting*, bearing on its reverse side the inscriptions, *Scribit quam suscitat artem*. It is not difficult to imagine that the portrait of Leonardo in the Uffizi attributed to *l'Altissimo*, but found to have been superimposed upon another painting, as revealed by radiography, may have derived its benevolent expression from that of a three-quarter representation in a lost portrait.

Concurrently with these, there evolves another majestic image, in which Leonardo's features are confounded with those of Aristotle. In this vein is a series of reliefs studied by Planiscig. These comprise a work in the P. Jackson Higgs collection in New York, executed by an early sixteenth-century north Italian artist; a bronze relief in the museum at Brunswick; a north Italian marble in the Castello Sforzesco which bears in Greek letters the inscription, "Aristotle, best of philosophers"; and similar small marbles in the Vatican museum and in the Aharon collection in New York.

The figure of Leonardo has often been recreated in more recent times—in engravings by Volpato and Mantelli, in the reconstructions of bust and figure made for various monuments (Magni's for the Piazza della Scala in Milan, for example, or Quadrelli's memorials for the town of Vinci and the Sala delle Asse of the Sforza castle in Milan, or the most recent monument by Francesco Wildt), and in paintings by artists from Cornienti to Ingres. For all these, the sources of inspiration have been limited to the drawing in the Turin Royal Library, the Uffizi painting, and the drawing reproduced in Vasari's *Life*.

Certainly, if Leonardo's image could have come down to us with the distinctness of Lorenzo di Credi's self-portrait in the Widener collection, or with the clarity of Perugino's and Botticelli's self-portraits, our desire to know how he looked would be fully gratified. From all that has been left to us, however, as well as from every idea of himself that Leonardo gives us, we know that the great man's person is epitomized in the grave and sublime tranquillity of the Turin self-portrait.

GIORGIO NICODEMI

Detail from *Marriage of the Virgin* –
Fresco by Bernardino Luini – Saronno

[24] A. Lensi, *Palazzo Vecchio*, Milan, 1929, p. 172.

Presumed portrait of Leonardo, by unknown Tuscan master of seventeenth century – Florence, Uffizi Gallery

This famous portrait of Leonardo has belonged to the Uffizi Gallery for almost two centuries. In the inventory of 1753 it was listed as from the hand of Leonardo himself.

Acquired by the directors of the Uffizi collection in the period of the rule of the house of Lorraine, it was considered a self-portrait until recent times. The doubts cast on its authenticity by many scholars during the last fifty years were justified by a radiographic examination. The thin oak panel bears under the portrait of Leonardo a composition that is certainly of the seventeenth century—a repentant Magdalene painted with hands crossed on her breast, with a book and a perfume vase beside her. The characteristics of the original painting on the panel leave no doubt that it should be attributed to an unknown artist, probably German, of the seventeenth century. We must conclude that the portrait of Leonardo was painted toward the end of the 1600's, on the model of the Da Vinci drawing now in the Royal Library of Turin. Piero Sanpaolesi has published the history of this portrait, with a careful study of the radiograph, in the *Bollettino d'Arte*, May, 1938.

The Archangel Michael, in Francesco Botticini's *Tobias and the Three Archangels* – Presumed to be portrait of Leonardo in youth

Portrait of Leonardo represented as Plato – Figure from Raphael's fresco, *The School of Athens* – Vatican, Stanza della Segnatura

3

17

Baptism of Christ – Leonardo and Verrocchio – Florence, Uffizi Gallery

THE LIFE AND WORKS OF LEONARDO

Leonardo's contribution to humanity appears even today so profound and real that it is as though this extraordinary artist mind must have foreseen the spiritual needs, the aspirations, and the technical achievements of modern times. His greatness was recognized even while he lived, and without him the Renaissance as a whole would have fallen short of those spiritual conquests that brought light to all of European civilization. To the thoughts and emotions stirred by Christianity he added his discovery of the affinities between human processes and those of nature, and through scientific studies he came to realize that the knowledge and application of nature's laws could carry human endeavor to greater and nobler heights. He sensed that the elements observed in nature could give order and form to the most sublime aspects of art. He was not unaware of the possible conflict between science and faith, but sought to reconcile the two in his notion that human knowledge and effort would be most perfectly fulfilled in art, which in turn was so bound to faith that it must be regarded as the highest possible means of serving God.

Raphael, who owed so much to Leonardo, and who, in the *School of Athens*, is thought to have portrayed him as Plato, pointing heavenward, robed Christianity in the ideal beauty of pagan classical form, giving us a vision of perfect and immutable serenity. Leonardo attempted to go further, and from the natural world about him he extracted whatever was worthy of being transformed into a living representation of truth and of the immortal essence of human life. Unlike Michelangelo, he did not need to create a world of sibyls and giants. Grace and truth seemed to him the outward expression of the soul "which rules and governs every body" (*Trattato della pittura*, ed. A. Bozzelli, Lanziano, 1914, p. 105); they confirmed for him the certainties arrived at through his perceptions of life and the world, and together with these made a timeless spiritual cycle.

By his contemporaries, even those who were most deeply convinced of his greatness, Leonardo was considered an investigator who became so engrossed in each artistic problem confronting him that he made it a field of scientific research. In order to represent the human body he studied its anatomy, but in the process became more intrigued with this science in itself than with its application to art; in order to paint plants, he delved into the laws of botany and geology; and so he was in turn geologist, physiologist, mechanical or hydraulic engineer, and astronomer. For all that he contributed in these fields, we may legitimately regret that as a result of such diversification of his interests he left only the small number of paintings that has come down to us.

All who knew him expressed their admiration for the talents which God had bestowed upon him, talents so great that Vasari numbered him among those who "represent not only humanity but also divinity itself." Leonardo's teachings seem to throw light into all the dark corners of knowledge, as if to demonstrate that it is never necessary to have recourse to the caprice of the senses or to mystery in the search for and conquest of truth. A myth of obscurity, almost of magic, has been woven around his brilliant figure, but the more his works are studied and comprehended, the more clearly and impressively the real man emerges. As we move away from the Leonardo legend toward what may be regarded as his true life story, his prophetic visions take on substance: mankind may avail itself as readily of his theorem on the composition and resolution of forces, or of his exploration of the principles of flying, as of the spiritual legacy of his paintings and drawings.

Early drawing by Leonardo – Florence, Gabinetto delle Stampe, Uffizi Gallery

Drawing for *Madonna and Child* – London, from the collection of British Museum

19

Drawing – *Woman with a Unicorn* –
Oxford, Christ Church College

Drawing – *Woman with a Unicorn* –
London, British Museum

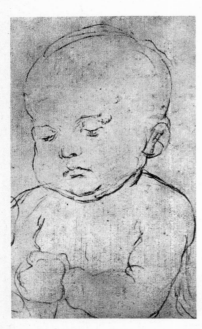

Head of child – Florence, Uffizi
Gallery

With each succeeding generation of scholars, renewed attempts have been made to reconstruct Leonardo's life and his multiple activities. The thousands of drawings and manuscript pages he has left us convey the notion that Leonardo sought to give the world a new concept of unity. Interspersed among the incomparably expressive sketches, we find admonitions addressed to himself, to his assistants, and to a general audience, as well as descriptions, formulas, and discussions of ideas which are clarified and perfected each time he returns to them.

Yet even today we are far from comprehending the whole of Leonardo's personality. Even if we restrict ourselves to a study of him as an artist, examining the various works that remain—as well as what is known about a few whose memory survives in written descriptions—and to his explanations in certain pages of the *Treatise on Painting* compiled by a pupil, of the things he did and those he might have done, we feel that centuries of admiration have not exhausted the range of thought that he encompassed. No approach, not even the so-called aesthetic one, which permits the writer to content himself with provisional assumptions, can completely explain his art. In each of his works an artist reveals not only his personal world, but also that general sense of the order of the universe which he derives from things and events, and in Leonardo the ramifications of this function are broad beyond measure. Painting, as Leonardo understood it, was the supreme end of knowledge, embodying more than philosophy, and synthesizing both science and art: "Painting extend to the surfaces, colors, and shapes of all things created by nature, while philosophy penetrates below the surface in order to arrive at the inherent properties, but it does not carry the same conviction, and in this is unlike the work of the painter, which apprehends the essential truth of these bodies, as the eye errs less" (*Treatise*, fol. 6).

He spoke of science as the "knowledge of things possible in the future, of the present, and of the past" (Cod. Triv., fol. 17 v), and defined it at the beginning of the *Treatise on Painting* as "an investigation by the mind which begins with the ultimate origin of a subject beyond which nothing can be found in nature to form part of that subject. Take, for example, the continuous quantity in the science of geometry; if we begin with the surface of a body, we find that it derives from lines, the boundaries of this surface. But we do not let the matter rest there, for we know that the line is bounded by points, and that the point is that [ultimate unit] than which there can be nothing smaller."

To clarify his definition further, Leonardo observed: "No human investigation can be called true science without going through mathematical tests; and if you say that the sciences which begin and end in the mind contain truth, this cannot be conceded, and must be denied for many reasons. First and foremost because in such mental discourses experience does not come in, without which nothing reveals itself with certainty" (*ibid.*, fol. 1).

In contrast to science, art—which for him attained its most complete fulfillment in painting—was "sole imitator of everything in nature, grandchild of nature, and related to God" (*ibid.*, fol. 8).

He saw too that "in imitable sciences the student can attain equality with the master and can produce similar fruit. These sciences are useful to the imitator, but they are not of such excellence as those which cannot be passed on by inheritance like other goods. Among the inimitable sciences painting comes first. It cannot be taught to those not endowed by nature, like mathematics, where the pupil takes in as much as the master gives. It cannot be copied, as is done with letters, where the copy has the same value as the original. It cannot be molded, as in sculpture, where the cast is equal in merit to the original; it cannot be reproduced indefinitely, as is done in the printing of books. It remains peerless in its nobility; in its singleness it does honor to its author, remaining precious and unique; it never engenders offspring equal to it; and this singularity makes it finer than the sciences which are disseminated everywhere. Do we not see great kings of the East going about veiled and covered because they think they might diminish their fame by showing themselves in public and divulging their presence? Do we not see that pictures representing divine persons are kept constantly concealed under costly draperies, and that before they are uncovered great ecclesiastical rites are performed, with singing to the strains of instruments; and at the moment of unveiling the great multitude of people who have flocked there throw themselves to the ground, worshipping and praying to those images in the pictures for the recovery of their health and for their eternal salvation, as if the Deity were present in actuality" (*ibid.*, fol. 4).

The various passages make a distinction between scientific and artistic activity, the first permitting one to amass knowledge, the other serving to express the function of the spirit.

Leonardo throws off such a wealth of diversified ideas and conceptions that each mind that comes in contact with his rediscovers him differently. All, however, are convinced of the methodical exactness with which he pursued truth. Each problem is presented in its essence and the definitions and solutions are entirely correct. His reasoning, or rather portions of his arguments, are not always so precise and flawless. At one time the positivists claimed him as their most brilliant precursor; more recently he has been acclaimed as an ardent idealist—indeed, a forerunner of Kant. Elements have been seen in his writings which to some have suggested a system linking Plato with Kant, the Stoics with Spinoza, or the Bible with Schopenhauer. By choosing passages which appear contradictory,

Head of Leonardo's angel in Verrocchio's *Baptism of Christ* – Florence, Uffizi Gallery

The Annunciation – Florence, Uffizi Gallery

Table in The Annunciation *– Florence, Uffizi Gallery*

Drawing for arm of angel in *The Annunciation* – Oxford, Christ Church College

scholars have thus attempted to suit Leonardo's observations to philosophical systems devised after his time. Such attempts, however, ignore the basic fact that for Leonardo, as for all sixteenth-century humanists, the natural sciences, art, philology, and archaeology were derived from an identification of spirit with life, and were naturally understood according to a notion of the universality of all things which bound them to the realities of nature. Spirit was the element which dominated and united all the phenomena of history. Thus it was possible for Leonardo to unite in art two rather uneasy bedfellows—a fervent religiosity and philosophical speculation. His method of research and his capacity for observation and ideation were translated into formulation of an absolute stylistic purity.

The fundamental aesthetic principle of the Renaissance, so far as it can be understood from a language that was simple but rather vague when referring to abstract ideas, was that art should be, as Vasari puts it, the imitator of nature. When trying to express the real value of a work of art, Vasari and all sixteenth-century writers continually refer to examples from life, and it becomes clear that nature is seen as a repository of that religious truth which allows the mind to function and the hand to obey the dictates of artistic creativity.

Fundamental to Leonardo is a principle which appears earlier in Leone Battista Alberti's *De pictura*: the painter must be "universal." He must be capable of representing not only man but also the objects and landscapes, the colors and shadows which constitute his world, as well as the myriad attitudes by which a human figure reflects its infinite psychological states. For Leonardo the process of artistic creation represented a constant referial back to the realities of an everpresent nature. Again and again he stressed the necessity for observing not only its resplendent visible surface but also its very viscera. Art, or rather, the artist, must be guided by the same laws that govern nature. These "force the mind of the painter to transform itself into nature's own mind, and to become the interpreter between nature and art" (*Treatise*, fol. 36).

Here we see emerging Leonardo's consciousness of the spirituality of art as contrasted with nature, and a point of view which explains the special quality of his work. In his paintings he achieves a reconciliation between nature and art, and arrives at a highly original determination of architectonic forms; in his activity as a theorizer and commentator on observable phenomena, on the other hand, he arrives at scientific accuracy and becomes the inventor of mechanical and hydraulic devices which vie with nature itself in giving to human faculties a heightened dynamic potential.

Of the many problems confronting the scholar interested in Leonardo, none is so attractive as the study of his thought process. Everything that he has left us contains something noteworthy and profound: every problem he posed, be it a question of the authenticity of a sketch for a machine, or one of his broad statements on ethics, opens such vast areas of inquiry and requires the aid of such a tremendous fund of knowledge that it makes the hope of comprehending his mind impossible. Not all of his manuscripts have yet been published. In many cases there exist only unreliable transcriptions, and no index has yet been made which would enable the student to trace any particular point through his writings. It is supposed that in his later years he meant to arrange his notes and drawings in order to publish them as an encyclopedia, but the form in which he intended

to present them is not known. Though a coherent arrangement of all the themes which Leonardo touched on might give us a clearer picture of his mind's range and understanding, we would still not have access to all that he thought about but did not write down: thus his words and his paintings will always have various interpretations.

The man whom Gabriele d'Annunzio called "master of truth," because he attempted to find a rational explanation for all things that were obscure, did not reveal to his acquaintances the order of his scientific treatises. But the ebullient vitality in every statement is enough to arouse a multitude of questions in everyone who wishes to understand what he has left to us.

Leonardo had a profound insight into his own life and work. His serene impassivity was only a surface aspect, and limited to matters of a practical nature. In remarking, "when you are alone, you are all your own" (*ibid.*, fol. 48), he wishes to say that he who controls himself best is by so much the better able to give all of himself to others. When at certain times of his life he drew back from the struggle, showing himself unafraid of changing course, it was certainly because he sensed the futility of a battle without reason, or because he had decided that his actions had not had the desired results. He never ceased his researches, for his thoughts and his works constantly dominated every "circumstance," as he would have called it, of his life. He may have intended to delineate his own attitude toward the world when he described (Cod. Arund., fol. 155 r) his vision of an extraordinary natural spectacle which he viewed from the entrance to a cavern. He records his feelings, torn between fear of the unknown and the desire to know, as follows:

"Nor does the tempestuous sea bellow so loud, when the northern blast dashes it, with its foaming waves, between Scylla and Charybdis; nor Stromboli, nor Mount Etna, when their sulphurous flames, having been forcibly confined, rend and burst open the great mountain, hurling stones and earth through the air together with the flames they vomit...

"Nor when the burning caverns of Mount Etna, rejecting the ill-restrained element, vomit it forth back to its own region, driving furiously before it every obstacle that comes in the way of its raging fury...

"Unable to resist my eager desire and wanting to see the great multitude of the various and strange shapes made by the work of nature, and having wandered some distance among gloomy rocks, I came to the entrance of a great cavern, in front of which for some time I stood, overwhelmed, having no knowledge of such a thing. Arching my back, I rested my tired hand on my knee and held my right hand over my lowered lids, frequently bending first one way and then the other, to see whether I could discover anything inside, though this was prevented by the deep darkness within. And after I had remained there some time, two emotions suddenly arose in me, fear and desire—fear of the threatening dark cavern, desire to see whether there were any marvellous thing within it."

The account is entirely symbolic, and throws light on all the vicissitudes of a life rich in events and triumphs, a life ruled by the harmony between the writer's noble concepts and aspirations on the one hand and his everyday activities on the other. Leonardo has no particular political importance in the complex life of his time. The great men of his day turned to him and his knowledge because they were aware of his fabulous capacity, but they never succeeded in changing his modest and benevolent attitude. He was his own counsellor when he noted:

"Words which do not satisfy the ear of the hearer weary him or vex him, and the symptoms of this you will often see in such hearers in their frequent yawns. You, therefore, who speak before men whose good will you desire, when you see such an excess of fatigue, abridge your speech, or change your discourse; and if you do otherwise, then instead of the favor you desire you will receive dislike and hostility."

He wrote in praise of patience, which "serves us against insults precisely as clothes do against

Study of figures and architecture for *Adoration of the Magi* – Florence, Uffizi Gallery

cold. For if you put on more garments as the cold increases, that cold cannot hurt you; in the same way increase your patience under great offenses, and they cannot vex your mind."

There has been too much emphasis on the notion that Leonardo's pages are full of designs for machines and projects which were never carried out or of thoughts made so secret by his "mirror" writing as to be inaccessible. In all likelihood his contemporaries often made use of his inventions and mechanical constructions, and the memory of his works survives in certain traditions and in documents. He had great respect for the inventor, saying:

"And those men who are inventors and interpreters of nature to man differ from boasters and declaimers about the works of others just as true objects differ from their reflections in a mirror. For the first are something in themselves and the others nothing—persons little indebted to nature, since it is only by accident that they are clothed, and except for this I might class them with the herds of beasts" (Cod. Atl., fol. 117 r-*b*).

He was certainly thinking of himself and of the fortune which his work might have merited when he wrote:

"If any man could have discovered the utmost powers of the cannon in all its various forms, and have given such a secret to the Romans, how swiftly would they have conquered every country and vanquished every army, and what reward could have been great enough for such a service? Archimedes, indeed, although he had greatly damaged the Romans in the seige of Syracuse, nevertheless did not lack offers of great rewards from these very Romans. And when Syracuse was taken, diligent search was made for Archimedes, and he being found dead, greater lamentation was made for him by the Senate and the people of Rome than if they had lost all their army; and they did not fail to honor him with burial rites and with a statue, in which they were led by Marcus Marcellus. And after the second destruction of Syracuse, the sepulcher of Archimedes was found again by Cato in the ruins of a temple.[1] So Cato had the temple restored and the highly venerated sepulcher... Whence it is written that Cato said that he was not as proud of anything else he had done as he was of having paid such honor to Archimedes" (Cod. Arund., fol. 279 v).

We must assume, naturally, that Leonardo's teachings were not all lost. Though many of his works have not survived, though the machines he built were destroyed and not reconstructed, and though the truths he established soon became separated from his name, they did not lack reverberations, and spread abroad in other guise and with other names, until evidence drawn directly from his writings in modern times revealed their origination in his mind. It was of course his paintings that established his fame and glory, and in painting, as he himself wished, he attained his loftiest

Study for *Adoration of the Magi* – Paris, Bonnat Collection

24

―――――
[1] Leonardo here confuses Cato with Cicero, who boasts in the *Tusculanae* of having found the sepulcher of Archimedes.

Angel by Leonardo, in Verrocchio's *Baptism of Christ* – Florence, Uffizi Gallery

Drawing for *Adoration of the Magi* – Paris, Louvre

heights. His ability as a writer, however, was no mean one, for he shows a great purity of expression, the clarity of scientific discipline, and a taste for expressive paraphrases. He says himself:

"I am fully conscious that, not being a man of letters, certain presumptuous persons will think that they may with reason discredit me by alleging that I am totally unlettered. Foolish folk! Do they not know that I might retort as Marius did to the Roman patricians by saying: 'They who deck themselves out in the labors of others will not allow me my own.' They will say that I, having no literary skill, cannot properly give words to that which I desire to treat of. But they do not know that my subjects are to be dealt with by experience rather than in words: and experience has been the mistress of those who have written well. And so, as mistress, I will cite her in all cases. Though I may not, like them, be able to quote other authors, I shall rely on that which is much greater and more worthy—on experience, the mistress of their masters. They go about puffed up and pompous, dressed and decorated with [the fruits of] not their own labors, but those of others. And they will not allow me my own. They will scorn me as an inventor; but how much more might they—who are not inventors but vaunters and declaimers about the words of others —be censured" (Cod. Atl., fol. 117 r-*b*).

He had an everyday wisdom which, where one grasps it, permits one to enter into an immediate and felicitous communion with him. He knows that "one can have no greater and no lesser mastery than that which one has over oneself" (Ms. H, fol. 119 v-*d*), that human life is short and must not be consumed in vain. "O thou that sleepest," he writes, "what is sleep? Sleep resembles death. Ah, why then dost thou not work in such wise that after death thou mayest retain a resemblance to perfect life, rather than during life make thyself like the hapless dead by sleeping?"

Noting the gentle appearance in death of an old man on whose body he had "made a notomia," [2] Leonardo observed that "just as a day well spent gives grateful sleep, so a life well spent gives grateful death" (*Treatise*, fol. 32).

Life and its necessities were ever present to him: he had seen the evils that must be avoided. In this connection he wrote:

"Lying is so vile that even if it were speaking well of godly things it would take off something from God's grace; and truth is so excellent, that if it praises but small things they become noble.

Detail from *Adoration of the Magi* –
Florence, Uffizi Gallery

------
[2] The word applies to dissection of a cadaver [translator's note].

"Beyond a doubt truth bears the same relation to falsehood as light to darkness; and this truth is in itself so excellent that, even when it dwells on humble and lowly matters, it is still infinitely above ambiguity and lies regarding great and lofty matters; because even if lying should be the fifth element of our minds, the fact remains that the truth of things is the chief nutriment of superior intellects, though not of wandering wits.

"But you who live in dreams are better pleased by sophistical reasonings and frauds of wit in great and uncertain things than by those reasoning which are certain and natural and not so exalted" (Ms. M, fol. 156 v).

His notions regarding the moral worth of life were in keeping with the respect he had for the human mechanism. Studies of anatomy roused him to such reflections as this:

"And you, O man, who will observe in these things I have made the wonderful works of nature, if you think it would be a criminal thing to destroy these, consider how much more criminal it is to take the life of a man. And if this, his external form, appears to you marvellously constructed, remember that it is nothing as compared with the soul that dwells in that structure; for that, indeed, be it what it may, is a thing divine. Leave it then to dwell in its function at its pleasure, and let not

Adoration of the Magi – Florence, Uffizi Gallery

Study for *Adoration of the Magi* – Windsor, Royal Collection, no. 12336

27

Studies for *Adoration of the Magi* –
Paris, Ecole de Beaux Arts and Louvre

your rage or malice destroy a life—for truly, he who does not value life does not himself deserve it. Indeed, it is not without reason that we are so loath to depart this life. Therefore take care to preserve your health" (Anat. Ms. A, fol. 2 r).

He advises his readers as follows:

"Avoid that study the resultant work of which dies with the worker" (Cod. Forst., III, fol. 36 v). "It is wrong for you to praise and worse to reprehend a thing if you do not understand it well" (Cod. Atl., fol. 284 b, 365 b).

"The acquisition of any knowledge is always of use to the intellect, because it may drive out useless things and preserve the good. For nothing can be loved or hated unless it is first understood" (*ibid.*, fol. 223 b, 671 b).

"Knowledge acquired in one's youth arrests the damage of old age, and if you understand that old age has wisdom for its sustenance, you will so conduct yourself in youth that your old age will not lack nourishment" (*ibid.*, fol. 111 b, 345 a).

"With what hope can poor students expect to be rewarded for their virtue? And in this case I know that I shall make not a few enemies, seeing that no one will believe what I can say of him. For only a few men are disgusted by their own vices; nay, vice is displeasing only to those who are by nature opposed to it. And many hate their fathers and break off friendship with those who reprove their vices; and they will not listen to any exhortations against them, or to any man's good counsel…

"If you meet with anyone who is virtuous, do not drive him from you; do him honor, so that he may not have to flee from you and betake himself to hermitages, or caves, or other solitary places or escape from your treachery. If there is such a one among you, do him honor, for these are our saints upon earth; these are they who deserve statues from us, images and honors…

"But remember that you are not to eat their images, as is done in some parts of India, where, when some image is thought to have brought about a miracle, the priests cut the wooden figure in pieces and give it to all the people of the country, not without payment, and each one grates his portion very fine, and puts it upon the first food he eats, and thus believes that he has eaten his saint, who then preserves him from all perils. What do you think here, man, of your own kind? Are you as wise as you believe yourself to be? Are these things that men should do?" (Cod. Forst., III, fol. 241 a).

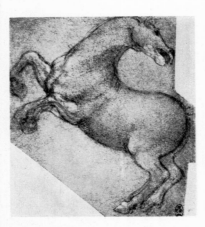

Study of horse for *Adoration of the Magi* – Windsor, Royal Collection, no. 12334

"Just as iron rusts without use, and water becomes putrid and with the cold freezes, so talent without exercise deteriorates" (Cod. Atl., fol. 284 b, 865 b). "The water which you touch in a river is the last of that which has passed and the first of that which is to come. The same is true of the present moment: life well spent is long" (*Treatise*, fol. 68).

It is very clear to him that life renews itself by passing through a succession of different stages:

"The body of anything whatever that takes nourishment constantly dies and is constantly renewed; because nourishment can enter only into places where the former nourishment has expired, and if it has expired it no longer has life. And if you do not supply nourishment equal to the nourishment

which is gone, life will fail in vigor... just as the flame of the candle is fed by the nourishment afforded by the liquid of this candle, which flame continually with a rapid supply restores to it from below as much as is consumed in dying above" (Quad. Anat. II, fol. 43 *b*).

Madonna and Child from *Adoration of the Magi* – Florence, Uffizi Gallery

Reflecting on the fossil fish which had for millennia "made the armature and support of the mountain above it," and observing that there appeared to be a kind of anonymous will operating in nature, he asked:

"Why did nature not ordain that one animal should not live by the death of another? Nature, being inconstant and taking pleasure in creating and continually producing new forms, because she knows that her terrestrial materials are thereby augmented, is more ready and more swift in her creating than time in his destruction; and so she has ordained that many animals shall be food for others. Nay, this not satisfying her desire, to the same end she frequently sends forth certain poisonous and pestilential vapors upon the vast multiplication and congregation of animals, and most of all upon men, whose numbers increase vastly because other animals do not feed upon them, and the causes being removed, the effects are lacking. And so this earth seeks to lose its life, desiring only continual reproduction. According to the clear logic of its own demonstration, like effects always follow like causes; animals typify the life of the world" (Cod. M, fol. 156 *b*).

Study for *Adoration of the Magi* – London, British Museum

29

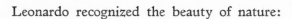

Lion at feet of saint in Leonardo's
St. Jerome – Vatican, Pinacoteca

Head of page – Detail from *Adoration of the Magi* by Bernardino Luini – Saronno, Sanctuary

Leonardo recognized the beauty of nature:

"Though human ingenuity may make various inventions which, by the help of various machines, answer the same end, it will never devise invention more beautiful, nor more simple, nor more to the purpose, than nature does; because in her inventions nothing is wanting and nothing is superfluous, and she needs no counterpoise when she makes limbs proper for motion in the bodies of animals. But she puts into them the soul of the body, which forms them, that is, the soul of the mother, which first constructs in the womb the form of the man and in due time awakens the soul that is to inhabit it. And this at first lies dormant and under the tutelage of the soul of the mother, who nourishes and vivifies it through the umbilical vein, with all its spiritual parts, and this happens because this umbilicus is joined to the placenta and the cotyledons by which the child is attached to the mother. And these are the reasons why a wish, a strong craving, or a fright or any other mental suffering in the mother has more influence on the child than on the mother: for there are many cases in which the child loses its life because of these, etc. This discourse is out of place here; it applies rather to the composition of animated bodies—and the rest of the definition of the soul I leave to the imagination of friars, those fathers of the people who know all secrets by inspiration. I leave alone the sacred books; for they are supreme truth" (Quad. Anat., fol. 184 *a*).

In contrast to the will of nature is the restless will of man:

"Now you see that the hope and the desire of returning to the first state of chaos is like the attraction of the moth to the light, and that the man who with constant longing awaits with joy each new springtime, each new summer, each new month and new year—deeming that the things he longs for are even too late in coming—does not perceive that he is longing for his own destruction. But this desire is the very quintessence, the spirit of the elements, which finding itself imprisoned with the soul is ever longing to return from the human body to its giver. And you must know that this same longing is that quintessence inseparable from nature, and that man is the image of the world" (Cod. Arund., fol. 156 *v*).

"One can have no greater and no lesser mastery than that which one has over oneself" (Cod. H, fol. 119 v-*d*).

Head of saint in Leonardo's *St. Jerome* – Vatican, Pinacoteca

But man's will depends on cognizance of law, which is attained through experience:

"But first I shall make some experiments before I proceed further, because my intention is to consult experience first and then by means of reasoning show why such experiment is bound to work in such a way. And this is the true rule by which those who analyze natural effects must proceed; and although nature begins with the cause and ends with the experience, we must follow the opposite course, namely (as I said before), begin with the experience and by means of it investigate the cause" (Cod. E, fol. 55 r).

Law is the mistress of events:

"Experience, the interpreter between creative nature and the human race, teaches how that nature works among mortals, and being constrained by necessity cannot act otherwise than as law, which is its helm, requires it to act" (Cod. Atl., 86 r).

Necessity, as an intrinsic element, regulates nature:

"Necessity is the mistress and the teacher of nature, it is the theme and the inspiration of nature, its curb and eternal regulator" (Cod. Forst., III, fol. 49 *a*).

St. Jerome – Bernardino Luini – Milan, Poldi-Pezzoli Museum

Madonna of the Carnation – Munich, Pinakothek

The Annunciation – Archangel Gabriel – Florence, Uffizi Gallery

Of the soul, as ruler of the body, he says:

"Every part always has a tendency to reunite with its whole in order to escape from its imperfection. The soul desires to remain with its body, because without the organic instruments of that body, it can neither act nor feel anything" (Cod. Atl., fol. 58 *a*, 180 *a*).

But the soul lives in a region of prayer. This idea is reflected in such passages as these:

"I obey thee, Lord, first for the love I ought in all reason to bear thee; second, for that thou canst shorten or prolong the lives of men" (Cod. Forst., III, fol. 29 r).

"O admirable impartiality of thine, thou First Mover; thou hast not permitted that any force should fail of the order or quality of its necessary effects" (Cod. Arund., fol. 24 r).

"God sells us all good things at the price of labor" (Quad. Anat. V, fol. 24 r).

Leonardo concludes with the wish, "May God, light of all things, deign to enlighten me, who here treat of light" (Cod. Atl., fol. 203 r).

In reply to some of his detractors Leonardo wrote:

"There are among the numbers of the stupid a certain sect, called hypocrites, who continually study to deceive themselves and others, but more others than themselves; though in reality they deceive themselves more than others. And these are they who reprimand the painters, who study on festival days those things belonging to the knowledge of all those forms which nature's works take on, and earnestly occupy themselves with trying to acquire as much knowledge of these as possible. But those who scold forget that this is the way of knowing the maker of so many marvellous things, and this is the way of loving such an inventor, because in truth a great love springs from a deep knowledge of the thing that one loves, and if you do not know it, you may love it but little or not at all. And if you love it for the good that may come to you from it, and not for its sublime virtue, you are like the dog who wags his tail and makes a fuss over the man who can give him a bone, and even if he knew the virtue of that man, would esteem it only if that virtue profited himself" (*Treatise*, fol. 74).

In the profound passage wherein the meager and false religiosity of his contemporaries is contrasted to his own absolute purity of faith, Leonardo not only shows his conviction that God is the source from which the order of all things emanates, but also affirms his certainty of a continual, intimate contact with God. This is the source of his naturalistic aesthetic. He feels that all rules have no other value than as a "corroboration of created form":

"For if you were to use rules in creating, you would never get to the beginning of anything, and your work would be confused" (Cod. Arund., fol. 218 *b*).

In the *Treatise on Painting* (fol. 29) Leonardo defines the process of creation from the inception of the idea, through the application of the principles of painting, the manual operation, to the final stage of actual expression:

"Painting begins in the mind of the contemplator but cannot be accomplished without manual operation. The scientific and true principles of painting first determine what is a shaded object,

Left: *Madonna and Child* – Attributed to Leonardo – London, Duveen Collection

Center: Drawing for Madonna – Dresden, Kupferstichskabinett

Right: Drawing for head of Madonna – Windsor, Royal Collection

Madonna – Attributed to Lorenzo di Credi – New York, R. M. Hurd Collection

Madonna – Attributed to Fernando de Llanos – Zurich, Gottfried Keller Institute

Madonna and Child – Bernardino de' Conti – Bergamo, Carrara Gallery

Right: *Virgin and Child* – School of Leonardo – Milan, Poldi-Pezzoli Museum

what is direct shadow, what is secondary shadow, and what is light—that is to say, darkness, light, color, body, figure, position, distance, nearness, motion, and rest. These are understood by the mind alone and entail no manual operation; and they constitute the science of painting, which remains in the mind of its contemplators; and from it is then born the actual creation, which is far superior in esteem to the contemplation or science which precedes it."

Thus the painter has a means of judgment:

"The adversary here says that he does not want so much science, and that practice in copying natural things is enough for him; to which one may reply that nothing is more deceptive than trusting to our judgment without other reasoning, as experience, the enemy of alchemists, necromancers, and other simple minds, always proves" (*ibid.*, fol. 739).

The painter's imagination, of which he may be only half conscious, plays a large part in the shaping of his creation. Leonardo addresses himself thus to writers:
"You have set painting among the mechanical arts, but truly, were painters as readily equipped as you are to praise their own works in writing, I doubt whether it would endure the stigma of so base a name. If you call it mechanical because it is by manual work that the hands body forth what is in the imagination—you writers set down with the pen by manual work what originates in your mind" (*ibid.*, fol. 15).

The possibilities of the imagination are infinite, even in relation to nature, and Leonardo repeats this more than once. The painter has reason to be proud of his originality, he says, and the famous passage which follows is an invitation to artists to express their own interpretation of nature: "I say to painters that no one should ever imitate the manner of another, for he will be called the grandchild and not the child of nature, because, since there is such an abundance of things in nature, it is better to go to nature than to the masters who have learned from her" (*ibid.*, fol. 78).

Madonna and Child – Attributed to Salaino – Piacenza, Collection of Count Piero Ricci Oddi

The virtues of originality are possible to the painter because the soul is divine by nature: "In similar proportion are the works of men to those of nature, as are men to God" (*ibid.*, fol. 10). The Platonic principle leads to the conclusion that painting directly reflects God, by recreating the face of nature:

34

Madonna Litta – Leningrad, Hermitage Museum

Left: Drawing for Madonna – Paris, Louvre

Right: *Madonna and Child* – Bernardino de' Conti – Milan, Collection of Prince Borromeo

"The deity which invests the science of the painter functions in such a way that the mind of the painter is transformed into a copy of the divine mind, since it operates freely in creating the many kinds of animals, plants, fruits, landscapes, countrysides, ruins, and awe-inspiring places" (*ibid.*, fol. 65).

The painter works back from the perceptions of the senses to the laws governing the world and to the mind of God, which gives them their supreme order, and then reveals what underlies the aspects assumed by nature:

"Necessity constrains the mind of the painter to transform itself into the very mind of nature herself, and to make itself the interpreter between nature and art, commenting in the one on the order shown forth in the other according to her laws" (*ibid.*, fol. 36).

For Leonardo the living world and art were not only closely bound together but were also to be considered equally as manifestations of the spirit become visible in reality.

In the course of combatting error and deeply rooted prejudices, Leonardo's science resolved for itself the problems of art. He saw art as an organic whole, in which the "scientific and true principles" are rules drawn from experience dominated by the faculties of the artist, which are "worthier" than the principles. Foremost among the rules drawn from experience are the teachings of tradition.

Though we cannot be sure that any coherent system of ideas on art was formulated during the fifteenth century in Florence, and though such language as was used in writing about art seems vague, there is much evidence for assuming that the means and ends of artistic activity were well understood. Leon Battista Alberti was the greatest art theoretician of the fifteenth century: Leonardo, intent on discovering a deeper root for the relationship between "judgment," "fantasy," and "manual operation," insists far more than his predecessor on the spiritual nature of art. The idealistic tradition which contributed to his development and to which he returned, the influence of the Platonic Academy with its purely spiritual conception of life, led him to see in nature the revelations of her own soul.

Not without casting barbs at Botticelli or Ghirlandaio, he describes his love for nature and revels in her garb of color. He insists that colors should appear limpid and transparent, like vibrations in

Drawing of Madonna – Florence, Uffizi Gallery

Benois Madonna – Leningrad, Hermitage Museum

Studies for *Madonna with Cat* – London, British Museum, and Paris, Louvre

Study for *putto* – Milan, Biblioteca Ambrosiana

Study for *Madonna with Cat* – Milan, from the collection of Biblioteca Ambrosiana

a vitreous atmosphere. He knows that they cannot be reduced to simple chiaroscuro, but that they must be seen in relation to shadow. Thus it follows that "the shadow of white seen in the sun and air tends to blue" (*ibid.*, fol. 192), and that "the shadows of plants are never black, because where the air penetrates there cannot be complete darkness." In following up the studies which first made him recognize the blue in shadows, he also noted that "the shadows are never of such a character that, because of their darkness, the color is lost where they fall, if the place where the bodies are situated be not dark" (*ibid.*, fol. 477). Leonardo's principle appears to give a theoretical basis to the most advanced coloristic perceptions in Venetian painting: was it from this principle, or, as Vasari would have it, from paintings by Leonardo that Giorgione worked out his artistic reform? Leonardo knew that "that body better shows its true color, of which the surface is less smooth and level" (*ibid.*, fol. 220), and he noted that color and light change according to shapes:

"The dilation or contraction of the shadow, that is to say, the greater or lesser area of the shadow and light on opaque bodies, will be found on the greater or lesser curving of the parts of the bodies which generate them" (*ibid.*, 634).

He finds rules for the appearance of near or distant objects as determined by light, and as a facet of chromatic effects also investigates aerial perspective, a phenomenon ignored by his predecessors:

"The eye would never through linear perspective, without moving, be able to perceive the distance between itself and the object which stands between the eye and another thing, except through the perspective of the colors" (*ibid.*, fol. 505).

The *Last Supper* shows the three types of perspective which he distinguished in this series of observations—perspective "of line," perspective "of color," and perspective "of recession" (*speditione*).

His capacity for probing every phase of artistic activity led Leonardo into the most diversified kinds of investigations. On folio 1412 of the Atlantic codex, in the middle of a passage exhorting mathematicians not to place their faith in books but rather to go back to experience of nature, may be read a rough outline of the history of Florentine painting:

"Hence the painter will produce pictures of small merit if he takes for his standard the pictures of others, but if he will study from natural objects he will bear good fruit—as was seen in the painters after the Romans, who always imitated each other, and so their art constantly declined from age to age. After these came Giotto, the Florentine, who—not content with imitating the works of Cimabue, his master—being born in the mountains, in a solitude inhabited only by goast and such beasts, and being guided by nature to his art, began by drawing on the rocks the movements of the goats of which he was keeper. And thus he began to draw all animals which were to be found in the country, and in such wise that after much study he excelled not only all the masters of his time but all those of many bygone ages. Afterward this art declined again, because everyone imitated the pictures already made; thus it went on from century to century until Tomaso of Florence, nicknamed Masaccio, showed by his perfect works how those who take for their standard anything other than nature—the mistress of all masters—weary themselves in vain."

Leonardo's critical evaluation does not venture outside his own Florentine milieu, and he sees only the original qualities offered by the two great artists, giving no weight to the influences that reached from Giotto to Masaccio along the direct road between master and pupil.

Leonardo expresses a sense of intimate communion with nature in describing the natural phenomena which struck him most forcibly in great moments of his life. His descriptions are comprehensive, and never seem to have been composed by piecing together disparate elements. His vision of nature is never an exercise in linking separate phenomena seen at different times, but bursts forth whole. Instances showing this in a truly amazing way are scattered through his writings.

Lomazzo, in his *Treatise on the Art of Painting* (Milan, 1584), records that "the learned Leonardo da Vinci was in the habit of often making poems, and among other *sonetti*, which are difficult to find, one reads this:

> "He who cannot do what he wishes, should wish to do what he can."

Unfortunately, not one of those "sonnets" which Lomazzo describes as "difficult to find" is known. The line that he quotes is actually the beginning of a poem by Antonio de Meglio, herald of the *Signoria* of Florence. Of the other few verses scattered through Leonardo's pages, none is by the artist himself.

On the other hand, we know that he had an admirable knowledge of music, and if Vasari's account is to be relied on, Leonardo took with him to Milan a silver lyre that he had made "in the form of a horse's skull." He cherished his friendship with Atalante Migliorotti and Franchino Gaffurio, both musicians, and with Lorenzo Gusnasco, a maker of musical instruments, and enjoyed talking with ordinary instrumentalists. Notes relating to sound devices and to acoustics, particularly in relation to methods for improving the acoustics of churches, may be found among his writings. In one of his designs for a musical instrument resembling a pianoforte, the strings are made to vibrate by means of drawing a bow over them. In the Forster codex an exquisite musical phrase springs suddenly from the page, and certain notations suggest that Leonardo toyed with ideas anticipating that instrumental polyphony which was to constitute Palestrina's glory fifty years later. Music, too, had its place in the artist's imagination.

Leonardo might well take a place among the perfect heroes of antiquity. Like them he was strong, possessed of a powerful will, and yet accessible to human emotion. Like them, he could meet adversity with intelligence and continue on the road before him, conscious of a heroic mission. There is no trace in his life of women who may have smiled at him or been his companions.

Leonardo's strength lay in his serene and accurate thinking. He accepted life's transient woes and its inevitable end with a stout heart. His feeling that existence had a social value was strong enough to alleviate all its sadness. He never expresses a trace of that feeling of melancholy isolation so often found in vain personalities. Study of Leonardo's life yields us the same profound joy that we derive from following the destinies of epic figures like Ulysses or Aeneas, or of historical personages such as Dante or Napoleon. A contemporary of Columbus and Copernicus and a discoverer

Studies for *Madonna with Cat* – London, collection of the British Museum

in his own domains, Leonardo opened the way not only to the deeper artistic insights of Raphael, of Giorgione, and of Michelangelo, but also to Galileo's scientific and mechanical conquests and to those achievements which in our time have made a reality of the world which he previsioned.

Leonardo was born April 15, 1452, from the love of Ser Piero da Vinci for a certain Caterina of the town of Vinci, of whom practically nothing is known. According to the Anonimo Gaddiano, she was "of good family." In 1457 she was the wife of Accattabriga di Piero del Vacca and lived in Anchiana on an estate belonging to the family of Ser Piero. A note in the Codex Forster, III (fol. 1) states simply: "Caterina came on the 16th of July, 1493," and another (*ibid.*, II, fol. 64 v), written about 1495, gives the "expenditures for the burial of Caterina." This latter suggests that she may have lived in Milan and that Leonardo was present at her death.

His father came of a family of notaries. Antonio di Ser Piero di Ser Guido, who lived from 1372 to 1468, was a man of law and a farmer: his two sons, Piero and Giovanni, were notaries. Just after the birth of his son Leonardo, Ser Piero (1427-1504) married Albiera di Giovanni Amadori. In Antonio's tax report for the year 1457 the five-year-old "illegitimate" Leonardo figures among the "mouths" of the house after Antonio, who was then eighty-five, Monna Lucia, his wife, aged sixty-four, Ser Piero, who was thirty, and Donna Albiera, aged twenty-one. The family lived modestly, and the early education of Leonardo must have been attended to by the good people about him—his grandmother and his stepmother.

"In the first memory of my childhood," Leonardo writes (Cod. Atl., fol. 162 r), "it seemed to me that, being then in the cradle, a kite came to me and struck me many times with its tail between the lips." Later, studying the flight of this bird of prey to discover the laws of its movements, he was to see in this early recollection a premonstration of one part of his researches.

But the hill and the castle of Vinci, the windmill, the fields, and such things as the men and the monuments of his birthplace could teach him, were abandoned when Ser Piero, soon after the death of Antonio, went to live in Florence, where, in 1469, he and his brother Francesco rented a house in the Sant'Apollinare quarter, in the Via delle Prestanze (today, Via de' Gondi). In 1471 Ser Piero appears as the *procuratore* for the convent of the Santissima Annunziata. In 1484 he is notary for the *Signoria*, counselling the first families of Florence, including the Medici.

In the tax report of 1469, Leonardo, aged seventeen, is still counted as one of the family, which at that time consisted of Antonio's widow, Monna Lucia, and her sons Francesco, with his wife Alessandra, and Ser Piero, with his second wife, Francesca Manfredini.

In 1480 Ser Piero moved to a house in the Via Ghibellina, in the San Pier Maggiore quarter. In the tax register of that year Leonardo is no longer among the mouths of his father's house, which little by little has become crowded with children—Antonio, Lorenzo, Violante, Domenico, Margherita, Benedetto, Pandolfo, Guglielmo, Bartolomeo, Giovanni—born to his third wife, Margherita di Francesco di Jacopo di Guglielmo, and to his fourth, Lucrezia di Guglielmo Cortigiani.

Vasari describes Leonardo's early assaults on the rudiments of learning at Vinci and in Florence, touching on the volatility characteristic of boys so richly gifted: "He took up the study of all kinds of things, and having begun them, dropped them. In arithmetic, in a few months of study, he made so much progress that by raising continuous doubts and difficulties for the master who taught him, he very often confounded him."

Leonardo's mathematical studies must in actuality have gone very little further than arithmetic, since he was to take them up again later, apparently without succeeding in penetrating algebra. No doubt music attracted him more, and from early musical impressions, cultivated and perfected in later years, he must have derived his capacity for detecting in every artistic form a real beauty of sensuous emotion freed of theoretical shackles.

In obedience to his natural bent he soon began to concentrate more earnestly on drawing than on music. Vasari records that Ser Piero showed his son's sketches to Andrea di Cione, called Verrocchio (1435-1488), who advised him to set the boy to studying art, and Ser Piero placed him in "Andrea's workshop." The exact year when Leonardo began to work with Verrocchio is uncertain, but the activities of both artists can be traced in works which Verrocchio is known to have executed during the time that Leonardo remained in Florence with him.

The first problem encountered by Leonardo scholars is that of the relationship between the pupil and his master. Marcel Reymond, the earliest modern student of Leonardo, held that he simply developed Verrocchio's inventions and motifs further. Others have believed that though Leonardo at first assumed Verrocchio's manner, he subsequently put his own stylistic imprint on the master, so that Verrocchio's later work was decidedly influenced by his pupil.

Some have even suggested that Leonardo's great genius needed no master at all, and have questioned the very actuality of his discipleship in the years before he received in January, 1478, from

the *Priori* of the city, a commission for a panel for the Palazzo Pubblico, which was carried out, on the basis of his drawing, by Filippo di Fra' Filippo. The commission is noted by the Anonimo Gaddiano and in the deliberations of the *Signori* and *Collegi* of Florence. The fifteen-year-old youth who presented himself to Verrocchio could have had only as much preparation as his early mental alertness would have enabled him to grasp, but when he left the master at twentyfive, he had already reached his full creative development. It must be supposed that he worked under Verrocchio and gave the master such assistance as was expected of him, especially in view of the fact that from 1472 on he was registered among the painters in Florence. The hand responsible for the subtle landscape drawing in the Uffizi, dated on the day of the Madonna della Neve, August 5, 1473, can hardly be considered that of an apprentice lad.

Much insight is needed to clarify the relationship between master and pupil. To define it as a simple transference to the younger painter of what the older had to teach would be misleading. Verrocchio was an accomplished artist, with a capacity for study and a breadth of mind which gave him access to a sound knowledge of sculpture, the goldsmith's art, music, engineering, and geometry, as well as painting. His style colored Florentine art in the years around 1475 with a refined elegance. His teachings must have been imposed with great respect for the bent and character of his pupils, however, for his workshop was a starting point in the development of the most varied talents. Francesco di Simone, Francesco Rustici, Benedetto Buglione, and Agnolo di Polo, sculptors, as well as Perugino, Lorenzo di Credi, Botticini, and Leonardo all passed under his guidance, and he kept up a close personal relationship with Botticelli and Ghirlandaio.

It appears that he did not give a great deal of personal attention to the finishing of his works, for in the *Baptism of Christ*, executed for San Salvi, he let his pupil Leonardo paint the angel at the left and also retouch the figure of Christ. He left the altarpiece for the Cathedral of Pistoia, commissioned from him about 1478, to Lorenzo di Credi, who may have received help from Leonardo, as is suggested by Leonardo's little *Annunciation* in the Louvre, which has sometimes been considered part of the predella.

Verrocchio also had his share in the pageantry which enlivened the late fifteenth-century Florentine artist's existence. For the tournament of Lorenzo the Magnificent in 1468, celebrated by Pulci, he painted a banner with Lucrezia Donati's device. He created an allegorical device and decorations for the tournament of 1475, famous because of the harmonious verses which Poliziano wrote for it. The festival apparatus arranged for Galeazzo Sforza's reception bore work from his hand, though only descriptions of it remain. Thus Verrocchio's activities reflected a Florentine gift for realistic storytelling, as well as an epic and dramatic sense of life. In this too he was a master worthy of Leonardo.

Left: Head of woman – Parma, Gallery

Right: Head of angel for *Madonna of the Rocks* – Turin, former royal palace

Madonna and Child – Formerly attributed to Leonardo, now to Boltraffio – Milan, collection of Prince Gilberto Borromeo

Virgin Enthroned (section) – Attributed to Lorenzo di Credi – Pistoia, Cathedral

According to early sources Verrocchio's activity as a sculptor began with the *Madonna and Angels* of Bernardo Rossellino's monument for Lorenzo Bruni in Santa Croce, though the only plastic work of his that can be dated earlier than 1470 is the bronze and porphyry tombstone of Cosimo the Elder, quite geometrical in style. In 1472 he carried out the sculpture of the tomb of Pietro and Giovanni de' Medici in the sacristy of San Lorenzo, which is of polychrome marbles decorated with bronze festoons and leaves. A fountain with a bronze *amorino* now in the courtyard of the Palazzo Vecchio, and a terra-cotta *Resurrection* made for the villa at Carreggi and now in the Bargello, were also executed for the Medici. E marble Madonna, another in terra-cotta from the *arcispedale* of Santa Maria Nuova, a bas-relief depicting the death of Francesca Pitti Tornabuoni—part of an unfinished tomb monument—and a bust of a gentlewoman holding a bunch of flowers to her breast are likewise to be found in the Bargello. Most important of his works housed in that museum, however, is the statue of David as a youth, executed in 1476 and sold by the Magnifico to the *Signoria* for the adornment of their palace—a figure so vibrant, animated, and graceful that it has often been thought to have been modelled after the young Leonardo. A representation of David, it is interesting to note, appears in one of the Leonardo drawings in Windsor Castle.

From 1476 on Verrocchio worked on the monument of Cardinal Niccolò Forteguerri for the cathedral of Pistoia, a work which was never finished. From 1478 to 1483 he was occupied with the St. Thomas group for Orsammichele, and in 1479 he began for the city of Venice the Colleoni equestrian statue, one of the noblest sculptures of the Renaissance.

If Verrocchio's work is set beside the Florentine production of Leonardo, it may become clear at what points the paths of the two artists converge, and where they become distinct.

In Verrocchio's studio Leonardo may at first have studied sculpture. Vasari writes of his having made some "heads of women laughing," and Leonardo himself, affirming that "sculpture is of lesser genius than painting," reminds the reader that he has worked "no less in sculpture than in painting, being equally adept at the one and the other" (*Treatise*, fol. 34); the note appears to constitute a backward glance over the activity of his entire life. Lomazzo, in his *Trattato dell'arte della Pittura* (p. 127), writes: "I too own a little head of Christ, as a child, from the hand of Leonardo Avinci himselft, in which are to be seen childish simplicity and purity accompanied by a certain something of wisdom, intellect, and majesty, and all with an air which is that of a tender child, while seeming to have something of the age of judgment—a truly excellent thing." To what extent can we trust

Left: *Madonna of the Spindle* – Attributed to Leonardo – London, collection of Duke of Buccleugh

Right: Portrait of woman – Attributed to Leonardo, but probably by Giampietrino – Montreux, Cuenod Collection

Madonna and Child – Attributed to Leonardo – London, Cecil Morgan Collection

43

Virgin of the Scales – Paris, Louvre

Christ Child and St. John – Bonn on Rhine, collection of Professor Paul Clement

Lomazzo's note? Certainly the qualities which the Milanese painter saw in the fragment in his possession were worthy of Leonardo.

Verrocchio's sculpture frequently has a dramatic and romantic aspect: how much of this was a result of the pupil's influence is not easy to determine. Some believe that the terra-cotta *Resurrection* should be ascribed to Leonardo in its entirety. Others even see Leonardo's hand in the figure of Colleoni. Both Verrocchio and Leonardo were capable of realizing an idea in plastic form, but Leonardo reveals himself a painter at the very first touch, and demonstrates an ability to define masses with a coloristic feeling for light and shadow. Verrocchio's work in the Colleoni monument and in the St. Thomas of the Orsammichele group seems in fact to embody something of the quality of Leonardo.

Vasari notes that Leonardo "in architecture prepared various ground plans and designs for the structure of entire buildings. He too it was who, though still but a youth, first suggested the construction of a canal from Pisa to Florence, by means of certain changes to be effected in the flow of the river Arno." In addition, "he made designs of flour mills, fulling machines, and engines which would be driven by water power; but as he had resolved to make painting his profession, he gave the large portion of his time to drawing from nature. He sometimes made models of different figures in clay, on which he would arrange fragments of soft drapery dipped in plaster; from these he would then set himself patiently to draw on very fine worn cambric or linen. These designs he executed in black and white with the tip of the brush in a most admirable manner, as may be seen in certain specimens from his hand which I have in my book of drawings. He drew on paper also with so much care and so perfectly that no one has ever equalled him in this respect.

"Leonardo was indeed so imbued by God with power and grace, and endowed with so marvellous a facility in reproducing his conceptions, while his memory also was always so ready and so efficient in the service of his intellect, that in discourse he won all men by his logic, and confounded every antagonist, however powerful, by the force of his arguments."

Vasari's descriptions of Leonardo's early activity come alive when he speaks of the youth in phrases that must certainly have been culled from accounts given by those who had known him. We see the young artist living among people who could not possibly have understood the fabulous works that he was turning over in his mind. Vasari recounts further:

"This master was also frequently occupied with the construction of models and the preparation of designs for the removal or the tunnelling of mountains, to the end that they might thus easily afford passage from one plain to another. He likewise showed how, by means of levers, cranes, and screws, great weights might be raised or shifted, in what manner ports and havens might be cleansed and kept in order, and how water might be brought from low places. From speculations of this kind he never gave himself rest, and of the results of these labors and meditations there are numberless examples in drawings to be found among our works of art; I have myself seen very many of them. Besides all this he wasted not a little time, to the extent even of designing a series of cords curiously intertwined, but of which any separate strand may be distinguished from one end to the other, the whole forming a complete circle. A fine and very complicated specimen of these coils may be seen in a print, and in the center of it are these words: LEONARDI VINCI ACADEMIA.

44

Portrait of young woman (Ginevra Benci) – Vienna, Liechtenstein Gallery

Christic child and St. John – Details
from *Virgin of the Rocks* – Paris,
Louvre

Virgin of the Rocks – Boltraffio –
New York, Hurd Collection

"Among these models and drawings there is one by means of which Leonardo often sought to prove to the different citizens who then governed Florence—many of them men of great discernment—that the church of San Giovanni in that city could be raised and steps placed beneath it without injury to the edifice. He supported his assertions with arguments so persuasive that while he spoke the undertaking seemed feasible, although every one of his hearers, when he had departed, could see for himself that such a thing was impossible.

"In conversation Leonardo was indeed so pleasing that he won the hearts of all hearers. Although possessing so small a patrimony that it might almost be called nothing, he nevertheless, while working very little, constantly kept many servants and horses, taking extraordinary delight in the latter. He was indeed fond of all animals, always treating them with infinite kindness and patience. As a proof of this it is related that when he passed places where birds were sold, he would frequently take them from their cages, and having paid the price demanded for them by the vendors, would let them fly off into the air, restoring to them their lost liberty. Leonardo was in all things so highly favored by nature that whatever the matters to which he turned his thoughts, mind, and spirit, he gave proof in all of such admirable power and perfection that everything he did bore an impress of harmony, truthfulness, goodness, sweetness, and grace, wherein no other man could ever equal him.

"Leonardo, with his profound knowledge of art, commenced various undertakings, many of which he never completed, because it appeared to him that the hand could never give due perfection to the object or purpose which he had in his thoughts, or beheld in his imagination—since in his mind he frequently formed some difficult conception, so subtle and so wonderful that no hands, however excellent or able, could ever give it expression. His fancy was so fertile that in philosophizing over natural phenomena he ranged from investigations of the properties of plants to observations of the movement of the heavens, the course of the moon, and the progress of the sun."

What may Verrocchio the engineer have taught Leonardo, and what assistance did the teacher have from his pupil? Certainly the most obscure part of Leonardo's activity is still that relating to his work as an inventor of machinery. In spite of the fact that none of his machines has come down to us, they are drawn with such precision and detail as to suggest that he must have designed and constructed many more than has been supposed by those who believe his activity in the field to have been purely an exercise of his prolific fantasy. However this may be, Vasari gives numerous notes regarding his preparation and training, through which we derive some notion of the inexhaustible variety of ideas fermenting in Leonardo's young mind, and their relation to the activities of Verrocchio.

A passage in the Atlantic codex (fol. 12 v) gives an idea of the milieu composed of scholars and students in scientific disciplines in which the artist moved. Here we find the names of the Hellenist Giovanni Argiropulo, translator of Aristotle's *Physics* and *On the Heavens*, Benedetto dell'Abaco, famous Florentine writer of mathematical treatises, Paolo dal Pozzo Toscanelli, mathematician, astronomer, geographer, and physician, Carlo Marmocchi, student of astronomy, Francesco Filarete, herald of the *Signoria*, Domenico di Michelino, painter and a pupil of Angelico, and "two other gentlemen." In Leonardo's notes may also be found suggestions of a friendship with Botticelli, with whom he debated the subjects of perspective (Cod. Atl., fol. 120 r, 313 r-*b*) and landscape (*Treatise*, fol. 57). He appears to have known Perugino, with whom he is linked in a famous verse in Giovanni Santi's *Cronaca rimata*; this is again suggested on folio 97 recto of the Atlantic codex. Leonardo and Botticelli were both acquainted with Antonio Segni. Leonardo worked for the latter in Rome in the mint of Leo X, and presented him with a drawing of a Neptune at the same time that Botticelli gave him the *Calumny of Apelles*. Some artists, like Ghirlandaio, are mentioned only in notes expressing a decided disapproval of their fashion of crowding figures into their pictures (*Treatise*, fol. 75, 116). Others, Lorenzo di Credi, for example, must have been associates and friends.

Leonardo's mode of life offers one aspect which led Vasari to record how "he liberally welcomed and gave hospitality to every friend, rich or poor, provided he had talent and virtue." This reflects the heterogeneity of his acquaintances and enmities, which may have been what brought about an infamous accusation of which he was acquitted on April 8, 1476, while the freedom with which he habitually expressed his thoughts laid him open to the charge of being an unbeliever.

In the circle of Verrocchio and his friends, Leonardo began to work out his aesthetic system. In the seventh decade of the fifteenth century in Florence, no form of thought was possible outside that promoted by the Platonic Academy: its outlook underlies both Leonardo's adherence to tradition and his new and confident approach to external reality. The beginnings of a system of precepts

47

Left: *Virgin of the Rocks* – Milan, Affori Church

Right: *Virgin of the Rocks* – Milan, Municipal Gallery

Virgin of the Rocks – Benevento, collection of Maria Pedicini-Foglianise

regarding painting, the art which increasingly seemed to Leonardo the logical aim of his activity, appear at this time.

There exists only a very small group of paintings by Leonardo on which no shadow of doubt falls. It is limited to the angel in Verrocchio's *Baptism of Christ*, the two paintings of the Annunciation in the Uffizi and in the Louvre, the *Adoration of the Magi* in the Uffizi, the Benois Madonna in the Hermitage at Leningrad, the *St. Jerome* in the Vatican Pinacoteca, the *Madonna of the Rocks* in the Louvre in Paris, the *Last Supper* in the refectory of the convent of Santa Maria delle Grazie in Milan, the *Gioconda*, and the *St. John the Baptist* in the Louvre.

The many other works which have been grouped around Leonardo's name are either not certainly by him alone or else they are altogether suspect. His authentic work is so profoundly expressive and so miraculous in technique that its authorship is incontrovertible. In sensitive and powerful forms, veiled in a luminous atmosphere which reveals their most delicate modulation, he conveys the ideas that he wishes to present with the effortless directness of a very great artist. From the restricted nucleus of authenticated works emerges a criterion of Leonardo's basic creative capacity which throws light on other paintings and on a few sculptures. His earliest work is linked with the activity of Verrocchio and other students in Verrocchio's workshop. Signs of his genius appear early and with a miraculous limpidity in the *Baptism of Christ* which Verrocchio executed for the church of San Salvi. The painting went later to the Vallombrosian monastery of Santa Verdiana, from there to the gallery of the Academy, and finally to the Uffizi. The contribution from Leonardo's hand, as noted above, seems to be limited to the figure of the angel at the left and to some parts of the figure of Christ. The sensitive modelling of the angel's captivating face, the fluidity of the drapery, the soft nuances with which the color moves from light areas into the darkest shadows, show how far Leonardo had already progressed in 1471 from the powerful yet arid style of Verrocchio. The characteristics of his hand have already become defined.

To Florentine realism, given impetus by Antonio Pollaiuolo's anatomical studies, Verrocchio had brought a fresh love for life and nature. His animals and plants, even those used for purely ornamental purposes, are not derived from classical prototypes but from living models. May not the agnomen Verrocchio, meaning "true eye," allude to the directness and purity of his vision? Leonardo appears to have followed his master's example, carrying his own insight to that high degree of perceptive sensibility which even so early appears in his part of the *Baptism*.

The panel of the *Annunciation*, taken in 1867 from the sacristy of the church of San Bartolomeo at Monte Oliveto outside the Porta San Frediano to the Uffizi Gallery, was variously attributed to

48

Virgin of the Rocks (section) – Paris, Louvre

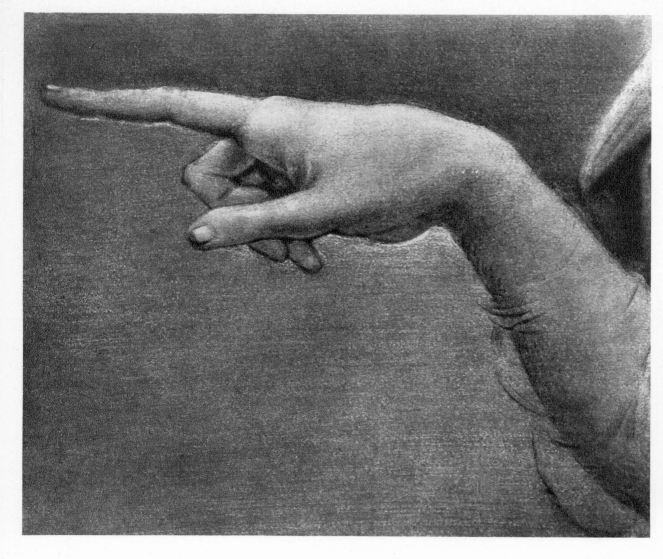

Study for Madonna – Paris, Louvre

Rodolfo del Ghirlandaio and to Verrocchio until the publication of a drawing now at Oxford, unanimously ascribed to Leonardo, for the right arm of the announcing angel. In this clear and serene work Leonardo is even closer to Verrocchio than in the angel of the *Baptism*, and the painting may be confidently assigned to about 1473, i.e., the period of his discipleship. It must have been not long after this that he made the other *Annunciation*, which came to the Louvre in Paris in 1861 as part of the Campana collection. It has been considered a predella for the canvas of the Madonna with St. John and St. Zeno commissioned from Verrocchio by the executors of Bishop Donato de' Medici's will and painted by Lorenzo di Credi with the collaboration of Leonardo and other Verrocchio pupils. The composition is similar to that of the *Annunciation* in Florence, but in the second painting the Virgin is no longer seated; she receives the angel's tidings kneeling, with her hands crossed on her breast. Both panels reflect profound emotion: the trees in the background, the architecture, the details of the flowers, of every object, constitute a setting of ecstatic mood for the miraculous moment of the action, transfiguring the forms of the Virgin and the angel, whose wings still vibrate from its recent flight. The atmosphere is crystalline, filled with that almost solidified light which Leonardo wove from his own fantasy to give his forms their magical and poetic semblance of life.

A number of works executed by Leonardo in his early years survive only in Vasari's account. They comprise a cartoon representing Adam and Eve which was to be woven into a tapestry in Flanders and sent to the King of Portugal; a *rotella* with a monster emerging from a cave, made at the request of his father for a peasant in Vinci; a figure of Neptune made for his friend Antonio di Neri di Antonio di Segna Guidi; a Madonna with a pitcher of water containing flowers, owned by Pope Clement VII; the *Medusa* which was in the Palazzo Vecchio; the head of an angel, known from a copy or an elaboration of the theme executed in Leonardo's own workshop, owned by Dr. F. Sarrasin and now in the museum at Basle. Perhaps the two "Virgin Marys" that Leonardo noted as begun "... ber 1478" have actually come down to us in some form—one in the Benois Madonna in the Hermitage at Leningrad, the other in a lost Madonna with a cat which may be traced through a series of drawings in the Uffizi collection, in Windsor Castle, and in the British Museum. The Benois Madonna's childish face, molded of transparent flesh finely veined with blue, has a delicate spirituality. The painting is strongly worked in chiaroscuro, but the left hand of the divine Child is unfinished.

Fortunately, two works of the first Florentine period remain—the *Adoration of the Magi* and the *St. Jerome*. The *St. Jerome* springs from those anatomical studies to which Leonardo had dedicated himself so earnestly. The saint squats at the entrance of a grotto, his emaciated body re-

Drawings after *Virgin of the Rocks* – Unknown artists of school of Leonardo – Paris, Louvre

vealing in its tormented pose and in the violent distortion of the arm—elongated to give force to the blow struck against the breast by the hand holding the stone—a tense muscular play which culminates in the passionate expression of the face with its fixed eyes and half-open mouth. The implication of religious fervor emanating from the penitent saint is heightened by the harsh light that accentuates the modelling of his figure. Rocks in the background, and a lion crouching in the foreground, set off the saint's figure with a grandiose decorative effect, emphasizing it as the focal point of the composition.

The painting has suffered through restorations and cleaning; Cardinal Fesch, who owned it before Pius IX secured it for the Vatican, is said to have obtained the picture by buying first the lower part, which was serving as the cover of a chest, and then the upper part from a shoemaker who had been using it as a top for his table. The panel is also unfinished in parts; yet it is of an amazing evocative power, and the strong impression that it made on Leonardo's contemporaries is evident from the variety of inspirations to which it gave rise.

The figure of St. Jerome is transfixed at the culminating moment of its movement. As in all his works, Leonardo here sustains the sense of action at a level not reached by any of his Florentine contemporaries: even Michelangelo preferred to represent his figures in the moment just preceding the climax of their movement.

More profound in its abstract ideas and more complex in its development is the *Adoration of the Magi*. The painting was not finished, but the composition is completely worked out, and even those parts left in the chiaroscuro underpainting are as eloquent as though they had been carried to detailed completion. The panel was commissioned from Leonardo in March, 1482, by the Scopetine monks of San Donato for the high altar of their church. The artist was to have delivered the completed work after twenty-four or thirty months. But Leonardo left Florence without finishing the painting, and the monks had another canvas made for their church, following the same specifications, by Filippino Lippi. Leonardo's half-finished work remained in the house of Amerigo Benci, then passed to the Medici family, and in 1794 was placed in the Uffizi Gallery, as was Lippi's.

The center of the painting is occupied by the seated figure of the Virgin, who bends over the Child a face suffused with a wonderful sadness. The Christ child reaches out for the gift offered by the eldest of the Three Kings. The two holy figures are barely sketched in, but toward them, toward the profoundly evocative revelation of the Son's divinity, is drawn a mass of awed and anxious faces under the high, immobile foliage of a tree. At either edge of the painting the crowd terminates in a standing figure: to the left, an old man wrapped in a mantle meditates with head bent and chin resting on his left hand; to the right a slender youth, in whom Leonardo may have been portraying himself, looks out at the external world from which the emotion of the faithful flows toward the Virgin. The background of ruins is animated by men on horseback. Endless time must have gone into the elaboration of the picture: so extensive a series of drawings as that made for this panel has not been found for any other work by Leonardo. The theme must have appealed to him greatly, and in the dynamic expression produced by the vehemence of gesture in the figures, he was perhaps attempting to symbolize the change which the coming of Christ was to bring to humanity. The pagan world, represented in perfect aesthetic beauty in the picturesque background of ruins traversed by horsemen, is a far different world from that in which mankind perceives simultaneously its own anguish and its salvation by the Redeemer.

In face of the miraculous science of the *Adoration*, we find it difficult to believe that Leonardo's hand was responsible for the almost naively naturalistic portrait of Ginevra Benci which hangs today

in the Liechtenstein Gallery in Vienna. On the back of the painting is a representation of a juniper branch entwined with a strip of paper on which are the words *Virtutem forma decorat*, within a crown composed of a laurel branch and a palm frond. As may be seen from the back, the lower part of the panel, which must originally have shown the hands, has been cut off. The young woman in the portrait was wedded on January 15, 1474, at the age of seventeen, to Luigi Niccolini; the portrait was probably made a short time later. Its attribution to Leonardo is relatively recent. Though the style of the painting shows that it is undoubtedly by an artist of the school of Verrocchio, we know too little of Lorenzo di Credi's early activity to ascribe to him a picture in which Leonardo's taste and observant eye are certainly present. According to Vasari, Leonardo painted the portrait of Ginevra at the time of his return to Florence in 1500, but in view of Leonardo's masterful handling of form in that period, it seems impossible that he should have returned to the simplicity of Verrocchio or of his fellow pupil, Lorenzo di Credi. Still more difficult to assign to Leonardo is the Madonna of the Munich Pinakothek, which is tinged with characteristics of Verrocchio but has a northern flavor. The work is not easy to evaluate because of dubious areas resulting from restoration and retouching. If it is ascribed to Leonardo himself, one must suppose him to have studied German paintings and prints; no trace of such influence, however, appears in any of his succeeding works.

From his drawings comes information regarding another painting made in execration of Bernardo Bandini de' Baroncelli, one of the leaders of the Pazzi conspiracy. Baroncelli fled to Constantinople, but from there was sent back in chains to Florence, where he was executed on December 19, 1479. A drawing of the horrible figure of the hanged man exists, accompanied by a note from Leonardo's hand describing the garments he wore: "A tan-colored small cap, a doublet of black serge, a lined black jerkin, a blue coat lined with fur from foxes' throats, and the collar of the jerkin faced in velvet stippled with black and red, black hose."

In 1482 Leonardo went to Milan. In a letter to Ludovico il Moro which is preserved in a rough copy by some other hand than his in the Atlantic codex (fol. 391 r-*a*), he describes his abilities as follows:

"Most Illustrious Lord, having now sufficiently seen and considered the proofs of all those who proclaim themselves masters and inventors of instruments of war, and finding that their invention and use of the said instruments does not differ in any respect from common practice, I am emboldened without prejudice to anyone else, to put myself in communication with Your Excellency, in order to acquaint you with my secrets, thereafter offering myself at your pleasure effectually to demonstrate at any convenient time all those matters which are in part briefly noted below:

"1. I have plans for bridges, very light and strong and suitable to be carried very easily, with which to pursue and at times flee from the enemy, and for others, solid and indestructible by fire or assault, easy and convenient to transport and place in position. Also plans for burning and destroying those of the enemy.

"2. When a place is besieged I know how to cut off water from the trenches, and how to construct an infinite variety of bridges, mantlets, and scaling ladders, and other instruments pertaining to the said enterprise.

"3. Also, if a place cannot be reduced by the method of bombardment, because of either the height of its glacis or the strength of its position, I have plans for destroying every fortress or other stronghold, even if it is founded upon rock.

Left: *Madonna with Christ Child and St. John* – School of Leonardo, sixteenth century – Milan, Burchil Sala Collection

Center: *Madonna and Child with St. John* – Cesare da Sesto – Milan, Melzi d'Eril Collection

Right: *Madonna and Child with St. John* – School of Luini – Bergamo, Carrara Gallery

Bernardino Luini – Madrid, Prado

Christ Child and St. John – Marco d'Oggiono – London, from the Mond Collection

51

Left: *Christ Child and St. John* – Mabuse – The Hague, Museum

Right: *Madonna of the Dove* – School of Luini – Milan, Galeazzi Collection

Christ Child and St. John – Boltraffio – Naples, National Museum

"4. I have also plans for making mortars, very convenient and easy to transport, with which to hurl a tempest of small stones, causing great terror to the enemy by reason of the smoke, and great loss and confusion.

"5. And if the engagement be at sea, I have plans for constructing many engines most efficient for offense and defense, and ships which can resist the fire of all the heaviest cannon, as well as powder and smoke.

"6. Also, I have ways of arriving at a given spot by mines and secret winding passages, made without noise, even though it may be necessary to pass underneath trenches or a river.

"7. Also, I can make covered chariots, safe and unassailable, which will enter the ranks of the enemy with their artillery, and there is no body of men-at-arms so great but they will shatter it. And behind these the infantry will be able to follow quite unharmed and unhindered.

"8. Also, if need should arise, I will make cannon, mortars, and light ordnance, of very beautiful and useful shapes, quite different from those in common use.

"9. Where it is not possible to employ cannon, I can supply catapults, mangonels, *trabucchi*, and other engines of wonderful efficacy not in general use. In short, as the variety of the circumstances may necessitate, I can supply an infinite number of different engines of attack and defense.

"10. In time of peace I believe that I can give you as complete satisfaction as anyone else in architecture pertaining to the construction of buildings both public and private, and in conducting water from one place to another. Also, I can execute sculpture in marble, bronze, or clay, likewise painting, in which my work will stand comparison with that of anyone else, whoever he may be. Moreover, I would undertake the work of the bronze horse which is to endue with immortal glory and eternal honor the auspicious memory of the Prince your father and the illustrious house of Sforza. And if any of the aforesaid things should seem impossible or impracticable to anyone, I offer myself as ready to make trial of them in your park or in whatever place shall please Your Excellency, to whom I commend myself with all possible humility."

On another page of the same codex (fol. 324 r) there is an inventory of the studies and objects which Leonardo took with him from Florence:

"Many flowers drawn from nature
A head, full face, with curly hair
Certain figures of St. Jerome
Measurements of a figure
Drawings of furnaces
A head of the Duke
Many designs for knots
4 studies for the panel of St. Angelo
A small composition of Girolamo da Figline
A head of Christ made with the pen
8 St. Sebastians
Several compositions of angels
A chalcedony
A head in profile with fine hair
Some bodies seen in perspective
Some machines for ships
Some machines for waterworks
A portrait head of Attalante raising his face
The head of Jeronimo da Feglino
The head of Gian Francesco Boso

Leonardo – Drawing – Studies of two children kissing – Windsor, Royal Collection

52

Study for composition of *Last Supper*
— Venice, Academy

Study for composition of *Last Supper*
— Windsor, Royal Collection

  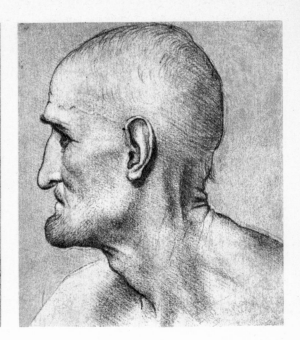

Many throats of old women
Several heads of old men
Several nude figures, complete
Several arms, legs, feet, and postures
A Madonna, finished
Another almost finished, in profile
A head of Our Lady ascending into heaven
A head of an old man with a very long neck
A head of a gypsy
A head with a hat on
A representation of the Passion, made in relief
A head of a girl with knotted braids
A head with a coiffure"

The letter to Il Moro gives a valuable list of the engineering abilities that Leonardo possessed, the artist receiving only a passing mention. The inventory, on the other hand, shows how greatly the artist valued his studies from life, and how strongly, in treating the St. Jerome theme, he felt his tie with such "anatomist painters" as Andrea del Castagno and Pollaiuolo, whose works represented a major stylistic trend in Florentine art. The detailed studies of coiffure are evidence of his training under Verrocchio. A strictly Tuscan theme is the "small composition of Girolamo da Figline." The "head of Attalante" probably portrayed the musician Atalante Migliorotti, who, according to the Anonimo Gaddiano, was Leonardo's companion on the trip to Milan and during his first sojourn at the Milanese court.

The "head of the Duke" suggests a portrait of Francesco Sforza, perhaps a first sketch of Leonardo's idea for the monument also referred to in the letter. The reference to a "Passion... in relief" possibly offers invaluable evidence as to sculptural works that he may have produced. These may be touched upon only by reference to certain works that have been remarked upon as revealing some affinity with Leonardian traits of the early Florentine period—the *Discord* in the Victoria and Albert Museum in London, the *Flagellation* in the Perugia Museum, and the *Deposition* in the Carmine (the last two in bronze). These are in some manner comparable to the *Resurrection* in the Bargello in Florence, in which another hand besides Verrocchio's reveals itself directly and with dynamic expressiveness in certain details of the faces and figures. However, the soundest attribution of these sculptures refers them to Francesco di Giorgio Martini. The piece of chalcedony was presumably a gem for engraving. Worthy of remark are the aquatic and navigational devices, a reflection of those studies in hydraulics to which Leonardo's first experiments as an inventor were devoted.

To Leonardo's Florentine period must also be assigned the singular outline of a romantic narrative found in letters addressed to a certain Diodarius of Syria, in which the author, speaking of a mission carried out in Armenia, describes strange places, the terrible catastrophe of a mountain falling into the sea, and the apparition of a prophet. These letters gave rise to the supposition that Leonardo lived in the Orient at some time between 1477 and 1480, but this hypothesis has been abandoned, since a number of documents prove that, until he went to Milan, his residence in Florence was uninterrupted.

The Anonimo Gaddiano, Leonardo's earliest and in general his most reliable biographer, relates that the artist went north with Atalante Migliorotti to present a lyre to Ludovico il Moro on behalf

Studies for figures and composition of *Last Supper* – Paris, Louvre

Last Supper – Milan, Santa Maria delle Grazie

Detail showing Saint Peter from *Last Supper* – Milan, Santa Maria delle Grazie

of Lorenzo the Magnificent. In his notes, however, Leonardo makes a point of recording that he was called to Milan to design and cast the statue of Francesco Sforza. Leonardo's letter may have been sent to the ruler of Milan by a representative at Florence. Certainly it describes the abilities which would have been required of a military engineer who could replace Bartolomeo Gadio, the Sforzas' military engineer, who had just then reached the end of his activity.

Two Leonardo codices, the Trivulzianus and that in the Institut de France bearing the designation *B*, are rich in references to military works and may be linked with the first period of the artist's activity in Milan. Corio records that early in 1484 representatives of Sixtus IV, the King of Naples, and the Duke of Ferrara met in Milan, joining forces with the Duke of Milan against the Venetian republic. It may have been in relation to this league that Leonardo speculated on ways of striking at an enemy with attacks carried out by men who could breathe under water through a double tube, or who travelled in apparatus for underwater navigation. Studies toward perfecting the mechanism of the ship's log, and probably also a model for automatic ignition of a fuse by means of a flint which could likewise be used under water, may also relate to this time. There are drawings for such military devices as those mentioned in his letter to Il Moro, which seem the forerunners of mechanisms used in more modern times, such as devices for strengthening fortifications and making them more easily defensible and others for effecting their capitulation more quickly. A sheet in the British Museum bears examples of battle cars, and in other places Leonardo demonstrates the use of high-firing mortars and hand grenades, and investigates the possibility of using asphyxiating gases.

A famous drawing in the Royal Library at Windsor represents a shipyard equipped with a powerful windlass to lift and haul pieces of heavy caliber. Fine drawings in the Atlantic codex (fol. 26 v-*b*, 9 r-*a*, 56 v-*a*, 56 v-*b*) picture small cannon mounted on trolleys and furnished with attachments to facilitate rapid aiming, small cannon formed of a fan of barrels, and a kind of machine gun consisting of small gun barrels mounted on a rotating prism bringing each barrel in turn into firing position. Drawings of weapons, of crossbows with shields, of devices for throwing darts, of steam cannon, are interspersed with others showing contrivances for stationary and rotating bridges, and designs for boats and fortifications.

Leonardo may have considered compiling his military studies into a treatise similar to that written by Roberto Valturio, which he must often have consulted. In fact, in the course of remarks on the need for defenses "to maintain the principal gift of nature, that is, liberty," and to "enable the people to support their good and just rulers," he states that he has begun to write of fortified walls. But Leonardo was engaged in many other labors. Notes in Ms. B relate to projects for work in connection with the castle of Milan, the cathedral, the church of Santa Maria in Pertica of Pavia, the church of Santo Sepolcro and the abbey of Chiaravalle in Milan, as well as in the Ticino region and in Brescia. His projects for a city to be built on the banks of the Ticino, perhaps enlarging the ducal city of Vigevano, may belong to the time just after the plague of 1484-1485, which left 50,000 dead in its wake. A passage in the Atlantic codex (fol. 65 v), perhaps addressed to Ludovico

Last Supper (section) – Milan, Santa Maria delle Grazie

Last Supper (section) – Milan, Santa Maria delle Grazie

Last Supper (section) – Milan, Santa Maria delle Grazie

Last Supper (section) – Milan, Santa Maria delle Grazie

Last Supper (section) – Milan, Santa Maria delle Grazie

il Moro, offers Leonardo's proposals for the construction of an ideal city—the dream of all Renaissance architects and princes—which seem to be based on themes taken from Hippodamus of Miletus. City plans are also frequently referred to in Ms. B.

For Leonardo the city was not simply a complex of buildings but a political and social entity. First, he proposed a double set of streets, an upper one for free circulation, a lower one for vehicular traffic and house services. The streets were to be as wide as "the general height of the houses" and equipped with valley tile for draining off water, which was then to be dispersed into a network of canals and sewers through special conduits on the street level. The houses and other buildings would have been constructed in obedience to that feeling for geometrical delimitation of space which inspired all Renaissance architecture, and which appealed to Leonardo because of the grace of its separate, three-dimensional elements.

Genoa gave itself up voluntarily to the Duke of Milan and Leonardo was called upon to devise means for defending the new territory. He designed and described (Ms. B, fol. 64) a way of "loosing a flood of water" in the direction of Lucca "against an army or a fortification," using the waters of the Arno. Between 1487 and 1490 he was occupied with work on the castle of Milan, designing a

Detail from *Last Supper* – Milan,
Santa Maria delle Grazie

Last Supper – Copy attributed to Marco d'Oggiono – Paris, Louvre

Last Supper – Attributed to Francesco Melzi – Ponte Capriasca (Lugano)

Copy of *Last Supper* (section) – Marco d'Oggiono – Leningrad

square before it that would have been dominated by a high domed tower. The military defenses were to have consisted of a surrounding moat always full of water, and the outworks were to be strengthened by concentric double interior walls. He also designed a secret passage, a new ravelin, and a pavilion in the castle garden for the Duchess of Milan.

Plans submitted by other architects for the roofing of the cathedral's transept, where an octagonal dome was to rise, did not inspire confidence in the *consiglio della fabbrica*, and the committee assigned to Leonardo the task of making a model for a central cupola with others grouped around it, and with spires which would have afforded architectonic effects suited to the Gothic lines of the whole. In 1490 he agreed to remake the model with some changes, but neglected to follow the plan through.

He was turning his attention to Lombard industry; it appears that at this time he was designing machinery for textile manufacturing. In his manuscripts are many drawings of machines for making warp cord (Cod. Forst., II, fol. 49 v, 50 r), for twisting yarn (Cod. Atl., fol. 2 v-*a*), for winding the yarn on a spindle (*ibid.*, fol. 393 v-*a*), and for shearing cloth (*ibid.*, 397 r-*a*, 161 v-*b*).

Leonardo's machines are directly expressive of their function; he appears to feel both their practical rationale and utility and their beauty. Delicate and almost sentient are those required to carry out fine, light work, massive and bulky those intended to exert greater force. The materials he uses, wood most usually constituting the main part, are always treated with simple elegance, never wasted. His machines are reduced to their functional essentials, and his drawings of them present marvellous

Portrait – *Lady with an Ermine* (Cecilia Gallerani) – Cracow, Czartoryski Collection

effects of lucidity. He seems to feel that the value and beauty of a machine must be immediately recognized in the sketch of it.

He showed the same familiarity with the laws governing the science of construction as do those who work in the machine idiom today. Through them he arrived at the principles governing friction and the mechanics of force. A poetic spirit underlies the conception of the builder and inventor when he writes:

"Force is a spiritual power, an invisible energy arising from motion which by impact of violence from without causes bodies to be distorted or displaced, imparting to them a marvellous animation; it compels all created things to assume new shapes and places. It runs with fury to its own desired undoing, expending itself as opportunity offers. Slowness strengthens it and speed weakens it. It is born of violence and dies through liberty" (*ibid.*, fol. 302 r).

All his explanations are given in precise language, language reduced to the essential tautness that characterizes also his moral observations. More purely scientific labors went hand in hand with his work as builder and artist. His workshop in the Corte Vecchio, which stood where the Palazzo Reale is today, must have been huge, and its various divisions must have been set up to carry out the different projects which occupied his mind.

At times these were purely mundane. Toward the end of 1488 he began working on the apparatus for the festival celebrating the marriage of Gian Galeazzo Sforza to Isabella of Aragon, which took place in January and February of the following year. In the Porta Giovia castle he made a leafy gallery which seemed a marvel to all who saw it. A year later he lent his hand to an allegorical representation entitled "Paradise," ordered by Ludovico il Moro and performed on January 13, 1490. Its libretto by the court poet Bernardo Bellincioni still exists. A half sphere gilded on the inside represented the sky, and in it were seven planets in niches rotating under the signs of the zodiac. The planets were represented by actors who stepped out to chant the praises of Isabella, Duchess of Milan. In 1491 Leonardo assisted in the preparations for another *divertissement*, the tournament held in honor of Ludovico il Moro's marriage to Beatrice d'Este. For this he devised an invasion by a company of dancing and singing Scythians or Tartars, costumed as savages and led by a rider mounted on a big horse and wearing a cloak covered with golden scales and painted with peacocks' eyes.

In these same years Leonardo busied himself with the problems of flight, resuming investigations and thoughts that had had their inception perhaps earlier in Florence. In Ms. B (fol. 74 v) there

60

Left: Study – Windsor, Royal Collection

Right: *The Resurrection* – Berlin, Kaiser Friedrich Museum

appears a completed design for a flying device, accompanied by cautionary directions for trying it out: "This device you should try over a lake, and you should wear at the waist an inflated skin, so that in falling you will not drown." He had already conceived of a machine to which a recumbent man would give the motive power necessary for raising and directing it by moving a rudder with his neck and a wing with each arm. We can imagine that the apparatus hung by a rope from the ceiling of his workshop, guarded by lock and key from spying eyes while its parts were being tested. Studies for mechanical flight were accompanied by investigations of living creatures equipped with wings—the bat, the eagle, the butterfly. Leonardo had no thought of recourse to magic in these things; his writings show him as consistently opposed to spiritism, astrology, and alchemy. After 1490 he broke off his studies on flight, resuming them only in 1505, at Fiesole.

Very little information remains regarding those who worked with him during this time. A certain carpenter named Bernardo Maggi di Abbiategrasso made the model of the dome for the cathedral under his direction. From Leonardo's own notes and from other documents we know that he lived together with his pupils and disciples, among whom were one Gian Giacomo Caprotti di Oreno called Salai, whom he had taken into his household as a boy, and two persons called Marco and Giannantonio; these were probably Marco d'Oggiono and Giovanni Antonio Boltraffio. We know too the names of several of Leonardo's friends—the De Predis, Fazio Cardano, the Marliani, Giovanni Taverna.

The first decade of Leonardo's stay in Milan, though it appears to have been taken up primarily with scientific researches and with military and mechanical works, was also rich in projects for paintings and for the great monument to Francesco Sforza. On April 25, 1483, he accepted the commission for an altar painting offered by the confraternity of the Immaculate Conception, which had a chapel in the now demolished church of San Francesco Grande in Milan. The brothers Evangelista and Ambrogio de Predis were to collaborate with him on the altar painting. The confraternity had previously had a richly carved *ancona* made by a certain Maestro Giacomo del Maino. The central part of the *ancona* was intended to contain the figure of the Virgin with the Christ child in a rocky landscape. It was agreed that the painting should be delivered in time for the Feast of the Conception of that year, on December 8, 1483; it was finished only in 1486, and became the object of a protracted quarrel concerning payment which was finally settled in 1509. The painting, first

Leonardo – Study – Hamburg, Kunsthalle

61

Madonna and Child – Fresco – Vaprio d'Adda, Villa Melzi

Drawing of St. Sebastian – Windsor, Royal Collection

Portrait of woman – Munich, Pinakothek

displayed for the devotion of the faithful in the confraternity's chapel, can be traced through its sale by the church of San Francesco to Gavin Hamilton in 1785, then to a Marquess of Lansdowne and again to an Earl of Suffolk, and finally, in 1880, to the National Gallery in London. However, a problem arises owing to the existence of another painting now in the Louvre, believed to have been in Paris since the time of Francis I, which repeats the same composition with only minor differences. Careful examination of the two paintings has convinced most scholars that only the Louvre painting is entirely from the hand of Leonardo himself. Various hypotheses have been advanced as to the history of the two paintings, none resolving the problem satisfactorily. In the Paris painting the angel beside the Christ child points to the infant St. John. It was believed that the gesture could have been understood only by the Florentine worshippers, who would have seen in it a glorification of their patron saint, and it was concluded that the painting was brought in its finished state from Florence. In a letter of August, 1507, which Charles d'Amboise gave to Leonardo for the *Signoria* of Florence, there is a reference to a painting that Leonardo was obligated to make for His Most Christian Majesty. It may be supposed that the original painting in the church at Milan was copied by Ambrogio de Predis under the direction of Leonardo himself. Certainly the Paris *Virgin of the Rocks*, which has in our own time been transferred to canvas, is finished in every part, and in such good condition that the hand of Leonardo can be clearly seen. Seated in the center of the painting, the youthful Virgin draws the infant St. John protectingly into the group by placing her hand on his shoulder. He joins his hands in prayer and kneels to Christ, who blesses him. Beside the divine Child is an angel looking out from the picture. A vast dark grotto in the background, its crags enlivened by flowering plants, sets off the figures in their sublime corporeal beauty and patterns them into a geometrical complex centering in the face of the Virgin. The iconography is very original: no angelic train accompanies the Virgin, who is sheltered only by an awe-inspiring geological setting, as she tenderly watches over the two nude babies, attended by the angel. The softness of every detail seems

62

to spring from the artist's miraculous ability to transcend the absolutist painting of his greatest Tuscan predecessors and to establish a direct communion with nature and life. The naturalistic aesthetic which Leonardo patiently built up in those observations from which the *Treatise on Painting* was compiled is fully revealed in this, his first finished work. Everything in this pictorial vision appears to come alive because of its own truth, and the spirit which animates it is a kind of poetry accessible to all.

It is difficult to establish a chronology of Leonardo's reading, for his mention in his notes of the books that he read is highly erratic. His study of Jordanus Nemorarius' *De ponderibus*, Euclid's *Elements*, and the *Prospettiva* of Witelo may undoubtedly be referred to the years around 1490, as may also anatomical studies continuing those begun earlier in Florence. Investigations regarding the effects of light and shade in perspective and the gathering of the philological notes comprised in the Codex Trivulzianus must have been carried on at the same time. We know that toward the middle of June, 1490, Leonardo went to Pavia with Francesco di Giorgio Martini to advise on the construction of the cathedral. When Beatrice d'Este and Ludovico Sforza were married in January, 1492, he directed the tournament of Galeazzo Sanseverino. He was also employed in many different kinds of work carried out at various times in the ducal residences in Milan, Pavia, and Vigevano.

At this time he also worked on the monument of Francesco Sforza. The political calm which descended on the duchy after 1485 made it possible for Il Moro to ask for speedy completion of the sculpture. In 1489, it appears, the preparatory studies were hardly finished, and presumably nothing visible or tangible was being accomplished, because on July 22 of that year the Duke wrote to Pietro Alemanni, the Florentine ambassador to Milan, asking him to find "a master capable of doing the work." The letter may have pushed Leonardo into beginning on the sculpture. An engraving by Antonio del Pollaiuolo, representing a rider whose horse rears above a fallen man, shows a motif designed earlier for the same monument. Leonardo appears to have used this as the starting point for his design. Frequent drawings accompany the development of the work, and on August 31 the model must have been quite far advanced, because at that time Leonardo asked Platino Plato, orator

and poet, for an epigram to put on the statue. Some notion of the sculpture may be derived from a number of small bronzes, like the rearing horse bearing a rider in the Budapest Museum, which were inspired by Leonardo's small models. It was not long, however, before Leonardo had a new idea for the monument which would make it easier to cast. At the beginning of Ms. C of the Institut de France he wrote: "On April 23, 1490, I began this book and began again to work on the horse."

In 1492 the model for the statue must have been finished. Vasari says that it was of a "marvellous size," and Luca Pacioli describes it more precisely in the *Trattato de divina proportione* as "12 *braccia* in height from the top to the ground, and weighing 200,000 bronze *libbre*." Giuliano da San Gallo saw it and "spoke with Leonardo about the casting that he wished to make of his horse." In November, 1493, the festival for the marriage of Bianca Maria Sforza, sister of Galeazzo, to Maximilian of Austria took place in Milan. At that time the clay statue dominated a square surrounded by "marvellous and beautiful edifices" which had been erected before the castle, and the enthusiasm which the work aroused has left an echo in verses by the poets Baldassarre Tacconi and Lancino Cuzzio.

According to what can be gathered from Leonardo's drawings, from miniatures, and from a print discovered by the French scholar Courajod, the statue represented Francesco Sforza on horseback, his head bare, holding the baton of command in his right hand and the reins in his left. The horse's forelegs rose above a fallen warrior. Leonardo's studies for the head of the *condottiere* appear to be synthesized in the very beautiful drawing in the Malcolm collection in the British Museum, showing the head and bust of a warrior in fanciful armor. The face in the London drawing is quite similar to profiles found in the Codex Trivulzianus and elsewhere, and if it was in fact intended as a likeness of Francesco Sforza, it does not show the physiognomic characteristics which we find in sculptures by other artists and in painted portraits of that duke. However, Leonardo may have wished to create and idealized head like those in the statues and reliefs of Verrocchio which he himself may have worked on in his master's studio.

But the casting of the statue never came about, and only the studies prepared by Leonardo with such infinite pains remain to us. Probably Il Moro was unable to find the money to pay for the

bronze that was needed, and the great model was abandoned. It may not have been entirely ruined in 1499 by the Gascon bowmen who used it as a target, as Vasari says, but Sabba da Castiglione reports that it suffered serious damage. Ercole I of Ferrara requested it of the Cardinal of Rouen, who at that time governed Milan for the King of France, but the Cardinal excused himself on the ground that he could not give it away without the King's orders.

Along with the works already mentioned, others followed each other in rapid succession. Leonardo designed bronze doors for the cathedral of Piacenza, executed a portrait, now lost, of Lucrezia Crivelli, a painting of the Nativity, also lost, for the Emperor Maximilian, a Madonna for Mattia Corvino, and a portrait of Cecilia Gallerani which may perhaps be identified with the *Lady with an Ermine* in the Czartoryski collection in Cracow. Though spoiled by restorations, this last painting is exquisitely graceful. The fine and animated head, presented in three-quarter view, shows direct study from life, as does the detail of the hand. It has been suggested that the ermine symbolizes Il Moro, because of a passage in Leonardo's notes comparing the little animal to the Duke of Milan. Others interpret it as an allusion to the name of the Gallerani, since the Greek γαλῆ connotes stone marten, weasel, or ermine—all belonging to the marten family, with which the animal held in the lady's arms may be identified.

The portrait, born of an affection to which it gives enduring life, must have seemed to Leonardo a task worthy of the painter's art. In its best-preserved sections—the breast, the hand, and parts of the dress—the Cracow painting bears that mark of truth which surely discloses the hand of the master. These portraits and the studies for the *Madonna of the Rocks* have a close relation to the lovely *Head of a Woman* in the Parma Pinacoteca. The period in which Leonardo painted the portraits of Il Moro's favorites seems to have coincided with a moment in which he became a courtier, seeking out and inventing examples of such literary forms as the fable, the prophecy, the allegory, the enigma. Here his scientific knowledge and his moral principles must have stood him in good stead, for even as a courtier he towers above the gentlemen and poets of the court of the Sforzas.

In September, 1494, having dropped the plans for the monument to Francesco Sforza until the work could be cast. Leonardo began reclamation work in the Sforza lands near Vigevano, freeing one vast tract of water and converting another to a grazing area.

Notes in the manuscripts allow us to assign to this time Leonardo's acquaintance with Luca Pacioli, with Giacomo Andrea di Ferrara, an architect and widely learned man, with Bramante, whose taste for centrally planned buildings he shared, with the Greek scholar Giorgio Merula, with the architect Giovanni Battaggio da Lodi, and with Pietro Monti, a curious soldier, engineer, and theologian who had lived for a while in Spain and returned to Italy to acquire great fame as a tactician. We find mention too of Fazio Cardano, a famous jurisconsult and amateur in the sciences, and of

Left: Drawing for *Leda* – Sodoma – Paris, Louvre

Center: Drawing for *Leda* – Sodoma – Paris, Louvre

Right: Drawing for *Leda* – Attributed to Leonardo – Paris, Louvre

Detail from the painting *Christ in Limbo* by Sodoma in the Pinacoteca, Siena

9

65

Giovanni Marliani's sons, authors of the *De proportione motuum velocitate* and accomplished scholars in the field of geometry.

Leonardo worked simultaneously on the Sala delle Asse in the Sforza Castle and on his *Last Supper* in the Dominican convent of Santa Maria delle Grazie. He was also asked by Padre Francesco Sanson, minister general of the Franciscan Friars Minor, for an altar picture for the church of San Francesco in Brescia, and made studies for the composition which date from this time.

The Sala delle Asse must have been finished in April of 1498, and shortly thereafter the Saletta Negra on the *ponticella*, which the painter was decorating for Il Moro under agreements with the architect Ambrogio Ferrario. The dates are established by two letters from Gualtiero di Bescapè to Il Moro. One, dated April 20, 1498, refers to the work in the Saletta Negra, and that of April 21 mentions it again, saying that "no time is being lost in the Saletta Negra." Bescapè adds that "on Monday the *camera grande de le asse*, that is, of the tower, will be cleared. Master Leonardo promises to finish it entirely for September, and that it can be used in the meantime, because the scaffolding he will put up there will leave space for everything below."

No trace remains of the few vestiges of painted decoration earlier found in the Saletta Negra. Only the black stone of the fireplace is left, with its inscription: *Atra in fine suo fiunt omnia quae inter mortales felicitatem habuisse videntur.*

Fragments of the decoration in the vault of the Sala delle Asse were still visible to those who cleaned off the whitewash—"a great motif of interwining cords [joining together the branches of trees] which rise from the imposts toward the top of the vault, where, as though on a keystone, was painted the ducal coat of arms surrounded by a crown. The recess of the vault described above was painted with extraordinary delicacy in such a way that the interlace of cords mentioned above formed a pergola. In the spandrels of the vault, between one lunette and the next, were painted great plaques bearing inscriptions in gold on a white ground." Beltrami, who gave the above-quoted description of the fragments in 1905, had the painting restored after removing what was still left, and succeeded in recreating something of the decorative suggestion evoked by the great trees with their interlaced boughs tied with cords in an austerely geometrical design.

It is the *Last Supper* that gives us the fullest idea of Leonardo's expressive power. Here indeed the unique personal character of the artist manifests itself supremely. Perhaps also the consciousness of his individuality functioning in the moral and social order is another of Leonardo's triumphs. As a man who knew himself to be at his best when he was his own master, his forcefulness derived not only from his works but also from his dialectic capacity. This last is confirmed by Vasari, the Anonimo Gaddiano, and that Milanese painter who in his *Antiquarie prospettiche romane* called him "another Cato in his speech." His extraordinary explorations gave him a masterful understanding

not only of nature but also of the men around him. Even the external history of the *Last Supper* seems to prove that Leonardo brought his intelligence to bear in art with such intensity that it was as though he were approaching his work with the aim of making it a complete justification of his spiritual life.

It is probable that he began work on the painting after 1495, when G. D. Montorfano painted the *Crucifixion*. The decoration in the lunette over the *Last Supper* was probably executed around 1494, since it includes the monograms of Ludovico and Beatrice, and that of their first son, Massimiliano, who was born in 1493, but not of the second, Francesco. Beatrice's monogram, however, was used even after her death in 1497, and the presence of the insignia of the Duke of Bari, without any indication as to the bearer, could be explained by the fact that the title was not at the disposal of Il Moro, because Gian Galeazzo Sforza's widow was still living. She in fact claimed it at the death of Il Moro.

Details of landscape background of *Mona Lisa* – Paris, Louvre

Study of clasped hands – Windsor, Royal Collection

67

Left: Copy of *Mona Lisa* – Spanish artist – Paris, Cheramy Collection

Center: *Mona Lisa* – Sixteenth-century copy attributed to Salaino – Innsbruck, Luchner Collection

Right: *La Gioconda velata* – Madrid, Prado

In a lost register of the church of Santa Maria delle Grazie could be read under date of the year 1497 a note on work done in the refectory, where Leonardo was then painting. In January, 1497, Raymond Pérault, Bishop of Gurk, visited Leonardo at his work. On June 29, 1497, Marchesino Stanga received an order to hasten the completion of the painting, and several anecdotes survive relating to the urgency with which both the prior of the church and Il Moro pressed the artist to finish his work.

Luca Pacioli mentions the finished work in his dedication to Il Moro of the *Trattato de divina proportione* (on which Leonardo had collaborated); this is dated February 9, 1498. He alludes to the religious value of "this beautiful symbol of the ardent desire for salvation in this solemn and dedicated place of bodily and spiritual refreshment," and observes: "It would be impossible to imagine with greater vividness the apostles' reaction upon hearing the voice of infallible truth pronouncing: "*Unus vestrum me traditurus est*." Leonardo's own thoughts regarding his work may be found in several notes from his hand. In the second manuscript of the Forster codex (fol. 62 v) he describes the attitudes of those grouped about the table:

"One who has been drinking and has left the cup in its place and turned his head toward the speaker;
"Another, twisting the fingers of his hands together, turns with stern brows to his companion;
"Another with his hands spread open, showing the palms, shrugs his shoulders up to his ears, making a mouth of astonishment;
"Another speaks into his neighbor's ear and he, as he listens to him, turns toward him to lend ear, while he holds a knife in one hand in the other the loaf half cut through by the knife;
"Another who has turned, holding a knife in his hand, upsets with his hand a glass on the table;
"Another rests his hand on the table and stares;
"Another breathes heavily with open mouth;
"Another leans forward to look at the speaker, shading his eyes with his hand;
"Another draws back behind the one who leans forward and looks at the speaker between the wall and the man who is leaning."

The interrelation of the figures in the four groups of the finished painting seems already determined. In the same manuscript are to be found suggestions for models for the figures:

" Christ
Count Giovanni of the household of the Cardinal of Mortaro
Alessandro Charissimo
of Parma for the hand of Christ."

Sabina Poppaea – French School, XVI century – Geneva, Museum of Art

The group of drawings in which Leonardo elaborated his various ideas for the painting, beginning with that for the head of St. John now at Windsor Castle, shows that the loftiness of the theme was

constantly present to him. One drawing among those at Windsor indicates that he thought at one point of depicting the moment which is the origin of the Communion. In all of his preliminary studies, the material offered by reality is immediately transfigured. To his contemporaries the fresco seemed a miracle, as is evidenced both by written commentaries and by the innumerable copies made of it, and the work still appears, when the light conditions permit of its being seen at its best, like a "legend which signifies great things." The moment portrayed is that in which Christ enters upon his martyrdom, setting himself apart from the humanity that has betrayed him in the person of Judas, accepting agony and offering his forgiveness. The Eucharistic symbolism is certainly present to the painter, but in a different and higher sense than the traditional one. Christ's figure is calm, more than human; each apostle is moved by terror or amazement according to his age and character; Judas is transfixed in his physical and moral baseness. The figures of the apostles thrust themselves forwarrd in agitated movement, their faces and the dynamic masses of their bodies forming geometrical arrangements. The expanse of white tablecloth before the figures is hardly broken by the marvellous detail of the objects on it. The partitioned walls, enlivened by the patterned hangings, converge toward three windows at the back: the light that comes through these openings seems to clash with that falling on the scene from the front and transfiguring every detail.

The *Last Supper* was not painted in water-based color on wet plaster, according to ordinary fresco technique. Leonardo appears to have painted on the dry plaster, using a medium containing oil and varnish. The exterior side of the wall was exposed to the north wind: quite soon the splendor of the tints became dulled, and the color flaked off. Unintelligent restorations, as well as the vandalism of the French soldiers who in 1796 used the refectory as a stable, have caused serious damage. Even in its mutilated state, however, the painting reveals the inspired quality of Leonardo's art, his mastery of subtly blended hues, and the magical truth of the various details which give the sublime scene its living reality.

To the right side of Montorfano's *Crucifixion*, Leonardo added the figure of Il Moro with his first-born, Massimiliano, and a Moorish page, and to the left that of Beatrice d'Este with their second son, Francesco. These were executed in oil, and nothing now remains but their partly effaced contours.

The misfortunes which beset Il Moro's life from the time of Beatrice's death became more and more grave. In imminent expectation of war with France, Leonardo had to resume his engineering. He dropped his work on "the horse," giving up the casting of it, and interrupted various other undertakings. In the summer of 1498 Ludovico gave the artist a vineyard of sixteen rods near San Vittore, a gift confirmed by a letter of April 26, 1499, in which are recorded the merits of both the painter "whom none of the ancients or moderns has surpassed" and the engineer. Leonardo was put to work on other tasks, among which may be mentioned a plan for a palace commissioned by a private person; on a sheet of the Atlantic codex we find a note from this patron in his own hand stating his wishes. Leonardo was also occupied with various fortification projects. He was very likely in Il Moro's suite during the journey of reconnaissance that the Duke made to his Ligurian possessions in order to ascertain the state of their defenses. The destruction of the harbor of Genoa, which occurred at the beginning of 1498, is in fact recorded by Leonardo. On April 1, 1499, he must

Monna Vanna Nude – Biblioteca Primoli – Kaupe Collection, Pallanza – Leningrad, Hermitage

Monna Vanna Nude – Rome, collection of Contessa Maria Cristina Pes di Villamarina

Monna Vanna Nude – London, Spencer Collection

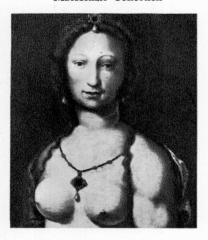

have returned to Milan; in a note on folio 249 recto of the Atlantic codex he says that he finds himself with "218 lire."

The events relating to the French invasion have left no trace in his writings. On folio 104 *b* of the Atlantic codex we have a note reporting: "On the first day of August, 1499, I wrote here concerning weight and motion." On the 19th of that month the French took Valenza. On September 2, Il Moro left for Innsbruck, entrusting military operations to Galeazzo Sanseverino and the custody of Milan and of the castle to Bernardino da Corte. In less than twenty days the French seized the duchy, and on October 6 the governor's treachery gave the city into their hands.

Leonardo remained; we know that Louis XII admired the *Last Supper* and the statue of Francesco Sforza, and perhaps the artist found friends and commissions among the invaders. However, in the beginning of January, after consigning six hundred ducats with a "letter of advice" to Giovan Battista Goro, he left for Venice in company with Luca Pacioli. At this time he wrote on the back of the cover of a manuscript, along with notes beginning with the words, "Buildings by Bramante," and referring to Milanese happenings: "The Duke has lost his state and his goods and his liberty, and no work will be finished for him."

After stopping for a short time in Mantua, Leonardo arrived in Venice. We know that he struck up a friendship with a certain Stefano Ghisi who lived in the parish of the Santissimi Apostoli, that he studied the movement of the ocean tides, and that he made geological observations and topographic reliefs in connection with projects for defenses on the eastern boundaries of the republic at Gradisca and Gorizia, on the Vipacco and the Isonzo.

When Il Moro returned to Milan on February 4, 1500, neither Leonardo nor Luca Pacioli moved from Venice. It is probable that Leonardo had returned to his music and painting. Lorenzo Gunesco of Pavia, wood carver and maker of musical instruments, wrote on March 13 to Isabella d'Este that Leonardo was in Venice, and had shown him a "very lifelike" portrait of her. The lovely drawing of Isabella's profile in the Louvre must relate to this portrait, which repeated one previously left in Mantua. It is rendered with that precise suavity through which forms fixed by the pencil take on a kind of intellectual enhancement, as though they represented a triumph of mind over matter.

Concerning Leonardo's influence in Venice, Vasari comments in his biography of Giorgione (ed. 1568, II, 12): "Giorgione had seen some things from the hand of Leonardo, with a beautiful subtlety of colors and with great relief, effected, as has been said, by dark shadows. And this manner pleased him so much that as long as he lived he always followed it, and in oil painting imitated it greatly."

Leonardo's invention of a *sfumato* manner did in fact come into Venetian painting with Giorgione, and through Giorgione and his staunchest follower, Girolamo Savoldo, Venetian art came to know the beauty of things seen in the open air, rendered in a crystalline atmosphere which appears as though filtered through veils of water. The manner in which Leonardo conveyed his pictorial magic is not known, and it may be that he made some essays in painting in Venice.

As early as April 24, 1500, Leonardo was in Florence, and of the monies which he had caused to be deposited in the Ospedale di Santa Maria Nuova he drew out fifty ducats. As Vasari relates,

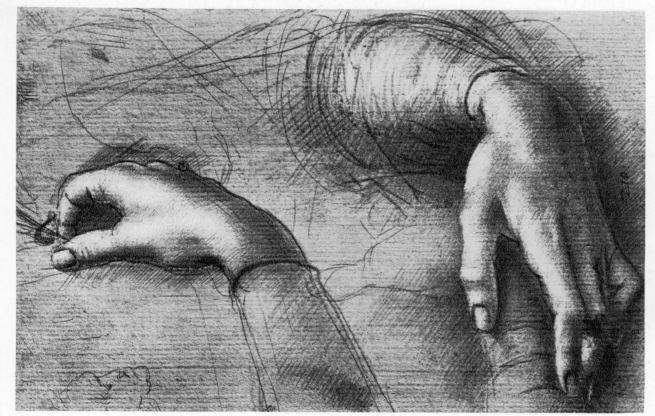

Left: Leonardo – Study of hands for *Mona Lisa* – Windsor, Royal Collection

Leonardo – Drawing for *St. Anne* – Paris, Louvre

he began a series of studies for an *Annunciation* commissioned by the Servite monks, but did not finish it. He resumed his Florentine life and work. Testifying to the impression that he must have made there are the precious verses of Giovanni di Francesco Nesi, a Neoplatonist, and some notes by Leonardo himself which refer to themes that he had discussed with those who were close to him.

The praise of the sun which Leonardo elaborates in Ms. F (fol. 4 v, 5 r) is very close in spirit to writings by Michele Marullo, a Byzantine Greek who fled from the Turks, took refuge in Florence, and there married Alessandra della Scala. The naturalistic aesthetic of Leonardo could not have existed without the concept of light, and the problems and enigmas of the Neoplatonists take on a lucid significance when seen through his thoughts:

"But I only wish I had words to serve me to blame those who are fain to extol the worship of men more than that of the sun: for in the whole universe there is nowhere to be seen a body of greater magnitude and power than the sun. Its light gives light to all the celestial bodies which are distributed throughout the universe; and from it descends all vital force, for the heat that is in living beings comes from the spirit; and there is no other center of heat and light in the universe, as will be shown in Book 4. And certainly those who have chosen to worship men as gods—as Jove, Saturn, Mars, and the like—have fallen into the gravest error, seeing that even if a man were as large as our earth, he would look no bigger than a little star which appears but as a speck in the universe, and seeing again that these men are mortal, and putrify and corrupt in their sepulchers."

Study for *St. Anne* – School of Leonardo – Paris, Louvre

Some light is thrown on the works which Leonardo carried out in Florence by letters from the Duke of Mantua's agents, who were given the task of soliciting from the artist works that Isabella d'Este hoped to obtain from him. In August, 1502, one of these, Francesco Malatesta, replying to the Duke, who had asked him for the design and measurements of the villa of Angelo del Tovaglia at Montughi, reported: "I send Your Excellency the design for the house of Agnolo Tovaglia, made by the hand of Leonardo da Vinci himself, who recommends himself as your servant, and similarly to your Lady... I did not have the drawing colored, nor ornamented with greenery... However, if Your Excellency wishes, the aforesaid Leonardo offers to do it, either in a painting or a model, as Your Excellency desires." On March 27, 1501, Isabella d'Este wrote to Fra Pietro di Novellara, then preaching in Florence: "If Leonardo the Florentine painter is to be found in Florence, we pray Your Reverence to find out what life he leads, that is, if he has begun any work as it has been said that he has, and what work it is, and if he believes that he will stay some time there—Your Reverence then sounding him out as to whether he will accept the undertaking of making a painting for our study, for the which, if he should so content himself, we shall leave the subject and time to himself; but should he appear unwilling, try to induce him at least to make a small painting of the Madonna, pious and sweet, as is his style." A few days later, on April 3, Fra Pietro replied: "I have Your Excellency's letter in hand, and shall do what you ask with all speed and diligence, but from what I can gather, Leonardo's life is varied, and highly uncertain, so that he seems to live from day to day. He has made, since he has been in Florence, only a sketch in a cartoon, depicting a Christ child about one year old who, almost slipping from his mother's arms, grasps a lamb,

St. Anne – School of Leonardo – Milan, Brera Gallery

71

Virgin and Child with St. Anne – Paris, Louvre

St. Anne and Virgin from *Virgin and Child with St. Anne* – Paris, Louvre

Madonna and St. Anne – Bergognone – Milan, Borletti Collection

and seems to hug it. The mother, half rising from the lap of St. Anne, takes the Child as though to separate him from the lamb, which signifies the Passion. St. Anne, also appearing to rise from a sitting position, seems to wish to keep her daughter from separating the Child and the lamb, and perhaps is intended to represent the Church, which does not wish the passion of Christ to be impeded. And these figures are life-sized, but they are in a small cartoon, because they are all either seated, or bending over, and one is placed in front of another, moving toward the left, and this study is not yet finished. He has done nothing else, except that two of his apprentices are making portraits to which he puts his hand from time to time; he is working hard on geometry, being impatient with the brush."

The information given here by Fra Pietro is invaluable, above all because it offers evidence as to the symbolic meanings which Leonardo gave to the religious themes that he carried out. With the same care that he lavished on investigating nature for pictorial ends, he also explored spiritual symbols, in order to render every element in his painting significant.

The friar succeeded not only in gaining information regarding Leonardo, but also in being presented to him, and he wrote to Isabella on April 4: "This Holy Week I had information regarding the painter Leonardo through Salai, his disciple, and others of his devotees, who in order to make all clear took me there on Wednesday. In sum, his mathematical experiments have so distracted him from painting that he cannot abide the brush. As for me, I first adroitly assured him of the good opinion of Your Excellency. Then, seeing him much disposed to gratify Your Excellency, I told him all freely, and at the conclusion things remained thus: if he can detach himself from His Majesty the King of France without trouble, as he hopes, at the latest within a month, he would sooner serve Your Excellency than anyone in the world. But in any case, as soon as he has delivered a little painting which he is making for a certain Robertet, a favorite of the King of France, he will make the portrait and send it to Your Excellency. I left with him two good petitioners. The little painting which he is making is of a Madonna who appears to wind thread on a spindle, and the Child, resting his foot in the basket of spindles, has grasped the distaff and looks attentively at those four rays which form a cross, as though desirous of that cross, and laughs and holds it firmly, not wishing to give it up to the mother, who seems to wish to take it from him."

The *Madonna with the Distaff* which Leonardo painted for Florimond Robertet, secretary of state to Louis XII, is lost. In the collection of the Duke of Buccleuch in England is a charming little painting in which there persists a delicate echo of the bland, pure tenderness with which Leonardo's picture was executed. The cartoon of the *Madonna with St. Anne*, now in the Royal Academy in London, recalls an idea that has appeared in drawings of his younger days. The group offered him a large variety of planes and lines; the religious theme gave him opportunity to develop those mystical meanings alluded to in Fra Pietro di Novellara's letter. The composition is again pyramidal; the central figures, seen one above the other, are balanced by the forms of St. John and the lamb. A landscape behind them was to have enfolded the figures. The cartoon described in the letter of 1501 must have corresponded in every particular to the painting preserved in the Louvre; this cartoon has been lost, but in the Royal Academy in London there is another cartoon, un-

Madonna and St. Anne – Engraving by Benaglia – Crema, collection of Count Stramezzi

Madonna and Child – Drawing attributed to Raphael – Budapest, Esterhazy Collection

Leonardo – Studies for *St. Anne* – Details from cartoon – London, British Museum

Leonardo – Drawing for *St. Anne* – Venice, Academy

Leonardo – Drawing for *St. Anne* – Paris, Louvre

doubtedly by Leonardo himself, which was probably executed at the time of his second Milanese sojourn. This last was preserved in Milan in the Arconati house, then in that of the Marquis Casnedi. From there it passed to the Segredo family of Venice, who in 1763 sold it to an Englishman, Robert Udny, and as early as 1791 it was in the possession of the British Academy. According to some interpreters of Vasari, the first cartoon was to have served for the panel of the high altar of the church of the Santissima Annunciata. The supposition is untenable, since the painting derived from the cartoon has dimensions very different from those of the *Deposition* designed by Filippino Lippi to take the place of the work which Leonardo did not finish: one measures 1.70 meters in height by 1.29 meters; the other, 3.38 meters by 2.18 meters. Lippi's painting was finished after his death by Perugino, around 1506. It has also been suggested that the cartoon which still exists, and of which beyond doubt Bernardino Luini availed himself for a painting of his now in the Ambrosiana, was produced during Leonardo's first Milanese stay. This does not seem possible, for with the exception of the Luini painting, it gave Lombard painters no such vast inspiration as had been induced by Leonardo's other works. The artist must have kept the cartoon with him in Florence

Cartoon for *Virgin and St. Anne* – London, British Museum

until 1508, when he returned to Milan; and it was from this that Raphael took his inspiration for the *Holy Family* in the Prado, which bears the date 1507.

Scientific work accounted for most of Leonardo's activity. The same thought that Descartes expressed in the *Discours de la méthode pour bien conduire sa raison* (ed. 1668, Paris, Bobin et Le Gras, p. 71), that observation and experience are the more necessary the more one learns, seems to have guided Leonardo's studies as his knowledge broadened. He emerged from his researches only to consider a means of regulating the Arno and of moving the baptistery of Florence, and to give an opinion concerning the cause of the ruin of Monte San Salvatore dell'Osservanza, ascribing it to the natural displacement of the walls owing to the infiltration of water after the work was finished. Leonardo had a companion in his studies, a certain Giovanni di Amerigo Benci, to whom he had confided his map of the world and with whom he discussed cosmography. Vasari reports that Leonardo painted a portrait of Ginevra di Benci at this time, but Ginevra, perhaps the sister of Giovanni di Benci, would at that time have been about forty, and the portrait that Vasari mentions could therefore hardly be identified with the one in the Liechtenstein Gallery in Vienna, and must be considered lost.

In his life of Michelangelo, Vasari says that the *gonfaloniere* Pier Soderini now urged Leonardo to make a statue out of the badly blocked-out piece of marble discarded by Bartolomeo di Pietro da Settignano from which Michelangelo later carved his *David*. During the first fortnight in May, 1502, Leonardo was in Florence. On behalf of Isabella d'Este, Francesco Malatesta asked him to appraise four *pietra dura* vases that had formerly belonged to Lorenzo the Magnificent, and the result of the appraisal is reported in a letter of May 12 preserved in the archives of Mantua: "I have shown the vases to Leonardo da Vinci the painter; he praises them all highly." Leonardo then went to Piombino to study the fortifications there, at the same time seeking a means of "drying up the Piombino marshes" and of building a canal in the valley of the Ombrone. After passing through Sienese territory he joined Vitellozzo Vitelli, one of Cesare Borgia's captains, and participated in the taking of Arezzo.

On June 13 Cesare Borgia left Rome, and by the 21st he had made himself master of the entire state of Urbino. He called Leonardo in haste, and entrusted to him the task of building stairs and drains, and of making various repairs and new constructions. Leonardo noted during this time that Borgia and Vitellozzo had promised to get him "an Archimedes" from the Bishop of Padua, Pietro Barozzi, a scientific writer and friend of Pomponazzi and Nicoletto Varnia. In early August of 1502 Leonardo was at Cesena, as indicated by sundry jottings in Ms. L (cover sheet and fol. 6, 78, 36, 46,

66). On the 18th of that month Borgia, in Pavia, where he had gone to meet Louis XII, signed the ducal letter preserved in the archives of the dukes of Melzi at Vaprio appointing Leonardo to inspect all the fortresses of his states as his architect and general engineer. Events then forced Leonardo to take refuge at Imola with Borgia and diverted him from his work at Cesena. He probably followed his patron, after the latter had put down the revolt of his captains, to Forlì, Perugia, Siena, and Rome. On March 4 Leonardo was again in Florence, where he withdrew fifty gold ducats from the Spedale di Santa Maria Nuova. Pier Soderini then employed him in connection with the construction of the new Sala del Gran Consiglio in the Palazzo Vecchio, together with Giuliano da San Gallo, Cronaca, Michelangelo, and Baccio d'Agnolo, and later asked him to decorate it with a fresco commemorating the battle of Anghiari.

Virgin and St. Anne – Two paintings by Bernardino Luini – Budapest, National Museum, and Milan, Ambrosiana

St. John – Bernardino Luini – Chiusa (Trento), Convent of the Capuchins

At the same time Leonardo must have been working on the portrait of Mona Lisa, daughter of Anton Maria di Noldo Gherardini, who lived in the Santo Spirito quarter of Florence. She was born in 1479, and in 1495 had married Francesco di Bartolomeo di Zanobi del Giocondo. We do not know whether it actually took Leonardo the space of four years mentioned by Vasari to finish the painting. Certainly he gave the highest proof of his qualities in this work. The young woman, dressed in the colors of mourning and seated, with her hands crossed, against the background of a rocky landscape, exercises such a tremendous fascination that every meaning the picture can possibly contain has been explored. The portrait has often been related to those passages in the *Treatise on Painting* (fol. 9) which set forth the aims of portraiture when confronted by "human beauty composed of finely proportioned members":

"Al the senses, together with the eye, wish to possess it, and it seems as though they would do combat with the eye. It appears as though the mouth wished to take it for itself into the body, the ear to be gratified by hearing of its beauties, the sense of touch to penetrate all its passages, the nose also to receive the air which continually breathes from it."

Vasari's not entirely accurate description of the painting sheds some light on the ideas concerning the relationship between art and life which were current in the early sixteenth century, and to which a complete explanation is yet to be given. Leonardo must have studied every element of the painting with the aim of penetrating its inner truth, in order to achieve such a glorification of reality that the portrait would take on a more than natural semblance of life. The landscape background accentuates the suggestion of such a purpose. In the *Treatise on Painting* Leonardo seems to regard the mastery of landscape painting an important part of the artist's technical equipment, and when he himself uses landscape, he appears to intend it not only to relate to the tone of the composition, but

Drawing – Bernardino Luini – Venice, Academy

Virgin and Child – Attributed to Salaino
– Rome, Tabacchi Collection

Virgin and St. Anne – Crema, collection of Dr. Paolo Stramezzi

as a spiritual concomitant illuminating the figure or action represented. The ruins is the *Adoration of the Magi*, the backgrounds in the paintings of the *Annunciation*, the *Last Supper*, and the *Virgin of the Rocks* have the same limpid intensity as everything else from Leonardo's hand. Mona Lisa has a sweet and intimate smile, but a mood of sadness seems to emanate from her tenuous setting of distant rocks stained with azure. The soft, full colors of the works of Leonardo, made more intense and intimate by a light filtered through a dewy atmosphere, reveal themselves as profoundly attuned, in such a way that they vibrate together in a complete harmony.

The picture had immediate reverberations in Florentine portraiture; Raphael and the painters of his time were deeply impressed by its grandeur. Leonardo kept the portrait with him, but had to give it up to the French king. In 1550 it was at Fontainebleau, where Cassiano del Pozzo saw and described it in 1685. It then went to Versailles, and after the Revolution to the Louvre.

During the time when he was painting the *Gioconda* and preparing the studies for the fresco of the battle of Anghiari, Leonardo carried on those investigations into the flight of birds which occupy a large part of Manuscript K. On folio 30 we find a cancelled outline for the study:

"Divide the treatise on birds into four books, the first to treat of flight by beating of wings, the second of flight without beating of wings and with the help of the wind, the third of flight in general, such as that of birds, bats, fishes, animals, and insects, and the last of mechanical motion."

In the same manuscript appear sketches and notes relating to the painting of the battle of Anghiari. We know that on October 24, 1503, after he had gone on behalf of the *Signoria* to "survey the Arno at Pisa to determine the level of its bed" (state archives, Florence, *Libri d'entrata e uscita dei Magnifici Signori*), Leonardo was given the key to the Sala del Papa and adjoining rooms in Santa Maria Novella. On February 28, Benedetto di Luca Buchi received payment for making a scaffolding with steps. On May 4, 1504, the *Signori* and *Collegi* stipulated that Leonardo should have the cartoon ready in February of 1505.

The painting of the battle that was fought at Anghiari on June 29, 1440, between the Florentines and the forces of the Duke of Milan, was to be matched with another by Michelangelo depicting an episode that took place at Cascina during the Pisan war.

On February 28 the cartoon was finished, and Leonardo made a scaffolding which seemed to Vasari a most ingenious device: "Upon compressing it, it went up, and upon lowering it, it became wider." The painting was begun, but Leonardo now wished to follow the instructions given in a passage in Pliny for preparing a plaster to be hardened by heat. Having first made a successful trial of the material, he applied it. However, when the painting was finished, according to what the Anonimo Gaddiano tells us, "below, where the fire reached, it dried out, but above, because of the great distance, the heat did not reach, and the material ran down."

For some time the cartoon remained on view for the admiration of the Florentines. In 1549, writing to Signor Alberto Lollio, Doni advises him to go to the papal palace near the cathedral: "Having gone up the staircase to the Sala Grande, be sure to look at a group of horses and men (a battle scene by Leonardo da Vinci) which will seem to you a miraculous thing." Echoes of the work have come down to us not only in Leonardo's preparatory drawings but also in the form of many copies. One of the most important of these is that by Rubens, an artist who well understood Leonardo's exceptional gift for discerning the character of persons and objects. The dynamism of the *Adoration of the Magi* here took on a fuller expressive power. The artist chose to represent the height of the struggle over the banner on the bridge, and a climactic moment of battle unfolded tempestuously before the eye. The supreme poetry of movement involving the utmost exertions of men and horses fascinated Leonardo. Michelangelo, in contrast, chose to represent a moment preceding the actual

Left: *Virgin and St. Anne* – Lund (Sweden), collection of Professor Lauritz Weibull

Right: Cartoon formerly attributed to Leonardo – Budapest, Esterhazy Collection

Painting attributed to Bernardino Luini – Milan, from the collection of Brera Gallery

79

combat. His soldiers were surprised on the bank of a stream in which they had been bathing, as they accoutered themselves to confront the enemy. They were transfixed in that heroic moment before action begins, when physical strength seems to increase as the heart beats faster.

The two cartoons, which seemed to Cellini as long as they existed "a school for all the world," are lost, but the memory of their heroic grandeur lingered on so long that their importance in the history of art must be recognized.

On May 14, 1504, while Leonardo was still working on his cartoon, Isabella d'Este wrote him: "Understanding that you are staying in Florence, we have entered into the hope of obtaining that which we so much desire—to have something from your hand. When you were in this region, and made a charcoal **drawing** of me, you promised to make a head from it, very soon, in color. But as this appears almost impossible, since means no longer exist for you to move here, we pray you to exchange our portrait for another figure, for which I would be even more grateful; that is, make me a young Christ of about twelve years, who would be of the age that he had when he disputed in the Temple, and made with that softness and subtlety of air which you possess with particular excellence in art. If we should be obliged in this our very great desire, you know that besides whatever payment you yourself wish, we shall be so grateful to you that we shall think only of how to oblige you."

To her agent, Angelo del Tovaglia, Isabella then wrote asking him to present her letter to Leonardo, adding that "If he should excuse himself, saying that because of the work that he has begun for Their Excellencies of the *Signoria*, he has not time, you can answer him that this will serve for recreation and lightening of spirit, when, tired of history, he takes an hour or so for his pleasure and convenience." On May 27, Tovaglia replied to Isabella: "I had Your Excellency's letter together with that for Leonardo da Vinci, to whom I presented it, urging him and counselling him with effective arguments to be sure to oblige Your Excellency with that figure of the young Christ, according to your request. He promised me to do it at such hours and times as were left to him from a work undertaken for the *Signoria* here. I shall not be remiss in pressing the said Leonardo and also Perugino in regard to that other piece; the one and the other both promise me fair, and appear to have a great desire to serve Your Excellency. Nevertheless I do not doubt that we shall have a competition in tardiness; I do not know which one is the more prone to this, though I am sure that Leonardo will be the winner. Nonetheless, for my part I shall be extremely diligent with them."

But Leonardo, who in July of 1505 began a series of studies on the transformation of solids, did not carry out the promised work, and renewed entreaties from Isabella had no power to move him. He had retired to Fiesole in company with Francesco Amadori and had resumed his investigations of flight. In March of 1506 he again notes details on the flight of birds. From the crest of Ceceri, outside of Fiesole, he may have attempted flight in some apparatus which was destroyed in the trials. On July 30 of the same year he obtained permission from the *Signoria* to go to Milan for three months, at the request of Charles d'Amboise, lord of Chaumont on the Loire, who governed Milan in the name of Louis XII. Before the three months were ended D'Amboise asked for an extension so that Leonardo might finish a certain work, and a extension was granted to the end of September. Leonardo did not return to Florence. The *gonfaloniere* Pier Soderini lamented that the artist, after having "accepted a goodly sum of money," had neglected to complete his painting of the battle of Anghiari. On December 16, D'Amboise furnished Leonardo with a letter to present in Florence, in which he remarks on certain excellent works already executed by the master, and

states: "Since we have used him here and by experience tested his different virtues, we see in truth that his renown in the art of painting is obscure as against that which he merits for the other talents of very great virtue which he possesses. And we wish to confess that in the trials made by him for some things which we asked of him in design and architecture, he has satisfied our requirements in such a way that we are not only contented with him, but have acquired great admiration for him."

In Italy, and even more so in France, it was usual to include military engineering and hydraulics under the term "architecture." The works which Leonardo may have carried out are alluded to in his manuscripts (Cod. Atl., fol. 231 *a, b, c*). We find notes on and elevations for a house in Milan in "the *nero* of Sancto Andrea," which may refer to a site near Nirone (now at the crossing of the Via Monte Napoleone and the Via Bagutta with the Via Sant'Andrea). The house may have been for Chaumont, with whom he seems to have lived. It must have been at this time also that Leonardo prepared drawings for the church of Santa Maria della Fontana, founded by Chaumont. A noble effect arises from the arcade surrounding the chapel that formed the ancient nucleus of the church, and from the deep feeling for architectural chiaroscuro and proportion within. At this time too Leonardo began the studies for a monument to Gian Giacomo Trivulzio, marshall of France.

Leonardo did not return to Florence. Francesco Pandolfini, Florentine representative at the court of Louis XII, wrote on January 12, 1507, that the King desired Leonardo to remain in Milan for his visit there, and the King himself wrote to Florence in this same sense. On May 24, 1507, the King arrived in Milan. Leonardo must have gone to Florence in September, however, to prosecute a lawsuit against his brothers, and presented Chaumont's letter to the *Signoria* at that time. The Anonimo Gaddiano says that Leonardo "for six months returned to the house of Giovan Francesco Rustici, a sculptor, in the Via de' Martelli." The lawsuit concerned a legacy from his uncle Francesco and involved possession of the paternal house in Vinci, which was willed to Leonardo with the stipulation that at his death it was to pass into the possession of Ser Piero's sons. The value of the bequest could have had only slight importance for Leonardo, who was assured of considerable income through the liberality of Louis XII. A much deeper concern must have been the desire to be recognized as belonging to the family, as he had been by his grandparents, his stepmother, and his uncle; his brothers had made a point of his illegitimacy. In the house of Piero Martelli, a noted mathematician and an intimate of Rustici, Leonardo began a notebook that survives as the Arundel manuscript. Vasari relates that "Gianfrancesco (who was working on the bronze group of St. John between a Pharisee and a Levite, for the door of the baptistery) would have no one about him but Leonardo da Vinci, who, during the making of the molds, the reinforcing of them with iron, in short, until the statues were cast, never deserted him."

Two notes in letters found in the Atlantic codex (fol. 317 r, 372 r) give information as to the succeeding events in Leonardo's life. Two Madonnas are mentioned in the letters, which may have been directed to D'Amboise and to the president of Dauphiné, Geoffroy Charles, vice-chancellor of Milan:

"I now send Salai to explain to Your Lordship that I am almost at the end of the litigation that I had with my brothers and that I hope to find myself back at Easter (April 23, 1508) and to bring

St. John the Baptist – Paris, Louvre

with me two pictures of two Madonnas of different sizes, which were made for our Most Christian King or for whomsoever Your Excellency may please."

One of these paintings may be that known as the Madonna Litta, now in Leningrad, to which two drawings in the Codex Arundel are related; the other is perhaps that in the Harrys collection in London, which is certainly related to a drawing in the Metropolitan Museum in New York.

In July of 1508 Leonardo was again in Milan, where he remained until September, 1513. Very little information regarding these years has survived; however, the number of sheets bearing studies by Leonardo which may be assigned to this period is huge. Among them are anatomical drawings, in connection with which he must have had some dealings with the Veronese anatomist Marco Antonio della Torre, who came to the university at Pavia from that of Padua in 1510, and who died in the following year at the age of thirty. There are also studies in Ms. F devoted to "aids" for use in hydraulic engineering, to instruments which he calls "aquatic," and especially to a pump for draining swamp land. Leonardo attacked all these studies with an admirable sureness, and the anatomical drawings remain even today the most perfect that have ever been made.

His scientific criteria and his observations as an experimenter give Leonardo the status of an astute precursor. He expanded his observations systematically, delving into matters such as phonetics, for example, which have become sciences only in modern times. He discusses hydraulic machines, the movements of water, the construction of canals for land reclamation, with remarkable thoroughness at every point. His anatomical studies were motivated only in part by artistic considerations. A note on a sheet of Ms. A (fol. 17 r) comments: "In this winter of 1510 I hope to dispatch all that anatomy." Research on the proportions of the human body, which he pursued for a time, was soon abandoned, as was the attempt to arrive at the impossible goal of perpetual motion.

His theory on the reversing of watercourses is discussed particularly in Ms. F, where, together with studies of whirlpools and intermingling currents, there are notes and sketches for a figure of Leda. While Leonardo was occupied with the Martesana canal, which was to be made navigable from Lake Como to Milan and continued from Trezzo to Brivio with two locks, he must have been working on two paintings—the *Leda* and a *St. Anne*, the cartoon for which he had brought from Florence. The *St. Anne* was later taken to France, and from there Melzi probably brought it back with him to Italy. It was bought in Italy in 1629 by Cardinal Richelieu, who twelve years later gave the picture, together with his palace and the collections in it, to Louis XIII. From the latter the painting passed to his successors, and finally to the Louvre. Perhaps Leonardo was helped by some pupil, but it is not inconceivable that the master's imprint is on the work as a whole. A subtle chiaroscuro infuses into all parts of the painting a tenuous softness which mitigates the harsh, plastic rigor of this very originally conceived composition. The rhythms underlying natural phenomena, the essential truths uncovered by a sensitive and passionate study of nature, give a pensive depth to the painting.

It is not certain whether or not the *Leda* has survived: the comments and descriptions of the Anonimo Gaddiano, Vasari, Lomazzo, and Cassiano del Pozzo, who saw the painting at Fontainebleau, have been associated with various works depicting this subject. The most acceptable of these appears to be the painting preserved in the Spiridon collection in Rome. Had Raphael perhaps seen a cartoon for the *Leda*, whose composition he recorded in a drawing now in Windsor Castle?

Left: *St. John the Baptist* – Bernardino Luini – Naples, National Museum

Center: *St. John* – Attributed to Leonardo – Genoa, Palazzo Rosso

Right: *St. John* – Pontedera, Crastan Collection

St. John – Paris, Cheramy Collection

St. John – Salaino – Milan, Ambrosiana

St. John represented with attributes of Bacchus – Paris, Louvre

Leonardo had relations with various personages at the Milanese court of Louis XII. He mentions Count Francesco Torello and Jean de Paris, a painter who accompanied the king in order to depict the country and the principal feats of arms. The poet Jean Lemaire de Belges in his *Plainte du désiré* praised both Jean de Paris and *"Léonard, qui a grâces supernes."*

Did Leonardo, then, inspire the *Bacchus*, executed by followers, which is now in the Louvre? An epigram of Flavio Antonio Giraldi's is thought to refer to it. The painting originally represented St. John; the thyrsus, the crown of grape leaves, the panther skin, and the grapes are later additions. Rather heavy and somber, the painting perhaps only took its inspiration from drawings of Leonardo's. The attribution to Melzi, a painter whose style is so much lighter, seems untenable, and the picture might be ascribed with greater validity to some good Lombard artist outside the immediate circle of Leonardo's followers.

In the years between 1510 and 1513 Leonardo visited various parts of Lombardy for different reasons. Various notes of his recall books that he studied and researches that he undertook. On March 10, 1511, he lost his great protector, Charles d'Amboise. Patronized by D'Amboise's successor, Trivulzio, the artist again began work on the latter's monument, as shown by a note on expenditures. At this time he had associations with sculptors like Benedetto Briosco and Bambaia. He must have retired to Vaprio to continue his studies and escape the disturbances produced by the advance of the armies of Ferdinand of Spain, Julius II, and the Venetians, whose intention was to drive out the French and bring back Massimiliano Sforza, son of Il Moro, to Milan. On May 11, 1513, Giovanni de' Medici was elected pope and took the name of Leo X. On September 24, Leonardo left for Rome, followed by four pupils, Melzi, Salai, Lorenzo, and Fanfoia. On October 10 he was again in Florence and deposited at Santa Maria Nuova three hundred gold florins. In December he was back in Rome, where the architect Giuliano Leni had prepared the room of the Belvedere palace which he was to use as his workshop. In the Atlantic codex (fol. 90 v) a note of July 7, 1514, says that he finished the treatise *"De ludo geometrico* in the Belvedere, in the studio made for me by the Magnifico."* The magnifico in this case is Giuliano de' Medici, connoisseur of the arts of mathematics and mechanics, student of philosophy and alchemy. For his protector Leonardo made a portrait of "a certain Florentine lady" that has been lost. For Baldassare Turini of Pescia, an enthusiastic patron of artists and executor of Raphael's will, he painted a Madonna and the portrait of a boy; these works too have been lost.

He must have occupied himself mainly with scientific studies, and these apparently alternated with

Left: *Holy Family* (section) – Attributed to Leonardo – Leningrad, Hermitage

Right: *The Goldsmith* – Fifteenth-century Tuscan master – Formerly attributed to Leonardo – Florence, Uffizi

St. John – Attributed to Leonardo – Basle, Municipal Museum, Sarasin Collection

Christ Carrying the Cross – Attributed to Leonardo – Vienna, Liechtenstein Gallery

Christ portrayed with donor - Andrea Solario - Milan, Grassetti Collection

Christ Carrying the Cross – Andrea Solario – Rome, Borghese Gallery

Christ – Giampietrino – Milan, Cagiardino Collection

experiments which seemed pure *bizzarrerie* to the papal courtiers, if Vasari's account is to be believed. Vasari also reports that he was then commissioned by Leo X to make a painting, for which he set about preparing a varnish before having even begun the painting, at which the Pope exclaimed, "Alas, this man will never do anything, for he starts to think of the end before the beginning of the work!" We know that during the period of his sojourn in Rome he made several excursions to other cities. He went to Civitavecchia and Florence; on September 22, 1514, he was at Parma, and on the 27th at Sant'Angelo beside the Po. He may have followed Giuliano when he went to Turin to wed Filiberta of Savoy, an event which took place on January 25, 1515. The curious allegorical drawing at Windsor, showing a barque bearing an olive tree drawn by a wolf toward the eagle of Savoy, may relate to this.

He never rested in his researches; during all this time geological studies were interwoven with studies of anatomy, of cosmography, of optics, acoustics, mechanics, and mathematics. He also sketched reliefs from ancient monuments. A note on the measurements of the basilica of San Paolo is to be found on folio 172 recto-*b* of the Atlantic codex, under the date of August, 1516. A certain German Giorgio, led astray by another German, Giovanni degli Specchi, his workman, for some time disturbed the smooth course of Leonardo's labors by causing the master's permit to work in anatomy at the hospital to be taken away.

In July of 1516, Francis I came to Italy, and Giuliano de' Medici, as *gonfaloniere* of the Church, was sent to meet him. Leonardo followed his patron, who fell ill and went back to Florence to stay with his nephew, Lorenzo di Pier Francesco. Vasari intended to record the friendship between Leonardo and Duke Lorenzo when he represented them together at one side of a fresco in the Palazzo Vecchio, as though in conversation. Leonardo followed the pontifical army, remained at Piacenza during the battle of Marignano, then went to Bologna, where the Pope and the King of France had come together. A reference to one of the personages among those assembled there accompanies a sketch of a beardless, bald, elderly man: "Portrait of M. Artus, chamberlain of King Francis I."

When Leo X and Francis I took leave of each other on December 15, Leonardo followed the King to France. He gave Salai permission to buid a house in his orchard at Porta Vercellina, while he took with him a new servant, Giovan Battista de Villanis. They left for France on January 6, 1517, in company with Francesco Melzi. Vasari speaks of Leonardo's departure as though it had resulted from disagreements between him and Michelangelo, perhaps because of the fact that both artists had been asked to prepare a work for San Lorenzo. It appears, however, that Vasari must have dramatized the actual differences existing between the two great men.

Some of the places through which Leonardo and his companions passed in the course of their journey are recorded in the Atlantic codex. On folio 103 recto appears the first note relating to his French sojourn: "On Ascension Day, in Ambosa [Amboise]; 1517, in May, at Cloux." The castle of Cloux had in fact been assigned as a residence to the artist. Leonardo's little band—Melzi, Giovan Battista, and a woman attendant named Mathurine—lived there in solitude. Leonardo did not neglect his studies, though he had been stricken with paralysis in the right arm.

The King came to visit him there, and Cellini leaves a curious record of Leonardo's relations with the French monarch: "I must not fail to repeat the words spoken of him by the King, who said to me in the presence of the Cardinal of Ferrara, the Cardinal of Lorraine, and the King of Navarra, that he believed no other man had been born into the world who knew as much as Leonardo—not so much speaking of sculpture, painting, and architecture, as saying that he was a very great philosopher."

Invaluable testimony regarding Leonardo's activity appears also in the account of a visit paid to him on October 10 of that year by Cardinal Louis of Aragon. It is given in a note written by Antonio de Beatis, the cardinal's secretary: "[His Eminence] with the rest of us went to one of the suburbs to see Messer Lionardo Vinci, the Florentine, an old man of more than seventy years,[3] an excellent painter of our time, who showed His Eminence three pictures—one of a certain Florentine lady, made from life at the instance of the late magnifico Juliano de' Medicis, another of St. John the Baptist as a youth, and one of a Madonna and Child seated in the lap of St. Anne, all most perfect, though one can no longer expect good work from him because of a certain paralysis in his right arm. A well-trained Milanese pupil of his works quite well. And though the aforementioned Messer Lionardo cannot color with that delicacy which was his wont, he works at making drawings and teaching others. This gentleman has written an extraordinary treatise on anatomy, with the demonstration in pictures of the limbs, as well as the muscles, nerves, veins, joints, intestines, and whatever one may wish to see of the bodies of both men and women, in a manner never before achieved by any other person. All this we saw with our own eyes, and he says that he has dissected more than thirty bodies, male and female, of every age. He has written concerning the nature of water, of divers machines and other things—according to what he says, an infinity of volumes, and all in the vulgar tongue, which when they are published will be most useful and interesting."

We know very little more of the activity of Leonardo in France. If Lomazzo is to be believed, he painted a smiling Pomona covered by a triple veil. Probably he also made the arrangements for

---

[3] Leonardo was actually only sixty-five at the time.

the festivities which were held in September, 1517, at Argentan in honor of the arrival of the King, and in May, 1518, at Amboise in connection with the baptism of the Dauphin and the marriage of Lorenzo de' Medici to Madeleine de la Tour d'Auvergne.

At Argentan, as recounted in a letter from Rinaldo Ariosto to Federico Gonzaga, dated October, 1517, Leonardo devised a lion which Francis I, when led up to it, "struck with a staff, and the said lion opened, and within it was all of azure, which signifies love according to the fashion here."

Folios 336 and 337 recto of the Atlantic codex relate to the Romorantin canal which was to link Tours and Blois to the Saône. Other folios bear architectural drawings for a "palace of the King," which some have tried to connect with the castle at Chambord. The last date which Leonardo wrote with his own hand is "June 24, the Feast of St. John, 1518, in Amboise in the palace of Cloux" (Cod. Atl., fol. 24 r); it appears inserted among exercises in geometry.

On April 23, 1519, the notary Guillaume Boreau received a will from Leonardo that gave profound proof of religious feeling and of affection for all who had been close to him. Leonardo was ending his days comforted by the faith of the Church, accepted in its fullest meaning.

On May 2 his life flickered out. Francesco Melzi sent the news to his half-brothers with the following letter:

"To Ser Giuliano and his honored brothers: I assume that you have already received the news of the death of Maestro Lionardo your brother, who was so good a father to me that it will be impossible for me to express the grief which afflicts me at his death. As long as my body holds together, I shall feel perpetual unhappiness, and rightly so, for he showed me daily a very warm and complete love. The loss of such a man is a sorrow to everyone, for nature will not be able to create his equal again. May Almighty God give him eternal rest. He departed this life on May 2, prepared for death, and with all the consolations of Holy Mother Church.

Christ Blessing – Bernardino Luini – Milan, Ambrosiana

"And since he had a letter from the Most Christian King, that he might make a will, and leave his goods to whomsoever he pleased, that is, *Eredes supplicantis sint regnicolae*, without which letter he could not have made a valid will, and everything would have been lost, that being the custom here, the said Maestro Lionardo made a will, which I would have sent you had I found a trustworthy person. I await an uncle of mine who will come to see me and then go to Milan. I shall give it to him, and he will convey it faithfully, since I have not found other means of sending it. As to what is contained in the will, in so much as concerns your part in it, there is only this, that the aforesaid Maestro Lionardo has deposited in Santa Maria Nuova, in the hands of the bursar, four hundred gold crowns, in marked and numbered notes, placed out at 5 per cent, which on the 16th of October will have been there six years, and also some land at Fiesole, which he wishes to have distributed among you.

"There is nothing more concerning you, nor shall I say more, except to offer you what I can of my services, remaining ready to do your will and recommending myself to you.

"Given at Amboise, this day of June 1, 1519.
"Please reply by the Gondi.
Tanquam fratri vestro Franciscus Mentius

GIORGIO NICODEMI

Head of Christ – Attributed to Leonardo – Antwerp, Cathedral

Drawing by Leonardo – Head of young woman – Windsor, Royal Collection

88

THE DRAWINGS OF LEONARDO

For Leonardo a drawing was a thought, a phrase, a sentence. His mind expressed itself in silverpoint, pencil, charcoal, or ink rather than in words. His sketches are a kind of ideography which follows the course of his thoughts and his observations of the life of things. The mobility of his thought can be traced on every sheet, often filled, like one example in the Louvre (no. 2022), with many different graphic ideas. Here is a man reaching out his arm, there an archer, a hygrometer, a Madonna and Child, a group of five apostles, the figure of Jesus from the *Last Supper*, two shepherds conversing, and a man covering his face in desperation. The Madonna and Child, in pencil, may have been sketched later than the rest, but the other figures, in pen and ink, all of the same type and in similar postures, were probably drawn at one time.

Besides the free sketches which express his observations and speculations, there are others revealing the genesis of the images that he painted and carved. The persistence with which he studied the aspects of his figures and the final form of his creation may be seen in such groups of studies as that for the *Madonna of the Cat*: now the Child clasps the cat in his arms; now he holds it under one arm, with the other beckoning to his companions to admire it; now he defends his possession of it; now he holds the cat out to show it off, and now he lays his little head against his friend the cat.

When Leonardo is planning the sculpture of a woman's bust, he moves around it, puts it aslant and erect, sketches it from fully nineteen points of view, lest from any one of them its line should not seem graceful and beautiful.

The first dated drawing by Leonardo da Vinci is in the Uffizi in Florence. On it is written:

"The day of *St. Mary of the Snow* on the 5th of August 1473."

The landscape has a life of its own. It is not simply the tract of countryside which appears in so many paintings as though seen through a peephole, but an extended scene, a panorama. At the left a mountain spur crested with castles and turrets lowers over the valley; and the valley fans out from the horizon into the foreground, among thickets at the foot of hills, and stretches along the banks of a torrent stream. At the right a great mass of stratified rock frames the scene, rising in one tree-crowned peak above another. The legend, which we have shown in reverse, was written in Leonardo's left-handed, mirror-image writing, and some parts of the drawing were also done with his left hand, as for example where the ground drops downward. Landscape as it had been drawn by Domenico Veneziano, by Piero della Francesca at the sources of the Tiber, by Baldovinetti and Pollaiuolo in the broad Tuscan valleys, is rendered by Leonardo with a new spaciousness. Above the heads of the two angels in Verrocchio's *Baptism*, Leonardo repeats such a vista opening out between two mountain masses.

A convention common to many early drawings may be noted in the drawing in question—a series of curling strokes which follow each other above the contours of the mountain, tufting them, echoing others repeated along the rise of the rocky mass.

On the reverse side of the sheet, at the left, is drawn a piled mass of rock at the foot of which springs a bridge. Here too, little spirals indicate the movement of the terrain, the precipitous slopes, the current of the river, and the foliage. Pinnacles rise behind the mountainous mass. Above the landscape is an inscription written with the right hand: "Zoa Morando. I like Anto." Below are a head crowned with leafy sprays, a running nude with lance, sketched in pen and ink, and a woman's

Drawing by Leonardo – Profile of youth – Windsor, Royal Collection

Drawing by Leonardo – Study for male portrait – Windsor, Royal Collection, no. 12498

12

89

bust in red crayon. We have already come upon one of those sheets which Leonardo covered with a multitude of different sketches, but the right hand is still used for the writing. In his earliest drawings he seems to have employed both the right and the left hand to some extent, but he soon uses the left exclusively.

As his touch becomes firmer, the spiral technique also disappears, and the pen runs ever more easily—fluidly, rapidly, flamelike. A growing maturity of line may be observed in comparing the early study *Purity* in Christ Church College, Oxford, with another figure representing the same subject in the British Museum in London. In the first the hand is restrained, almost modest, tracing groups of parallel strokes and defining the tree branches with spirals. The maiden points to the unicorn with the index finger of her right hand. In the second study the symbolic maiden is grouped with the mythical beast, and the line runs flexibly, breaking among the contours, flowing over the damsel's hair, flying among the tree branches, leaping along the distant hills. The conventional spiral appears here and there, as for example in indicating the unicorn's dark hide, but the line is already masterful, moving freely, seeming to turn fluid in defining the forms.

A second convention is established—a flamelike tuft, or breath or tongue of fire, over the foreheads of the figures. In studies for Madonnas, the brows of the Child and the shepherds are topped by flamelike locks which seem to vanish in thin air. These conventions come to an end with the Florentine period, and in the Lombard period only an occasional head appears with feathery, wind-tossed curls.

Once out of Verrocchio's studio, Leonardo begins to touch his drawings with *sfumato*, a subtle shading which etches and veils the flesh with its light vapors, softening all the surfaces. The swift, light line appears to be consumed and rarefied by the atmosphere. It traces vaporous contours, quivers in imperceptible, exquisite modulations of light and shade. Within the nebulous penumbra that seems to caress the faces, under a veil of tenuous shadows, the flesh becomes tender, the eyes languid in the uncertain, reflected light, the features attenuated and consumed in the evanescent shadow, the forms immersed in the suppressed light that expands them in an atmosphere moved as though by tremulous reverberations from some watery surface. The *sfumato* seen in the drawing of 1477, as in the Benois Madonna in Leningrad, reveals that at twenty-five Leonardo had mastered his own means of expression and was an accomplished painter.

After this time he rarely used his right hand in drawings. Those which are erroneously attributed to him may be detected at a glance, for the stroke runs from right to left, as is the case in a

Left, right: Drawings by Leonardo
– Windsor, Royal Collection

drawing which many (Richter, Seidlitz, Giovanni Poggi) have assigned to Leonardo, but which is probably by Francesco di Giorgio Martini. This is also true of a drawing published by Beltrami, which was discovered to be a study not by Da Vinci but by Andrea Solario for the *Virgin with Green Cushion*.

It has been suggested that Leonardo's left-handedness resulted from a disability of his right hand. Antonio de Beatis, secretary to Cardinal Louis d'Aragon, when he visited the painter in the castle of Cloux between 1517 and 1518, noted that the great old man was paralyzed in his right hand. Because of this, he believed that Leonardo was unable to paint any longer. However, even if the painter's right hand had been disabled by some infirmity, he had much earlier found the way to overcome the handicap by making use of his left hand. It is more likely that his left-handedness was congenital and, in the absence of any definite proof that the disuse of his right resulted from illness or injury, we must limit ourselves to noting that, after the earliest drawings, in which he occasionally used his right hand, the stroke consistently runs from left to right.

Prince of draftsmen was Leonardo: no one before him had given such full pictorial life to a drawing. As though with a dagger, he renders all the deep and intimate subtleties of the human body, animates inorganic material with living power, unleashes human conflict with the fury of a tempest. He undertakes to render the inner life of things—of clouds, of rocks, of war horses, of everything in the world, in a shower of strokes like lightning bolts or darts flashing between light and shadow.

ADOLFO VENTURI

Leonardo – Drawing for *putto* –
Bayonne, Museum

91

Portrait of gentlewoman – Drawing – Florence, Uffizi Gallery

LEONARDO IN FLORENCE AND TUSCANY

When Leonardo, some time after 1460, came down from his native Vinci to the capital, Medicean Florence in full flower lay before him.

Newly crowned with its lantern was the shapely mass of Brunelleschi's dome, which gave the city its definitive and characteristic appearance. San Lorenzo, the Annunziata, and Santo Spirito had just been finished, or were in the final stages of their construction; the Pazzi palace had just been begun, or rather, work on it resumed. For some decades the unfinished palace that Brunelleschi began for Luca Pitti had stood, impressive for its style more than its bulk, against the Boboli hill. On the other side of the Arno, Alberti's palace for the Rucellai offered a stately harmony in the classical taste, to which the traditional robustness and vital grace of Michelozzo's palace for the Medicis presented an inspired contrast. In these and in other elegant houses, in churches and convents, could be seen a wealth of splendid sculptures and paintings.

How old Leonardo was when he found himself for the first time surrounded by so many marvels is not known exactly.

He was born in Vinci in 1452 to Ser Piero, a notary of a family "from Vinci" which had counted many notaries among its members, and to a certain Caterina, who was soon afterward married to a complaisant countryman. In that same year Ser Piero himself, twenty-seven at the time, wedded a lady named Albiera degli Amadori.

It may be that at the time of Leonardo's birth Caterina lived in Anchiano, not far removed from Vinci. An old but dubious tradition points out the house there in which Leonardo was supposed to have been born. It does not seem very likely that the woman should have gone to bear her child in the house in which her seducer lived with his family and to which, indeed, he was about to bring a new wife. It may be this same Caterina whom the artist later mentions on several pages of the Atlantic codex as having come to Milan to live with him, and as having died there. It does not appear to have been an event which weighed very heavily in his life.

According to the tax register of 1457, Leonardo's grandfather owned and lived in a house with an enormous garden in the village of Vinci, in the Santa Croce area. Living in the house with him were his consort Lucia, his son Piero with his wife Albiera, the other son Francesco, still a bachelor, and "Leonardo son of the said Ser Piero, illegitimate... five years old."

As Albiera bore her husband no children, it may be presumed that Leonardo, a beautiful and very intelligent child, was kindly regarded and well treated in the family—the more so since at that time legitimate and illegitimate children were brought up together, even in the grandest houses, without protests or opposition on the part of the lawfully wedded wives.

In the sunny countryside around Vinci the boy could enjoy at leisure a blue sky, crystalline air, green fields and woods, and he must then have begun to accustom his prodigious eye to the tremendous hovering mysteries of nature. Of his life in the country as a child, however, our artist records no other memory or dream than that of the kite: "Among the first recollections of my infancy," we may read in the Atlantic codex, "it seemed to me that as I was in my cradle, a kite came to me and opened my mouth with its tail, and struck me several times with its tail inside my lips."

A later tax report, made by Ser Piero for the year 1469, informs us that Leonardo at that time lived with the family in Florence in a house sublet from the *Arte di Calimala* and located in the Via della Prestanza (later Via de' Gondi), by the Palazzo Vecchio. Ser Piero's father, Antonio, and Piero's first wife, Albiera, were both dead. He lived there with his mother Lucia, his second wife

Hanging of Baroncelli, assassin of Giuliano de' Medici – Paris, Bonnat Collection

Tuscan landscape – One of Leonardo's early drawings – Florence, Uffizi Gallery

Drawing of Michelangelo's *David* – Windsor, from the Royal Collection, no. 12591 r

Francesca Lanfredini, who was also childless, and his brother Francesco, married to a certain Alessandra, and the seventeen-year-old Leonardo, again declared "not legitimate."

How long before this had Ser Piero settled in Florence? Possibly he went there after his second marriage in 1465; perhaps after the death of his father, which occurred in 1466 or 1467. It might be thought that even while at Vinci the self-taught youthful prodigy had taken to drawing, and that Ser Piero had taken some of his sketches to Verrocchio from there. But considering the attempts at sculpture, the studies in arithmetic, the time given to music—all described in Vasari's account—and especially considering the fact that by 1472 Leonardo was a painter of such proven worth as to be inscribed in the Company of St. Luke, it must be concluded that his family had arrived in Florence some years previous to his entry into Verrocchio's studio (*ca.* 1468), that is, at least as early as 1465.

It takes one's breath away to think what artists Leonardo must have seen at work around 1470, when he was in the master's shop.

Fra Filippo, Donatello, and Desiderio had disappeared from the scene shortly before, but their schools continued their traditions. Still alive, though in their seventies or over, were Michelozzo, Paolo Uccello, and Luca della Robbia. Benozzo Gozzoli, Antonio Rossellino, Giuliano da Majano, Mino da Fiesole, Antonio del Pollaiuolo, Bertoldo, Verrocchio, and Signorelli were all between thirty and sixty years old and actively at work. Botticelli, Perugino, and Giuliano da San Gallo were very young men at the time. Domenico Ghirlandaio was twenty-one and Benedetto da Majano twenty, Filippino Lippi only thirteen, and Michelangelo not yet born.

Leonardo did not stay long in his father's house. When Ser Piero bought a house in the Via Ghibellina in 1480 and went to live there with his third wife, Margherita, and with the children of this marriage—Antonio, four years old, and Giuliano, one—Leonardo, now twenty-eight, no longer appeared among the "mouths" listed in the tax report. In certain "deliberations of the *ufficiali di notte*" in 1476, regarding a base accusation against him which was adjudged groundless, it is recorded that "Leonardo di Ser Piero da Vinci is with Andrea del Verrocchio."

He lodged and worked in the studio there for at least eight years, as we have pointed out. It is a logical inference that Leonardo, though self-taught in many ways, owed his artistic formation to Verrocchio. Support for the inference appears in the tradition repeated by Vasari and in the artist's own youthful drawings. Granted the power of the pupil's genius, it is easy to believe that the influence later became reciprocal. A subtle Leonardesque smile seems to touch the face of the bronze *David*, which Verrocchio must have modelled before 1476, while Leonardo was still in his studio, for in that year Lorenzo and Giuliano de' Medici gave the work to the *Signoria*, who set it up in the Palazzo Vecchio. It is an exaggeration, however, to attempt to invert the poles, upsetting the

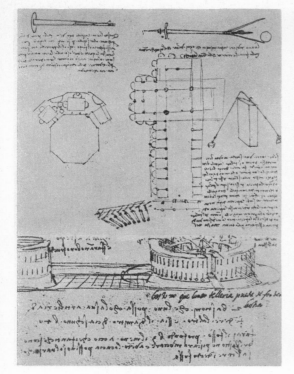

laboriously constructed chronology of Leonardo's early artistic activity and attributing to him as a stripling youth works that he never painted.

In the well-known Uffizi landscape drawing dated August 2, 1473, Leonardo already reveals a new and personal manner of depicting or rather interpreting reality. The youth also shows strong originality of spirit and form in the angel that he painted in Verrocchio's *Baptism of Christ*, commissioned by the Vallombrosian monks of San Salvi. The angel has been attributed to Leonardo since 1510, when Francesco Albertini ascribed it to him in the first guidebock on Florence. The date of the painting is still uncertain and disputed, but a comparison of the landscape in the background, already somewhat Leonardesque, with the above-mentioned drawing supports the notion that it was begun around 1473.

In this period, which we might call Verrocchiesque (*ca.* 1468-1476), the studio had much work to do for the Medicis—for the tournament of Lorenzo in 1469, for the festivities held in 1471 when Galeazzo Maria Sforza came to Florence, and for the tournament of 1475. The festive apparatus got together for these occasions must have fascinated Leonardo and excited his inventive spirit. To this period Vasari assigns various lost works: the cartoon for a tapestry representing Adam and Eve; the famous *rotella* requested of him by his father for a peasant of Vinci; the so-called *Madonna of the Pitcher*; a drawing of a Neptune illustrating Virgil's *Quos ego*, and the celebrated *Medusa*.

To this period also belong the two paintings of the *Annunciation* in the Louvre and the Uffizi, though they are not recorded by the biographer.

The painting in the Louvre reveals originality in feeling and interpretation in spite of a certain timidity, and may be dated between 1469 and 1470. If, as has been suggested, it formed part of the predella for Verrocchio's altarpiece in the cathedral of Pistoia (the Madonna between St. John the Baptist and St. Donato), the date of its execution would have to be moved forward to 1475 or even later. This date, however, would be entirely incompatible with its simple style.

Somewhat later than the Louvre *Annunciation* is the one in the Uffizi, almost unanimously assigned to 1472 and attributed in its entirety or in large part to Leonardo. The figure of the Virgin, the architecture which almost overshadows her, and the classical marble table are motifs from Verrocchio, but the full and abundant folds of her great mantle show an attentive study of beautiful drapery, and the hands are already done with all of Leonardo's exquisite sensibility. The flower-dotted field, reflecting so much love for natural things, the angel's more than human beauty and its divine gesture, at once devout and timid; the magnificent landscape, in which objects become ever more indistinct as they recede toward the horizon, ever more wrapped in a luminous blue which finally melts into that of the sky, reveal a very new personality, that of Leonardo. He would have been about twenty when he painted the picture, and even so early he was capable of applying his original researches and the observations of his acute eye.

In 1478 Leonardo had probably left the master's *bottega*, since on January 10 of that year the Florentine *Signoria*, with at least the consent of Lorenzo de' Medici, assigned to his hand the altarpiece of the tiny chapel of San Bernardo on the third floor of the Palazzo Vecchio, a chapel later decorated by Ridolfo del Ghirlandaio. The panel had been ordered on December 24 of the preceding year from Piero del Pollaiuolo, who also worked for the Medicis. We do not know whether the exchange of artists only fifteen days later was made because Pollaiuolo himself gave up the commission, or as a result of some influence brought to bear by Ser Piero, who was notary to the *Signoria*. However this may be, Leonardo, having received twenty-five florins on account on March 16, paid no further attention to the commission—with the result that in 1483, after he had gone to Milan, the *Signoria* gave the commission for the picture to Domenico del Ghirlandaio, but with equal lack of success.

It appears that the artist had already begun to drift away from his profession, devoting himself

Left: Plans of churches of Santo Spirito and Santa Maria degli Angeli in Florence – Ms. B, fol. 11 v

Center: Drawings by Leonardo – First Florentine period – Florence, Uffizi Gallery

Right: Architectural drawings – On the back of the sheet is written: *Benedictus de Veneclusis de Pisis amicus Leonardi Vinci*, a reference to Benedetto da Vinchiusa – Cod. Atl., fol. 362 v-*b*

Handwritten list of works of art owned by Leonardo da Vinci when he moved from Florence – Cod. Atl., fol. 324 r

95

Head of woman – Oxford, Christ Church College

Verrocchio – Drawing of woman's head – Paris, Louvre

to satisfying his vast curiosity and releasing all his enthusiasm in a multitude of wonderful drawings in which his hand, tracing variations on a theme, seems barely able to keep pace with his imagination. By now there were also mathematical problems and naturalistic investigations to attract and distract him, not to mention attempts at sculpture and architectural exercises.

It was not that Leonardo lacked good intentions; on one of his drawings may be read the notation, "...mber 1478. I began the two Virgin Marys." These were very probably the Benois Madonna in the Hermitage and the so-called *Madonna of the Cat*. The first he left unfinished. Perhaps he was dissatisfied with it—and he was always dissatisfied—for the left hand is only just sketched in, and the mouth of the young mother, who is playing and laughing like a child, is all but toothless. The *Madonna of the Cat* may never have been carried beyond the initial ideas, which have come down to us in drawings in Florence, Windsor, London, and Bayonne. The studies reveal successive moments of a vivid, joyous quality, almost as much as a finished whole.

By now Leonardo was curious about everything; everything interested him; everything distracted him from painting.

On December 28, 1479, Bernardo Bandini de' Baroncelli was hanged outside the windows of the Palazzo del Capitano di Giustizia (later called the Bargello). Bandini had taken part in the conspiracy headed by Francesco de' Pazzi, which led to the assassination of Giuliano. He fled to Constantinople in vain, for the Sultan immediately sent him back to the Magnifico. Leonardo went with the rest

Madonna of the Cat before restoration

Radiograph of *Madonna of the Cat*
made by Dr. Flavio Gioia

Among Leonardo's drawings for Madonnas is the series of studies for the *Madonna of the Cat* reproduced on page 38 and following. They are generally attributed to his first Florentine period, more precisely to the years between 1475 and 1478. From this latter year is Leonardo's note on a drawing now in the Uffizi: "...mber 1478. I began the two Virgin Marys."

One of these was probably the *Madonna of the Cat*, a painting which he may never have completed. It was considered altogether lost until Carlo Noya, a Savona industrialist, pointed out the close resemblance between some of the drawings for the *Madonna of the Cat* and a painting in his possession.

Giorgio Nicodemi, with the concurrence of such Da Vinci students as Mons. Enrico Carusi, Pietro Toesca, and Bernard Berenson, dated the painting around the end of the fifteenth century, and assigned it to the Tuscan orbit of Da Vinci. Adolfo Venturi believed the precious document so close in technique, style, and composition to Leonardo's *Madonna of the Cat* that he did not hesitate to recognize in it the hand of the master himself. Radiographic examination revealed no reasons for denying the attribution. The painting is excellently preserved in its essentials. Professor Hans Sendresen made some slight restorations, repairing a crack in the panel, arresting the flaking off of the color in the background, and restoring the freshness of the original tones.

Verrocchio – *Incredulity of St. Thomas* – Florence, Orsanmichele

to the palace to look on, and portrayed the hanged man in a rapid sketch, adding careful notes on the colors of his clothes.

Some time after this, probably about 1481, he started the *St. Jerome* now in the Vatican Gallery. It is in very poor condition today and is also unfinished in parts. Leonardo did not complete it, nor did he complete the *Adoration of the Magi* (today in the Uffizi), a painting which is very close in spirit and form to the Vatican painting.

The *Adoration* was commissioned in March, 1481, for the high altar of the church of San Donato a Scopeto, just outside the city walls, and Leonardo remained there up to the end of August of that year. In 1482, however, he was already in Milan, and the Scopetine monks turned to Filippino Lippi, who painted his *Adoration of the Magi* to replace Leonardo's. Lippi's painting is now also in the Uffizi.

A glance is enough to show that Leonardo's work must have been considered unfinished by those for whom it was intended. Considered from an artistic point of view, however, the *Adoration* is indeed quite perfect just as it is, in its incomplete preparatory state. Color, of which there are as yet only a few areas in muted tones, might have been too much. Spacious in the background with its strange buildings and band of horsemen, the composition is tumultuously crowded toward the center, calmer in the foreground. Amazingly enough, the painting offers in embryo the master's entire pictorial work: at thirty Leonardo had already created and defined his own almost superhuman imaginary world.

The eternal discussion as to the factors which pushed Leonardo into abandoning Florence cannot be avoided, but it will suffice simply to advance some plausible reasons.

It is hardly credible that the artist should have considered himself unappreciated and neglected, even though a note of depression creeps into some of the Florentine folios of the Atlantic codex. At thirty he had had at least two important commissions, and if he had not carried them out the fault was his and his alone, or better, that of his restless genius.

Nor can it be said that Lorenzo the Magnificent had so slighted him as to oblige him to leave his native city. The Anonimo Magliabechiano, on the whole so accurately informed about our artist, definitely suggests that he frequented the San Marco gardens, but this is a piece of information very difficult to fit into Leonardo's early biography. On the other hand, the Anonimo's statement that Leonardo worked for Lorenzo must derive from some precise information and not simply from a general belief. The interpretation given by Girolamo Calvi to the famous phrase in the Atlantic codex, "The Medici created me and destroyed me," seems the most convincing.

Since friendly relations existed between the artist and the Florentine ruler, it may be concluded that Lorenzo himself either spoke of or presented Leonardo to Ludovico il Moro during the latter's brief sojourn in Florence in 1478, or, when asked to suggest an artist capable of executing the monument to Duke Francesco, proposed Da Vinci.

Three pieces of documentary evidence may be adduced in support of this hypothesis: the record of a "head of the Duke" among other drawings and works mentioned in a list probably compiled

Verrocchio – Detail of monument to Giovanni and Piero di Cosimo de' Medici – Florence, San Lorenzo

13

Detail of Verrocchio's Colleoni monument – Venice

Verrocchio – Angel – Paris, Louvre

Coat of arms of city of Pistoia –
Pistoia, Palazzo Comunale

when Leonardo left Florence; the artist's laconic suggestion at the end of his famous letter to Ludovico, that "the bronze horse may be made," offered as if he were referring to something definite; and the statement in a rough draft for one of his letters: "There is one whom the Duke has brought from Florence to do that work of his..."

The episode of the lyre is only a circumstance, even though the Anonimo Magliabechiano refers to it without mentioning the monument: "When [Leonardo] was thirty, Lorenzo the Magnificent sent him to the Duke of Milan, together with Atalante Migliorotti, to present him with a lyre."

This lyre, and, even more, the many marvels enumerated in the letter to Il Moro explain well enough how Leonardo preferred to spend his time and employ his talents. The letter is certainly authentic, though it is not in Leonardo's own hand.

In April, 1500, after eighteen years of absence, Leonardo found himself once more in Florence, which had been a republic for the past sixteen years, the Medicis having been exiled, it was believed, forever.

Florence was perhaps only a stage between Milan and Naples, where Da Vinci may have followed Louis of Luxembourg, Comte de Ligny. Ligny went to southern Italy in an attempt to assert certain of his rights, or better, to satisfy some of his great ambitions in Naples, relying on French help. Between April and August, however, he left Italy and returned to France, where he died three years later.

Filippino Lippi then ceded to the disillusioned Leonardo, again in Florence, a commission that he had received from the friars of the Annunziata for a double *ancona* destined to ornament the main altar of their church. On September 15 of that year the Servite Fra Zaccaria allocated to Baccio d'Agnolo a commission to make a frame for this *ancona*.

Happy that such a painter deigned to work for them, the Brothers "took him into their house," says Vasari, "paying his expenses and those of his household... and thus he held them in expectation for a long time, but never began anything."

Since the biographer proceeds immediately to speak of the cartoon for the *St. Anne*, to be further discussed below, it has often been concluded that this cartoon was intended for the Annunziata

Verrocchio – *Madonna and Child with Angels* – Paris, Jacquemart-André Museum

Verrocchio – Two representations of Madonna and Child – Florence, National Museum

Detail of Verrocchio's monument to Giovanni and Piero di Cosimo de' Medici – Florence, San Lorenzo

100

ancona. However, the subject would hardly have been suitable for the solemnity of a high altar. Furthermore, the *St. Anne* of the Louvre, a painting undoubtedly derived from this cartoon, is too small for either the specified position in the church or the frame made by Baccio d'Agnolo, assuming that it was his frame that was used for the paintings finally executed for the altar by Filippino and Perugino. The subjects of these had in all probability also been imposed on Leonardo. A *Deposition* from the front of the *ancona*, begun by Filippino Lippi and finished by Vannucci after Lippi's death, is now in the Uffizi, but the *Ascension* that Perugino painted for the back of the *ancona* is still in the Annunziata. The theme for an altar picture was not generally a matter left to the caprice of the artist, even though the artist were Leonardo. One or more erudite ecclesiastics generally worked out the subject and its form.

In the meantime Da Vinci was "living from day to day," as Fra Pietro da Novellara wrote in the spring of 1501 to Isabella d'Este, who was consumed by the desire to have something from the artist. The friar, who was preaching in Florence during those months, goes on to say that Leonardo, "in a year" (that is, since his return to Florence), had worked only on the cartoon for a St. Anne painting, and occasionally added a stroke to portraits that his pupils were executing for him. A short time later Novellara wrote that he had succeeded in learning more about the master from Salai and from other intimates, and that Leonardo was working on a little painting (the so-called *Madonna with the Distaff*) for Florimond Robertet, secretary of state to Louis XII. He was, however, more devoted than ever to mathematics, which had so distracted him from painting that "he could not suffer the brush."

Of the *Madonna with the Distaff* nothing is known. If Da Vinci ever finished it, it must be considered lost, and the presumed derivations from it are not very convincing. Lost to us also is the *St. Anne* cartoon from which Leonardo and his assistants later made the painting of that subject in the Louvre.

To this period the Aretine biographer also assigns a portrait of Ginevra de' Benci, recorded and praised by the Anonimo Magliabechiano as well. But in 1501 Ginevra was more than forty, whereas the woman portrayed in the Liechtenstein picture is much younger, nearer to her age at the time of her marriage to Luigi Niccolini (1474). The Liechtenstein portrait is now generally assigned to Leonardo's youth, or better, to the workshop of Verrocchio. Hence it must be concluded either that Leonardo's portrait is lost, or that Vasari erred in his dating and attribution.

In the meantime Leonardo put his mind to his own fortunes, for the painter's trade suited his temperament very little. Perhaps, having lost all hope in Ligny, he now began to think of Borgia

as a patron. In the first fortnight of May, 1502, he was still in Florence, where he evaluated several precious vases formerly belonging to Lorenzo de' Medici which had been offered for sale to the Marchesa Isabella. In the latter part of the month he was to be found at Piombino, where he investigated the possibility of draining the local marshes. There he was invited to Foligno by Vitellozzo Vitelli, one of Borgia's captains, who was moving on Arezzo, then on the point of rebelling against Florence. Leaving Piombino, Leonardo went through Siena—where he was much interested in the works of the clock in the Mangia—and joined Vitelli at Foligno, accompanying him on his march against Arezzo (June 4-7) and remaining until the city fell, on June 18. He then went to join Borgia at Urbino.

Among Leonardo's papers is a topographic map showing the itinerary followed by Vitelli's army, as well as some sketches of siege apparatus which may relate to the siege of Arezzo. There are also remarks and notes which suggest that Da Vinci profited by this trip to consider the possibility of reclaiming the Chiana valley—a problem which had again come under discussion at the close of the fifteenth century. Perhaps it was then that the artist began to cherish a much expanded plan for the Florentine canal which would have regulated the waters of the entire valley of the Arno all the way down to the sea.

In the documents which can be assigned to the time of this trip may also be read a note to the effect that Vitelli had promised Leonardo an "Archimedes" which existed at Borgo Sansepolcro, and it may have been this promise that moved him most.

Borgia named the artist his "architect and general engineer," and Leonardo stayed several months in Romagna. Before March 4, 1503, however, he was back in his native city, for on that day he drew in person fifty gold florins from the deposit he had made in the Ospedale di Santa Maria Nuova. Evidently, he had not acquired a fortune in Borgia's service.

Now begins the third Florentine period, dating from March, 1503, to May, 1508—a period which could have been extremely productive for Leonardo the painter, as evidenced by the quality of the *Mona Lisa* and the fame of the *Battle of Anghiari*.

He must have set to work on the portrait immediately after his return, for Vasari says, probably depending on some verbal tradition, that "having toiled four years on it, he left it unfinished." Vasari's statement that it was unfinished must also have been culled from contemporary myth, for it is in complete contradiction to his own very minute although second-hand description. Vasari could never have seen the masterpiece.

Mona Lisa di Anton Maria Gherardini, born in 1479, married in 1495 to Francesco del Giocondo, was twenty-four years old in 1503. The portrait did not remain with the fascinating Lisa, probably because the reason for its coming into being was that Leonardo had wanted to paint this magnificent model for his own pleasure, and not that Francesco had commissioned it. It is certain that the artist took the beautiful painting with him to France, where in 1550 it formed part of the royal collection at Fontainebleau.

101

Two Madonnas by Verrocchio –
Kaiser Friedrich Museum, Berlin

Section from *Virgin and Child with
Saints* by Verrocchio – Florence,
Uffizi Gallery

Such was Da Vinci's fame by now that the *Signoria*, headed by the *gonfaloniere* Pier Soderini, commissioned him early in 1504 to paint a fresco for the great Sala del Consiglio. There he was to depict the battle of Anghiari, won on June 29, 1440, by the Florentine and papal armies over the forces of Filippo Maria Visconti. Michelangelo was asked to make a companion fresco representing the battle of Pisa.

Leonardo set to work on the painting with a will, beginning by having himself provided with a description of the battle, which may be found written in the Atlantic codex by some other hand than his (but not by the hand of Machiavelli, as has been ingeniously suggested). He drew group after group of combatants like those on the pages now in the Venice Academy and the British Museum, and in order to execute the enormous cartoon more easily, invented an "ingenious scaffolding which went up when it was compressed, and widened out when it was lowered," as Vasari records.

Toward the end of October of that year, Leonardo set to work on the cartoon in the huge Sala del Papa at the convent of Santa Maria Novella. In February he finished it, according to the agreement that he had made. Since the scaffolding in the great hall of the Palazzo Vecchio was finished in that month, it may be assumed that he began his painting almost immediately, assisted by some of his pupils. Up to October 31 of 1505 salaries were paid and expenditures made in

connection with the *Battle*: in fact, a reimbursement was made to two pupils for colors and grinding as late as December 31 of that year.

Leonardo, however, may have already abandoned the work in October for a reason revealed to us by the Anonimo Magliabechiano. "And from Pliny," writes the biographer, "he got the idea for that plaster with which he worked; but he did not rightly understand it, and the first time he tried it in a painting in the Sala del Papa, as he was working in that place, and leaning the painting against the wall, he built before it a great fire of coals, whereupon the great heat of the coals dried up the material; and then he wanted to follow this procedure in the Sala [Grande], where at the bottom the fire reached it and dried it out, but above, because of the great distance, the heat did not reach, and the material ran down."

The damage may not have been irreparable. The *Signoria* long hoped that Leonardo would resume the interrupted work, but in vain. Probably the master was disgusted with his unfortunate painting, in which art had been sacrificed to science. Though hope must have receded yearly, the *Operai di Palazzo* had it protected with a boarding when some work was done in the hall in March of 1513.

However, even in its fragmentary and ruined state the work was for some decades recorded among the things in Florence worthy of a visit. Thus wrote Francesco Albertini in 1510, and then Giovio, the Anonimo Magliabechiano, and Anton Francesco Doni in 1549; this went on until—after 1557— Vasari caused the ever more damaged remains of Leonardo's painting to be destroyed, in order to transform the Sala Grande del Consiglio into the Salone dei Cinquecento which we see today.

Some historians are still of the opinion that Leonardo, like Michelangelo in his *Battle of Pisa*, depicted only one episode—that of the struggle for the banner, the theme best adapted to his taste and genius, and the only one described by Vasari or reproduced in copies and prints. However, Leonardo's drawings offer views of other episodes from the battle, and the Anonimo Magliabechiano says quite clearly that when Leonardo finally left Florence for good he took many drawings with him, but left to the Ospedale di Santa Maria Nuova "the greater part of the cartoon of the Sala del Consiglio, of which *the drawing for the group of horses which today [before 1548] one may see finished, remained at the palace.*" In 1558 or shortly thereafter Cellini wrote that the cartoon had been brought back to the Sala del Papa, but his statement, although awkward, is not sufficient to weaken the conclusion that may be drawn from the Anonimo's information. Hence we may believe that the contest for the banner constituted only one episode in the cartoon, even though it was the central and principal one, and was depicted in vast dimensions, since the upper part of the painting was not reached by the fire that Leonardo lit at the foot of it.

It may be added that in referring to the interrupted work Soderini called it "the small beginning of a large work," and that Anton Francesco Doni, writing in 1549 to Alberto Lollio, spoke of a "piece of a battle." Also, the old copy of the painting formerly in the Uffizi storerooms and now in the Palazzo Vecchio certainly seems to represent a "piece" of a battle.

The misunderstanding arises partly from the ambiguity, intentional or not, in Vasari, who apparently wished to make the reader believe that he was describing the cartoon, which he had very

Left: Portrait of Verrocchio by Lorenzo di Credi – Florence, Uffizi Gallery

Right: Self-portrait by Di Credi – Florence, Uffizi Gallery

Verrocchio – Profil of gentlewoman – Detroit, from the collection of the Institute of Art

103

Di Credi - *Adoration of the Shepherds* - Florence, Galleria Antica e Moderna

Di Credi - *Virgin and Child with the Infant St. John* - Dresden, Museum

Di Credi - *Portrait of Caterina Sforza* - Forlì, Pinacoteca

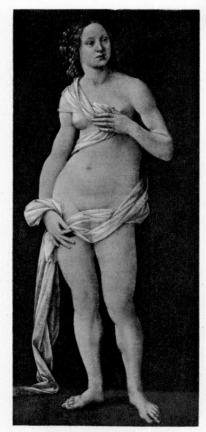

Di Credi - *Venus* - Florence, Uffizi Gallery

likely not seen. In his 1550 edition he actually described what was left of the painting, and in 1568 he repeated this passage without noting that all of the fresco had been gone for ten years.

Suter has demonstrated that Vasari was speaking of the painting by pointing out not only his reference to the "old soldier with a large red cap" (a cap which in the cartoon was most probably in grisaille, like the rest) but also his omission of the warrior crouching under a shield, a figure also missing from the Uffizi copy, which was accurately made from the painting. This figure, on the other hand, does appear in the copy in the Horne Museum and in the print by Zacchia (1558). Both of these contain other details also taken from old copies of the cartoon. That the Uffizi copyist faithfully reproduced only what remained on the wall is further shown by his attempt to render the upper part of the copy uncertain and indecisive, as the original must have appeared after the unfortunate running of the color.

During his third Florentine period Leonardo, then over fifty, engaged in a prodigious number of activities. In July of 1503 he was in the countryside about Pisa on behalf of the *Signoria* to study methods for the possible diversion of the Arno, with the aim of facilitating the surrender of that city. Together with Machiavelli he continued to busy himself with the grandiose project, which failed beacause the government was reluctant, and because adequate means for the purpose were lacking. On January 25, 1508, he was among those who gave counsel on the placing of Michelangelo's *David*, and advised that it be set up in the Loggia della Signoria. He was then particularly occupied with hydraulics, studying ways and means for constructing the above-mentioned Florentine canal. He made researches and experiments on flight, dating an observation in this connection from Monte Ceceri on March 14, 1505. He intensified his mathematical studies, starting a notebook concerning the geometry of solids on July 12.

On July 9, Ser Piero da Vinci died, and Leonardo made a simple record of the fact in his papers, though elsewhere we find traces of affectionate words for his father, who could never have lost interest in his prodigiously endowed illegitimate son.

Detail from *Tobias and the Three Archangels* by Francesco Botticini – Florence, Uffizi Gallery

Di Credi – *Adoration of Christ* – Florence, Uffizi Gallery

Piero di Cosimo – *Madonna and Child with Saints* – London, Matthiesen Collection

Detail of the above *tondo* by Piero di Cosimo – *Madonna and Child with Saints* – London, from the Matthiesen Collection

Isabella d'Este, still not discouraged, again insisted on having something from his hand, even writing him directly. But Angelo del Tovaglia, a Mantuan agent dealing with the Florentine *Signoria*, replied that in spite of promises from both Leonardo and Perugino, he feared that there would

Putto by Verrocchio – Florence courtyard of Palazzo Vecchio

Bust of warrior – Polychrome ceramic
– Della Robbia workshop – Lisbon,
National Museum

Verrocchio – Idealized portrait of
Alexander the Great – New York,
Strauss Collection

be a "competition in tardiness" between them, and concluded: "I am sure that Leonardo will be the winner." He was a true prophet.

That matters did not go well in the Palazzo Vecchio has already been noted. Leonardo drew his wages but, discouraged, lost all interest in the painting of the *Battle*, to the indignation of Soderini, who later, when Da Vinci had gone back to Milan and gave no signs of returning to his own city, wrote rather sharply to the vice-chancellor, Goffredo Carles: "He has accepted a goodly sum of money and has made only a little beginning on a big work that he was to do."

In May of 1506 the artist obtained three months' leave and went again to Milan, where Charles d'Amboise was governor. What with postponements and pretexts and recommendations from the king of France himself, he returned to Florence only on September 14, 1507, armed with a letter of recommendation from Robertet. He was involved in a lawsuit with his stepbrothers concerning a legacy from his father and his uncle Francesco, and this was the real motive for his return, so little did he think of setting hand again to the battle painting.

This last time he went to stay for several months in the house of Piero Martelli, in the Via Martelli, as evidenced by a note dated March 22, 1508, in one of the Arundel codices of the British Museum. There he was much occupied with Giovan Francesco Rustici, who also lived in the Martelli house, and who was then working on a bronze group of St. John between the Pharisee and the Levite destined for one of the doors of the Baptistery. Leonardo helped the young sculptor with such diligence that attempts have been made to see his hand in the skillful group.

In the meantime the artist worked wearily in his spare time on "two pictures of Our Lady, of different sizes, which were made for our Most Christian King, or for whomsoever your Excellency

106

may please," as he wrote in a draft of a letter in the Atlantic codex, perhaps directed to Chaumont. Very little is known of these Madonnas. Since two drawings in the Arundel codex and one in the Louvre correspond to the Madonna Litta in the Hermitage, this picture has been considered to be one of them. The work is so Lombard in style, however, as to exclude the possibility of Leonardo's having worked on it in Florence, even in his spare time. It is just conceivable that he worked out the composition of the panel, or very little more, and then, after returning to Milan in July of the same year, confided its execution to a pupil.

He left Florence for Rome on October 10, after the election of Leo X. Perhaps he came back in the winter between 1515 and 1516, accompanying the Pope on his return from the Council of Bologna, but documents contradict the tale that he was angered on this occasion because the commission for the façade of San Lorenzo had been given to Michelangelo.

Leonardo may have seen his native city again for a last time on his way to France. There, on April 23, 1519, he made his will, not forgetting his Florentine stepbrothers, to whom he left land in Fiesole and his deposit in the Ospedale di Santa Maria Nuova. In spite of the lawsuit, relations between the very humble legitimate offspring of Ser Piero and the very famous illegitimate one must have been re-established on a cordial basis.

NELLO TARCHIANI

Left: Filippino Lippi – Detail from *Virgin Adoring the Christ Child* – Florence, Pitti Gallery

Right: Filippino Lippi – *Virgin Adoring the Christ Child* – Florence, Pitti Gallery

Below: Filippino Lippi – *Esther before Ahasuerus* – Chantilly, Museum

Studies for equestrian monument to Marshal Trivulzio – Windsor, Royal Collection, no. 12355

LEONARDO IN MILAN AND LOMBARDY

"In time of peace I believe that I may satisfy as well as any other in architecture, in the design of public and private buildings, and in conveying water from one place to another. Also, I will execute in marble, bronze, or terra cotta, or in painting, whatever may be desired, to the equal of any other man, whoever he may be. Then the bronze horse may be made, which will be a monument to the immortal glory and eternal honor of the Duke your father, and to that of the illustrious house of Sforza."

This famous letter to Ludovico Sforza, known as Il Moro, begins the first chapter of Leonardo da Vinci's two Milanese decades.

The Milan of the Sforzas cast a blaze of unprecedented magnificence over the Italian peninsula. Its richness was not only material but also intellectual, for noted men, scholars, and artists surrounded the splendid Maecenas like a brilliant constellation. The castle rooms swarmed with a chosen crowd of courtiers and ducal guests. Pre-eminent among them, after the pallid duke, Gian Galeazzo Sforza, and his powerful uncle, Ludovico, were the representatives of foreign powers resident in Milan, the ducal advisors, the men of law, the cavaliers and soldiers. Even these last were brilliant —especially at tilting in jousts and tourneys, for in Renaissance Italy war too had become an art form.

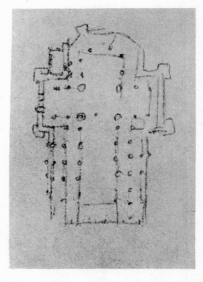

Plan of Milan cathedral – Cod. Forst., III, fol. 55 v

The word *virtù* no longer had the austere meaning given it by Brutus or Lucretia: *virtù* was now seen as the quest of success, as cunning in politics, literary elegance in the turning of a Latin phrase, luminousness in a painting, or victory in love, especially if the victory were obtained under the ancient rules of the divine Plato. An elegant and wealthy society sought refined pleasures inspired by Hellenism, without, however, renouncing the fat feasts to be enjoyed after lofty discussions of ancient philosophy or Latin literature.

Earlier, Bramante had arrived in Milan, bringing a mind as clear as a May dawn, to revive Lombard architecture, still steeped in the Gothic twilight. Now came Leonardo, perhaps in the winter of 1481 to 1482, with his exquisite mastery of art, to revive Milanese painting, which was still bound to the traditional archaistic forms of Foppa, Bergognone, and the De Predis.

The life of this supremely great man is still obscured by a host of mysteries. Why did he leave Florence? Lorenzo the Magnificent had certainly given him much protection; yet in the Atlantic codex may be found the enigmatic note, "The Medici created me and destroyed me." Does this allude to his failure in Rome, where he had gone into the service of Giuliano de' Medici, who had made a studio for him in the Belvedere? This is one of the many questions that fill Leonardo's biography.

The fact remains that though Leonardo was in Florence at the end of September, 1481, by April of 1483 he was in Milan, already familiar with Milanese circles.

As Calvi points out, at the close of the first thirty years of his life, spent in Tuscany, Leonardo's financial condition was that of an insolvent debtor. He had not finished the altarpiece for the chapel of San Bernardo, nor the picture commissioned from him by the monks of San Donato. His interest was mainly engaged by the creative, intellectual phase of his works. His aims were accomplished only when he was personally satisfied as to their perfection, and he was more or less indifferent toward his practical commitments. For the rest, his temperament inclined toward a cosmic mysticism, toward a pictorial ideal that respected all the forms of life.

Vasari and the Anonimo Gaddiano attempted to connect Leonardo's departure for Milan with the presentation of a lyre to Ludovico il Moro on behalf of Lorenzo the Magnificent. Friendly rela-

Cross section of church of San Lorenzo – Cod. Atl., fol. 7 v-*b*

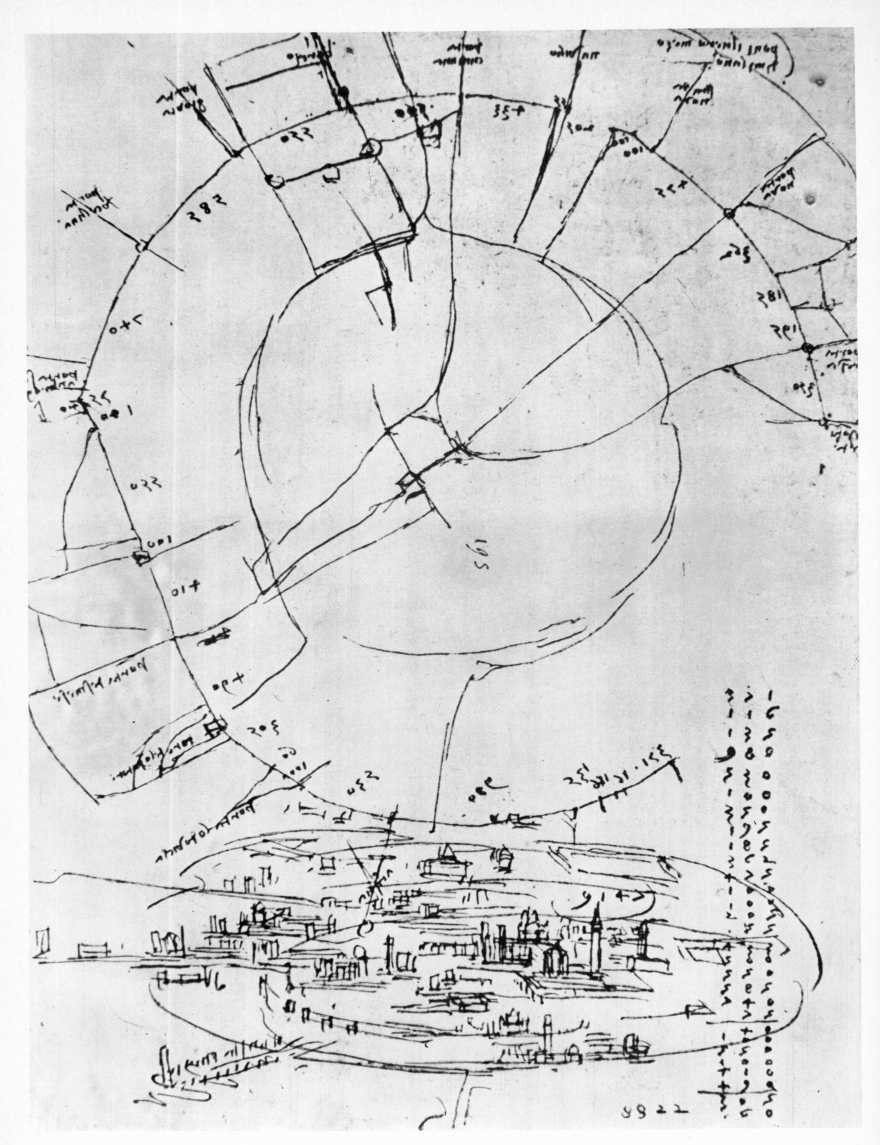

Plan and perspective view of city of Milan – Codex Atlanticus

tions certainly existed between the Medici and the Sforza, hence at that time between Florence and Milan, while those between the Republic and the Visconti had been correspondingly bad. Calvi does not deny the actuality of the episode: he notes only that the biographers have elevated a concomitant to the importance of a primary fact. Besides, it is not unlikely that Ludovico, in looking for a Florentine artist with the qualifications that Leonardo certainly describes in his letter, should have communicated with Lorenzo through the Medicean representative at Milan.

The artist's arrival may have come about through Lorenzo. It is also possible that the Florentine ruler had entrusted the master with a gift which he knew would be welcome to Sforza, whom he had had occasion to know intimately, and who at that moment had assumed a place of primary importance in the Italian political scene. But it is probable that Leonardo was called to Milan principally in order to execute the equestrian monument to Francesco Sforza—the famous "horse" which was never finished. Leonardo himself presumably alludes to it in the following note: "There is one whom the Duke has brought from Florence to do that work of his: a worthy master, but he has so much to do that he will never finish it."

He is, then, in Milan: and as early as the first months of 1483 we see him, together with the brothers Evangelista and Giovanni Ambrogio de Predis, contracting for the painting of the *Virgin of the Rocks*. The work, done for the Confraternita della Concezione della Vergine in the church of San Francesco, was far superior to all that Milan had possessed in the way of paintings up to that time. It is likely that the artist who asserted himself so vigorously in the first year of his Milanese sojourn gained no little fame thereby.

Many biographers have stated that Leonardo was somewhat neglected by the Sforzas during the first period of his Milanese residence. Malaguzzi-Valeri, without making a thorough critical examination of the facts, maintains that the young artist came almost unknown to Milan and that the Sforza court, busy with other matters, was more or less unconcerned with his position there, leaving him in penury almost up to the time when he painted the *Last Supper*.

It is not impossible that the great hopes Leonardo had built up on engaging in Sforza's service were somewhat disappointed. But negative conclusion must not be drawn from the mere fact that there are only sparse documents on his life from 1482 to 1489. He must have become known with the painting of the *Virgin of the Rocks*, as noted above. It should also be remembered that in 1484 and 1485 Milan was desolated by a plague no less disastrous than that of 1630, though the latter scourge had the relative advantage of being described by famous writers and finally immortalized by Alessandro Manzoni.

In these years, too, there was intense military activity; and it must not be forgotten that Leonardo presented himself in the famous letter as an expert military engineer. It is likely that he was much engaged on military engineering and the casting of mortars and cannon. Many folios of the Atlantic codex bear studies of cannons. The military preoccupations of Ludovico il Moro between 1482 and 1485 must have influenced the direction that Leonardo's activities took, and studies and sketches in the manuscripts show that the artist also collaborated with Ludovico on a great plan for rebuilding the city after the plague.

Sforza had princely notions on the matter of building. Behind him, bent to his ear, we discern the "pensive figure of Leonardo, who, a fantastic dreamer of future things, seer of strange cities that never rose, must often have suggested grandiose and original ideas." That Leonardo was occupied with a redevelopment plan for Milan is proved by the schematic sketch of a design for the city found in the Atlantic codex; this is complemented by another, dating perhaps from 1506 or 1510, on a folio of the work on anatomy now at Windsor, containing the design for a third circle of walls. This last project, for the *Redefossi*, was in fact carried out in the middle of the sixteenth century. There is such a complete picture of the hydrographic system around Milan that Beltrami considered the sketch to represent a project for some co-ordination of the network of watercourses vital to the city.

Statements by the Florentine ambassador, Sabba da Castiglione di Pietro Alemanni, and by Leonardo himself, make it even clearer that the supposed neglect was more mythical than real. The horse for Francesco Sforza's monument and the portrait of Cecilia Gallerani both belong to those apparently obscure years. Evidence as to his activity in Milanese court life also comes from the jesting poet Bellincione, who assigns Da Vinci a not unworthy place in the Sforza Olympus. The artist was in contact with the great personalities of the court—with Galeazzo Sanseverino, Marchesino Stanga, Gualtieri da Bescapè, Bergonzio Botta, and Ambrogio Ferrario. These were people ranking high in the state administration and in the circles closest to the Sforzas.

In his manuscripts there are traces of payments received before 1490, and references to benefits enjoyed before that time. Drawings, sketches, and allegories testify to his participation in the life of the court. Such things, as Calvi rightly says, must be evaluated before subscribing to the too rigid opinion that Leonardo was neglected and isolated during the first fifteen years of his Milanese stay. It is understood that what is meant here is an isolation imposed on the artist, not that to which he betook himself once he had become immersed, "alone and all his own," in his beloved studies.

As regards this taste of Leonardo's for meditation and study, it must be borne in mind that Ludovico, as though aware that his career was ephemeral, was devoured by an almost desperate dynamism. He wanted to see any idea of his carried out immediately. Though he undoubtedly recognized Leonardo's genius, he must sometimes also have rebelled against the artist's uncertainty, against his inability to be satisfied, and against his absences—if not material, at least spiritual. Leonardo often stopped work to meditate, to abstract, becoming totally absorbed in soaring thoughts. Once, perhaps abruptly recalled to his task, he noted disdainfully and aristocratically: "To give orders is a gentleman's work; to carry them out is the act of a servant." And because of this he never finished anything, as Solmi remarks.

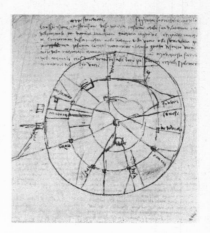

Plan of city of Milan – Windsor, Royal Collection, no. 19115

Moat of castle of Milan – Ms. B, fol. 36 v

Pavilions on towers of Milan castle – Windsor, from the Royal Collection, no. 12552

The Musician – Milan, Ambrosiana

Portrait of Beatrice d'Este – Milan, Ambrosiana

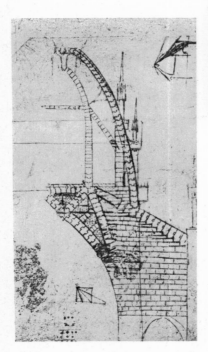

Study for dome of Milan cathedral – Cod. Atl., fol. 310 r-*b*

When he studies hydraulic problems he is arrested by the sight of some natural phenomenon, hastily jotting down a phrase which for us is an enigma but for him perhaps signified an entire thought: "A lily placed itself on the bank of the Ticino, and the current carried off the bank together with the lily." His inner life would be, if we knew it, the most beautiful psychological romance in the world. "It seems," Croce says, "that in him all modern science is born, and that he is passing it on to succeeding centuries as in a grandiose sketch."

From his point of view Ludovico was not entirely to blame if he became impatient because the "horse" did not progress. Leonardo, eternally dissatisfied, filled his notebooks with sketches, with anatomical details concerning horses—horses from classical monuments like the famous *Regisole* of Pavia; horses from the stables of Sanseverino, the handsome "sporting general," a great wielder of the lance in tourneys, a great courtier of beautiful women, and a pitiful leader of men in serious warfare.

Perhaps in 1489 Ludovico, irritated by the artist's delays, considered taking away from him the commission for the monument to Francesco Sforza, which everyone now called "the horse." It

Portrait of a young woman – Milan, Ambrosiana

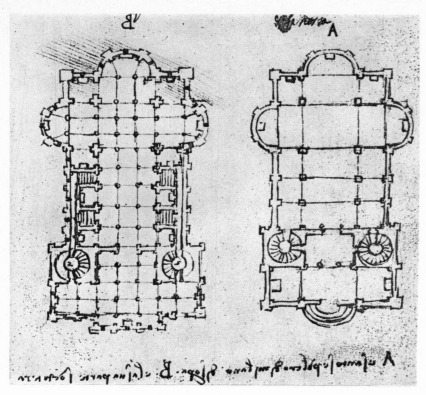

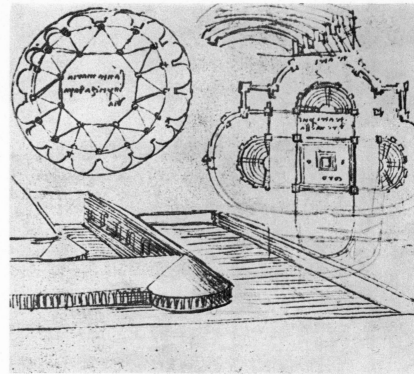

appears that Pietro Alemanni actually wrote to Lorenzo the Magnificent on Ludovico's behalf, asking for another sculptor, but there is a great deal of controversy among critics as to the date at which the request for a new artist was made. Some also suggest that Sforza's aim in threatening to entrust the project of the great monument to another sculptor was simply to goad Leonardo into completing it.

However this may be, in one of his notebooks, known as Ms. C, the artist writes: "On April 23, 1490, I began this book and again set to work on the horse."

No doubt the duke and the artist had reached an agreement and the work was resumed, though not without a thousand mundane interruptions. Leonardo was required to organize wedding festivities in 1489 and again in 1490. Leonardo as producer—this was another aspect of his many-sided activity. When one reflects that his genius was often thus employed in the service of empty worldliness, it does not seem strange that he sometimes became indignant and took refuge in his meditations. But for the *beau monde* of his time he was still that strange man who had invented "the Festival of Paradise in honor of the Duchess of Milan."

"And it is called Paradise because in it was made, with the great ingenuity and art of Master Leonardo Vinci the Florentine, Paradise, with all the seven planets which turned; and the planets were represented by men who looked and were dressed like poets, and each of these planets spoke in praise of the Duchess Isabella." Thus wrote the court poet Bellincione.

The Festival of Paradise was one of the many impressive celebrations by means of which the astute Ludovico hoped to give the figurehead couple, Gian Galeazzo Sforza and Isabella of Aragon, the illusion that they actually ruled Milan, and thus to mask the extent of his own power. Bernardo Bellincione and Leonardo da Vinci contributed all their combined poetic, pictorial, and mechanical abilities to create a marvel which would bedazzle an era already so accustomed to courtly brilliance —and at the same time, adds Solmi, so sad. He was not wrong. Leonardo, the poet of mechanics, concerned himself with theatrical devices, with fabrics, with colors, and collaborated on the festivities for the weddings of Ludovico il Moro and Beatrice d'Este, of Anna Sforza and Alfonso d'Este. May he not have invented the pastime of the rebus, as Beltrami observes in connection with a book by Baratta, to make himself acceptable to the court and thus save the independence of his unquiet soul? Such an artifice might also have been devised to call Ludovico's attention to a phrase intended as a justification of his own conduct, and as a renewed promise to live up to the confidence the Sforzas had placed in him. The phrase, which still leaves its interpreters in doubt, is this: "Up to this time I have never accomplished anything, but I know that those who are here will cause me to triumph."

His private life, his tastes, his relations with contemporaries would offer posterity a fascinating subject for study, were there documents or other evidence less vague than the notes which the artist scribbled on the run between a sketch, a study, a recollection. Was it a sympathetic feeling, or perhaps psychological curiosity, that made him record the misdeeds and knaveries of Giacomo, a boy of ten who had come in some unknown way into his service? "Jachomo came to stay with me on the day of the Magdalene in 1490, at the age of ten years." In Ms. C (fol. 15) he relates that the boy had stolen money intended for his new clothes, and dubs him "thief, liar, mulehead, glutton." At dinner with M. Giacomo Andrea da Ferrara, "he ate enough for two and made mischief enough for four, for he broke three cruets and spilt the wine." Giacomo's every misdeed is patiently and precisely set down, the master limiting himself to reporting with a bookkeeper's accuracy the money value of the damages and thefts perpetrated by this diabolic ten-year-old.

Along with such curiosities appear hints concerning some of his disciples. The recurring names Marco and Gianantonio suggest that Marco d'Oggiono and Boltraffio were among them. A phrase of 1497, "Salai stole the money," has led to the belief that the incorrigible boy of seven years before

Left: Plan of church of San Sepolcro in Milan – Ms. B, fol. 572

Right: Plan of church of Santa Maria in Pertica, Pavia – Ms. B, fol. 55-a

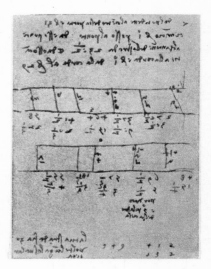

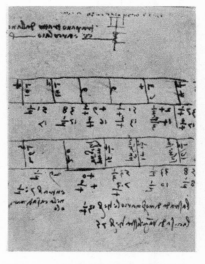

Map of Leonardo da Vinci's vineyard, which was situated in San Vittore section in Milan – Ms. I, fol. 118 v, 119 r

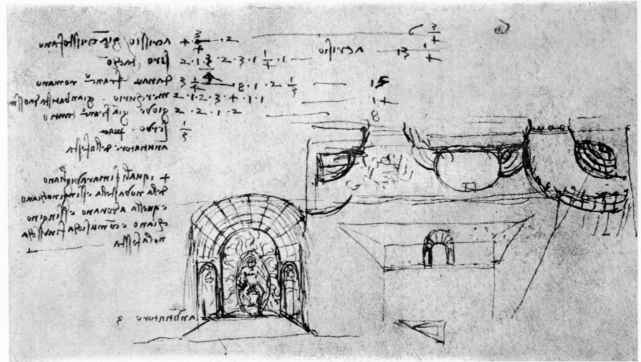

Costumes for performance of Festival
of Paradise – Windsor, from the
Royal Collection

is the same person as Salai. The difficulty regarding the name (according to tradition, Salai was called Andrea) may be surmounted by noting that the name Andrea does not appear in connection with Salai either in Leonardo's notes or elsewhere, whereas in a notary deed of 1527 (*rog.* Pasio Isolano) there is mention of a "domiciliary, Jacobo de Caprotti, called Salai," son of Giovanni Pietro Caprotti, who lived in the Porta Vercellina quarter near San Martino al Corpo. Calvi has found other documents according to which Salai—Gian Giacomo Caprotti—appears to have died in 1523 from a gunshot wound (a hunting accident?) and left his not inconsiderable estate to two sisters. The name of Andrea wrongly given him may be explained by his having been confused with Andrea Solario in an epoch in which excessive accuracy in matters of art criticism was not considered particularly important.

In 1490 Leonardo went to Pavia with Amadeo and Francesco Martini of Siena, to inspect the work on the cathedral there. With a train of servants and horses, they boarded at the Hosteria del Moro, at the expense of the cathedral building committee. During this time our artist meditated, designed, sketched projects: and if these drawings are compared with the final wooden model for the cathedral, it will be seen that the model follows Leonardo's drawings very closely.

Solmi points out that this model represents the only completed effort by Da Vinci in the art of church construction that has come down to us. The sketches naturally recall other buildings that he has seen, and from a series of observations the artist works up to a general theory about ecclesiastical architecture, as is his habit with regard to everything that he studies. For him, observations in any scientific field had to lead to a principle, a precept—in sum, to pure science. Some of the studies suggest the possibility that the lantern crowning the cupola was to serve as a bell tower, as at Chiaravalle. From here he leaps to the church of the Holy Sepulcher at Milan; dissatisfied, he unexpectedly changes his mind and casts a yearning look toward a round structure similar to Santa Maria in Pertica at Pavia; in yet another study he develops architectural concepts suggested by San Lorenzo in Milan. He wavers between two distinct ideas: from a simple plan like that of the Grazie in Milan, he enlarges his concept to a type of Greek cross with a great dome, the prolongations of its crossarms ending in semicircles, then passes to an octagonal plan with eight apses. He continually varies the combinations, amusing himself by resolving difficulties for his own pleasure.

It is no wonder that his clients and patrons sometimes wearied of this exacting artist who, in search of perfection, never finished anything. Vasari says of him: "He began many things, and never finished any of them."

It is not certain whether Leonardo in 1490 made a protracted stay at Pavia, or whether he went back and forth repeatedly. The fact remains that after 1487, from the time when Gian Galeazzo Sforza retired to Pavia, leaving the entire direction of affairs of state to his uncle Ludovico, relations between the two cities became closer. The park of the Pavia castle echoed to the joyous shouts of the court in the excitement of autumn hunting and feasting days. Probably our artist was engaged in engineering work about the castle, and perhaps also painted pictures which were lost when the most splendid wing of the ducal dwelling was blown up in 1527. Manuscript B is full of drawings and comments relating to his Pavian sojourn. Amid exalted thoughts are noted trivial matters which must have cost him more irrigation than anxiety, such as the construction of the ducal bath, undoubtedly a marvel of hydraulic engineering and built "in the middle of the Duke of Milan's labyrinth," as recorded by Breventano. The latter also informs us that Da Vinci devised a similar elegant marble pavilion, covered with metal foil, in Vigevano.

Almost all of Manuscript B was written at Pavia, and testifies to his having been much occupied with work in ecclesiastical, civil, and military architecture. He also studied a great deal, making use of the very rich ducal library in the castle and taking part in the intellectual life which pulsated around the university during these years.

The long Lombard sojourn served Leonardo in his scientific formation just as Florence, in his green years, had shaped his feeling for and mastery of art. "Having come to Lombardy in 1482 as a musician, painter, sculptor, and architect," we may conclude with Solmi, "he left the great valley of the Po in December, 1499, as a scientist and thinker, second to none of his time."

At Pavia he read Witelo's *Perspective* and Roberto Valturio's *De re militari*, found in the ducal library, but it was the university that made him a scientist. His bent toward science eventually threatened to overwhelm his artistic impulse: such was the opinion held by Vasari and by Leonardo's contemporaries.

Pavia was in a period of great intellectual flower, her philosophers tending to a freedom of thought in which all scientific currents were welcomed. To paraphrase Solmi again, Italy's future was hammered out on the plains of the Po, and the brilliant light of a new philosophy radiated from the hoary Lombard university. Men like Lorenzo Valla, Tommaso da Vio, called Cardinal Gaetano, the unjustly forgotten Ludovico Pendasio, Cornelius Agrippa of Nettesheim, Gerolamo Cardano, Cristoforo Magneno, and Andrea Alciato left luminous and lasting traces at Pavia. Leonardo sought out books by earlier men like Biagio Pelacani of Parma, Giovanni Taverna, Ugo Bensi, Francesco Filelfo, Giovanni Marliani, Giorgio Valla; he delved into the private library of Giovanni Ghiringhelli; but above all he had close personal relations with Fazio Cardano, that most unusual jurist and mathematician, father of another famous scientist, Gerolamo Cardano. Nor did he overlook Giorgio Merula, Nicolò Antiquario, Andrea and Alessandro dei Ghiringhelli, Franchino Gaffurio, Nicholas of Cusa, Gerolamo Marliani, Ambrogio Varese di Rosate, and Marco Antonio della Torre.

His geological observations concerning the age of the earth and the different areas once covered by the seas, his famous investigation of the *nicchi*, or fossil conch shells, were the fruit of discussions with such learned men as Fra Luca Pacioli, Fazio Cardano (so passionately devoted to the occult sciences that he was publicly believed to be accompanied by a familiar spirit), and Giorgio Merula, whose debates Bellincione describes in a sonnet.

Had they been carried through, his studies in anatomy, made in colloboration with Marcantonio della Torre, would have led to such far-reaching conclusions that they would have obscured the fame of Vesalius and Harvey.

During his Pavian sojourn he went to the hall of anatomy at the university and studied with such single-mindedness that the disorder of the students made him indignant. In one of their tumults he may even have harangued the ignorant and restless goliards: "Make a homily," he writes in his book, "of the reproaches which should be made to unruly students." Reflections of such a polemical discourse recur in other, contemporaneous passages written with his left hand: "Peroration: But such as these may remain in the company of the beasts; and those who seek their favor are dogs and other animals full of rapine, and accompanied by them they always hunt him who flees, following the innocent animals who, in their hunger, in the time of the great snows, come to your house asking for charity, as from their master." Such are his strange and obscure words, the phrases often inverted as are his left-handed letters.

At intervals he dashes to the ducal courtyard to work on the "horse," which is still not ready to be cast. The *Regisole* in Pavia suggests new studies and new observations, new enigmatic notes: "In that of Pavia the movement is to be praised more than anything else. The imitation of the most ancient things is more laudable than modern things. Can there not be beauty and utility? As appears in men and in fortresses? The trot is almost the characteristic [gait] of a free horse. Where natural vivacity is missing, it must be supplied by art."

In painting Leonardo sought effects of light and air: he felt the countryside, and above all the sweetness of the Lombard landscape. He knew it, our Lombardy, and his manuscripts are full of recollections of his travels.

In 1491 preparations were on foot for the Sforza-Este nuptials, and a draft of artists was made, Leonardo being among the first. He studied costumes for the great tournament of Galeazzo Sanseverino: "On the 26th of January being in the house of messer Galeazzo da Sanseverino to direct the festival of his joust..."

Meanwhile the colossal equestrian statue was ever more eagerly awaited, and on the occasion of Bianca Maria's marriage to Maximilian, king of the Romans, the model was apparently put on exhibit. But where? In the "old court," that is, the ducal palace where Leonardo worked, or in the courtyard of the castle? It appears that in honor of this wedding Ludovico il Moro sent the Emperor a painting by Leonardo, an altarpiece.

A rich cortege escorted Bianca Maria on her journey toward Germany, across Lake Como and the Valtellina. Calco describes the most interesting places in Lario—the Pliniana, Bellagio, Fiumelatte. It is interesting that his observations correspond to notes jotted down by Leonardo in the Atlantic codex. Da Vinci may have been among the train, or perhaps he saw these sights during a stay at the villa of his friend Marchesino Stanga on the Bellagio promontory. "At the head of the Valtellina are the mountains of Bormio—terrible and always covered with snow. Here ermine [marmots?] are born." Leonardo was struck with the imposing might of the Alps. Then the phenomena of the Pliniana caught his interest, and of Fiumelatte, which he calls "Fiumelaccio," in the dialect of the natives of the region. He consistently gives the names of the places as he must have heard them pronounced, writing "Borme" for Bormio, "Porta Sinese" for Porta Ticinese, "Serio" for Alserio, "Voltolino" for Valtellina, "Corduse" for Cordusio, and so on.

He traversed Lombardy from north to south, from the Adda to the Ticino. He stopped in Brianza and went to Como, where he studied the architecture of the cathedral. In 1498 he seems to have been at Genoa with Ludovico to examine the fortifications there in view of a French attack that was feared and later became a reality. Leonardo comments on a heavy sea that had ruined the jetty and notes that the party entered Genoa on March 17 at five o'clock—"the which hour he

Costumes for Festival of Paradise – Windsor, Royal Collection

Portrait of Massimiliano Sforza – Drawing – Milan, from the Pinacoteca Ambrosiana

115

Study for monument to Francesco Sforza – Windsor, Royal Collection, no. 123582

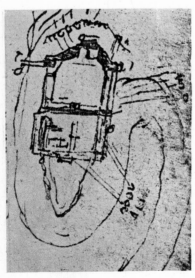

Plan of castle of Trezzo – Quad. Anat. II, fol. 7 v

had from his astrologer Master Ambrosio de Rosate, from whose advice he never deviated," as Marin Sanudo wrote. The devastating tidal wave is reported in Bartolomeo Senarega's chronicle as well as in the acute and curious observations of Leonardo. The artist noted some pieces of iron drawn out by the pressure of the granite mass which had gone to the bottom of the sea, and in a later study for a machine for drawing wire he recalls the iron drawn out "by a ruin of a part of the jetty at Genoa."

The itinerary of the return from Genoa may be traced in his notes. Mentioned in them are the Genoese Casale (part of Montoggio), Mongiardino, Ronco, Alessandria, Candia di Lomellina, Chiaravalle, and finally Milan. He could not pass by the marine deposits visible in the Montferrat rocks without comment, and he also remarks on the finding of "an ancient boat ten *braccia* under the earth" at Candia di Lomellina.

These were years intensively lived, with intense activity. Ludovico, after a second *coup d'état* following the death of his nephew Gian Galeazzo, in which he had deposed the "little duke," as Francesco, the son of the unhappy duke, was called, had become uncontested ruler of Milan. The court was now more brilliant than ever, but beneath the glowing splendor of art, concealed under the magnificence of the house of Sforza, was a gnawing corrosion which must have been the cause of that indifference of the people to foreign intervention that embittered the centuries that followed.

On January 2, 1497, Beatrice d'Este, the wife of Il Moro, died. She was only twenty-three. With her death the Sforza court lost that intelligent smile which had embellished it in so many ways and had seemed to protect it from the tempests that threatened to founder it momentarily. Leonardo's nature would appear to have become still more unreliable and unsteady, while from every side the portents of ruin became ever more menacing.

116

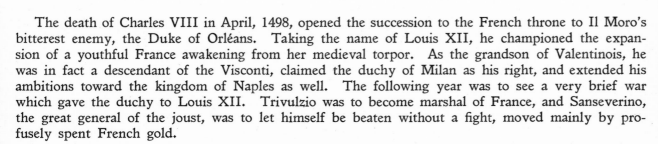

The death of Charles VIII in April, 1498, opened the succession to the French throne to Il Moro's bitterest enemy, the Duke of Orléans. Taking the name of Louis XII, he championed the expansion of a youthful France awakening from her medieval torpor. As the grandson of Valentinois, he was in fact a descendant of the Visconti, claimed the duchy of Milan as his right, and extended his ambitions toward the kingdom of Naples as well. The following year was to see a very brief war which gave the duchy to Louis XII. Trivulzio was to become marshal of France, and Sanseverino, the great general of the joust, was to let himself be beaten without a fight, moved mainly by profusely spent French gold.

On September 2, 1499, Ludovico left his castle, as Napoleon left Fontainebleau, though without the heroic farewell to the Guard: for Il Moro was no lion, but a fox.

117

Left: Studies for casting of bronze horse – Windsor, Royal Collection, no. 12349

Right: Studies for casting of bronze horse – Cod. Atl., fol. 216 v-a

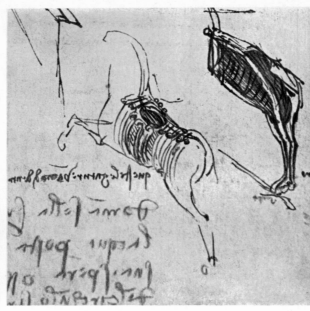

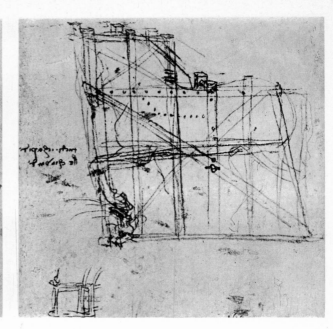

Study of rearing horse for monument to Francesco Sforza – Venice, Academy

Study for monument to Francesco Sforza – Windsor, Royal Collection, no. 12356 v

Studies for monument to Francesco Sforza – Windsor, Royal Collection, no. 12359

And Leonardo? The famous horse was still in the form of a clay model, but it was nonetheless an "admirable and stupendous equestrian statue," as Luca Pacioli expressed it, twelve *braccia* (7.64 m.) high from crest to ground, and the weight of the bronze necessary to cast it was estimated at about twenty thousand pounds. Poets and learned men of the court busied themselves with praising it, Pietro Lazzaroni, Baldassare Tacone, and Lancino Curzio in particular.

In a letter to the Duke, Leonardo complains of two years' arrears in salary. "I have kept 6 mouths for 36 months," he writes, "and have had 50 ducats." There is a moment in which he is indignant because of the neglect in which true scholars and artists have been left, in favor of intriguers and such unworthy people as "potters and armorers, bell founders and bell ringers, even bombardiers, among them one in His Lordship's service" (Giannino Alberghetti). He gives vent here to the spleen of an artist who believes himself to be misunderstood. With regard to the work on the horse, however, evidently suspended for lack of funds, he adds: "Of the horse I shall say nothing, because I know the times." Even the artist was aware that the current situation was not propitious for luxury expenditures.

At this moment, which must have been a difficult one for him, he agreed to go to Piacenza to Bishop Fabrizio Marliani. The letter is very strange, because it is written as though by a third person, but it is in the hand of the artist, who finds a curious way of praising himself. The letter reads: "Piacenza is a land of passage, like Florence... where numerous foreigners gather, who, seeing the excellent works there, form the impression that the city is filled with worthy inhabitants." It is the importance of the city as a tourist center that he emphasizes, insisting on it as a goal for travellers. And here are the eulogistic words: "I can tell you that from this town you will get only makeshift works and unworthy and crude masters: there is no capable man, believe me, except for Leonardo the Florentine, who is making the bronze horse for Duke Francesco, and who has no need to praise himself, because he has a task which will take him all his life, and I doubt that he will ever finish it, because it is such a large work."

He did not go to Piacenza, however, but remained in Milan.

It appears from documents that during that year, 1498, Leonardo worked in the famous Sala delle Asse. On April 21, 1498, Gualtiero, an intimate of the ducal family, wrote to Ludovico: "Most Illustrious and Excellent Lord. On Monday the *camera grande delle asse* will be cleared, that is, of the tower [the scaffolding put up for the plastering of the vault]. Master Leonardo promises to finish it by the end of September, and says that during this time it may be enjoyed all the same, because the scaffolding that he will make there will leave enough space under it for everything."

Leonardo then worked, as Beltrami relates, on the *saletta negra* and in the *camerini*. It is probable that the Sala delle Asse was completed some time between 1498 and 1499. It is very much in Leonardo's taste, for he amused himself here with complicated designs, with interlaced trees and fanciful knots. Lomazzo says in his treatise on the art of painting: "in the painting of the trees may also be found a beautiful invention of Leonardo's, who wrought so that, by weaving them all together, the branches formed various bizarre groups; which fashion Bramante later used." He comments further on an intimacy between Bramante and Leonardo, who was named official ducal engineer together with Bramante, Giangiacomo Dolcebuono, and Giovanni Bataggio da Lodi. If Bramante served chiefly as a creator of ecclesiastical and civic architecture, Leonardo must have been most often employed as a military architect and hydraulic engineer. However, the inspired technician did not entirely stifle the artist.

The *Last Supper* in the monastery of the Grazie was probably commissioned from him after 1495. How much study was expended, how many uncertainties encountered by the never satisfied artist and scientist! In this work he sought to achieve new artistic effects by means of new techniques. He would suddenly leave the "horse" being constructed in the ducal palace and run to the Grazie to give another touch of the brush to the *Cena*. "He went," Bandello writes, "from the old court, where he was working on that magnificent clay horse, to the refectory of the Grazie," and there, having mounted the scaffolding, took up the brush "to give one or two strokes to one of the figures,

Studies for monument of Marshal Trivulzio – Windsor, Royal Collection

Drawings for monument to Marshal Trivulzio – Windsor, Royal Collection, no. 12343, 12356 v

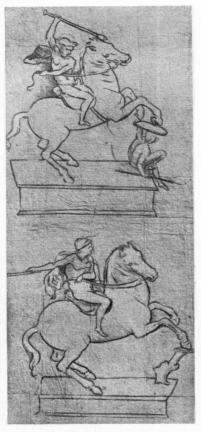

Projects for equestrian monument to Francesco Sforza – Engraved after drawing by Leonardo da Vinci – Milan, Castello Sforzesco (Gabinetto delle stampe)

and of a sudden departed.'' He must often have crossed the city at the height of a summer day, when the air in Milan becomes burning hot, goaded by a fleeting inspiration. And on his way something would strike him: he would hurriedly scribble piecemeal phrases in his notebooks to serve as memoranda, or make summary sketches for later development. Then, seized by other thoughts, he would drop the idea. But the sketch remained.

He observed everything: in fact, on a page of the Atlantic codex (fol. 225 r) may be found a reference to a book dealing with Milan and her churches, perhaps Beroldo's, and a note, "The last stationer toward the Corduse has it." In his dash between the ducal palace and the castle, or the Grazie, he stopped, as all cultivated spirits are bound to do, before the bookseller's shops.

The idea for the *Last Supper* is generally considered to have come to him in Tuscany, where Andrea del Castagno and Domenico Ghirlandaio had created precedents. At the beginning of the nineteenth century a painting of the *Last Supper* similar to Leonardo's came to light in a monastery at Lucca. A painter named Stefano Tofanelli attempted to maintain that it was older than that in the Grazie, and that Leonardo must therefore have plagiarized it. The absurd calumny vanishes at a breath. Leonardo never copied: he studied and created. A red-crayon drawing in the Venice Academy has long been considered a precious document of the endless preparatory labor that went into the masterpiece. Though some hypercritical historians have contested the authenticity of the drawing, there is now general agreement that it is from the master's hand.

The *Last Supper* immediately became famous. Leonardo, generally so dilatory in executing his commissions, had carried out the work with enormous energy. The court, foreigners, artists, vied with each other in singing praises to this marvellous creation of the master's matured art. Even today, ruined as it is, it entirely justifies Prudhon's words: *Le tableau de la cène de Milan est le premier du monde et le chef d'œuvre de la peinture.*

120

Projects for monument to Marshal Trivulzio – Windsor, Royal Collection, no. 12354, 12356

Neighing horse – Windsor, Royal Collection, no. 12327 r

But the masterpiece was doomed from birth: the Cardinal of Aragon in his *Itinerario* (published by Pastor), writing before 1520, noted that the masterpiece was already threatened with ruin. He added a realistic detail undoubtedly conveyed to him by someone on the spot: "The characters in it (the *Last Supper*) are done from life, painted from several personages of the court, and from Milanese of that time." Leonardo had not, however, used a sacred representation as an excuse for portraiture. On the contrary, his insatiable spirit of research into living reality had made him select from the faces around him those elements through which he aspired to render the sublime scene true for all time. Considering this, we may trust that the tale according to which the prior of the Grazie is portrayed as Judas is only a malicious invention. All the paintings of Leonardo's Milanese period

Drawing of horse – Windsor, Royal
Collection, no. 12345 r

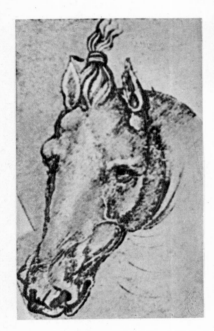

Head of horse – Windsor, Royal
Collection, no. 12288

Head of horse – Windsor, Royal
Collection, no. 12287

Hindquarters of horse – Windsor,
Royal Collection, no. 12335

have been the subject of much controversy, furiously negated as being his and attributed to this or that artist. Today, however, the critical pendulum has swung so far the other way that he has been assigned the paternity of many Lombard paintings of the time, along with this masterpiece.

As for the more "human" branch of painting, as Lesca styled portraiture, many works expressing the individual and the characteristic in the subjects were produced during Leonardo's epoch, but his portraits surpass them all with a quality of modelling peculiarly his own, and with the breath of a higher life that seems to hover around his figures. The portraits of two of Ludovico's favorites are now generally accepted as from his hand—that of Lucrezia Crivelli, known in the Louvre as *La Belle Ferronnière*, and that of Cecilia Gallerani, which must have been among the first works that he carried out in Milan.

The latter painting was attributed to Leonardo as early as the seventeenth century by Cardinal Federico Borromeo, when he secured it from the Gallerani family for the Ambrosiana. We also have contemporary testimony to his authorship of it in the sonnet by Bellincione which begins:

"At whom dost rage? Of whom art envious, Nature?
Of Vinci, who has drawn down one of thy stars...."

Some comment must be made regarding Leonardo's activity in connection with the greatest church in Lombardy, the Milan cathedral. We must go back to 1487, when the carpenter Bernardo Maggi da Abbiategrasso helped him to construct a model he had designed for the *Duomo*. From a page in the Atlantic codex (fol. 270 r) it seems that the artist intended to accompany the model with a report explaining the concepts he had followed in its creation. Addressing himself to the "Venerable Building Committee," he declares that he wished to find a remedy for that ailing organism, "the sick cathedral," by means of a rational composition of the various elements and stresses. He writes that he will return to the rules from which good building proceeds, and which are founded on scientific principles of weight and force.

The project was accepted for examination, and then, at the request of the master himself, was given back to him to make some modifications. It appears from the documents that there was a group that would have favored him and his proposals, but he seems to have lost interest in the problems of the cathedral as they became buried under other newer ones that occupied his mind. Thus, on the point of gathering the fruit of his meditations, he drew back and changed course, as he so often did during his life.

In the Sforza territory near Vigevano various hydraulic works and reclamation projects were being carried out, as the notes of the Leicester codex attest. Leonardo may have had a hand in these as well as in the conception of an entirely new city plan for Vigevano, the Sforza's favorite summer residence. A note refers to his having also put the finishing touches on "the mills of Vigievine."

From the Sforza lands he admired the spectacle offered by the solemn circle of the Alps, their snows splendid against the blue of the sky under the morning sun. He admired and meditated. Perhaps he went to see Monte Rosa from close by, going up the Val d'Ossola, than a Lombard territory besieged by the Swiss from the northern cantons, or the valley of the Sesia.

Leonardo now became the owner of a plot of land in the outer zone of Milan, between Porta Vercellina and the *Pusterla* of Sant'Ambrogio. This area, given over to the cultivation of vineyards, had taken on some importance through the opening of a road between the *Pusterla* and San Vittore. Together with others, Leonardo stepped forward to petition the duke for a vineyard of sixteen rods

122

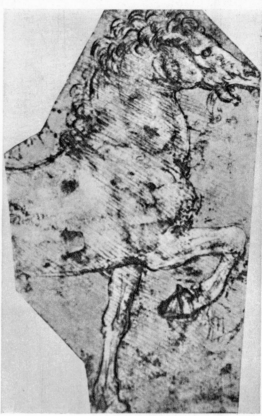

on the road paralleling the Porta Vercellina ditch. Ownership of real estate represented an important step, for it was the necessary prelude to the concession of citizenship, which Il Moro would undoubtedly have granted Leonardo had it not been for the catastrophe which occurred only a few months after he got his land. Leonardo also wished to build a house on his plot, so conveniently located in relation to both the castle and the Grazie, which would have offered a refuge for his artistic and cultural studies. It is not known where the master actually lived: it is presumed that he had a house near the ducal palace, since in 1503 the brethren of the confraternity of San Francesco, during their quarrel with Leonardo over the *Virgin of the Rocks*, refer in a court document to the dwelling place of the artist in the "Curia Arenghi Mediolani," that is, in the parish of Sant'Andrea near the Muro Rotto, now the Via Larga. Biscaro conjectures that Leonardo came into possession of the piece of land between September and October of 1498, and that he built a workshop on it, bringing there the plaster which was to go into the horse.

The duke, after a sharp altercation with the artist in 1496 because of some scandal presumably connected with Leonardo's beginning to paint the *camerini* in the castle, had once again taken him into favor. Ludovico was no doubt encouraged by the enthusiasm aroused by the *Last Supper*, which was finished toward the end of 1497, for it was then that Leonardo received the commission for the Sala delle Asse and the *saletta negra*. What the scandal was, is not known. It is supposed that Leonardo alone had the commission to paint the *camerini* in the castle, but whether there were actually other painters too is not certain. The letter from Bartolomeo Calco to Archbishop Arcimboldi simply asks for Master Pietro Perugino to replace "the artist who was painting our *camerini*," who "today caused a certain scandal because of which he has absented himself." The ducal secretary does not give the name of the artist. Why?

Whatever the situation in that respect, the fact is that this was a prosperous moment for the artist, at which he probably received payment of certain arrears in salary, for a short time later, on December 14, 1499, before leaving Milan with Luca Pacioli, he sent a remittance of six hundred *scudi* to the Ospedale di Santa Maria Nuova in Florence. It was a way of placing his money in safety. Leonardo had not lost sight of the possibility that he might have to live on his own means during the general war that was threatening in both northern and southern Italy. Patrons would then be few and far between.

Bandello relates the anecdote about the artist and the Bishop of Gurk, who stopped in admiration before the *Last Supper*. Leonardo climbed down from the scaffold where he was working, to pay his respects. In the course of a conversation with the master concerning artistic matters, the Cardinal asked him what salary he received, and Leonardo replied that he had a regular stipend of two thousand ducats, not counting the gifts and presents given him by the Duke.

If these figures are truthful, and not an exaggeration on the part of Leonardo, his economic situation was certainly far from bad in the last years of the Sforza rule. The grant of the vineyard could not have been made exclusively as a recompense for the *Last Supper* and for the relief of Leonardo's poverty, as was believed by Amoretti and other writers after him.

Before leaving the city, Da Vinci rented his vineyard to Giovanni Battista da Oreno, a citizen of Milan.

By now events pressed close upon one another. The Graces and the Muses, frightened away by the military clamor, abandoned Milan and its castle. Bands of fierce, warlike, and unscrupulous troops camped all around and within the city walls amid the desolated populace—foot soldiers and cavalry quite different from the Sforza forces and the brilliant *condottieri*, more adept at jousting

Rearing horse with and without rider
– Budapest, National Museum

Rearing horse – London, Pierre Jeannerat Collection

Warrior repulsed – Bronze statuette –
Formerly owned by the Trivulzio
Collection

and at negotiating the surrender of fortresses than at capturing them. It was a moment of grave crisis for the duchy. A Milanese citizen was commander-in-chief for the king of France: the brave Marshal Trivulzio, who had come in at the Porta Vercellina, "not without wrath," attempted to keep the French troops from occupying the city, but the violence that he feared occurred all the same.

It is said that Gascon archers used Leonardo's horse as a practice target. The damage must have been less serious than might be imagined, since in November, 1499, Louis XII went to see the monument, and since in 1501 the Duke d'Este officially requested to be allowed to take it to Ferrara, for the reason that "every day it becomes more ruined, because it is not taken care of." Cardinal d'Amboise, the French governor, replied that since his Majesty the King had seen it, he could not undertake to move it without the royal authorization. Leonardo, far away from Milan, was no longer interested in it; he had abandoned it. His genius was going forward to new conquests.

"The Governor has been made prisoner, the Viscount carried off, and his son killed: the Duke has lost his state and his goods and his liberty, and none of his works has been finished by him." Leonardo thus summarizes in his notes the bloody end of the splendid Sforza meteor. After Ludovico il Moro's disaster at Novara, Leonardo left Milan in what we must believe was a very melancholy frame of mind. His studies and his greatest works of art had been carried out in Lombardy: even the background for the Gioconda portrait was to be a nostalgic Lombard landscape with its soft and veiled colors.

But he was to return again after having been in Romagna, in Venice, and in Florence. Charles d'Amboise requested him from the Florentine *Signoria*, and with some difficulty Leonardo was able to obtain a regular permit for residence in Milan, without arousing the jealous republic's displeasure. D'Amboise held the artist in the highest esteem, and immediately gave him back his vineyard, which had been confiscated during the French occupation. It appears that Leonardo now lived in the Porta Orientale section in a parish referred to as *S. Babilae foris*. For D'Amboise, Grand Master and marshal, lord of Chaumont-sur-Loire, he apparently projected a sumptuous palace to be built in the region bounded by the streets now called Monte Napoleone, Sant'Andrea, Spiga, and Corso Venezia. There are designs for it among the drawings and sketches in the Atlantic codex, accompanied by directions to this effect: *a* is the court of the Grand Master; *b, c,* are his rooms; *e* is his hall; "and it may be all open in front." Another sketch informs us of a project for an aviary "along a stream; covered with a copper net and full of birds." The same sheet (fol. 231) of the Atlantic codex bears a reference to the *Neron da Sancto Andrea*, which would have been the watercourse called the Nirone, while the "stream" would have been the small Acqualunga, which emptied into the Seveso after running through the Porta Orientale suburb (Corso Venezia).

124

Leonardo's mind now turned primarily to scientific speculation, hydraulic engineering, and perhaps the military arts as well. If the sketches for a monument to Marshal Trivulzio and an expert opinion regarding the work in the cathedral, and especially the new choir stalls, are excepted, the rest of his activity bears on projects for rendering the Adda navigable between Lecco and Milan. It may be that he lodged in the Villa Melzi at Vaprio, and there formed a friendship with the young Francesco, who became his passionately devoted disciple and followed him to Cloux, where he remained up to the master's last breath.

Leonardo perfected a system of basins for river navigation, acted as overseer on the work then in progress for making the Martesana canal navigable, and also directed the building of locks for the great irrigation canal near San Cristoforo.

For these works King Louis XII ceded him the water rights in San Cristoforo. A note in the Atlantic codex refers to the "canal of San Cristofano of Milan, finished on the third day of May, 1509." The water rights are mentioned in his will, in a letter of 1510, and in a comment in the Atlantic codex: "This His Majesty knows: what he gives to me he takes from himself," and Leonardo seems to be arguing against those who protested against the excessive generosity of the gift. It is apparent that the French were not miserly with Leonardo, for in ten months he had put aside 390 scudi and 200 francs. Actually, the stories of his poverty are only stories. He earned large sums and enjoyed the highest consideration.

Small bronze model of monument to Marshal Trivulzio – Sixteenth century – Milan, Castello Sforzesco

His leisure hours were now devoted to anatomical studies, to problems in geometry and flight. After his Tuscan attempts, he investigated in Milan a type of flying apparatus not strictly bound to the human body and muscle power.

Once again the plain of the Po became the scene of war—a very different war from the formalized, almost bloodless warfare of the *condottieri*. This was a stern and bloody conflict in which new machines and new weapons played an important role. War was being modernized. Leonardo devised new types of arms and new systems of defense. The war of the League of Cambrai was carried on over a far-flung strategic checkerboard, and Leonardo sketched for the French king schematic military charts which appear to anticipate the field maps of later date.

On the first of May, 1509, Leonardo left his meditations on geometry to ride with a group of Milanese gentlemen to meet the king of France. He appears to have followed the King in his expedition against Venice from that time on. He must also have been present at a crossing of the Adda under the protection of intensive artillery fire.

Rearing horse with rider – Venetian master of sixteenth century – Amsterdam, Rijksmuseum

There are sketches for a port at Cassano, and Leonardo probably remained there for a time, because no trace of reference to the battle of Agnadello is to be found among his drawings. He notes that Trezzo has become a French base, and he may have been present at the capture of Caravaggio (called "Carovazo" in his notes), which was accomplished through extensive use of artillery. There is a drawing of a fort being blown up. He must have followed the military operations very closely, almost in advance of the staff officers. His topographic sketches of Lake Iseo, of northern Brescia, of the courses of the Serio and the Oglio suggest in fact a clearly military scope, as does the schematic relief of the hydrographic system of Lombardy between the Brembo and the Mella.

He was made "painter to the King," and also directed a band of artists charged with substituting the French lily for the lion of St. Mark, step by step, as the advance progressed. Sanudo

Horse, *écorché* – Bronze – Basle, Luthy Collection

Small bronze horse – Palermo, collection of Duchess of Arenella

Detail of bronze horse shown above – Palermo, collection of Duchess of Arenella

relates an episode that occured at Bergamo. "The great St. Mark which was in the piazza" was taken down and "was sent to Milan." The people said: "He goes to Milan because soon he will be lord of Milan. And the French disliked these words but were unable to find out who said them." Though Leonardo participated in military operations, he did not hesitate to declare war "a most bestial madness." In its wake followed spectacular celebrations, in connection with which Leonardo had again to display his talents as director and as designer of triumphal machinery. The common people and the gentlemen of the court marvelled. "The street where they passed from the Porta Romana up to the castle was covered with hangings, and at many points there were triumphal arches."

Milan became the arena for new conflicts: France, attacked by the league formed under Julius II, had to withdraw from Lombardy. The investiture of France with the duchy by Emperor Maximilian had cost Louis XII a good 55,000 ducats, but Massimiliano Sforza was now restored to his ancestors' rights, with strong support from the Swiss.

Leonardo found that the city of Milan was no longer for him. He was attracted to Rome, where the best artists of Italy had begun to gather, sensing, perhaps, the coming splendor of the pontificate of Leo X. "I left Milan on the 24th day of September with Gian Francesco Melzi, Salai, Lorenzo, and Fanfoia." The master worked on in his studio in the Belvedere, but he did not lack enemies, among them Michelangelo. He followed Giuliano de' Medici to Bologna, where he met the impetuous and chivalrous Francis I. The old artist, weary now, listened to the young sovereign's words: *Mon père, venez à ma cour. Vous y serez respecté, aimé, écouté. Vous serez le maître dont tous les artistes, mes sujets, voudront se faire les disciples.*

In the plains around Cloux, where the Loire flows gently, in the tranquil sky, the old master saw a distant reflection of the Lombard plains. There he rested his head forever in the arms of Francesco Melzi, the Milanese patrician who had followed him faithfully to the end of his eventful and magnificent life.

ALESSANDRO VISCONTI

126

LEONARDO IN ROME

The learned enthusiasm that many men of the Renaissance felt for ancient Rome, for classicism, and for the glory of the Caesars, which they were almost convinced they could bring back to life in their own day, seems never to have fired Leonardo. The great names of antiquity are rarely mentioned in his writings, and though his contemporaries devoted much admiring study to the marbles, paintings, and ruins of imperial buildings, Leonardo lumped all these things together as *queste anticaglie*—"those antiques." When he inspected Trajan's port at Civitavecchia he was interested primarily in matters of building technique.

His exclamation, *Dimmi se mai, dimmi se mai fu edificato in Roma alcuna cosa* ("Tell me if ever, tell me if ever anything was built in Rome": Cod. Atl., fol. 216 v) has no specific meaning for us. It presents only another instance of Leonardo's total spiritual independence of his contemporaries.

Leonardo seems to have gone to Rome several times during his life, but the discussions of scholars have established definite data relating to only two trips there. One was the brief stay that Leonardo made in the papal city at the beginning of 1505, during which visit he was consulted on the minting of the new coinage of Julius II. The other was the much longer sojourn of about three years, from 1513 to 1516, when he stayed as the guest of Giuliano de' Medici in the Belvedere palace of the Vatican.

Edmondo Solmi has proved that Leonardo came to Rome early in 1505.[1] This information he derived, first, from the briefs of Julius II relating to his reform of the currency; second, from the fact that a close friendship existed between Leonardo and Antonio Segni, who had been engaged by the Pope in 1504 to make new coins in the Roman mint; third, from Leonardo's own drawings and annotations relating to methods for coining money, among which is the famous passage beginning, "Mint of Rome—it may also be done without a spring"; and, finally, from a document published by Gaye, in which we read: "Leonardo di Ser Piero da Vinci, paid for him to Mariotto Galilei, functionary of the Customs, for duty on a case of his clothes sent to Rome—18-9-8."[2]

This document cannot possibly refer either to the Roman trip that Leonardo is supposed to have made when he was in the service of Cesare Borgia or to another journey, never carried out,[3] which is suggested in the note: "*Truova Ingil e dilli che tu l'aspetti a morra e che tu andrai con seco in lo panna...*" (Cod. Atl., fol. 247 r). In this note Leonardo reverses the spellings of the proper names: "Find *Ligny* and tell him that you await him at *Rome* and that you will go with him to *Naples*." The journey was to have begun from Milan, as can be inferred from a reference to Santa Maria delle Grazie, and its aim was primarily artistic. In fact, in the list of things to be done, such as the buying of caps, shoes, hose, and jerkins, which suggest to us a Leonardo richly dressed and very fastidious in his person, may also be read: "Get from Gian de Paris the way of coloring *a secco*, and the method of white salt, and how to make tinted paper, single and in many folds, and his box of colors. Learn to work flesh colors in tempera. Learn to dissolve gum shellac..."

Of greatest importance in the life of Leonardo—and hence to us—was the trip to Rome that began when the master noted: "I left from Milan for Rome on the 24th day of September, 1513, with Gianfrancesco de' Melzi, Salai, Lorenzo, and Fanfoia."[4]

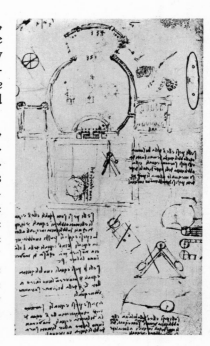

Drawing of port of Civitavecchia – Cod. Atl., fol. 271 r-*a*

Drawing for archaeological reconstruction of port of Civitavecchia – Cod. Atl., fol. 63 v-*b*

---

[1] E. Solmi. *Scritti vinciani*, Florence, 1922, p. 239 f.
[2] Gaye. *Carteggio inedito di artisti*, II, p. 89-90.
[3] M. Cermenati. "Leonardo in Rome," in *Nuova antologia*, 1919.
[4] Ms. E, fol. 1 r (Paris, Institut de France).

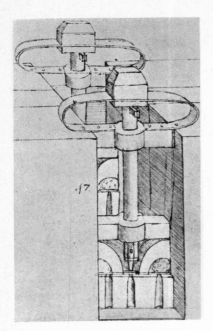

Mint of Rome designed for Julius II
– Two-hole stamp actuated by sledge
– Cod. Atl., fol. 3 r-*a*

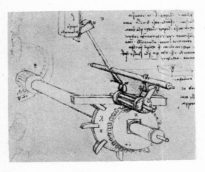

Study for gold beater – Cod. Atl.,
fol. 11 r-*a*

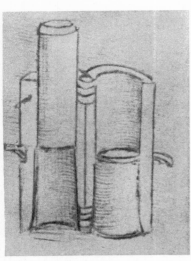

Leonardo's details for mint – Ms.
B, fol. 43 r

The notation, " 13 ducats for 500 pounds [of weight] from here to Rome, 120 miles from Florence to Rome, 180 miles from here to Florence" (Cod. Atl., fol. 400 r), is perhaps related to the same trip.

Leonardo went to Rome on this occasion at the invitation of Giuliano de' Medici. The greatest artists of the time were gathering at the court of Giovanni de' Medici, lately become Pope Leo X. Both Giuliano de' Medici, and Giovanni ever since he had become a cardinal, must have known Leonardo. It is logical to suppose that Giuliano, seeing his brother surrounded by a kind of fantastic Olympus of human intelligence, should have sought to enlist for himself the services of Leonardo—the outstanding man, the great painter, the scientist and hydraulic engineer, the builder of fortifications and designer of cannon. Giuliano at that time held the post of commander in chief of the papal armies, and would certainly have been able to make use of Leonardo's multiple talents in this connection.

Leonardo must have been appropriately welcomed to Rome. He was assigned a lodging, which was also to serve as his workshop, in the palace built by Innocent VIII at the highest point of the Vatican hill, the Belvedere, overlooking the fields that then stretched behind the Castel Sant'Angelo.

The exact date of Leonardo's arrival in Rome is not known, but we may suppose, from a document published in part by Müntz and Pastor, and later in full, with ample notes, by Cermenati,[5] that it was in November or December of 1513. The document in question is a notebook kept in 1513 by the members of what we would today call the maintenance office of the Vatican palace. In it is recorded the work that Giuliano Leno, a contractor and an architect of some worth, was to do, as well as that which he in fact executed, "in the rooms of Messer Leonardo da Vinci." On this occasion rather extensive changes were made in those rooms: the width of a window was altered, the frames and fittings of five other windows were refurbished, partitions and floors adjusted, new cupboards, seats, benches, and work tables constructed. The descriptions of the alterations to be carried out and of the work which was actually done are so detailed as to leave no doubt that Leonardo himself had a hand in dictating them.

It is difficult to determine just what position Leonardo's protector gave him. It is certain that the artist worked on mechanical devices for the Magnifico, who was an amateur student of such things, and that he received a stipend from his patron. The Magnifico also paid Leonardo's apprentices and assistants, among whom he had placed two Germans whose proximity soon became a great trial to the master. This irritation appears in a letter which Leonardo himself wrote to the Magnifico after a period in which both he and his patron had been in ill health.

Preserved in the Atlantic codex are notes that Leonardo made for the letter, two almost complete drafts of it, and the beginning of a third. The development of his thoughts and the revisions he made cast light on certain aspects of Leonardo's character and explain the source of his malaise during his stay in Rome. The letter speaks of two Germans, Giovanni degli Specchi ["Mirror John"] and a certain Maestro Giorgio, the assistants whom the Magnifico had placed with him.

The earliest note relating to the letter is probably the one which reads: "I have ascertained that he works for everyone, and that he keeps a shop for the people, because of which I wish him not to work for me for a salary, but to be paid for each work that he does for me; and since he has his shop and lodging from the Magnifico, he should be held to doing the Magnifico's work before anything else" (Cod. Atl., fol. 92 r).

Evidently Leonardo has become aware that Giovanni degli Specchi, to whom the note refers, neglects the work for his patron and "keeps a shop for the people." Leonardo, here jotting down his thoughts, finds this offensive. The other mysterious phrase, "They spy on everything I say, for the adversary"[6] must likewise relate to this period.

Then something new must have happened, perhaps some complaint to the Magnifico by Giovanni degli Specchi, and Leonardo decides to write a letter to his patron. First he sets down the facts without giving them the form of a letter. He is speaking of Giovanni degli Specchi:

"I wanted him to eat with me, being at... He went to eat with the guards, where, besides spending two or three hours at table, he very often took up the rest of the day going out with a gun, killing birds among those *anticaglie*.

"And if none of my people entered the shop and reprimanded him, and if someone scolded him, he replied that he worked for the Wardrobe, cleaning armor and guns.

"Very quick to take the money at the beginning of the month.

"And in order not to be asked to do anything he left the shop and set one up in his room, and worked for others, and if I finally sent word to him...

"Seeing that he only rarely stayed in the shop and that he ate a great deal, I sent him word that if he liked I would make a price with him for each thing that he did, on an estimate, and would give him what we might agree on. He consulted with his neighbors and quit the room, selling everything, and came to find...

"That other one has hindered me in anatomy, belittling it to the Pope, and also at the hospital, and he fills this whole Belvedere with tools for making mirrors and with workmen, and he did the same thing with Maestro Giorgio's room. This latter did not do any work without consulting with Giovanni every day, who published everything abroad, saying that he was master of that art, and spoke of things which he did not understand, saying that I did not know what I was doing, accusing me of his own ignorance.

"No..."

At this point Leonardo breaks off and, following some geometrical idea, traces two intersecting circles with a square inscribed in them. Then, half bored, he continues:

"Because of this fellow I cannot do any secret thing, because he is always at my shoulder. Be-

[5] Cermenati, *op. cit.*
[6] "Etudes et dessins de mécanique," Rouveyre Collection, fol. 1 r.

cause one room leads into the other... But his whole intent is to gain possession of these two rooms to work on mirrors, and if I set him working on my tasks he complains.

"He said that he had been promised eight ducats every month starting from the first day when he began, or at the latest when he spoke to you, and that you accepted" (Cod. Atl., fol. 182 v).

This outline of the letter is without doubt the most interesting of the three drafts, for in it Leonardo appears to us in all his humanity, very sincere, and intent on finding the weak point in his enemies. Giovanni has little desire to work, employs his time badly, spends hours and hours at table with the Swiss guards, and then goes off "with a gun, killing birds among those *anticaglie*." And here we seem to feel not only his disapproval of the idler but also his regret for the birds slain with the shotgun, and a half-veiled contempt for the "antiques" that were the object of such universal admiration.

What disappoints him most of all is that Giovanni "has hindered me in anatomy, belittling it to the Pope, and also at the hospital," while he also goes about talking of everything that Maestro Giorgio has described to him of what is being done in the shop, and of "things which he did not understand, saying that I did not know what I was doing, accusing me of his own ignorance." And the master can do nothing in secret because they spy on him, and all this because they want to take away those two rooms to work on mirrors in them. It is almost piteous to see Leonardo fretted by such paltry matters, and his spirit must have winced at writing down certain things.

Then, finally, he begins to compose his letter, for which we have two consecutive drafts on folio 247 verso of the Atlantic codex, and the beginning of a third on folio 283 recto. There is not enough space to give the three passages here in full. Leonardo now avoids mentioning the question of the anatomy studies, and the intention of the Germans to take the two workrooms away from him, matters which might appear unduly colored by personal feelings. A comparison of the beginnings of the various versions shows us Leonardo intent on finding obsequious and respectful modes of address for his patron, and trying his hand at a fine piece of epistolary prose.

The first draft is full of cancellations and corrections. It is given here with the cancelled words in parentheses: "Most Illustrious Lord... I am greatly rejoiced (by the) Most Illustrious Lord by your..." Then he makes a fresh start, and gets a good idea: "I rejoice so (I) Most Illustrious Lord (of the great acquisition) of the (famous)..." But "famous" pleases him no better than "great" and he proceeds with "longed-for restoration of your health, so that I have almost..." Then "almost" must have seemed niggardly to him, and he writes ("so that I have entirely gained back my own health... I am now at the end of my illness"), all of which he crosses out in favor of a simpler and more elegant form: "My own ill health has fled because of the almost complete recovery of Your Excellency's (which is as mine). But I am extremely regretful (of the malignity) that I have not been able to satisfy Your Excellency's wishes in full because of the wickedness of that deceiver, for whom I have left nothing undone in which I could have been of service to him, which has not been done by me for him..."

Study of horses for *Battle of Anghiari* – Windsor, Royal Collection, no. 12315

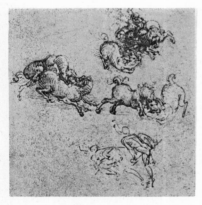

Study for *Battle of Anghiari* – Windsor, Royal Collection, no. 12330 r-a

Study of horses – Windsor, Royal Collection, n. 12328 r

In the next draft the preamble is shorter and less obsequious, and thus passes more effectively to the facts. The same is true of the third draft, of which we have only the beginning (Cod. Atl., fol. 283 r). It runs: "I have been so greatly rejoiced, Most Illustrious Lord, by the longed-for recovery of your health, that my own illness has almost left me, for which God be praised." Leonardo must have felt that the additional note of gratitude to God for his patron's recovery and his own would moderate the obsequiousness and exaggeration of the idea that the Magnifico's recovery had given him so much pleasure that it became the best medicine for his own illness.

Certain exaggerations, which I should call Ciceronian, were then fashionable, but Leonardo could not have loved them, since he manages to tone them down with such elegance. He proceeds: "But I am extremely regretful that I have not been able to satisfy Your Excellency's wishes in full because of the wickedness of that German deceiver, for whom I have left nothing undone by which I could hope to please him. First, he was paid in full before the beginning of the month; second, I invited him to lodge and board with me, for which purpose I would have a table fixed at the foot of one of these windows, where he could work with the file and finish the things made below; and thus I could constantly see the work he was doing, and it could be corrected with greater ease. And besides, he would learn the Italian language and be able to speak with ease without an interpreter..."

Leonardo is calmer here: the Magnifico might be displeased by his outbursts. He now speaks almost good-naturedly of "that German deceiver," whom he would still be willing to take into his shop, putting him to work with the file "at the foot of one of these windows." We can picture Leonardo in his huge rooms in the Belvedere, occasionally raising his eyes from his closely written pages, from his machines, from his strange drawings, and looking out of "these windows" high above the Vatican. He can see all Rome, and in the distance the blue circle of the Alban hills and Tivoli, and the snowy summits of the Sabine country.

This letter must have been written at some time in 1514, a year during which Giuliano was often in Florence. In September the Pope recalled him, and his nephew Lorenzo as well, because he felt that both had abandoned themselves to a mode of life that ill accorded with the reserved demeanor befitting relatives of the Pope.

In that same month of September, 1514, Leonardo too was travelling, toward the north. He may have gone to Milan on business connected with his vineyard there. The trip is reported in two notes. One reads, "At Parma at la Campana on the 25th day of September, 1514" (Ms. E, fol. 80 r); the other, "On the bank of the Po near Sant'Angelo in 1514 on the 27th day of September." [7] The first refers to a stay in the then famous Parmese inn, La Campana, and the second to Sant'Angelo, a charming town situated near Lodi on the Lambro, not far from where it empties into the Po. The second note accompanies a drawing of a rugged and gloomy place, a kind of canyon caused by fluvial erosion.

At the end of 1514 Leonardo must have been in Rome once more, because his sister-in-law Alessandra, writing to her husband, who was also in Rome, asked to be remembered "to your brother,

---

[7] Cermenati, *op. cit.*

Studies of horsemen for *Battle of Anghiari* – Left: British Museum – Right: Windsor, Royal Collection, no. 12339 r

that excellent and distinguished man." On the back of that letter (Cod. Atl., fol. 287 r) Leonardo noted: "My book 'On Voice' is in the hands of Messer Battista dell'Aquila," which confirms the fact that in that year Leonardo had finished a book with that title. Messer Battista dell'Aquila, to whom Leonardo had perhaps lent it, was Gian Battista Branconi, a prelate favored by Leo X, well known in the papal court and a friend of Raphael.

The famous note, "Have them draw for you where the shells are on Monte Mario" (Cod. Atl., fol. 92 v), must also be assigned to the first period of his Roman stay. Anyone who knows Monte Mario knows that there are fossil shells more or less everywhere there, and it seems odd that an acute observer like Leonardo should not have noticed them wherever he may have ventured on that hill. To that same period must be assigned a jaunt to Tivoli and Hadrian's villa—"Rome, old Tivoli, house of Hadrian" (Cod. Atl., fol. 227 v)—which appears to have made no greater impression on Leonardo than visits to other Roman ruins.

In that year, however, the first of his Roman stay, Leonardo was charged by his patron Giuliano de' Medici with a great project—the study of a plan for reclamation of the Pontine marshes.

Leo X, ambitious to revive the glories of the ancient Caesars during his pontificate, had no sooner assumed St. Peter's chair than he determined on an undertaking of impressive magnitude—the draining of the marshes.[8] There is a brief of December, 1513, addressed to Guglielmo Caetani, to the effect that the Pope was minded to begin the work and that he was willing to indemnify the prince, who had vast holdings in that part of the country, for any damages resulting from the operation. The projected work was to be done at the expense of the Camera Apostolica and under the guidance of "geometers" ["land measurers," i.e., surveyors]—*geometrarum arte et industria*. A year later the plans were changed. In a *motu proprio* of December 14, 1514, Leo X, after speaking of the detrimental effects produced over such a vast area by the deadly exhalations from the fens flanking the Appian Way, confided to his brother Giuliano the task of draining *pigram paludem Pomptinam*. And Giuliano, having listened to the *peritissimorum geometrarum giudicia*, assumes the undertaking *sua impensa ac periculo*.

Edmondo Solmi has made an excellent study of Leonardo and the reclamation work in the Pontine marshes, tracing and reconstructing those works which were actually carried on for Giuliano by a notary of the Camera Apostolica, a certain Domenico de Juvenibus. Giuliano deputized De Juvenibus as his legal agent in an act of December 14, 1514, the very date of the *motu proprio* of Leo X.

In a later document, of January 9, 1515, Giuliano, who left on that day for his wedding in Savoy, ceded to this Domenico de Juvenibus a fourth part of the marshland which was to become his property when reclaimed. He also promised at his own expense to procure for the notary the office of apostolic scribe. De Juvenibus for his part agreed to spend up to twenty-four thousand ducats on the work, and further obligated himself, in the event that he did not actually spend this sum, to reimburse Giuliano for whatever the latter might have spent in securing for him the desired office.

From these documents we learn that Giuliano, who had obtained the contract for the work of draining the swamps from his brother the Pope, was to be recompensed for his expenditures by re-

Study for *Battle of Anghiari* – London, C. F. Clarke Collection

Horseman – London, Norman R. Colville Collection

---

[8] Solmi, *op. cit.*, p. 323 f.

131

Studies for *Battle of Anghiari* – Windsor, Royal Collection, no. 12340, and Venice, Academy

Study of horses – Milan, Ambrosiana

Episode in battle of horsemen – Drawing attributed to Michelangelo – London, British Museum

Horseman – Study for *Battle of Anghiari* – Oxford, from the collection of Ashmolean Museum

ceiving land in the reclaimed area. He in turn ceded the actual direction of the work to De Juvenibus, who would receive a quarter of the land eventually gained. Giuliano would also have manipulated his connections in the offices of the Curia in such a way as to obtain for the new contractor the office of apostolic scribe.

Seen across a considerable span of time, the documents, that *sua impensa ac periculo* of the papal *motu proprio*, have an almost ironic flavor. The great undertaking was completed only four centuries later. How the works recommended by the "expert geometers" developed under the direction of Fra Giovanni Scotti of Como, and how, after the resolution of serious differences arising among those citizens of Piperno, Sezze, and Terracina who held or claimed rights over different tracts of the swampy land, the point was reached when actual work was begun, as well as how the undertaking was later abandoned after the deaths of Giuliano and Lorenzo, and finally of Leo X himself, may all be read in Solmi's study. Here we need only say that the operations carried out under the direction of the Comasque friar were highly successful. His accomplishment consisted in draining the lowest part of the marsh by directing the water into a new channel dug for the Ufente. This river had formerly taken a very long and tortuous course to its mouth near Monte Circeo. It was made instead to flow directly into the sea near Torre di Badino, carrying off the stagnant waters from the surrounding countryside, which now rose above the swamps. The new channel was called the Giuliano or the Portatore di Badino. The reclaimed land was divided between Giuliano and De Juvenibus, and the friar who had directed the work received donations.

The documents cited here, and others published by Solmi and various scholars who have studied the work done in the Pontine marshes, never mention Leonardo's name. And yet it is to Leonardo, as Cian first correctly assumed and Solmi later amply demonstrated, that the credit must be given for those plans which in so short a time produced such marvellous results.

Leonardo had already worked on a system of canals in the Lombard plain, had studied methods for turning the Arno and other rivers from their courses, and had traced out the direct lines for canals which would drain the Chiana swamps. He must certainly have been among those "expert geometers" who originally convinced Giuliano de' Medici and the Pope himself that the work was possible. Furthermore, granted the absolute pre-eminence that his genius and experience had won for him among his contemporaries, it must be believed that it was he who proposed the over-all plan on which the undertaking was based.

Evidence for this assumption is found in his beautiful map of the Pontine marshes preserved among the manuscripts in Windsor Castle (no. 12684; see below, p. 473). A birds'-eye view from near the coast shows the great expanse of marshy land traversed by the Via Appia, the Monti Lepini sloping down to the plain, the towns of Sermoneta, Sezze, Piperno, and Terracina, the ruins of the temple of Jupiter Anxur on the height above the city, the rivers running down from the hills, and Monte Circeo standing out at the edge of the sea. The names of the places are written from left to right, clear for all to read and understand.

A map of the Pontine marshes would be of little significance in itself, but here are indicated the works that the friar from Como began and carried to a rather advanced stage. Leonardo traces a new channel for the Ufente, to which he gives its old name, Levola, and draws in a new course for the Rio Martino. The creation of a new channel for this river was the first step taken when, many years later, the inhabitants of Sezze and Sermoneta finally came to some agreement as to the value of carrying out reclamation work in the swamps below them.

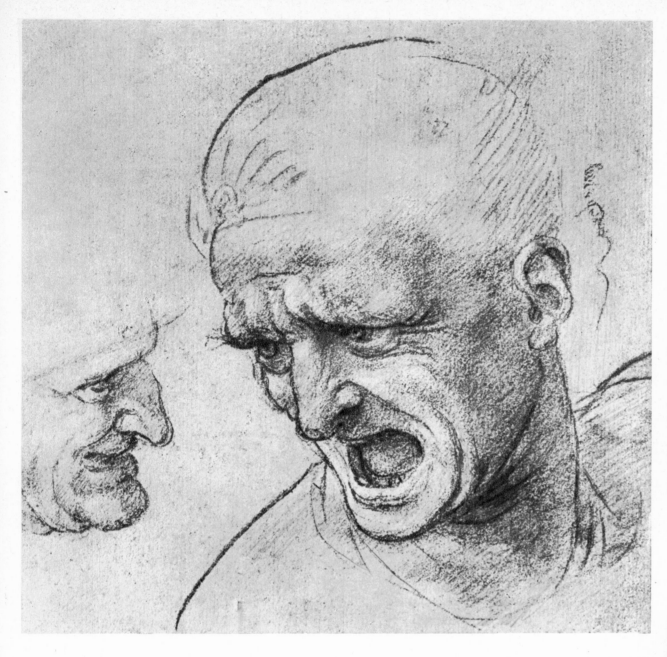

Studies of expressions for *Battle of Anghiari* – Right: Venice, Academy – Left: Budapest, Museum of Fine Arts

Head of warrior with turban – Oxford, Ashmolean

Struggle between nude men – Drawing attributed to Michelangelo – Paris, Louvre

The clear-cut line of the Via Appia divides the plain into two distinct parts. Above are the Lepini, with their wooded valleys seen as if lit by the slanting rays of the westerly sun. Sermoneta, Sezze, Piperno, Terracina, Anxur are the place names given for these heights; from them the rivers come down and turn into the swamps in the Appian flats. The Teppia, which Leonardo marks "Tivera," the Nympha, the Puzza ditch, and the Fiumicello flow together near a tower. Beside the Appian Way, at the mountain, he again puts the name Lympha. From the valleys of Sezze and Piperno, the Amaseno and the Portatore run down, meet, and go toward the Appian Way, running beside the road, or so it seems, toward the south.

Now we must cross the road. Moving up the coast from Terracina, we encounter the village of Badino. Here is the mouth of a canal marked by Leonardo on the tortuous course of the river Ufente. It is the canal, the Portatore di Badino, which kept the river from backing up. The river is here designated "Levola," and we see it following the broad curve of the coast and emptying into the sea near Circeo.

Halfway up the great arc of the coastline between Circeo and Torre Astura, which is too far north to be included on the map, we see clearly marked a drainage canal, the Rio Martino, designed to carry off the waters which had previously spread out into the swampy area of the great flats.

Leonardo thus indicated with great precision the means of resolving at least in part the great problem of reclaiming the land: the Medici might have made their name resound through the centuries by virtue of this truly remarkable project. Meanwhile, Leonardo himself, the experimenter par excellence, was held back from the studies he loved: "[He] has hindered me in anatomy, belittling it to the Pope, and also at the hospital." This was certainly the Santo Spirito hospital, only a few hundred yards from the Vatican. Sixtus IV, the Della Rovere pope, had made it one of the most modern of its time when he renovated it with the help of the architect Baccio Pontelli. The proscription of the anatomy studies by Leo X is not to be wondered at; Leonardo himself may have been expecting it, for he notes with some anxiety: "The Pope has found out that I have skinned three corpses."[9]

Leo X was a strange man in his continual contrasts of good and evil, his fervent enthusiasms and

---

[9] "Fragments d'études anatomiques," Rouveyre Collection, R. C., fol. 9 v.

Studies for *Battle of Anghiari*

Right: Venice, Academy

Left, above: Windsor, Royal Collection, no. 12326

Left, below: Windsor, Royal Collection, no. 12332

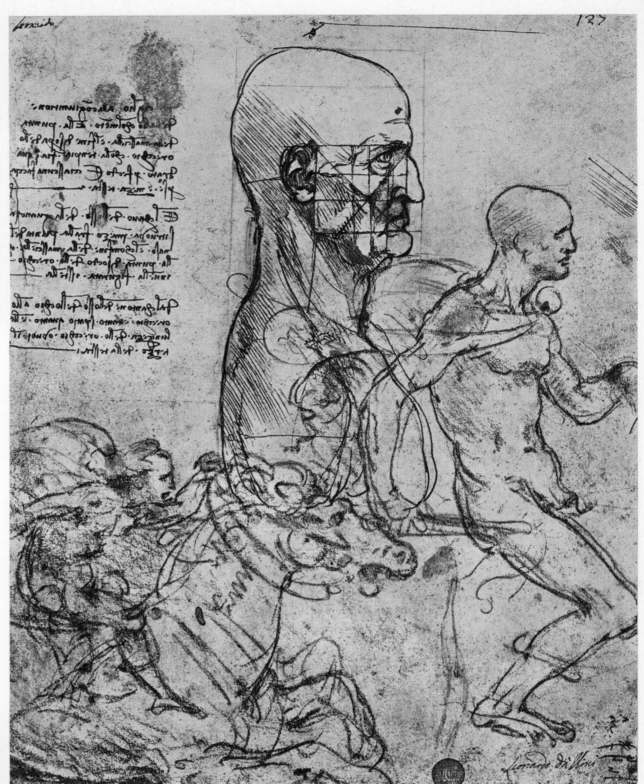

Study of running horses – Windsor, Royal Collection, no. 12328 r

Battling horseman – Oxford, Ashmolean

unexpected apathies, his ardent faith and fearful superstition. He seems in truth to sum up and epitomize the world in which he was the highest authority, and in which the last remnants of a culture were being extinguished, overshadowed by the new culture that was then moving to the fore. The Pope could certainly not have been altogether pleased that the Vatican itself, his own palace, should be inhabited by a kind of witch doctor who made unheard-of experiments, and skinned and dissected corpses—by Leonardo.

Since Da Vinci apparently did not engage the sympathies of the Roman milieu, he was forced into a solitary existence in his Belvedere rooms, far from the papal court. In the course of his life he had already met Bramante, Michelangelo, even Raphael, who as a lad had admired his works in Florence. He was acquainted with Fra Luca Pacioli, whom the Pope had named teacher of mathematics in the revived Sapienza school, and also with Fra Giocondo, who had been active in the Venetian camp at the time when Leonardo accompanied Louis XII on his expedition against the Venetian republic. Everyone in the court knew of Leonardo's genius, of his military works, of his infinite learning, his beautiful painting. In the *Last Supper* in the Grazie he had appeared as the greatest artist of the day: even Raphael would have been disposed to call him Master. All would have wished him to paint. They did not understand his continual filing away at odd kinds of gear, his spending hours and hours tracing intersecting circles, and his continual discourses on angles and quadrants, his piling figure upon figure, only to lose himself again in the thread of new reasonings. Castiglione wrote: "Another of the greatest painters in the world despises that art in which he is

so rare: he sets himself to studying philosophy, from which he derives such strange concepts and novel chimeras that with all his craft he would not be able to paint them." In the account that Vasari gives of Leonardo's Roman period there is a clear echo of what the Pope must have felt on seeing the master so inactive: "It is said that when the Pope commissioned him to make a painting, he began at once to distil oils and herbs to make the varnish, because of which Pope Leo said: 'Alas, this man will never do anything, for he begins to think of the end of the work before the beginning.'"

Vasari has narrated just before this the tale of the lizard that Leonardo disguised as a little dragon, and has told of his blowing up a wether's gut so that it occupied an entire room, and adds: "He perpetrated many such follies and worked on mirrors." The mirrors must have been those of Giovanni, the "German deceiver" who had given the master so much trouble.

Of the two pictures that Vasari says Leonardo painted for Messer Baldassarre Turini da Pescia, no trace remains today.

Certainly, in that feverish milieu of practical men, who were at that very time transforming the face of Rome and with it the face of the world, and creating new models of beauty, expressing a civilization which had reached its highest point, and, conscious as it were of its inexorable fate, was making haste to immortalize itself in monumental works—in that milieu Leonardo, the philosopher, the experimenter, the untiring searcher, uncompromising and unappeased, could not have succeeded.

Leonardo worked for the Magnifico, occupying himself with designing a great stable to shelter his patron's horses (Cod. Atl., fol. 96 v-*a*); he read, and worked over his books, especially those on geometry. During the year 1515 his contacts with the Magnifico were less frequent than in the preceding year; Giuliano in fact left Rome on the very day of the signing of the above-mentioned contract with De Juvenibus: "The Magnifico Giuliano de' Medici left Rome on the 9th of January, 1515, at dawn, to take a wife in Savoy, and on that same day the king of France died."

Leonardo too travelled in northern Italy in 1515, but there are no grounds for supposing that he accompanied his patron on that trip. Luca Beltrami discovered a document establishing the fact that Leonardo went to Bologna: "1515—expenditures made by M. Paolo Vittori, major-domo of His Excellency, for the trip to Bologna, in Bologna, and elsewhere. Note of the stipends to be paid by me in the name of our excellent Signore Bernardo Bini and his company from Rome. To L.do da Vinci for his stipend xxxiii ducats, and another vii ducats to the same for the salary of Giorgio the German, which is in all xl ducats." [10]

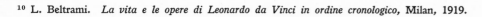

[10] L. Beltrami. *La vita e le opere di Leonardo da Vinci in ordine cronologico*, Milan, 1919.

Tuscan master of sixteenth century
– Episode from *Battle of Anghiari* –
Florence, Horne Museum

Giovanni Francesco Rustici – Battling
horsemen – Terra-cotta sculptures –
Florence, Palazzo Vecchio and Bargello

Leonardo, then, was in Bologna during that year, and toward the end of it we find him also in Milan.[11] From there he wrote a letter to his steward, Zanobi Bono, who had sent him samples of the new wine from his vineyard at Fiesole: "The last four carafes were not up to my expectations, and I have had vexation because of it." He goes on to explain the reasons why the wine is not as it should be, concluding: "Although if you and the others would make note of these things, we should have an excellent wine."

Leonardo's trip to Bologna coincided with the Pope's journey to meet Francis I. Evidence for the assumption is given in a fine map, from the artist's hand, of the territory immediately north of Rome (Cod. Atl., fol. 336 v). This map, so far as the writer is aware, has never been connected with that trip, yet on it are marked all the places that the papal cortege touched at during the first part of the journey. Paride de Grassis has left us the itinerary: "On the first day of October, 1515, Pope Leo left Rome, taking his way to Viterbo, Montefiascone, Toscanella, and finally Civitavecchia. Stopping here, the Pope was advised that Milan had been occupied by the French, and that King Francis with his army was preparing to go to Rome, fearing which the Pope wished to intercept him, in case he should be planning some new thing in Tuscan and Roman territory, and moved with his entire court to meet him at Bologna."

Was it then that Leonardo, waiting on events with the Pope and the pontifical court at Civitavecchia, observed, made drawings, and arrived at inferences regarding the construction of the ancient port of Trajan, or was it at some other time? It has been suggested that he was with the Pope when the latter went to Civitavecchia, accompanied by Antonio da Sangallo and other courtiers and architects, to study the fortifications of that town.[12] Whenever it may have been, it is certain that at Civitavecchia Leonardo inspected the remains of the ancient imperial port (Cod. Atl., fol. 63 v), drew a reconstruction of the ancient buildings facing the sea, and above all observed with keen interest the workmanship in the laying of the ancient stones "which are at the front of the mole." He is standing on the pier called today the Calata; lowering his eyes, he sees the finely smoothed masses, "4 ells long, 2 ells deep, 2½ ells wide." He makes a few sketches and is pleased at how the stones are laid: "And the surface of this cement is well plastered with perfect mortar and sand." He also describes the "imperial rooms built over the mole of the port."

What seems to have interested him more than anything else was the motion of the waves. He noted on the same sheet (Cod. Atl., fol. 63 r): "The wave moves under the skin of the sea and leaves behind it all the foam that is worked up ahead of it." For him the sea, like all created things, was a living entity.

"Write to Bartolomeo the Turk about the flow and ebb of the Black Sea, and whether he knows if there be such a flow and ebb in the Icarian or the Caspian Sea," he reminds himself (Cod. Atl., fol. 260 r), and further on he notes: "Consider the attraction and respiration in the lungs of man, and whether the attraction which the earth has for the water in the 12 hours of the ebb and flow could evenly

[11] Beltrami, *op. cit.*
[12] Guglielmotti. *Storia della marina pontificia*, Rome, 1881-1893.

136

show us the measure of the earth's lung, reasoning thus: the lung is half an ell square and breathes 270 times each hour: how great, then, must be the lung of the earth to breath once in every 12 hours?"

Here Leonardo begins one of those long discourses bristling with figures. But this is of little importance: reading the passage above, we feel Leonardo's ample respiration, his broad chest lifting two hundred and seventy times an hour, his breathing deep, almost solemn. And he seems to feel that the earth, from which his precise reasoning has torn so many secrets, is living: it breathes. The earth breathes once in every twelve hours, and the high and low tides, the ebb and flow of the sea, are the index of its calm and even respiration.

On March 17, 1516, Giuliano de' Medici died of phthisis, and with his death Leonardo lost his only protector. Life in Rome must have seemed increasingly difficult for the master, though nothing authorizes us to believe in his alleged envy of this or that artist whose fortunes in the papal court had risen higher than his own. Leonardo could not have been ambitious in that sense. So long as they let him work in peace, follow his dreams, try out his machines—so long as they let him live as he wished, he was content. What irritated him was to feel himself watched, spied on, misunderstood: "They spy on everything I say, for the adversary." There is the note, "Because of this fellow I cannot do any secret thing." And again, "First the favors, then the work, then the ingratitude, and then the base lamentation, and then..." But not a word is found in his writings against those whom historians have tried to picture as his enemies.

Perhaps only that phrase, "The Medici created me and destroyed me," reflects a profound regret over what he might have done and had wished to but had not been able to do. He too, perhaps more than many others, was afflicted by the somber melancholy that spread like a veil of sadness over the splendors of the Renaissance.

In August, 1516, he was still in Rome, and measured the basilica of San Paolo: "San Paolo in Rome has five naves, 80 columns, and its width across the naves is 130 ells, and from the steps of the high altar to the door is 155 ells, and from these steps to the furthest wall at the back of the high altar 70 ells. The portico is 130 ells long and 17 ells wide. Made on the... [?Aug]ust, 1516" (Cod. Atl., fol. 162 v). On the same manuscript sheet may be seen sketches which appear to be a study for removing or replacing a column on which there rests an architrave with a flat molding. It is not possible to determine what relation, if any, this sketch may have had to the restorations then being carried out in San Paolo. On those sheets of the Atlantic codex which may be assigned to the Roman period, the master has left numerous studies for methods of reinforcing arches which threaten to collapse. Does this suggest that Leonardo worked as a restorer of ancient buildings?

The passage giving the measurements of the Ostiense basilica is the last certain document of Leonardo's Roman activity. It is probable that he left Rome for France toward the end of the year 1516.[13] It seems impossible, however, that he should have gone "almost in flight before his hated rival, Michelangelo Buonarroti." He may never have thought of Michelangelo as his rival. And even though there may have been no sympathy between the two, both were of a stature that allowed them to contemplate the world and life from a height that we cannot know.

EMILIO LAVAGNINO

[13] E. Solmi and G. B. Toni. "Leonardo da Vinci's Trip to France," in *Atti del Reale Istituto Veneto di Scienze, Lettere e Arti*, Vol. LXIV (1904-1905), p. II.

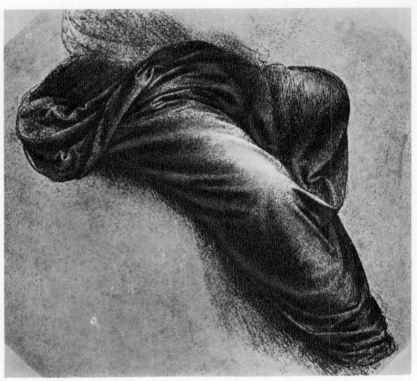

Studies of drapery – Paris, Louvre

LEONARDO IN VENICE

It would be gratifying to have some beautiful, profound phrase, some poetic "illumination" of Leonardo's, which refers explicitly to Venice. Failing this, one would wish at least to be able to attribute to Venice certain of his magic formulae to define the motions of water.

"Man has within himself a lake of blood wherein the lungs expand and contract as they breathe. Just so does the corpus of the earth have its ocean sea which expands and contracts every six hours so that the world may breathe." In Venice this "breathing of the world" is more perceptible than elsewhere, for the sea laps the thresholds of the houses, mounts the marble stairs, is ever and everywhere before one's eyes. But who knows whether Leonardo's stupendous figure of speech was born from exact observation, registered on the spot, of that ebb and flow that is "two ells at Venice."

Certain other fragments have a Venetian flavor: "And the high walls of the great city will be seen upside down in their ditches." Though this was certainly not written about Venice, it reminds one that in no other great city of the world is the spectacle of high walls reflected upside down in the mirror of the waters so frequent and familiar: "The fens will be so muddy that men will climb the trees of their towns." Here interpreters of Leonardo would have us understand that men must walk on stilts to avoid the mud. But how much more beautiful it would be—and it seems quite likely to me—if Leonardo had meant that they would walk over marshy ground that had been dotted with lake dwellings raised on piles.

When we think that the Venice that Leonardo saw was the Venice faithfully recorded by Gentile Bellini, Carpaccio, Mansueti, and Bastiani, it seems all the more regrettable that there is no interpretation of the city by Leonardo, not even a little drawing. The many sketches of horses which closely recall those of St. Mark's and of the Colleoni are definitely Venetian, but we must freely admit that this is an occasional and not an essential theme in Venice.

Moreover it is well established that, by the time the master came to the shores of the lagoons in his forty-eighth year, he was no longer interested primarily in painting. Entirely occupied as he then was with the knottiest theoretical speculations, deeply involved with ideas that were to engage the science of the future, he had come to despise that art in which, in Castiglione's words, he was most rare. "Science is the captain, and practice the foot soldiers." Art, a practice like any other, was thus relegated to the incoherence of creative passion.

The fact is, therefore, that Leonardo did not leave any pictorial record of Venice, nor can we honestly say that his Venetian sojourn gave rise to any of his remarkable philosophic speculations or poetic fantasies. But he stayed there three or four months, he looked, he observed, and from the particular conditions of the environment and of the given historical moment came the impulse to create new and daring things, things which seemed to the matter-of-fact Castiglione strange, indescribable "chimeras."

The year 1499 drew to as sad a close for Ludovico il Moro as for his enemy, Venice. On October 6, Louis XII, king of France, arrived in Milan with a vast train of French and Italian cavalry, among which was the Duke of Valentinois. Louis had been called thither by that Serene Republic. But on that same day the Turks, incited by the Duke of Milan, who had fled to Innsbruck, arrived at the Tagliamento with their infantry. A few months earlier they had won a victory at Zonchio over the fleet of the sea captain Antonio Grimani, and had taken Lepanto, capturing many prisoners. Now they descended from Friuli to threaten the state of St. Mark on its home territory.

Male garment – Florence, Uffizi Gallery

Study of drapery – London, British Museum

Studies of garments – Florence, Uffizi
Gallery

Studies of drapery – Florence, Uffizi
Gallery

In that tragic close of the year and of the century, Leonardo did not leave Milan. The preceding April, he had received a gift from Ludovico il Moro of a vineyard outside Porta Vercellese; in fact, on December 14, he had sent money from there to Florence in two letters of change. Perhaps that was the time of his first encounter with a captain of Louis XII, Count de Ligny, Louis of Luxemburg, whose goal was to reassert the rights over Naples where he had been with Charles VIII. This is a thread we shall find again in the hodgepodge of Venetian notes in the Atlantic codex.

It is difficult to say exactly when Da Vinci left Milan, the city of his most intense work and greatest glory, in order to begin what is called his wandering phase. We know only that on March 3, 1500, he was in Venice where he showed the lutanist, Gugnasco, the charcoal sketch for the portrait of Isabella d'Este. If we bear in mind that Milan was seething with unrest from December to February in preparation for the brief return of Il Moro, it is reasonable to assume that Leonardo felt it advisable to avoid any possible meeting, under precarious and painful circumstances, with his sore beset lord, and had therefore taken refuge in Venice. A few unequivocal words he had jotted down not long after, along with others of a more obscure nature, suffice to give us a picture of his state of mind at that moment. They are to be found on the inside front cover of Ms. L: "The Duke has lost his state and his goods and his liberty, and none of his works has been finished by him."

The trip, then, can be dated in the early part of 1500, and it is certain that his friend, the mathematician Fra Luca Pacioli, accompanied him. The latter may have been well known in Venice already, for he had given lectures in geometry at the Church of St. Bartholomew. They stopped over in Mantua where Leonardo made that charcoal sketch of the divine Isabella which was to have served later as a basis for the portrait of that lady she had so eagerly wanted him to paint. Another unkept promise; but the drawing, now in the Louvre, is a masterpiece.

In Venice, where the two great Tuscans arrived toward the end of January, they met another citizen of their province, the Sienese doctor Paolo di Vanozzo. The mathematician recalls he was among his audience when he spoke again at St. Bartholomew's, and there were many important persons whose names the painter marked down in the notebook he always carried with him. There was "Salamon" whom we may identify as Alvise Salamon, galley captain against the Turks (unpublished papers at Windsor, XVI, fol. 28-a); "Pier Pagolo da Como" and "Marco da Rimino, sheriff at Ravenna" (Rouveyre Collection, fol. 6-b); Stefano Chigi or Ghisi "canon...at the Church of the Holy Apostle" (Cod. Arund, fol. 274 r); "Antonijo of Padua" (Ms. I, fol. 107 r); "Antonio Frisi [who] is on the Council of. Justs.ice" (Ms. I, fol. 135 r); and perhaps also the great architect from Verona, Fra Giocondo (Ms. K, fol. 100 r). Particularly noteworthy, as we shall see, was the name of Salamon.

Study of drapery, on canvas – Paris, Louvre

Draperies – Windsor, Royal Collection, no. 12525

This is the point at which Leonardo made his report on the military problem of Friuli to the heads of the Venetian department of arms and fortifications. That this report was entirely worked out and presented seems beyond question in the light of the full, minutely detailed notes conserved in the Atlantic codex (fol. 234-*a*, *b*). The raid by the Turks, who had come as far as the very walls of Vicenza, had proved that the vulnerable point of Venetian defense to the north lay in the Isonzo valley. Some barrier against the invader must urgently be created at that point. Leonardo, no less famous as a military engineer than as a painter, must have been sent to the spot to study the situation. He went to the Isonzo valley, took notes and made sketches tracing the course of that river and of the Vippacco near Gorizia ("The bridge of Gorizia... Vilpago... high... high"), stopped at Gradisca ("Bombardments... at Venice... as I said at Gradisca"), and conceived the idea of a "movable dam" with "dentellated supports" strong enough to withstand the current which could, if need be, raise the waters high enough to flood the plain, thus rendering it impassable.

"Illustrious Sirs, having noted that from whatever part of the mainland the Turks may reach our Italian lands, they must pass by the Isonzo valley. Although I recognize the fact that no lasting defense can be set up at that point, still we must admit that a few men with the help of such a river are worth many without it... I have concluded that there is no single place where the defense of a site would be of more universal value than at that river." The defense was, then, that "dentellated" and "movable" dam to be made of wood, with due consideration given to the force of the river current (for "the more rapid the water's descent, the more furiously will it hurtle against anything in its way"). The height of the banks must be carefully gauged too so that the dam, when raised, would force the river out of its natural course, causing it to flood the woods, root up the trees, and hurl them against the dam.

Perhaps Leonardo's idea remained only an idea, but he did not abandon it because of that. So true is this that, in the last years of his life, we find him discussing the use of a "movable barrier" in France ("which I planned in Friuli") in order to fertilize certain fields lying along a branch of the Loire (Ms. B. M., fol. 270-*b*).

Another invention, another "chimera" of the brief Venetian sojourn, was an apparatus for swimming under water.

Female garment – Windsor, Royal Collection, no. 12524

Studies of drapery – Windsor, Royal Collection, no. 12523 r

Windsor, Royal Collection, no. 12528

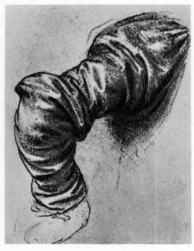

Windsor, Royal Collection, no. 12546

Windsor, Royal Collection, no. 12527

Right: Windsor, Royal Collection, no. 12532

Edmondo Solmi's interesting hypothesis that the drawings of submarines in the Atlantic codex date from this period is based largely on a note in that codex. There Leonardo mentions a certain Manetto, who may be identified as Lodovico Manenti ("Alvise Manetti," according to Sanudo), Secretary of the Venetian Republic entrusted with negotiating with Sultan Bajazet II the return of Lepanto and the release of Italian prisoners. Manenti, who returned from his mission in March, reported the inacceptable terms and haughty words of the Grand Turk. Some decisive, energetic action was imperative. Leonardo thought of sending submarines to "gore the flanks" of the Turkish galleys, and threw himself heart and soul into the task of perfecting the necessary instruments.

An initial apparatus that would permit the submerged human body to breathe by means of a tube protruding above the water's surface held up by "pontoons or cork," was discarded because it would be too readily detected by the enemy. Something else was needed, and in fact this remarkable engineer invented another device. "A diving suit which covers the body from top to toe, with a vent to urinate, and a breast plate that contains an air tank which, by means of an iron semicircle, is held well away from the chest itself..." Every detail of the diving suit is then minutely described. Leonardo even anticipates that the diver may be sighted and trapped by a net ("Take a stout knife with you so that you cannot be caught in a net."). He recommends secrecy: "Get a simple-minded fellow to do the job and have him sew the suit up for you at home." In conclusion, Leonardo details his possible earnings from this invention, and this is where the name of Manetto recurs: "But first come to an agreement for [the use of] this device, so that half the rights are yours free and clear. And the prison deposit should be in Manetto's hands, so that the payment should be made to him." The "payment" was that offered by the Venetian Republic, half to Leonardo and half to his divers, if the undertaking proved successful, and the "prison deposit" was the sum deposited by relatives of the prisoners of Zonchio as a reward for their eventual liberation. All this must be agreed on "in writing," drawn up as a sort of contract and signed before a notary.

This is the passage on which Solmi [1] bases his findings. His reasoning is hard to refute, especially if we recall the reference to Alvise Salamon which also indicates that Leonardo had some direct contact with the military authorities of the Republic.

It is almost certain that the undertaking went no further than the planning stage. Leonardo wrote later that he did not want to release his "methods of staying under water" as he felt man's native iniquity was such that he would use the discovery to "sink ships and thus cause loss of life to those who sail them." But it seems that he would have set aside these scruples for Venice at that moment.

On April 10, at the battle of Novara, Ludovico il Moro was taken prisoner and his power came to an end. Now Leonardo need no longer seek protection under the wings of the lion of St. Mark's and, on April 24, we find him in Florence with his friend Pacioli.

He was to have gone on to Rome to meet Count de Ligny, as he notes enigmatically in the Atlantic codex (fol. 246-a): "Find Ingil [Ligny]; tell him you'll wait for him at mora [Roma] and go to ilopanna [a Napoli] with him."

But after Novara, the prince left suddenly for France, and Leonardo's trip to Naples, like so many of his other projects, never took place.

DIEGO VALERI

---

[1] E. Solmi. "Leonardo da Vinci and the Venetian Republic," *Archivio storico lombardo*, 1908, p. 327 f.

LEONARDO IN FRANCE

In the spring of 1516, Leonardo da Vinci left Milan for France in the retinue of Francis I. The underlying reasons and circumstances attending this event are sufficiently well-known. However, if we were to consider the move as a fortuitous "exile," [1] we should be forced to ignore the fact that, despite the work Leonardo performed so freely in Italy, he had actually been in "the service of the king of France" for fifteen years. It seems remarkable, almost like predestination, that this obligation, which survived so many crises, should have arisen and developed, and a brief examination of it is worth our attention.

Leonardo went to Milan in 1483 under the patronage of Ludovico Sforza, enjoying the full favor of the Prince. During his long residence there, a stay interrupted by occasional visits to Florence, his fertile genius was productive. On September 24, 1499, Ludovico fled from Milan before the approaching French army, leaving behind him, stunned, the artists who had been grouped about his throne. But the liberal proclamations of Louis XII from the time he entered Italy, and the spiritual independence evident even in that war-torn world, allowed Leonardo and his fellow artists to appear before the King fifteen days before his triumphal march into Milan, and from that meeting was born a remarkable adventure.

At the instant of their encounter, a spark was struck which united the two men: the cultivated Florentine artist who became a Lombard by choice and adaptation to a milieu to which he was at bottom akin, and the monarch—alien in customs and separated from the Italian by a vastly different culture. Nevertheless the conquering King was overcome as by a "bolt of lightning": he was captivated by Leonardo and his work, and wanted only to acquire the work and take the artist with him.

The *Last Supper* amazed him, and it was his intention to cut it from its resting place so that he might adorn one of his cathedrals with it; the equestrian statue of Francesco Sforza would rise in a public square—the model later came to the Louvre—and Leonardo himself must follow the King almost as if he were the chief hostage in a war involving the conquest of all Italy.

For his part, the artist did not refuse: on the contrary he was agreeably tempted. He promised all that was asked of him and entered the "service of the King."

As we assess the situation today, what was the basis for so unexpected and precipitate a friendship? Can we suppose that Louis XII had on the instant divined the profundity and restlessness of Leonardo's art, that sense of the mysterious, that intuition full of doubts and irony that reclothed the visible world with a kind of supernatural unreality? Surely not; Louis was struck, first of all, by the "perfection" [and the word is his] which until that time had never been seen in art, a perfection whose harmony of detail determined the unity of the whole, a perfection then unknown in France, and even in Italy. Louis also voluptuously savored the sweetness, the tenderness, the divine beauty in the exquisite grace of the figures in such works as the *Virgin of the Rocks*, the *St. John* of the *Last Supper*, and the *Annunciation*. He was obsessed by this new world revealed to him. He could never again forget it or ignore it.

And is it not possible that Leonardo discovered in the Northern king—a man of ordinary physical qualities and perhaps a bit ponderous of gait—a spirit new to him, embodying an ingenuousness at

School of Clouet – Portrait of Francis I – Paris, Louvre

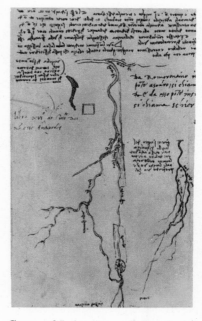

Course of Loire river – Cod. Atl., fol. 336 v-*b*

---

[1] In *Sapere*, 1938, p. 365, E. Carusi employs the phrase "voluntary exile in France, where he seeks asylum, invited by the knightly king of France," without giving any evidence for this statement.

Fresco composition in chapel of Clos-Lucé in Amboise, probably drawn in by Leonardo

Leonardo Da Vinci's memorandum of his stay in Cloux near Amboise (Indre-et-Loire, France) – Above at side one can read: *Il di dell'Asensione in Ambosa 1517 di maggio nel Clu* – Cod. Atl., fol. 103 r-b

once subtle and shrewd, a simple and generous loyalty, and a genuine enthusiasm devoid of vanity and selfish calculation? This devoted lover of Anne of Brittany who had waited for her for ten years in spite of another marriage and the duties of the throne, this sovereign "who did not know how to avenge" the injustices of the Duke of Orleans: did not Leonardo find this candor something at once surprising and attractive?

What a joy to meet a truly "royal" soul that with heart and with faith reached the highest summits of the spirit; what joy to the painter who, in his career, had known only such cruel and perfidious lords as Ludovico il Moro and Cesare Borgia or pedantic, mediocre bourgeoisie like Soderini or the Prior of Santa Maria delle Grazie, who tried to draw up contracts to limit Leonardo's sacred freedom of inspiration and to bind his artistic accomplishments to their bidding!

Should we agree with Müntz in seeing this effect as a kind of "foreordained harmony" between the native country of the King—that valley of the Loire with its graceful landscape tinted by gradations of a mother-of-pearl light, and the very similar plains of Lombardy, where Leonardo seems to have found an atmosphere so propitious to his genius? Müntz writes that "the union, the communion of French and Italian art took place on the plains of Lombardy between the mountains and the lakes. The French Renaissance, offshoot of that of Italy, retained a quality of youth and ingenuousness that the Florentine school, already in decline after having reached its peak, could not maintain."

But an argument of this kind, however ingenious and even plausible, leaves out of account another affinity too long neglected by historians. Let us make bold, as was done apropos of Virgil, to seek for this affinity in a common ancestry. Research by Camille Jullian has suggested that the poet of the *Georgics*—in which we find again and again descriptions of landscapes more Gallic than Italian— was the direct descendant of a family of Anjou still in existence today, the Marot family, who had come to Mantua two centuries before Virgil's birth. And on the other hand, who would not seek to establish the fact that the elegant Prince of Blois, the clever and ironic countryman of Rabelais, a dreamer, poet, and lover of art, was a Lombard and a Visconti by descent through his grandmother, Valentina of Milan?

Certain it is that in October, 1499, an agreement was made between the artist and the King; it was duly registered and adhered to. This is evident not only through orders and continued execution and acquisition of works, but through written statements and official relations of the artist with the King's representative in Milan.

In 1499, Louis stayed only a month in Milan (Oct. 6 – Nov. 7). Leonardo, now morally in the King's service, remained in Milan, which was French territory, and was commissioned a work which was to be the cause of much vacillation and complaint: a painting of the Holy Family which must

La Gioconda – Paris, Louvre

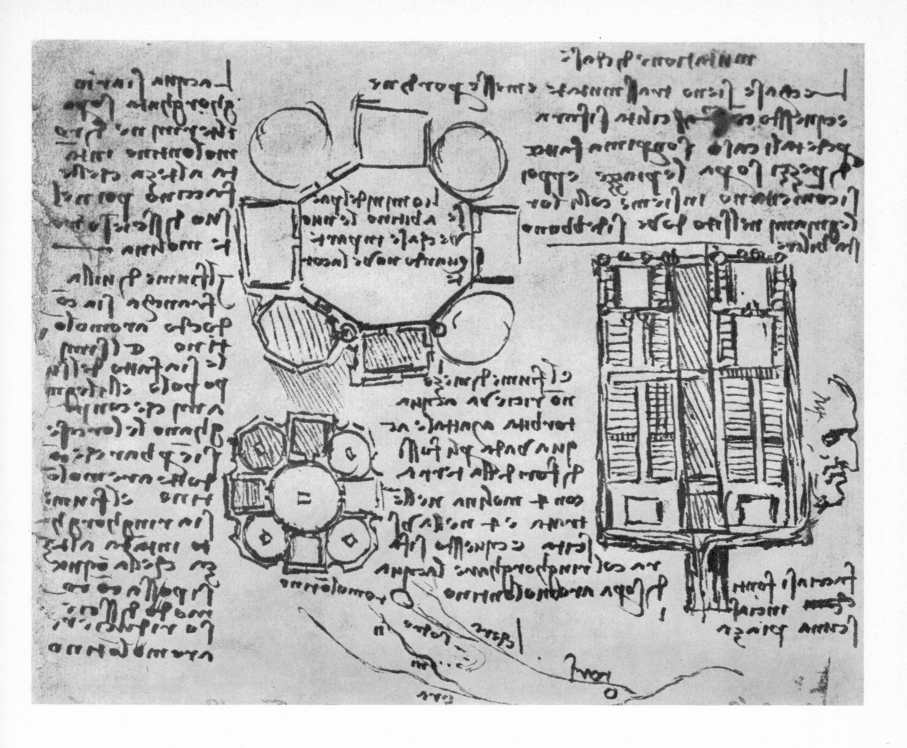

certainly be that of the Louvre, although planned at first for the Servites, and which led to the *St. Anne*, executed later but only as a sketch.

Leonardo used his title of "painter and sculptor to the king of France," given him in 1501 by the Cardinal of Amboise, as an excuse for refusing to hand over the model of the statue of Francesco Sforza to the Duke of Ferrara. He used the same excuse to Isabella d'Este when she insisted upon having her portrait painted. However, neither this office nor his journeys to Mantua, Venice, and Florence prevented him from completing his chief works, the *Battle of Anghiari*, the *Gioconda*, and the *St. John*, from forming an alliance with Cesare Borgia, and from dedicating himself with increasing ardor to physics, mechanics, and applied sciences.

In April 1507, a letter from Fra Pietro da Novellara reminds the Marchioness of Mantua, who is still pleading for her portrait, that Leonardo is first of all "in the service of the King." Doubtless Da Vinci could have put aside his obligations for one month without falling into disfavor, but at that moment he was under the orders of a functionary of Louis XII, one Robertet, for whom he was painting a small picture, the *Madonna of the Distaff*.

In the meantime, living up to his contract, he worked on the *St. Anne*, the cartoon of which he sent to France. This was to become the subject of special negotiations with Louis XII in 1507.

In 1504, during another stay in Florence, a rivalry with Michelangelo over the completion of the Church of San Lorenzo so disgusted Leonardo with faithless and unreliable patrons, that he decided to go to France where he knew he was awaited and welcomed. He was to make this decision twice again before he actually left Milan in 1516. Each time the pleadings of his friends and his awareness of his total ignorance of the French language dissuaded him.

The time was coming, however, when another voyage of Louis XII was to renew the bonds that linked Leonardo to France. For some years Leonardo had been in close and constant relations with Charles d'Amboise, lord of Chaumont, who obtained from the *Signoria* at Florence (which desired to have the *Battle of Anghiari* completed) the release from the service of the King that had been requested.

145

Francesco Melzi – *Columbine* – Leningrad, Hermitage

Drawing executed by Francesco Melzi when he was at the age of nineteen – Milan, Ambrosiana

Müntz gives in full an interesting letter from Chaumont to Soderini, expressing not only his satisfaction with, but his admiration for, Leonardo.

The fond friendship of the King for his painter was such that the Florentine envoy, Pandolfini, addressed a letter from Blois to the *Signoria* which is a rather astonishing epistle. "His Majesty called me to tell me: 'Your Signori may do me a service. Write them that I wish to employ master Leonardo who is in Milan... Have the *Signoria* enjoin him to place himself at my disposal and not to leave Milan before my arrival.'" Pandolfini answered that, if Leonardo was already in Milan, he was under the jurisdiction of the King and could not possibly elude him. "All this was provoked by a small picture Leonardo has recently sent to Blois and which is considered an excellent work."

The King concluded: "Perhaps I will have him paint a portrait of me."

It is a curious fact that no such picture exists—no sketch nor design of a likeness of Louis XII made either by Leonardo or by one of his pupils. Doubtless the King would have been too busy during his rare visits to Milan, and Leonardo, always the procrastinator in painting—especially in portraiture—would have managed to evade this specific wish.

Francesco Melzi (?) – *Lute player* – Detroit, Fisher Collection

Melzi: *Columbine* – Paris, Van Berbrock Collection

Finally on January 14, 1507, Louis XII announced from Blois a projected visit to Milan and again personally requested his Florentine friends to send there Leonardo "from whom I desire work as soon as possible, and wish that he be not far from that city." Such a document is truly unique. We find nothing comparable to it in the letters of Francis I nor in those of Louis XIV.

The King did not betake himself either to Italy or to Milan, but from afar he wrote Leonardo expressing his continued intention to do so. The painter, however, went on with his work without altering his habits of leisurely reflection, without giving in to his sovereign's demands, affectionate though they were, any more than he had bowed to the meanness of Soderini's wishes. He simply accepted this commission calmly, and was, in fact as in name, in the "service of the king of France."

On May 24, Louis XII made a triumphal entry into Milan and told the artist that he had decided to take him in his retinue. Several historians believe that he succeeded, among them a scholar of outstanding merit, Charles Ravaisson-Mollien. He told me his reasons for thinking so, chief of which was a letter written in 1509 to "the Signor Lyonnard, painter of the King at Amboise"; but I agree with Müntz in recognizing that Uzielli has demolished this theory.

Melzi (signed) – *Portrait of girl with parrot* – Milan, Gallarati-Scotti Collection

147

Mimicry and posture – Drivers of a scythed chariot – Ms. B, fol. 10 r

Defenders of fortress – Cod. Atl., fol. 49 v-*b*

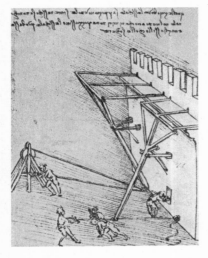

Ratchet catapult – Cod. Atl., fol. 51 r-*a*

Horseman – Windsor, Royal Collection, n. 12713

Unfortunately, the results of that second meeting were far from making the desires of the King a reality. Louis XII had wanted too much; he had dreamed of introducing France to Leonardo's genius, and with this purpose in mind he had brought with him Jean Perréal, the most renowned and representative painter of Paris, whom his compatriots called, with naïve erudition, "a second Zeuxis or a second Apelles." With Perréal were the court chronicler, Jean d'Anton, and Jean Marot, the poet, who were to note down the "marvels" Louis had promised to reveal to them in an artistic domain unknown to France.

But, as Müntz says, "Louis XII was remarkably in advance of his subjects." The three uprooted and offended Jeans [Perréal, d'Anton, and Marot] were incapable of understanding the genius to which Louis XII was exposing them. Here and there they took a few vivid notes, made some realistic sketches and returned to France more Parisian and less Lombard than ever. Once back in Paris, they roared with laughter at the episode, and what they believed was the simplemindedness of their King.

After the King's departure from Milan, Leonardo went to Florence for a legacy and then returned to Milan.

This was the period of his career when he was especially absorbed in work on geodetics and the construction of canals. The French-held territory profited greatly by his works, and in recompense Louis XII granted Leonardo rights in the waters of the San Cristoforo canal: another proof that during this time Leonardo was indeed "in the service of the king of France."

Once again, in May 1509, surely drawn by his desire to see Leonardo, Louis XII returned to Milan; and Da Vinci was responsible for all the details of invention and execution in preparing the city for the King's triumphal entry, the most important ceremony of its kind ever seen in Milan.

But the death of Charles d'Amboise in 1511 and that of Gaston de Foix (killed at Ravenna), his successor in the governorship of Milan, resulted in the evacuation of the French troops and shortly thereafter in the return to power for a short time of Massimiliano Sforza, the son of Ludovico.

Leonardo had only two choices: to go to France where his King desperately wished him to be, or to remain in the quiet district in Milan where he lived, paying no heed to the political ferment which seethed about him. He remained there, and moreover it seems that he had some contact with Massimiliano. The defeat of the French army at Novara in 1513 cut off his every relation with France, for the time being.

It took the victory of Melegnano to reinstate the artist in the "service" which he had deliberately chosen, and to prepare him for his withdrawal to that country to which he had so long been devoted.

The circumstances which brought about the meeting and subsequent agreement of Leonardo with Francis I are fully recorded. After the evacuation following the defeat at Novara, and after a brief contact with Massimiliano Sforza, Leonardo went to Rome to see Leo X who at that time had worn the triple crown of the papacy for two years. The new Pope highly esteemed the painter, and considered entrusting to him the completion of the Church of San Lorenzo in Milan; second, he wanted the artist to paint his portrait. To complicate matters, however, there were the brutal rivalry on the part of Michelangelo and the Pope's own fear of Leonardo's slow methods and vacillating techniques. In the end, Leo changed his mind and Leonardo, discouraged, returned to Florence, which had been the cradle of his genius and was to remain his true fatherland.

Figures of fighters – Venice, Academy

But here the same difficulties, the same jealousies, the same bitterness awaited him. Public opinion had changed greatly toward Leonardo; favor had now turned to younger, sprightlier men, witty and easy to get on with, like Raphael who became Bramante's successor. Leonardo said to Lorenzo the Magnificent, as he had said to Leo X, when the latter had urged him to adapt new techniques to the new times, "I cannot change my art."

Shortly afterward, at the beginning of 1515, his patron Giuliano de' Medici having been struck down by a mortal illness, Leonardo decided to return to Milan where once again the French declared they were ready to satisfy his desires.

By hurrying, he preceded by a few days the triumphal entry of the victor of Marignano into Pavia, and for that ceremony fashioned a "mechanical lion which took several steps and then its breast unfolded to reveal a mass of fleurs-de-lis." It was an imaginative symbol of his loyalty to the royal house of France.

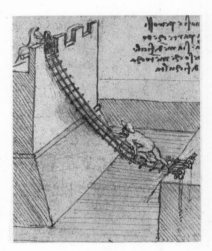

Fighter scaling walls of fortress –
Ms. B, fol. 50 r

After a brief meeting with Francis, Leonardo returned to Milan, leaving the King to continue his triumphal tour to Bologna and Florence. In Milan he resumed his "service to the king of France," establishing close relations with Messer Artus, master of the chamber, and a favorite of the King.

Here is a curious situation which tells us many things about Leonardo's method of work. The artist who never condescended to finish a portrait of Isabella d'Este, who never even began a portrait of Louis XII, and who was equally difficult with Francis I, three times drew the likeness of this man Artus, whom the King had left behind him in Milan almost as if he were a hostage.

How can we explain such a paradoxical preference? Undoubtedly there must have been an opportunity for long, friendly conversations during a period of relative rest for the painter, and then certainly there was the attraction of the face of the old man, a face strangely furrowed by meaningful lines in which we can read all the vicissitudes of a stormy life. This is, of course, merely a question of the artist's sketching, almost caricaturing, a face in order to get into contact with that French spirit which is so different from the Italian, and with which he was destined to pass the last years of his life.

It was in this way that Leonardo learned to assess in line and relief what a peasant or bourgeois of France was like, a son of the Beauce or Touraine.

Müntz feels justified in attributing other works to this time of relative repose: some sketches of young French noblemen and pages, whose fresh and frank faces attracted the artist, who was so accustomed to the elegant artifices of the Italian courts. In short, Leonardo was preparing himself for his inevitable departure from Italy, for it is all too apparent that for him the land of his birth held neither favors nor further resources. Florence, his birthplace, Milan, where he had lived, struggled, and suffered, had now become distasteful to him: the illustrious old artist, exhausted by work, by restlessness and meditation, no longer had the fortitude to shoulder new burdens. He was ready at last for the execution of that plan so often envisioned and as many times abandoned—his exodus to France.

Types of combatants – Windsor, Royal
Collection, no. 12653

To Leonardo the new King was not so worthy a person as Louis XII had been. Louis had said one day, "After me, that boy will destroy everything." And in truth, although Francis I was an ardent, generous, and chivalrous soul and a lover of beauty, he was at the same time frivolous and incapable of appreciating the profound, mysterious art of Da Vinci. Most pleasing to Francis were magnificent exteriors, ornate decorations, and the play of color and movement, from all of which Leonardo grew daily more detached. On the other hand, Francis I did not lack intuition and taste; moreover he knew that Leonardo's genius had been "in trust" for the greater glory of France for fifteen years, thus constituting a portion of the nation's heritage which had been extended by legacy

149

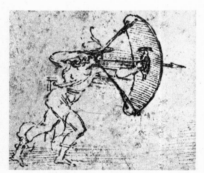

and by conquest. Leonardo was a glorious "legacy" from Louis XII who had acquired him in the only way one can "acquire" a free spirit, through fervent admiration and unswerving devotion. Recognizing this, and Leonardo's spiritual isolation, Francis I no longer hesitated. He made the artist a truly regal offer, a pension of 7,000 gold scudi a year and "a palace of his own choice in the most beautiful region of France."

Moreover, Francis I flattered Leonardo in that he did not take him into service only as a painter and sculptor, but also as an engineer, architect, "master of every science and art."

In an interesting article in the *Gazette des Beaux-Arts* (1915), Pierre Gauthiez told the story of the journey upon which Leonardo accompanied the King to France. Francis I sought to please the aging artist in every way; they were accompanied by Leonardo's favorite pupil, Francesco Melzi, and a devoted servant, Battista de Villanis.

They started for Provence in January, 1516, and on the way stopped to meet the Queen Mother, Louise of Savoy, who was delighted to receive her illustrious guest and offered him as his residence a small castle at Cloux (Clos-Lucé), near Blois, which she had recently purchased—one of the most delightful spots in all of that lovely region.

The journey continued by easy stages, filled with long conversations in which the reminiscences, thoughts, and inventions of the master stirred and fascinated Francis and his retinue.

Passing through Fontainebleau they left there some pictures brought from Italy. Finally they arrived at Blois and at Clos-Lucé, where Leonardo declared he was as if "in paradise." It is an elegant little castle on the Loire. The Loire at Amboise? For an Italian recently arrived from Milan, Piacenza, Cremona, or Parma, it must have made the same impression as the Mississippi at St. Louis would have with its islands, inlets, and currents. Leonardo was enchanted—he went out of the castle to the terrace to drink in the magnificent, changing view.

What was to be his destiny during his remaining three years of life? Even more important, what had he brought with him from that beloved, sparkling, heartbreaking land, Italy, which he had left with such regret? What significant works had he taken with him to testify to his greatness, and which would constitute in some way a "dowry" for this marriage *in extremis* which united the supreme genius of Italy with the country best suited to receive it?

"He carried in his luggage," writes Pierre Gauthiez, "not only the cartoon of the *St. Anne* (a second cartoon, that of 1507, which was never executed in paint, is now in the Royal Academy of London), but also two finished paintings, the *Leda* and *La Belle Ferronnière*, as well as two other works which were almost completed, the *Gioconda* and the *St. John*. The first two were left at Fontainebleau; the two latter Leonardo could not bear to part with." He dreamed each day of modifying or adding a detail because he saw these paintings as a mirror of the human soul, of his own soul, something which could never be completely defined nor expressed.

Besides these, there were numerous notebooks, albums, and memorandum books in which he had drawn the fantastic creatures, plans, sketches, and ideas still fresh from his inspired hand.

In the three years which were still left to him, he wanted to work out his plan for an ideal world, not only in conception but also in the world of action in which Leonardo aspired to express himself.

As Solmi writes, Leonardo "had invented and undertaken everything; he succeeded in all of these fields, without finishing anything, but proposing and leading up to everything in a way that seems almost miraculous."

It is difficult to say what part of his work in the notebooks and manuscripts stems from this final period in France. When he arrived at Amboise, Leonardo had reached a point in his life and career

that represented the culmination and the end of both. Gradually he was to discard all the parasitic elements with which nature, his profession, and his character had encumbered his life.

First of all he rejected all "subject" paintings and frescoes with their conventional, fictitious action, in which the artist dissipates and loses both the fruits of his observation of reality and his originality. The *Adoration of the Magi* is perhaps the only composition in which he took joy in the interplay of perspective and planes, and in the carefully composed grouping, which Raphael was to use in all his work. The *Last Supper*, which is a static and ideal representation depicting, in the figures of the Apostles and Christ, erring humanity and absolving divinity, is a work of a far different nature. The *Battle of Anghiari* was a failure precisely because of the artist's abstract studies and scruples, his anatomy and kinetics. And even the sacred themes of religious iconography wearied Leonardo with endless doubts and complications: the paintings of the Holy Family, of St. Anne, and of the Madonna. Leonardo could paint or carve one figure at a time, putting into it his incomparable wealth of experience transformed by his own meditation. In painting he had now succeeded in eliminating everything that seemed nonessential to him, color, for example, which he considered a superficial and external factor.

Very early in his work Leonardo had replaced diversified coloring by chiaroscuro, a combination of shadow and reflections, with which Correggio and Rembrandt achieved effects unforeseen by the master who had invented it.

I do not wish to dwell on this point because, by the time Leonardo had settled at Amboise, he had long since gone beyond this stage, as he had previously gone beyond color. For some time he had no longer painted in the literal sense of the word but had turned to drawing, which from then on was the basic form of art for him, because it penetrates to the essence of things.

Indeed, the "form" of beings is the aspect given them by the action that constitutes, conserves, and changes them. "The function creates the organ," we are told by physiology and morphology. Thus every being is the result of its own life, and it is in the concrete and embodied product of this continual action, in the intimate structure, that we must search for the secret nature of the thing, which is the supreme object of art.

In his new world, Leonardo wanted only to draw the things that attracted him, moved him, interested him. At Montargis he made a "schema" of the horizon to which some weeks later he added one made at Amboise. Studying the broad, changing channel of the Loire, he perceived the currents and eddies, and his keen mind discovered the laws of their changes and realized how they could be put to use. He dreamed of diverting the waters that flowed uselessly to the sea in order to irrigate the too arid soil, and of deepening the channels to make them navigable.

These were the things that occupied Leonardo's mind at the moment when the phantoms of his past were being slowly obliterated. It was of such projects that he talked with Francis I when the monarch left the festivities at Blois or Fontainebleau to pay a brief visit to the aged artist.

We may draw one conclusion from the years between 1516 and 1519: Leonardo did not paint. Aside from other testimony, that of Don Antonio de Beatis, secretary of the Cardinal of Aragon, leaves us no doubt on this point. When De Beatis visited the château of Cloux (Oct. 10, 1517), he wrote: "Since the master has been afflicted with a paralysis of the right arm, we can no longer expect great works of art from him." We might remember, too, that the dampness of the Loire country aggravated an ailment which had appeared in Rome in 1515.

The rash hypotheses of Bérence (p. 357) to the effect that the *Leda* and the *Bacchus* were modified or finished, if not actually created, during this period, are thus out of the question. The romantic or

Peasants plowing – Windsor, Royal Collection, no. 12643

Postures and figures of men working – Windsor, Royal Collection, no. 12641 v

151

mystical dreams of writers who see in the completion of the *Gioconda* and the *St. John* the last efforts of the genius of the master are equally unfounded.[2] It may be that Leonardo may have added a touch to the two pictures here and there, for they were close to his heart. Yet they reveal no signs of resumption of work or alterations. For Leonardo, from the moment the essentials of the composition were there, the picture was finished.

Antonio de Beatis, in line with all the evidence we have concerning that period, wrote that Leonardo had the active help and collaboration of a "pupil who came from Milan and worked excellently under the master's direction." This of course was Melzi.

There is certainly no doubt that Melzi, during this sojourn, continued to work in Leonardo's studio under the direction of the master, turning out some cartoons for a fresco (of which there are still traces in the chapel of the little château at Cloux), and an occasional portrait for which Leonardo suggested the main outlines. More often, Melzi drew a sketch or a characteristic head such as that of the old man, reproduced in the work of Calvi,[3] on which Leonardo invigorated the softish profile in sanguine with a bold black stroke. But there must have been other occasions on which real paintings were produced which may at first have been attributed to Leonardo, and which later, upon closer scrutiny, were seen as the product of one who had been working with and under the eye of the master, namely Melzi.

It seems to me that two of the pictures which should be included in this category are the *Vertumnus with Pomona* in Berlin and the *Columbine* in the Hermitage museum. The first was admired for a long time and considered worthy of Leonardo himself; however, a certain flabbiness of touch, the ever so slight affectation in the smile, and finally the late date of the composition, which seems to come from the Cloux period, mark it as the work of Melzi.

Wilhelm Bode is alone in rejecting it as the work of a mediocre, second-rate artist.[4] But the prestige of the Berlin director, so far as Da Vinci matters are concerned, suffered serious blows as the result of the latest acquisitions of the Emperor Wilhelm II, and I confess that I find more probability in Bérence's hypothesis, according to which, while basically agreeing with Müntz, he sees the painting *Vertumnus with Pomona* as a work by Melzi from a cartoon conceived, if not actually created, by Leonardo. Everything speaks in favor of this interpretation: in the first place, the subject is more French than Milanese, being naturalistic mythology and not a mystical allegory. It is conceived in the spirit of the frescoes at Fontainebleau and was beyond doubt done at the suggestion of the King. Moreover, the composition itself has a stark suggestive simplicity, completely in accord with the spirit of Leonardo's thinking at that time. Lastly, the young man's smile is very like that of the figure of St. John, although drawn with a weaker hand.

With the above reservations, one can in truth trace these pictures back to the influence of Leonardo, as they appear to the eyes and the spirit of visitors at Clos-Lucé.

The second picture attributed to Melzi is the *Columbine*, of which there are several replicas, the most famous being in the Hermitage museum.[5]

A very interesting example is owned by the eminent collector van Berbrock. Still another admirable *Columbine* is that of the museum at Blois. The latter is certainly a copy executed by a French artist who must have intended to protest, in the name of French national realism, against the "portents" which surrounded the figure painted by Melzi.

If one wishes to indulge in the belief in a legend which sounds plausible, it has been said that the figure of Columbine is an exact likeness of a court lady, Babou de la Bourdaisière, a favorite of the French king, who is said to have brought her to Leonardo and begged the artist to immortalize

[2] See Merezhkowski, *Romance of Leonardo da Vinci*.
[3] Calvi, *Manoscritti di Leonardo da Vinci*, p. 261.
[4] In *Gazette des Beaux Arts*, 1889.
[5] Haufstaengel Collection.

her lovely image. Leonardo, according to this tale, promised to fulfill this request, entrusting the work to Melzi under his own watchful supervision. Melzi did not betray the trust placed in him. The *Columbine* of van Berbrock is delightful with its freshness, youth, and grace. It is even over-supplied with those perfections, which are surrounded by all the ornaments that nature and luxury can provide. The young woman Columbine is no longer a pretty courtesan, but a veritable nymph of the court, with the too affectedly tender smile and glittering Italian charms so despised by Jean Perréal in all his Gallic robustness. Comparing this *Columbine* with that at Blois, we can discern the profound difference between Leonardo and the country that was host to his luminous genius.

The *Vertumnus* and the *Columbine* are the only two easel paintings which can rightly be placed in the Amboise period. We must add, of course, the frescoes (many times retouched) that still cover the walls of the chapel at Cloux. Nevertheless, it is difficult to distinguish the mark of the master there because of the inroads of time upon the work. Let us not delude ourselves that Leonardo at Amboise spent much time on frescoes and paintings. Indeed, he gave himself completely to science and to the study of mechanical, utilitarian applications of science. We need only examine the drawings and manuscripts of this period.

An allegorical drawing, often differently interpreted, may give us the key to the work upper-most in Leonardo's mind when he began his residence in France. It was a task assumed as "engineer and architect, master of all structures and works." The drawing bears the date 1516; this was after his arrival in France, the moment when the master realized how much prodigious activity would be open to him in his new homeland.

The drawing is that of a boat whose mast is a living plant thick with foliage. The sail is wind-filled, and the boat is driven by the strong current of a river. At the helm sits a wild, shaggy bear

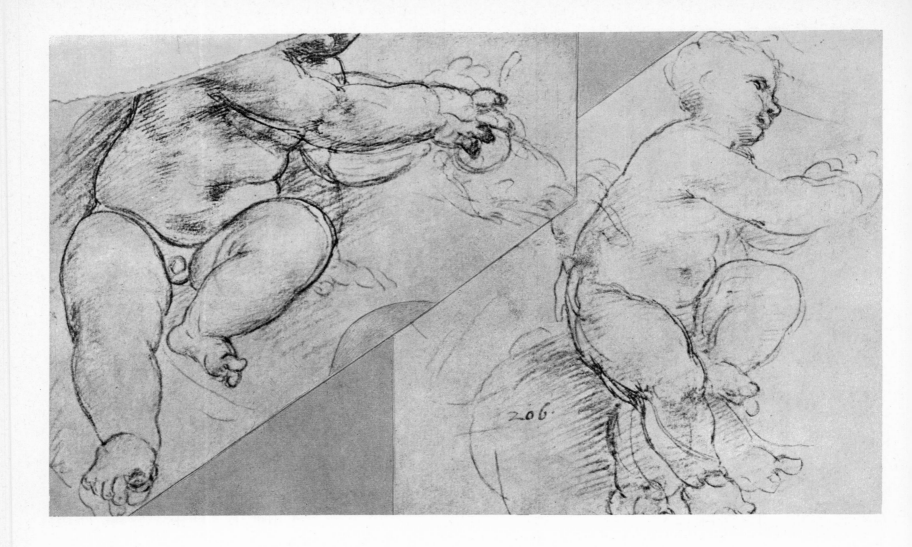

Postures of babies – Studies for fresco at S. Onofrio in Rome – Windsor, Royal Collection, no. 12565, 12566

Pilgrim – Windsor, Royal Collection, no. 12620 r

who directs his frightened gaze upon a compass which is illumined by a shaft of light originating in the heart of a crowned eagle seated on the bank, on a globe which dominates the entire scene.

This drawing of 1516 marks the arrival of Leonardo at Amboise; my awareness of the plans that absorbed Leonardo at that time forces me to discard the historical symbols and political images concocted by many imaginative writers. Here is what I read clearly in this allegory:

The bear is the peasant of this countryside, blessed by heaven but ignored by men. Nothing is clearly defined: neither the sandy river with its winding veins of waters which holds the flat plain in a deep bed of heavy, stagnant water, nor the land of Sologne, now dry, now swampy, nor the cultivation of the fields, now inundated, now sere. The bear can never guide his ship to his destination, he must have the help of genius which alone can send a powerful, illuminating ray down upon his compass, showing him the way to productive labor.

This allegory is a program, such as we find again and again in the drawings of the master. In this program all the general views of Amboise, Romorantin, Montargis, and Blois are drawn, in order to show and define the areas to be controlled. Leonardo then drew schematic maps of the basins of the Loire and the Cher, of the terraced lands of the Nivernais, of the slopes which descend toward the Saône. Thus we see clearly that Leonardo had planned to dig a canal to unite the two great rivers whose waters were, at that time, wasted. Leonardo had conceived a comparable scientific transformation in the region of Milan and the river Adda. Francis I had looked with favor on the project, but postponed its execution because of the enormous expense involved. The Tourangeois today who rereads Leonardo's maps may see in them the vanity of human plans: for in 1939, the Loire was still sandy and inaccessible to any shipping whatsoever; the Cher slept on in its indolent uselessness; the district of the Beauce continues to be dry and sere, and that of Sologne, marshy and unhealthy. Neither science nor industry has ever attempted to reactivate the projects conceived by Leonardo. So many successive disillusionments must certainly have discouraged and exhausted the master.

At this time, an evolution of thought and feeling began to take place in Leonardo that caused profound changes in his inner life. For the first time, he turned his faculties of intuition and observation upon himself. Until now they had been turned outward upon the spectacle of the world or concentrated upon research into the bases of the laws by which he worked.

All at once he realized that there was no full likeness of himself, nothing to tell the world of the external characteristics of the genius he knew himself to be. Here and there were rapid sketches of a profile drawn in the corner of a painting—yet there was nothing to reveal to mankind the image of one who surpassed and dominated them.

And so Leonardo did a self-portrait. In sanguine, with an implacable hand, he drew the likeness which is now preserved in the former Royal Library at Turin. It is the picture of an old man, a face at once terrible and magnificent with the eyes deeply sunken, the lips tight-drawn and scornful. In the lines we read struggle, pain, and sorrow: a Moses descending from Mount Sinai with empty

154

Studies of men digging – Ms. B, fol. 51 v

hands, and without that divine light upon the face that had softened the expression of the prophet. I would set aside two or three small drawings in which Leonardo seems to have had a desire to leave some record of certain aspects of himself, and consider instead that of his last days, to me the most moving and most significant.

We know, in addition, that for some months the master had shown revulsion toward art and distaste for science and philosophy, and turned to the study of religion. He consented to be deeper instructed in Catholic doctrine. Vasari may have overdramatized Leonardo's "conversion," depicting the artist as crushed beneath the weight of his guilt and sorrow. But Leonardo's own last will and testament clarifies this. There is one phrase which is singularly moving: he asks God to forgive him for not using all the resources of his spirit and his art. I firmly believe that this was Da Vinci's supreme thought at the last moment of life—the moment in which our entire destiny lies cruelly bare before us. He felt uncertain in his genius and the image of his magnificent work had begun to dim and vanish before his eyes.

Thus he turned to God without any reservations but rather in pitiful resignation. The highest expression of this I find in the last drawing of himself on the terrace at Cloux. It is of an old man wrapped in a cape, seated on a tree trunk with his chin resting on a shepherd's crook; he contemplates the whirlpools of the Loire, the river he had dreamed of controlling and turning into a useful tool for mankind. Now he is content merely to watch it in its vain wanderings, as if he were watching the futile meanderings of his own life. In this forlorn, melancholy attitude there is neither anger nor rebellion, only serenity and resignation.

In an essay of this limited scope, one too quickly arrives at the end. This is surely the most difficult and thankless portion of my task. Leonardo went to France with great plans; he lived there for three years in close contact with the court, surrounded by royal favor and the respect and admiration of all. But, in the last analysis, what did he accomplish? What were the useful results of his activity? The most optimistic wishful thinking is checked by the evidence.

First of all, let us have no illusions upon this point: France had no effect upon either the content or the form of Leonardo's work. In the "service of the king of France," Leonardo remained more specifically Italian in spirit than, perhaps, even he realized. The subjects of his works, the conception, execution, and inspiration do not show, during the last fifteen years of his life, the

Study of peasant digging – Ms. B, fol. 51 v

155

Left: Horses and horsemen – Turin, former Royal Library

Right: Men digging – Ms. B, fol. 52 r

Hunter – Ms. H, fol. 63 v

Bell-ringer – Windsor, Royal Collection, no. 12716

least influence of the spirit of the King nor of the protector nation. The French kings admired him, gave him commissions, bought and paid for paintings, received and supported the great artist who lent his genius to their culture, but they never for a moment labored under the illusion that they either directed or assimilated him. This was a notable example of a liberality he had not enjoyed on the part of his many Italian protectors; neither the Florentine *Signoria* nor the Prior of Santa Maria delle Grazie had done as much.

Let me add that this does not apply to all the artists Italy gave France in that period. Rosso, Primaticcio, Fra Colombo, and even Cellini followed the suggestions and sometimes even the dictates and orders of the patron king in whose service they worked. Leonardo remained completely untouched in that milieu, which never fully understood him. Nor is there any trace of specific influence of Leonardo upon France. Not one French pupil during those three years! Not one eager youth to study, not one mature man to reflect on and investigate the master's work! No, the artist remained alone in the manor house which royalty had prepared for him, unable to honor him as he should have been honored. Not even the works left at Fontainebleau, which the King enthusiastically exhibited, provoked any movement of emulation or imitation, nor were the French artists who had been informed of the great genius in their midst, enlightened, attracted, or influenced in any way. The comments made about the Blois *Columbine* serve only to confirm this conclusion.

Three schools of painting which developed in France from the period of Charles VIII to that of Henry IV could have been enriched by the splendor of this sovereign of art. First of all, the school at Tours with its dry precision and heavy realism completely escaped the spiritual and mystic influence of the master. The Fontainebleau school remained sumptuous and decorative, and it is impossible to discover in its leaders, Primaticcio and Rosso, both of whom had attracted a host of French pupils, any trace of Leonardo's profundity and mystery. Finally the Flemish school of Clouet, with its emphasis on the study of physiognomy and penetration into the soul, should have betrayed some greater preoccupation with the element of "magic" emanating from the *Gioconda* and the *St. John*. And it is quite certain that the Flemish school did not remain insensitive to this potent spell.

But it seems impossible to point with assurance to an artist or a work and positively link it with the period of Clos-Lucé. The single exception is the beautiful painting called *Sabina Poppea*, whose ambiguous smile does evoke an inevitable comparison; otherwise the work is rather superficial.

Even the kings of France were not unswerving in their admiration of the magnificent works housed in their palaces. Louis XIII sold the *St. John*, which he believed of dubious origin, to Charles I of England, and the financier Jabach had to buy it back to restore it to Louis XIV who really preferred Poussin and Lesueur to Leonardo.

Nevertheless, the record and, more important still, the mortal remains of the master stayed at Amboise, and around this consecrated rock there is an indescribable aura of genius. *In confinio immortalium, aliquid immortalitatis odorat*, wrote Pomponazzi, Leonardo's compatriot.

The seventeenth and eighteenth centuries in France were still more ungracious than the sixteenth to the memory of the great man. But the nineteenth century restored the artist to vital and understanding admiration.

It was the romantic movement that discovered the *Gioconda* and the *St. John*. If Ingres preferred Raphael, Delacroix had eyes only for Leonardo. The great French poet Baudelaire dedicated one of his most beautiful quatrains in "Phares" to Leonardo, and around him there rose a Leonardesque school which influenced the critical and literary works of the day. Arsène Houssaye wrote the painter's life history, Joséphin Péladan formed a cult which spread rapidly, and Seailles discovered in Leonardo the founder of modern science.

Oddly enough, the theft of the *Gioconda* made the entire world conscious of its strange, incomparable fascination.

And so Leonardo da Vinci is re-established upon his throne, or better still upon the altar which two kings of France had prepared for him. They had not formed him, but they had recognized, aided, and welcomed him in the most difficult days of his career. They obtained his most beautiful and significant works in a legitimate fashion with his full consent, and little by little these have been incorporated into the national heritage of France.

LEOPOLD MABILLEAU

L E O N A R D O ' S   M A N U S C R I P T S

The life of an author has more or less intimate connections with his work, especially if that work takes the form of methodical, ordered compositions reflecting the habits and the feelings of the person who thought them out and set them down in writing. But when a many-sided genius like Leonardo, in the fever of work, dwells even for a moment on one of the various topics that attract him, and leaves his powerful imprint on it, the work, even though incomplete, is an interesting episode or chapter of his biography.

From his youth to his declining years, Leonardo left many mementoes of himself; if he was taciturn,[1] as all innovators of genius are, we can find proof of this attitude of his in the artistic and scientific drawings, which I should call silent—never used preferentially by Leonardo, because, as he says, "the more minutely you describe something, the more you will confuse the reader's mind and the further you will remove him from knowledge of the thing described."[2]

His left-handed or mirror writing, so characteristic of him, has revealed to us the phases of his development and the physiological factors that brought it about, after the acute studies of Calvi,[3] Baratta,[4] and Favaro.[5]

We would know still more about Leonardo's life if his manuscripts had all come down to us intact. He had the habit of conversing with himself in his writings, and of putting his thoughts into the clearest and most simple form, which makes it still more regrettable that we have lost a large number of his folios, and have to try to find them and put them together, in some way, out of the disorder in which in many instances they have been transmitted to us. There is no doubt that in the case of the Arundel codex, or of the rich collection of separate sheets at Windsor, our first impression induces a bewilderment which can be overcome only after patient and devoted research to find the sequel of a theme that interests us, or to get the best possible framework for a phrase left broken off in the middle.

This handicap arises from the way in which Da Vinci's works have come down to us, but it is not entirely absent in regard to some manuscripts that have suffered little or not at all through time and the hand of man. It is instructive in such cases to examine and explain a more or less evident disorder which may also indicate a personal characteristic; in these cases it would be useless to insist on finding an integrated, completed work according to our way of looking at things, when Leonardo had his particular methods of work and was able to leave many important fragments of meditations and researches, marked with his great genius, in the various fields over which his mind ranged.

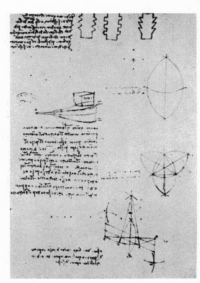

Ms. A – 43 numbered sheets – 146 × 212 mm. – Fol. 15 v: Demonstration of Pascal's principle

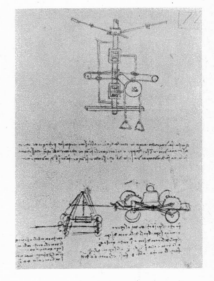

Ms. B. – 84 sheets – 176 × 235 mm. – Fol. 77 r: Automotive wagon with two driving axles

---

[1] This point is convincingly stated by G. Uzielli, *Ricerche intorno a Leonardo da Vinci*, Ser. I, Vol. I, Turin, Loescher, 1896, p. 374.

[2] Anat. Ms. A, fol. 14 v, ed. Sabachnikoff-Piumati, Paris, 1898, p. 32.

[3] G. Calvi, "The Manuscripts of Leonardo da Vinci from the Chronological, Historical, and Biographical Points of View," in *Pubblicazione dell'Istituto Vinciano di Roma*, dir. M. Cermenati, Vol. VI, Bologna, Zanichelli, 1925.

[4] Mario Baratta, "Why Leonardo da Vinci Wrote 'Backward,'" in *Curiosità vinciane*, Turin, Bocca, 1905, p. 3-55.

[5] G. Favaro, "The 'weary' hand of Leonardo," in *Annuario della Regia Università di Modena*, 1929-1930; idem, "How Leonardo Wrote," in *Rivista di storia delle scienze mediche e naturali*, An. XXI, No. 11-12 (Ser. 4), Nov.-Dec., 1930.

Ms. C – 30 sheets – 210 × 220 mm. – Fol. 25 v:
Study of currents in liquids

Ms. D – 10 sheets, with four blank sheets –
160 × 222 mm. – Fol. 88 v: Study of flight

Ms. F – 96 sheets – 100 × 145 mm. – Fol. 48 v:
Study for tachometer

I shall not go into the question of the reconstituting of some manuscripts, such as Ms. A, which was seen and examined by Oltrocchi and Venturi before it was mutilated,[6] or the Codex on the Flight of Birds, which formed a part of Ms. B and has now been reconstructed in its entirety.[7] Likewise as regards folios taken out of various codices, we see some phrases[8] that can help us to trace, in the most unexpected places, scattered sheets of Da Vinci manuscripts.

We shall instead dwell on three little codices, published by the Reale Commissione Vinciana, which are in the Forster collection[9] and have come to us in a fair state of preservation.

Volume I,[10] which is the most recent, may be assigned to the year 1505 or thereabouts; its contents are homogeneous, and it has a page numbering added later. Leonardo did not mark the folios, but if we look at them attentively it is possible to see in them an original order given to the single propositions which the books comprise, perhaps three in number; a first proposition is indicated on folio 39 verso, while the second is on the recto, and so forth. Thus Leonardo was habitually left-handed in an eccentric manner[11] even in the use of his sheets, and like the Orientals started from the last page.[12]

Before the division of his treatise into books and propositions, Leonardo set down definitions and rules, which include not merely those given on folio 40, but also those in the early folios from 3 to 19. From the contents, Marcolongo supposes that folio 5 should be next to folio 35,[13] and that folios 11 and 12 also belong there,[14] while folio 13, which treats of the transformation of lunules, should be put between folios 28 and 29. Accordingly, an arbitrary reshuffling of the folios has taken place, as is shown by the irregular and artificial arrangement of fascicles I and II, while one sheet is missing from fascicle III.[15]

As for the development of the three books identified by Marcolongo, the first, from folio 40 to folio 35, contains eleven propositions; the second, from folio 34 to folio 28 verso, comprises thirteen propositions, repeating propositions 6 and 9, while there is no number assigned to the proposition developed on folio 29 verso and corrected on folio 28 verso. The third book includes all the rest, from folio 28 recto to folio 20, in perhaps twenty propositions; but proposition 10 is repeated (fol. 26), since it is corrected on folio 24 recto, and numbers 11, 12, and 13 are likewise repeated.

If we shift folio 3 to the end, we also have a simple explanation for the title, "Book entitled *De Trasformazione*, namely, of the conversion of one body into another without diminution of matter," which Leonardo added in his own hand to the little treatise, and the chronological note, also an autograph: "Begun by me Leonardo da Vinci on July 12, 1505."

The second part of this codex is obviously an addition, with sketches of machines and hydraulic projects that have no relation to the work preceding it.[16]

Codex Forster II is likewise made up of two quite distinct parts. The first part, with several sheets missing and various numbering systems, has every mark of being a little memorandum book for receiving Leonardo's daily notes in the period when he was working on the *Last Supper*. There are few notes on mathematics and mechanics, and many isolated entries of personal and intimate nature.[17] There are frequent names of persons, moral aphorisms, fables, sketches for drawings; red crayon is used almost exclusively. But the sheets must have remained separate to a great extent even after the death of Leonardo; this may explain why the subsequent numbering is often misarranged with respect to the reading order of the pages, and is frequently at the top or the bottom of the sheet without any visible reason; it is true that sometimes Leonardo himself wrote with the manuscript upside down.[18]

The second part of this second volume, although like the first part in externals, differs in content. Whoever it was that in the seventeenth century gave it the title *Mechanica potissimum* ["Mostly mechanics"][19] hit the nail on the head, and the other reader[20] who added to it, *In fine incipiendum* ["To be begun at the end"], was not mistaken either. I have no way of knowing

[6] For Oltrocchi, cf. S. Ritter, "Baldassarre Oltrocchi," in *Vinciani d'Italia*, Vol. III, Rome, 1925. It is known that Oltrocchi's work was revised and published by Amoretti; this was discussed by S. Musitelli, "An Eighteenth-Century Miscellaneous Writer from Oneglia: Abbé Carlo Amoretti," in *Bollettino della Società Storico-archeologica Ingauna e Intemelia*, An. I (1934), p. 3-56. On Venturi's work, cf. G. B. de Toni, "Giambattista Venturi and his Work on Da Vinci: Unpublished Works and the *Essai*," in *Vinciani d'Italia*, Vol. II.

[7] Cf. *I fogli mancanti al codice di Leonardo da Vinci sul volo degli uccelli nella Biblioteca Reale di Torino*, ed. E. Carusi, Rome, Danesi, 1926.

[8] Venturi gives some extracts from Da Vinci sheets that were removed from the originals after he did his work. Cf. De Toni, *op. cit.*, p. 73 f.

[9] All three manuscripts have been published with prefaces and indexes by the Reale Commissione Vinciana in the collection, *I manoscritti e i disegni di Leonardo da Vinci*, Ser. min.: *Il Codice Forster I*, Rome, Danesi, 1930; Vol. II-V, Rome, Libreria dello Stato, 1934-1936.

[10] Comprising fol. 1-40 of the manuscript, p. 70-99 of the published book.

[11] G. Favaro, "The 'weary' hand of Leonardo," p. 21 f.

[12] Manuscript A, in the form in which it has come down to us, has Leonardo's numbering from left to right. Manuscript B, which has no traces of the original pagination, is one of the characteristic examples of this backward progression; the topic taken up for the first time on folio 39 recto is taken up again with a reference to column 5 on folio 38 verso, where the text is preceded by the note, "Here follows what is missing below at 5," i.e., at the end of folio 38 recto.

[13] Professor Marcolongo, who has done so much for the cause of Leonardo's scientific studies, has made a special study of Codex Forster I, and was the first to recognize the composition of a Da Vinci treatise. Cf. "Il trattato di Leonardo da Vinci sulle trasformazioni dei solidi: Analisi del Codice Forster I nel Victoria and Albert Museum," in *Atti della Reale Accademia di Scienze Fisiche e Matematiche di Napoli*, Vol. XX, Ser. II; republ. in *Studi vinciani o memorie sulla geometria e la meccanica di Leonardo da Vinci*, Naples, 1937, p. 311 f.

[14] Marcolongo, *op. cit.*, p. 312.

[15] Cf. "The Forster Codices I-III: Prefaces, Indexes," in *I manoscritti e i disegni di Leonardo da Vinci*, Ser., min., V, 13.

[16] The text is given by Marcolongo, *op. cit.*, p. 338 f.

[17] They are practically all written in red crayon. Cf. "The Forster Codices I-III," *op. cit.*, p. 20 f.

[18] Folios 47 verso and 48 recto are written in reverse as compared to folio 43 recto, likewise folios 54 recto and 54 verso; the photocopies have been adjusted for ease in reading. Cf. *ed. cit.*, V, 24, which mentions the seventeenth-century glosses.

[19] Cod. Forst., II, 2, fol. 64.

[20] *Ibid.* The hand that wrote this and other similar notes in Latin does not seem to me to be Italian.

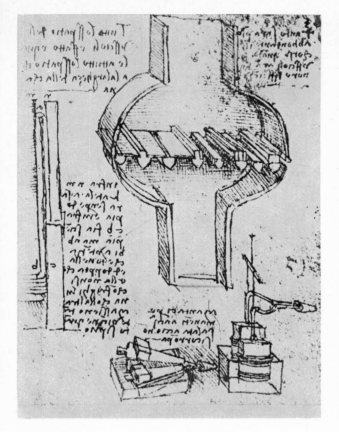

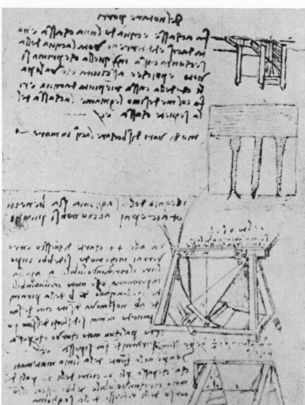

Left: Ms. E – 80 sheets (originally 96 sheets; last 16 sheets missing) – 99 × 150 mm. – Fol. 34 r: Studies in hydraulics

Right: Ms. G – 93 sheets – 95 × 140 mm. – Fol. 51 v: Studies in mechanics

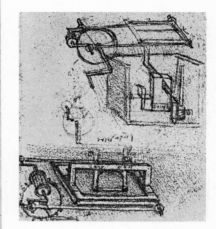

Ms. H – 142 sheets, divided into three parts with separate numberings – First part, 1–48 – Second part, 1–46 – Third part, 1–47 – 74 × 104 mm. – Fol. 28 r: Drawings of machines

whether it was the last-named reader who began to number the sheets, and stopped doing so at the fifteenth, when he realized that there was an original enumeration by Leonardo in a backward order.

It is hard to find any other Leonardo manuscripts that have come down to us as nearly complete as this one; it is composed of six fascicles of sixteen sheets each, a total of ninety-six sheets, all numbered by Leonardo at the upper left of the back of each folio.[21] Manuscripts E and I of the Institut de France, which are most like the one we are dealing with now, have not come down to us intact and do not contain Leonardo's original enumeration, which was removed in order to conceal the mutilations that had been committed.

The pocket-sized manuscripts were for taking notes to be developed at greater length thereafter, while the little Forster codex that we are examining offers us one of the best of examples for studying Leonardo's methods of work.[22] The principal subjects treated are balances, weights, and frictions, but the text is in the form of notes that are often incompletely developed; here too there are references to parts of treatises which—in contrast to what we find in the first volume—are not present in our codex, as, for example, a Book 7 *de confregazione*, a second book *de percussione*, and then a book *de ponderibus, delle piramide*, etc.[23] Other codices, moreover, repeat some of the topics that are referred to here or developed; thus in the Codex Atlanticus (fol. 348 r-*a*) there is a repetition of a series of *ludi* that have an extra figure or two in our codex (fol. 87 v). But the characteristic feature of the Forster manuscript is its extremely neat external form; it is virtually without erasures or cancellations, so that when a correction has been necessary, as in folio 103 verso (Leonardo's folio 56), it is strikingly obvious. Even here Leonardo did not strike out the text, but made the correction in smaller writing in the upper margin, bringing the lines closer together, and since there was not enough space, he continued the demonstration on folio 104 (55 v by his numbering), whereas according to his system he should have written on folio 103 recto.[24]

He was to return later to the theme discussed on folio 103, when, in the first pages of the Arundel codex,[25] he proposed to set down his notes in order in a clean copy, but refused to "read over again all the past" and so excused himself for any possible repetitions. At that time, in 1508, he was at Florence in the house of Piero Martelli and was transcribing the first fascicle of the Arundel codex; he had before him the sheets of the Forster codex in which, as early as the period between 1495 and 1497, he had taken up the problem of the tension in a cord supported at its ends by pulleys in turn supporting two weights, and in its own turn supporting at its middle another weight. In the clean copy he repeats the figure but not the words of the little notebook, and applies one of his theorems on the moments of concurrent forces, when the axis is taken along one of the component courses. In this definitive formulation he takes advantage of the old correction, and adds another theorem on moments, making many beautiful applications of it which are absent in the Forster codex, as Professor Marcolongo writes me.[26] Now, it is of interest to note that Leonardo had dis-

Ms. I – 140 sheets, in two parts with separate numberings – First part, 1–48 – Second part, 2–91 – 74 × 102 mm. – Fol. 28 v: Study in hydraulics

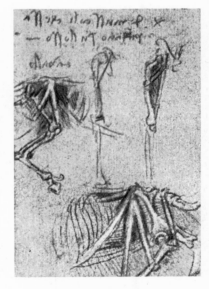

Ms. K – 128 sheets, in three parts with separate numberings – First part, 49 sheets – Second part, 32 sheets – Third part, 48 sheets – 65 × 98 mm. – Fol. 102 (22) r: Anatomical drawings

---

[21] This is Leonardo's habit, but I have already noted that in Ms. A Leonardo's numbering is consecutive, and on the recto of the folios, which may have been displaced.

[22] Marcolongo, *op. cit.*, p. 331, reports an instance in which Codex Forster I was taken into account in drawing up the Arundel codex; the latter, it should be remembered, is a revision and not a mere copy. For other examples, cf. *ibid.*, *passim.*

[23] "The Forster Codices I-III," *op. cit.*, p. 55, *s.v. Leonardo, Sue opere cit.*

[24] See, e.g., fol. 132 v, which is a continuation of fol. 133 r, and fol. 137 v, which is a continuation of folio 138 recto.

[25] *I manuscritti e i disegni di Leonardo da Vinci*, Vol. I: Il Codice Arundel 263, Pt. 1, Rome, Danesi, 1923, p. 1.

[26] I make use of Professor Marcolongo's observations in this contribution, which does not take into account the scientific contents of Codex Forster III.

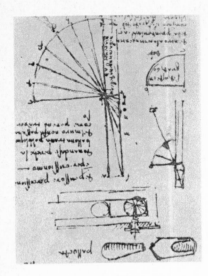

Ms. L – 90 sheets – 75 × 101 mm. – Fol. 43 v:
Studies in statics

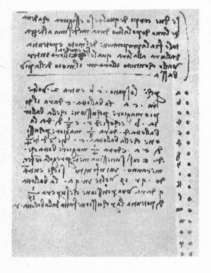

Ms. M – 94 sheets – 70 × 98 mm. – Fol. 52 v:
Studies on the fall of heavy bodies

The manuscripts of the Institut de France
formed part of the works inherited by Melzi, and
after his death they were dispersed and sold.
They were donated by Arconati to the Biblioteca Ambrosiana in 1637, where they remained
until May, 1796, when a decree of Napoleon I
ordered their transfer to Paris. The box containing the twelve manuscripts was consigned
to the Institut de France, while that containing
the Codex Atlanticus was consigned to the
Bibliothèque Nationale. This latter manuscript
was the only one returned to Italy

Codex Arundel – 283 sheets, 150 × 220 mm. –
Fol. 141 v: Various studies – London, British
Museum. — The manuscript was bought by
the Earl of Arundel in Italy after the death of
Pompeo Leoni, and after Arundel's death passed
to his heirs. In 1831 it became part of the
collections of the British Museum

covered this theorem on the moments of forces more than ten years previously, and that in giving it final form he was not content with a mere calligraphic copy, but changed both the content and the form. This does not contradict but rather remarkably confirms what he says about the nature of his mind.[27]

There is nothing especially characteristic about the way in which Volume III of the Forster codices has come down to us; it is like Volume II with respect to both numeration and arrangement of the folios.

These three codices, which have been left to us in a fairly good state of preservation, help us to understand Leonardo's method of work. He continually collected studies and observations as materials for a fuller and more systematic development in his treatises; and it is perhaps precisely for this reason that the composition of the little volumes was probably never quite definite, but subject to constant additions until he began to write the works based on them. It would seem that there were separate fascicles of paper held together for convenience in simple parchment covers; thus Codex Forster I may contain two groups of fascicles of slightly different format, each with a numbering not due to Leonardo, while Codex Forster II is composed of two quite different parts, one numbered by Leonardo, with the two bound together in a customary calf binding.

This may explain why other codices, similar to the ones we are discussing, like those in the Institut de France labeled with the letters H and I, seem to have entered the Ambrosiana with a smaller number of sheets than they formerly possessed.[28] Here too Da Vinci's original cover probably held separate groups of fascicles, so that in Paris they must have done what was done in the Victoria and Albert Museum as well: that is, the sheets were numbered consecutively and sewed to the covers some time after the manuscripts were received in the respective institutions.[29] If this work had been done at the outset, all the mutilations of the Leonardo manuscripts, including those committed by Libri, would at least have been more difficult to effect.

MANUSCRIPTS C AND D

Of the codices of the Institut de France, two are of interest because of the history of their transmission.

The first is the one marked with the letter C by Venturi.[30] It did not form part of the Arconati donation and is also known under the title "Light and Shade"; it was one of the six "that returned to the Mazenta house,"[31] that is, the house of the brothers of the Barnabite, Father Ambrogio, and that was given to Cardinal Federico Borromeo in 1603.[32] Father Mazenta describes it as follows in his *Memorie*: "One was given to Cardinal Federico of glorious memory, and is now preserved in his Biblioteca Ambrosiana, in folio, covered with red velvet, and it deals with shadows and light in a very philosophical manner, and very usefully for painters and for those who deal with perspective and optics." Even while in the Ambrosiana the codex lost the "red velvet" of its cover, and it now has a brown leather binding tooled in gilt on the two faces and gilt ornaments at the four corners, while the back has gilt decoration. The front cover of the binding bears in small capital letters an inscription giving the name of the donor: *Vidi Mazentae – Patritii Mediolanensis – liberalitate – An. MDCIII*.[33] The new codex must have lost some folios when it passed from Gavardi's hand to Mazenta; the latter at least says nothing on the subject, but what disorder there is in the few sheets composing it—thirty in all by the modern numbering!

Taking away sheets 11 and 29, which cover the entire fascicle, we have left sheet 1 to 28, consecutively numbered by a hand dating from the seventeenth or eighteenth century. Some of these sheets have Leonardo's original numbering, on the back, as is his custom, and the original numbers can be read on the verso of folios 1 to 7, 14 to 17, 21 to 28; folios 8 to 13 and 18 to 20 do not have Leonardo's numbering.

We can easily reconstruct a fascicle of sixteen sheets with Leonardo's numbers from 1 to 8 and from 9 to 16; these numbers are present on the back of sheets later numbered with the figures 15, 28, 27, 26, 25, 24, 23, 22, 7, 6, 5, 4, 3, 2, 1, 14.

For a second fascicle we have only three numbers written in Leonardo's hand, namely, the numbers 17, 18, and 19, which are found on the backs of sheets later given the numbers 21, 17, and 16, to which folios 13, 12, and 8 of the still later numeration correspond. There is no precise determination of the folios marked with the numbers 9, 10, and 11, corresponding to the later numbers 18, 19, and 20; these have no original numeration by Leonardo and give no indication in their context for a more rational arrangement, for one thing because the subjects treated are completed on the single sheets and there is no reference to topics in later folios.

Hence Ms. C should be rearranged as follows[34] according to the original numbering: 1 (15 v), 2 (28 v), 3 (27 v), 4 (26 v), 5 (25 v), 6 (24 v), 7 (23 v), 8 (22 v), 9 (7 v), 10 (6 v), 11 (5 v), 12 (4 v), 13 (3 v), 14 (2 v), 15 (1 v), 16 (14 v), 17 (21 v), 18 (17 v), 19 (16 v), which should be followed by folios with only the later numbering (13), (12), (8), since they are connected to the former group, and folios (9), (10), (11), (18), (19), (20), which would form a set of six sheets.

---

[27] See Cod. Arund., ed. cit., p. 1.
[28] S. Ritter, *op. cit.*, p. 21 f.
[29] The so-called *capitelli* of the sewing of the folios in the three Forster codices appear to be relatively recent work.
[30] G. Uzielli, *op. cit.*, p. 302, and plate following p. 256. Cf. H. Ludwig, *Leonardo da Vinci: Das Buch der Malerei*, Vol. III, in *Quellenschriften für Kunstgeschichte und Kunsttechnik des Mittelalters und der Renaissance*, XVII (Vienna, 1882), 2 f.
[31] *Le memorie su Leonardo da Vinci di don Ambrogio Mazenta ripubblicate ed illustrate da D. Luigi Gramatica prefetto della Biblioteca Ambrosiana*, Milan, Alfieri e Lacroix, 1919, p. 39, n. 28. Mazenta's memoirs were written about 1635; *ibid.*, p. 18.
[32] Cardinal Federico Borromeo died in September, 1631.
[33] Cf. *Le memorie*, etc., p. 63-64, n. 28, where the handwriting of G. B. Bosca appearing on the flyleaf is identified.
[34] The numbers within the parentheses are those of the later pagination, while the numbers outside the parentheses are Leonardo's.

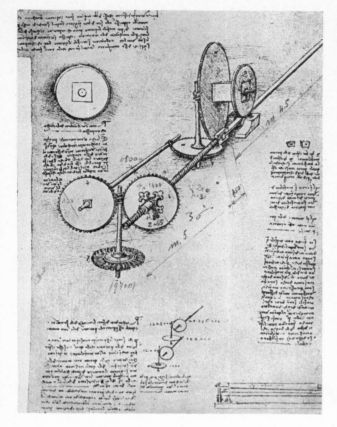

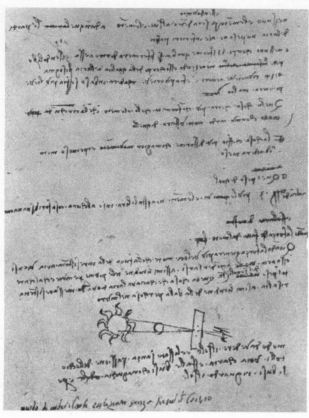

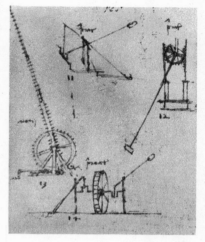

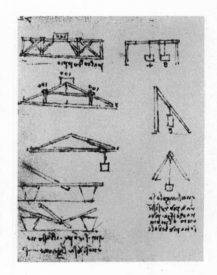

Manuscript D, a small codex whose origin is unknown,[35] was marked with the letter *S* by Oltrocchi.[36] It seems to have come down to us with its pages intact; it is a little volume of modest appearance, but written with great care and on a subject very dear to Leonardo, optics and the eye. I have no way of assigning any date to the cover, which is made up of two coarse cardboards of a dirty grey color, one of which bears the letter *D*, put on by Venturi.[37] But the numbering of the sheets is not Leonardo's, though fairly old, dating perhaps from the sixteenth century. The form of the few numbers there recalls those of Codex Forster II, 2; here the numbers 3 on folio 67 recto, 8 on folio 72 recto, and 9 on folio 73 recto are like the corresponding numbers in our Ms. D; the same numbers can be seen in Codex Forster I, folios 5 recto, 10 recto, and 11 recto. This brings up once more the question as to the paternity of this system of numbering,[38] which may go back to Melzi, according to Calvi.[39] However, in this respect Ms. D goes together with the Forster codices, and may have been a little booklet already numbered before it came into the Ambrosiana, and containing an entire treatise on optics.

The few manuscripts that have been briefly discussed here have, therefore, external signs that may cast some light on their vicissitudes and give us some idea as to the state they were in when in the hands of their author. The external evidence we have about Leonardo's works consists mostly of fragmentary references, usually richer in laudatory remarks than in precise descriptions. The secretary of the Cardinal d'Aragon, who visited the great painter at Cloux in 1517, saw and admired only the anatomical drawings, and with respect to the other works reports information given vaguely by Leonardo himself, and does not describe them: "He also wrote concerning the nature of water, of divers machines and other things—*according to what he says*, an infinity of volumes, and all in the vulgar tongue, which when they are published will be useful and most interesting."[40]

The evidence in Vasari,[41] Pacioli,[42] and Cellini[43] referring to the treatise on painting as being ready for the press is not confirmed, and vague also are Vasari's indications regarding the "sheets on anatomy," almost all in the hands of Melzi.

We know moreover that the compiler of the Codex Urbinatus Lat. 1270, which is the fullest version of the book on painting, had at his disposal at least eighteen distinct books with special designa-

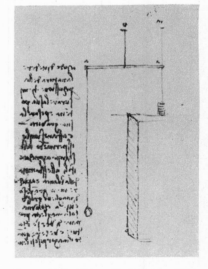

---

[35] Cf. Uzielli, *op. cit.*, p. 303, and plate following p. 256.

[36] Cf. S. Ritter, *op. cit.*, p. 21. See also Ludwig, *op. cit.*, p. 11 f. It is supposed that Arconati put together Ms. D and offered it to the Ambrosiana in exchange for another manuscript which later became the Codex Trivulzianus.

[37] Venturi naturally made use of this codex in studying Leonardo's optics and in his *Essai*. Cf. G. B. de Toni, *op. cit.*, p. 87 f., 186 f.

[38] The problem of this sixteenth-century numbering which keeps cropping up in the Da Vinci codices that have been bound or put together, and in the sheets that make up the Codex Atlanticus or the Windsor collection, has directed my attention to sheet 19145 of the latter collection, designated by an old number, 8, which also is identical with the numbers of the codices mentioned above. The Windsor sheet is of importance because it is dated and refers to the well-known studies *de ludis geometricis* which Leonardo made later at Rome in the Belvedere.

[39] Cf. *ed. cit.*, *I manoscritti*, etc., p. 269. Clark (see n. 49, below) supposes (p. XIII) that the numbering of the Windsor sheets is by Leoni; if this is so, the numbers in the Atlantic codex, which are like those of the Windsor folios, should have some continuity.

[40] In L. Beltrami, *Documenti e memorie riguardanti la vita e le opere di Leonardo da Vinci*, Milan, Treves, 1919, p. 149, no. 238.

[41] In L. Beltrami, *op. cit.*, p. 175 f.

[42] Cf. the passage of the *Divina proportione* given by Marcolongo, *op. cit.*, p. 41.

[43] Before 1542; cf. Ludwig, *op. cit.*, p. 8

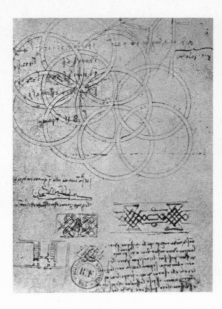

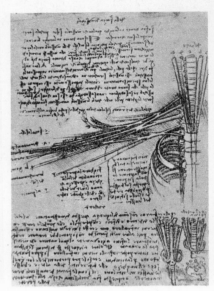

Codex Leicester – Fol. 7 r: Studies of moon – Holkham Hall (Norfolk), Library of Lord Leicester
Manuscript of 36 sheets, 295×218 mm. Acquired, during a voyage in Italy, by Lord Leicester, who was in Rome several times between 1713 and 1717, and on one of these visits may have met Giuseppe Ghezzi, to whom the codex belonged

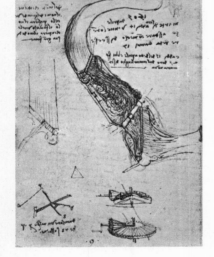

Surviving sheets of Codex on Flight – Turin, former Royal Library
Originally the codex consisted of 18 folios, as is seen from Arconati's deed of donation, and from the note on the outside of the cover, which reads: "There are 18 folios." Only four have come to light again

tions,[44] among them the two books of "Shade and Light," one of which was marked with the letter *G*.[45]

After the death of Melzi (1570), the marks on the outside of the codices disappeared, and there was no longer any kind of order among the loose sheets, which had perhaps been grouped by subjects and may have had consecutive numbering.

The account given by Father Ambrosio Mazenta does not provide us with any data that can be used for reconstructing, in their state at the time, the thirteen manuscripts that Gavardi had; he must have taken with him from Vaprio to Pisa the codices rather than the loose sheets in large format. Mazenta's gifts to Cardinal Federico Borromeo, to the painter Figini, and to the Duke of Savoy marked the beginning of the dispersion of Da Vinci's manuscripts; seven of them, which came back to Melzi's hands, along with the three others kept by the Mazenta family, were finally obtained by Pompeo Leoni, who in part "undid them and made a big book of them, which was then left to his heir, Cleodoro Calchi, and sold to Signor Galeazzo Arconati."[46] It is known that Leoni took the Da Vinci manuscripts to Spain, and after the death of Philip II trafficked in them in Milan, where we lose trace of him about 1610, and that later Lord Arundel[47] was able to buy some of them for himself and for the library of his king. A worthy competitor in the acquisition of Da Vinci manuscripts was Count Arconati of Milan, who succeeded in obtaining the Codex Atlanticus as Leoni had put it together, along with eleven other codices of various origins, and gave them to the Ambrosiana in 1637. In 1674 the Ambrosiana received as a gift the Codex Archinti (now Ms. K), and at that date had a total of thirteen manuscripts of Leonardo.[48]

The fate of these codices after the Napoleonic invasion and the mutilations they underwent when they could have been thought to be in safety is known. Da Vinci manuscripts streamed into England from the dismemberment of the manuscripts of the Ambrosiana that had been taken to France; Lord Ashburnham acquired some of them, but other manuscripts now preserved in the British Museum, in the Victoria and Albert Museum, by Lord Leicester, and the many loose sheets of the royal library at Windsor, have origins that are hard to trace, although for the most part they go back to the Melzi inheritance.[49] And all over Italy, in various other countries of Europe, and now in America as well, there are in circulation sheets or groups of sheets written by Leonardo, some of which might go toward completing manuscripts that have been brutally mutilated, not only out of the love of collecting but out of greed for money.

The national edition of Da Vinci's manuscripts and drawings, especially if the tempo of its publications is accelerated, is designed to aid a great deal in this delicate and necessary work of reconstructing the Da Vinci codices in order to come close to their original form. To this end it will help to collate the sheets with respect to their content as well, keeping in mind the history of the dispersions and mutilations they have undergone, and correcting arbitrary rearrangements given to the individual manuscripts at various times.

E. CARUSI

[44] Given in Ludwig, *op. cit.*, p. 456.
[45] It is interesting to note that on the flyleaves of the Paris codex *Della luce e dell'ombra*, as Oltrocchi calls it, the letter *C* cannot be seen today; instead, we find the letter *G*, crossed out and replaced by the letter *O*. This is the letter that Visintin used to designate the Naples codex containing the transcription of the Paris Ms. C. Cf. the codex of the Biblioteca di Reggio, marked CXXI, B, 10, fol. 98 v. But it is certain that Venturi designated the Paris codex *Della luce e dell'ombra* with the letter *C*. See letter *G* of the corresponding Paris codex, written by Venturi.
[46] *Le memorie*, etc., ed. cit., p. 39.
[47] Ludwig, *op. cit.*, p. 11.
[48] Cf. G. Uzielli, *op. cit.*
[49] Cf., for the English manuscripts in general, G. Uzielli, *op. cit.*, p. 317-323; E. MacCurdy, *Leonardo da Vinci's Notebooks*, New York, 1938, p. 35-39, in addition to the prefaces in the editions of the codices, and K. Clark, *A Catalogue of the Drawings of Leonardo da Vinci in the Collection of His Majesty the King at Windsor Castle*, Cambridge University Press, 1935, Intro.

162

THE THOUGHT OF LEONARDO

Leonardo, the "divine" Leonardo of the writers of the sixteenth century (like the "divine" Ariosto or the "divine" Michelangelo), is one of the most complete expressions of the Renaissance personality. His contemporaries felt vaguely that there was divinity in the creative power of Leonardo's artistic genius, a typical embodiment of the humanist ideal which was the most exquisite fruition of that marvelous age of poetry, intelligence, and indomitable energy of character.   This ideal took form within life itself, after humanism had freed the most gifted individuals from every prejudice and arbitrary presupposition, and given them an unlimited confidence in their own powers and in the freedom of the spirit as capable of building its world for itself.   But through life this ideal came to the light of consciousness, and became a meditated doctrine, a philosophy, a great faith that could direct life.   Not only in art and the exercise of intelligence, but also in warfare and the winning of wealth and the building of the state by craft and force, things worthy of being called *virtù* (as they were in fact called), since they were truly a plenitude of human activity for ends transcending the individual, man idolized himself in a wondrous representation of a conscious power, as a creature able to solve the problem of his life and to be what he ought to be, starting from himself alone and relying only on himself.   This was Machiavelli's faith as it was that of Leonardo.   It was a faith in man, who is spirit, who is that being which is not naturally, but makes itself what it is by rising from itself by means of study, by means of will power, by means of persevering in study and will until it reaches the plane on which it wills to live, to conquer fortune, to establish itself, to gain honor.

Allegory of peasant removing weasel from its nest – London, Clarke Collection

It was a faith that multiplied the native vigor of the human individual and instilled into him an acute and persistent need for making the most of all his energies, for testing all his capabilities, for mastering all the instrumentalities that could add to his powers, for trying all the ways that opened out before him or that he could open up by his ingenuity and his determination to engage in every battle and win every victory over the surrounding hostile forces of nature and men.   From this sprang an unquenchable thirst for knowledge and a proud dissatisfaction with all particular and limited knowledge, along with an irresistible desire to break down every barrier between theory and practice, science and art, thought and action.   For this man, the child of humanism and the creator of the Renaissance, every action had to be a trial of thought in reality, in which it was to unfold and prove its worth;   thought could be no mere impotent and inert contemplation shutting the mind within the narrow confines of the individual personality.   Science was man's tool for founding that dominion of man over nature (*regnum hominis*) which Francis Bacon was to proclaim throughout all Europe as the great task of modern times.   For man can never be at ease in his belief in his own liberty if he does not feel himself altogether as a being that cannot be split up in the dichotomy of theory and practice, which only an abstractly intellectualist and hence at least in tendency materialist philosophy can differentiate as two effectively distinct and divergent forms of human activity.

Allegorical subject for medal or gem – Windsor, Royal Collection, no. 12700 v

Unity of theory and practice—a Herbartian philosopher would call it many-sidedness of interests, and the writers of the Renaissance spoke of universality.   The complete artist is not only a painter, not only a sculptor, not only an architect.   He is if possible a poet, or at least a writer with a feeling for art.   At the same time he is an engineer, whose point of departure is geometry, and who studies mechanics and hydraulics and propounds problems of every kind—in agriculture, in regard to soil

Group of dancers for allegorical composition – Venice, Academy

Allegorical mythological scene – Bayonne, Bonnat Collection

Girl holding up mask – Allegorical drawing – Windsor, Royal Collection, no. 12700 v

improvement, in the art of war. The mathematical and physical sciences were just taking form at that time; their individual contours were not yet firm, and their distinction and connections both inchoate. He who took up one of them as a guiding light for his practical functioning became interested in all of them. All the arts and all the sciences, if they are to be learned deeply or touch the ideal, are intertwined inextricably and endow man's soul with a complex of varied interests, at that point in history bringing together in the breast of a single individual various urges which in more advanced and more analytical ages might reflect the spirits of artists and scientists of differing tempers and orientations.

The breadth and multiplicity of intellectual interests was accompanied, as it usually is, by an interest in fundamental matters which in periods of greater maturity and scientific specialization men try to reject and smother, and in any event are ashamed to be found supporting, inasmuch as it has become accepted doctrine that science is limitation and admits no syntheses proffered as solving problems of a universal and strictly philosophical nature. The Renaissance thinker did not set himself any limits except to surmount and go beyond them toward the All, the One. To this goal, although he was not sure of being able to attain it, his eye turned with longing, since he felt within himself that if this is not the source of the light by which everything would be illuminated, it is the secret of all motion and life: the mystery is to be found there. For him a philisophy, positive or negative, was at the bottom of all thought and all scientific research; from the still obscure concept of the All to which philosophy led him, he drew inspiration and strength for the intuition of art in fancy, and back into it he poured the deep emotion that seizes on the soul of man at the immediate vision of what is called the Absolute, or the All, or God; or it may be called Nature, as the Renaissance thinkers were more wont to name it. In these thinkers, therefore, philosophy and poetry and art in general are more intimately connected than they later appeared to be, when rigorous thought was chilling the warm sense of the divine, of the holy, that is always present in the mind of the artist, filling it altogether and moving it with the powerful pulsation of its infinite life.

This was the root of the universality of those marvelous geniuses who were scientists—and scientists in every science to which they were led by the circumstances of life and the problems presented to them by those circumstances—and at the same time artists, at work in several branches of art, and poets who, when they did not prove themselves in the measured rhythm of verse, breathed a lyric sweep into their prose, like that of Leonardo's lofty and eloquent discourse. But they were all more or less philosophers; and the intellectualist tendencies of scientific thought flowed together with the impetus and power of what I should call their artistic instinct, which too is a sort of divine afflatus.

Leonardo's universality can be better understood if we go on from the threshold of the Renaissance, over which he towers like a colossal boundary statue set in the vestibule of those times, and compare him with one of the great figures which tragically conclude that age—with Giordano Bruno or Tommaso Campanella, who likewise were universal geniuses, but oriented in a direction opposite to that in which Leonardo looks. He was artist principally, and a scientist in so far as he was an artist, by virtue of the problems to which the exercise of art gave rise in his restless and powerful intelligence. They were philosophers, constrained by the direction of their philosophizing to interest themselves in the most vital scientific problems of their times. At the same time, however, they were artists and poets; in their treatises, as in their poetry, there vibrates the intense emotion deriving from a certain deep mysterious sense of an immanent divinity that is their own very essence—a sense

Allegory of boat, wolf, and eagle –
Presumably devised for celebration of
marriage of Giuliano de' Medici with
Filiberta of Savoy – Windsor, Royal
Collection, no. 12496

of Nature as divine, of Wisdom as absolute, of Truth as infinite. Just as in Leonardo the thinker (the scientist and philosopher) is contained in the artist, so in Bruno and Campanella there is, within the thinker, the poet. This is one of the characteristics of the epoch, and explains such a large part of Leonardo's mind as epitomizing the spirit of that glorious civilization.

There is a famous letter of Leonardo's calling to mind all those missives which Campanella wrote to popes, cardinals, and emperors during his imprisonment in the castles of Naples to ask their intercession in his favor, in order that he might at last, after so many tortures and sufferings, obtain his freedom and devote himself to their service with the ability and the enormous learning acquired in so many years of solitary meditation. And he makes long lists of the marvelous things he is able to do. Campanella's promises comprise great plans for religio-political action—a field that Leonardo does not enter. The difference between these documents of the Renaissance at its rise and at its decline is as significant historically as their similarity: for the passage of the Renaissance spirit from contemplation of nature to contest with historical (politico-religious) reality marks the beginning of the tragic end of that era.

The letter of Leonardo, to be found in the Codex Atlanticus, dates from 1483, when he had already taken up residence in Milan and wanted to have a settled place in the service of Ludovico il Moro. It presents the credentials of the candidate: "Having now, Most Illustrious Lord, sufficiently seen and considered the proofs of all those who proclaim themselves masters and inventors of instruments of war, and finding that their inventions and use of the said instruments are nothing different from common practice, I am emboldened, without prejudice to anyone else, to put myself in communication with Your Excellency, in order to acquaint you with my secrets."

Finally, Leonardo recalls that he also has some ability applicable in times of peace: "In time of peace I believe that I can give you as complete satisfaction as anyone else in architecture pertaining to the construction of buildings both public and private, and in conducting water from one place to another. Also, I can execute sculpture in marble, bronze, or clay, likewise painting, in which my work will stand comparison with that of anyone else, whoever he may be. Moreover, I would undertake the work of the bronze horse, which is to endue with immortal glory and eternal honor the auspicious memory of the Prince your father and the illustrious house of Sforza."

In the last sentence the writer's return to the center of his own personality, in which he feels his true greatness, lifts him to a loftier style, to a heightened self-consciousness. And the applicant does not hesitate to set himself above the potentate to whom he is addressing himself, and above his "il-

Leonardo da Vinci's allegorical design
for gem or emblem – Windsor, Royal
Collection, no. 12700 v

165

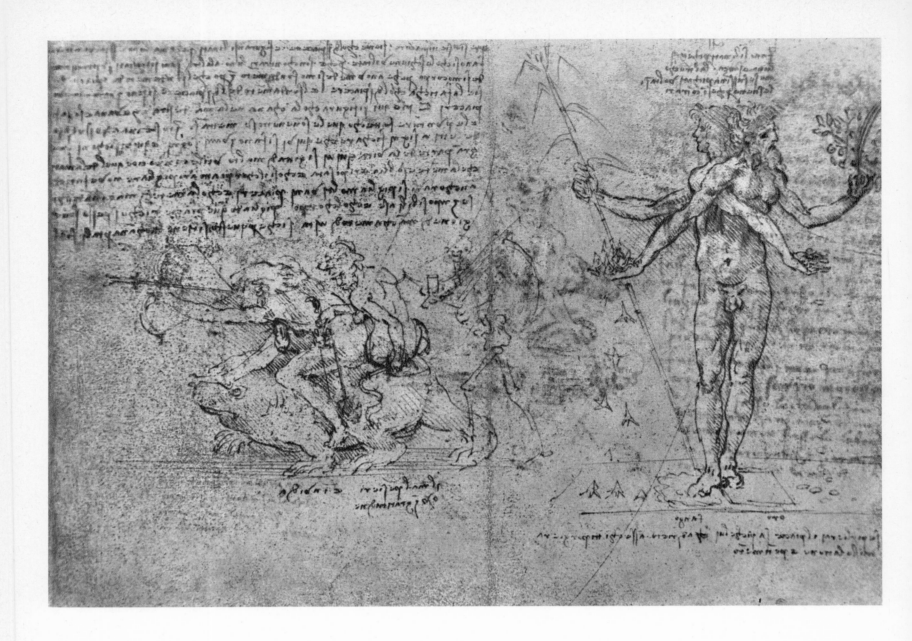

lustrious house," from whom he does not expect honor, but upon whom rather he intends to confer it—eternal honor and immortal glory, such as only art can bestow. But in painting, as in every other art or technique to be used in war or peace, Leonardo is proudly aware that his work "will stand comparison with that of anyone else, whoever he may be." He knows that he can do everything in this field as no one else can.

Able to do everything—the effect of study, for no one believes in technique as much as he does, and in his *Treatise on Painting*, which does not even bring together everything that his reflection on his art suggests by way of precepts, there is the general theme of the science in his art. It is a logical corollary of the thoroughly humanistic and Renaissance notion of the divine nature of thought, which is identical in God and in the man who studies in order to rise above his immediate humanity; thus it is possible for man to investigate and reproduce within himself the secret processes by which the divine thought creates living nature, which man prompts and urges to live the outer life of art.

But Leonardo knows that study, reflection, and technique by themselves can only prepare art, not generate it: they are the condition of the creative process, which requires that more strictly and directly divine thing which moderns call genius, while Leonardo, using a no less suitable term, calls it *naturale*, which is in fact nature.

"Anyone who argues by referring to authority," he says, "is not using his mind but rather his memory. Sound learning is born of a sound spirit [*naturale*], and since the cause is more to be praised than the effect, I shall praise a sound spirit without learning more than someone well lettered but without spirit." [1] And, being a man "without letters," [2] he was content to be looked on as such, as long as the men of letters did not proceed from this to accuse him of not being able to say well that which he had to present. "Foolish folk! Do they not know what I am capable of, so that I might retort as Marius did to the Roman patricians by saying: ʻThey who deck themselves out in the labors of others will not allow me my own.ʼ" Leonardo's manuscripts frequently wage a polemic against the bookish learning of erudite men content to be wise at second hand, strangers to the custom and desire of those who write well to return to the source, which is experience, namely, nature itself.

When he comes to speak of the power of his painting, he boasts as one who possesses a divine power: "If the painter wishes to see beauties to fall in love with, he is master of producing them; and if

[1] Cod. Atl., fol. 76 *a*.
[2] *Ibid.*, fol. 119 v-*a*.

he wishes to see monstrous things to terrify, or clownish and ridiculous things, or things that are truly moving, he is lord and god thereof. And if he wishes to produce desert places, groves shady and dark in hot seasons, he represents them, and likewise warm places in cold seasons. If he wants valleys, if he desires to disclose a great plain from the high summits of mountains, and if he desires thereafter to look on the horizon of the sea, he is the master, and likewise if from the low valleys he wishes to see the high mountains, or if he wants to view the low valleys and beaches from the high mountains. And what the universe contains by essence, presence, or imagination, he has first in his mind and then in his hands; and these are of such excellence that in equal time they generate a proportionate harmony in a single glance, as things themselves do." [3]

And elsewhere he says: "The deity that resides in the science of the painter causes the mind of the painter to transform itself into a similitude of the divine mind, since it proceeds with free power to generate the diverse essences of various animals, plants, fruits, landscapes, plains, ruins of mountains, tremendous fearful lakes that inspire terror in those who look upon them, and likewise pleasant, gentle, and delightful places, variegated meadows moved in gentle waves by gentle motions of the winds, looking back at the winds that fly from them; streams coming down from the high mountains, swollen with the rains and driving before them uprooted plants along with rocks, roots, earth, and foam, driving before them whatever resists their ruin; and the sea with its squalls wrestles and battles with the winds, which fight against it, rising up high with its proud waves, and falls crashing down with them on the wind that strikes their bases, and shutting it up and jailing it under itself, tears and divides it. Mixing it with its turbid foam, it cools its infuriated rage; sometimes, overcome by the winds, it escapes from the sea and passes over the high summits of the neighboring promontories, where it flies over the summits of the mountains and descends into the valleys on the other side, and part is carried off by the fury of the winds, and part escapes from the winds by falling in rain back on the sea. And part descends ruinously from the high promontories, driving before it whatever opposes its destruction; and often it clashes with the wave following after, and shocks against it, rising to heaven, filling the air with confused foamy mist." [4]

---

[3] *Treatise*, fol. 13.
[4] *Treatise*, fol. 68.

There are many such pages, both in the *Treatise on Painting* and in other writings of Leonardo's, in which the artist lends a helping hand to the thinker, as in this case, where it almost seems that in order better to convince himself and feel that deity characteristic of his science as a painter able to raise before the astonished eyes of men spectacles no less marvelous and sublime than those that nature offers us when it unleashes the fury of its elements, he is not content with theoretical assertions but exemplifies them and thus passes over to practice, and paints in broad strokes, even with the simple means of the ready word—whatever theories he may form in the abstract—no less powerfully than with the brush, receiving and remolding in eternal forms the fluid wave of his mighty fantasy. And the burning word dramatizes its own nature, and becomes a picture, which the painter, in a frenzy of his *naturale*, unfolds before us as seen and imaged by his inner eye. The eye that he endeavors to praise as the privileged organ of the art of arts—which for him is, above music and poetry, painting—is not really the material eye, but the eye of the mind, the divine fantasy in which the eye sees and in general the soul feels. Thus painting (and Leonardo knows this well) first evokes within the mind its figures and their movements and their expressions, and the landscape and the light and shade bathing it all with the art whose secret Leonardo possesses, because it can make itself hand and brush, and become a painting evoked in the fullness of its life and set down on the canvas or the wall.

This divinity of art which Leonardo feels within himself does not inhere in technique or reflection, although the richness of his experience in art and the reflective and speculative quality of his spirit led him to lay great weight on technique; it is rather a prerogative of that fortunate *naturale* which passes beyond study and every kind of knowledge to turn to nature itself. This is the world of Leonardo, as it was in general that of the man of the Renaissance, for the Neoplatonism of Ficino and the other Florentine thinkers had made familiar the idea that man is of a piece with nature, which is also possessed of a soul, since it is all divine, and essentially spiritual, as man surprises it in the inner pulsing of its consciousness, where it is concentrated and revealed.

This eternal and infinite nature is before the eyes of our senses and is in fact present in sense; from it all the normal life of the human spirit begins, although that spirit then goes forward with the mind, or reason, or judgment, which Leonardo well realizes is necessary for the completion of the cognitive act, into which sensation itself enters and in which it is reflected in the light of consciousness. But Leonardo mistrusts this judgment which, working on what is felt, is a source of error [5] whenever it departs from the sensible datum; and above all he distrusts the argumentation of reason in the void, giving rise to empty sciences that start and finish in the mind,[6] as Leonardo says, or a priori sciences, as we should say. For that which has to be known is not in the mind, but out there in nature, which to be sure is internally reason, as is found in the end, once it is known by means of our reason, with which natural reason converges. Hence the definitive form of knowledge, the end point aimed at, which is constructed by means of attentive examination of the effects of natural operation, derived from sensible experience, is rational knowledge. But reason, which is the starting point for nature, is the end point for us, who have first, to open our eyes, and observe, scrutinize, discover. Once the reason of the natural fact is understood, Leonardo says, experience is no longer required. But

[5] "There is nothing that deceives us more than our judgment" (*Treatise*, fol. 65); cf. Richter, no. 1153, 1199.
[6] Cf. *Treatise*, fol. 1.

in order to arrive at the point where the reason is understood, we must open our eyes, and see, see.

Allegorical composition – Oxford, Christ Church College

He was indignant at those philosophers who consider much seeing as a distraction of thought, which calls for withdrawal. "And if you will say that seeing hinders fixed and subtle mental cognition, which is the means of penetrating into divine sciences, and that this impediment led one philosopher to deprive himself of sight, the answer to this is that the eye, as master of the senses, does its duty in impeding false and confused, not sciences, but talk, the discussions that are always carried on with loud cries and gesturing with the hands... And if that philosopher put out his eyes to remove the impediment to his discourses, the fact is that this action was a worthy companion to the brain and the discourses, for everything there was madness. Could he not have closed his eyes when he entered upon this frenzy, and kept them closed until the paroxysm had passed? But the man was mad and mad the discourse, and most idiotic was putting out his eyes."[7] Theology, metaphysics (as we should say), sciences of crotchets and authorities, sciences of "enthroned letters," as Leonardo calls them, are all stuff for friars—holy friars, but pharisees,[8] as he says in a phrase that breaks from him at one point, to be lumped together with the astrologers, the alchemists, and the speculators on perpetual motion,[9] and perhaps as well with the many who "trade in deceits and feigned miracles, deceiving the stupid multitude: and if anyone proves to have uncovered their deceit, they beat him."[10]

There is irony in a note in the Quaderni di Anatomia (IV, 10 a): "I leave the definition of the soul in the minds of the friars, the fathers of the people, who know all secrets by instigation. Let enthroned letters alone, for they are highest truth." This parallels the disdain with which, in the Codex Atlanticus,[11] Leonardo compares the originality of inventors and direct interpreters of nature with the mechanical relations of the "reciters and trumpets of the works of others." There is as great

[7] *Treatise*, fol. 16.
[8] "Pharisees, that is, holy friars": Cod. Triv., fol. 34 a.
[9] See Richter, no. 1206 f.
[10] Ms. E, 6⁶.
[11] Fol. 117 a.

Sleeping peasant, weasel, and serpent – Allegory – New York, Metropolitan Museum of Art

a difference, he exclaims, "as between the object outside of the mirror and the image of that object appearing in the mirror: the one is something in itself, and the other is nothing. Men who owe little to nature, since it is only by accident that they wear clothing, and otherwise could be classed among the herds of beasts."

As an admonition he writes: "O wretched mortals, open your eyes."[12]

His assiduous uninterrupted labor of observation every day, even on festival days, scandalized some people. And he reacted with bitter sarcasm: "There is among the number of the foolish a certain sect called hypocrites, who constantly strive to deceive themselves and others, but others more than themselves: yet actually they deceive themselves more than others. It is they that reprove painters who study on holy days, on matters concerning the true knowledge of all figures that the works of nature have, and eagerly strive to acquire that knowledge so far as they are able."

He rises up against this brood of hypocrites with all his proud awareness of the religious nature of his tireless study of nature: "But let these reprovers be silent, for this is the way of knowing the performer of so many wonderful works, and this is the way of loving so great an inventor! For in truth great love is born of great knowledge of the thing loved: and if you did not know it, you could not love it, or could love it but little. And if you love it for the good you expect to get from it, and not for its sublime virtue, you are acting like a dog that wags his tail and fawns before someone who can give him a bone. But if the virtue of that man were known, he would love him much more, if that virtue served his designs."[13]

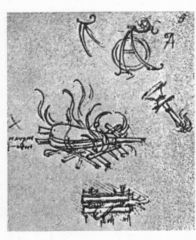

This was the religion of the Renaissance, which sought God in nature. Hence, to fix his glance on natural things was Leonardo's perpetual longing and joy. It was an anxious longing, as he expressed it in a symbolic representation of nature and in the trembling, careful scrutiny with which he explored it: "The stormy sea does not roar so loud when from the north Aquilo strikes it with foaming waves between Scylla and Charybdis, nor Stromboli or Mongibello when the sulphurous flames shut up within them break forth and open up the great mountain, and throw into the air rocks and earth, together with the flame they vomit; nor when the glowing caverns of Mongibello, vomiting forth again the ill-contained element and urging it to its own region, furiously drive before them every obstacle that comes in the way of their impetuous fury... Drawn by my eager wish, desirous of seeing the great confusion of the various strange forms created by ingenious nature, I wandered for some time among the shadowed cliffs, and came to the entrance of a great cavern. I remained before it for a while, stupefied, and ignorant of the existence of such a thing, with my back bent and my left hand resting on my knee, and shading my eyes with my right, with lids lowered and closed, and often bending this way and that to see whether I could discern anything within; but this was denied me by the great darkness inside. And after I had stayed a while, suddenly there arose in me two things, fear and desire—fear because of the menacing dark cave, and desire to see whether there were any miraculous thing within."[14]

This is religious terror. The keenness of that marvelous eye which Leonardo, whether writing or painting, casts on nature cannot suffice to quench his insatiable thirst for knowledge. His glance lights on all the surfaces of living things, perceives their constant motion, catches every vibration, adhering to and moving with the object, almost merging with it. Whether the object be near or far, in an unending perspective, in a living light that also moves and trembles and plays with the shadow,

[12] Richter, no. 1182.
[13] *Treatise*, fol. 77.
[14] Ms. Brit. Mus., fol. 155 *b*.

he takes advantage of the circumstance to illuminate it by veiling it with gradations of shading that are light and shadow at once, in a velvety delicacy of surface. When we read the minute and yet vivid description of trees moved by the wind, and of the branches, and of the leaves and the flowers, and of the ground in which they are planted, and of the rocky background against which they stand out in a complex which the words analyze and embrace and hold close in a living nexus, we behold the restless mind and the anguish of the artist who strives by means of his numberless sketches and drawings and notes to retrace the infinite path that nature has run to attain any one of its slightest effects. And on this path, what man ever labored as much as Leonardo? But he knew well that there is one thing "that is not given, and if it were given would not be," namely, the infinite, "which would be limited and finite if it were given, for that which can be given has a boundary with the thing that surrounds it at its ends, and that which cannot be given is that thing which does not have ends." [15]

Untiringly he follows up the unattainable idea. "O Leonardo, why do you labor so?" he says on a folio of the Codex Atlanticus.[16] And in a prayer he turns to God with these sad words: "Thou, O God, sellest us all good things at the price of labor." His mottoes are of this sort: *Sine lassitudine*; "Death before weariness. No work shall tire me. I do not grow weary of serving." [17] And his warning runs: "A life well spent is long. Just as a day well spent gives grateful sleep, so a life well employed gives grateful death." [18] Campanella's great imperative, "Think, man, think," is anticipated in Leonardo's severe judgment, "He who thinks little errs much." [19] Thinking—this is "serving" as one should, up to death. And not sleeping; for "sleep resembles death," and one should act "in such a way that after death you resemble one completely alive" rather than "living make oneself by sleep like unto the gloomy dead." [20] Memory conqurs time,[21] and the glory of imperishable works conquers death.

But what works are imperishable? Do not perfect works also require an infinity that will assure them immortality? And is this infinity at least given? Even if Leonardo had not expressed his thought in a single note, there could be no doubt that his answer would be negative. But in fact he has written memorable words on the inevitable dissatisfaction of every excellent author with respect to his own work. Every master, it is known, must be surpassed by his disciple: "It is a sorry disciple that does not go beyond his master." [22] But the master himself, if he realizes what art is—how can he help feeling sadness in face of his work, when he sees it falling below his ideal? "It is a sorry master whose work surpasses his judgment; and that master tends toward the perfection of art whose work is surpassed by his judgment." [23] At bottom such a man will always retain a doubt, a discontent, a desire for something better. "The painter who does not doubt achieves little. When

Left: Allegorical drawing – London, British Museum

Right: Allegory – Windsor, Royal Collection, no. 12585 r

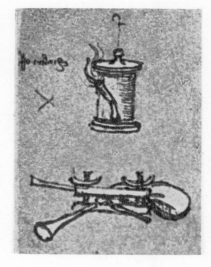

Drawings for rebuses – Ms. M, fol. 4 v

Rebus – *Felice sarei se dell'amore ch'io ti porto resta orna* [?] *fossi* – Windsor, Royal Collection, no. 12699

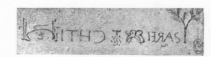

Rebus – *Felice sarei se* [l] *l'amore ch' ti porto* – Windsor, Royal Collection, no. 12694

[15] Cod. Atl., fol. 131 *b*.
[16] Fol. 71 *a*.
[17] Ms. H, fol. 48 *b*.
[18] Cod. Triv., fol. 34 *a*, and 72 *a*.
[19] Ms. H, fol. 119 *a*.
[20] Cod. Atl., fol. 76 *b*.
[21] Cf. Fum., fol. 356 f.
[22] Richter, no. 498.
[23] *Treatise*, fol. 57.

Studies of struggle between horse and dragon – Windsor, Royal Collection, no. 12331

the work surpasses the judgment of the worker, that worker achieves little; and when the judgment surpasses the work, that work never ceases to improve, if injury does not supervene." [24]

This discontent was therefore not flightiness, as Leonardo's contemporaries sometimes whispered among themselves, nor was it a result of "caprices," as Vasari says.[25] Rather, it was due to that divergence between idea and hands to which Vasari himself refers: "It is obvious that Leonardo, because of his knowledge of the art, began many things, and never finished any, for it seemed to him that the hand could not attain the perfection of art in the things that he imagined—since in his idea he formed certain subtle difficulties so marvelous that hands, no matter how excellent, could never have expressed them." This was the necessary consequence of the conception that Leonardo had, and had to have, of art, of human thought, and of nature, which he followed so closely. This is the secret cause of his travail ("O Leonardo, why do you labor so?"), and hence of the dispersion of the powerful vigor of his activity, as well as of the shadow of melancholy that suffuses the creations of his art.

It is a mysterious melancholy rising from the soul of the artist anxious for light and fascinated by mystery, divided between the sense of the divine in nature, which is unity and life and is essentially spirit, as nature was felt to be by the man of the Renaissance, once Ficinian Platonism had enlarged the capacity of his breast, with its boldness and its faith in human freedom, to a sense of the infinite life in which his individual soul expands into the breast of nature—and the concept of the unattainability in concepts of that universal unity, since nature is known only by way of sense experience. And this is shown through a numerable multiplicity, susceptible of mathematical treatment, which Leonardo was among the first to proclaim, anticipating the canons of Galilean science, which is modern science. It is a multiplicity that can be ordered in a closed and fixed system, necessary and mechanically invariable, according to causal relationship, which is nothing but the factual connection

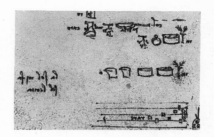

Rebuses and figured words – First line: *Colpa dell'amore mal collocato* – Windsor, Royal Collection, no. 12699

Rebuses and figured words – Windsor, Royal Collection, no. 12697

[24] *Ibid.*, fol. 62. On this subject, compare: "When the work is equal to the judgment, it is a bad sign for that judgment; and when the work surpasses the judgment, it is a most evil judgment, as happens to one who is surprised that he has done so well; and when the judgment surpasses the work, it is an excellent sign; and if the man in such a state, is young, he will without doubt be an excellent worker, but will compose few works, though they will be full of qualities that will fill men with admiration at contemplating their perfection" (Cod. Atl., fol. 80 *b*).

[25] Vasari, *Vite* (ed. Milanesi,) IV, 22.

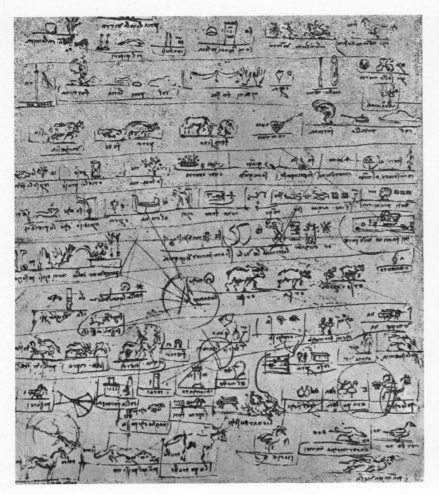
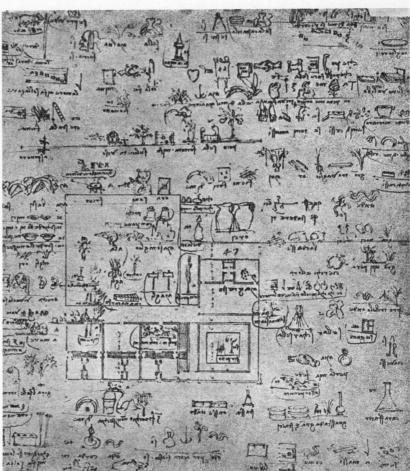

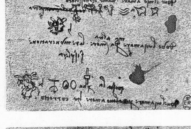
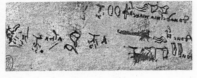

Rebuses and figured words – Windsor, Royal Collection, no. 12692 r, v

Rebuses and figured words – Windsor, Royal Collection, no. 12693, 12696, 12695

between the condition and the conditioned, capable of endowing the totality with the mechanistic character proper to the single elements—the character of the fact that exists, though we do not know how nor why. Science grows and the unknown grows.

The little facts, whose number is infinite, become an enormous fact enveloped in the same darkness as each minutest object of the initial observation. Why? How? Questions without a reply.

Science must silence these questions. From Galileo's day on, rigorous scientific method has rejected such questions as undue and illegitimate, and limited itself consciously to what are called appearances, or phenomena (as they were later to be termed) of nature—that is, to the surface. But Leonardo, while looking to such an ideal of scientific knowledge, cannot be satisfied with the surface. His keen unsleeping eye penetrates deeper; and when observation, the experience that is so greatly praised and exalted, no longer serves him, he intuits or evokes the inner life, the secret soul setting in motion the great machine that he has taken apart and studied piece by piece, watching, espying, scrutinizing, by means of mathematics, mechanics, anatomy, and every instrument that might enable him to follow the operations of nature step by step.

The painter, the artist, seeks and glimpses the infinite from afar; the scientist, who would wish to introduce into painting the certainty of facts and of the external manifestations of the All, and rigorously measure and count—*pondere numero et mensura*—whatever can be observed, strives to confine himself within limits. The unity of the inward illuminates the fantasy; and the intellect comes to break up this unity into the endless multiplicity of sensible appearances.

Hence the anguish and the innermost tragedy of this universal man, divided between two irreconcilable worlds. Hence the desperate lifelong labor of this implacable self-torturer, whose marvelous work of gleaming phantasms of art, spread from full hands day by day on paper, on canvas, and on storied walls, and of precise concepts and inspired researches which in many fields of scientific knowledge are portentous anticipations of the future, leaves in the mind an infinite longing, made up as it were of regret and sadness. It is the longing for a Leonardo different from the Leonardo that he was, one who could have gathered himself up at each phase and remained closed himself off either altogether in his fantasy or altogether in his intelligence, in order to taste the pure joy of divine creation. It is an anguished longing such as always welled up in Leonardo's heart each time that he put down his brush, his charcoal, or his rod, or had to break off setting down his secret thoughts.

Secret thoughts—and on this account entrusted to that most singular handwriting which Leonardo was pleased to use, as if in despite of anything easy and usual, that mirror writing which was to hinder the profane from setting eyes at once on his thoughts. He felt that he was thinking for himself, to bring together bit by bit the materials for the works that, once they had come to maturity in the fullness of their being, and hence in the logical and persuasive coherence of their elements, could come to light like the bodies generated by nature that are brought to birth when their time has come.

GIOVANNI GENTILE

174

STUDYING LEONARDO

There are Da Vinci specialists, as there are Dante scholars. Every age has its own, and can be recognized in them, by and large. But even within any given single epoch, the representatives of the various cultural tendencies have each practiced their own methods in studying authors, have had different preferences, and have picked out one problem rather than another. Hence various styles and orientations coexist in literature and the plastic arts. When I was studying Leonardo as a Neo-platonist—an I was not the first to do so—Dr. Gerolamo Calvi, the late lamented specialist, was studying Leonardo as an Aristotelian; he had commenced before I had.

It should be granted at the outset that it is possible to discuss Leonardo, and to do so with learning and taste, even without having gone through the entire history of Da Vinci studies. This applies particularly in relation to those men who hit the mark by way of intuition, who know as they search what they will find. Thrusts and anticipations of this sort may form the basis for treatments that in a few pages lay the foundations of a book, a book that may perhaps have to be written later on by someone else. What counts is working without preconceived ideas, and admitting to one's initiation into Da Vinci studies not merely those authors who speak of Leonardo, but likewise all those who treat of art, culture, and philosophy in general. This enables one not only to observe, in the body of Leonardo studies, truthful statements that may well have been put forward by writers who did not make Leonardo the sole content of their existence, but also to see that decisive judgments concerning Leonardo may have been uttered by persons who did not even mention him by name, and perhaps were not thinking particularly of him, since their judgments deal with problems that the Da Vinci scholar identifies with Leonardo, or still better, take up principles that apply to the understanding of those problems. In that event the Da Vinci scholar may find his own Leonardo in the works of other scholars, but in a new guise, recognizing him and knowing him better, as a beloved friend who has returned after a long absence: the features, voice, and action that were all so familiar still hold surprises, truths unsuspected confirmation of older explanations, offered in words that say everything better. It may be because ideas are not pure schemes, systems interposed, but realities in a dimension in which we participate in knowledge as it realizes itself, realities that sprout on the trunk of their secret life and branch out, producing flowers and fruits with their seeds within. And among all potent ideas, Leonardo's is most potent, like a tenacious brood, incessantly bountiful: it is the idea of what man is capable of—a question that does not dissociate the problem of the triumphs of thought from that of the triumphs of nature.

And if in such a treatment the Leonardist now and then Leonardizes, by all means let him do so. There is a limit, in any case, to that kind of Leonardizing, namely, that of the space given in the total organization of the discussion to the examination of critical positions already taken on the same subject and of others that depend on it, and in the requirement of a certain scientific good taste (not merely the deference to a deontology), presenting a brake, I should almost say a canon of gracious dignity or (amounting to the same thing) of liberty well enjoyed.

Caricatured expressions from Vallardi
Album – Paris, Louvre

175

Studies of heads – Turin, former Royal Collection

Head of old man – Venice, Academy

Man's head in profile – Drawing in the Venice Academy

An evaluation which would indicate that limit with some open-mindedness should not in any event meet with a cool reception in the field of Da Vinci studies, be they "positive" or analytical studies. No divergence of interests and orientations would justify an attitude of rivalry, or even of disparity. Rather, the philosophers, although some pure Vinciologists (as there are also pure Dante scholars) may have leaned somewhat on the philosophers, owe to positive Da Vinci studies a clear and public contribution of whatever can help toward a scientific organization, on solid bases, of the researches evaluating Leonardo's position in the history of thought. Each must act according to what is closest to his heart, but with such bountifulness on both sides that any temptation to avarice is excluded.

This is why, when a Polish woman student asked me for a bibliography in connection with her doctoral dissertation on the subject of *"La Gioconda" and Its Critics*—a subject in regard to which heaven and earth could be dragged in—I advised her merely to plunge head first, swimming under her own power, into the three thousand volumes of the *Raccolta Vinciana* of the Castello Sforzesco— —a monument to the infinite love of the man who has collected and is still collecting everything about Leonardo, down to the splinters and scraps. For there is no datum or testimony or biographical detail of which we can say that it is more or less important than any other when dealing with the theme of "all of Leonardo," at which one always arrives, no matter from what point one commences. In that *Raccolta* the history of the historiography of the arts, the theory and the history of criticism in the plastic arts, the theory and history of philosophy and science, and of taste and culture in general, are integrally linked with the theory and history of exact speculation and experimental investigation, with the history of technology, and with the analysis of the factors of human life as they are brought together to converge from great distances to a single point. In a word, the very vastness and capillarity of Da Vinci studies reveal the unity of Leonardo.

Now, it can be said of this unity, conceived of as realized in a process of research that has successive phases in time, that it is the cause (Leonardo would have said the "form") of the process itself, which at first was thought to be the causal factor in a pattern of continually perfected stages of appreciation, but has latterly been held to be caused by the unity, that is to say, impelled by an idea.

If we now consider the value of Da Vinci studies from this point of view, a sort of Rickertian point of view, it is impossible for any research on Leonardo to take form either as a system indifferent to the appreciation of Da Vinci studies as a tool and a method, or even (whether the philosopher or the historian of science or of art and literature is concerned) as a system indifferent to the problem of the general value of culture and of the ascertainability, within that problem, of the significance of Leonardo's appearance within the world of men. Today the most vital direction of Da Vinci studies seems to inhere in the aim of reintegrating Leonardo's humanness with ours, understanding his work as the profession of a civilizing project whose essential outlines we are disclosing just at this time because there seems to have come at last a fortunate moment that gives a clearer idea of what our ancestors meant by the continuity of culture, what they expected of us, what they wanted to be present in us. Nevertheless, everyone can rediscover Leonardo anew in his paintings, his calcula-

The Condottiere – Silverpoint drawing – London, British Museum

Drawings of women's heads – Paris, Louvre and Florence, Uffizi Gallery

tions, his drawings, his texts, his structures and his machines, and in the criticisms and the testimonies that different people use for different ends. When, in conformity with this presupposition, we move to the search for Leonardo's unity, we renounce in advance the ambition of a Leonardo encyclopedia; and if there is one obvious difference to be remarked between the Leonardo celebrations of 1919 and those of 1939, it consists in the acceptance of the changes that twenty years of labor have made in the myth of Leonardo as encyclopedic.

For during the last thirty-five years or more, work has gone forward on Leonardo as a thinker (I speak now of the most worthy work) for the purpose of learning what it was that Leonardo wanted to be when he wanted to be (and was) encyclopedic. He was seeking the unity of knowledge in the principle of a knowledge that would suffice for everything.

In this sense Leonardo's demand for a unified science has recently been interpreted also by me as the demand for a *knowledge of ideas*, whatever the expression thereof might be, in mathematics or botany or painting or anthropology. The problem raised here is that of how to conceive of these ideas, which are the object of knowledge and which knowledge itself makes one. It is well known that I have a propensity toward a Platonic interpretation, which has sought its position between the concepts of the ideas represented in contemporary thought on the one hand by the thesis that the idea has the function of a figure, or sign of a reality, and that which regards it as a reality. Relating Leonardo to the problems of today, with an inclination toward the second of the position above mentioned, shows quite naturally the vitality of Leonardo's thought, although in my opinion there is still much work to be done on this formulation of the problem, since it poses the necessity of placing the historical interpretation of Leonardo within the general question of the reality of ideas.

Head of young woman – Florence, Uffizi Gallery

At the time of the Renaissance this question was at an important turning point, whose features deserve to be reconsidered by someone who is well aware of the inheritance that the Renaissance has handed down to our century. Senator Bodrero has pointed out to me, in this connection, how much still remains to be found out with respect to the sources of Leonardo's erudition, the history of the Leonardist movement, and the scholars of the Renaissance as a whole, not merely in so far as these matters concern the prospective organization of present-day studies on the Renaissance, but also as they relate to the studies on scientism and on the view to be taken of the Middle Ages. Even out-

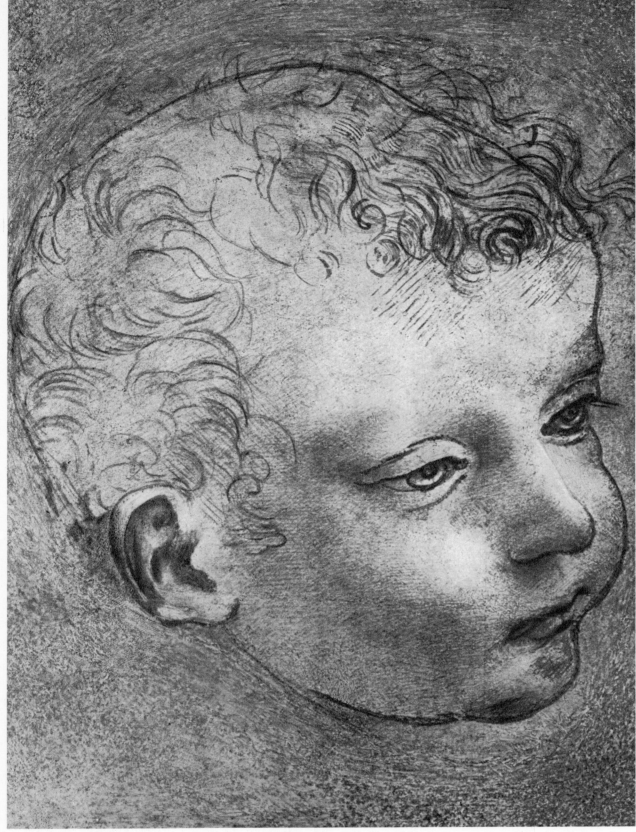

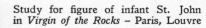
Study for figure of infant St. John in *Virgin of the Rocks* – Paris, Louvre

Drawing – Infant's head – Paris, Louvre

Drawing – Infant's head – Paris, Louvre

Drawing for head of infant Jesus in the picture of the *Virgin of the Rocks* – Paris, Louvre

side of the neo-scholastic camp, anyone who loves calm research and disinterested conclusion will find reason for welcoming a revision of the polemics of the Renaissance against the Middle Ages, with respect to which the history of philosophy in the past has taken a position well known for its own polemical factors. The new principle for defining the boundary between the two epochs would seem properly linked up not so much with criteria based on sweeping syntheses of the history of culture overburdened with promises and prophetic intentions, and deriving from work with old materials, as with a detailed and methodologic revision of the materials themselves, which, with respect to the study of Leonardo, may well be undertaken in the process of reconstructing the history of any branch of the knowable that he even so much as touched on. For in every field Leonardo's work constitutes an epilogue of technico-cultural situations that bespeak an old cosmopolitan tradition, and a phase of revival and rejuvenation of these in a period during which the center of cultural cosmopolitanism was located in Italy.

179

But if Leonardo is to be taken as the simplifier of these situations, many of which present stratifications and interferences whose cosmopolitan and encyclopedic physiognomy must be delicately effaced in order to bring out the vitality and unity as well as the national quality of their process, it is necessary to know not only what the learned men of the Renaissance knew but also what they thought they knew and what they thought they could learn to do, which requires a philological reconstruction of the relevant documents and, moreover, a realization of the psychology of the personalities. The two go hand in hand, and the savor of poetic novelty in the fruits of their respective labors may become equally precious to both. Each will have the merit that monograph studies, when well carried out, always possess as compared with general histories on a grand scale; they will have greater precision of aim, more vivid and better-ordered proportional presentation of the various planes, greater power of conviction because of an organic isolation of documentary bases subjected to direct study.

One of the first results of such a method is to resolve any apparent contradiction between Leonardo as a scientist and Leonardo as an artist, and to justify his position as a man who began more than he finished. By and large, the men of the nineteenth century were too greedy for conclusions to permit the philosophy of research to be detached from results: their writings on Leonardo show the effects. Leonardo, however (and this is where we feel him to be a modern man), never intended to work for progress. In fact, no man of his time had such an intention. This matter of progress is a task we have taken upon ourselves, a burden inherited from the Enlightenment, and we do not always have the courage to say that the figure of Leonardo is so human and beautiful a figure precisely because he aims at realizing in pure mental luxury what to us are practical goals. Just see how, in one of the finest passages of the *Treatise on Painting*, this robust laborer praises the work of the painter as an agreeable and harmonious idleness that creates everything without being enslaved by care, effort, or disciplinary tasks: for him, the painter is the total man. Leonardo's ideal of conduct is gratuitous action, the eradication from life of any sign of toil, of any compensation. Free as a god, the painter plays as he paints; the realm of ideas, or the reality of the activity of painting, is the realm of liberty. Within this ambition, the method of knowledge appears as a method of liberation, and painting as perfect knowledge, as "science" of the truth.

Leonardo paints what is commonly called reality precisely in order to make it true. Expressing knowledge of reality as idea is something other and something more than symbolizing nature: for painting is not a system of writing, a way of putting nature down in signs. It is invention. And it could not be otherwise, since painting is identified with science. Now, anyone who undertakes to organize a study of Leonardo from this point of view will give up the myth of Leonardo as the "great misunderstood man," the "noble victim," the "absolute exception," both as a personality and

Head of old man - Paris, Louvre

180

with respect to his historical position, and will do this gladly if he loves scientific work and has any taste in art. Leonardo is at home in the Italian Renaissance, by the consensus of his contemporaries. He is in tune with his stock, his civilization, his century. The purpose, and even more so the tone, of the agitated demands for a vindication and restitution, indicate more than anything else the carry-over into the method of Da Vinci studies, at the end of the nineteenth century and roughly through the first quarter of the twentieth, of ideational and sentimental factors derived from the romantic conception of the inevitable sufferings of genius, of the expiation, always coming too late, of the injustice committed, to its own loss, by a history lived contrary to history.

It is not true that the Renaissance did not appreciate Leonardo; the fact that a short time later a large part of his work (which he himself during his life kept secret, out of scientific patience) fell into oblivion has its basis in the very rhythm of civilization, which feeds on its own products in accordance with a pattern of avarice and, by and large, of dispersion, that characterizes every epoch. This leads to the surprises encontered in the rediscoveries and exhumations made by later generations, surprises which are a reflection of the realization, in the course of living, of the antiquity of life. There is nothing exceptional about this, and not even anything malevolent.

Moreover, if some day it should come to pass that everything about Leonardo has been discovered and investigated, this would not mean that Leonardo would be dropped from sight, either as a painter or as a thinker. The studies on the subject may change their perspective in a way that we are unable to envisage today, but with respect to which we may reasonably predict that it will constitute a step beyond specialization, provided of course that specialization has exhausted the data on which it can work. One example is the number of "discoveries" appearing in the study of Professor C. Horst on the proportions of the *Last Supper*; this work may be considered as a model of research through which, from a descriptive point of view, an entire critical panorama opens up. The measurements of this diligent and intelligent investigator (the two qualities do not frequently go together) on an isolated piece of Leonardo's production remind us, in the use that is made of them, of the method through which the reading of a single dialogue of Plato may broaden out into a criticism of all of Plato, without ever losing sight of the initial theme.

The idea that Leonardo as thinker cannot be separated from Leonardo as painter is supported, as we know, by the subtlety of Da Vinci's constructive canons or criteria, though there is at the same time no reason to conceive of this set of canons as a symbolist expression, as a figurative language. Leonardo employs it as a syntax of the painter's language. It represents the internal order of the liberty of invention that within its structure remakes nature, to the extent that nature is conceived of not as mechanical repetition but as invention. Leonardo's tendency to a compositional rhythm that collects pictorial invention into a single whole does not, either in the *Treatise* or in the paintings

Left: Studies of expression – Caricatures – Venice, Academy

Center: Expression of man shouting – Paris, Louvre

Right: Caricatures – Paris, Louvre

Grotesque profile – Paris, Louvre

181

that have come down to us, show any sign of a resolving of the single whole into a uniform whole;
nor should we be led into error as to the meaning of the realistic notes scattered here and there
through the *Treatise* ("How to depict a battle," etc.), for what is involved is a fantastic realism that
draws its unity from the unity of the depiction and not from the unity, however given, of the thing
depicted.

This is a principle that should be kept in mind when studying the landscapes in Leonardo's pictorial production. Naturalistic conceptions easily slip into decoration, reducing landscape to the background of a portrait or an action, and excluding it from the conceptual unity of the painting precisely
by means of enriching it with incidental items—such as the hamlet on a hill, the lonely castle, the
sanctuary, the detailed panorama—or with little episodes drawn from human life, such as the troop
of horsemen, the hunter going into the woods, the carpenter in his shop, the travellers chatting on
a bridge, all of this being fantasy that repeats the play of memory by juxtaposing bits of composition
which remain bits and do not produce unity. On the other hand, Leonardo's conception of an
unpeopled landscape, making no pretense of pleasing, indifferent to any thought of human existence,
and all concentrated in an idea of cosmic life, is the conception of a poetic philosophy that Leonardo
could well say he had attained if he could hear modern geologists expressing astonishment at his scientific accuracy and aesthetes expressing equal admiration for the truth of his fantasy. Here reason
coincides with liberty; and this is what Leonardo meant to speak of when he described the effects
of painting on the beholder—the ape saluting as truth the portrait of his master, or the dog barking
at a painted dog, or the mass of people adoring the painted divinity.

In any case, therefore, "invention" appears in Leonardo's art and science to be a step forward in
creation, an agreement with the nature of being, discovered by knowledge of its laws, and producing
a new value which had not possessed any effectiveness in nature. We are at a higher level than that
of Bacon's idea of man as *minister et interpres naturae*; here in truth we discover man as *magister
naturae*. And the difference between the methodism of Bacon, who reduces reason to utility, and
the scientific, pansophic idealism of Leonardo, is brought out as well by the personal psychology of
the two. Bacon inherits from the alchemists his absorption in useful and potent knowledge, and we
may say this even after taking into due account the distinctions he is at pains to draw between his

182

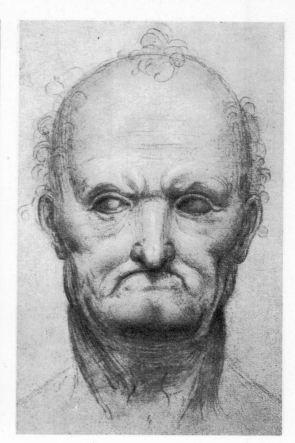

program and that of the alchemists. But the knowledge at which Leonardo aims is gratuitous knowledge, a beautiful perspicacity that asks nothing more, indeed, than to be beautiful, a knowledge that illuminates the world; and in this lies the true "power" of man. This is precisely why it was possible for the thinker, the scientist, and the poet to coexist in Leonardo, and the unity of Leonardo is the unity of a fully realized integration of human normality.

Within the framework of this unity, the picture of Leonardo as a thinker can be supplemented by that of Leonardo as a poet as well. The recent success of Giuseppina Fumagalli's *Leonardo "omo sanza lettere"* is justifiably spreading from the literary field to that of philosophy, giving rise to a fruitful re-evaluation of Da Vinci's thought. A similar situation exists in regard to the work arising out of the edition of Leonardo's writings which was undertaken on the occasion of a centennial celebration but has outlived that occasion. The contribution that Signora Fumagalli has made toward the understanding of Da Vinci's philosophy will have effects that will endure and grow with time. Indeed, it is not an idle question to ask whether it is Leonardo's writings or his paintings that tell us most about him.

From one point of view, it is his writings. In addition to the greater coverage inherent in any written work, the tone of his writings has something that is more urgent, more apt, more subtle, and of greater evocative power. The problem is more explicitly posed in them: and it is always a problem that is not divorced from the problem of the paintings, as Leonardo consciously poses it—the problem of the meaning of the world, of the value of reality. In the paintings, however, it seems to be posed from a formal point of view, while in the writings it is posed from a point of view more often discursive and moral, for which the general run of mankind is better prepared, and to which its response is less indifferent.

Not that Da Vinci's writings have the familiar quality of improvisation. In them, too, we feel the results of long meditation and subterranean incubation, as we do in the drawings, because those drawings which seem to have been made most summarily, and portray the aspects of life in motion with the certainty of a snapshot at 1/400 second, are the fruit of rigorous and systematic observation, by means of which Leonardo sets down in a rational synthesis the necessity of an isolated moment of disorganized expression. In other words, these are observations to be taken as eminently mental constructions, in which calculated synthesis picks up the sensible observation, gives it form, and fills up its lacunae. The Leonardo who draws birds in flight and men leaping is not a man endowed with an exceptional perception span, one whose sensory apparatus operates like a film in slow motion, but a man who, without any external aid, sees flight and jumping *mentally* for the first time: he sees in a calculated way. The predominant feature in Leonardo's drawings, as in the rest of his work, is a realization of the structural necessities of reality, organized as known reality. It is this necessity that Leonardo seeks for, in order to supply a foundation for knowledge itself as idea, not as a conventional

183

Left: Girl's face – Vienna, Albertina Collection

Center: Young woman – Turin, former Royal Collection

Right: Profile of young woman – Florence, Uffizi Gallery

fiction. In the famous dream of the grotto we see a myth of introspection. Discovering nature means discovering an order of connection of which the discoverer is a part; it means identifying the correspondence of man with the system of being under the aspect of the capacity of the all to be idealized.

But there is more than this: the more deeply we go into this method in the field of a philosophy of invention, the more effectively we justify the value of hypothesis in scientific research—that is, the inevitability that nothing is invented that has not previously been known, and as such sought for in invention. Hypothesis is the necessary premonition of it. This eliminates any illusion that may exist as to the possibility of fortuitous inventions in any field. A philosophy of invention that would do away with the standard of a merely psychological inquiry, and base itself on the theory of knowledge and on metaphysics, could today take on new interest and prestige, and contribute something new to learning. This is one more chapter in the program of work that a "rediscovery" of Leonardo might suggest.

The next step is to see to what extent Leonardo's conception of the "world-mindedness" of the painter-philosopher, of the painter as prototype of sage, constitutes a paraphrase of the theme, popular at that time, of the correspondence of the microcosm to the macrocosm, and the extent to which, on the other hand, the conception of such a world-mindedness expresses a new content. The true significance of experience considered as an original value, as reality which is not a term produced by other terms, but the source and foundation of its own being—this we can find there, if it is true that in Leonardo's intention the painter causes this value to be true, makes it real, makes it a value (satisfies it) *by knowing it* (that is, by painting it). We have said that Leonardo's painter is a sage—not someone who merely has sensation, but someone who constructs; not someone who imitates, but someone who creates.

This enables us to see at last the meaning of Leonardo's concept of "imitating nature." As we have seen, this conception can be subjected to examination without contradicting the conception of the originality of a painter's knowledge. Consider for example the way in which, up to the time of Kant, the philosopher designated by the word "subject" an existence that was termed "object" after Kant, and applied the word "object" to another existence which since Kant's time has been called "subject." This happens in the case of many words, both in scientific and in ordinary usage. Then precisely what is "imitating nature" in Leonardo? First of all, it means that the painter should not imitate other painters, as a writer should not imitate other writers, etc. Originality here is seen in the light of the criterion of unrepeatability. All this may seem obvious, since Leonardo holds a place in the history of the reaction against all formalisms in general; but if this were everything new that he had to say, it would not be enough. The fact is that there is more. This new thing consists in the way in which the idea of imitating nature fits into the idea of invention, which is more than mere-

Woman's head – London, British Museum

184

ly knowing, since we know by means of the intellect, but invent by means not of the intellect but of reason. And nature is not intellect: it is reason. I have already said, in *Leonardo pensatore*, that at this point Leonardo faces the most terrible problem of his life—the problem of going so deeply into nature, of becoming so absolutely reason, that he may become inhuman, that he may break the equilibrium of microcosm and macrocosm. At that time I called this intent a plan of cosmic incest. In Leonardo's moral experience this dizziness constitutes one of the decisive factors in his religious conversion. I do not regard this theme as exhausted, and it should be taken up again, both by students of the history of the Christian Renaissance, and by students of religious philosophy, with special attention on the part of the latter to the connection between religion and knowledge, a problem connected to the problem of the relationship between the mind and truth.

Finally, another question should be raised in discussing the personality of Leonardo, the question as to whether the man of genius must necessarily be aware of his own genius. Here I shall only draw the consequences of the thesis stated above, namely, that it is impossible that there should be any fortuitous invention that has not previously been known in the structure already given to the research. Here we depart not only from the old notion of the genius unaware of himself and his value, but also from the relatively more recent conception—and this may take a longer time to die out— which would justify from an industrial point of view the right of every inventor, or even of every possessor of a profilate patent, to the title of benefactor of humanity. The moral personality of Leonardo is in complete contrast to any such notion. Nevertheless, it would be out of place to make any comparative judgment between the two moral positions with the purpose of qualifying one as morally "better." Today the idea of the gratuitousness of scientific work, in the sense of disinterestedness as regards the purposes of application, goes beyond the limits of any such comparison, even in the evaluation of scientific work as a social fact. The multiplying force that animates and guides the refinement of special competences within the framework of scientific collaboration is not a divergence nor a dispersion but a qualitative enrichment of a single noetic system—the system that is the source of the very possibility of science. All culture today is on the march toward a society in which the unity of science, even in its most disinterested or "poetic" aspects, is hypostasized; and it should be noted that none of us is far from a frankly philanthropic conception of such a society. And in Leonardo too we find that sense of a "calling" which characterizes all of the greatest geniuses of the Renaissance, including the great saints and the great heretics.

Young   woman's head – Bayonne,
                Museum

FAUSTO M. BONGIOANNI

Flemish school, formerly attributed to Leonardo – *Joan of Aragon* – Rome, Palazzo Doria

LEONARDO IN BELGIUM

In Brussels in 1919, the Belgian Friends of Italy organized an academic gathering to commemorate the four-hundredth anniversary of the death of Leonardo da Vinci.

In the handsome setting of the Stodet palace, various speakers recalled the chief scientific and artistic accomplishments of the man of genius who had turned his "searching gaze upon all the profundities," as Gabriele d'Annunzio had said. The president of the Belgian group, M. Fierens-Gevaert, later published a well-documented article on "Leonardo da Vinci in Belgium" in the *Revue générale*, and, as additional homage, a long procession of admirers of Italian art set out, one bright spring morning, April 23, 1919, for the abbey of the Premonstrants at Tongerloo in the country near Antwerp, which has a remarkable and almost unknown copy of the *Last Supper*, Da Vinci's immortal masterpiece.[1]

In the Brussels Museum, under the name of Domenico Puligo (previously in the collections of Queen Christina of Sweden, the Duke of Orleans, and Lucien Bonaparte), there exists a copy of the celebrated *Leda*, a composition which would be unknown if it were not for the drawings in the library at Windsor and the painting in the Borghese Gallery in Rome. This has been copied by the Flemish painters [2] and recently, in a study on Vincent Sellaer of Malines,[3] I suggested that it was he, under the influence of Frans Floris, who was responsible for the painting *Charitas*, still in the Prado, which is a copy of the seductive Da Vinci *Leda*, without the swan. Castor and Pollux, who accompany this attractive, sinuous female figure, attest the vogue in Flemish painting of depicting children as little cupids, and cherubs, a characteristic theme of the Italian Renaissance. We shall have occasion to mention this "children's crusade" later on.

It goes almost without saying that the ineffable smile of the *Mona Lisa* made a profound impression on our compatriots, and they gave it many varied interpretations. I shall mention but one of these, that of Martin-Le-Roy now in Paris (note how differently the long, tapering fingers were treated in the original in the Louvre).[4] In 1911, when the *Mona Lisa* was stolen from the Salon Carré, the Burlington Fine Arts Club of London, not without a certain ironic intent, organized an exhibit of nude Giocondas, several of which were Flemish. It is possible to recognize in one the hand

Joos van Cleve – *Virgin of the Cherries with Child* – Brussels, Leu de Cecil Collection

---

[1] According to an old tradition, this handsome big picture, which has been at Tongerloo since 1545, was ordered by King Henry VIII of England. A note by Canon Erens, archivist at the abbey, gives its history. Fierens-Gevaert suggested attributing it to Boltraffio. I shall not go into the influence of Da Vinci's *Last Supper* on Flemish painting. We need only recall the predella of Joos van Cleve, the painter of the *Death of Mary* in the Louvre, the miniature of the Hennessey *Hours*, and later the series of compositions connected with the name of Pieter Coeck van Aelst, who treated the Last Supper in various paintings.

[2] Paolo d'Ancona "Leonardo da Vinci's *Leda* in an Unknown Flemish Version," in *Arte*, 1920. See also the Johnson Collection, Philadelphia, Cat. Valentiner, 1913, II, 393.

[3] *Revue belge d'archéologie et histoire de l'art*, VII (1937), 337. In a communication to the Royal Belgian Academy of Archaeology, Mlle. S. Bergmans puts forward Vincent Sellaer as one of the main interpreters of the art of Leonardo da Vinci in the Low Countries.

[4] Cat. Le Prieur et Pératé (1909), IV, no. 24.

Jan Metsys – *Flora in the Garden* – Stockholm, National Museum

Joos van Cleve, the Younger – *Leda* – Philadelphia, J. C. Johnson Collection

of Joos van Cleve,[5] the author of the *Death of Mary*, and there are others which reveal French origins, since the prototypes of Diane de Poitiers and Gabrielle d'Estrées, emerging from the bath, had prolonged this style of painting from the beginning of the 17th century; the entire Fontainebleau school was markedly inspired by it.

Da Vinci's paintings of the Madonna exerted their fascination in our provinces thanks to the works of the master's Lombard disciples. Andrea Salaino, in particular, is closest to the Flemish artists.[6] The Benois Madonna in Leningrad[7]—the smiling girl tenderly fondling the infant Jesus—is linked to the Flemish school through a copy which is now in the Colonna Gallery in Rome,[8] as is a banal copy of the *Madonna of the Carnation*, the original of which is in the Old Pinakothek of Munich with the copy, in turn, in the Louvre. This is a phenomenon analogous to copies made by Flemish painters of the works of Raphael (Flemish copies of the Bridgewater Madonna) and of Michelangelo (a Flemish copy of the master's *Holy Family* in the Uffizi is now at the Fogg Art Museum in Cambridge, Mass.).

Leonardo's characteristics are most clearly apparent in the group of saints of the *Sacred Conversation* in the Brussels Museum, painted by our own Quentin Metsys; here something of Gioconda's

[5] Max J. Friedländer, *Altniederländische Malerei*, IX, 55. In addition to Joos van Cleve, the author mentions a copy of the nude Gioconda by Barthel Bruyn at the Munich Pinakothek, formerly at the Augsburg Museum. See also André de Hevesy, "Leonardo da Vinci: Found Works and Lost Works," in *Gazette des Beaux-Arts*, I (1931), 114.

[6] It should not be forgotten that Ambrose Benson, who settled at Bruges and belonged to the circle of Gerard David, was of Lombard origin.

[7] S. Reinach, "Flemish Imitations of the Benois Madonna," in *Burlington Magazine*.

[8] Herbert Cook, "Leonardo da Vinci and Some Copies," in *Burlington Magazine*, XX, 128. Morelli already considered the Colonna picture as being a Flemish work.

enigmatic smile survives in the pallid faces of the group of women around St. Anne and the Virgin. The formula of complicated, dark-bluish landscapes with the mountains arranged as a receding backdrop is directly derived from Lombard painting. This landscape met with special sympathy from our painters for it gave them inspiration without forcing them to abandon what was, essentially, a clear view of their own homeland. The painting by Metsys, formerly in the Raczynski collection of Poznan and now in the municipal gallery there,[9] recaptures in its grouping of the figures of the Virgin and Child with lamb the composition of its model, the *St. Anne* of the Louvre,[10] except that the figure is draped in Flemish style and is framed against a landscape attributed to Patinier depicting the valley and rocks of the Meuse. Hulin de Loo has brought to light the Metsys-Patinier collaboration in this work as an element of special interest. We should note that the reclining pose of Mary who, "thanks to an instinctive girlish trustfulness, has resumed her earlier position at her mother's knee" (Gabriel Séailles), is quite inexplicable and the figure is as if suspended, while the St. Anne has disappeared.

Left: Quentin Metsys – *Virgin and Child* – Paris, Darcy Collection

Right: Flemish copy of painting by Leonardo – Paris, Louvre

Another Da Vinci motif, that of the Madonna embracing the Child, has been used by Quentin Metsys in his painting in the Berlin Museum.[11] Many copies of this subject are known, but perhaps the least familiar of these is that in the Darcy collection in Paris.

The gentleness of the Lombard models is even more sensitively captured by that epigone of Metsys called the Master of the Mansi Magdalene. We need not enumerate here all the proofs of the influence of the Metsys circle. It should suffice to mention an interesting composition, that of the *Virgin of the Cherries*, which is a popular subject in our region among the followers of Quentin Metsys and Joos van Cleve. There are examples of this in Munich and in the Cook collection in Richmond, and I would like to add here that one version of this subject belongs to M. de Leu de Cecil of Brussels.

We have emphasized the work of Quentin Metsys and Joos van Cleve, yet the same Lombard influence can be traced in the work of Bernard van Orley and Jan Gossaert, called Mabuse. Leonardo's influence in portraiture, aside from that which is so obvious in the painting of *Anna de Berghes*,

[9] Friedländer, *op. cit.*, VII, 47, no. 19.

[10] The *St. Anne* had been at Fontainebleau since 1529.

[11] The *Virgin Embracing the Child* in the church of S. James in Antwerp, a very weak variant with its directions reversed, is attributed to Jan Metsys. J. Sanders van Hemessen should likewise be cited among the Flemish painters in whose works the influence of Leonardo can still be traced.

Early school of Low Countries – *Charitas* – Madrid, Prado

189

Peter Paul Rubens – *Head of Medusa* – Vienna, Art Museum

Quentin Metsys – *Madonna with Child* – Berlin, Kaiser Friedrich Museum

Jan Gossaert, called Mabuse – *Infants Embracing* – Collection Professor G. Bellesi

Quentin Metsys – *Madonna and Child* – From collection of municipal gallery in Poznan

Marquise de Veere, directly inspired by the master's *La Belle Ferronnière*, can be observed in the use of melting blue alternating with darker blue landscapes behind the half-length portraits, arranged in the style of Solario.

Gossaert possibly took one motif from the Milanese masters in his *Virgin of the Veil*, with its capricious infant Jesus who is trying to conceal himself in the folds of his mother's mantle. We could cite innumerable examples of this treatment, even in the later and less felicitous copies.

It is impossible to recall all the Flemish embodiments of the Da Vinci ideal. There are gaps in such a brief recapitulation, of course, but we must conclude by mentioning the charming group of the Christ child embracing St. John the Baptist, which Leonardo placed in the foreground of the *St. Anne*.[12] Taken from the painting as a whole, this group has been treated again and again with many variants by Marco d'Oggiono and the master's principal disciples.

I mentioned earlier the Flemish enthusiasm for painting sacred and profane "putti," those little cupids of the Italian Renaissance; this subject had extraordinary success. One example, described in an inventory of 1523, adorned the palace of Marguerite of Austria at Malines: *Item ung aultre tableau de deux petitz enffans embrassant et baisant l'ung l'autre sur l'arbette.* The best examples are in Naples, at Hampton Court and in the Mond collection in London; the painting of the Mauritshuis at The Hague should be attributed to Gossaert or van Orley.

In contrast to the sweetness of infancy which Leonardo treated so unforgettably, we must not omit recognition of another facet of the master's universal genius: his tremendous skill at caricature. A merciless observer of the physical and moral weaknesses of his fellow men, he caught up with and surpassed both Quentin Metsys and Hieronymus Bosch. Those strangely distorted faces, those expressive grimaces, have been much imitated in the Low Countries. Let us glance at the *Christ at the Pillar* by Mabuse (the original bears the signature, 1527 *Malbodius invenit*), of which there are numerous copies.[13] The keen profile of the old man who clutches a purse to his chest, the man with the turban shouting insults, they are familiar to us, for we have already seen them in the Da Vinci sketches, along with drawings for equestrian statues or war machines.

To conclude this brief sketch, I should like to ask the reader to consider for a moment a sentimental comparison between Italian and Flemish art. Could not Peter Paul Rubens, Flemish genius par excellence, have had at least partial knowledge of the famous *Battle of Anghiari* painted by Leonardo da Vinci in the Palazzo Vecchio in Florence? I was thinking of this as I studied the *Battle of the Flag*,[14] that marvelous Rubens drawing in the Louvre which was exhibited in the Palace of Fine Arts in Brussels.

PIERRE BAUTIER

---

[12] B. Luini, in the Prado. Compare the *Virgin at the Fountain* in the collection of the Abbé Thuélin, Paris.

[13] P. Bautier, "Mabuse's *Christ at the Pillar* and Its Various Versions," in *Revue de l'Art*, XXIII (1922), p. 32.

[14] *Drawings of Peter Paul Rubens at the Palais des Beaux-Arts at Brussels*, 1938-1939, Cat. no. 1. It is known that Rubens had also made a drawing of the Last Supper under the inspiration of Da Vinci (Dijon Museum, Coll. His de la Salle, no. 847).

LEONARDO IN ENGLAND

The subject "Leonardo da Vinci in England" makes an interesting chapter in the history of artistic relations between Italy and the British kingdom. Although for obvious reasons the most important foreign influence on England during the Middle Ages was French, the artistic bonds between Great Britain and Italy were of considerable importance. At the beginning of the sixteenth century, Henry VIII, the sovereign who represented the dawn of the Renaissance in England, encouraged the importation of Italian artists much as did his brilliant French contemporary, Francis I. With Henry VIII, however, we deal more with sculptors than with painters: the most famous of the sculptors was Pietro Torreggiani whose uncomplimentary remarks concerning the English won immortality when Benvenuto Cellini included them in chapter XII of the first book of his autobiography. It is interesting to imagine what fascination Leonardo's personality would have exerted upon Henry VIII. That monarch appointed Girolamo da Treviso to his service, an Italian who combined the talents of painter and military engineer, like Leonardo, although on a far smaller scale. No invitation was sent to Leonardo from England, however; and the master never crossed the English Channel on the "ebb and flow" of which he had made a note in one of his manuscripts.[1]

The break between Henry VIII and the Roman Catholic Church took place in 1534, fifteen years after Leonardo's death. This resulted in a radical reduction of artistic exchanges between England and Italy. In fact, the Italian art of the sixteenth century must have been in large measure unknown to England at that time. During this century, however, we do find the origins of what much later was to be termed the "grand tour"—a journey through France and Italy considered as an essential part of an English gentleman's liberal education. It is true that Sir Philip Sidney, one of the greatest of the Elizabethans, formed friendships with Tintoretto and Paolo Veronese in Venice, but this is an isolated instance, and the situation in general remained as outlined above. Significant proof of this can be found in the fact that the only reference to the Italian art of the Renaissance extant in the works of Shakespeare is the passage in the second scene of the fifth act of *The Winter's Tale* in which the dramatist alludes to "that rare Italian master, Giulio Romano." Romano is referred to, however, not as a painter but as a sculptor, which he probably never was. In the same passage he is called an "ape of nature," an expression which was applied in the history of Italian art to one of the followers of Giotto known by the name of Stefano. From this we can deduce that whatever affinity one may discover between Leonardo and the Elizabethan thinkers and artists must be attributed in every case to "spontaneous generation." There cannot have been any direct influence from Leonardo. Even though it is true that an echo of the "Paragone" may be found in the dialogue between the painter and the poet which takes place in the first scene of Shakespeare's *Timon of Athens* it is quite certain that he had no knowledge of the writings of Leonardo.[2]

It would be interesting to be able to state the precise date on which the name of Leonardo first appeared in a printed book in England. As far as we know, it was in a translation done by Richard

---

[1] J. P. Richter, *The Literary Works of Leonardo da Vinci*, 2d ed., Oxford, 1939, p. 959.
[2] Karl Borinski, *Die Antike in Poetik und Kunsttheorie*, I (1914), 167; cf. *Journal of the Warburg Institute*, II (1939), 260-262.

Masculine headdresses – Windsor Royal Collection, no. 12478 and 19122 r

Haydocke published at Oxford in 1598.[3] It was called "Treatise on the Art of Painting" and referred to Leonardo by the Anglicized name of "Leonard Vincent." We know without doubt that Leonardo's first painting to come to England was the *St. John the Baptist* that Charles I, a noted patron and collector of the arts, obtained from Louis XIII of France in exchange for the portrait of *Erasmus* by Holbein, now in the Louvre, and a *Holy Family* by Titian.[4] When the collection of Charles I was dispersed at the time of Cromwell, the painting was acquired by Jabach who sold it to Louis XIV, and it has been in France since that time.

There is nothing to substantiate the attribution of any of the few paintings listed in the inventory of Charles I's collection to Leonardo. As for the collection of drawings by Leonardo which now may be found in the Royal Library at Windsor, the major part of them (formerly belonging to Francesco Melzi and later to Pompeo Leoni) were not brought to England by Charles I, as has frequently been claimed. They were acquired by the "father of English art collectors," Thomas Howard, Earl of Arundel (1586-1646), from a Spanish nobleman, Don Juan de Espina, probably shortly after 1637. Some of these figure drawings, while in the Arundel collection, were reproduced in engravings by Wenceslaus Hollar between 1645 and 1651. We then find a gap in the history of the drawings, until they appear again in London in 1690 in the hands of Constantine Huygens, secretary to King William III, who acquired them for three and a half guineas. Then there follows a still longer period without any mention of the existence of the drawings, and it is not until the beginning of the reign of George III, who ascended the throne in 1760, that they again come to light. This time they are the property of the royal house of England, after having been unearthed "from the bottom of a chest of drawers."[5]

Not all the Windsor drawings, however, come from the Pompeo Leoni collection. It has been established that one of them was in the collection of Buonfiglioli in Venice.[6] The complete history and genealogy of the collection still needs investigation. The Leonardo codex, given in 1831 to the British Museum by the Royal Society (Arundel 263, now Pl. CLXV), also comes from the Arundel collection.

Turning to the end of the seventeenth century, we find that appreciation of Leonardo in England was constantly increasing. Aside from occasional references to the artist in various guidebooks, we note that William Aglionby, in his extremely interesting but little-known book, *Painting Illustrated* (1685), traced the history of Italian painting; after mentioning the "sweet union of colors" of Francesco Francia and Pietro Perugino, he said it was "so pleasing to the eye that people flocked to admire their works, believing it impossible to surpass them; but they were soon undeceived by Leonardo da Vinci whom we must recognize as the father of the third stage of painting, that of the modern method; in him nothing was lacking. Not only were his drawings strong and true, he also gave clearer rules and more exact measurements, and showed more profundity in art than anyone who had preceded him."[7] I believe this may be the first time that Leonardo's personality and historical position were defined in England. Aglionby's book also contains a life of the artist, among the translations of eleven of the biographies of Vasari's *Lives*.

Among the references to Leonardo which date from the beginning of the eighteenth century, the one by Edward Wright, one of the most learned and cultured of early English art collectors, is worthy of notice. The following passage appears in his description of Milan (1722):

"As S. Carlo is held in the highest esteem at Milan upon the account of his piety, so is Leonardo da Vinci upon account of his skill in arts and sciences. His paintings are esteem'd there at least equal to Raphael's; and his twelve volumes of mechanical designs, which they preserve in an apartment near the library, almost with veneration, are held inestimable. They were given to the library by count Galeaz Arconato, and receiv'd with an upparallel'd solemnity. The donation was register'd in great form, in presence of the conservators of the library, the syndic and notary, and a solemn message of thanks was sent to the count; the form of which is also register'd among their archives. A large inscription in marble over the place where the volumes are kept, sets forth that the king of England [James I] had offer'd the count three thousand pistoles for one of the volumes, which he, *regio animo*, refused. There is likewise register'd an affidavit made by an agent of the count, of the reality of such offer, by James king of England, and of letters from the earl of Arundel, and of other pressing instances, to have obtain'd the book upon any terms."[8]

In the same year, 1722, when Edward Wright made his visit to Milan, the first edition of *An Account of the Statues, Basreliefs, Drawings and Pictures in Italy* by J. Richardson was published. Richardson was a painter and a collector of drawings, and he made ample mention of Leonardo in his book. Some years earlier, between 1713 and 1716, Thomas Coke, who later became Earl of

[3] "A Tracte Containing the Artes of Curious Painting, Caruinge & Buildinge." I am indebted to my friend, Mr. Charles F. Bell, for calling my attention to the importance of this translation for the subject treated here.

[4] Sir Claude Phillips, *The Picture Gallery of Charles I*, London, 1896, p. 85.

[5] For the original of the Windsor drawings, see Sir Kenneth Clark, *A Catalogue of the Drawings of Leonardo da Vinci in the Collection of His Majesty the King at Windsor Castle*, Cambridge, 1935, p. IX-XI.

[6] G. Poggi, *Leonardo da Vinci*, Florence, 1919, p. 59, no. 1.

[7] William Aglionby, *Painting Illustrated*, London, 1685, p. 73.

[8] Edward Wright, *Some Observations Made in Travelling through France, Italy, Etc. in the Years MDCCXX, MDCCXXI and MDCCXXII*, 2d ed. London, 1764, p. 467 f.

Madonna of the Distaff – Oil on wooden panel – London, Collection of the Duke of Buccleuch

Madonna of the Distaff – Montreal, Robert W. Reford Collection

Madonna of the Distaff – Collection of Prince Rupprecht of Bavaria

In April 1501, Fra Pietro di Novellara wrote to Isabella d'Este that Leonardo was painting for Florimond Robertet, a gentleman of the French court, a "Madonna seated, as though she wanted to reel spindles, and the Child, with his foot in the basket of spindles has taken the distaff and is looking attentively at the four spokes, which are in the form of a cross, as if desirous of the cross, laughing and holding it firmly and not willing to give it to his mother, who seems to want to take it from him."

Various versions of this composition are known, but none of them answers exactly to Fra Pietro's description. The best-known versions are in the collections of the Duke of Buccleuch, of Lord Battersea (now Reford), and of Prince Rupprecht of Bavaria. The Reverend Emil Möller believes that the Buccleuch Madonna is Fra Pietro's Da Vinci painting, while William Suida prefers the Reford version.

Most students consider all these paintings as copies of Leonardo's painting, made by pupils or masters of Leonardo's school. At the Leonardo Exposition, the Buccleuch Madonna proved its nobility of composition and figure work, but showed obvious retouching throughout the landscape and sky. The X-ray picture made by the radiologist of the Commune of Milan, Flavio Gioia, confirmed this observation, showing Leonardo's design in its first form; the original composition excluded the entire landscape. Moreover, the broad strokes seem in fact to have been drawn by the "left hand," and at the feet of the Child on the Mother's knees there will be noted a change in the composition that might represent painting over the basket of spindles.

S. P.

Leicester (1697-1759), had acquired the codex which since then has remained at Holkham Hall. He got it from Giuseppe Ghezzi in Rome and brought it to England. To another eighteenth-century English connoisseur and collector of art objects, John Udny (1727-1800), British consul, first at Venice and then at Leghorn, goes the credit and honor of having imported into England one of the greatest of Da Vinci art treasures, the cartoon for the *St. Anne*, showing the figures of the Madonna, the Child, St. Anne, and the infant St. John. Udny owned this before 1763 and the Royal Academy had acquired it by 1791.[9]

Toward the end of that century, in 1785, Gavin Hamilton brought another Leonardo treasure to England. This was the *Virgin of the Rocks*, which Leonardo had been commissioned in 1483, and which had been placed in the chapel of the Confraternity of the Conception in the Church of San Francesco in Milan, 1506. The picture was sold to Lord Landsdowne in England, who transferred it to the Earl of Suffolk in an exchange. It was acquired from the Suffolk collection by the National Gallery in 1880, and it can now be considered the only painting in England attributed to Leonardo the authenticity of which can be documented. (The lateral paintings by Ambrogio de Predis were acquired only in 1898 from the Melzi collection in Milan.) There are many works attributed to Leonardo in the English catalogues of the nineteenth and twentieth centuries, but they consist for the most part of paintings by pupils or followers of the master. Some of these have real value in themselves, but it is absurd and inaccurate to attribute to them such exalted paternity. Let us add that the nineteenth century saw the importation of five manuscripts of Leonardo into England —the three codices, now in the Victoria and Albert Museum, which were given as a bequest by Mr. J. Forster; and the two codices of the Ashburnham Library which remained only briefly in England and are now in the library of the Institut de France in Paris.

The English contribution to Leonardo literature during the 1800's has been considerable. Let us cite first the essay by Walter Pater on Leonardo (1869) which was included in his *Studies in the History of the Renaissance* (1873). This essay influenced the development of aesthetic thought in England, even though the author based part of his discussion on works which had been recognized for some time as having been wrongly attributed to Leonardo.

J. P. Richter's book *The Literary Works of Leonardo da Vinci* (1883; enlarged, 2nd ed., 1939), although not the work of an Englishman, is unquestionably connected with England in that it was published in that country and in English. The work of the late Herbert Horne, a translation of *The Life of Leonardo* by Vasari with commentary (1903), represents a solid contribution to Leonardo studies.

It is perhaps not generally known that Sir Joseph Crowe, Cavalcaselle's English collaborator, constantly urged the latter to write a book on Leonardo. It is even said that the fruit of their collaboration, the *History of Painting in Northern Italy* (1871), consisted in large part of material sent by Cavalcaselle to Crowe to keep him occupied while he himself worked out his ideas on Leonardo.[10] There is only one short article by Crowe extant on "Two Little Known Years in the Life of Leonardo da Vinci," published in the first volume of the weekly periodical *The Academy* (London 1869-70). Apparently the two authors did not pursue their research beyond this point.

It is not possible to speak here of those who have written in England on Leonardo and who are fortunately still with us. Anyone familiar with the subject is well aware of the importance of the contributions brought to the study of Leonardo by these writers and art critics.

TANCRED BORENIUS

Caps and helmets – Pinacoteca Ambrosiana and Royal Collection at Windsor, no. 12590, 12491, 12441 r, 12498, 12442 r

---

[9] Sir Herbert Cook, *Reviews and Appreciations*, London, 1912, p. 1 f.
[10] Crowe and Cavalcaselle, *History of Painting in Italy*, ed. T. Borenius, 2d ed., 1914, VI, p. 115, 126, 191.

Hairdo for head of Virgin – Study for *St. Anne* – Paris, Louvre

LEONARDO IN GERMANY

This is primarily a spiritual problem, as the traces left by Leonardo's personality and work in Germany are present chiefly in the history of the mind, and particularly in the history of Goethe's work. Leonardo has been and remains to this day a living and active spiritual force in Germany. The master's personality has been particularly effective in Germanic lands as the expression of matchless art.

For this reason, it is strange that there is no monument evident to all marking German veneration for Leonardo.

Although Rubens definitely set himself to study the cartoon for the *Battle of Anghiari*, and Raphael's *Sistine Madonna* in Dresden has brought so many Germans to ponder the essential characteristic of art, it is not a simple matter to establish the extent of Leonardo's influence. It may be explained by the small number of works by the master to be found in Germanic lands.

Straight through the eighteenth century, Germans cherished the illusion that a whole series of paintings by Leonardo were in their possession. These attributions, to be encountered in many an old museum catalogue, serve today only to remind us of how little was known of the personality of the master.[1] For a great work by Leonardo which could give in synthesis the art of this master was lacking, as it is today.

It is relevant to ask, first of all, what the influence of Leonardo on German contemporary artists has been. Since the contacts between German and Italian art in the sixteenth century were so numerous, one might suppose that research regarding the elements acquired by German artists from Leonardo's work would be a rich haul indeed. But the harvest is, as we all know, a curiously meagre one.

We may be sure that Albrecht Dürer had many direct contacts with Leonardo's works, exposures possibly going back to the days of his first Venetian sojourn.[2] And it has often been suggested that Jacopo de' Barbari was a go-between in these developments. Without dwelling too extensively here on the recognized fact that Dürer did use motifs recalling Leonardo, it is still evident that such an influence existed although it had less importance for the German master than, for example, the influence of Venice itself or Mantegna.

People have sought to recognize, in the *Opus quinque dierum* of Dürer, in that singular painting, *Christ among the Doctors*, dated 1506, echoes of Leonardo's studies of faces. It seems certain that Dürer at least knew about the existence of such studies, and the old man to the right of the Christ Child definitely recalls Leonardo's work.[3]

There is a kinship too between the horse in Dürer's copper engraving *The Knight, Death and the Devil* (Bartsch no. 98) and Leonardo's study of an armed horse in the Ambrosiana.[4] In this case, Jacopo de' Barbari could have been the link between Dürer and the studies in construction and proportion by Leonardo.

St. Sebastian – Marble sculpture in style of Cristoforo Solari as influenced by Leonardo – Milan, Cathedral

---

[1] See also *Allgemeines Künstlerlexikon*, Zürich, Füssli, 1818.
[2] G. Pauli. "Dürer, Italy, and Antiquity," *Vorträge der Bibliothek Warburg*, Leipzig, 1921-1922, p. 51; see also W. Suida *Leonardo und sein Kreis*, Munich [n.d.], p. 253.
[3] The painting, formerly in the collection of the Palazzo Barberini, Rome, now in the Thyssen Collection, Lugano, is reproduced in F. Winkler, *Albrecht Dürer* (*Klassiker der Kunst*, Vol. IV), Pl. 35. See also W. Waetzoldt, *Dürer und seine Zeit*, Vienna [n.d.], p. 169.
[4] Reproduced in H. Bodmer, *Leonardo da Vinci* (*Klassiker der Kunst*, Vol. XXXVII), p. 274. See also H. Wölfflin, *Die Kunst Albrecht Dürers*, Munich, 1905, p. 188.

195

Left: Bust of unknown woman – Formerly attributed to Verrocchio, now to Leonardo – Florence, National Museum

Right: Bust of gentlewoman – Glazed terra cotta, attributed to Leonardo – Rome, Lidia Doria Collection

Flora – Wax sculpture, formerly attributed to Verrocchio, now to Leonardo – Berlin, Kaiser Friedrich Museum

The Christ Child seated with a bird in his hand, which we find in Dürer's copper engraving *Mary with the Monkey* (Bartsch no. 42), is impressively reminiscent of the Child in Leonardo's *St. Anne* in London.

It would not be hard to establish other interrelations of artistic motifs without, however, being able to determine with any degree of certainty just how the contact between Dürer's art and that of Leonardo came about. The fact that the "six knots" of Albrecht Dürer (wood cuts, Bartsch no. 140-145) are taken from Italian copperplates clearly marked ACADEMIA LEONARDI VINCI [5] cannot be ignored.

This clearly indicates that Dürer must have known Leonardo's studies of faces, his studies in proportion, numerous sketches and perhaps even the cartoon for the *St. Anne*. It is less easy to say that he had surely seen the cartoon for the *Battle of Anghiari*. However, it is certain that Dürer had never seen Leonardo's masterpiece, the *Last Supper*, although he may have known of its existence.

As for Lucas Cranach the Elder, in whom people have often sought to recognize the influence of Leonardo,[6] no single piece of evidence has come to light until now which would establish the least proof of contact between that artist and Da Vinci's work. Nor is any influence Leonardo may have exerted on the work of Hans Holbein the Younger [7] any easier to establish, for the latter had never been to Italy—as Karel van Mander has unquestionably proved. Yet many feel they see in his work elements which are indubitably of Leonardesque origin. Ulrich Christoffel, for example, has pointed out that, in certain portraits such as the *Cecilia Heron* at Windsor, Holbein is close to that ideal female figure created and established forever by Leonardo.[8] Even prior to this, an internal affinity was noted between certain works of Holbein and Leonardo. Indeed, the famous *Little Moor* of the Dresden gallery was bought in 1746 as a Portrait of Ludovico Sforza and attributed to Leonardo da Vinci. Of course certain motifs characteristic of Leonardo may have reached these German painters by indirect routes and complicated means, but the sum total of them is not great and is limited to details rather than to indications of direct and intense penetration.

[5] *Burlington Magazine*, XII (1907), 41 f. See also Seidlitz, *Leonardo da Vinci*, II, p. 268, 438-b; V. Scherer, *Die Ornamentik bei Albrecht Dürer*, Strasbourg, 1902.
[6] Suida, *op. cit.*, p. 255.
[7] W. Suida. *Hans Holbein der Jüngere und die Kunst der Lombardei*, in *Bericht der Amerbach-Gesellschaft in Basel*, 1921, p. 13 f.
[8] U. Christoffel. *Hans Holbein d. J.*, Berlin [n.d.], Pl. 33.

Yet with this brief roster, Leonardo's importance in German spiritual history has scarcely been exhausted. An awareness of his greatness was never completely absent in the 16th and 17th centuries. For instance, Sandrart, in his *German Academy* [9] speaks of Leonardo in several places without, however, having been able to reach a true understanding of his genius.

These German writers of the baroque period did not go beyond conventional notions based, in large part, on Vasari. In short, Leonardo's fame was recognized without any just interpretation of the master.

This situation changed radically at the time of Goethe who must have felt a strong spiritual affinity for Leonardo. There was a bond of kinship between Goethe and the universal mind of Leonardo. Though the great German poet was continually interested in the artist in Leonardo, he was no less attracted by the scientist, the indefatigable researcher, for also with Goethe studies in natural science played a not inconsiderable role. [10]

The primary source for Goethe's ideas on Leonardo da Vinci may be seen in the well-known essay which derives from the work of Giuseppe Bossi on the *Last Supper*. [11] There it is shown clearly that Goethe felt attracted to Leonardo because he found in him his own aspirations, his own inner turmoil. At the very start, he writes: "I was moved above all by the unusual configura-

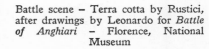

Battle scene – Terra cotta by Rustici, after drawings by Leonardo for *Battle of Anghiari* – Florence, National Museum

Noli me tangere – Detail from relief by Rustici – Florence, National Museum

---

[9] Joachim von Sandrart. *Academie der Bau-Bild- und Malerei-Künste*, ed. by A. R. Peltzer, Munich, 1925, p. 411, n. IV.
[10] Walter Jablonski. "The Place of Goethe's Natural Investigations in the History of the Mind," in *Jahrbuch der Goethe-Gesellschaft*, XV, 22 f.
[11] J. W. Goethe. *Kunst und Altertum*, in *Werke: Ausgabe letzter Hand*, Vol. 39 (1817). Cf. Giuseppe Bossi, *Il Cenacolo di Leonardo*, Milan, 1810.

Details of Verrocchio's *Resurrection* – Florence, National Museum

Verrocchio – *Resurrection* – Terra-cotta relief – Florence, National Museum

tion of the faces, which reveal both the permanent character of the individual human beings and their passing emotions, and this is the aspect of the *Last Supper*, on which we shall dwell at some length." Reading these lines calls to mind Goethe's interest in the studies of faces by Lavater.[12] And on many other occasions he speaks of this aspect of Leonardo's art, which proves how easy it was for him to orient himself in Da Vinci's world. The analysis of the expression on the individual faces of the Apostles and of Christ makes evident Goethe's intense interest in physiognomies.

He recognized more clearly than any German before his time the problems of composition with Leonardo, and developed this theme using the *Last Supper* as an example. Thus Goethe is a fore-runner of the history of art in Germany, which was later to deal, on many occasions, with the problem of form in Leonardo and in general with the art of the Renaissance.

It is only natural, therefore, for Goethe to have been interested in Leonardo's studies of propor-tion and perspective, of the laws of organic construction and in general in the scientific side of Leo-nardo's personality as well as in his rules for art. Goethe thought too that he found in Leonardo corroboration of his own theories on the function of the eye, which was for him far more than an organ of sight. "The many gifts with which nature had endowed him were chiefly concentrated in his eye, for which reason, though he was capable of everything, he seems to us especially great as a painter."

But above and beyond all the individual elements Goethe noted in the world of Leonardo, he recognized the universal mind expressing itself in the most diversified manifestations and capable

Francesco Rustici – *Holy Family* – Marble sculpture – Florence, National Museum

---

[12] Johann Kaspar Lavater. *Physiognomische Fragmente zur Beförderung der Menschenkenntnis und Menschenliebe*, 1775-1778.

199

Figure of St. John preaching – Statue over north door of baptistery in Florence – Executed by Rustici with collaboration of Leonardo

Wax bust of young girl – Attributed to Leonardo – Lille, Museum

Francesco di Giorgio Martini – *Flagellation* – Perugia, National Gallery of Umbria

Rustici – *Moses Trampling on the Golden Calf* – Terra cotta – Florence, De Mari Collection

of finding unity in them. Goethe also believed that the external appearance of the artist corresponded to his inner spirit. This theory conformed with his own ideas on the superior individual, above and outside of time, fitting with Goethe's classical concept: "Of regular and well-formed features, he seemed a man who could serve as a model for all humanity."

At this point, we should recall that the Romantic Movement in Germany, though opposing Goethe's classicism to a certain extent, found its own ways to understand Leonardo. It was but natural that the romanticists, aspiring to the infinite and loving the enigmatic, should be drawn to an artist like Leonardo. In fact the veneration in which Da Vinci was held by the romanticists was enormous. They saw in him "the man of many arts and theories," whose depth and "great, open soul" they could never admire enough. The complex and enigmatic aspects of Leonardo have never ceased to exercise a magic attraction for romanticists.

The most noteworthy example of this exalted admiration is to be found in Wilhelm Heinrich Wackenroder's work whose title alone is characteristic of the romanticist mentality: "The model of a man at once expert in art and erudite, as seen in the life of Leonardo da Vinci, famous founder of the Florentine school." [13] Da Vinci's scientific research seems shrouded in mystery; yet in it, too, the romanticists admired the unity of Leonardo's life and the multiplicity of his artistic expression.

We would be justified in saying that Goethe and the German romanticists formed an entirely new idea of Leonardo, which was to become a part of the German artistic inheritance. And from this concept stem the scientific advances of the late eighteenth and nineteenth centuries.

Although every country has studied the magnificent body of material left to the world by Leonardo, it is not too much to say that German art history has brought an essential contribution to the study of Da Vinci. Leonardo is, as we have said, a living, active spiritual force in Germany. The inscrutable and mysterious elements in his nature, to which Burckhardt refers in the words quoted at the beginning of this essay, have never failed to fascinate Germans. In the endless research, the tireless aspiration of Leonardo, every German thinks that he finds some aspect of himself.

GERT ADRIANI

[13] Wilhelm Heinrich Wackenroder. *Herzensergiessungen eines kunstliebenden Klosterbruders*, publ. anonymously by L. Tieck, 1797; re-ed. by E. L. Schellenberg, Weimar, 1928.

THE MATHEMATICS OF LEONARDO

Speaking of Leonardo's mathematics should not lead us into the error of thinking that so great an intellect as his should have regarded the special study and activity he devoted to this branch of human knowledge as ends in themselves. There is always present in his mind an almost exclusively practical conception of the mathematical sciences, along with which he recognizes and grants their importance and above all their necessity.

I like to recall two very well-known sayings of Leonardo's in this connection: "Mechanics is the paradise of the mathematical sciences, because in it we come to the fruit of mathematics," and, "There is no certainty as to where one of the mathematical sciences cannot be applied, nor as to where mathematics is not connected with them."

Just because Leonardo's scientific activity always has a primarily practical and constructive character, and is dominated by a restless and almost anxious inventive spirit, it is difficult if not impossible to separate the results he arrived at in mathematics from those he achieved in other fields. The line of demarcation becomes cloudy in the concrete reality of a Leonardo who was a mathematical physicist, mathematical painter, and mathematical architect. In his complex personality as artist and scientist, mathematics as creation rather than as knowledge has the function of a tool.

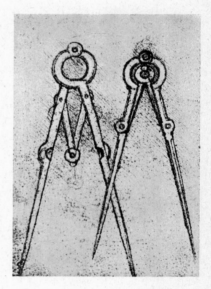

Compasses – Ms. H, fol. 108 v

For example, how can we avoid referring to his geometrical investigations aimed at the solution of problems of perspective and optics? And were not his special studies on lunes directed toward satisfying the artistic spirit of the great investigator rather than the research of the mathematician? I think that this is certainly one of the basic reasons why students of Leonardo have neglected an aspect recently illuminated by Marcolongo in particular.

Leonardo as a pure mathematician must be set in the framework of his time. There is no doubt that his culture and orientation were influenced by Luca Pacioli, the mathematician, whom he had the opportunity of knowing during his stay in Milan at the court of Ludovico il Moro. Leonardo's knowledge was limited to geometry; it does not appear that he concerned himself with algebra, although there has been some dispute with reference to the matter. However, even his geometrical knowledge was not very advanced and does not seem to have gone beyond the usual Euclidean notions of his time.

The conditions of the mathematical sciences in that epoch, and above all the prodigious and manifold activity that absorbed his energies unceasingly in other fields, are sufficient explanation for the fact that Leonardo, a self-taught man, who had only a rather elementary body of transmitted mathematical knowledge available to him in any case, did not reach the same degree of excellence here that makes him a source of pride for the human race in so many other fields.

An expression that I borrow from Leonardo himself well describes his production—"geometrical recreations." This is what a large part of his investigations amount to, after all; and like the consummate artist that he cannot avoid being, he always brings an acute aesthetic spirit to them. He liked to drill himself in elementary problems of plane geometry, which the painters of that time solved empirically, such as approximate constructions of regular polygons made by inscription in a circle, given the length of the side; the division of a circumference into equal parts; the division

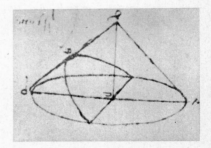

Construction of parabola as conic section – Cod. Atl., fol. 32 r-*a*

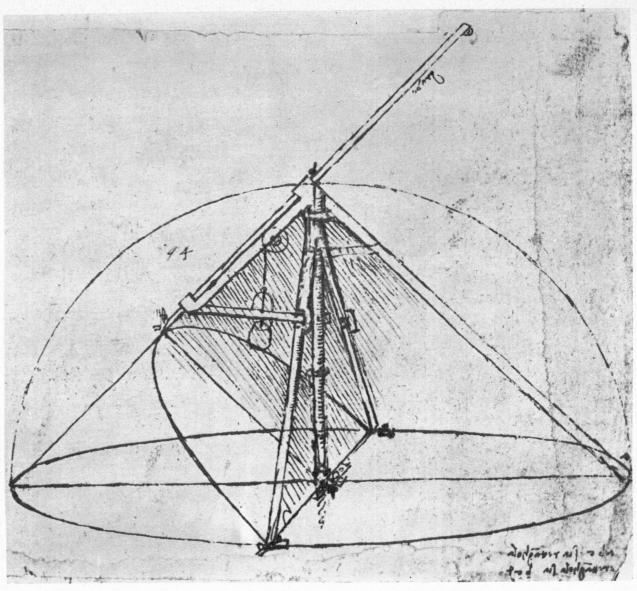

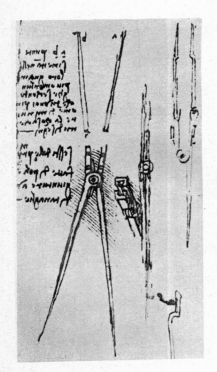

Parabolic compass – Cod. Atl., fol.
394 r-*a*

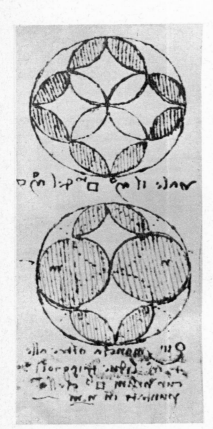

Studies on lunes – Cod. Atl., fol.
172 v-*a*

of a segment into equal parts; inscription of a regular octagon in a square, etc. In any event, there is more simple curiosity here than anything else.

Of much greater weight, and of definite originality, are his researches into the transformations of solids "without decrease or increment of volume"; this work was always suggested by practical needs. Leonardo seems to have had the intention of collecting these investigations and arranging them in a treatise in three books, which was never completed, if it was ever begun. It seems certain [1] that he drew his inspiration from the *De transformationibus geometricis* of Nicholas of Cusa (1401-1464). The transformations in question are those of a square or circular column into a cube; of a cube into a sphere; of a cylinder into another cylinder with a given different height; of a sphere into a pyramid; and, finally, of two spheres, one double the other, into a cylinder. He obtained the solutions to some of the problems by resorting to mean and fourth proportionals, and those of others by means of simple solid-geometry constructions.

He also made considerable progress in researches relating to the centers of gravity of various solid figures, in the course of which he brought out interesting geometrical properties, some of them original findings—for example, with reference to the geometry of the tetrahedron. Here Leonardo formulates a double theorem: "The center of all the weight of a pyramid is at a quarter of the axis of that pyramid, and if the axis is divided into four equal parts and you make the axes of the pyramid intersect two by two, this intersection will occur at the aforesaid point." According to an authoritative opinion, [2] Leonardo demonstrated this theorem "as we should today, with the elementary knowledge of Euclid's *Elements*."

In the same field of investigation we have the formulation of the principle that "any solid body that has its opposite parts similar and equal to one another will have its center of natural gravity coinciding with the center of its magnitude."

Now, it is obvious that in these investigations the geometrical study is merely accessory to the solution of mechanical problems; the very terms Leonardo adopts show an aim that is not merely speculative but experimental. Thus, for example, the determination of the center of gravity of an

---

[1] On all this see Roberto Marcolongo, *Studi vinciani*, Naples, 1937, p. 65.
[2] *Op. cit.*, p. 85.

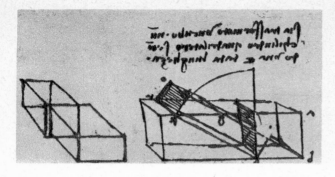

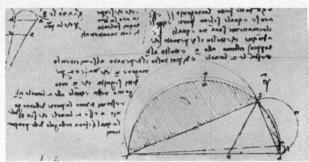

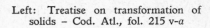

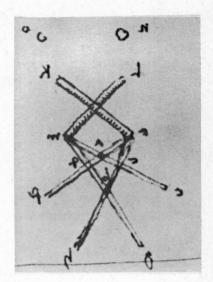

Studies on theory of shadows – Cod. Atl., fol. 177 r-*b*

isosceles trapezium is presented in the form of a calculation referring to a console table: "For any console table [top], the center of its gravity lies in the line dividing it into two equal parts when two of its sides are equidistant."

A conspicuous place in Leonardo's geometry is occupied by the studies on lunes that he developed in the *De ludo geometrico*. It is here particularly that he combines his artistic temperament with the gifts of a scientific researcher. Starting with the first lune of Hippocrates of Chios, he proceeds, with copious pen-and-ink illustrations, distributed over many codices, to formulate and demonstrate the theorem of the sum of two lunes constructed on the two legs of any right-angled triangle, which had been found some centuries earlier by Alhazen, the Arab mathematician and astronomer, but which, it seems certain, was not known at the time of Leonardo. The elegant combinations he derives from it are obtained chiefly by the simple method of adding or subtracting equal parts from a figure to be squared.

Roberto Marcolongo [3] has made a preliminary classification of the large number of diagrams. This comprises:

1. Diagrams derived from the first quadrable lune of Hippocrates;
2. Diagrams derived from ninety-degree angles whose two sides form a quadrant of a single circle;
3. Crescent-shaped lunes;
4. Studies on equivalence between crescents and circular segments;
5. Crescents derived from the equilateral triangle.

Even further removed from the field of mathematics, strictly so called, than the topics referred to above, is the solution of the problem known as the problem of Alhazen, or still better, the problem of "incidence," the solution of which was found by Leonardo with the aid of a special compass based on the use of an articulated parallelogram, which he was probably the first to employ. This problem as we know, concerns the path of a light ray from the source to the eye after reflection on the surface of a sphere. The complex reasoning adopted by the Arab mathematician was obscure to Leonardo in several places; and in any case he did not have enough mathematical knowledge to reach the result which was obtained only later by the Dutch mathematician Huygens. Leonardo could only follow the ingenious road that so often bore him fruitful results, the "instrumental way."

To conclude this rapid survey, brief reference must be made to the construction of mathematical instruments, i.e., those inventions which may in some way concern the field of geometry. Many students of Leonardo have dealt with these instruments; but whereas the nature of some, such as the parabolic and elliptic compasses, is not too definite and must be determined largely on the basis of interpretative inference, we have for others, such as the proportional compasses, illustrative drawings and satisfactory explanations. Actually, the proportional compasses are nothing more than reducing compasses, which are used to form a figure similar to another figure, and in a given proportion to it.

There is also some uncertainty as to the precise nature of the oval lathe referred to in Leonardo's manuscripts. Writers have labored the subject down to the present time, and not all of them share the opinion of Chasles [4] that Leonardo was the inventor of the dual method in kinematics, i.e., that he observed that in hypocycloid motion, which is the frictionless rolling of one circle on another, both situated on the same portion of the common tangent at the point of contact, a point bound to the moving circle describes an ellipse. This is the method on which the principle of the elliptic lathe is based.

In conclusion, we may point out that it adds nothing to the splendor of the many-sided figure of Leonardo to isolate him as a mathematician, especially in the modern sense of the term; his name cannot be handed down to posterity as a reformer of the mathematical sciences. However, we still cannot but recognize that here too, as in any other sector of the arts and sciences to which he turned, the traces of his creative genius can be seen, leaving the signs of his particular originality.

UMBERTO CISOTTI

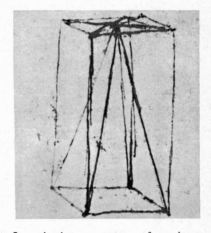

Investigations on centers of gravity – Cod. Atl., fol. 146 r-*c, d*

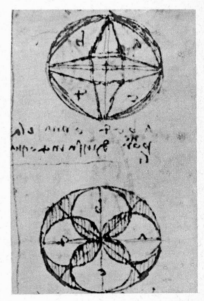

Study on equivalence of areas – Cod. Atl., fol. 85 r-*a*

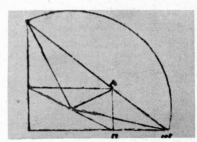

Studies on lunes – Cod. Atl., fol. 44 v-*a*

[3] *Op. cit.*, p. 58 f.
[4] Cited by Marcolongo, *op. cit.*, p. 98.

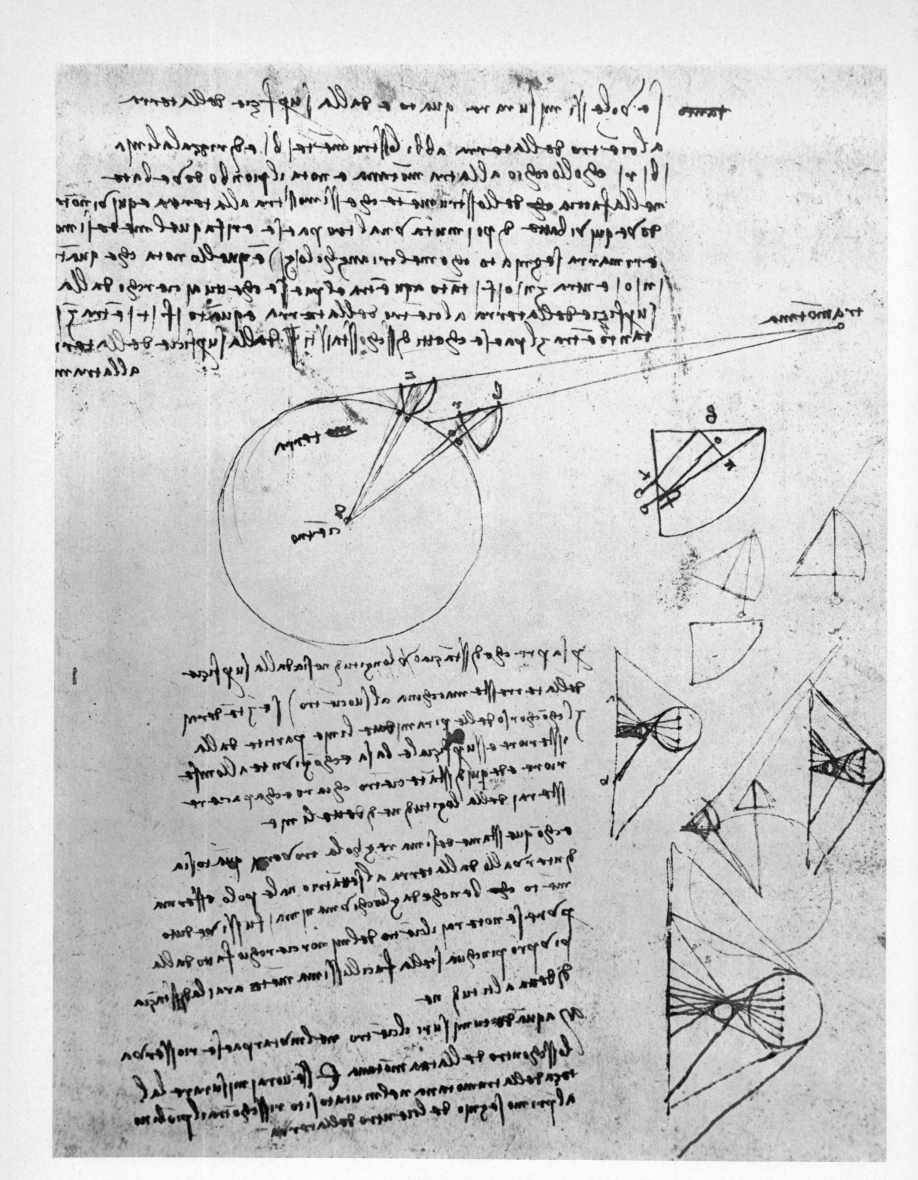

Study for measuring the earth, from surface to center — Windsor, Royal Collection, no. 19148

204

DA VINCI'S ASTRONOMY

Leonardo cannot in any way or for any reason be considered an astronomer. It was impossible for him to be one because of the very nature of his mind, which was essentially encyclopedic and tended to sudden leaps and fragmentary treatments.

In studying any branch of what can be known scientifically, it is necessary to have a mental discipline made up of orderliness and perseverance; but in studying the science of the heavens that discipline has to be present in its most rigorous form, and makes special demands, because of the vastness of the field of research and the difficulty of the problems to be attacked and solved. Astronomy requires systematic method, assiduous application, constant and regular work, and above all persistence in prosecuting investigations that may have to be conducted on a single topic for years and years. Moreover, the life of the astronomer should be as calm and serene as possible. Leonardo, occupied in a thousand of the most different kinds of work—he is a painter, a sculptor, and an architect, and deals with the art of war, with hydraulics, anatomy, mechanics, botany, geology, the flight of birds, and still other matters—for various reasons was unable to enjoy the tranquillity of a permanent residence. With a mind often troubled by adverse circumstances and the hostility of enemies, Leonardo was perhaps the worst-suited person in the world to apply himself to astronomical studies. The science of the skies absorbs all the activity of anyone who dedicates himself to it, and does not permit straying or absence of any kind. Copernicus, the great astronomer who was almost a contemporary of Leonardo, arrived at the enunciation of the heliocentric theory after a process of elaboration that lasted for decades, and filled his thoughts from the years of his youth down to his death. Newton was once asked how he was able to arrive at so many marvelous scientific results. "By always thinking of a single subject," he answered. The celebrated Italian cosmologist Paolo del Pozzo Toscanelli lived at the time of Leonardo, and Giovanni Müller, known as Regiomontanus, the equally celebrated German astronomer, had recently died: a brief glance at the work of these two investigators of the heavens is enough to realize the characteristic qualities that guided the working methods of the fifteenth-century astronomer. None of these qualities seems to be discoverable in Leonardo.

But if Leonardo was not an astronomer in the ordinary sense of the word, he was still not entirely a stranger to investigation of and meditation on some particular problems of the science of astronomy.

Terrestrial globe – Depressions — Dead Sea – Cod. Leices., fol. 36 r

In his days the telescope did not yet exist. It seems practically certain that this precious instrument is of purely Italian invention, and that in Italy it was constructed for the first time toward the end of the sixteenth century. If this supposition, which rests on trustworthy historical evidence, is accurate, as there is every reason to believe, we may conclude with practical certainty that the telescope had not yet been invented at the time of Leonardo. This does not exclude the fact that the properties of concave and convex lenses were known then, and were made use of for correcting and improving vision. It is very likely that the "glass" used by Leo X, who was an enthusiastic huntsman, to see distinctly at a distance during his hunting excursions, did not consist of a single lens,

Proportions of land and water – Cod. Leices., fol. 35 v

205

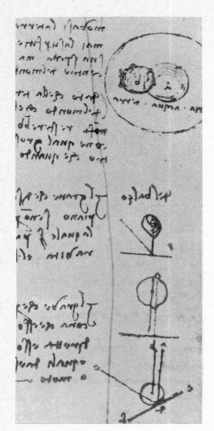

Studies on sphericity of earth and law of universal gravitation – Ms. F, fol. 22 v

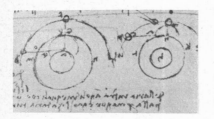

Studies to prove that earth is star – Ms. F, fol. 25 v

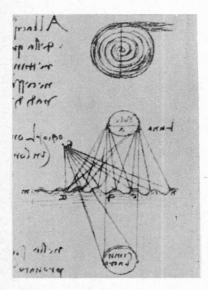

Astronomical studies – Ms. G. fol. 3 r

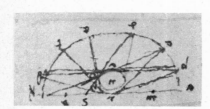

Studies regarding reflection of lunar and solar light – Cod. Arund., fol. 25 r

but of two, one biconcave held close to the eye and the other biconvex which was held as needed at a little distance. It is obvious that it would have been a very short step from this optical device to inventing the telescope, and the reason for its not having been made at that time is one of those many mysteries that encompass the history of science. At all events, it is our opinion that Leonardo, although he knew the properties of lenses, never constructed or possessed a genuine telescope. For if he had one available to him, he would not have failed to direct it at the skies, if only for curiosity's sake. By that he would have anticipated by about a century the memorable celestial discoveries made by Galileo in 1609-1610. It would be a deprecation of Leonardo's lofty genius to suppose that he had invented the telescope and then had not used it even once to look at the moon, Jupiter, and the stars of the Milky Way; for that would mean that he had not understood the importance and usefulness of the instrument. News of the celestial discoveries that he would inevitably have made with the telescope would have spread rapidly through Italy and Europe, arousing surprise and enthusiasm, and the echo of this memorable event would have come down to us, directly or indirectly. And this is without denying that he might have set it down, if it had happened, in one of his notebooks, which might then have failed to come down to us. For it is extremely probable that he would have told friends and acquaintances of the extraordinary discoveries; and they in turn would have spread the tidings to others, especially if they were astronomers or had some kind of interest in astronomical studies. But the history of astronomy has not handed down to us any hint, any slightest suspicion of this presumed invention or the discoveries to which it must undoubtedly have led.

Moreover, it would be very strange if Leonardo, who was concerned with military technology and weapons, had not realized from the very first moment of the invention what a powerful unsuspected aid in war an instrument like the telescope would have been, which could have discerned the enemy troops and their movements afar off, when they were invisible to the naked eye. And it would be strange as well that he should not have constructed more than one instrument, to bestow on the princes and petty nobles of the time, either as a compliment or for money. It is certain that history would not have failed to take note of this too, if only in an indirect manner.

All this leads to the conclusion that Leonardo did not invent and hence did not use the telescope. The manuscripts of his that have come down to us do not contain a single observation, celestial or terrestrial, that could even vaguely prove or support such a supposition. In the Arundel codex (fol. 104 r) there is a sketch of the face of the moon, obviously made by the naked eye or using some kind of lens to improve the view. If Leonardo had known the telescope at that time, he would not have drawn a sketch of that kind, but something that would have resembled the first hasty sketches of the surface of the moon that Galileo put down for his *Sidereus Nuncius*.

Several major celestial phenomena quite visible to the naked eye appeared during the lifetime of Leonardo (1452-1519). There is no reference to them in the Da Vinci manuscripts. We may recall, among other things, the great comet of 1472 (when Leonardo was twenty), which was accurately observed by the celebrated Regiomontanus, and those of the years 1491, 1500, 1506, and 1516. The comet of 1472, which the chroniclers of the time described in their usual style as "horrible and fearful," was so bright that it was seen distinctly (January 21, 1472) in the daytime, in the full light of the sun. It had a very long tail, and was visible for three months. It is impossible that Leonardo should not have seen it, as it is likewise impossible that he should not have seen any of the eclipses of the sun and moon that occurred in Italy and France between 1460 and 1518. The eclipses of the sun were recorded for the years 1460, 1478, 1485, 1502, 1518 as reaching a maximum phase above seven tenths in Italy and France.

But although the Da Vinci manuscripts do not contain references to astronomical observations, arguments and speculations of an astronomical nature are sometimes found there. Leonardo is not always clear in his thought, and is not always of the opinion on a given subject. He often contradicts himself, and not infrequently presents things as novelties that were quite well known. His astronomical speculations, with a few exceptions of which we shall speak presently, are not in advance of the views that were generally held in his time. According to Leonardo and the old Ptolemaic astronomy that still prevailed in the fifteenth century, the earth is at the center of its elements. The sun revolves around it, as does the moon. Leonardo maintains, correctly, that the sun is in reality larger than it appears, and attacks Epicurus, who maintained the opposite. But Epicurus was never regarded as an authority in astronomy, neither among the scientists of antiquity nor still less among those of the Middle Ages, and in Leonardo's day, and for a long time before that, everybody believed without question that the sun was at least as large as the earth. For example, Regiomontanus, about 1470, estimated the angular radius of the sun as equal to 16' (a value that is fairly close to correct), with a parallax of 3'. Assuming, with Ptolomy, that the circumference of the earth was 180 thousand stadia, and taking the measurements given by Regiomontanus, the size of the sun would come out considerably more than that of the earth. Furthermore, various astronomical treatises of the time—virtually all of which bore the generic title of *Sphaera*, the best-known of them being that of Sacrobosco [John Holywood]—state that *"sol in se continet terrae magnitudinem 166,"* in other words that the volume of the sun was 166 times that of the earth. We know today that the ratio between

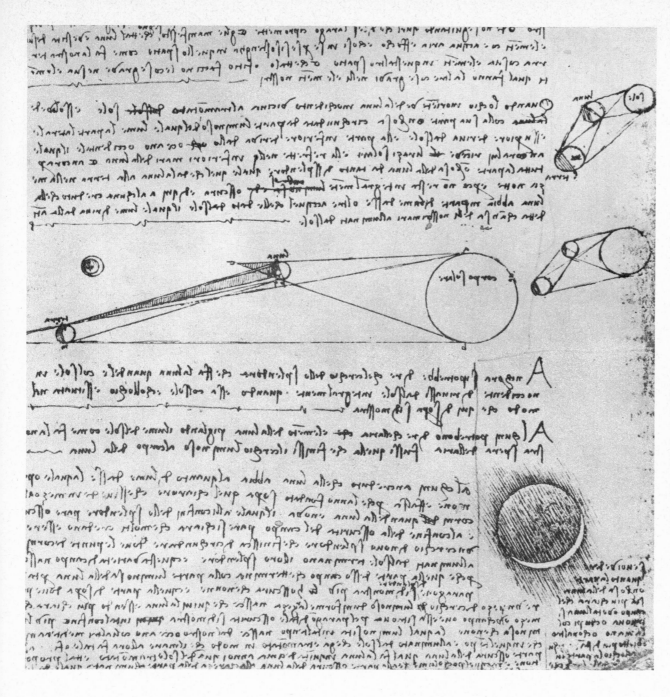

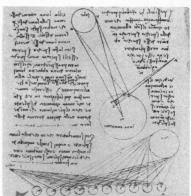

Eclipses of moon – Cod. Leices., fol. 2 r

Moon reflecting light of sun – Cod. Arund., fol. 28 r

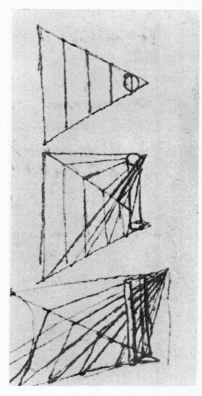

Another drawing regarding studies of moon – Perspective of mirrors – Cod. Arund., fol. 94 r

the volume of the sun and that of the earth is not 166 but 1,300,000 so that the figure of 166 was far from correct, but this does not do away with the fact that the conception that the sun was larger than our globe had been fully and officially accepted since the Middle Ages, and was commonly granted and taught in Leonardo's time.

The twinkling of the stars is a phenomenon known to everybody. In the winter, on a cold calm night, it strikes the eye of anyone observing the celestial hemisphere even accidentaly. The stars look like diamonds, whose light is subject to a rapid twinkling, because of the intermittent emission of light rays. Aristotle gave an erroneous explanation of this, attributing its cause to the weakness of the sight as compared to the distance of the stars. This explanation was universally accepted, and handed down without discussion, until the great Arab philosopher Averroës gave a very nearly exact explanation, attributing the phenomenon of twinkling to the atmosphere and its irregularities. Leonardo follows Aristotle when he says: "First define the eye, then show how the oscillation of some stars comes from the eye, and why the oscillation of those stars is greater in some than in others, and how the rays of the stars arise in the eye." Accordingly, Leonardo did not know the explanation given by Averroës, nor that of Alhazen and Witelo, and stuck to the common opinion which was based on the authority of Aristotle.

Detail examination of the astronomical passages that are found in the Da Vinci manuscripts would require much more space than we have been granted in this publication. We therefore feel it advisable to discuss only two, which are the only ones among all those referring to astronomical subjects that say something really new: two grains of gold in a great deal of sand.

In Leonardo's time it was held that the earth was at the center of the universe, steadfast and immutable down through the ages; *fundasti terram super stabilitatem suam, non inclinabitur in saeculum saeculi*, says the Psalmist. There is no movement of diurnal rotation nor of annual revolution. It is true that there had already been a philosopher, Cardinal Nicholas of Cusa (Cusanus), who had maintained that the earth moved; but his views on this point do not seem to have any value except

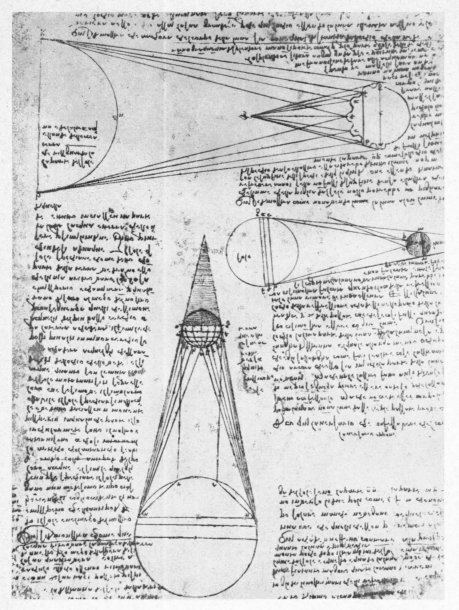

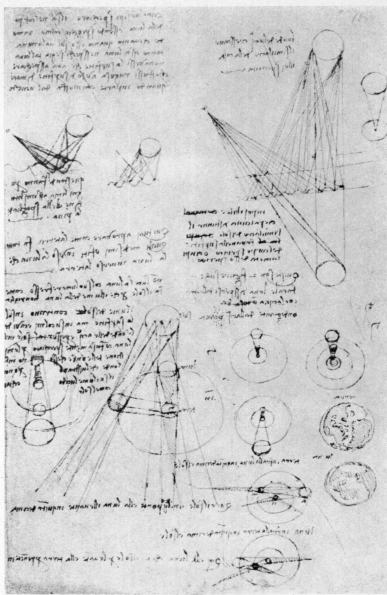

that of mere philosophical, or rather metaphysical speculations. Moreover, it seems very unlikely that Leonardo ever read the *De docta ignorantia* of Cusanus; and we voice this doubt although we are aware that it contradicts the thesis advanced by a master of the history of science, Duhem, who is certain that the works and ideas of Cusanus had a considerable influence on Leonardo's mind. Be that as it may, Leonardo, in a passage discussing the fall of bodies, upholds the notion of the diurnal motion of the earth. The passage dates from 1510. So far as we know, he never returned to this important subject. If he had only developed it or at least stressed it, he would have been able to deduce other brilliant conclusions from it. He is silent as to the motion of revolution of the earth about the sun, and the astronomical drawings of Codex Arundel (fol. 104 r) assure us that he did not admit it.

The second passage deserving mention has reference to the explanation of the gray light on the dark hemisphere of the moon. Immediately after the new moon, a more or less whitish or grayish light is seen on the part of the lunar disk not directly illuminated by the sun. The explanations given by the ancients are rather few in number. Cleomedes attributed it to a certain transparency of the lunar globe. And although this interpretation is in contradiction with what is observed during total solar eclipses, it enjoyed general approval for many centuries, so that Witelo still emphasized it in the thirteenth century. Leonardo senses the true cause of the phenomenon, and says correctly that it consists in the reflection of the light the earth sends to the moon after receiving it from the sun. The reasoning is not quite correct, and the premise he starts from is false, but the conclusion he comes to is exact. Moestlin, Kepler's teacher, later came to the same explanation as did Leonardo.

We conclude by saying that although Leonardo cannot be considered as being an astronomer, still his speculations on some celestial phenomena deserve to be recalled, without giving them any excessive importance.

PIO EMANUELLI

THE PHYSICS OF DA VINCI

Some fine pages have been written on Leonardo's physics, but it cannot be said that we have any exhaustive treatment of the subject, and perhaps the time has not yet come to write it. The Da Vinci manuscripts are now all, or virtually all, available to students, but the problem of their source is still partially unexplored, and the problem of their chronology is a hopeless puzzle. The best that can be done is not to attach excessive importance to questions of priority and chronology, and to try to judge Leonardo from within; in fact, I believe that to be the only solution. There are some questions that are insoluble but, at least so far as Leonardo is concerned, it is not absolutely essential to solve them.

Leonardo Da Vinci derives from the Greeks, the Arabs, Jordanus Nemorarius, Biagio da Parma, Albert of Saxony, Buridan, the doctors of Oxford, Duhem's unknown precursor; but the ideas he derives are more or less open to question. What is his alone, and new, is the curiosity concerning every natural phenomenon and the ability to see with the naked eye things that are very difficult to see even with the aid of instruments. This powerful and unique spirit of observation differentiates him from his predecessors and from Galileo. His writings are essentially not ordered; to attempt to translate them into treatises of purest modern science is to distort them. Leonardo—we must say this emphatically—is not a super-Galileo; he is a great intellect who is curious about nature, not a scientist philosopher. In some respects perhaps he even goes beyond Galileo, but he does so in a different spirit. Where Galileo would write a treatise, Leonardo writes a hundred aphorisms or a hundred notations of facts; while Galileo is so consistent that consistency sometimes becomes a sort of obsession with him, Leonardo watches and makes note, without worrying too much about theories. Many times he sets down the fact without even attempting to explain it. (This is one of his merits: when it is impossible to make a good theory, it is better to get along without any.)

Since it is impossible to study all of Da Vinci's physics within the space limits assigned to me (and I should be trespassing on the fields of collaborators, into the bargain), I shall confine myself to saying a few words on some of the most important or most neglected aspects.

Leonardo made a contribution of the first magnitude to the fundamental principles of mechanics. He can be said to have contributed to all three of the principles. He was not aware of the second principle, since he always remained faithful to the Aristotelian theory that was later to be demolished by Galileo in the dialogues of the *Massimi sistemi* and the *Nuove scienze;* but some properties of the inclined plane discovered by him are in conformity with Galileo's law. His contribution to the first principle is so important that many speak of the principle of Leonardo da Vinci instead of the principle of inertia. It has also been said that Galileo did not succeed in rising to the degree of generalization attained by Leonardo. "Every motion," says the *Codex on the Flight of Birds* (fol. 12 r), "tends to maintain itself, that is, every body that is moved always moves as long as the impression of the motive force continues in it." And in the Codex Atlanticus (fol. 109 v-*a*) he says: "Every body will follow its path in a straight line as long as the nature of the violence done by its motive force persists in it."

Here we undoubtedly have the principle of inertia of classical mechanics, but it is complicated by the theory of impetus developed by Buridan and Albert of Saxony. It is true, as Marcolongo

Leonardo's experiment on heat with *ampolls* or *amola,* according his own words: "As regards the proof that heat draws moisture, this is proved as follows: Heat a flask and put it in a dish with the mouth downward and put a burning coal in it, and you will see that the moisture, in order to follow the heat, will climb and fill the flask with water, and the air that was within the flask will escape by the mouth of that flask" – Ms. A, fol. 56 r

"To raise a heavy body with fire, as a cornet or cupping glass, and the vacuum vessel should be an ell [wide] and 10 long, and strong, and let the fire be from underneath as in a bombard, and suddenly this orifice closes, and immediately afterward the one above; then the bottom will come up, which has a leather contrivance like a very powerful bellows, and this is a way of simulating every great thing" – Ms. F, fol. 16 v

"Very rapid rubbing together of two dense bodies generates fire" – Ms. F, fol. 85 v

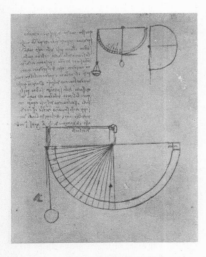

Drawings for calculating balance – Cod. Ashb., I, fol. 8 r

remarks, that this theory more or less implicitly contains the idea that the motive power communicated by the mover to the object moved may be neutralized by the passive resistances, whereas in the absence of perturbing factors it should persist indefinitely, but it is also undeniable that these consequences, which seem obvious to us, are not granted by Leonardo, who is convinced, with Aristotle, that a vacuum is impossible. While Galileo says that although a mover is necessary to start the motion, it suffices for its continuance that there should be no opposition, Leonardo writes (Ms. A, fol. 22 v): "Against perpetual motion.—No inanimate object will move of itself; hence if it moves, that motion will be due to an unequal power, that is, unequal in time or movement, or of unequal weight, and once the impulse of the first mover has come to an end, the second will cease at once." These words have an Aristotelian flavor. Leonardo believes firmly, with classical mechanics, that bodies tend to persist indefinitely in a state of rest if no external cause intervenes to set them in motion; but, with Aristotle, and common experience, he believes that all movement is temporary and cannot be "perpetual." The idea that in a vacuum movement could be endless does not come to his mind, for he does not believe that a vacuum can exist. In the same manuscript of the Institut de France, and on the same sheet, Leonardo has said that if a force moves a body, it finally exhausts itself and then the body stops. "Hence no object that is moved can have an operation of long duration; for when the causes are absent, so are the effects." One of the most original aspects of Galileo's method was that it abstracted from friction and the resistance of the medium.

The most important contribution that Leonardo made to the laws of motion seems to me to be in connection with "Newton's principle," or the principle of reaction. "An object offers as much resistance to the air as the air offers to the object" (Cod. Atl., fol. 381 v-a). "It is as hard to move the oar against the stationary water as it is to move the water against the stationary oar" (Cod. Atl., fol. 175 r-c). "The operation of the motion of water against the motionless air is equal to that of the air against the motionless water" (Cod. Arund. 263, fol. 135 r). For even greater generality, a Newtonian generality in fact, consider this passage (Cod. Arund. 263, fol. 85 r), which I do not see cited: "Every body goes in a direction opposite to the place from which it is driven by the object that strikes it... The body strikes the object in the same measure as the object strikes the said body." Here we no longer have the air and the object, the water and the oar, the water and other water, or the air and the bird, but bodies in general; and Leonardo says clearly that the action is equal to and contrary to the reaction.

Of course, Newton's contribution is not diminished, as Galileo's is not, by Leonardo's anticipation of the principle of inertia. The two creators of classical mechanics do not merely enunciate the principles and make modest application of them: they make those principles the foundations of their systems of the world. The only possible conclusion is that reached by Marcolongo: "Leonardo thus had a clear idea of the first and third laws of motion"—and, I add, much clearer in regard to the third than to the first—"and this, it seems to me, should give him one of the outstanding places among the predecessors of Galileo and Newton." I add further that if Leonardo had freed himself of every residue of Aristotelianism as regards the principle of inertia, he might have anticipated Galileo's principle, and decisively and radically abandoned Aristotle's mechanics.

Leonardo anticipated the fundamental experiment on the central impact of elastic bodies: "There are two kinds of percussion, namely, when the object flees from the moving thing that has struck it, and when the moving thing rebounds backward from the object that is struck. In the first case the object that is struck may be equal in weight and size to the moving thing that strikes it. In percussion of this kind the object that is struck leaves the moving thing that struck it in its place, while for itself it goes through the remainder of the motion left in the first moving thing" (Cod. Arund. 263, fol. 83 v). It is not explicitly stated that this relates to central impact of elastic bodies (which is why I have spoken of an anticipation, and not of a discovery), but it is understood that the reference is to a precise experiment. Leonardo knew that the result is different in the case of inelastic bodies. He says (Ms. A, fol. 32 r): "If you take a small portion of a uniform kind of fresh earth, and make it into a little ball with your hands, and throw it into the original pile of earth, you will see that the said ball will penetrate into it, partially preserving its round form in the portion that sinks in."

Likewise in Ms. A (fol. 31 r) Leonardo says that a blow struck on a stone in the water kills fish in the immediate neighborhood, and that a blow struck on any hard and heavy body hurts things in surrounding bodies, whether they are dense or rare. It will be seen that these are qualitative anticipations of Pascal's principle.

Leonardo knew Archimedes' principle and was able to apply it (although he held that ice floats on water even though it is "denser" than water); he knew the theory of the syphon as well as the theory of communicating vessels, even where the liquids are of different densities; he had some idea of capillary phenomena.

I shall not take up his studies on the flight of birds and on human flight, merely mentioning his research on the parachute and on the screw as a propelling instrument. I shall also pass over his studies on simple machines and on the polygon of forces, his anticipation of the principle of virtual work, and his writings on hydraulics and meteorology.

In relation to optics I instance the fact that Leonardo was aware of the camera obscura, of the persistence of images on the retina, of the phenomena of contrast; he knew that an inverted image can be obtained with a convergent lens, and that it can be rectified by means of another lens; he

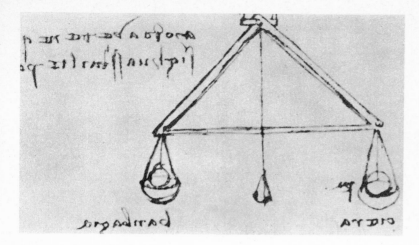
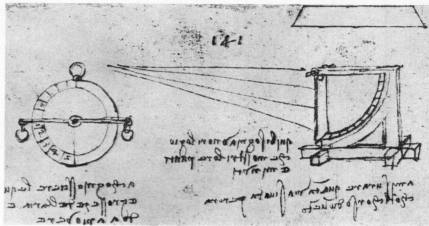

studied the eye and binocular vision, colors, the theory of shadows, perspective. He knew the theory of reflection from plane mirrors. He did not succeed in theoretically solving the problem of reflection from a spherical mirror, but solved it by means of an instrument that has been reconstructed by Marcolongo. I also mention his famous saying, "Make glasses to see the moon enlarged," which is one of Galileo's great themes.

His finest discoveries in optics are those relating to the blue color of the sky and the blue appearance of smoke, and to the colors that have the most blue in them (Cod. Leic., fol. 4 r, 20 r, 36 r; Ms. L, fol. 75). "I say that the blue that the air exhibits is not its own color but is caused by the hot humidity, evaporated into most minute and insensible atoms, which receives the percussion of the sun's rays and becomes luminous under the darkness of the immense shadows of the region of fire that covers it over from above; and this will be seen by anyone, as I saw it, who will go up Mon Boso [Monte Rosa]... As an example of the same sort as the color of the air, we may cite the smoke coming from dry wood, which seems very blue as it leaves the chimney, when it is between the eye and a dark place; but when it rises and lies between the eye and the illuminated air, it immediately appears to have a bluish color; and this happens because it no longer has darkness behind it, but luminous air instead. And if the smoke comes from green and young wood, it will not tend to blue because, being transparent and full of excess moisture, it acts like a condensed cloud, taking on lights and shadows with definite outlines, as if it were a solid body. Air acts in the same way if it has been rendered white by excess of moisture, and dark—of a dark-blue color—by a too slight infusion of heat; and this is sufficient for us with respect to defining the heat of the air. Although it could also be said that if the air had this transparent blue as its natural color, it would follow that where a greater quantity of air lies between the eye and the element of fire, its blue should appear darker in that place, as we see in blue glass and in sapphires, which show darker the larger they are. And the air acts quite to the contrary in this case, for where it interposes in largest amount between the eye and the sphere of fire, there it shows itself whitest, and this occurs toward the horizon; and the smaller the amount of air interposed between the eye and the sphere of fire, the more darkly blue it appears, even when we are in the low plains. It therefore follows from what I say that the air receives the blue color by means of the corpuscles of humidity, which receive the luminous rays of the sun. Also, see the difference in the atoms of dust and the atoms of smoke in the sunbeams that pass through holes in walls in dark places: the first ray will seem to be ashen, and the other ray, in fine smoke, will seem to be of a beautiful blue. Also note that in the dark shadows of mountains far from the eye the air between the eye and those shadows seems very blue, while on the luminous portion of the mountain it does not change much from its original color."

Excess of smoke interferes with the perfection of the blue, while too little smoke does not form the color. To prove that the air seems blue because it has shadows behind it, the following experiment may be made: "Let smoke be made from dry wood in small amount; let the sun's rays strike this smoke; and behind this smoke place a piece of black velvet on which the sun does not fall, and you will see all the smoke that comes between the eye and the darkness of the velvet shows a beautiful blue color; and if you put white cloth in place of the velvet, the smoke is ashen gray. Just as water drawn up as atoms in a dark place where the sphere of the sun passes will make the sunbeam blue, and especially so if that water is distilled, so fine smoke makes blue. This is said in order to show that the blue of the air is caused by the darkness that is above it; and the examples given may be cited to anyone who has not confirmed the experiment of Mon Boso." Leonardo writes further: "Of the colors that are not blue, the closer they are to black, the more will they partake of blue when seen at a long distance. And conversely they will the more retain their own colors when seen at a great distance, the more they are unlike the said black. Hence the green of the fields will change into blue more than yellow or white does, and pure red changes less than green."

I have quoted these passages virtually in full, because I am sure that without the text in front of him the reader would find strange what I am about to say, whereas now it will seem natural. Leonardo anticipated Lord Rayleigh's theory regarding the blue color of the sky, and practiced the

Left: Hygroscope utilizing cotton wool and wax – "Method of seeing when the weather is turning bad" – Cod. Atl., fol. 8 v-b

Right: "To know the qualities and density of the air, and when it is going to rain" – Hygroscope resembling type drawn on sheet at Louvre (see below) – Study of anemometer – Cod. Atl., fol. 249 v-a

Hygroscope consisting of rod oscillating about pivot, with sponge at one end and wax counterweight at other – Drawn on sheet containing studies for *Last Supper* – Paris, Louvre, drawing no. 2022

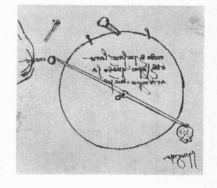

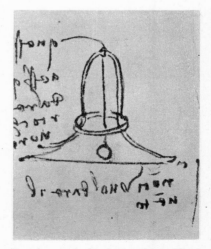

Drawing made by Leonardo da Vinci showing a study on Inclinometer Apparatus planned for finding inclination of his flying machine – Cod. Atl., fol. 381 r-a

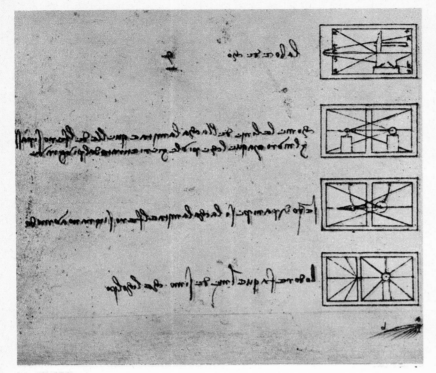

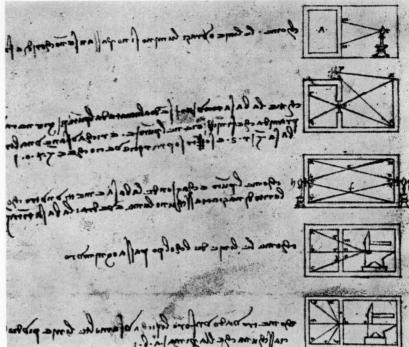

"How the attraction of the lodestone and that of iron pass the wall, but the lighter object is drawn by the heavier. When they are of equal weight, lodestone and iron attract each other in the same way" – Cod. Atl., fol. 126 r-*a*

Drawing made by Leonardo Da Vinci showing how he conceived an apparatus for testing expansion of steam – Christian Huygens and Papin were to adopt an identical arrangement in their engines – Cod. Leic., fol. 10 r

dark-field vision that is essential in ultramicroscopy. I point out that, according to Lord Rayleigh, the blue color of the sky is an effect of selective diffusion. The white light, encountering "insensible granules," or "most minute and insensible atoms," such as the molecules of air or smoke or fine water vapor, is partly diffracted around them and in part dispersed or scattered. The radiations that are most easily scattered are those whose wave length is small in comparison to the dimensions of the particles, namely, violet and blue light; the least dispersed radiations are the red and the yellow. Every corpuscle is thus turned into a little blue star by the light that is diffused. Leonardo did not know nor suspect the existence of diffraction phenomena, which were to be discovered later by Grimaldi, but he saw everything. And he knew that if we desire ho see clearly the faint blue light scattered by fine smoke, we must look at it against a dark background and not against a white field. Today we know why: the light scattered by the white screen would mask the effect.

In the other branches of physics, the contributions of Leonardo are not of basic importance but a good deal more noteworthy than is usually believed.

He knew (Cod. Atl., fol. 41, 126 r-*a*) that the action between the lodestone and iron is reciprocal, a matter that is not as evident as it seems to us today, if we consider that Albertus Magnus, as Govi observes, writes in his work on stones and minerals: "One of my comrades, a curious investigator and experimenter on new things, told me that the Emperor Frederick had a lodestone that did not attract iron and was attracted by it instead." Leonardo knew that the action is exerted even through a wall and says, in conformity with the principle of reaction that he considers as applying in this case as well, that when they are of equal weight, "lodestone and iron attract each other in the same way."

There is a curious reflection entitled "Perspective and Motion" (Ms. A, fol. 26 v): "Every body that moves with velocity appears to tint its path with the likeness of its color. This proposition is seen from experience, for when a lightning bolt moves among the dark clouds with the speed of its serpentine flight, its entire path appears like a luminous snake. And similarly, if you move a burning coal in a circular movement, its entire way will seem to be a burning circle. And this is more a matter of the perceptive faculty than of the judgment." This is curious, not so much because of the experiences of the persistence of images and their skillful interpretation, but because the lightning is thought of as a heavy body, and hence contradicts the law of inertia by its serpentine flight. "Every movement arising out of a free movement," Leonardo says in another place (Cod. Forster, II, fol. 32 r), "goes along or keeps to the line of the motion that generates it, except for the lightning that descends from the clouds." (It will be seen that the principle of inertia has exceptions that Leonardo does not take the trouble to explain; and this is not strange, given his point of view. This is one more proof that the principle as he conceives it is not quite the same as that of Galileo and Newton.)

There is an interesting experiment on heat, dealing with a flask—an *ampolla*, or *amola*, as Leonardo writes it, using a word not in the dictionaries (Ms. A, fol. 56 r): "As regards the proof that heat draws moisture, this is proved as follows: Heat a flask and put it in a dish with the mouth downward and put a burning coal in it, and you will see that the moisture, in order to follow the heat, will climb and fill the flask with water, and the air that was within the flask will escape by the mouth of that flask." The interpretation of this experiment does not present us with any difficulties today. As the flask is heated, the air expands and escapes; later it contracts, and the

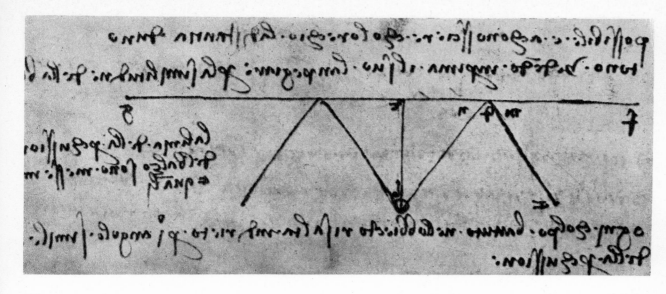

water tends to fill the flask by reason of atmospheric pressure. Obviously, however, Leonardo could not furnish the explanation. A similar experiment is described without interpretation in Ms. F (fol. 16 v), in which Leonardo shows how a heavy body can be lifted by means of fire.

The idea of heat following moisture [?] made Leonardo wonder whether heat might cause iron to become magnetic. He says (Ms. F, fol. 10 v): "Test whether hot iron attracts iron filings to itself." He thus poses, in his own way, the problem of the relationship between temperature and magnetism.

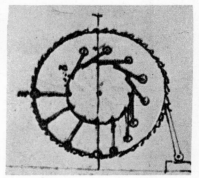

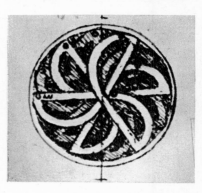

Leonardo knew that "fire, or other heat, lessens the weight of moisture and makes it lighter than air" (Cod. Atl., fol. 279 r-*b*); that "where flame is generated, there wind is generated around it" (Cod. Atl., fol. 237 v-*a*); that "very rapid rubbing together of two dense bodies generates fire" (Ms. F, fol. 85 v). And he wrote those lucid words (Cod. Atl., fol. 76 v-*a*) which any physicist today could repeat: "If you will heat water made turbid by mud, it will clear up at once; and this takes place because, as the water is heated, it increases, and as it increases it tends to rarefy, and being rarefied it does not support things heavier than itself that are within it."

In acoustics Leonardo gives many observations and experiments, from which a treatise could be written. In Ms. A (fol. 19 r) he says that "it is possible to tell the distance of thunder by the ear after seeing its lightning flash, from its resemblance to the tone of an echo"—a fruitful idea. He knew that sound is reflected in conformity with the same law that governs elastic vibrations and light rays; he had a clear idea regarding pitch in sounds and sensed its laws; he was aware of the phenomena of resonance and indicated experiments (Ms. A, fol. 22 v) that are still repeated today in school courses. "A blow struck on a bell," he wrote, "will answer and move to some extent another bell similar to itself; and a lute string played on will respond and move another similar string of similar tone in another lute; and you may see this by placing a straw on the string that resembles the sounded string." For bringing out the presence of vibrations, he was aware not only of the device of the rider but also of the powder method that Chladni was to employ so much: "If you beat a flat board, you will see the dust on it come together in little heaps" (Ms. A, fol. 32 v).

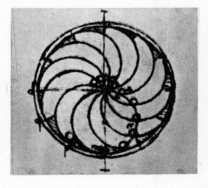

Graphic researches on impossibility of perpetual motion – Cod. Forst., II, fol. 90 v, 91 r, v

He often asked whether many small voices put together would make a sound like a large one (Ms. A, fol. 23 v), and whether a bell sounding two miles away would, if converted into many small bells sounded all at once, be heard at the same distance (Cod. Forst., II, fol. 32 v). His answer was in the negative: the small voices and the small bells would carry for a shorter distance. He was right, because the vibrations would necessarily interfere, and this would partly weaken the sound.

I should like to conclude with the remark in which Leonardo shows (Cod. Forst., II, fol. 133 r, 132 v) that a perfect circle cannot be made with a compass. If you grant, he says, that the point must be worn down by long motion, it must be granted too "that a part will be consumed in a part of this time, and that the indivisible will give a beginning to this consumption in an indivisible time. And likewise, the opposite point of this compass, which turns on itself at the center of this circle, undergoes consumption of itself and of the spot supporting it, at every step of the movement; so that we shall say that the end of the circle will not meet its beginning, and the end of the line comes by an insensible amount closer to the center of the circle in question."

This is a thought that would have pleased Galileo and Volta greatly. It is subtle, but has nothing sophistical or paradoxical about it; the assertion that the point must be insensibly worn down in an infinitesimal time is modern.

Leonardo's language too is admirable—lucid, close to the idea, like his drawings and paintings. And this is natural, because Leonardo's science is an aspect of this vision of the world, and surprising, as is his art.

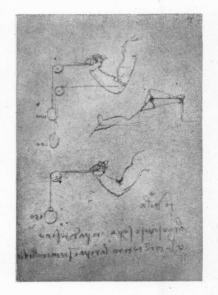

Dynamometer for muscles – Ms. H, fol. 44 r

SEBASTIANO TIMPANARO

213

PRAYER – I obey thee, Lord, first for the love that I should reasonably bear thee, second because thou canst shorten or lengthen the life of men – Cod. Forst. III, fol. 29 r – Drawing in Vienna, Albertina Museum

214

DA VINCI'S PHILOLOGY

"The Philological Section of the Leonardo Exposition has undertaken to re-examine the question of Leonardo da Vinci's *grammar* and *dictionary*": these were the words with which Luigi Sorrento began his essay, "Da Vinci's Philology," in the first edition (1939) of this book. In it he was kind enough to announce a forthcoming article by the undersigned dealing with the so-called "dictionary," while he would confine himself to a discussion of the "grammar." My work became much more extensive than had been foreseen, and was published in two volumes (at different times) constituting a critical edition of all Leonardo's linguistic notes, along with a detailed examination of the various problems connected with them.[1] The results of this study have put the problem in such a new light that a complete revision of Sorrento's essay has been required, although the title has been kept for reasons of historical continuity, and as a tribute to the memory of the late scholar. I should point out, however, that despite the qualifications stated by Sorrento himself (for whom Leonardo "on the whole exhibits the characteristics of a philologist, not specifically in the determinate sense of the word as used in modern times, but as one who was always conscious of the importance of the scientific study and the expressive value of language"), this title has always seemed to me a little excessive, for it would still permit the attribution to Leonardo of some kind of theoretical and scientific approach to linguistic problems, whereas his notes always show a practical and personal purpose. This is not of course to deny categorically that Leonardo ever thought of the possibility that his notes might be useful to other people as well; but we are unable to see any definite proof that this was so. Moreover, although we do find theoretical statements in Leonardo, such as, "The derivation of Latin words is necessary to... good grammarians," we must recognize that these are passing thoughts set down in quite different connections, and it would be exaggerating them grossly to try to make them the basis for some philological doctrine said to be held by Da Vinci.

In 1939 the problem we were studying appeared in the following light. There exist a quantity of notes by Leonardo dealing with the study of Latin and Italian grammar and vocabulary. What was the purpose for which they were compiled? Was Leonardo planning some kind of grammatical treatise or dictionary, or was he studying language from a philosophical and philological point of view, or was he merely looking after his own literary education? Between 1872 and 1918 various scholars, to the accompaniment of some violent polemics, had proposed various solutions for our problem, which may be summed up in three basic positions: that this work was for self-instruction (Solmi), that it was philosophical (Geymüller), that it was didactic, for the use of others (Govi, Beltrami, Morani, Olschki). The last position had decidedly come out ahead in the contest, and it seemed to be universally admitted that Leonardo had arranged materials for the first grammar and the first dictionary of the Italian language.[2] It is important to remember, however, that most scholars approached Leonardo with their minds prepared to admire the "universal genius and forerunner," and that in such a euphorically heightened atmosphere the picture of a Leonardo studying para-

FABLES AND JESTS

THE CRAB – The crab stayed under a rock to catch fish that swam under it. The flood came, ruinously bringing down rocks that crushed the crab with their rolling. – Cod. Arund., fol. 42 v – Drawing in Cologne, Wallraf-Richartz Museum

THE FALCON AND THE DUCK – The falcon, indignant because the duck had escaped and hidden from it by diving under the surface of the water, wanted to do likewise plunging down under the water, and as its feathers got wet in this way, it was caught there, and the duck, rising in the air, mocked the drowning falcon – Cod. Atl., fol. 67 v-*b* – Drawing at Windsor, Royal Collection, no. 12395

---

[1] A. Marinoni, *Gli appunti grammaticali e lessicali di Leonardo da Vinci*: Vol. I, *L'educazione letteraria di Leonardo*, Milan, 1944; Vol. II, *Testo critico*, Milan, 1952.

[2] The reader will excuse me from citing a long list of publications to be found in C. Trabalza's "History of Italian Grammar" in *Enciclopedia italiana*, s.v. *Lessicografia*.

215

THE DOG AND THE FLEA – While a dog was sleeping on a sheepskin, one of his fleas smelled the odor of the greasy wool and thought that this would be a place where he could live a better life than by feeding off the dog, and be safer from the dog's teeth and claws, and at once he left the dog and went into the thick wool and began with hard labor to try to get to the roots of the hairs: but after much sweating he found this vain, for the hairs were so thick that they touched, and there was no place for the flea to test the skin; hence, after long trouble and toil, he began to wish to go back to his dog, but the dog had gone, and he, after long regrets and bitter tears, died of hunger – Cod. Atl., fol. 19 r-a – Drawing at Windsor, Royal Collection

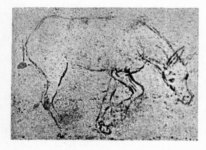

THE ASS AND THE ICE – A donkey fell asleep on the ice of a deep lake. His heat dissolved the ice and the ass went down into the water, to his loss, and was drowned at once – Cod. Atl., fol. 67 v-b – Drawing at Windsor, Royal Collection, no. 12362

THE FIG TREE – The fig tree was barren and without fruit, and it was ignored by everyone. Its desire was to be praised by men for the fruit it bore, but instead it was bent and broken by them – Codex Atlanticus, fol. 76 r-a – Drawing at Windsor, Royal Collection, no. 12644 r

digms of verbs and the "parts of speech" *for his own benefit* had a rather chilling effect, like an anticlimax.

We point out how the various theses took form. The first section of Da Vinci's linguistic notes to attract the attention of students, because of its impressive and enigmatic appearance, consists of the approximately nine thousand words (although it should be noted that if repetitions are not counted, the total is reduced by about half) arranged in long, dense columns on fifty-one sides of the sheets of the Codex Trivulzianus (fol. 30 r and v are reproduced on p. 225 below). There are four pages of the codex which alone contain about three hundred words in alphabetical order, accompanied by a sober interpretation (see below, p. 225, first reproduction, upper left); the other words are not in any visible order and have no explanation. To these lists in the Codex Trivulzianus we may add some pages of the Codex Atlanticus, such as folio 367 recto-c, with a list of two hundred and two verbs, and folio 213 verso-b, with forty-four words, as well as some shorter notes scattered in Mss. H and I, Anatomical Ms. B, Codex Forster II, and various sheets in the collection at Windsor. In explanation of these lists of words in the vernacular, Govi, in his *Saggio delle opere di Leonardo da Vinci* (Milan, 1872), was the first to propose the hypothesis that Leonardo intended to put together a dictionary of the Italian language, in order to defend it against the "distortions it was undergoing in the usage of Neapolitans, Romagnols, Bolognese, Venetians, and Lombards." Govi saw the three hundred words ordered and defined as a part of the work already completed, while the remainder seemed to him to represent raw materials awaiting arrangement and definition. But even here Govi felt that he found signs of a proposed alphabetical order, since the words beginning with the letter *A* are almost always accompanied by a dot.

On the other hand, in 1894 Henri de Geymüller, in the *Gazette des Beaux-Arts*, put forward a much bolder and more ambitious interpretation. He remarked that in the mass of words listed some were interconnected by links of synonymity, derivation, opposition, etc., as for example *militare* and *militia*, *exerciti* and *exercizi*, *notare* and *nuotare*, etc. He supposed therefore that Leonardo had reflected on those groups of words related through similarities of sound or sense, with the purpose of explaining the philosophical problem of the origin, nature, and mechanism of language. It must be pointed out at once, however, that the pairs or sets of words in which these parallelisms are to be seen are a small minority. Geymüller solved the difficulty by defining the enormous mass of disconnected and unrelated words as "raw material" accumulated for purposes of study.

Edmondo Solmi, in the preface to his famous anthology, *Frammenti letterari e filosofici di Leonardo da Vinci* (Florence; reprinted several times), rejected the dictionary hypothesis with these simple words: "This catalogue of words, which has suggested the strangest hypotheses to Da Vinci scholars, even to that of alleging him to have been the tutor of the young prince Maximilian, is merely an effort on the part of the founder of Italian scientific prose to define the exact meaning of terms."

Nonetheless, the didactic hypothesis, which had meanwhile obtained the support of Beltrami, the editor of the Codex Trivulzianus, was taken up again enthusiastically by Luigi Morandi, in a book which seemed to many to be an exhaustive and definitive examination of the problem we are considering.[3] The didactic hypothesis had been formulated in 1872, when Leonardo's manuscripts, still unpublished, were wrapped in mystery. Govi (*Saggio*, p. 9) expressed himself as follows: "Leonardo left some documents in his manuscripts which show how close the native tongue was to his heart. Thus we know from Comolli's *Bibliografia architettonica* that one of the Da Vinci codices formerly owned by the Ambrosiana, and now withheld in France, contained 'grammatical conjugations.'" Govi therefore did not know Mss. H and I, and could suppose that the "grammatical conjugations" they contained related to Leonardo's "native tongue" rather than to the Latin language. By the time Morandi took up the problem, the Paris manuscripts had been published by Ravaisson-Mollien, and there was no more room for doubt. Notwithstanding the evidence to the contrary, however, Morandi reverted to Govi's hypothesis, and extended it by increasing the number of projects attributed to Leonardo as efforts in defense of the "native tongue." The few lines written in the upper part of folio 213 verso-b of the Codex Atlanticus (cf. below, p. 223) are enough to make him declare: "That Leonardo attempted to make an Italian grammar, even if only for his own use, is adequately proved by a passage in the Codex Atlaticus (fol. 213 v)." But, according to Morandi, Leonardo had been composing "a Latin-Italian dictionary as well. This newest hypothesis is proved by the fully two hundred Latin words, translated by him into the native tongue, that are found in Ms. I." As regards the Italian dictionary, Morandi holds that the words in the Codex Trivulzianus prove "that their collector could not have had any other intention in mind than that of putting them together later in alphabetical order, and defined in a true and proper dictionary... His intention was... to compile the dictionary of the common language, and to compile it for the use of others, probably to have it printed, rather than for his own use" (*op. cit.*, p. 12, 31, 45, 53).

Govi could not examine many writings of Da Vinci's; but Morandi certainly was not an expert on them. The strength of his convictions was not founded on a general study of Leonardo's thought and work. Morandi was an ardent supporter of Alessandro Manzoni's linguistic doctrines, which favored the spoken language as against any attempt at archaistic imitation. The possibility of reinforcing his own theories with such a sensational example, such a great name as that of Leonardo, was the main cause of his enthusiasm. "Leonardo, with his sample of a Latin-Italian dictionary, his sketch of an Italian grammar, and the thousands of words collected for the Italian dictionary, anticipated in deeds that opposition to Cardinal Bembo's baneful doctrine which Machiavelli and

[3] L. Morandi, *Lorenzo il Magnifico, Leonardo da Vinci e la prima grammatica italiana*, Città di Castello, 1908.

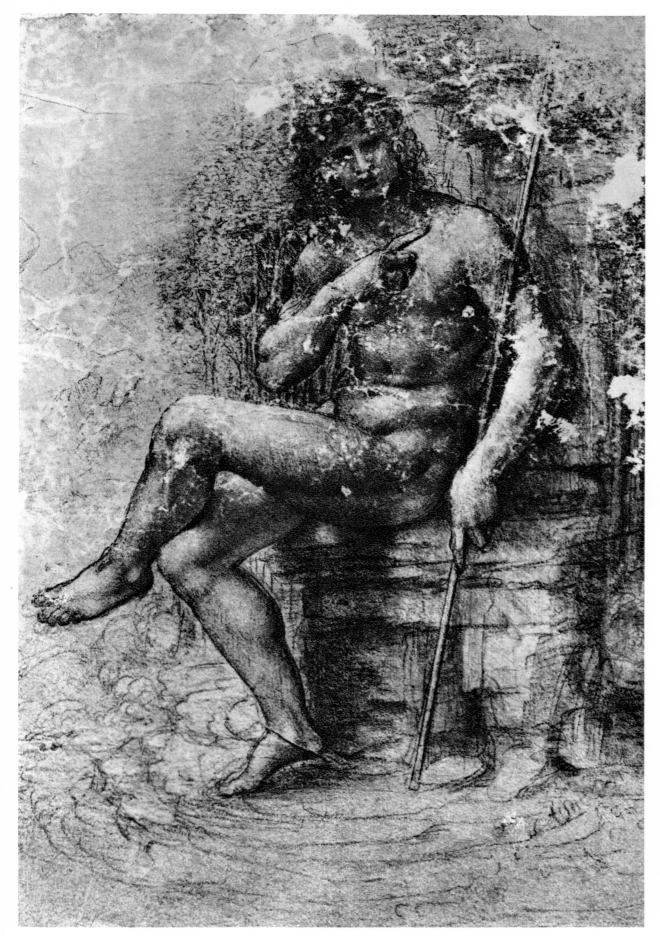

Bacchus – Painting in oil on wooden
panel – Paris, Louvre

St. John in the Desert by Cesare da
Sesto – London, Earl of Crawford
Collection

Flavio Antonio Gisaldi, a sixteenth-century scholar of Ferrara, mentions in an epigram a painting of Bacchus by Leonardo. Very few Da Vinci drawings drew their inspiration from pagan subjects. We have not been able to find any preliminary study for the Bacchus. It is, however, regarded as certain that Leonardo painted a Bacchus beside Leda, since in 1515 Antonio Pallavicino, owner of the painting, promised it to the Cardinal of Rouen. This painting, however, cannot be the great *Bacchus* of the Louvre, because in 1695 it was still appearing in the inventory under the title, *St. John in the Desert*, and the figure was described as pointing with the index of his right hand to a cross and not to a thyrsus.

Most experts are of the opinion that the painting at the Louvre originally represented St. John and was only subsequently transformed into a Bacchus. The crown of vine leaves is believed to have been superposed in the eighteenth century; also, the fawn has a religious rather than a pagan significance. On the other hand, critics do not agree in attributing the painting to Leonardo. Various hypotheses have been put forward on the subject.

Some attribute to Leonardo the drawing in red pencil preserved at the Sacro Monte sanctuary in Varese, others ascribe it to Cesare da Sesto. At any rate, the drawing reveals that the composition of the *Bacchus* was executed over the preliminary study for the *St. John in the Desert*. The composition of the *St. John* by Cesare da Sesto (London, Earl of Crawford Collection) here reproduced is identical with the Sacro Monte drawing. There is, however, in the inclination of the head and the expression of the eyes, a closer resemblance between the drawing and the *Bacchus* at the Louvre.

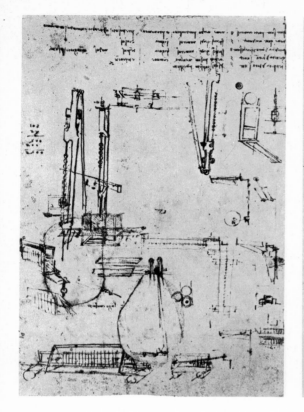
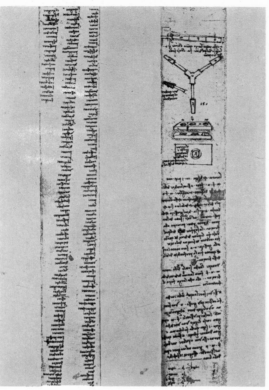
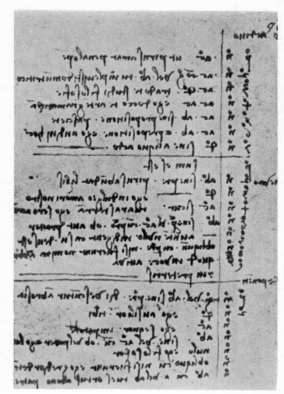

others of the period vainly offered, but which had its final triumph only with Alessandro Manzoni." [4] Moreover, the public was so willing to ascribe to Leonardo the most unexpected projects for works anticipating future advances of any kind that Morandi's thesis had an easy victory, despite the protests of a genuine (although philologically vague) Leonardo scholar, namely, Solmi. The principal argument on which Morandi based his assertions was always that of chronological priority. "In view of the lack of an Italian dictionary at that time and in view of the nature of Leonardo's mind... all doubt as to the true intent of this part of his works vanishes... Likewise, ignorance of the fact that when Leonardo made his experiments toward an Italian grammar and a Latin-Italian dictionary, these two tools of culture may be said not to have been in existence, caused these experiments to pass... unobserved by all." The dogma of the "universal genius and precursor," Leonardo, did away with any need for further evidence.

But there still remained the "grammatical conjugations," as they are called, namely, a large group of notes on Latin grammar, in which tables of verb conjugations predominate (see the three reproductions from Ms. H, p. 221). Since there were so many Latin grammars, old and new, in Leonardo's time that it was impossible to ascribe any anticipatory function to these "exercises," Morandi condescended to recognize in them a simple purpose of self-instruction, on this occasion, at lest, in agreement with Solmi. But the time of re-evaluation came for these notes, after they had remained for a while without being given any special value. In 1918 Leonardo Olschki, in his valuable *Geschichte der neusprachlichen wissenschaftlichen Literatur* (Vol. I, Heidelberg), went beyond Morandi's assertions; feeling perhaps the contradiction they contained in presenting Leonardo as a schoolboy in relation to some notes and as a master of grammar in relation to others, he got around the difficulty by lending Leonardo the intention of writing a Latin grammar as well. He did not subject the linguistic notes to a new and searching examination, but accepted Morandi's statements as definitive and irrefutable, seeing them as the model for a new general and unified interpretation of all of Leonardo's manuscript work.

As we know, Olschki did not believe that Da Vinci's writings had any scientific validity, and preferred to consider them as a conglomeration of materials prepared for a hoped-for scientific encyclopedia for the use of "unlettered men," a sort of great *Summa* in the vernacular, a new *Convivio*, larger and grander. "As a scientific method, Leonardo's way of research is inconceivable and unfruitful, but as an undertaking of collection for a systematic comprehensive work it is explicable and possible, by all our presuppositions," he says (*op. cit.*, p. 329). This great scientific encyclopedia in the vernacular would have had room, along with including a treatise on painting and others on anatomy, hydraulics, optics, etc., for a grammar and a large Italian dictionary, a Latin-Italian dictionary, and, besides, a Latin grammar written in the vernacular, to teach even the "unlettered" the rudiments of Latin. In this way all of Leonardo's manuscripts enter into a huge pedagogic program, although lowered to a plane of undoubted mediocrity. Reasoning thus, Olschki did not take into account, among other things, a solid article by E. Solmi [5] which pointed out some sources of Leonardo's grammatical notes and raised grave objections to the didactic thesis of Govi and Morandi. How could the three hundred ordered and defined words of the Codex Trivulzianus, Solmi remarked, prove that Leonardo intended to define all the others, if they were nothing but a transcription

Left: Parts of speech, in Latin – Cod. Atl., fol. 358 r

Center: Note on four Latin verbs, in first and second person, present tense, with Italian translation (below, right, turning page) – Cod. Atl., fol. 367 v

Right: Examples of Latin syntax – Ms. I, fol. 138 r

INTEMPERANCE – The *alicorno* or unicorn, through its intemperance and its inability to control the delight it takes in young maidens, forgets its fierce, savage nature and puts all suspicion aside, approaches the seated maiden, and goes to sleep in her lap; and thus the hunters take it – Ms. H, fol. 11 v – Drawing in London, British Museum

FOLLY – Since the wild bull cannot abide the color red, some hunters drape the trunk of a tree in red, and the bull charges at it with great fury and drives his horns into it, so that the hunters are able to kill it – Ms. H, fol. 8 r – Drawing at Windsor, Royal Collection, no. 12364 r

[4] L. Morandi, "For Leonardo da Vinci and the Grammar of Lorenzo de' Medici," in *Nuova antologia*, 1909, Oct. 1, p. 1.
[5] "Niccolò Perotti, Luigi Pulci, and Leonardo da Vinci's Autodidactic Studies in Latin and Italian," in *Nuova antologia*, March, 1910.

WATER – When the water was in the majestic sea, its element, it got the desire to ascend above the air, and raised by aid of the element of fire into a fine vapor, it all but seemed to have the lightness of the air; and mounting on high, it came to the thinner and colder air, where it was abandoned by the fire; and the little granules, being pressed, united and became heavy, whereat, in falling, pride turned into flight, and fell from the heavens; so that then it was drunk up by the dry earth, where it was shut up for a long time, doing penance for its sin – Cod. Forst. III, fol. 2 r – Drawing at Windsor, Royal Collection, no. 12393

THE TORRENT – The torrent bore down so much earth and rock into its bed that it was later forced to change its site – Cod. Arund., fol. 42 v – Drawing at Windsor, Royal Collection, no. 12398

THE EAGLE – An eagle, wishing to defend an owl, remained with its wings full of birdlime, and was taken and killed by a man – Cod. Atl., fol. 67 v-b – Drawing in Ms. B, fol. 89 v

THE CEDAR – A cedar, proud of its beauty, suspected the plants around it and had them removed; and then the wind, no longer being broken, tore it up by the roots – Cod. Atl., fol. 67 v-b – Drawing at Windsor, Royal Collection, no. 12402

218

of a little dictionary compiled by Luigi Pulci, the author of the *Morgante Maggiore*? The alphabetical order and the definitions reflect an idea of Pulci's which Leonardo did not apply anywhere else in the Codex Trivulzianus. And how can we consider the definitions of the eight parts of speech given on folio 213 verso-*b* of the Codex Atlanticus as a sketch of an Italian grammar when they do not even deal with the article? Solmi later made a valuable identification of the *Rudimenta grammatices* of Niccolò Perotti as the source of the tables of Latin conjugations in Mss. H and I.

These were the terms in which "the question of Leonardo da Vinci's *grammar* and *dictionary*" was presented in 1939, when I began a thorough examination of all Leonardo's grammatical and lexical notes, with a view to preparing a critical edition of them. Most of the scholars referred to above not only ascribed to Leonardo a polemical attitude toward the humanists (thereby indulging a critical prejudice of romantic origin), but could not even stop to consider the hypothesis that Leonardo did not have, aside from speaking of a refined knowledge, even a reliable knowledge of Latin. Olschki, for one, peremptorily excluded the possibility that the conjugation tables for *amo, doceo, lego, audio,* etc., may have served Leonardo himself, regarding it as impossible that the latter, at forty, when he had filled whole pages of Ms. B with many citations of Latin authors, should still be struggling with *rosa, rosae* or *amo, amas, amat.* Again, Duhem and Solmi himself, in the course of their researches on Leonardo's sources, had attributed to him extensive reading in difficult Latin works. But all these are convinctions that had to be, and still have to be, revised. The citations in Ms. B are evidence of the reading of a single book from which they all come—the *De re militari* of Roberto Valturio, which Leonardo read in the vernacular version of Paolo Ramusio. When Leonardo tackled the Latin text directly, he was capable of translating the phrase *Caelidonium auctores vocant ipsi falcastrum* ("The same authors call the *caelidonium* a scythelike weapon") as "The autors, as Celidonius says, is a scythelike weapon"; *faber Tyrius* ("a Tyrian mechanic") as "Febar of Tyre"; and *Callias Rhodum cum venisset* ("when Callias had reached Rhodes") as "Callias the Rhodian" (see my *Gli appunti,* etc., I, 134-140). It is quite evident that Leonardo knew his not very numerous Latin authors by way of vernacular translations, or through conversations and the help of learned friends. There is a significant note in this connection to be found in the Quaderni di Anatomia, which runs: "Have Avicenna's *De giovamenti* translated"; but even if we did not have the facts already mentioned, examination of the notes on Latin grammar would suffice to prove that Leonardo at forty had a shaky knowledge of Latin.

In the first place, the spelling of the Latin is that of non-Latinists, "vulgar" or "unlettered" men, *produttam* (Ms. I, fol. 80 r), *michi contengit, protter=propter, pose=post se* (Ms. I, fol. 137 r, v), *ic, ec, oc, uius, uic, lettus=lectus, letis=lectis* (Ms. H, fol. 126 r). And even later, when he is fifty-six, Leonardo writes a satirical Latin sentence as follows: *Non prestavis bis [si prestavis non abebis] si abebis non tam cito [si tam cito non tam bona] e si tam bonum perdas amicum"* (Ms. F, cover). It is hard to see in these examples the hand of a master, who plans to teach Latin to the "unlettered." But let us look at a page in which Morandi sees the sketch of the first Latin-Italian dictionary. The first lines read:

accidit	*acchade*
aliquid	*alcuna cosa*
congruo	*conveniente*
uniuscuiusque	*di ciascuna cosa*

If we really believed in the idea of a projected Latin-Italian dictionary, every word here would bring us up short. Why is the verb in the third person, and why are the two pronouns in the neuter and the genitive? And is *congruo* an ablative, or is it already a vernacular form? And why does the translation of *uniuscuiusque* say specifically *of each thing,* when the Latin form could also refer to a man or a woman, etc.? Is a dictionary of the Latin language contemplated here, or is a particular text being translated? Actually, as we proceed, we find the verbs listed in the forms for all the persons and numbers at random: *aditur, utuntur, ripricor, sorbet, disces.* We find *quibus* translated now *da questi* ["by these"] and then *alli quali* ["to which"]. We find other genitives *cuiusque, utrius, agentis.* We find many other forms that seem to be vernacular rather than Latin —*appellativo, particulare, mancipio, concisione, cogiente, regresso, pretermittente*—and also spellings tending toward the vernacular: *abentia, abietta, cogiente, agies, pracipue, gieri, fervessco.* Nor should we overlook the mistakes or inexactnesses in translation: *dulcedo=dolce; interimit=amazare; lituris= =cancellare; abentia=avere cose; agies=fare; excipiuntur=si trae fori; vapulant=è battuto;* etc. All in all, is it conceivable that a Latinist at the height of the Renaissance would dream of making a dictionary with materials of this kind?

The reason for this disorder and looseness and for these errors became clear to me when an attentive examination of some pages of the *Rudimenta grammatices* of Perotti enabled me to discover the origin and hence of course the reasons for these notes of Da Vinci. Leonardo, reading a passage like this, "Numerus quomodo *accidit* syllabae? Dictio unde dicitur? A dicendo quod dicit *aliquid*... oratio *congruam* sententiam demonstrans... notemus *uniuscuiusque* substantiae qualitatem," certainly was not perfectly clear as to the meaning of the words here italicized. In point of fact, he copied them into his notes, keeping the order they had in the text, without making any attempt to put them into the form of the paradigms that constitute the listings of a dictionary (the most likely assumption is that he had no idea of the technique of lexicography). It was only his weakness in Latin that made him change spellings in some cases and use as his examples, instead of nominative

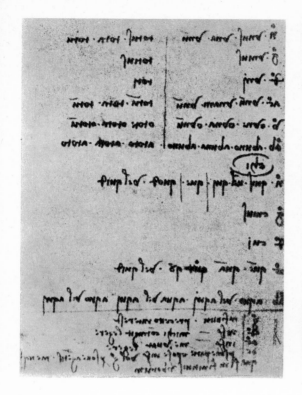
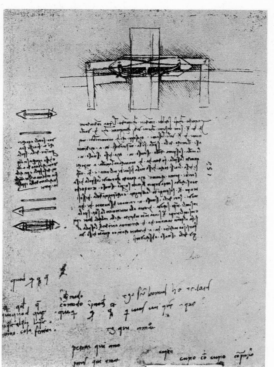
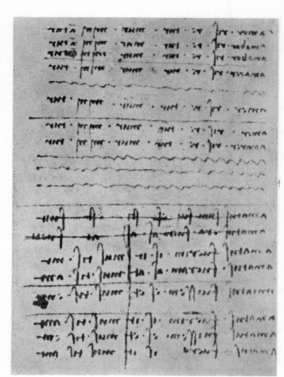

forms, apparent ablatives (*congruo, appellativo, mancipio,* etc.) or neuters (*particulare*) which really are Latinisms current in the vernacular. These considerations enabled us to reconstruct the genesis of the entire alleged Latin-Italian dictionary, and to set down in footnotes in our edition of it the passages from the reading of which the project arose. In the process Da Vinci's work was reduced to its actual dimensions, eliminating Morandi's exaggerations. Leonardo acted exactly as we do when reading a text in a language we do not know perfectly. Newish words are underlined, the translations of them are written in the margin, and they may even be put into a notebook, the better to fix them in the memory.

We also find in this Latin grammar the solution of another enigma, constituted by folio 138 recto of Ms. I (reproduced on p. 217). This gave a good deal of trouble to its first transcriber, Ravaisson-Mollien. It is an arrangement in columns of signs and numbers which seem obscure; they are in three groups—*verbo attivo, neutro, deponenti* (a fourth group is on the opposite page, fol. 137 v). We reproduce the first group.

verbo activo

p^o n^o	ac^o ut pirus amat penalopem
2° n^o	ac con g^o vel ab^o tu inplevisti domum tritico
3° n^o	ac d^o trado te studii filosofie
4° n^o	ac ac ego doceo te artem grammaticham
5° n^o	ac ab sine prepositione pascie te
6° n^o	ac ab e prepositione ego audivi hoc
7° n^o	d^o sine aliquo acto [=accusativo]

Perotti's Latin grammar centers the treatment of syntax around a classification of the verbs governing the various cases. The classification and verb constructions are given as follows (we italicize the words copied by Leonardo into his list).

"Quot sunt ordines *verborum activorum*? Septem. Quæ sunt verba primi ordinis?

"Quæ exigunt *nominativum* ante se pro re agente et *accusativum* post se pro re patiente, ut '*Pyrrhus amat Penelopen*...'

"Quæ sunt verba *secundi* ordinis? Quæ exigunt *nominativum* ante se et post se *accusativum cum genitivo vel ablativo*, ut '*tu implesti domum tritico*...'

"Q. s. verba *tertii* o.? quæ exigunt *nominativum* ante se et post se *accusativum* et *dativum*, ut '*trado te studiis philosophiæ*...'

"Quæ s. v. *quarti* ordinis? Q. exigunt *nominativum* et *accusativos duos*, ut '*ego doceo te artem grammaticam*...'

"Q. sunt v. *quinti* ordinis? Q. exigunt *nominativum* et *accusativum* cum *ablativo sine prepositione*, ut '*pascie te* liberalibus studiis...'

"Q. sunt v. *sexti* ordinis? Q. exigunt *nominativum* et *accusativum* cum *ablativo* a vel ab mediante, ut '*ego audivi hoc* a pretore...'

THE SNOW – A little snow was once caught on the top of a rock hanging at the peak of a very high mountain; and gathering its thoughts, it began to use its imagination, saying to itself: "Now should not I be held to be proud and haughty, being in so lofty a place, when I am but a little pinch of snow, and realize that all the snow that I can see is lower than I am? Certainly my small quantity does not deserve this height, and I know well, by the witness of my little shape, what the sun did to my comrades yesterday, for they were all undone by the sun in a few hours; and this happened because they had placed themselves higher than befitted them. I wish to flee the ire of the sun, and abase myself, and find a place suited to my little quantity."

And throwing itself violently downward, it began the long journey, rolling along from the high mountains and gliding over other snow, and the more it sought lower ground, the more its amount grew, so that when its course finally came to an end on a mound, it was not much smaller than the ground that supported it; and therefore it was the very last patch of snow to be annihilated by the rays of the sun that summer. Let it be said for those that humble themselves: They shall be exalted – Cod. Atl., fol. 67 v-*b* – Drawing by Leonardo da Vinci at Windsor Royal Collection, no. 12405

"Q. sunt v. *septimi* ordinis?   Q. exigunt *nominativum* ante se et *dativum* post se *sine aliquo accusativo...*"

In this case too we note that Leonardo's weakness in Latin gives rise to a certain hybridization with the vernacular, into which Leonardo slips with great ease, not because he is intending to write a Latin grammar making use of the vernacular, but by the spontaneous force of the latter, which takes the place of its delicate rival whenever it can: e.g., *verbo activo*; *n⁰=nominativo*; *ac⁰=* *=accusativo*; *con* instead of *cum*; *e* instead of *et*.   We can also observe the true originality of these Da Vinci notes, which consists in the stressing of the visual element.   Leonardo is constantly making tables, substituting graphic elements for Perotti's long discourses.   The vertical line indicates the position of the verb in the sentence, the number indicates the class to which it belongs, *n⁰* before the line and *ac⁰* or *ab⁰* after it indicate the cases governed by the verb *ante se* and *post se*.   Then comes the example.   However, it cannot be said that Leonardo is very accurate in taking his notes, and it may well be that he is not always master of the material.   The examples for the fifth and sixth orders are limping, and the situation gets worse in the following groups.   This is especially true as regards the fourth and last group (see lower portion of fol. 137 v, reproduced on p. 219), in which we read:

THE LILY – The lily placed itself on the bank of the Ticino, and the current tore away the bank with the lily – Ms. H, fol. 44 r – Drawing at Windsor, Royal Collection, no. 12418

g⁰	*infinitum precetto interest*
d⁰	*infinitum michi contingit legere*
ac⁰	*infinitum me iuvat legere*
ac⁰	*persone patien e pose infinitum vel g⁰ persone agentis me miseret*
que si infinitivis verborum	

This relates to the five classes of *impersonalia*, which Perotti defines as follows:

"*Quæ exigunt ante se genitivum et post se infinitivum, ut 'preceptoris interest legere...'* Quæ exigunt *dativum ante se et post se infinitum, ut 'mihi contigit legere...'* Quæ *accusativum* exigunt et *infinitum, ut 'me iuvat legere...'* Quæ ante se *accusativum* habent *personæ patientis, et post se infinitum vel genitivum personæ agentis, ut 'me miseret calamitatis humanæ...'* Quæ si infinitivis verbis personalium iunguntur, personalia sunt...*"

LION – This animal wakes his young with his thunderous cry three days after they are born, opening all their sleeping senses and putting all the beasts in the forest to flight. This may be compared to the way of children of virtue, who are waked by the cry of praise and increase their honorable studies, which always ennobles them more, while all the dullards flee them, yielding place to the capable – Ms. H, fol. 18 r – Drawing at Windsor, Royal Collection, no. 12586 r

Here we note not only the intrusion of the vernacular into the Latin (e.g., *vel genitivo, e* for *et*) and the pronunciation of the Latin after the fashion of the vernacular (*michi contingit, pose* to be read *possè=post se*), but also the abridgment of various words (*precetto, patien*) and sentences (*que si infinitivis verborum, me miseret*), which makes the rule incomprehensible and detracts from its value. Leonardo seems here to be chiefly concerned with an over-all synthetic bird's-eye view of Latin syntax as outlined in a series of grammatical categories; the precise and complete formulation of a large number of particular rules is something that for the moment lies beyond his limited requirements.

In order to get a better idea of the personal and private nature of these notes and their inapplicability for the "use of others," it should suffice to consider Ravaisson-Mollien's transcription of the fifth-order rule for intransitive verbs: *Ab. F: Sine præ: ab. f ab; cum præ, ob, aut, propter,* instead of *ab⁰ sine prepositione vel ac⁰ cum prepositione "ob" aut "protter,"* corresponding to "*...et post se ablativum sine præpositione vel accusativum cum præpositione ob aut propter...*" in the original source.

It is also likely that Leonardo had the help of some educated friend.   The translation of the words written down in the little Latin-Italian dictionary must have been suggested, at least in part, by a person with better knowledge, who may have been present while Leonardo was taking the notes that fill the lower portion of folio 326 verso-*a*, Codex Atlanticus (reproduced on p. 219).   It seems to me that they were intended to accompany a discourse, I might say a "lesson," dealing chiefly with the relative pronoun.   The group of notes at the left remarks on the relative pronoun in an abbreviated separate entry.   In the center there is a translation of an interrogative adverbial *qui*, "in what way?", and probably of a causal *quod*, "whereas, so that."   Next there is the declension of the relative pronoun; the agreement of *qui* with the first and third persons of the verb is studied (*qui amo, qui amat*).   Another study of agreement is the sentence *ego sum bonus homo et datis*.   The last line at the right comprises a study of verb derivation and composition—*cupio, concupio, concupisco* (wrongly written *compiosco*).

THE MOUSE AND THE CAT – The mouse was besieged in a little house he dwelt in by the weasel, who waited with unceasing vigilance to undo him; and from a little hole the mouse looked out at his great peril. Meanwhile along came the cat and suddenly seized that weasel and devoured it at once. The mouse then sacrificed some of his nuts to Jupiter, thanking his deity for everything, and went forth from his lair to take advantage of his once-lost liberty, of which, along with his life, he was at once deprived by the fierce claws and teeth of the cat – Cod. Atl., fol. 67 v-*a* – Drawing at Windsor, Royal Collection, no. 12363

What shall we say now with respect to folio 213 verso-*b* of the Codex Atlanticus (reproduced on p. 223), in which Morandi saw a preliminary formulation of an Italian grammar?   First of all, we compare the notes on this folio with those of folios 358 recto-*c* and 280 verso of the same codex. All three folios deal with the classification of the eight parts of speech—eight, in accordance with the structure of Latin grammar, and not nine, as Italian grammar would require.   Folio 358 recto-*c* (reproduced on p. 217) clearly shows that Latin grammar is involved here; the page contains a table taken, as usual, from Perotti's *Rudimenta grammatices*, and gives us fresh proof of how weak Leonardo's Latin was, and how easily it slipped into the vernacular.   The first line says: "*Quot sunt parte orationis?   8 nomen verbum participivo et pronomen prepositio adverbio interiectio et coniuntio.*"

Where Perotti writes *Quot accidunt nomini?* Leonardo copies it as *Nomen quot accidunct*. And note the fourth line, *Gienera verborum sunct 5 activo passivo neultro commune e deponente*, in which the vernacular definitely has the upper hand.

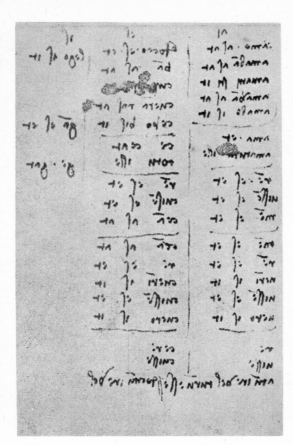

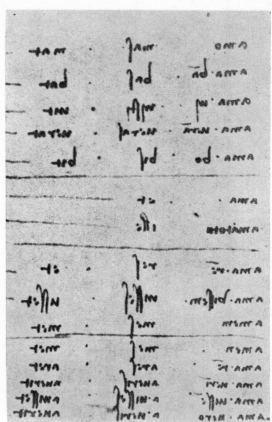

Left: Notes on conjugation of Latin verb *amo*
    – Ms. H, fol. 139 r

Center: Notes on conjugation of Latin verb
    amo – Ms. H, fol. 4 r

Right: Notes on conjugation of Latin verb
    amo – Ms. H, fol. 3 v

It is therefore certain that here Leonardo, following Perotti step by step, is continuing to study Latin grammar, as he does in the other notes, dealing with the conjugation of *amo, doceo,* etc. What reason is there for us to assume that on folio 213 verso-*b* he has turned to laying the groundwork for an *Italian* grammar? Merely because the arrangement of the eight parts of speech is accompanied by examples or definitions in the vernacular? But the fact is that ever since there had been a vernacular, Latin had always been taught on the basis of vernacular themata. Perotti's Latin grammar too contains phrases and words in the vernacular, and there are an enormous number of medieval manuscripts in which Latin grammar is accompanied by explanations in the vernacular. One of the reasons that Dante himself gives for his preference for his mother tongue is that "this vernacular of mine was my introducer to the way of learning, which is the highest perfection, since by it I came into Latin, which was shown to me in it" (*Convivio*, I, XIII, 5). A further proof that the purpose of folio 213 verso-*b* is that of an introduction to Latin is the presence of various exercises, logical and grammatical. In fact, *nominativo – Giovanni, verbo – pingie; nome – Antonio, verbo – studia* is nothing but the logical analysis of the two propositions *Giovanni pingie, Antonio studia* ("Giovanni paints"; "Antonio studies,") *nominativo* and *nome* corresponding to "subject" in our terminology. The expressions *bella donna* and *bello homo*, on the other hand, receive grammatical analysis, the single words being classified according to their role as their parts of speech—*adgiectivo, sustantivo*—for which definitions and examples follow. Special attention is given to the relative pronoun, which is of greater importance because of its special syntactical functions. The repetitions, corrections, and cancellations to be found on this page indicate, in my opinion, a state of uncertainty that would be astonishing in a teacher.

Furthermore, folio 280 verso of the Codex Atlanticus, which Morandi did not know, since Piumati had left it out of his transcription of the codex (he must have thought it apocryphal because the writing is not left-handed, though today he would hesitate before pronouncing a judgment of this kind; and incidentally a closer examination I have recently made of the original in place of the reproduction has enabled me to make a correction in Galbiati's transcription: in the series of pronouns, instead of the strange *overo*, the reading should be *questo*), contains a *divisio* of grammar into four elements—*littera, syllaba, dictio, oratio*—and a second *divisio* or partition distinguishing the eight parts of speech, accompanied by copious illustrations in a vernacular that seems to me to be tinged with Lombard turns of speech. At the top, the folio bears a large title, GRAMMATICA, but there is nothing to justify us in holding that the compiler of these notes was already thinking of an autonomous grammar of the vernacular. On the contrary, the absence of the article, and an ancient tradition, still strong at the end of the fifteenth century, are our guarantees that here too *grammar* is equivalent to *Latin*, and that we may place this page together with the thousands of others in which beginners were introduced to the study of Latin by means of vernacular themata or examples.

Our examination of the grammatical notes has led us to deny the existence of three of the projects attributed to Leonardo—a Latin grammar, an Italian grammar, and a Latin-Italian dictionary —and to point out how slight a knowledge Leonardo had of the Latin language. Since he shows such a limited knowledge of Latin (which may have improved in later years, but hardly to any

THE STONE – A stone of fine size, recently uncovered by the waters, was standing on a certain high place, where a pleasant little wood ended at a rocky road, and it was surrounded by herbs and various flowers of all kinds of colors; and as it looked at the great number of stones all together in the road below it, the desire came to it to drop down there, and it said to itself: "What am I doing here with these little plants? I want to live with my sisters there." And down it dropped, and rolled to a stop among the comrades it longed for; and soon it began to be in constant travail from the wheels of the carts, the hooves of iron-shod horses, and the travellers' feet: this one turned it, the other kicked it, sometimes a chip was taken off, or, again, it was covered with mud or the dung of some animal; and it looked back in vain to the place it had departed from, to that place of solitary and tranquil peace. And this is what happens to those who desire to go from a solitary contemplative life to live in cities, among people full of infinite evils – Cod. Atl., fol. 175 v-*a* – Drawing at Windsor, Royal Collection, no. 12399

221

TALE – A certain man said to an acquaintance: "Your eyes are all changed to a queer color." The other man said that this often happened to them. "But haven't you done anything about it? And when does it happen to you?" The other replied: "Every time my eyes see your queer face, the violence done them by such a great displeasure makes them turn pale and change to a queer color." – Cod. Atl., fol. 76 v-a – Drawing at Chatsworth, Museum

LAZINESS – A certain person was told to get out of bed, because the sun was already risen, and he answered: "If I had to go as far and do as much as he, I should be up by now too, but since I have so short a way to go, I do not wish to get up yet" – Cod. Forst., II, fol. 31 r – Drawing at Chatsworth, Museum

PORTRAIT- A certain sappy weed grown in the shade, like a squash or melon for excess water, or like a withered plum for wrinkles—no, you're not saying it right, you know.... He's a real jackass... shaved as close as a pinhead, but he lacks the cabbage or squash-vine leaf to drain off the scabs. What do you think, Sandro? I'll tell you the truth: I didn't succeed in telling you the truth – Cod. Atl., fol. 313 r-b – Drawing in Milan, Ambrosiana

great extent), it is much more logical to believe that he wanted to learn Latin rather than to teach it to others. There still remained the task of accounting for the imposing mass of words arranged in columns in the Codex Trivulzianus, and here and there in other codices, on the basis of which scholars had agreed on the conclusion that Leonardo's intention had been to prepare the first dictionary of the Italian language. Morandi, who also credited him with the polemical intention of supporting living Tuscan usage, the "native tongue," against the learned and artificial language of the humanists, preferred to believe that Leonardo drew his words from his memory or even from books, but always following living usage and avoiding any archaism "like the plague." And yet he should have known that on folio 367 recto-c of the Codex Atlanticus (a long, narrow strip of paper, reproduced on p. 217) Leonardo had arranged 202 verbs in three columns, fully 180 of which are copied from a page of the *Rudimenta grammatices*, where they appear as the translations of the same number of Latin verbs. (On the back of the sheet Leonardo had begun to copy this list of Perotti's in full: *amo as...* for *amare*; *audio is...* for *odire*. But here he abandoned the Latin to copy out only the Italian verbs.) Moreover, it was known that the 300 words arranged in order and defined in the Codex Trivulzianus (fol. 23-26) were also copied from a small dictionary of Latin words composed by Luigi Pulci. The alphabetical order and the definitions for the words are not, therefore, an innovation of Leonardo's but merely reflect the situation existing in the source; these lists too are the fruit of reading a text.

What sort of thing was Pulci's dictionary? Its title, *Latin Words*, is enlightening. The grammarians of that time designated as "Latin" words, or "French" or "Provençal" or "Spanish" words, those terms which did not belong to popular Tuscan usage but had been inserted (or "derived," as they put it) into Tuscan from the Latin, French, Provençal, or Spanish language. This observation in and of itself refutes Morandi's affirmations. Leonardo was not taking the words of his normal language from his memory, but was looking in the books of grammarians for a special linguistic material, namely, Latinisms. Now we are able to understand the significance and importance of a passage written by Leonardo in Anatomical Ms. B (fol. 4 v), just two pages after a little list of Latinisms (fol. 2 r, v): "This [anatomical] demonstration is as necessary to good draftsmen as the *derivation of Latin words* is to good grammarians." This was an idea common to all men of letters of the time. From among their views we may cite the recommendation of Cristoforo Landino: "One who wants to be a good Tuscan must be a good Latin... everyone sees that if we wish to enrich this language [Tuscan], we must *derive Latin words* every day, without distorting their nature, and introduce them into our tongue." Castiglione recommended to the protagonist of his *Courtier* (I, 34) that he form new words, "drawing them well from the Latins, as the Latins once drew them from the Greeks." Later, the first grammarians and lexicographers of the vernacular were to stress this argument, defending the legitimacy of "deriving" the "Latin words." Alunno speaks of "many Latin words... finer and more sonorous than the vernacular words, as *macilente* is better than *macro*, *impudenti* better than *sfacciati*, *memorando* better than *recordevole*, *auriga* better than *carrettiero*, and *esterno* better than *forestiero*." Aracisio compiles a long list of Latin words used by Boccaccio, such as *abstratto, abominevoli, accendere, acume, amaritudine, amanti, amatore, amabile, animali bruti, annali*, which are completely like those of Leonardo's lists; and he recommends their use for the reason that "we should follow in the steps of the writers we approve of... and avoid those less attractive ones who are in the mouths of the people" (*Vocabolario et grammatica*, etc., Venice, 1550, chap. 20). Tolomei records in the *Cesano* (Venice, 1555) that Dante "was forced to make use of the riches of others, and to take idioms from all the rest of Italy, from France, from Spain, often taking words from the Roman tongue and giving them a Tuscan form... sometimes the Latin words themselves without changing them in the least or departing from their natal form," that is, "foreign words, and *pure Latin* words, and *Latin* words Tuscanized" (p. 67, 70).

Instead of a polemical opposition on Lenardo's part to the linguistic doctrines of the learned, we find here a concordance of ideas that definitely contradicts Morandi's assertions. The latter's mistake was that he anachronistically attributed his own problems and conceptions to a man and an age that had quite different problems and ideas. From its beginnings, the development of the vernacular as a literary language had taken place under the wing of "grammar," that is, Latin. Grammar was the only *ars* that taught how to compose either in Latin or in the vernacular, how to write either a *dictamen* or a *diceria*. In many instances the bilingualism of the writers, enhanced by the humanistic experiment, dims the line of demarcation between the vocabularies of the two languages, so that it seems natural for them to draw copiously on the stores of Latin words for writing in the vernacular, provided that the characteristics of the two languages are skillfully enough adapted and fused, "imitating sounds and accents, and aspirations and endings." The Latin word becomes an Italian one by a mere adaptation of the ending (Latin words Tuscanized), or unchanged, as we see in the apparent ablatives used by Leonardo—*congruo, pretermittente, appellativo, particulare, concisione, mancipio*, etc., all pure Latin words.

Now, it is of importance to remark that not only do we find the words transcribed from Pulci's little dictionary to be "Latin" or Latinisms; not only can the verbs of folio 367 recto-c of the Codex Atlanticus, transcribed from Perotti's Latin grammar, be so described; but all the nine thousand terms in the Codex Trivulzianus, and also the shorter lists scattered in other manuscripts, come under the heading of "Latin words," by and large, and with some random infiltration. Isidoro del Lungo (*Conferenze fiorentine*, Milan, 1910, p. 290) was the only scholar to point out, with respect to the words in the Codex Trivulzianus, "the attention that Leonardo devotes to synonyms, abstract words, and in general to the possible relations of any word that gives rise to a family of words," but he did not note the virtually total absence of concrete words, "corporeal" words, to use the Renaissance terminology, from Da Vinci's lists. If Leonardo really intended to prepare a Tuscan vocabulary, Morandi might have been asked, why did he systematically exclude the names of corporeal objects and physical persons, and collect only verbs, adjectives, adverbs, and abstract

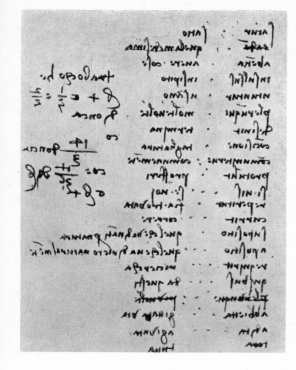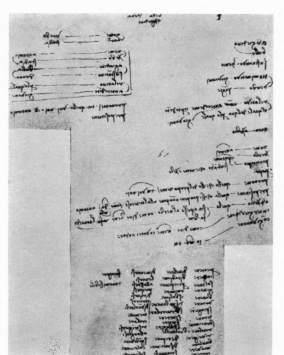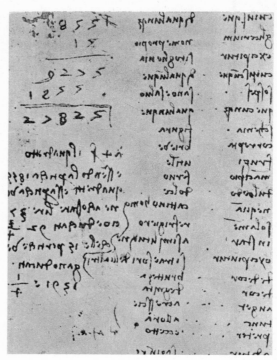

nouns? In connection with these observations, it may be noted that even Solmi, although he pointed out the autodidactic nature of these lexical collections, was unable to realize the very special nature of the linguistic material Leonardo had searched out. Solmi found in it "an effort on the part of the founder of Italian scientific prose to define the exact meaning of terms," suggesting as it were a search for special technical terms, which are all but absent from the lists of the Codex Trivulzianus (only a dozen words relate to hydraulics, and a few more than that to military matters).

Furthermore, we must note in the Trivulzianus lists too that absence of any strict criterion in the formulation of the paradigms already mentioned in connection with the little Latin-Italian dictionary of Ms. I, in which the word forms are not constant types, such as lexicographers use—the nominative case for nouns and adjectives, and the first person singular of the present indicative for verbs. In the Codex Trivulzianus we find verbs in the form of the infinitive, the gerund, the participle, or even the third person of the present indicative; we find adjectives in the masculine or feminine form, the singular or plural, or even the superlative, indifferently throughout. The reason for this apparent disorder, so far as the little Latin-Italian dictionary is concerned, was elucidated by the discovery of the source, which enabled me to see how Leonardo had taken the words from the text he was reading, transcribing them in the same order and practically without changing their form. A similar discovery, and an even more important one, enabled me to make the same finding in regard to the lists of the Codex Trivulzianus. Repeated and patient probings in the pages of the *De re militari* of Valturio, as rendered into the vernacular by Paolo Ramusio, enabled me to reconstruct the history of many pages of the Codex Trivulzianus, and to follow closely Leonardo's work in gleaning words from the texts that he read.

I give below some passages from the Valturio-Ramusio work, comparing them with the corresponding pages of the Codex Trivulzianus.

THE WARRIOR – A certain man saw a great sword at the side of another man, and said: "Oh, you poor fellow! It's a long time now that I've seen you tied to that weapon. Why don't you undo it? Your hands are free and you are at liberty."
To which the other answered, "That's an old joke; it's not yours."
The first one, piqued, replied, "I know that you know so few things in this world that I thought any old thing would be new to you" – Cod. Atl., fol. 13 r-d – Drawing in Milan, Ambrosiana

Valturio Ramusio, sheet 250 v et seq.	Cod. Triv., fol. 51 r (p. 93)		

..... Le nebule discendando da li monti overo dal cielo *caschando* overo *dimorate* ne le valle... se 'l nasce ne le parte *meridionale, condurà* grande *effusione di acqua,* quale non poterà essere *superata* dal fervore dil sole: sol risplenderà circa *occidente...* se aparerà in *oriente...* serà li tonitrui magiori che li *lampezi... descenderanno* le pioge... da queste *regione* vigniranno li venti con pioze... quando in *septentrione* solamente serano li lampezi... se vederà la fiama dil fuocho essere *palida* et extenderse con *murmuramento...* non drita ma *tortuosa...* il *sonito* audito in el mare *tranquillo:* overo le *spume disperse* overo quando *boglieno* le acque et subito *cessa* et fa le spume bianche et *batendo* ne li saxi *concita voce* et *murmuramenti atroci...* natura apta a dare *presagii* et *pronostici...* Quali *remedii* debiano pigliare quelli che sono oppressi dal *periculo...* contra li periculi che molte fiate *occurreno...* il stomaco *turbato* subito se *aquietarà* per la *insparsione* di olio, inperò quelli che *nodano* in esso se *ongieno* la boca cum quello perché *mitiga* l'aspera natura di l'acqua... lo *absinthio* bevuto non lassarà venire il *vomito...* ancora il *remedio* di questa cosa; le lane distese *intorno* a le nave se bagneno prima che lo *spiramento* dil mare da le quale se poterà *exprimerse humore* dolce... vasi vodi et *submersi...* in lo mare *sorbeno* l'acqua dolce. Ancora l'acqua marina perde la sua *amaritudine* se la mesederai con l'argilla

cascare	disperse	attorniare
cadere	b[o]gliente	spiramento
caduco	cessare	exprimere
dimorare	abattere	radicale
meridionale	concita voce	humore
condurre	atroci	submerso
effusione d'acque	presagii	subbisato
superare	pronostici	amaritudine
occidente	remedii	
oriente	pericolare	
la[n]pegiare	occurrere	
descendere	turbare	
regione	aquietare	
septentrione	isparsione	
palido	notificare	
murmurio	longitudine	
tortuosità	mitigare	
sonito	absumpto	
tranquillo	vomitare	
spumegiante	remedio	

BAT – An image of vice, which cannot stay where virtue is. The more light there is, the more it squints, and the more it looks at the sun, the blinder it gets – Ms. H, fol. 14 r Drawing from Ms. B, fol. 89 v

223

THE MERCHANT AND THE FRIARS – The Franciscans have certain periods of abstinence during which they do not eat meat in their monasteries; but when travelling, since they live by alms, they have license to eat whatever is set before them. Now, on one such journey a pair of these friars stopped at an inn in the company of a certain peddler, who was at table with them, the inn being so poor that only one boiled chicken was served; whereat the peddler, seeing that the chicken was but little for him alone, turned to the friars and said, "If I remember aright, you do not eat any kind of meat in your monasteries these days." To these words the friars were compelled by their rule to say without hemming or hawing that this was true; so that the chapman had his desire and ate the chicken all by himself, and the friars got along as best they could.

Now, after this dinner, these table mates left together, all three; and after going a way they came on a river, good and broad and deep, and as all three were on foot, the friars by reason of poverty and the other by reason of avarice, it was necessary for company's sake for one of the friars, being barefoot, to take the peddler on his shoulders; so the friar took off his clogs and carried that man. Now it befell that when this friar was halfway across the river, he too remembered his rule; and stopping, like St. Christopher, he raised his head toward his human burden and said, "Tell me, do you have any money on you?" "Of course," the other answered, "how do you think we traders can get about any other way?" "Alas!" said the friar, "our rule forbids us to carry any money," and all at once threw him off into the water. When the merchant saw how amusingly his own previous trick had been avenged, he laughed, half blushing for shame, and accepted his punishment – Cod. Atl., fol. 150 v-b – Drawing in Milan, Ambrosiana

JEST – Someone said that the strangest things in the world grew in his district. His companion replied, "Your being born there proves it to be true, your ugly face is so queer" – Codex Atlanticus, folio 76 v-a – Drawing by Leonardo da Vinci in Lille, Museum

---

Valturio-Ramusio, sheet 252 v

..... la qual cosa de nemici prima fu *sbefata* dicendo che li Prusiani voleano combatere con li vasi *fictili*... ma quando comincionno essere *persequitadi* da li serpenti *territi* et *spauriti*... perché fanno le tavole et asse tanto *lubrice* che non ponno *firmarse* in piedi li adversari a conbatere. Anchora se alcuno volesse *approbare* questo: la qual cosa in molti exempli è *annotato*, elegere alcuni giovani atti et *prompti* quali sapiano nodare soto le aque et quando se acostano le nave foraranno cum le trivelle il fondo di esse: per la qual cosa se submergeveno. Il *transito* et passare di fiumi *anumerato* tra le *inventione digne* di *memoria*. Anchora è da agiongere questo *adviso* et *precepto*... dimostraremo *dichiarando* di tale chosa facta molti exempli: Alexandro *subiugò* la India... colocò li soi *alogiamenti* sopra la ripa dil fiume... largo circa stadii quatro et alto et *profondo*... il quale *simigliava* ad lui che facesse la *guarda* al campo...

Cod. Triv., fol. 50 r (p. 91)

sbeffare	approvare	subiugare
fittiva	proibire	allogiare
fintione	notitia	profondità
persequitare	prontitudine	simigliante
territi	transito	guardia
spauriti	situare	
lubrice	anumerare	
sdruciolente	degnità	
infermare	momentana	
amalare	memoria	
sanare	adviso	
ghuarire	precepto	
approbare	dichiarare	

Valturio-Ramusio, sheet 246 v

..... è *custodita* et *observata*... agiongeno altri tanti *inserandoli* et metandoli intra li altri... et a ciascuno di venti ne *computeno* dui altri... nasce overo *descende* in occaso... per le dodece *divisioni* quali se atribuisseno a l'aere... quali *concitano* et moveno la triplicità di segni... Sonno adoncha li venti principali dodece *distincti* in questo ordine, come dimostra la descriptione *infrascripta*... il più *debile cessa*... Sonno cioè da *nutrire* perché sonno *generatori* di ogni cosa: in quel medesimo tempo *exercitano* sue force et virtute et *molificano* il tempo di l'inverno... La stella caniculare sotto a la quale è il *fervore* di l'estate cioè quando il sole... per *continuo* spacio di giorni trenta... Aphrico nasce *incontrario*... et il verno non se *fortificase*... sencia *periculo* perché è *benigno* et *pacifico* sencia fortuna. Il resto dil tempo è *sotoposto* a lo inverno et avenga che li corsari cum il periculo di la morte primi habiano cominciato a navigare per il mare al tempo de lo inverno

Cod. Triv., fol. 55 r (p. 101)

custodia	superiore	benignio
observatione	nutrire	pacifico
inserando	gieneratione	mansueto
inestando	esercitatione	umano
i[n]sidendo	mollificare	pericolo
conputare	continuo	sottoposto
descendere	fervore	servitudine
diversioni	contrario	servitio
divisioni	averso	obedientia
concitare	oposito	
distintione	retroso	
infrascritta	antiporre	
debilità	fortificare	
cessare	altrettanto	

Cod. Triv., fol. 54 v (p. 100)

..... simelmente li mercadanti *avari* et *audacissimi* per la *immensa cupidità* di la roba non habiano curato la navigatione hybernale, *nondimeno*...

timore	scharsità	cupidità
subgiectione	parsimoni[a]	nondimeno
domabile	aldacia	
avaritia	imensa	

The specimens reproduced here represent only a portion of the coincidences found in comparing Leonardo's lexical lists and the Valturio-Ramusio text (for all the others, cf. *Gli appunti*, etc., I, 238 f.). Many conclusions follow from this discovery. Just as the sources previously mentioned showed us, we see that here too the words listed by Leonardo follow the order they have in the source. But while these sources are already in the form of lists chosen and arranged by Pulci or Perotti, we see Leonardo here gleaning his words in the course of reading a technical book. However, he does not pick out a very special scientific terminology, but deals with a part of the vocabulary that may seem very general and common to the modern reader, at first glance. It was just this aspect of the collected material which suggested that it was not meant to serve Leonardo for his own use, but only for the compilation of a dictionary for the use of others. Actually, however, we should realize that it is "Latin words" that are involved here, Latinisms, learned or semilearned terms that were strange to an "unlettered man" and presented semantic or orthographic problems.

There is a passage in a dialogue of Gelli[6] that seems to me very instructive in this connection. The Shoemaker asks the Soul: "What is the meaning of *negoziare* ["carry on a trade"]? I do not understand the word." The Soul replies: "*Negoziare* means nothing more than doing business, and being busy at something, doing everything necessary in it, and it is a verb that comes from a word that the Latins call *negotium*, which in our language means *faccenda* ["business"]." "It must be only a short time that it has been in use," the Shoemaker says, "because I for one do not remember ever having heard it spoken." "That is so, but have I not told you that as languages become more perfect, they are constantly being made over and taking new words as they are needed?" This was the situation of "unlettered" men in the sixteenth century, and if we examine the lexical lists of Leonardo, we see that all the words collected there are of the same class as *negoziare*, and many of them are even more uncommon, e.g., *concita voce, presagii, remedii, isparsione, absumpto, spiramento, exprimere, humore, submerso, amaritudine, fittiva, territi, lubrice, prontitudine*, etc. If we compare these words with the "Latin words" listed by Acarisio (cited above), we see that they are similar or identical.

Perhaps the most useful aspect of these comparisons with the Valturio-Ramusio text is that they make it possible to determine more precisely how much Leonardo transcribes and how much he adds out of his own head, and the proportion between the two parts. If we start with the first specimen given above, we see that after Leonardo has copied the verb *cascare* he adds on his own account the two words *cadere* and *caduco*, clearly connected with the first by synonymity and derivation. Similar

---

[6] "The Shoemaker's Caprices," in *Opere*, Milan, 1885, II, 83.

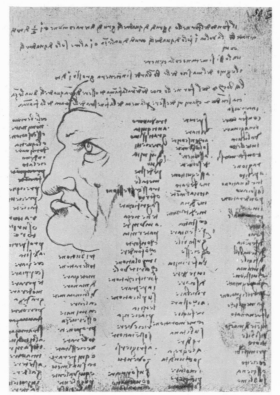

groupings in the Codex Trivulzianus lists struck Geymüller, who saw in them the beginnings of a philosophical dissertation on languages, as well as Morandi, to whom they represented a simple device for amassing words, and Del Lungo, who came closer to the truth, and saw them as signs of a special interest in synonyms, abstract words, "the possible relations of any word that gives rise to a family of words," and "the possibility [for a language] of logically taking form in new words." At this point it would have been enough to examine the teaching practices of the grammar schools of the Middle Ages and the Renaissance, in which the *disciplina derivationis*[7] was of considerable importance and constituted the normal practice of all men of letters, who drew up extensive λεξικοί ἐλέγχοι in their notebooks, revising and expanding them from day to day, to realize that this work, in which Leonardo drilled himself in "deriving" and "introducing into his tongue" the "Latin words" and grouping around some of them other related words, enriching his own vocabulary and making his language finer in its nuances, was an absolutely normal phenomenon at that time. Note how in the last of the specimens presented above Leonardo, having transcribed the word *contrario*, groups around the concept of contrariety the terms *averso, oposito, retroso, antiporre*; how the concept "subjected" (*sottoposto*) suggests *servitudine, servitio, obedientia, timore, subgiectione, domabile*; how *pacifico* is linked up with *mansueto, umano*, and *avaritia* is followed by *scharsità, parsimonia*.

Left: List of words – Cod. Triv. – Pl. 22, fol. 13 v

Center: List of words – Cod. Triv. – Pl. 54, fol. 30 r

Right: List of words – Cod. Triv. – Pl. 55, fol. 30 v

It is no marvel if here and there we find a word or two that has no connection whatever with those around it, and for which we can find no corresponding term in the source. This means that we have not yet managed to unearth it. Leonardo must have read the *De re militari* primarily for its extremely interesting content (our minds run to those underwater swimmers who bore holes in the bottoms of ships—the subject of a famous note by Da Vinci—and to the many notes on arms transcribed in Ms. B). Ramusio's prose is full of heavy Latinisms and Latinizing constructions that must have wearied Leonardo, who was still not an expert at Latin. It is probable that during his reading of the work, or during a rereading, he underlined the terms that were most striking or interesting to him. Later he must have gone on to collect this material, and in this phase of the work some errors in reading must have taken place, so that *se ongieno* has become *longitudine*, and *absinthio* has become *absumpto* (for some even more curious errors, cf. *Gli appunti*, etc., I, 284). Here Leonardo was under no obligation to follow strictly the order of the words in the source; sometimes his eye may have gone back over fields already harvested, to glean some ear that had been overlooked, or he may have skipped pages, or changed books. It is to one of these backward glances that we should attribute *altrettanto*, inserted on folio 55 recto between *fortificare* and *benignio*, but corresponding to *altri tanti* (*inserandoli*) at the beginning of the list. (With respect to *inserandoli*, it will be remarked that some vernacular idioms that are not Tuscan are also inserted among the "Latin" words).

WINE – Wine drunk by a drunken man revenges itself on the drinker – Cod. Forst. III, fol. 21 r – Drawing by Leonardo from Cod. Triv., fol. 28 r

The conclusions to which we have been led by our examination of Da Vinci's linguistic notes have also called for the revision of some ideas that are current among students of Leonardo. For example, the study of the sources has had to be put on a new basis.[8] It has been realized how much

---

[7] See, in *Gli appunti*, etc., the chapter on "Lexicography and the *disciplina derivationis* in the Humanist Schools."

[8] Cf. the essay by E. Garin in *Atti del Convegno di studi vinciani*, Florence, 1953.

harm has been done by the mania for discovering anticipatory divinations in everything Leonardo wrote, and we have come to see more clearly into the problems of his literary formation. He came from one of those artisan *botteghe* which were producing the future masters of the "mechanical arts," experts at shaping matter into all the forms created by fantasy, for all the material and spiritual needs of life. The instruction given there was practical rather than theoretical; the grammatical discipline of Latin was absent from them. When we come to think of it, the true meaning of Leonardo's famous declaration, "Since I am an unlettered man," boils down to a confession of not having Latin, the true entry to all the sciences. But in the artisan *bottega* Leonardo had discovered another way by which he could come even more surely to science; this is the way that passes through "mathematical demonstrations," the method of experiment, which cuts through the interminable sophistical disputations of the philosophers with the indisputable certainty of facts proved and proved over again. It is just toward his fortieth year that Leonardo challenges the boastful philosophers and dreams of a scientific treatment of mechanics, anatomy, hydraulics, etc., in order to arrive at a deeper knowledge of nature that would make it possible for the painter to repeat the images of the world with absolute faithfulness, without reducing them to the surface alone, and with all the richness of the life that palpitates in them through infinitely varied structures.

The artist-scientist must therefore make himself a writer: this is the problem that Leonardo sets himself at forty. Along with Ms. B, which is full of transcriptions from the *De re militari*, the Codex Trivulzianus collects the booty of "Latin words" derived from the same source. These are the first of Da Vinci's manuscripts to have a certain unity. Since he was unable to obtain from a direct knowledge of Latin the flow of words that the literati were deriving from it every day, in order to insert them into the mother tongue and bring it to "perfection," Leonardo was compelled to obtain them by way of the books written by the men of letters, and as he copied them out he also learned the secret of their formation, exercising himself in "deriving and introducing" them on his own account. The more specifically Latin exercises based on the *Rudimenti grammatices* date from a few years later, and show the modest progress made along that road. It is, however, very significant that this effort to master "letters" occurs just at the beginning of Leonardo's literary activity in the laborious peace of his first Milan period, when the great artist shone in the conversation of the court as well, as a teller of fables and riddles (*profezie*), as a creator of rebuses,[9] games, festivals, and theatrical devices.

THE FLINT AND THE STEEL – The flint, being struck by the steel for a spark, was astonished, and said harshly, "What arrogance makes you do this to me? Don't hurt me; you take me for somebody else, for I never did any harm to anyone." To which the steel replied, "If you are patient, you will see what wonderful fruit will come forth from you." At which words the flint was pacified and patiently endured the torment, and saw born from itself the wondrous fire, whose power operated in an infinite number of ways. This is said for those who take fear at the beginning of their studies, and then show that they can be masters of themselves and patiently give continual labor to their studies, from which marvelous things are seen to result – Cod. Atl., fol. 257 r-b – Drawing from Cod. Atl., fol. 56 v-b

Although advancing age and the troubles of the later years may have interrupted his study of Latin, Leonardo was able, by means of the study shown by his linguistic notes and the frequent practice of writing, to achieve a proud awareness of his own literary mastery, even without Latin, and, in a word, to liberate himself from the ingrained humanistic prejudice against the vernacular. "I have so many words in my mother tongue, that I am more concerned about not understanding things well than about lacking the words to express the ideas in my mind" (Quad. Anat. II, fol. 16 r). But we know that he too, "an unlettered man," following in the footsteps of the men of letters enriched and brought to perfection his mother tongue, deriving and introducing into it a stream of "Latin words."

AUGUSTO MARINONI

---

[9] I have brought these all together in a volume entitled *I rebus di Leonardo da Vinci, raccolti e interpretati con un saggio su "una virtù spirituale,"* Florence, 1954. This problem is presented on p. 37 f.

Before dealing with this fascinating aspect of Da Vinci, it must be stated that, in the present condition of our knowledge, the figure of Leonardo as a musician is the vaguest among all the images of the many-sided genius that have been left to us. And it should be added at once, for the information of the unspecialized public, that the solution of the problem is of more interest to the musicologist than to the musician. The scientist looking for new light on the history of the art of a little-explored period will profit more by the inquiry than the artist who may hope to find unknown music worthy of the great master. The latter may still hope for discoveries of this nature, but the musicologists no longer hope.

Without further examination, it is hard to believe that Leonardo was a "great musical figure." We know that the period from 1474 to 1519, in which he may have worked practically as a composer, was completely dominated, in the schools and in the official world, by the Flemish masters of what is called the "third period," and in popular art by forms not as well known as they ought to be, which, in any event, were the *frottola*, the *villotta*, the *rispetto*, the *strambotto*, and the ubiquitous polyphonic *canzone*, which was courtly in Italy and France, and spiritual in pre-Lutheran Germany and mystical Spain—in the former marked by the influence of the Meistersinger, and in the latter by troubadour or Moorish survivals, with varying accompaniments played on plucked instruments.

Now, the first printed works of Petrucci, which reflect the fashion of the times in Italy, offer us motets and *canzoni* by De Orto and Agricola, by Okeghem, Josquin, and many other Flemings, as well as by innumerable Italian *frottolisti*, but do not present a single *canzone* by Messer Leonardo da Vinci, a Florentine engineer in the service of the Duke of Milan, who was so well known, so famous in that intelligent and intellectual world to which the well-informed publisher dedicated the *Odhecaton A* and the *Canti B*, the ten books of *frottole*, the lute tablatures, and all the varied production of his print shops at Venice and Fossombrone.

And not only did Petrucci, Antico, and the successors to their printing art not know, while Leonardo was alive, that he was an important musical figure; no more did Attaignant and the other French publishers, who were vigorous revivers of works of the past, recall the great protégé of the king of France ten, twenty, or thirty years after Leonardo had died.

In a word, we are without the most important kind of evidence, printed works; and besides this absence there are circumstances that compel us to interpret it rather as negation than as forgetfulness.

This is a disconcerting beginning for investigation of the "excellent musician" of whom Vasari speaks. But if we overcome our disappointment as musicians and listen to the patient musicologist as he goes to the other sources, in biography and iconography, we find assertions that gradually increase in number and thereby in weight until they come to assume very great importance. Leonardo was not a composer; at least, he did not have the will nor the patience to write. But he knew music, loved it, practiced it, and made an important contribution to it.

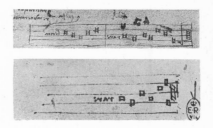

Two musical phrases by Leonardo – Windsor, Royal Collection, no. 12697, 12699

Study of mechanical violin conceived by Leonardo da Vinci – Cod. Atl., fol. 218 r-c

Study for "bow" of "viol" – Ms. H, fol. 28 v

"Bow" for "viol" – Ms. H, fol. 28 r

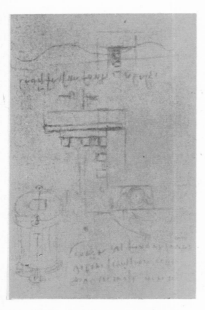

"Bow" for "viol" – Ms. H, fol. 29 r

The biographical sources, summed up by Vasari, tell us that when Leonardo was a youth in Florence, he attended schools of all kinds, besides Verrochio's. We believe it. These sources tell us that he studied music: we do not doubt it. And it is of little importance to us to know whether his teacher was, as Peladan asserts, no other than the great old Squarcialupi, or some other one of the twelve able masters set to teaching music under Medicean auspices.

They say that he made rapid progress: this is accepted without the shadow of a doubt, for it would be astonishing if it had been otherwise. But we are even more willing to believe, without asking for further proof, that he was primarily self-taught in this subject, as in every other.

We believe that he sang with a fine voice, both in polyphonic groups and solo, accompanying himself on the lyre, which he played extremely well. This is an important point that comes to us from Vasari.

We believe that Leonardo played the lyre extremely well; in fact, we believe, because of what we have said earlier, that he played it like an autodidact of genius, better than anyone else.

Did he not sing to his own accompaniment? This statement of Vasari's, fully confirmed in other ways, is supported by the preceding data and confirms them in turn; it enables us to regard it as certain that Leonardo's musical studies were not only "fairly profound," but decidedly so, comprehensive and continuing.

For we must not forget that the accompaniment of singing at the end of the fifteenth century was not and could not be of the very simple type that any dilettante, from the seventeenth century to our times, has been able to perform on the guitar; it was not chord strumming of a harmonic sort. The Camerata at Florence and Grossi da Viadana came almost a hundred years later, and harmony was unknown, even though it existed and governed composition (just as the law of gravity, while it ruled the universe at that time as well, was still unknown as a law).

When Leonardo presented himself to the Duke and Duchess of Milan with his famous horse's-head lyre, the instrumental accompaniment of a *canzone* was contrapuntal in style; it was an arrangement for the instrument (*in chordis*) of the two, three, or four parts in horizontal motion, without which no proper *canzone*, learned or popular, was conceivable before the Florentine revolution of the Casa Bardi. Hence the dilemma: either Leonardo also invented both accompanied monody and the art of accompanying it (and this we do not believe), or else he performed "out of his head," in the 1480's and 1490's, what Franciscus Bossiniensis was to write and give to the press of Petrucci some years later, in 1509.

This is possible. And it says in the clearest manner that Leonardo knew music splendidly, and better than most.

"He surpassed all the other musicians," says Vasari. And how well he puts it! The practice of accompanying song with one or more instruments is a good deal older than Leonardo; it is as old as the singing schools of the Carolingian era. The voice is accompanied at all stages, in unison, in diaphony, with *gemello* and faux-bourdon, with mile-long tenor notes, with free and capricious descants, with canons. But all this was outmoded at the end of the fifteenth century, when people accompanied themselves with Flemish-style contrapuntal imitations. This was the manner, very fashionable in his time, but the most difficult when used for improvisation, in which Leonardo must have accompanied himself when he astounded the audience in the Sforza house. He knew the craft like a master. Vasari, with a single phrase, has enabled us to be sure of it.

We pass to other historical sources. Some assertions in them are obscure or of no significance. They tell us that Leonardo came to Milan (but was it in 1483 or 1494?) bringing with him a pupil, Atalante Migliorotti. But the latter took part, at Mantua, in the first performance of Politian's *Orfeo*, which occured in 1471. Is it possible that Leonardo brought with him as a pupil an artist who was already well known and who was at least as old as he, if not older?

He is said to have had some other "pupils" and to have been in touch with musicians of some importance—Gusnaschi, Gisiberti, Gian Giani, Gherardini, at Milan, at Florence, at Venice. But this means nothing for our purposes, and is at best tentative evidence.

He served together with Franchino Gaffurio. This is an indisputable fact and of considerable importance. He was very friendly with a family of four lutanists from Lyons called Duiffopruggar (=Tieffenbrucker); and this is information of capital importance, although there is little reliable confirmation of it. His friendship with Gaffurio, his fellow worker in the services of the court and the city, could not but have given rise to academic discussions of the mathematics of sound, and his intimacy with the lutanists could not but have given rise to discourses on the physics and mechanics of sound. This we shall see later. Let us therefore give a passing glance at the pictures decorating the 1490 and 1496 editions of Gaffurio's *Musica practica* (which are so crude that no one could reasonably conceive of attributing them to Leonardo, although some have done so) and at the "portrait of a musician" in the Ambrosiana, which may not even represent Gaffurio, but which at all events was never touched by Leonardo's hand, and go on to Leonardo's drawings, to the iconographic sources and the manuscripts.

It would be in point to start by reading some of Da Vinci's words with reference to music. But we do not believe that those pretty dreams, worthy of a troubadour at the court of Frederick II in Palermo, shed any light on the musicianship of the man who wrote them: "A garden covered

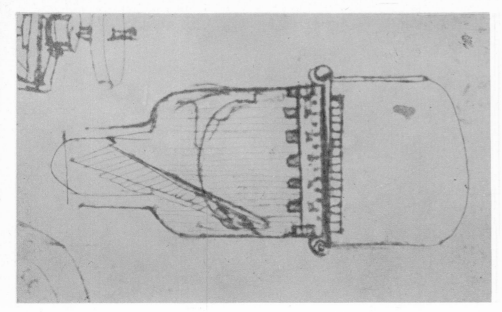
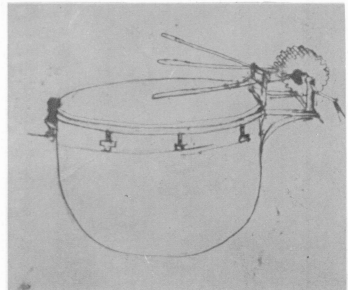

with a net and full of singing birds;" "A mill that gives forth sound as it turns"; and then: "There should be made" fountains in tune. And this, that, and the other thing "should be made." All this is in character for a decadent poet, not for a musician or someone who knows music.

On the other hand, Leonardo's assertions regarding the greater power of visual emotion as compared to auditory emotion, and his often repeated demonstrations of the superiority of painting to the other arts, are philosophical disquisitions that do not give us the right to conclude, as has been done, that the great man had a sort of insensitivity to music. That would not do at all, after the academy in which Leonardo "surpassed all the other musicians!" Let us see what the manuscripts say.

We shall divide the Da Vinci drawings into two categories—those depicting instruments without any other specific purpose, and those which appear to be genuine studies for creating new instruments or modifying old ones. The first kind might include the drawing of the lute player, with the little volume of highly legible written music. But criticism tends to exclude this work from the catalogue of Leonardo's productions. Then we find drawings of the viol, as an entity or shown in its parts, in certain manuscripts. Here some students seem to have gone astray.

In verbal descriptions of Leonardo's drawings, some writers have gone so far as to state that he designed viols "with a new finger board." The word has betrayed the thought. It has led people who had not seen the drawing, but were familiar with musical terminology and jargon, to imagine that Leonardo tried to change the proportions of the distances between frets, that is, the distances separating the little crosspieces that are found in almost identical form in the lute and its derivatives, and which, on the neck of the old fretted viol, marked off precisely the fractions of the length.

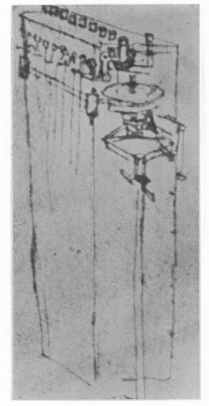

This would immediately give Leonardo a place among the theoreticians of music, beside his contemporaries Gaffurio and Burzio, Pareja and Spataro; but nothing of the kind ever happened. Instead, Leonardo made many studies in an effort to make it easier to handle the keyed viol (*viola a tasti*), or *gironda*, also called *sinfonia* and *lira da orbo* in Italy, *vielle* in France, hurdy-gurdy in England—a wheeled viol, in short, and something very hard to find today, even among old street mendicants.

How many times did Leonardo draw the finger board and the box or sound chest of the hurdy-gurdy? Innumerable times—in the Codex Atlanticus, in the Codex Arundel, in all sorts of places. It could be truly said to have been an obsession of his. The matter interested him. We shall go further, and at the risk of hurting the feelings of the sentimental, assert that he was very much interested in it, but from an entirely different point of view than they in their enthusiasm imagine: it was from the mechanical point of view, and within a frame of reference in which all Leonardo's activities as an instrument designer are to be located. He always tended to mechanize the player's performance. Why? Perhaps because replacing the hand made superhuman in the miracle of art seemed to him the supreme and most difficult conquest that the science of mechanics could make. And just as he designs a trumpet with keys, but with the keys arranged like those of keyboard instruments (Cod. Arund., fol. 175 r), and as he draws snare drums and kettledrums equipped with a toothed wheel to make the roll easy and regular, and with a screw to stretch the skin systematically, and as he draws a cylinder with pegs that can perform a canon merely by being turned (in total defiance of the learned composers of rounds, canons, and so-called fugues), just so he draws and draws again the apparatus with frets for dividing the length of the string, the sound box with its jacks and tangents, the finger board of the *viola da orbo*.

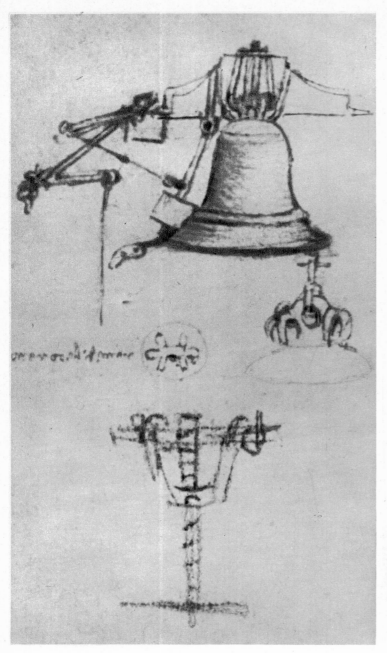

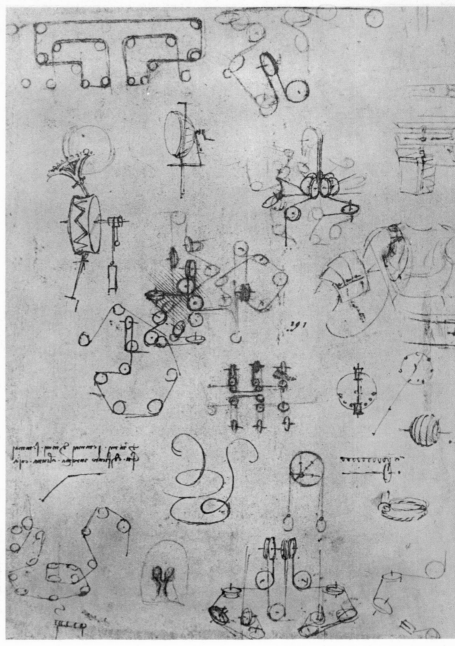

The player may go ahead with confidence and turn the crank, only pressing the keys; the sound will come out much better than before, since mechanics has taken the place of his skill.

The cylinder with pegs, mentioned above, is another of Leonardo's favorite themes. It is to open in order, at the will of the person setting the pegs, the stops of organ pipes (Cod. Arund., fol. 137 v); it is to actuate the clappers of the bells of a carillon; it is to perform a canon with variable time intervals. Twice, unless we have overlooked other cases, he sets up a canon mechanically—once in the Arundel codex and once in the Windsor drawing no. 12697, which is reproduced in the *Enciclopedia Treccani*. In both instances he also writes musical notes; these, on the basis of what we said at the outset, are the only notes from his hand that have come down to us.

The musical reader will prick up his ears at this point and put the challenge: "Is the theme worth anything or not? This is the point at which to test whether Leonardo was a musician and understood composition." We do not have the proof. Our only response to the musician consists in the two themes that might be based on the modern pentatone, and an invitation to resolve the two canons. First, however, a word of advice: there are certain harsh successions that did not frighten the musicians of Da Vinci's period. Second, not all Flemish canons can be resolved without "mutation."

Was Leonardo da Vinci, then, a finished musician? After tests of this nature, there can no longer be any doubt: he was a finished musician. He knew how to state a canon. He did not work it out, perhaps because he had neither the time nor the desire to do so, and perhaps because his mind was dedicated to the mechanical problems involved and suggested in music more than to music as an art.

He planned a new instrument which he called the *viola organista*. He drew it twice on a page of the Codex Atlanticus. With two lines he crossed out the second drawing and condemned it with the word *falso*. Later, he took up the idea again (Cod. Atl., fol. 218 r-*c*) and brought it to completion with modification which, conceived by a mechanical mind, anticipate one of the most interesting of modern automatic instruments, whose only impediment to being artistic is precisely

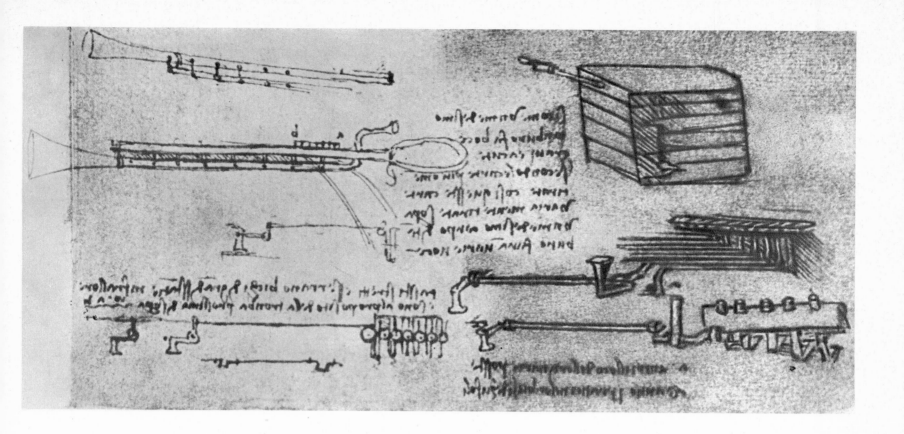

that they are automatic. The difference is that Leonardo's "organist viol" is not automatic and, if it had been built, could have become an artistic instrument.

We do not think that a detailed description of Leonardo's organist viol would be in place in this article. The design and a hint or two will suffice. There are two drawings, as we have said. In the instrument shown in the first, the strings are stroked by a wheel; in the final form they are brought into contact with a moving bundle of horsehairs. The finger board brings the given string (mounted on an independent guide) into contact with the horsehair.

The feat most recently attributed to Leonardo is that of having had a share in the invention of the violin. The question may be stated in the following terms. It is asserted that Leonardo not only knew the Duiffopruggar "family" of lutanists, to whom criticism both recently and in the past has been inclined to assign a rather large share in the invention of the violin, but was also very intimate with them. We speak of the "family" and not specifically of the bearded Caspar Duiffopruggar of Voeriot, because, as Mme. Roux Champion asserts, there were four lutanist Duiffopruggars—grandfather, father, son, and nephew. This implies a much longer period of activity as lutanist than has previously been supposed, and makes it possible that a violin was in existence as early as the first years of the sixteenth century. Where was it made? In Milan or Florence, in some household where Leonardo was a frequent guest. And nothing of this sort would have taken place in a house that he visited as a friend without his knowing it; it is impossible that Leonardo, knowing what the lutanist was doing, should not have lent a hand to it, or words or a drawing or advice.

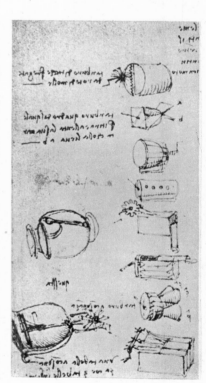

Now we need only find some proof for this gratuitous supposition. Does the famous 1506 violin given to the Emperor Maximilian exist? Did it exist? Did anyone see it? Was it a head by Leonardo that was carved on the violin seen and owned by the lutanists cited by Mme. Roux Champion? Was this instrument a violin or a small viol? Did it have a sound post, bass bar, sloping finger board, and scroll? The scroll itself has been said to be of Leonardian paternity. Does it not have the form of a snail, and is not the snail one of Leonardo's symbols, repeated so many times— appearing, as one instance, in the painting of Leda, in which there are the two *putti* bearing the legend "Caspar" amid their blond curls? These are vague hypotheses; we put them aside.

There is, however, a much more weighty fact, although it comes out of a problem that has not yet been solved. Since the violin was created while Leonardo was alive, who else in his time could have conceived its geometrical construction, and definitely and completely solved that tremendous problem in acoustics? A craftsman like the Duiffopruggars or Bertolotti? It is not desired here to make risky assertions; but there are people who think of Leonardo as the most probable theoretician of the structure of the violin.

We end in the only way possible—by bowing our heads in reverence before the genius who saw and chose what he pleased in every field of thought, heedless of fate and all but heedless of his own creative power, who passed by music and possessed it as if in sport, and, if he endowed it with a gift or gave it a thought, did so by chance or by caprice. The flight of the genius had another goal.

ENRICO MAGNI-DUFFLOCQ

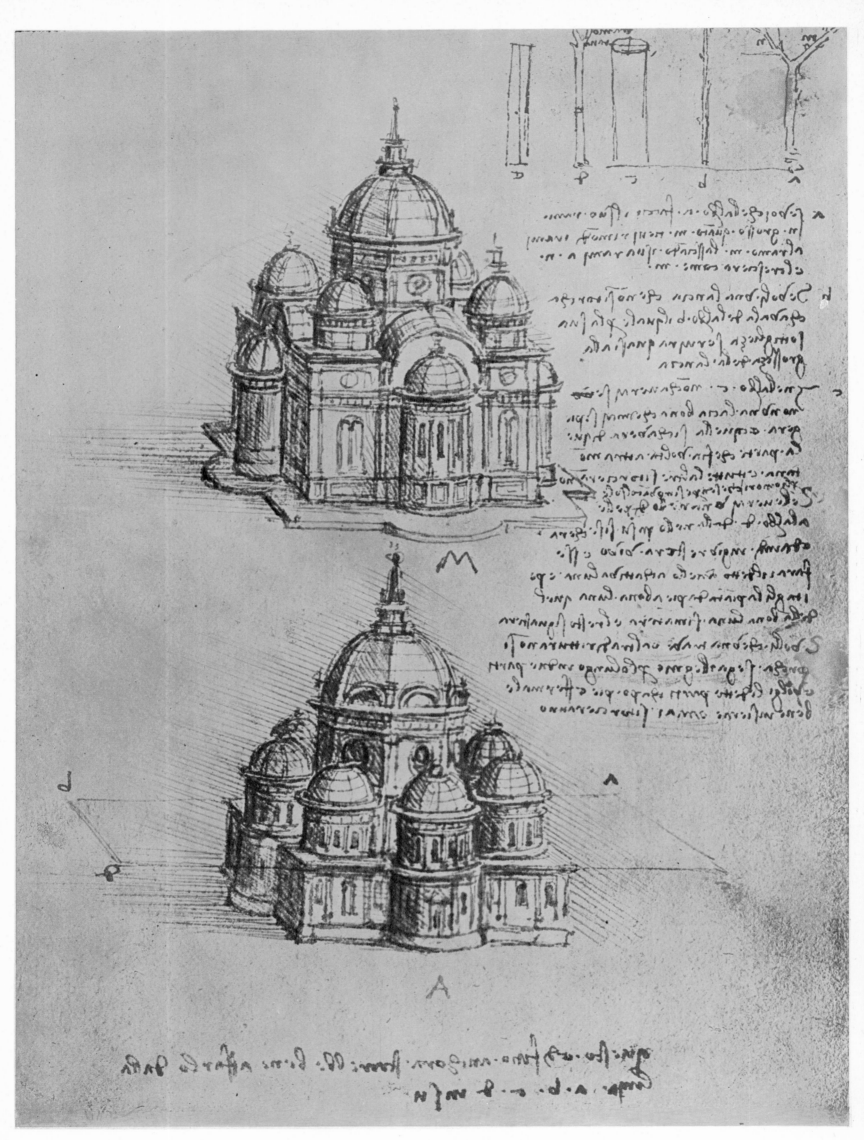

Domed churches with central plans – Study of proportions – Ms. B, fol. 17 v

Leonardo is to be considered as a theoretician in architecture. It was only in a very few cases that he faced concrete problems of construction, as for example the project of erecting the *tiburio* (crossing tower) of the cathedral of Milan; in all likelihood, the ultimate purpose of his studies was the compilation of a treatise like those of Vitruvius, Alberti, or Filarete. The only basis for attributing the church of Santa Maria della Fontana to him is a drawing in the Codex Atlanticus that is too vague to have any value as evidence; nor can we with any certainty assert the existence of precise directives emanating from Leonardo in relation to the construction of the cathedral at Pavia.

Nonetheless, the further we go in examining the Italian architecture of the Renaissance in its aspiration toward complete expression of that perfect eurythmya, that rigorous equilibrium in which the harmonic and firm unity of Platonic thought seems to have taken concrete form, the stronger and clearer does the figure of Leonardo stand out, for no one seems to have felt as he did the importance of the central plan in the statement and development of the new style.

The sketches scattered in the various codices, and concentrated in greatest number in the Codex Atlanticus, show us the torment and travail of a man who was endeavoring to go beyond any solution yet reached, in order to study all the possibilities of a given scheme. The research is motivated by the irresistible creative need of the fantasy, aroused by the scientific curiosity that we find at the bottom of every one of Leonardo's activities. The artist puts signs down on paper to fix the solutions that are ripening in his mind. They are notes that may perhaps be developed some day, quick comments recorded in order not to forget a sudden thought or the fruit of a long meditation, sketches that seem to comment on and illustrate an entire train of reasoning. This has been taken sometimes, all too hastily, as mere dilettantism, and it may give the appearance of an academic exercise; but it represents Leonardo's concrete contribution to the architectural development of the Second Renaissance.

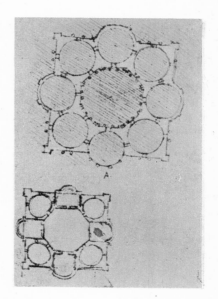

Plans of domed churches shown on opposite page – Ms. B, fol. 18 r

Leonardo resided in Florence during his youth, from about 1470 to 1482, and for the greater part of that time he was in Verrocchio's studio. Filippo Brunelleschi had recently died, and Leon Battista Alberti followed him in those years; but the impetus the two great men had imparted to the new architecture that was transforming the city and making its way everywhere in the world can be said to have been in full flower. The fellow student of Perugino and Sandro Botticelli, living as a youth in constant contact with the scientists collected in the *Studio fiorentino*, in an environment of living humanistic culture, could not but catch fire from such a tremendous striving for renewal; and certainly even in that early period he must have posed to himself those problems which he was to meditate on all through his life.

The memories of the Baptistery, of Santa Maria degli Angeli, and of Santo Spirito, long and lovingly studied, were never to leave him again; but when he was far away, it was principally Santa Maria del Fiore that would be before his eyes, the model of the attempted fusion of two schemes —the one of central symmetry, the other of development in length. The portion of the church

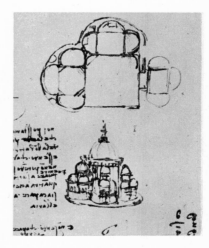

Apse with plural chapels – Type of tribune of Santa Maria del Fiore in Florence – Cod. Atl., fol. 265 v-*a*

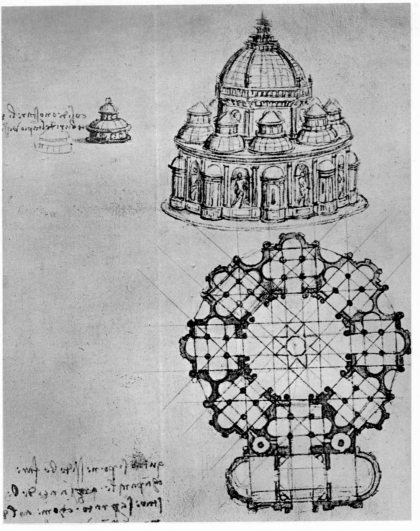

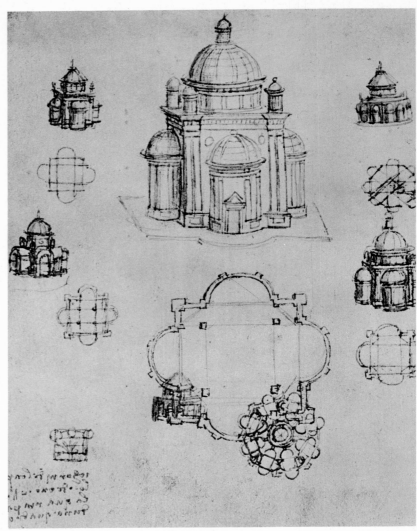

designed for the clergy must have been especially interesting to him for its harmonious distribution of volumetric values, for its gradual transition, through the phases of hemispherical and pyramidal surfaces, from dominated multiplicity to dominant unity, and for the sense of serene power given by its immense dome, sustained and secured by the closed circle of the chapels. Few structures of this type offer a richer ensemble of structural solutions and plastic conceptions. The influence of this edifice was tremendous in the development of Leonardo's architectural thinking, which was to find new food for reflection and a new impetus in the church of San Lorenzo in Milan.

To realize the value of Leonardo's contribution to the development of structures built on a central plan, we must take into consideration the achievements of the architecture of imperial Rome and the new affirmations of the Florentine masters of the fifteenth century.

In the resources of Roman technique, the theme of the central plan had had every possibility of answering to the basic conceptions of the formation of spaces and of a monumental plasticity that would go beyond the iron discipline of the trilithic system and seek new elements of beauty in curved lines and surfaces. In the Roman architects' temples, fountains, baths, and mausoleums, bold and brilliant inventions seem to have run through all the possibilities. After the building of the Pantheon and the temple of Minerva Medica, the Serapeum at Pozzuoli and the four-faced arches, the mausoleum of Diocletian and that of Santa Costanza, and above all after the creation of the Laurentian group, it was a difficult matter to add anything new to such a rich repertory. The Byzantines made the attempt with Santa Sophia and San Vitale, but, we feel, without achieving results of absolute originality.

Throughout the Middle Ages the pattern continued to flourish, alongside the basilica plan, taking the form of the Byzantine church in the Orient and that of the baptistery in the Occident; and although there are other religious structures with central plans, the reference is perfectly clear in the case of baptisteries. Moreover, the attempt to fuse the central and the longitudinal conception, which had been made even before its expression in the *Duomo* at Florence, shows that the former idea always was present in the field.

With Brunelleschi, the Florentine fifteenth century took up the theme again and worked it out once more with a clear and serene sense of proportion and that simple and aristocratic grace which is characteristic of Tuscan art. The spaces, harmoniously composed and cleanly formed by smooth luminous walls under slender cornices, recall solutions of Roman architecture, expressed, however,

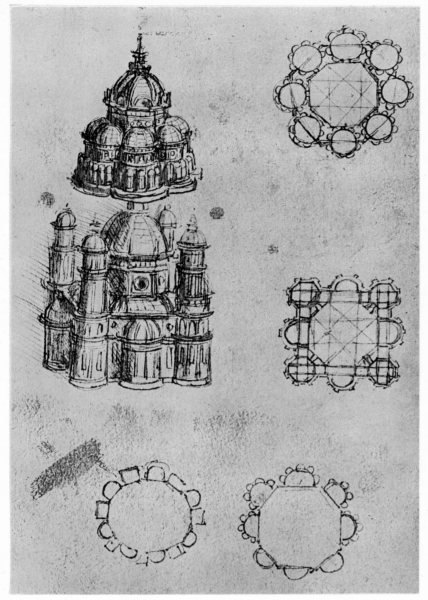

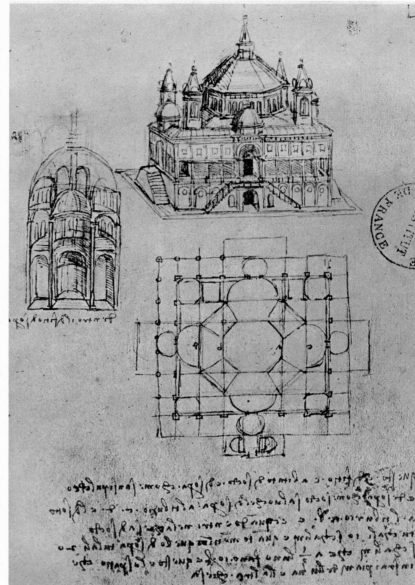

with the new spirit that modelled the delicate framing of San Lorenzo and the Pazzi chapel. Leonardo thus was confronted, if not with a revival, at least with a re-evaluation of buildings with central plans, which must have been of deep interest to his speculative mind.

Leonardo's architectural sketches, scattered in the various manuscripts, may be divided as follows: notes on solutions seen and put down on paper in the desire not to let anything escape that was worthy of attention (San Lorenzo in Milan, the *Duomo* in Florence); memories of edifices called to mind with a subtle nostalgia for his distant native land (Santo Spirito); problems confronted with a view to a concrete solution (*tiburio* of the Milan cathedral, planning of the Romorantin island); quick notations of original ideas set down to be reworked later in a meditated development.

Now, it is in this last-named activity that Leonardo's contribution to the architecture of the Second Renaissance will be found; and it is a contribution to other things as well.

In the case of the "ideal city," the objection might be raised that he had proposed its embodiment in reality to Ludovico il Moro, but we believe that this proposal followed rather than preceded the urbanistic vision projected into a future that had not yet been reached. But there is no doubt in the case of the buildings with central plans. Here we find the exercise of thought on a problem that we can consider as abstract, for all its seeming concreteness. In what different ways can spaces be grouped around a vertical axis? And in how many ways are these spaces susceptible of material definition? And, again, what new solutions can be given for the structure-space relationship?

The inquiry extended not only to the program of classical and medieval architecture, but also to the masters of the Renaissance, and led up to the extreme possibilities of complicated but logical and harmonious associations and interpenetrations of volumes. Around cubical, polygonal, or cylindrical structures, smaller volumes are massed and multiplied, and the hollows of recesses are scooped out in ever accelerated rhythms, until we reach sensations of rotatory motion that the rigid lines of the pilasters and buttresses cannot hold back. The arches with their extrados to the outside, the crowd of cupolas surrounding the central dome, almost always with spires, the superimposed drums, the lanterns, the cusps—all are, as it were, the inevitable outcome of such an overwhelming *élan vital*.

The memory of the monuments of Florence keeps coming back in the sketches, especially the recollection of Santa Maria del Fiore and the Baptistery. But these are not the only buildings that

Left: Plans and perspective views of churches with plural cupolas – Ms. B, fol. 25 v

Right: Plan, section, and perspective view of domed structure of square plan with porticoed façades – Cod. Ashb., II, fol. 4 r

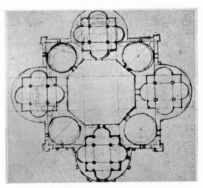

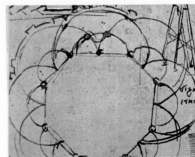

Plans for many-domed churches – Ms. B., fol. 19 r, 35 r

235

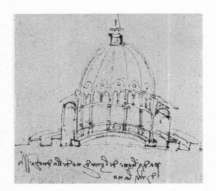

Pavilion in maze of Duke of Milan – Ms. B, fol. 12 r

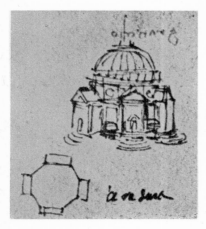

Domed church with cruciform plan – Ms. B, fol. 12 r

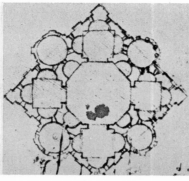

Plan (below) and perspective view (above) of many-domed church on square plan, with four apses – Ms. B, fol. 22 r

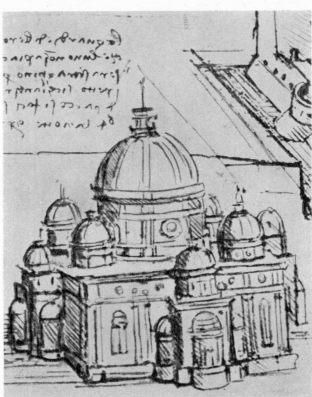

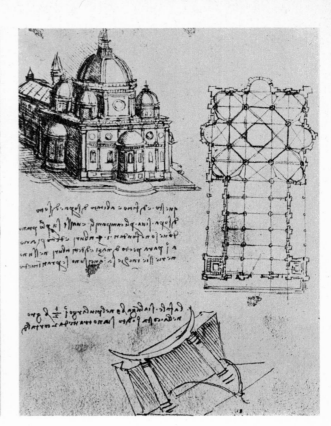

arouse Leonardo's fantasy: San Lorenzo in Milan is always vividly before his eyes, and Santa Maria in Pertica at Pavia and even the monuments of Venice are not strangers to some of his most fortunate ideas.

Leonardo is all taken up with the essential problem, and hardly pays attention to the architectural details, which are a matter of indifference to him; but not infrequently we are surprised, as if by an unexpected gleam, by precursory hints at new sensibilities and manners that were to come much later: we are surprised and disconcerted.

Do these summary expressions of Leonardo's thought, which never took form in works fully studied and translated into reality, suffice to prove his influence on the development of architecture? We have no doubt of it. Leonardo is an architect potentially. In him artistic intuition runs before scientific investigation, but the one and the other, although completing each other, never give him the joy of attaining the goal. In the very action that creates a new form he detects all the possibilities which that form suggests to him, and he follows them up, reaches them, and goes beyond. Even if men and means had permitted, he might never have completed an edifice he had planned. He would work for years on a picture or a statue, making and remaking it with that thirst for perfection which made him infinitely discontented. And this could not have been permitted him in such a practical field of work as building.

But we think of what an irresistible power of persuasion and force of inspiration there must have been in the words of this artist whose habit it was to scrutinize the mysteries of nature, to understand and unveil the great harmony of the universe, and of how these words must have affected those who approached him and were fortunate enough to speak with him.

About 1496, Donato Bramante was erecting the dome of Santa Maria delle Grazie; toward the end of that year Leonardo was deep in his work on the *Last Supper*. The two masters worked side by side, and perhaps as night was falling, when they came down from the scaffolding with tired bodies and minds still vibrating from the effort of creation, they met and spoke to each other of their art under the arcades of the silent cloister. And they had other opportunities of discussing architecture together when the question of the *tiburio* of the Milan cathedral came up, or when they went to Pavia for the construction of the cathedral there. Is it not to be assumed that Leonardo, enthusiastic over his studies on buildings with central plans, must have discussed them with his friend, showing him all the possibilities he had worked out, revealing to him new points of view that no one had ever thought of before? And his talks, which all listened to with an attention tempered with amazement and respect—must they not have been a fertile seed in the minds of the architects who met him in Milan and Pavia, in Florence and Rome?

After Leonardo's time, the development of the idea of the central plan seems to be filled with a new spirit, directed to a reappraisal of spatial values, which multiply and become stabilized and fused, dominated by the cupola, that Roman element *par excellence*. The derivation of many later structures, or at least their relationship with Leonardo's solutions, is plain; but the boldest and most impressive of them still represent, after four centuries, suggested possibilities that have never been realized, not even by the fanciful architects of the Baroque period.

GINO CHIERICI

Centered plans – Perspective views of churches with plural cupolas – Arches – Architectural elements – Cod. Atl., fol. 362 v-*b*

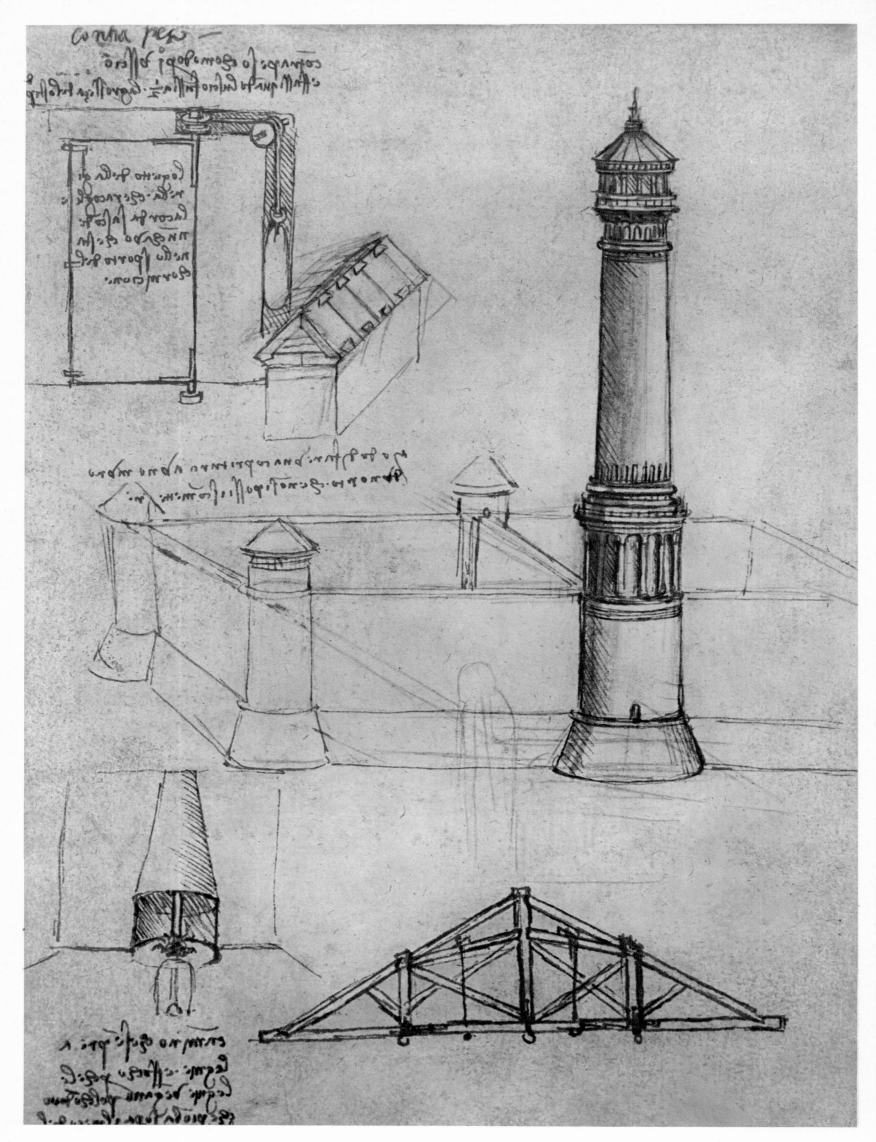

Architectural drawings – Projects of towers – Ms. B, fol. 23 v

LEONARDO AS ARCHITECT

The studies that have been made of the most versatile and inclusive genius that humanity has produced have always, by an irony of fate, been fragmentary and one-sided, because all who undertake such inquiries must be contented with a partial knowledge, attained often with great struggles; and it is hard to see as of now how anything better can be hoped for.

Investigations into the artistic power and achievement of this miraculous researcher in art and in science, this man of thought and harmonious action, have usually stressed his matchless value as a painter and searched for the basic principles of his activities as sculptor and architect as though these had been accessory expressions of an essentially pictorial genius.[1] The internal dynamics of Da Vinci studies have tended in the same direction, for the reasoning went by deduction on the basis of inspection of intrinsically pictorial materials, the drawings of Leonardo. On the other hand, the researches conducted by more understanding minds either were confined to the precise determination of well-documented chronologies or have produced more or less accurate anthologies, such as Richter's, which is inadequate to a great extent today, because of our demand for more exact and methodical analysis. It may be useful for the collection of specific data to limit the scope of the investigation in order to make it more intensive, but that also means precluding any genuine critical understanding of a phenomenon that can be evaluated only as a whole. This is why Heydenreich, who has written very useful pages full of observations and data on Leonardo as a church architect, never arrived at any final conclusions, confining his field of study to a limited number of Da Vinci's architectural drawings.[2] These drawings, however, are related on the one hand to the subjective background of Da Vinci's tendencies and artistic tastes and on the other to active experimentation on the norms that guide the positive sciences, and must therefore be studied with both aspects in view.

Detail of façade for two-storied palace – Windsor, Royal Collection, no. 12759 v

Beltrami well says that in Leonardo "the natural, instinctive tendency to take up architectural themes" was but a manifestation of the "spirit of inquiry that drove his mind to cope with and exhaust every element of art or science."[3] Even as early as the end of his first Florentine period, the investigative drive of the artist isolated him in an intense experimentation in the most diverse sectors of that knowledge in relation to which "no human investigation may deem itself true science if it has not passed through a mathematical demonstration."[4] This later led Fra Saba da Castiglione to mourn that "when he should have attended to painting, in which he would have been a new Apelles, he devoted himself altogether to geometry, architecture, and anatomy."[5] But it was also the reason why, in the famous draft of a letter to Ludovico il Moro found in the Codex Atlanticus (fol. 391 r-a), the artist appears already endowed with that tremendous knowledge oriented to deeply moral considerations and purposes by a kind of cosmic mysticism of Pythagorean tinge.[6]

Cathedral of Faenza – Ms. L, fol. 15 v

[1] G. C. Argan, in "The Problem of Bramante," in *Rivista marchigiana*, no. 7-9 (reprint), p. 6, sees as characteristic of Leonardo "a taste for forms that appear, with a sudden formal suggestion, from the vague atmosphere, or that are softened by the atmosphere to go off into the gentlest, most imperceptible of planes."
[2] L. H. Heydenreich. *Die Sakralbau-Studien Leonardo da Vincis*. Leipzig, 1929, p. 98.
[3] L. Beltrami. *Leonardo e i disfattisti suoi*, p. 179 f.
[4] *Idem. Leonardo, scritti*, p. 41.
[5] S. da Castiglione. *Ricordi*, Venice, 1560, p. 57.
[6] G. Calvi. *Contributi alla biografia di Leonardo da Vinci*, p. 15, no. 1.

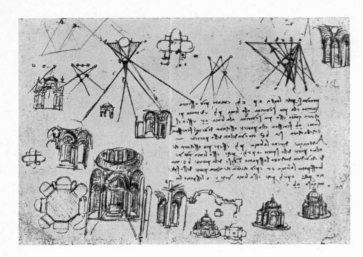

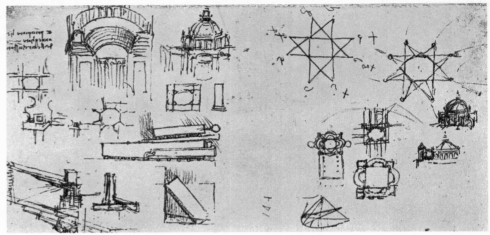

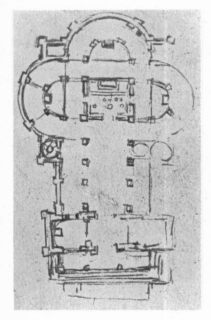

Plan of basilican church – Ms. B,
fol. 35 v

Section and external development of
church with four chapels – Cod. Atl.,
fol. 205 v-*a*

Idea of church with cross-shaped plan
– Cod. Atl., fol. 362 r-*b*

Gerolamo Calvi has subtly tracked down the most hidden meanders of the complex experimental development that culminates in Leonardo's superb power of invention,[7] and his observations are of especial importance with respect to such of the artist's researches as those in architecture. Da Vinci constantly asserts and investigates the connection of architecture with the experimental sciences, relating it to statics with respect to the causes for the cracking of arches and vaults, to geometry as regards the symmetrical development of proportional masses, to physiology in relation to the requirements of a rational and ethical organization of urban and rural building.[8] To Leonardo, the divine harmony of the universe is likewise due to the parallelism of the norms that govern phenomena, which can be explained in terms of the analogies between them: in presenting to the deputies in charge of the construction of the Milan cathedral the reasons in favor of a certain plan for the *tiburio* [tower at the crossing of nave and transept], he resorts to principles identical with those underlying the physical soundness of a human being.[9]

It will be seen, therefore, that a simple listing of the number and types (already widely known) of the architectural elements delineated by the master will be of little help in solving the more general architectural questions that are posed today on the basis of more rigorous methods of research. Moreover, we need no longer debate whether these architectural drawings were connected with actual construction work carried out by Leonardo, or whether they are to be regarded as mere conceptual exercises, "architectonic combinations not designed to be constructed but to show the characteristic features of a given conception or its consequences in statics and aesthetics," as Annoni puts it.[10] The precise observations of Beltrami on the subject of the *tiburio* of the cathedral of Milan,[11] and of Calvi on the projects for the house of the great patron Charles d'Amboise [12] that are referred to in the Codex Atlanticus (fol. 231 r, v-*a*),[13] and indeed any systematic and complete study of Da Vinci's drawings and notes on building matters (quite apart from other documentary evidence), suffice to make further doubt impossible. Even though it is true that scientific considerations predominate in most of the architectural notes in Leonardo's manuscripts, so that they seem to apply only incidentally to structures—as, for example, ruptures of arches serve to explain the action of the laws of gravitation, and the raising of a bell upon a tower, or of some weight upon a colonnaded loggia, is used to determine the forces acting on a lever and on an inclined plane [14]—these considerations are nonetheless not ends in themselves, but rather aspects of a general tendency to consider art as a theoretical entity, a form of knowledge, a *scienza*.[15]

On the other hand, we should never lose sight of the basic intention that inextricably connects Leonardo's architectural notes with positive practical data and goals. This is likewise the conclusion of the detailed and realistic observations that are suggested to him by the logic of the habits and needs of individual and social living. The essential factor is not that the inventive solutions reached in Da Vinci's studies almost never received actual material application. This negative aspect of his work concerns only a different and secondary phase of it, the sphere of application; it does not affect its core, the fact of original creation. As compared with his actual building practice, the historical rank of an artist whose intentions included the composition of a treatise on architecture, and who was familiar with the writings of Leon Battista Alberti, should be evaluated in accordance with the defini-

[7] Cf. Dami, "Leonardo's Edifices," in *Marzocco*, May 4, 1919, p. 5 f.; G. Calvi, "Observation, Invention, Experience in Leonardo da Vinci," in *Istituto di studi vinciani in Roma: Per il quarto centenario della morte di Leonardo da Vinci*, p. 331-335.

[8] Favaro. "Leonardo in the History of the Experimental Sciences," in *Leonardo da Vinci: Conferenze fiorentine*, p. 177.

[9] Cod. Atl., fol. 270 r-*c*.

[10] Annoni. "Thoughts on Leonardo da Vinci as Architect," in *Emporium*, April, 1910.

[11] L. Beltrami. *Leonardo e i disfattisti suoi*, p. 181.

[12] G. Calvi. *I manoscritti di Leonardo da Vinci*, p. 239-243.

[13] There are references to another organized project for a private house, definitely commissioned from the artist by a specific client, in the Codex Atlanticus (fol. 158 r-*b*, v-*a*), which also contains a memorandum of the requirements for the building, written from left to right, possibly by the hand of the client himself or of an agent of his.

[14] An account of Leonardo's studies on the strength of materials along the lines of the treatise *De ponderibus* is given in P. Duhem, *Etudes sur Leonardo da Vinci*, I, p. 257 f.

[15] B. Croce. "Leonardo as Philosopher," in *Leonardo da Vinci: Conferenze fiorentine*, p. 243. Cf. Beltrami, *Leonardo, Scritti*, p. 40, 42.

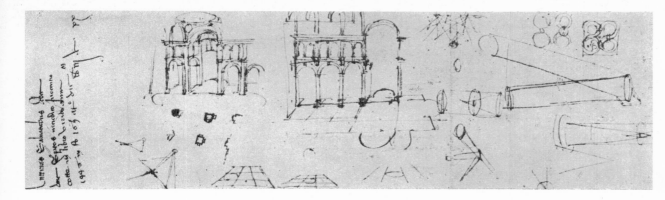

Façade of church – Venice, Academy

tion of an architect given by Alberti himself. All too often it is forgotten that our appraisal of Bramante's project for St. Peter's is based on reconstructions largely derived from study of the drawings of other masters.

Considerations of this nature can lead us to a precise evaluation of the principles of Da Vinci's architecture, and possibly to discovery of structures that can be attributed to him. To this end we shall have to abandon preconceived doctrines and in their stead initiate a stylistic research similar to that undertaken to identify Da Vinci's handiwork in paintings or sculptures, which themselves are often searched out on the basis of his designs (I cite the case of the little Budapest bronze), precisely as must be done for the architectural works. In this light, for example, we might once more take up the study of the original part of the cathedral of Pavia, which recent criticism has been all too positive in attributing to Bramante in its entirety. At the very least, any observer will note that polygonal configuration of the sacristy is in complete conformity with the ideas set down in Da Vinci's drawings, even when masked by all the adaptations to the local building traditions that appear in the wooden model of the edifice, although an attempt has been made to draw inferences from the identity of Leonardo's plan with that of the classic hall "outside of Rome three miles on the way to Marino" noted by Giuliano da Sangallo on folio 8 of the Codex Barberinianus and on folio 16 of his Sienese pocketbook; the plan is repeated by Baldassarre Peruzzi in the Uffizi drawing numbered 1657.[16]

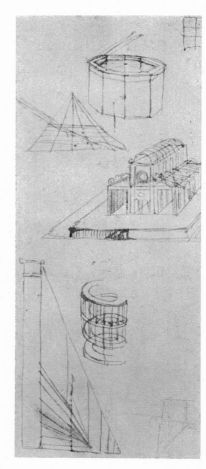

Pattern of three-aisled building – Basel, formerly K. Geigy Hagenbach Collection

Posed in these terms, the question may be only hypothetical, but as a logical and methodologic requirement it should not be ignored. There is a priori tendency to stop short with the statements that there are no known structures erected by Leonardo, and that he must be regarded as the theoretician for whom Bramante was the practical constructor.[17] These statements are too generic to be of weight in criticism, and are not far from mere *petitio principii*. In an extensive review of the volume that Venturi devotes to the architecture of the Renaissance in his monumental *Storia dell'arte italiana*, Gustavo Giovannoni has maintained that the importance of Leonardo's architectural work is decreased by the fact that his studies remained in the stage of mere possibilities or sketches. We cannot contrast a Leonardo, designer of unbuilt edifices, with a practical Bramante represented by monuments of which he is by no means conceded to have been the author, such as the church of Santa Maria delle Grazie. Agnoldomenico Pica, in his recent monograph on that remarkable shrine, has classified me as one of those who, like Richter, Müller-Walde, Beltrami, Strzygowsky, and Annoni, are alleged to have "made much of Leonardo's influence on Bramante, especially here at the Grazie church."[18] I believe, however, that he has not visualized quite clearly the problems I have tried to bring out; if he had, he would at least have realized that the way I posed these problems was entirely original and that I did not speak of *influences*, but aimed merely to shed light on still controversial aspects of a question in criticism that is far from being resolved.

Pica is usually very quick in his judgments and examinations of style, a matter that is not simple in the case of such a structure as the tribune of Santa Maria delle Grazie, which shows such clear-cut discontinuities in form. At any rate, there is no point in stating that "there is not the slightest old evidence" of Leonardo's *influence* in the Grazie church, when the evidence for attributing the work to Bramante is sought in a marginal note taken from a mutilated copy of the De Pagave manuscript —a note ascribed to the chronicle of Padre Giorgio Rovegnatino[19]—without the precaution of finding out whether the note appeared also in the original manuscript[20] or whether it should be considered an easily detectable interpolation. Nor is the note regarding the marble sent to Bramante by the Certosa di Pavia between 1494 and 1499 at the order of Il Moro of great probative value from this point of view, since in the first place it represents only a nineteenth-century digest, rather inexact

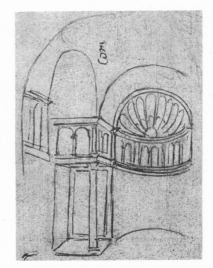

Idea for apse of Como cathedral – From Windsor Royal Collection, no. 12609

[16] Huelsen. *Il libro di Giuliano Sangallo*, text p. 15, Pl. E. There is a good plan in the series of Brunelli's engravings, after a drawing by C. Amati. See also Gianani-Modesti, *Il duomo di Pavia*, p. 54.

[17] Heydenreich, *loc. cit.* This author returns to the same notion in an article, "On the Genesis of Bramante's Design for St. Peter's," in *Forschungen und Fortschritte*, 1934, p. 367.

[18] Pica-Portaluppi. *Le Grazie*, Rome, 1937, p. 133.

[19] C. Casati. *I capi d'arte di Bramante da Urbino nel Milanese*, Milan, 1870, p. 44.

[20] This is preserved in the library of the Municipal Art Museums in the Sforza castle, under the listing C.VI.28. The "marginal note" is not in it, nor in the definitive redaction given in the Codex Ambrosianus, S 157 *sup.* As for the copy in his possession, Casati himself stated that it lacked the portion relating to the artist's Roman period and contained corrections, but does not say whether these were in the same hand as the original version.

Left, right: Projects for dome of Milan cathedral – Cod. Atl., fol. 310 v-*b*, 310 r-*b*

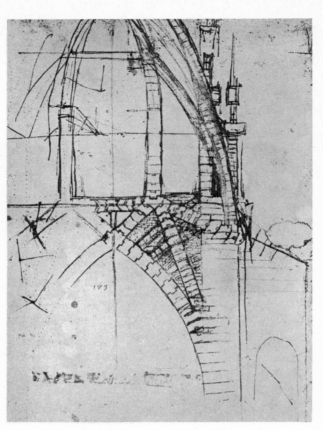

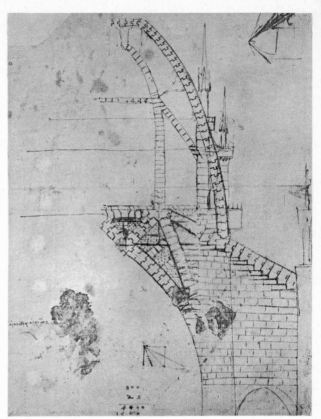

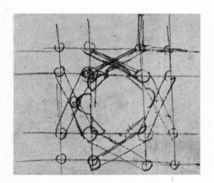

Exterior development of dome of Milan cathedral – Cod. Atl., fol. 266 r

System of piers for supporting dome of Milan cathedral – Cod. Triv., fol. 21 r

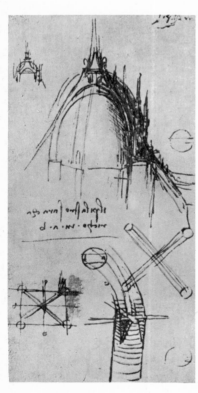

Study for dome of Milan cathedral – Cod. Triv., fol. 22 v

at that, and since in the second place it may well be maintained that the marbles were sent to the artist in his capacity as the duke's architect. The silence of Cesariano, Gaspare Visconti, and the very diligent Padre Gattico should therefore have led Pica to take a less dogmatic position in the face of doubts that were based, if on nothing else, on the intelligent and minute technical observations of Tito Vespasiano Paravicini.

However, if we wish to do more than mention an affinity between the expressive forms of artists who could be pointed out to have had common aims merely by reason of identical requirements arising out of the common historical milieu, we must emerge from the nebulous position that deals with the question of the relationships of the styles of Leonardo and Bramante by cautiously recognizing a "solely spiritual" collaboration between the two masters,[21] or by more boldly stating that "the superiority of Bramante must be attributed primarily to the influence of Leonardo."[22] As for the well-known similarity of some sketched plans by Da Vinci to the original drawings of Bramante for the Vatican basilica, the conclusions adopted on this basis suffer from an excess of haste; here too the respective chronological and conceptual positions must be examined.[23] Similarly, it is not quite accurate to assert that Leonardo's "sketches preserved in the various codices of Milan, Paris, and London" deal with "almost exclusively Milanese structures, in which the traditional forms seem to have been followed."[24]

The fact is that if we desire to make a more reasonable and conclusive stylistic investigation, we must first of all make a decisive separation between those of Leonardo's architectural drawings that give observations and notes on structures studied by the artist—although with those arbitrary variants that always proclaim the presence of an individual taste and its irrepressible tendency to burst out even during the passive experience of reception—and those drawings in which the master really studies original new solutions. In the latter the echoes of existing buildings should always be especially stressed for their possibilities of individual expression. We need only point to the drawing numbered 12609 verso in the royal collection at Windsor, which bears the little note *Com*, and compare it directly with the two wooden models preserved in the cathedral of Como, to see the originality of the architectural solution devised by Da Vinci as compared with the broad-based solution proposed by Cristoforo Solari and by Rodari. On other occasions, however, inspection of the manuscripts will show the artist intent on merely recording the data and his observations. Thus, folio 225 recto-*b* of the Codex Atlanticus indicates studies "of the measurements of San Lorenzo," and on folio 64 of Ms. H, in a note dated January 29, 1494, he reminds himself to find out "how many ells high the surface of the wall is, how wide the hall," apparently a hall of the castle of Milan; he also seeks to find out how wide the *Ghirlanda* is. The answer to one of these questions is found on folio 49 verso of the third of the Forster codices: "The hall of the court is 128 paces, and 27 ells wide."

[21] Giovannoni. *L'architettura del Rinascimento*, p. 72.
[22] Lukonsky. *Maestri dell'architettura classica*, p. 365.
[23] Cf. Geymüller, *Les projets primitifs*, text p. 336; *idem*, "Architectural Designs," in Richter, *Leonardo da Vinci*, II (1st ed.), p. 42; K. Frey, *Bramantes St. Peter Entwurf und seine Apokryphen*, p. 76, 79. The ideas set forth by Heydenreich, "On the Genesis of Bramante's Design for St. Peter's," *loc. cit.*, are more prudent but also vaguer.
[24] Lukonsky, *op. cit.*, p. 29 f. Cf. Reymond, *Brunelleschi et la Renaissance italienne au XVe siècle*, p. 64.

A typical example of an exercise in documentation is the determination of the measurements of a city district traversed by the Naviglio and near a church; it is found on folios 118 verso, 119 recto, and 120 verso of Ms. I. There are many such examples. I have already had occasion to show that the two plans of the Florentine churches of Santo Spirito and Santa Maria degli Angioli on folio 11 verso of Ms. B should be considered as taken unchanged from the Codex Barberinianus of Giuliano da Sangallo; recourse to the knowledge of others in order to have observational data is also shown in the passage in Ms. M, folio 53 verso, that indicates "the kind of drawbridge Donnino showed me." The investigator who applies to "messe[r] Attavian Palavisino for his Vetruvius" and to Bartolomeo Turco for information on the "ebb and flow of the Black Sea" also gets information on the amphitheater at Verona from "Giovan Lombardo." He is also an active collector of manuscripts and printed books, and as he frequents "the last stationer toward the Cordusio" and looks there for "the book that deals with Milan and its church," [25] he obtains possession of the document now called Codex Ashburnham 361 of the Laurenziana, ascribed to Francesco di Giorgio, on which he also writes some notes.[26] And he keeps the "book...that was got at Rome," with notes on local archaeological monuments, and accords the privilege of consulting it to the still unknown writer of the so-called Codex Bramantinianus of the *Rovina di Roma*, now preserved in the Ambrosiana library.[27]

When he can, therefore, he makes his observations directly from the buildings. Thus there are the precise plans of the cathedral and the church of San Sepolcro at Milan, the round church of Santa Maria in Pertica at Pavia, the archaeological area at the port of Civitavecchia, as well as measurements of San Paolo in Rome and observations on Hadrian's villa at Tivoli.

In other cases it is not so easy to decide whether we have purely receptive notations or more or less original developments. This happens when Leonardo sets down the pattern of the staircase at

---

[25] Cod. Atl., fol. 225 r-*b*.

[26] Cf. G. Mancini, "An Artistic and Scientific Fourteenth-Century Manuscript with Some Autograph Notes of Leonardo da Vinci," in *Archivio storico italiano*, p. 354-363; *idem, Vita di Leon Battista Alberti*, p. 287.

[27] See the note on Pl. LVII of the Mongeri edition.

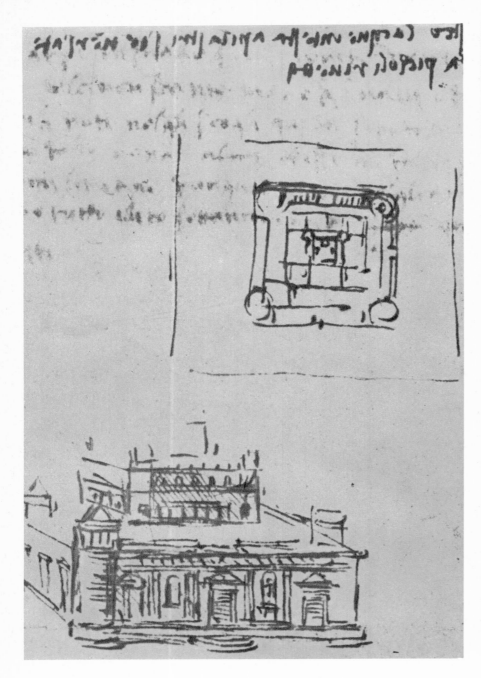

Left: Façade and plan of turreted palace – Windsor, Royal Collection, no. 12591 r

Right: Façade and plan of villa – Ms. I, fol. 56 r

Façade of house, with chimney detail – Ms. K, fol. 116 v

Urbino [28] or shows "the pavilion that is at the center of the maze of the Duke of Milan" [29] or "the stable of the Magnifico." [30] The references to persons and places are not always a sure guide. As I have said, the research must be conducted anew each time, with the aid of all the resources of methodology—paleography, comparative analysis of style, chronology, and historical integration.

A differentiation of this kind was made by Heydenreich, in part; but it is of value only if applied integrally. Dami said rightly of Leonardo as an architect that "his temperament led him to saturate himself with experiences, and once he was full of them and had digested them with great rumination, to go in search of 'reasons,' as he himself said. Architectural experience consisted for him, and he was basically not a professional, in keeping abreast of the discoveries of others and assimilating them. Studying the 'reasons' meant investigating them down to the bottom, mastering all their possibilities, employing them to the point of exhausting them." [31] Careful graphic and mnemonic recording of the data as they were observed, as he recommends in his *Treatise on Painting*, was his constant practice in the many architectural notes that describe the elements of the buildings to which he could have access or about which he could obtain knowledge in some other manner; the references to instances show that his critical and comparative spirit was always alive; for that spirit, as Calvi says, "the communication of every activity, every difficulty, and every step forward on the path of truth and usefulness, is a stimulus, an increase, a completing of his inventive powers." [32]

There can be no doubt that this highly original interpreter of the finest expressions of Italian genius took advantage of the experience offered him by historical developments and the contemporary

[28] Ms. L, fol. 19 v.
[29] Ms. B, fol. 12 r.
[30] Cod. Atl., fol. 96 v-*a*.
[31] Dami, *op. cit.*
[32] G. Calvi. "Observation, Invention, Experience in Leonardo da Vinci," *op. cit.*, p. 341.

Façade, plan, and details of lordly residence – Cod. on Flight of Birds – Turin, former Royal Library

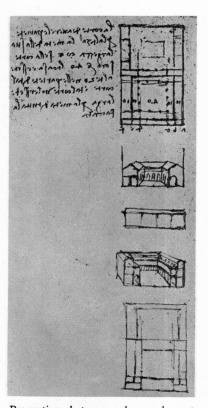

phenomena of the culture around him. The formal expressions of his art arise all the more out of external observation when they relate to works involving knowledge traditional in the profession, as is the case in architecture, which interests Da Vinci not only as an artist but also as a scientist investigating the functioning of the laws of statics and formulating the principles of hygiene and ideal communal life in an ethically organized society.

The same research method that has brought out in Leonardo's technology the contribution of the scientific work of Alberti and Francesco di Giorgio,[33] and explored the relationships of his painting to the art of Verrocchio and Lorenzo di Credi,[34] must now be applied, therefore, to the examination of Da Vinci's architecture. Just because the forming of this supreme artist proceeds from intense cognitive experimentation, it is plain that following out the successive stages of this experimentation, realizing his preferences and tastes, and seeing the affirmation of an individual style by way of original developments born of examination and criticism of school data already assimilated, mean the same thing as defining the figure and the work of the great artist as an architect.

In this research the questions of chronology, which are basic, are uncertain and complex, from various points of view. It is true that Heydenreich has taken up the problem of dating Da Vinci's architectural drawings, conforming in principle to the conclusions arrived at by Gerolamo Calvi, but it should be pointed out that, although some kind of result has been reached for the drawings in which Leonardo made notes of his architectural knowledge and intuitions, no progress has been made in going beyond the surface of the paper to which the rapid sketches were entrusted: the core of Leonardo's architectural conceptions has hardly been touched by the inquiry.[35] Thus, when it is observed that the plan of Santo Spirito in Florence, in Ms. B, folio 11 verso, shows that the artist is aware of the discussions that took place in 1486 concerning the projects for the façade of the church, this gives us something by which to date the drawing; but we have not gone far enough to pose the question of how Leonardo, a permanent resident of Lombardy at that time, could have come to have such precise knowledge of graphic details; the assumption that the two Florentine plans on the sheet were drawn from memory alone is too much oversimplified to inspire confidence.[36] And yet it is just this point that might have made further critical developments possible.

Once we have traced the lines of the complex formative process that leads from Da Vinci's collection and elaboration of observed data to original creation, we must use these lines to guide us through the hitherto confused web of experimental results and highly personal creations in the architectural drawings of Leonardo. Further, it should never be forgotten that these drawings represent only a part of all that the artist must have made; consequently, the critical conclusions drawn from them

[33] G. Calvi, *Ibid.*, p. 337 f.
[34] Degenhart. "Some Problems of the Development of Painting in the Atelier of Verrocchio, Leonardo, and Lorenzo di Credi," in *Rivista d'arte*, 1931, p. 263, 403, 444.
[35] Heydenreich. *Die Sakralbau-Studien Leonardo da Vincis*, p. 14 f.
[36] *Ibid.*, p. 15.

Country house with roof garden –
Ms. B, fol. 19 v

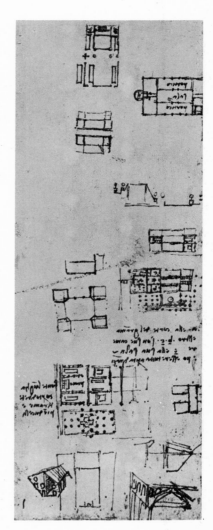

must be complemented by factors derived from other sources. The very way in which the Da Vinci manuscripts were composed, as shown for example by an autograph statement in the Codex Arundel, folio 1 verso, gives notice of Leonardo's habit of resuming the study of themes begun in the past, and developing them in accordance with new opinions and requirements; and references to notes or proposals previously made are found in various codices, proving the existence in the artist's lifetime of other manuscripts now lost to us.[37] We may therefore assume that substantially identical elements of design may refer to quite different periods. A typical case appears in the designs for the equestrian compositions of the Sforza and Trivulzio monuments, which in turn have a common point of prior attachment in the background groups of the *Adoration of the Magi* at Florence and come to expression in the central core of the *Battle of Anghiari*. Since Leonardo himself informs us that he recopied notes in his notebooks, perhaps because they were dispersed on various sheets, it may be possible that drawings or notes that are not in agreement with the chronological indications of the text should be retrodated.

Great case must be exercised in doing this, of course. Uccelli, who started by trying radically to undermine the critical authority of the historicochronological method in the field of Da Vinci studies, to the point of stating that by the use of the method "we should like to arrive at some precise data concerning Leonardo's compilation," [38] ends by saying more prudently that he only desired "to point out the difficulty and virtual impossibility of reconstructing a text of Da Vinci on the basis of purely historical and chronological criteria." He seems to overlook the fact that the few dates and historical and biographical references may be supplemented by paleography and other ancillary disciplines. However, the method he proposes is indeed well contrived for the purpose of reconstructing Da Vinci *texts*, co-ordinating and critically organizing propositions and demonstrations as *rules* in the various fields discussed—painting, hydraulics, aviation, etc. But it does not always seem possible, at least as regards architecture, to make the connection between the notes and drawings and a proposed treatise. Sometimes, as I have tried to indicate, the entries are merely references to the structures of other architects, or practical projects for buildings to be erected—for example, the house of Charles d'Amboise. In these cases, and in general whenever organization into precepts has not become very definite, we shall be obliged each time to combine paleographic study with analysis of biographical and historical data and the suggestions by analogy that arise from constant reference to the milieu.

[37] A. Uccelli. "Vicissitudes and Methods in Da Vinci Reconstruction" in *Il Politecnico*, 1937, p. 329.
[38] *Ibid.* p. 335.

Project of house of Charles d'Amboise
in Milan – Cod. Atl., fol. 231 r-*b*

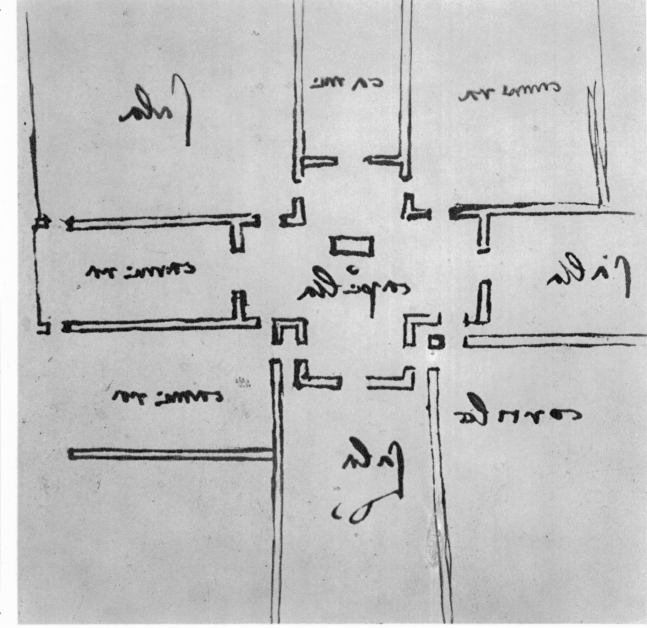

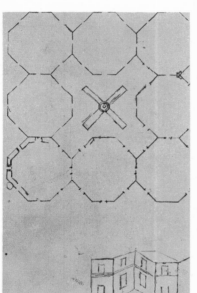

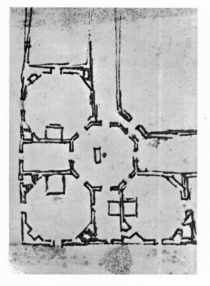

It is thought, with good reason, that Leonardo intended to write a treatise on architecture. This is indicated by the solid theoretical tendency of his work in the thousands of manuscript sheets we know of, and emerges clearly from some quite explicit statements. For example, there are the places where he shows "the way to design a stable" [39] and "how frameworks for ornaments in the form of buildings are assembled," [40] or "a coping for a garden wall," [41] or "how to decorate a scaffold for festivals." [42] These sketches are clearly expository. On folio 52 recto of Ms. B the connection between the long church plan and the sketch of the "theater for preaching" is indicated just as it would be in an illustrative plate for a text: "Building for the foundation illustrated below." These are clearly not notes that Leonardo intended to keep to himself. In some cases he speaks directly to the future reader: "If you have a family in the house, act thus..." [43] or "Know that anyone who wants to travel all over the world by highroads may do so." [44] Even when he is laying down a rule for proportions his conceptual position does not change. In the Codex Atlanticus, folio 235 recto-*b*, he states: "The capital is to be in this form: Divide the distance from top to bottom in seven and take 5/7 from the base, and have it 5/7 high and it will be square; then make the ovolo 1/8 and the thickness of the plate above the column another eighth," etc.

This last sheet, however, exhibits one of those mixtures of unrelated observations that confuse us in our task of methodical restoration. Precepts like the one just given, and others likewise, are references to technical points in architecture, as we see not only from the solemn introductory passage at the top of the folio, taken from Diodorus Siculus, but also from the realistic desire to leave "the sculptors free" to determine the *ornaments* of the capital. Nevertheless, apart from the preamble,

[39] Ms. B, fol. 39 r.
[40] *Ibid.*, fol. 28 v.
[41] *Ibid.*, fol. 23 v. Cf. Cod. Atl., fol. 357 v-*a*, "Types of garden walls."
[42] *Ibid.*, fol. 78 v.
[43] *Ibid.*, fol. 12 v.
[44] *Ibid.*, fol. 16 r.

248

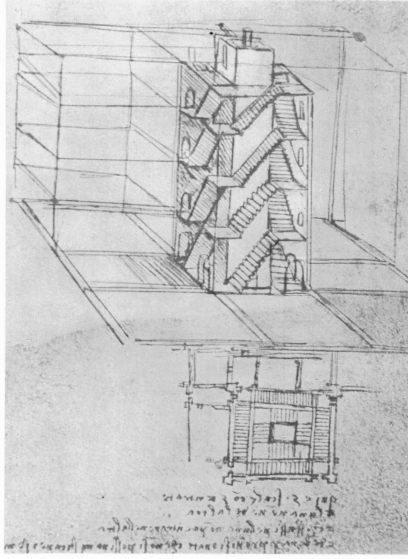

the page opens with a note on gravitation ("The column which has its thickness at the third is likely to break there") and ends, as if after a parenthesis, with a return to the study of the same physical laws: "But to return to columns and show the reason for their strength or weakness as the result of their form, I say..." Now, it is known that Leonardo had accumulated data for a treatise on the strength of construction materials and the causes of damage to them; these data are scattered in several manuscripts. He outlines a definite project in the well-known note of the Codex Arundel (fol. 157 r): "First write the treatise on the causes of the giving way of walls and then, separately, treat of the remedies." Once again it is very difficult to determine the dividing line between one of Leonardo's researches and another. This dividing line exists really only for us and not for Leonardo. In the course of an experiment or demonstration his speculative curiosity will suddenly be drawn to other suggested phenomena and unrelated notions. A fundamental trait of the genius of the great masters is his desire to grasp the reason for the facts that reach his senses and to do this at all costs and sometimes without any logical concatenation.

Any reconstruction of the treatise on architecture that may be attempted cannot make use of the schematic indications given by Leonardo himself—a useful method in reconstructing other treatises, as Uccelli has indicated.[45] How conclusive in this connection are the suggestions for returning to the classic treatise of Vitruvius, which, as we know, was of tremendous theoretical importance for the architects of the Renaissance and was much used by Da Vinci? He seems to have consulted Vitruvius constantly on the spur of the moment, and got from him not only such matters as the proportions of the human body or the citation of the work of Trypho of Alexandria, along with other ideas less related to architecture in the strict sense,[46] but also the pattern of the Attic base of a column and the relevant nomenclature.[47] Nevertheless, his objectivity made him avoid absolute acceptance of a single source of doctrine, no matter how authoritative. In addition to ancient texts, such as that of Diodorus Siculus or the *Frontino de acquidotti*,[48] he consults Valturio, from whom he gets the *nomi ingiegnieri* ["technical terms"] given on folio 50 verso of Ms. B; he also derives principles and

[45] Uccelli, *op. cit.*
[46] Cf. De Toni, "Outline of a Da Vinci Nomenclature," in *Raccolta vinciana*, XIV, p. 116 f.; H. Solmi, *Le fonti dei manoscritti di Leonardo da Vinci*, p. 310.
[47] Cod. Forst., III, fol. 44 v. 45 r.
[48] Cod. Leices., fol. 13 r.

Left: Double staircase – Ms. B, fol. 68 v

Right: Quadruple staircase – Ms. B, fol. 47 r

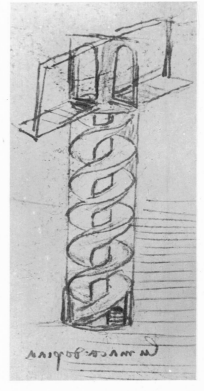

Double spiral staircase – Ms. B. fol. 69 r

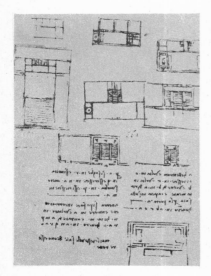

Country house – Cod. Atl., fol. 220
r-c

Stairs with three flights – Cod. Atl.,
fol. 220 v-a

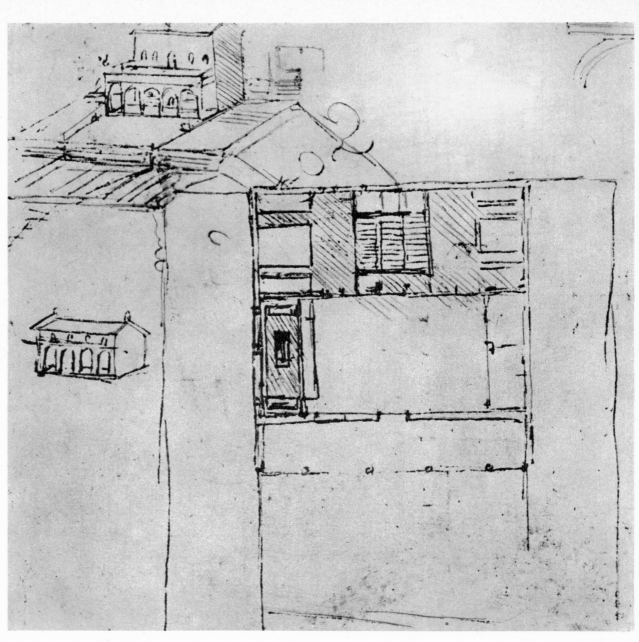

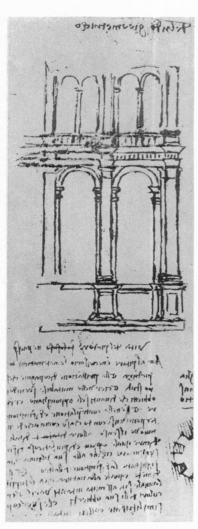

Façade of double loggia – Cod. Atl.,
fol. 184 v-c

rules from the building practice of the time, or from classical examples, from which perhaps he obtains the singular Ionic capital with five ovoli.[49]

From all this wealth of information, those guiding principles should be singled out which Leonardo may have derived directly from personal experimentation: for example, the rules that the "*latastro* [abacus or plinth] should be (*g*) as broad as the thickness of the wall to which the *latastro* is attached," [50] and that "the height of the walls of the courtyard should be half its breadth, that is, if the court is to be 40 ells, the house should be 20 ells high in the walls facing on the court, and the court should be half the width of the entire façade." [51] As we know, Vitruvius prescribed the ratio of 1 to 3/4 in this case, and Cesariano, who claimed to sum up the knowledge of his master Bramante, wavers in his statements of the proportion in use.

In general, the essential characteristic of Leonardo's architecture may be said to be vigorous and constant assimilation of stylistic elements variously interpreted by a taste formed principally through hard study of the possibility of atmospheric merging of geometrically developed perspective planes. His search for the laws that give reason and nobility to man's constructions brought together the deep-seated tendencies that inspired him as a scientist to inspect the geometrical postulates and urged him as an artist who, like Alberti, always considered perspective to be the basis of true art, to embody the magic charm of a soft and penetrating atmospheric light. His evident absorption in perspective inspired clear-cut statements like the following: "A building should always be detached on all sides in order that its true shape may be seen," [52] and again, "It never looks well to see the roofs of a church." [53] But in the designs suggested by his heated imagination these considerations are subsumed

[49] Ms. H, fol. 121 r. I have shown elsewhere that this capital may have been taken from the *Taccuino senese* of Giuliano da Sangallo.
[50] Ms. L, fol. 20 r.
[51] Windsor, no. 12585 v. Cf. Cod. Atl., fol. 76 v-b: "The principal division of the façade of this palace is into two parts, that is, that the width of the court should be half the aforesaid façade."
[52] Ms. B, fol. 39 v.
[53] *Ibid.*, fol. 18 v.

Above: Project of stable with automatic feed to mangers – Ms. B, fol. 39 r. — Left: Section of country house with variant of stable shown above – Cod. Triv., fol. 21 v (43). — Right: Terraced house – Cod. Arund., fol. 126 r

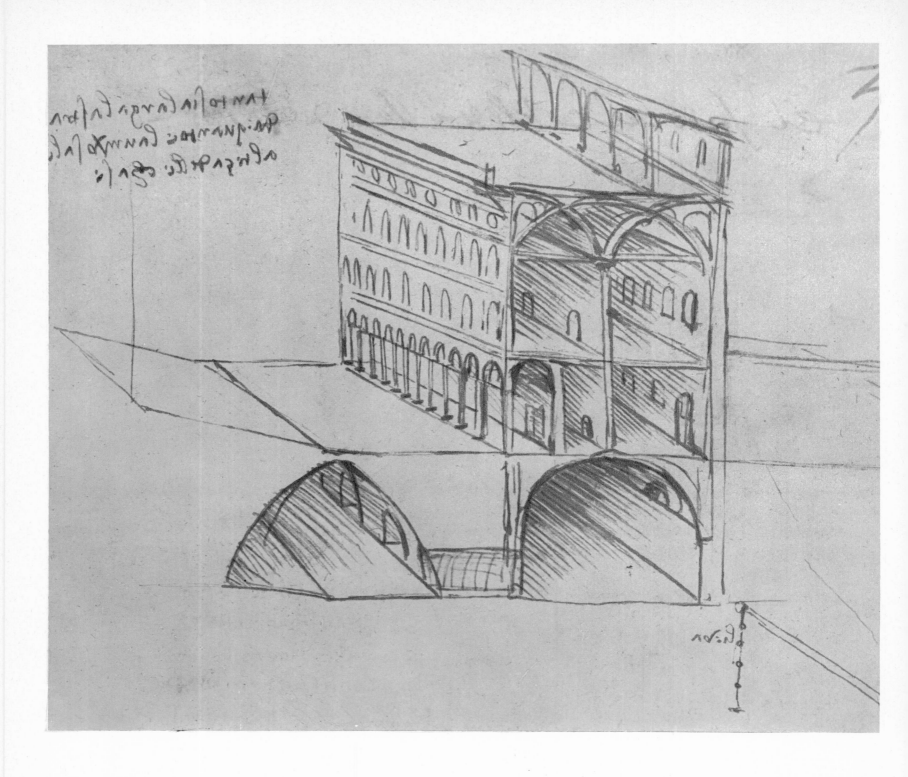

Exterior and section of palaces in city with raised streets – Ms. B, fol. 36 r

in a more general geometrical investigation. The artist who has laid down the principle that "no human investigation may deem itself true science if it has not passed through a mathematical demonstration" [54] requires that the rigid symmetry of star-shaped polygons furnish architectural plans for buildings in which men can live and pray.

The tendency toward many-celled radial plans with central symmetry was already present in the Florentine architectural practice which Leonardo took as his starting point. Alberti had shown how it was possible to have cells grouped in simple or alternate symmetry around a polygonal nucleus,[55] while later the study of complex plan developments by means of addition and combination of spaces was taken up by Francesco di Giorgio, Peruzzi, and Giuliano da Sangallo, with the classical architecture of Rome once again as a guide. It is only in Da Vinci, however, that it can be said to have been fully carried out. His thirst for knowledge drives him to study exhaustively the causes for any given mode of being. A simple initial theme leads him to infinite complex embodiments, always varying and always rich in new formal and practical resources. These developed plans have an intimate genetic connection with their "lucid mathematical elements," and the insertion of circular, oval, or ellipsoid figures in squares is a determinant factor both in the studies on quadrable lunes and in the definition of the spaces organized and enclosed by architectural creation.

Spatial research is of the essence of Da Vinci's architecture. The delicate suggestion of chiaroscuro in his drawings of churches with multiple cupolas is only a contingent element, and adaptation to the formal pictorial factor that is always at the base of Leonardo's activity, to this taste for the

Tympanums of windows – Cod. Forst., III, fol. 22 r

[54] Beltrami. *Leonardo, Scritti*, p. 41.
[55] Frey. *Bramantes St. Peter Entwurf*, etc., p. 76.

Communications and buildings of city
with raised streets – Ms. B, fol. 16 r

sinuous vibrant line. But this taste, we should repeat, is merely a taste in draftsmanship; it does not affect the architectural conception, which is built up in terms of large structural masses. We need only translate the drawings into plastic terms in models to fall in with Heydenreich in seeing in Da Vinci's architecture the aspiration toward spatial quality, *Körperraum*,[56] and to realize the absurdity of the skepticism of such critics as Malaguzzi Valeri in holding[57] that such constructions cannot stand the test of actual construction. Gustavo Giovannoni, a master in the study of Renaissance architecture, would not have been so positive in stating, as he has, that Leonardo's drawings comprise "outlines of ideas, fantastic compositions possibly thought up for backgrounds in pictures, but no concrete architectural drawings,"[58] if he had given closer study to the clear and precise section and plans of castles, houses, street tunnels, and stables. It does not seem altogether realistic to label the designs of even the most complicated many-domed churches as paradoxical utopian exercises if we discern in them the origin of the type of the Vatican basilica. The jaded skepticism of Malaguzzi Valeri, Annoni, and so many other students of Da Vinci's architectural activity, with the "defeatism" against which Beltrami reacted so sharply, is merely an attitude, quite epidemic, that critics have taken to in dealing with the words of the great master. Uccelli has fairly attacked these quietists of Da Vinci studies.[59]

The factor of constructive *necessity* is even more clearly apparent in Leonardo when he is drawing elements or systems in private architecture; then everything is reduced to the essential pattern. The pictorial appeal of the delicate divided windows, of the grilles, niches, and fountains, is something

Communications and buildings of city
with raised streets – Ms. B, fol. 16 r

Palace doorway – Ms. B, fol. 68 r

Portico – Cornice of recess – Cod.
Atl., fol. 148 r-*b*

[56] Heydenreich, *op. cit.*, p. 86.
[57] Beltrami. *Leonardo e i disfattisti suoi*, p. 202.
[58] G. Giovannoni, in *Palladio*, 1938, p. 109.
[59] Uccelli, *op. cit.*, p. 329.

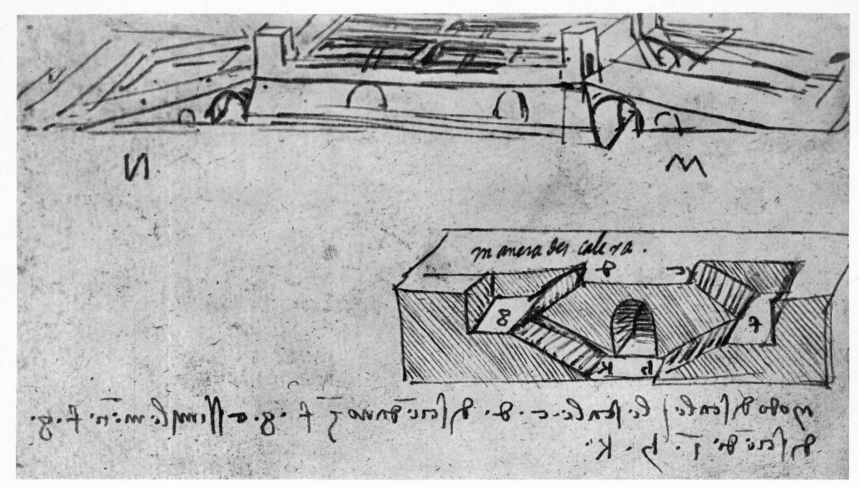

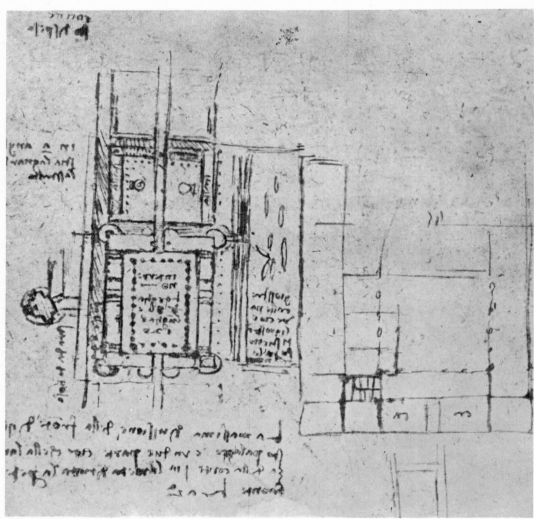

Above: Organization of city with raised streets – Details of stairs connecting streets at different levels – Ms. B, fol. 15 v. — Below, left: Organization of spindle-shaped city with districts for artisans and merchants – Cod. Atl., fol. 217 v-*b* — Below, right: Plan of royal court at Romorantin – At side of palace, pool for sham naval battles – Cod. Atl., fol. 76 v-*b*

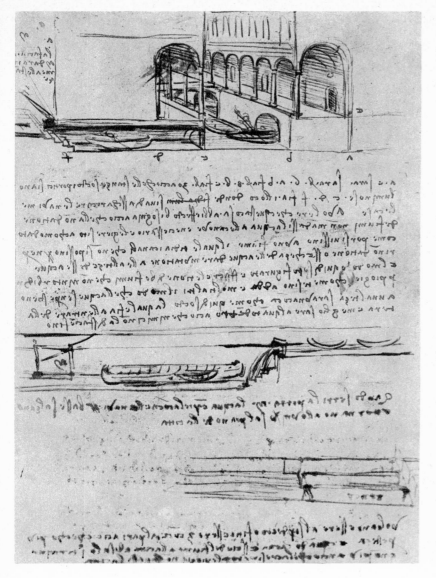

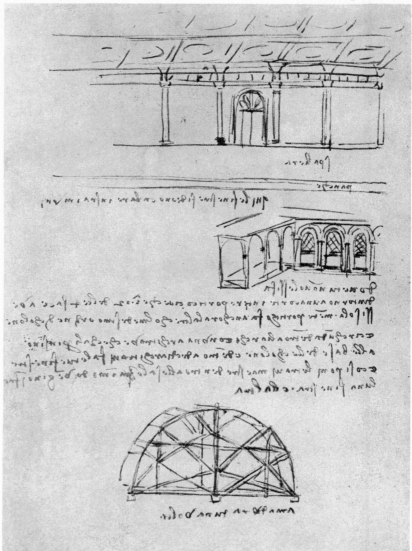

that engages the curiosity of the master in an episodic way; in architectural practice he prefers to deal with the technical questions of materials and the mechanics of building in adaptation to the needs of real life, leaving aside the decorative element, which he considers as merely accessory and hence consigns to the inventiveness and skill of the sculptor and fresco painter.

Left: Waterways and arcades in city with raised streets – Ms. B, fol. 37 v

Right: Interior of hall – Portico – Centering – Ms. B, fol. 67 v

The science of materials, functionality of structure, and exactness in perspective are the decisive factors in Da Vinci's conception of architecture, in which, as in the most daring constructive works of our times, the art of building is an attempt to adapt the environment to man, viewed from the standpoint of his needs and of the manifestations of his existence in society. This is the modernity of Leonardo as an architect, best expressed in the well-known city plans, although it would be an error to try to set these apart from his other designs, as if they were the end point of a separate research; actually, his drawings are all directed to the study of groupings, of the services and communications among the individual churches, houses, groups of houses, palaces, and buildings for diversified uses, which he was the first to consider, from the "palace of the prince" to the "theater for preaching" and to the street tunnel. So much so, that along this line Da Vinci arrives at solutions that seem to be fecund anticipations of today's architectural tendencies, such as the conception of buildings with setbacks,[60] or of complexes of multiple dwellings with a high hexagonal tower form and with an external wall built up of wedge-shaped elements, an even more rational conception than Le Corbusier's skyscrapers of cross-shaped plan with set-back surfaces.[61]

In tracing out the pattern of a city Leonardo does not, like his contemporaries, stop at the traditional type of an urban aggregate on a concentric plan enclosed by the polygonal perimeter of the walls. He is concerned primarily not with the customary generic questions of military defense, but with precise urgent social and hygienic goals. Back of these there is always the political concept of the stability of the civic organization that is to provide the bases of well-being for the population. When the artist arrived at the Sforza court, he saw the disorderly tangle of narrow streets encumbered with the heterogeneous traffic of the busy city, with its often improvised shops and stalls, and his mind, remembering deadly pestilences, was deeply moved by the sight. Moreover, his aristocratic spirit must have been offended by the plebeian aspect of the streets and the squares, full of the movement and noises of the craftsman's shops and the merchant convoys coming to or going from the great Lombard market town.

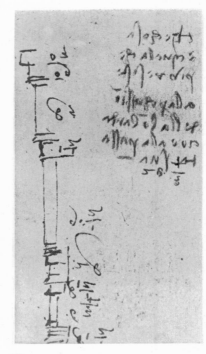

Measurements for palace profile – Cod. Forst., II, fol. 53 r

---

[60] Cod. Arund., fol. 126 r.
[61] Cod. Atl., fol. 114 v-*a*.

255

Water system and cross streets in
city with raised streets – Ms. B,
fol. 37 r

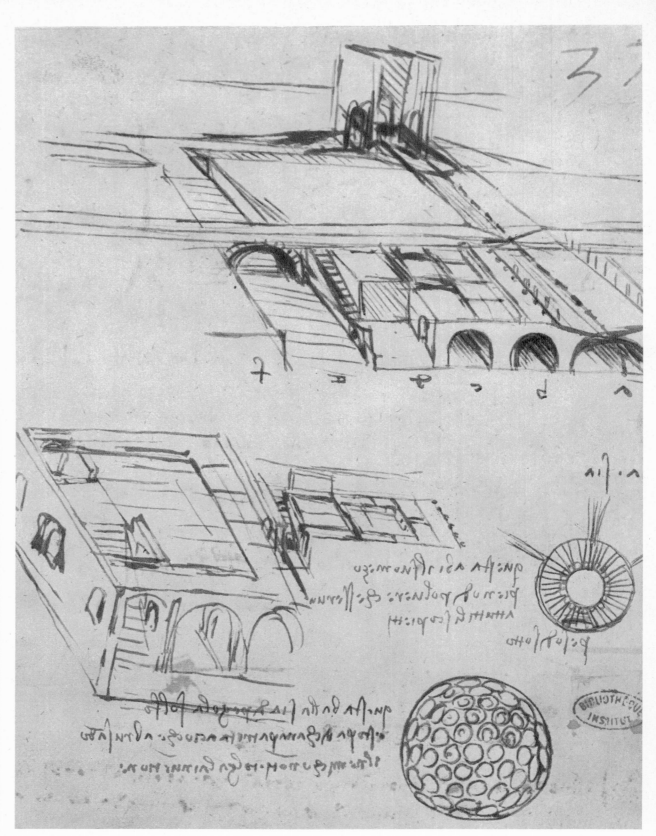

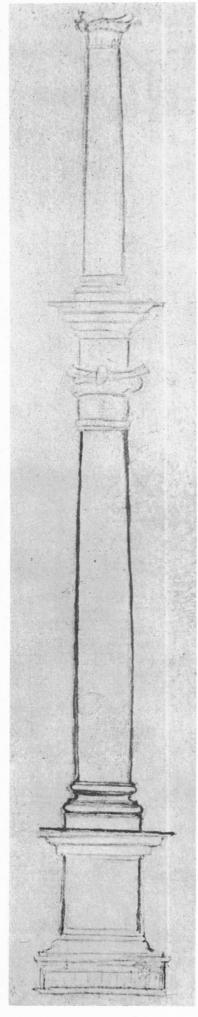

Here for the first time Leonardo abandons the literary conception of the walled city with its polygonal perimeter, the fortress city designed according to the precepts of Vitruvius, and takes up the problem of a purely rational city plan of an open type. Decentralization of the urban agglomeration will make it possible to spread out into the country with inhabited centers made available to the poorest classes, hitherto packed together like goats, with a constant danger to public health; and this will be a good way of binding the tenants and the proprietors to the land, and of safeguarding the rule of the overlord. These centers might be formed in the vicinity of Lodi in Lombardy, and in France near Romorantin; here the artist imagines building, on the banks of the river, a village of demountable wooden houses where "the people of the place live in the new houses in part, when the court is not there." [62]

With the urban population pressure reduced in this way, Leonardo envisages the city as arranged in a checkerboard pattern between spindle-shaped groups of main arteries, the principal axis being formed by a grand canal with a rapid flow—"so that the air of the city may not be polluted"—to be

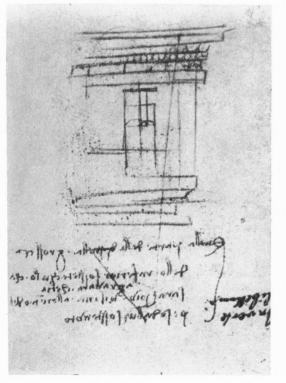

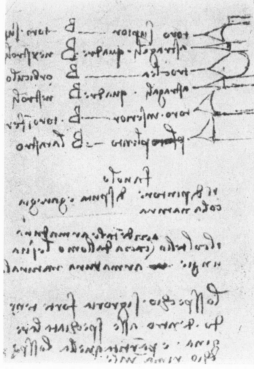

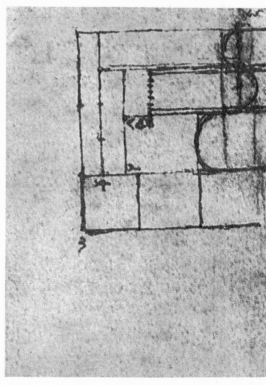

Above: Monumental building along river – Windsor, Royal Collection, no. 12292 v. — Below, left to right: Study of entablature – Cod. Forst., III, fol. 13 v – Base and nomenclature – Cod. Forst., III, fol. 44 v – Proportions of base – Cod. Forst., III, fol. 45 r

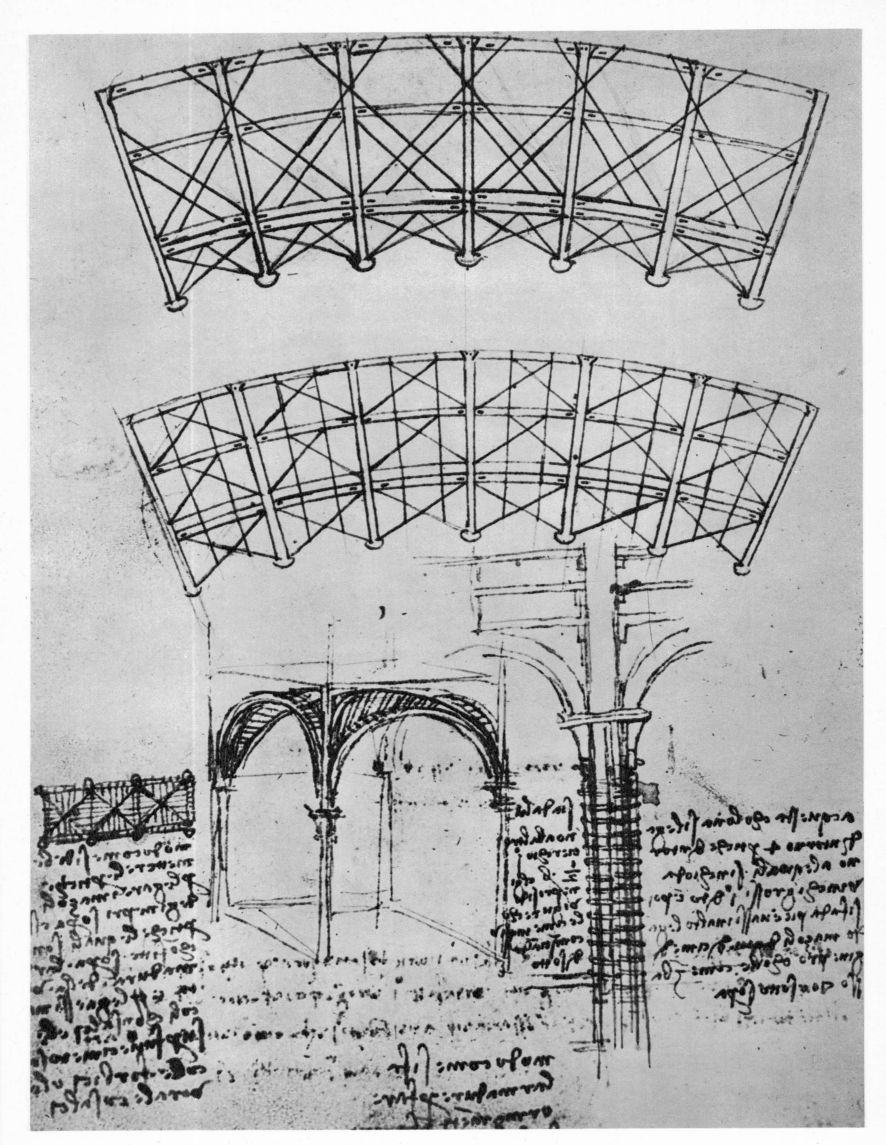

Scaffolding and framework in wood for festival architecture – Ms. B, fol. 28 v

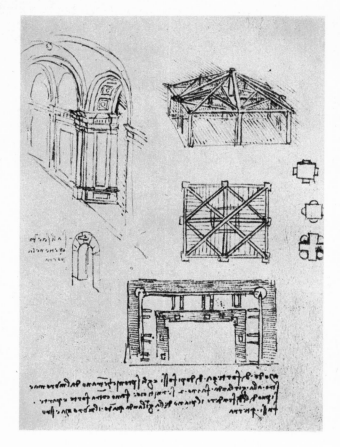

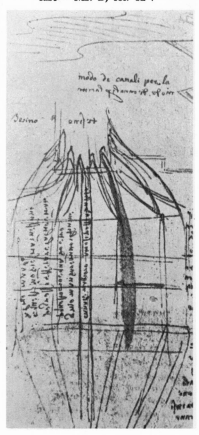

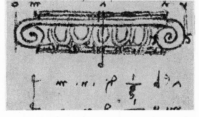

flanked by smaller canals.[63] Large cross streets mark the boundaries of the separate districts to be inhabited by artisans, merchants, and gentlefolk, the latter being given access to the prince's dwelling. This urban pattern seems to express convictions that are rooted deep in Da Vinci's mind. Not only does he emphasize it during his first Milanese period when he is outlining his well-known projects for Ludovico il Moro, but he comes back to it later in a drawing of an ideal improvement of Florence,[64] and again in depicting the plan of the demountable village of Romorantin.

Leonardo believes that a large watercourse must be present and flow through the city, not only for the sake of economy in transport but even more so for sanitary reasons. He thinks of the possibility of locating dams and mills at the point where the canals enter the city, to obtain effective street washing and complete disposal of refuse. To this end the canals are to be at a lower level than the low streets that will be open to the passage of the "carts and other loads for the use and convenience of the people," so that they can come directly into the cellars and places for collecting refuse, since Leonardo desires "that nothing be thrown into the canals, and that these canals go direct to the houses," at their entrances.[65] Again, the earth excavated for the canals and foundations will serve to raise the high streets, reserved for the movement of the gentlefolk, one story above the level of the low streets. Skylights are to let in light for the traffic below, and spiral staircases will afford communication between the levels of the streets.

The higher harmony of such a well-made urban scheme is utopian only with respect to Leonardo's time and its historically conditioned society. This may be the reason why Leonardo's system of city planning found no echo even among those architects close to him who were ready to interpret and make use of the formal elements of his church and secular buildings. Today we can profit by his farseeing vision. Leonardo's city is not the impossible dream of a poetic architect, but a concrete project thought out with a view to embodiment in monumental reality. It is not of importance that the design has only the status of a part of Da Vinci's doctrine and was destined to remain an abstract precept. There was no economic and political organization at the time that could understand the profound reasonableness of such an undertaking. What remains is the rational and critical conception of a city with its traffic separated into distinct street systems, the urban agglomerations relieved of population pressure, the width of streets and the height of houses kept in proportion, and with unified sanitary measures and proportional planning of built-up and open areas.

What is lacking is only a moral attitude rising above the realistic adaptation to the contingent requirements of the social structure inherent in the prevailing political system. At bottom, the thinker who is concerned with relieving man's sufferings and eliminating the causes of death, and gives careful attention to the needs of animal life, remains bound to an aristocratic way of thinking that has no sympathy for "paupers" and assigns sharply separated districts even to artisans and merchants. Leonardo's city, in tendency the city of the spirit, is the expression of the civilization of the Renaissance.

CONSTANTINO BARONI

---

[63] Ms. B, fol. 38 r.
[64] Windsor, no. 12681.
[65] Ms. B, fol. 16 r.

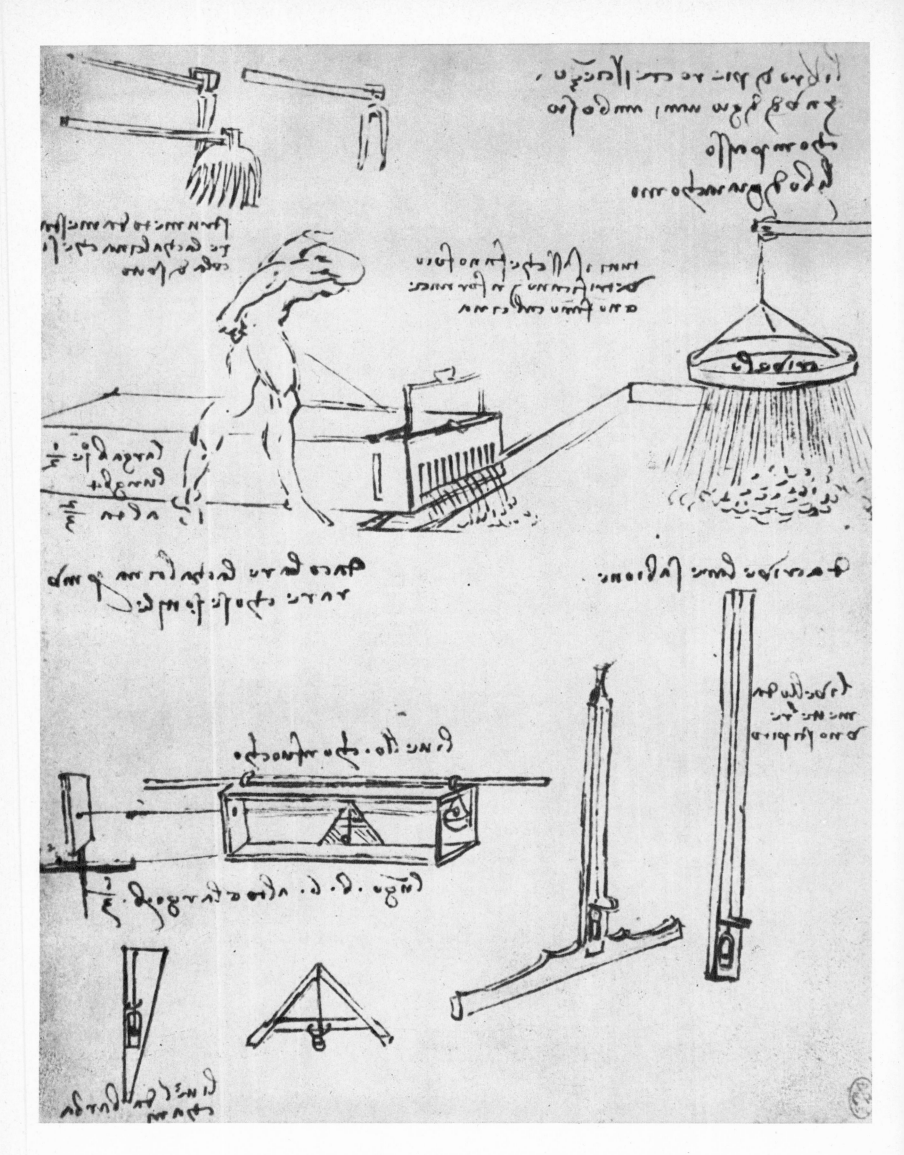

Apparatus for preparing lime – Building tools and instruments – Windsor, Royal Collection, no. 12668

THE SCIENCE OF STRUCTURES

At a time like the present, which is marked by the way in which the use of new materials is influencing architectonic lines, it would be worth while to make a detailed study, from the historical and technical point of view, of the evolution of constructive forms in relation to the scientific and practical concepts gradually acquired in the course of the historical development. Analytical researches conducted in this sense would undoubtedly lead to a conclusion not too far from the following:

Lack of information regarding the strength of materials, coupled with the need for some degree of safety in the structures, gave archaic buildings crude and massive forms. As time went on, empirical data derives from repeated observation and from greater experience made it possible to lighten the primitive forms and led first to the beauty and purity of Greek architecture and then to the greater lightness of the Roman arch. When the old empirical rules were lost as a result of the barbarian invasions, the Gothic style arose out of the need to solve the problems of strength and safety in another way. Following on from that point with a rigorous analysis free of any reference to true art in itself, we could come down to the daring modern structures based on the greater knowledge we have today regarding the strength and use of materials.

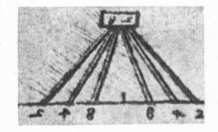

When we speak of the strength of materials, we come face to face with an apparent contradiction, at least from the historical point of view. The history of science attributes to Galileo Galilei the first researches on the strength of materials—in particular of beams—on the bending of rods fastened at one or both ends, and on columns and pillars loaded at the upper end. Galileo himself, because of the neglect and dispersion of Da Vinci's manuscripts, was unaware of the researches the latter had made, and in his *Discorsi e dimostrazioni matematiche intorno a due nuove scienze* he claimed to be the first author to have dealt with this special branch of research.

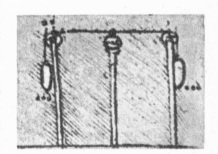

However, we find in classical antiquity some traces of what might be termed the experimental observation of facts that may be considered the foundation of the theory of the strength of materials.

Even in prehistoric times man must have realized that it is much easier to break a stick if the middle of it is put over the knee and force is applied to the two ends rather than near the point of support.

Without going into the question of the authenticity of Aristotle's *Mechanical Problems*, we find a very important point raised in the first and seventeenth of the "mechanical questions."

The Stagirite asks: "Why will a given stick held over the knee break more easily in the middle if the hands grasp it at the ends rather than at points near the knee? Similarly, if the rod is held firmly against the ground with one foot, does the hand succeed in breaking it more easily by grasping it at a point as far as possible from the foot? Perhaps because the knee in the first case and the foot in the second constitute a kind of center, and anything moves more easily the farther it is from the center. To break an object it is necessary to move it."

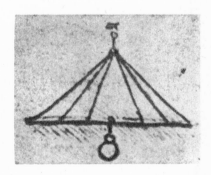

In the seventeenth question Aristotle poses a problem that goes beyond the physical knowledge of his time, for nothing was known then about the theory of elasticity. The great philosopher writes:

"Why are branches the weaker, the longer they are? And why do they bend in such a way when they are lifted that a thin pole two ells long bends less than a heavy pole a hundred ells long?"

Elementary researches on constrained reactions – Ms. A, fol. 47 v

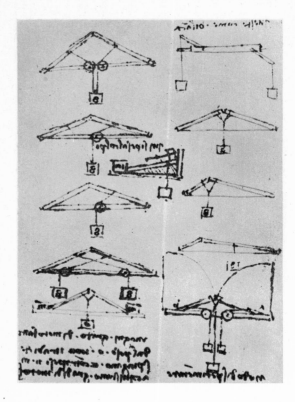
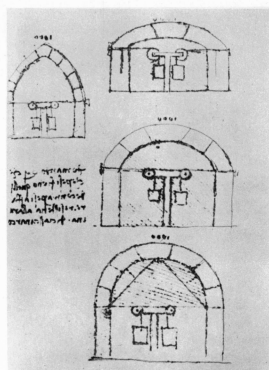
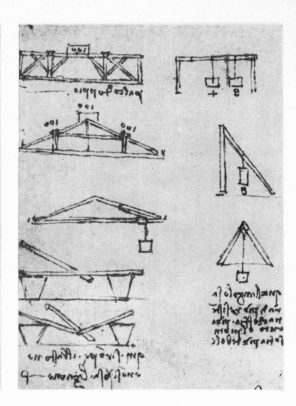

Study of arches – Ms. H, fol. 35 v

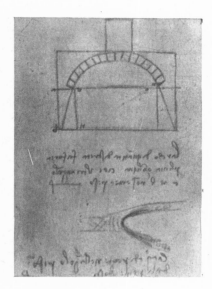

Another study of arches – Ms. H, fol. 36 r

The arguments used by Aristotle are found amplified in the *Mechanics* of Hero of Alexandria, a book whose Greek text we do not have, and which we know only in the Arabic translation made long ago by Kosta Ibn Luka and in the French version that Carra de Vaux gave us over sixty years ago.

In the Middle Ages, the Peripatetic commentator on the *Elements* of Jordanus Nemorarius, the unknown author of the *De ponderibus* whom Duhem calls the "precursor of Leonardo," resumes the Aristotelian line of argument in his own treatise, in the eleventh proposition of the fourth book, and comes to a conclusion in due scholastic form:

"The greater the length of the object under consideration, the more easily can its extremities be bent; the reason is the same as the reason why the weights in a balance are heavier, the further they are from the center, since they describe greater arcs."

There is more of an apparent than of an essential contradiction between the history of science, which points to Galileo as the first investigator of the strength of materials, and the record—which could be given much more extensively than we have done here—of the statements of some ancient authors that have passed through the scholastics to the *auctores de ponderibus*.

The fact is that, setting aside some purely philosophical considerations related to certain geometrical considerations arising out of the foundations of Aristotelian mechanics, Leonardo should be considered the true inaugurator of research on the strength of materials and in the science of structures—this, of course, without detracting from the merit of the great Pisan mathematician and astronomer, who certainly had no knowledge of Leonardo's manuscripts.

In Ms. A, preserved in the library of the Institut de France, we find in embryo the foundations of the theory with which the present commentary deals. On folio 33 recto we read:

"*Of the weakest part of the thing bent*.
"In a body of uniform thickness, the part that is further from the end will bend more easily than any other.

"*Of the arrangement of the thing bent*.
"If you wish to bend two things of equal thickness, the longer will be bent by a smaller force than the shorter."

On the same sheet of this manuscript, in one of the notes that Leonardo wrote as a memorandum, we find:

"Reminder to make an experiment.

"Make the experiment: If a thin piece of wood upheld on two supports at its ends bears ten pounds, what will a beam of the same proportions bear? And see whether the rule of three serves you, because experience makes good rules."

We find once again in this passage the searching and experimental spirit of Leonardo, as he abandons the tradition of the scholastics to initiate his own investigations, excluding sophistry and dog-

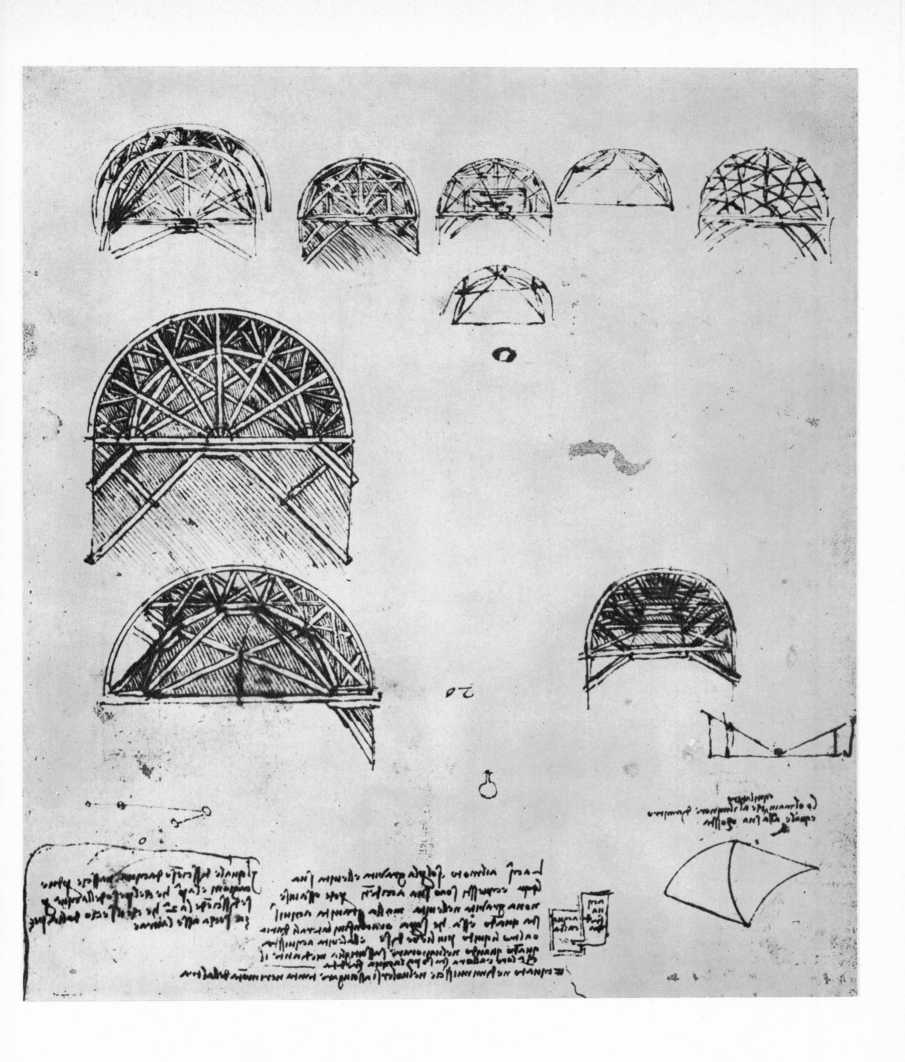

Researches on types of centering – Cod. Atl., fol. 200 r-*a*

Studies of strength of beams – Ms. A, fol. 33 r

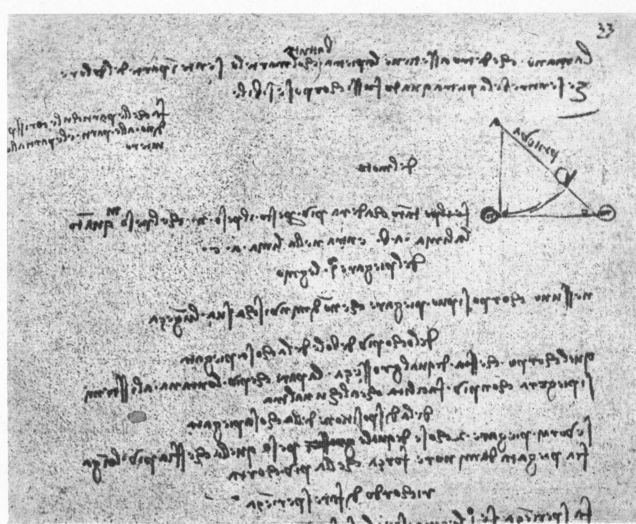

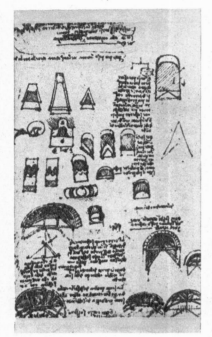

Centerings for arches – Cod. Atl., fol. 225 r-a

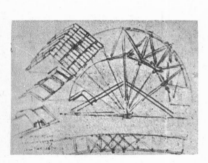

Study for covering of roof – Ms. B, fol. 22 v

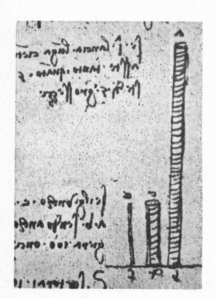

Study of resistance of pillar – Ms. A, fol. 48 v

matism, and launches out on the same path that will be followed by the Accademia del Cimento many decades later. It is a passage that may be taken as the starting point for Da Vinci studies in our particular field.

Today, when we have the mathematical bases of the special branch of the science of structures that aims at rationally determining the stresses to which the parts of a machine or the structures of a building can be subjected, we can also realize why it was essential for Leonardo, in his prolific activity as designer and constructor of machines of the greatest technical variety, to get a clearer picture of measurements and ratios, stresses and strains, strengths and loads, in order to assure the necessary quality and suitability in the materials used in construction.

The only difference between the researches we make now and those conducted by Leonardo lies in the fact that we solve all our problems today by application of our knowledge of the theory of elasticity, a theory that was unknown in Leonardo's time and Galileo's as well. In the absence of any conception of this theory, the only method of investigation available to Leonardo was to compare the resistance of beams and columns made of the same material but having different heights and identical cross section.

Let us look at some passages in Da Vinci that will serve better to illustrate our subject than any discussion. In Ms. A, where we came upon the passages cited above, which may be considered as anticipative of the treatment that follows, we find along with other, heterogeneous concepts and discussions, as is usually the case in Da Vinci's writings, material most valuable for our purposes.

Using the method of comparison, Leonardo writes in Ms. A, folio 48 verso:

"Of the supports.

"A pillar whose thickness is increased will gain more than its due strength in direct proportion to what it loses in relative height.

"Example. If a pillar is nine times as high as it is thick—that is to say, if it is one ell thick, and according to rule 9 ells high—then, if you place 100 such pillars together in a mass, this will be 10 ells broad and 9 high. And if the first pillar will carry 10,000 pounds, the second, being only about as high as it is wide, and thus lacking 8 parts of its proper length, will bear eight times more; that is to say, each of the pillars thus united will bear eight times more than when disconnected; that is to say, if at first it would carry 10,000 pounds, it will now carry 90,000.

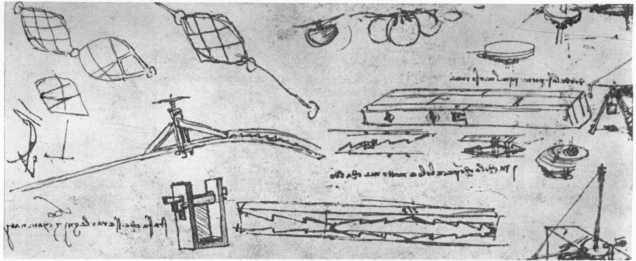

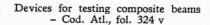

Devices for testing composite beams – Cod. Atl., fol. 324 v

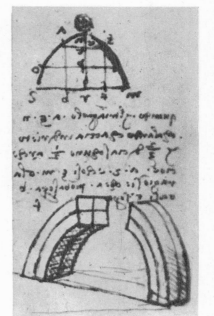

"For example: if you take a reed a hundred times as high as it is thick and place it perpendicularly, and let an ounce of weight be put on it, which it will carry.

"Then bind 100 reeds together continuously; these reeds will form a body five times its thickness. By as many times as 5 goes into 100, by so much will this body support more weight than if it were of a hundred thicknesses; and since 5 goes 20 times into 100, by virtue of this binding each reed will support 20 times as much weight as before binding; that is, if at first it supported one ounce, it will then support 20.

"If a lance one hundred times as long as it is thick will bear 20 pounds, what will a similar rod of five times its thickness bear? By as many times as 5 goes into 100, by so much will the rod of 100 thicknesses bear less than the rod of 5 thicknesses.

"If reed *ef* bears one ounce and its height is 100 diameters of its thickness, *ab* also comprising 100 diameters and 100 reeds, it will support 100 ounces, since the reed is 100 times the proportion of reed *ef*.

"If you take 100 similar reeds like *ef* and bind them together firmly and continuously, since *ef* is of 100 thicknesses and *cd* of 5 thicknesses, 5 goes 20 times into 100 and so each of the reeds bound together will support 20 times as much as when single; so that if *ef* bears one ounce, *cd* will bear 2000."

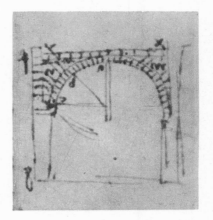

Above, below: Study on strength of arches and on sections – Ms. A, fol. 49 v

In connection with the method employed, we transcribe a further passage written by Leonardo in Ms. A, folio 3 verso. All the passages of this folio are crossed out. Probably Leonardo copied them out onto some other sheet that has not come down to us. As a matter of fact, the Da Vinci manuscripts show a clear distinction between the various ways of crossing out a passage or a phrase. When Leonardo realizes that the form or the matter of what he is writing does not satisfy him, he uses a stroke for crossing it out that is quite different from the stroke he employs when, although he finds the idea to be exact and the form clear, he crosses out a passage to transcribe it—at least we presume this is the case—into another notebook. At any rate, here are the three crossed-out passages that concern our theme:

"Of supports.

"Many small supports joined together will support a larger total weight than when they are separate. For example: 100 reeds of the same thickness and length, when separate, and each one placed vertically, will bend when loaded with one denaro [?] of ordinary weight; and if you bind them together with close bindings wound so that they touch, they will be capable when vertical of supporting so much weight that each reed will sustain more than twelve times the weight it would bear before.

"Supports.

"If [two] columns separately can each support 100 pounds, they will support 300 pounds if you join them together.

"Of the pressure of weight.

"It is impossible that a support of uniform thickness and strength should ever twist or break when loaded vertically with weight equidistant from its center; it will rather sink [into the ground]; but if the superimposed weight should be more to one side of the support than to the other, the support will bend toward the side where the greater pressure of the greater weight lies, and will break in the middle on the other side, that is, the further part."

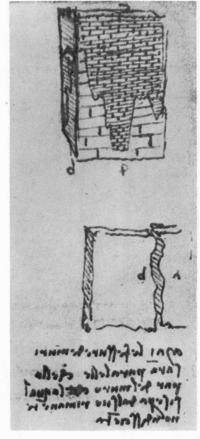

Researches on causes of fissures in walls – Cod. Arund., fol. 157 v

Before proceeding with other citations, may we point out that the method followed by Leonardo in his researches, that of comparing the strength of beams or columns of different height and iden-

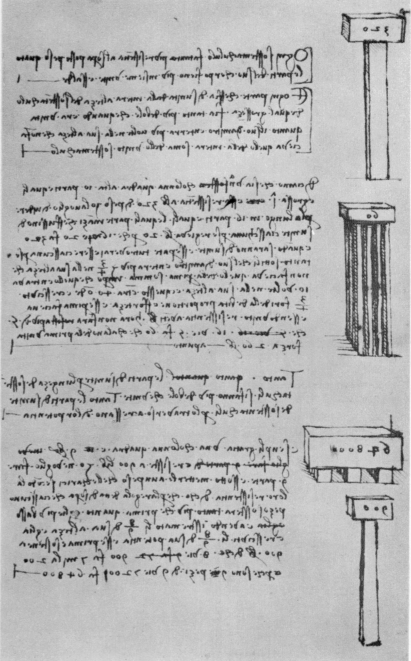

Studies and experiments on strength of beams or columns – Left: Ms. A, fol. 45 v – Right: Ms. A, fol. 46 r

Researches on fissures in walls – Cod. Arund., fol. 138 r

tical cross section, or vice versa, the beams or columns being of course made of the same material, considers relationships that eliminate the modulus of elasticity as it enters into modern calculations. In considering beams with the same cross section, the moment of inertia enters into modern calculations, while with the method of comparison followed by Leonardo this term as well is eliminated.

To bring out the keenness of Da Vinci's thought in these researches, the results of which are so close to ours of today, we transcribe from Ms. A, folio 45 verso:

"The force of the weight placed on supports affects and overcomes them in greater degree halfway up their height than at any other point.

"This is proved by experience. For if you take three pieces of wood of similar proportions, and set them up in triangular formation, that is, apart at the foot and together at the top, and load them with such a weight that they will bend, you will see that the middle will bend first. And the reason is that the weight applied from above goes down through the entire support and is as great at the base where it terminates as it is at the top; and since, as has been said above, the weight is entirely everywhere in every part of its support, and the part that is weaker offers it less resistance, that part can therefore be said to be weaker that is further from the attachments, that is, the middle, which is equally distant from the fixed ends, the one at the weight and the other on the ground. And if you pull a bowstring tight, holding it firm at the two ends, you can say that the part of the wood that is furthest from the cord is the weakest, and that is the middle.

"A support that is perpendicular and placed outside the center of the superposed weight will slope toward the larger part of the weight.

266

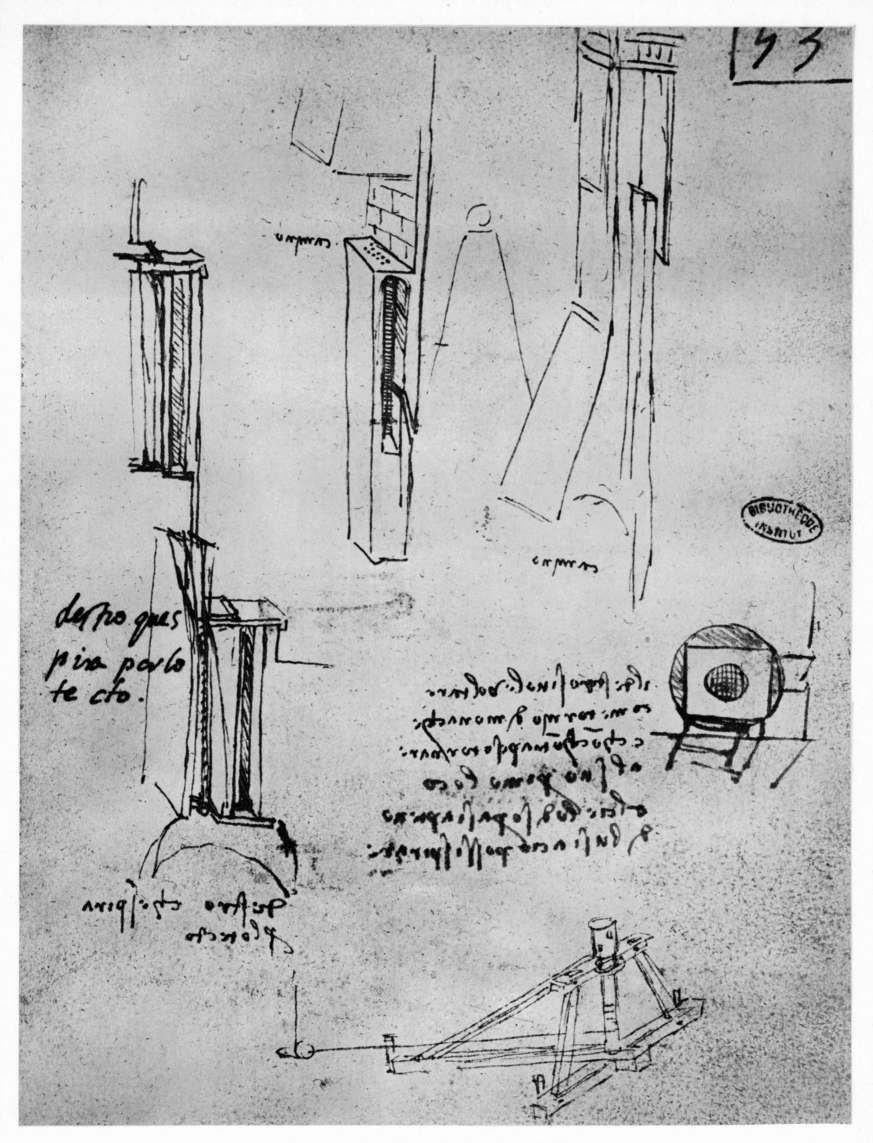

Studies on indirect draft in chimneys – Ms. B, fol. 53 r

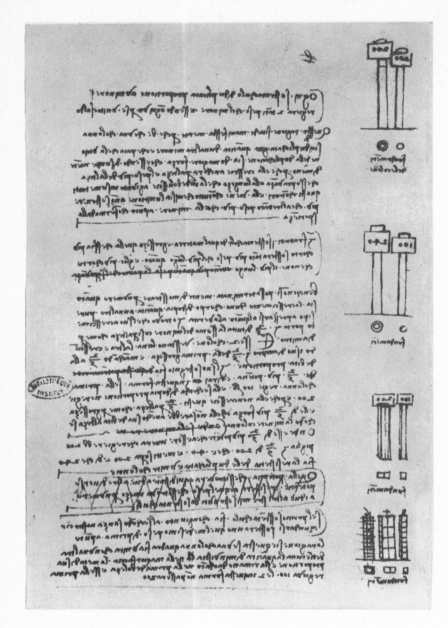

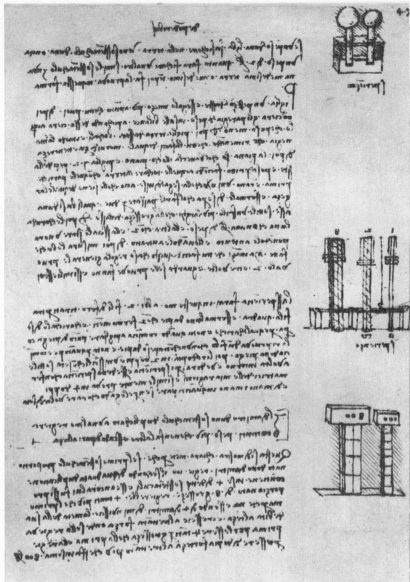

Left: Studies of strength of supporting beams – Ms. A, fol. 46 v

Right: Experiments on strength of
beams – Ms. A, fol. 47 r

"This too is proved by reason and confirmed by experience. The reasoning goes as follows: If you load a support, placed perpendicularly, in such a way that the center of this support is under the center of the load, it will sooner sink in than break, because all the parts of the load correspond to the parts of the resistance.

"It is impossible that a support, placed perpendicularly, whose center is under the center of the superposed load, should ever bend; it will sooner push its base underground.

"The reason for the statement is that the part of the support that is under the center of the load is as it were the pole of this weight; and since this is so, practically all the force remains there, and when the part of the support that constitutes the pole is not surrounded and reinforced equally by the entire thickness of the support, the part that is weaker gives way."

On folio 46 recto of Ms. A, we read:

"Every support offers the more resistance to the load imposed, the more compact and solid the parts of its substance are.

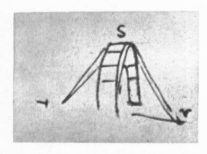

"And every part of equal thickness, and having the entire height of the support, if separated will be by so much the weaker than when it was joined with the other parts, the more times its diameter enters into its height, as compared with the ratio of the diameter of the entire support to its height.

"Let us say that there is a square column 10 parts high and one part thick, and let it resist a weight of 320 pounds. I divide it lengthwise into 16 equal parts; before these parts were separated, each supported 20 pounds, since 20 times 16 makes 320. And when these parts are separated, you will find each one so thin that its diameter will enter four times as many times into its height as the diameter entered the height in the first combined unit; for that was ten times as high as it was thick, and this is 40 times as high as it is thick, so that it has grown by 3/4 out of due proportion and strength, and if before, when united, it carried 20 pounds, now it will not take more than 5; and 16 times 5 makes 60 [sic], so that just 260 pounds are taken from the original combined strength.

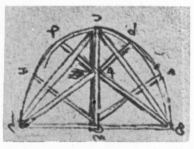

Study of strength of arches – Ms.
B, fol. 19 v

268

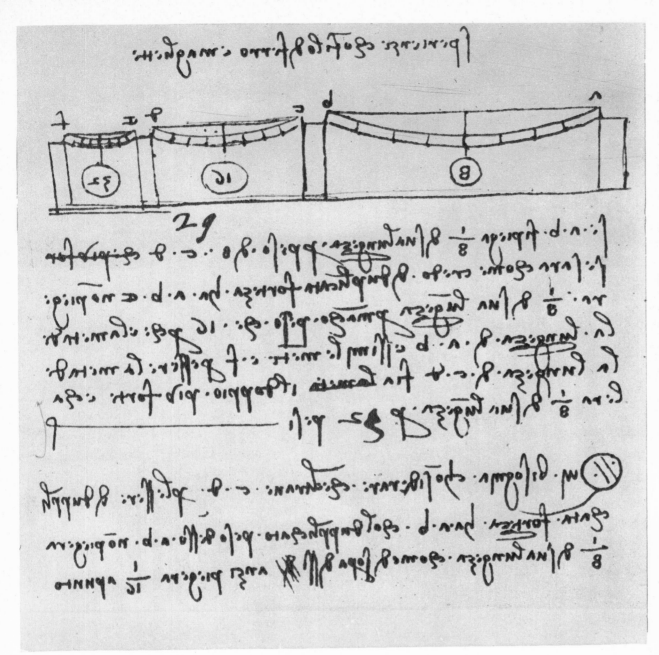

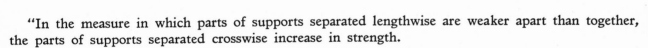

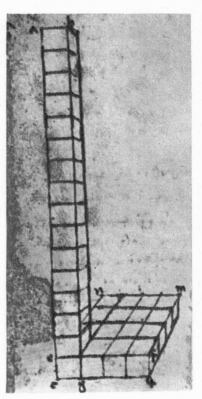

Study of elastic deformation of beam supported at both ends – Cod. Atl., fol. 332 r-b

Elementary study of strength under stress – Cod. Atl., fol. 224 v-a

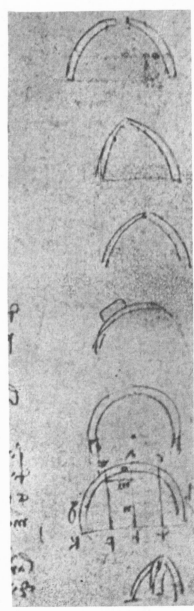

A further Leonardo da Vinci's drawing regarding study of strength of arches – Ms. A, fol. 50 r

"In the measure in which parts of supports separated lengthwise are weaker apart than together, the parts of supports separated crosswise increase in strength.

"For example: A square column 9 ells [long] stands a weight of 900 pounds; I divide it into 9 [transverse] parts and subject them to a load to the limit of their strength. I say that according to the rule given above, each piece will now support the more [weight], the lower it is; and since it has lost 8/9 of its height, it has increased its strength by 8/9. And if it carried 900 pounds before, I say that 8 times 9 makes 7200, and since there are 9 pieces, 9 times 7200 makes 64,800."

On folio 46 verso of Ms. A, Leonardo writes:

"Any support of twice the proportions of a smaller one will carry twice as great a load as the smaller, each of the two being in one piece and solid.

"This is evident, for although one column may have twice the substance of a smaller column, and it might seem that the union of the duplication would give greater strength than when they were separate, the fact is nevertheless that since it increases in height as well, the greater weight for the increased height and the length which weakens it join together to the contrary effect, so that despite the union the column supports no more than twice as much as the smaller one, as experience confirms.

"Of all supports of similar material and equal thickness, the shorter one will sustain more weight than the longer one by as much as it is shorter than the longer one.

"Although it is not possible to prove definitively in figures the amount of increase of a body that has twice the quantity of another, it is possible to come close to the truth. I find that its increase comes to 2/5 of the entire amount of the smaller one, as regards both height and diameter.

269

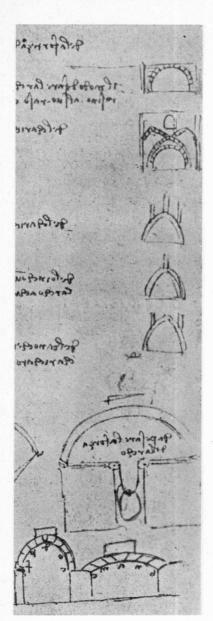

Study of strength of arches – Ms. A, fol. 50 v

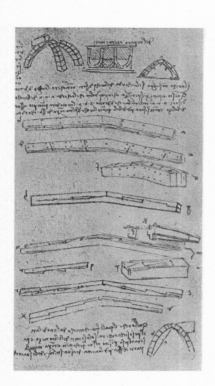

A further study of strength of arches and on composite beams – Ms. A, fol. 51 r

"And if two columns should fit one into the other, with the diameter increased by 2/5 of the original thickness, and with 2/5 coming off the due proportion, its strength would be 2/5 greater. And you will say: If the first column bears 100 pounds and the second of double proportions bears 200, and since it does not increase these 2/5 in height as in thickness, it has 2/5 more strength than it would have if it had its due height as in the smaller column.

"Now being 2/5 stronger than by itself, in which case it would bear 200, take 2/5 of 200, which 40 [?], and add 200 to this, and the strength of the doubled and combined columns will be 240."

This passage is followed by another, also crossed out:

"A force equidistant from two other different forces will resist the load that is the numerical mean of the other two extremes upheld by supports."

Folio 46 verso of Ms. A ends with the following proposition:

"If the first support is joined to the second without surrounding it, they will carry precisely the same load as before."

The proof that follows runs:

"The reason is thus: if a square column is united to another, although the entire quantity is cut down by half the proportion of the larger face, it retains its previous weakness sideward, and if the first carried 100, the 2 in this form will not go above 200."

On the next sheet Leonardo, before proceeding with the discussion, goes into a kind of experimental excursus that casts a great deal of light on the general method he followed in his researches and on the practical experimental details. Under the generic title *De ponderibus* he writes (Ms. A, fol. 47 r):

"If a weight of one pound drives a support one ounce [1/12 ell] into the ground, how far will a two-pound weight drive a similar support into the ground in the same time? Make the test in this way: Take a piece of rod and saw it in two as exactly as you can; then equalize the weight of the two halves in a balance with wax, adding wax to the one that weighs less; then take pottery clay and knead it so that it will be of uniform softness and smoothness; then beat it out flat on a flat place and take the two pieces of rod and set them upright, making them touch the clay with the parts that were originally together, that is, the sawed faces, so that they will be of equal breadth, and fasten them above by having them pass through two equal holes in a thin strip of board, a hairs-breadth larger than the thickness of the rod. Then load one with a pound weight and the other with two and let them stand an hour, setting them down at the same time and taking them off together; then measure the indentations made. But before you take this case as a general rule, try it two or three times and see whether the effects are similar in every test.

"Experiment. You will perform the experiment in this manner: Have two square-drawn iron wires, and fasten one upright with two stops at its foot, and load it from above with some weight and note when it begins to bend, and check by means of a wire with a counterweight at its foot, and note the weight under which the said bending begins. Then double them and tie them together with thin silk around them, and you will see by experience that this experiment will confirm my reasoning; and similarly try four together and so forth, and as many as you please, always binding them with a few turns of silk."

After this experimental parenthesis, Leonardo goes ahead with his presentation on the same folio 47 recto:

"If the diameter of a support is double that of another, it will support 8 times as much weight as the other, the two being of equal height.

"This is proved clearly, for if the first support proportioned to its diameter supports 100, the second, having the square of the duplication, comprises within itself 4 of the said supports, and even if it had the proportion of 8 thicknesses, it would carry 4 times as much as the first; but since it is of 4 diameters [has four times the cross section?], it decreases by half of its due height and its strength increases by that much, so that if it originally carried four times as much weight because of having four times the thickness [cross section], it will carry as much more for being of double strength, which makes 800 pounds altogether."

To conclude and sum up the passages referred to above, we should point out that Leonardo was perfectly well aware that the resistance to pressure of beams longitudinally loaded is proportional to the stressed cross section.

He is in error when he holds that the pressure is inversely proportional to the ratio between the height of the beam and the side of the square cross section or the radius of the circular cross section of the cylinder.

Today we know, on the basis of the theory of elasticity, that in the cases given above the pressure is in fact proportional to the stressed surface and inversely proportional to the square of the above-

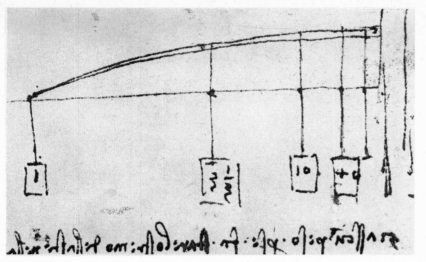

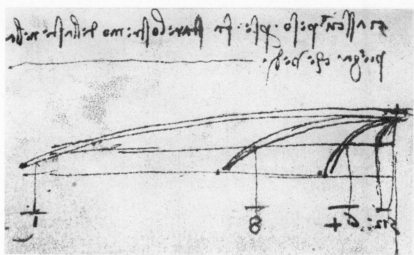

mentioned ratio. In other words, if the height is kept constant and the side of the section or its radius is doubled, the strength will vary, according to Leonardo, as the cube of the side of the section or its radius, and so will be eight times as great, whereas actually it varies as the fourth power, and is sixteen times as great.

Likewise, if the cross section is kept constant, the strength, by Leonardo's reckoning, will be inversely proportional to the height, whereas actually it will vary inversely as the square of the height.

With respect to the experiment cited, which refers to beams of square cross section loaded at their upper ends and rigidly fastened at their lower ends, we should note the perfect harmony between theoretical research and practical experiment that is manifested in Leonardo, even though his method seems primitive by modern standards, for all its ingenuity.

We now take up the researches of Da Vinci on the problem of a beam fastened at one end and stressed at the other, and on the bending of a beam supported at its two ends and stressed in the middle.

Again in Ms. A, folio 49 recto, we read:

"If a rod projecting by one hundred thicknesses [100 times its diameter] from a wall carries ten pounds, how much will be borne by a hundred similar rods similarly projecting and bound together into a unit?

"I say that if the [rod of a] hundred thicknesses will carry ten pounds, the [bundle of] five thicknesses will carry ten times as much as the [rod of] 100 [thicknesses], and if ab is the [bundle of] five thicknesses, the hundred rods will carry 20,000 pounds."

As regards a beam set horizontally and supported at its two ends, we have wonderful researches into flexion in the Codex Atlanticus.

Modern theory tells us that in a square beam raised at its end and stressed at its midpoint, the bending is directly proportional to the weight and to the cube of the length, and inversely proportional to the fourth power of the side of the square.

In the Codex Atlanticus, folio 332 recto-b, Leonardo gives us an anticipation of the modern theory, at least in relation to the first part of it as we have just stated it. He says:

"If ab bends 1/8 of its length for a weight of 8, cd, if it is, as I believe, twice as strong as ab, will not bend 1/8 of its length for a lesser weight than 16, since it is half the length of ab; and likewise ef, being half the length of cd, will be twice as strong and will sag 1/8 of its length for 32 weights.

"It should be kept in mind here that beam cd, being twice as strong as ab, will not bend 1/8 of its length under twice the load of ab, but will bend precisely 1/16."

The Codex Atlanticus also contains conclusions based on experimental data relating to the passage cited.

Among other comments, we read (fol. 211 r-b):

"I have found that when a weight of a pound is hung from the middle of a rod of 12 ells, the rod curves by one ell, and I wish to know what weight will cause a rod 6 ells long, of the same thickness, to have the same one-ell bend.

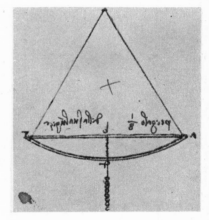

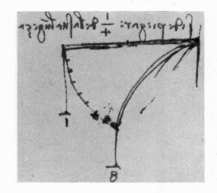

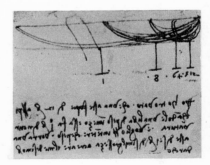

271

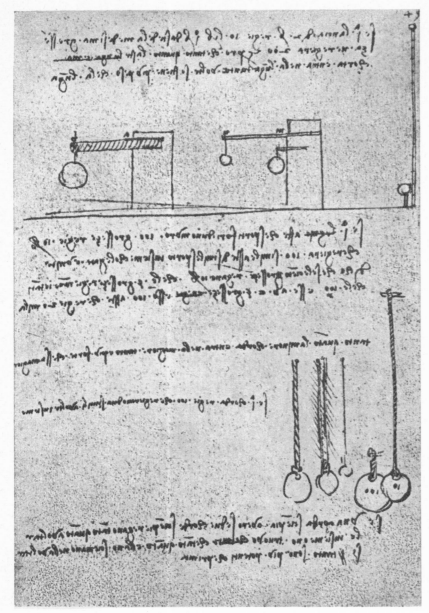

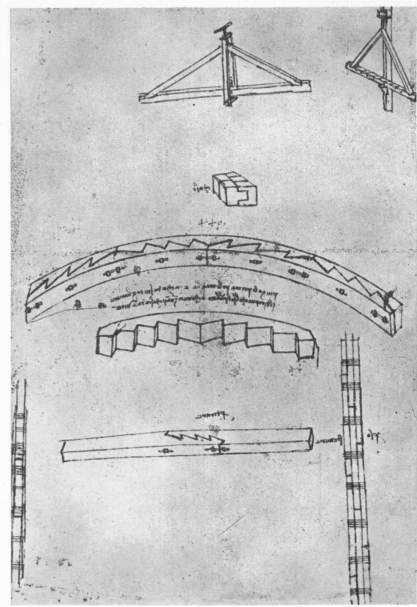

Left: Study of beams supported at one end – Ms. A, fol. 49 r

Right: Studies of composite beams – Cod. Atl., fol. 344 v-a

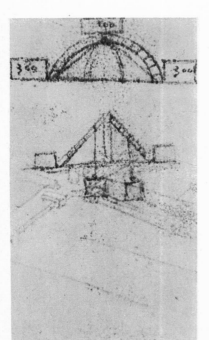

Researches on statics of arches – Cod. Forst., III, fol. 79 v

"The 6-ell rod is twice as strong in the middle as four 12-ell rods of the same thickness bound together.

"If all these weights were hung on this rod at once, how much would the rod curve?

"And what would be the weights that if hung at each of these places at the same time would cause the rod to retain ... the same curvature?

"And what weight should be placed at each of these points so that the rod ... *co* may have the same sag? It should bend 1/4 of its length.

"If a rod is fixed at one of its ends, and the other end in bending describes the twelfth part of a circle, the degrees of its flexion, if caused by equal weights, will be equal to each other."

And alongside a figure we find:

"Bend it 1/8 of its length. The curvature of rod *abc* comes to the sixth part of a circle; the degrees of the descent to this curvature will be equal to each other if caused by equal weights.

"I desire to hang a weight from the middle of a uniform rod, and have it keep the same curvature, and change that weight in 5 different places on the rod, coming closer and closer to an end, and always doubling the previous weight, to find for each weight the exact position that will keep the rod at its original curvature.

"Each weight in and of itself causes the end of the rod to take the bend that you see. I desire only to see the weight that, by being hung in the middle of the uniform rod, will give it a certain degree of curvature; then touch the rod anywhere you please, and I shall tell you what weight must be hung at that point to give the same curvature to the rod.

"The strength will be proportional to the length."

272

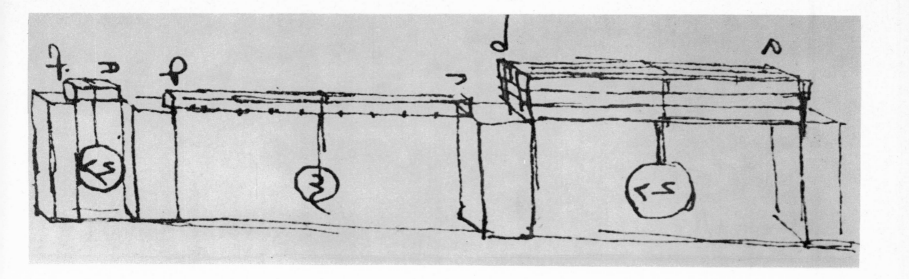

A similar notion, also based on an experimental criterion and the method of comparison, is expressed in the following passage of the Codex Atlanticus (fol. 225 r-*f*):

"If a rod 10 ells long bends one ell with a weight of 100 pounds, 4 similar rods tied together will bend 1/2 ell, and the half rod [half as long] is as strong as 8 full-length rods bound together, or as one full-length rod so thick that it has twice the diameter of the half-length rod."

At another place in the Codex Atlanticus we find precise references to experiments and to conclusions reached by Leonardo in his study of the problem of the bending of beams supported at the ends and loaded in the middle.

On folio 152 recto-*b* of the Codex Atlanticus, after discussing supports in the form of vertical beams loaded on one end, he says:

"Among supports of similar material and equal thickness, that one will be the stronger whose length is shorter."

Then he gets to the heart of the question and writes:

"If you will place crosswise a support of like thickness and material which has a strength of 100, and then take away nine tenths of its height, you will find that its remainder, if supported at the ends, will have a strength of a thousand.

"You will find as much force and resistance in a collection of 9 beams of equal quality as in the ninth part of one of them."

This last paragraph, as the figure shows, refers to beams supported at both ends. In a note next to the figure itself, explaining his treatment, Leonardo says that

"*ab* supports 27 and is 9 beams, while *cd*, which is the ninth part of it, supports 3; since this is so, *ef*, which is the ninth part of the length of *cd*, will support 27, because it is 9 times as short."

In this case, as in the previous ones, Leonardo considers beams with square cross section. He comes to the conclusion that the strength is inversely proportional to the length and directly proportional to the square of the side, whereas we know today that it is proportional to the cube of the side and inversely proportional to the length.

The examples that have been cited should suffice to prove that Leonardo's researches anticipate by about a century those published by Galileo in 1638, although completed forty years before that date.

On reaching this point it would be necessary to extend our discussion to the part of the Da Vinci manuscripts that apply the ideas given above as the first rudiments of a theory of the arch. Starting with folio 29 recto (28) of the Codex Trivulzianus, we should observe the sketch in which Leonardo considers a certain weight sustained by a vertical support and subsequently the same weight placed on the keystone first of a Gothic arch and then of a round arch. Doing this, however, would mean going beyond the limits set for this note of ours. The question is a very important one and is much studied by Leonardo, both in Ms. A, from which we have derived most of the passages cited here, and in other manuscripts that we hope to examine in another note.

Before ending this one, however, we should like to refer to an experimental apparatus devised by Leonardo for investigating the strength of material that shows him, as ever, anticipating a similar mechanism first used hereabouts some fifty years ago.

On folio 82 recto-*b* of the Codex Atlanticus we find this entry:

"Experiment regarding the strength of an iron wire in various lengths.

Study of laws of elastic line in beam – Cod. Atl., fol. 152 r-*b*

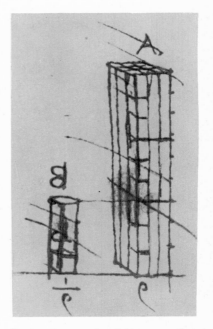

Study of strength of beams – Cod. Atl., fol. 152 r-*b*

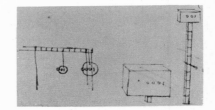

Study of strength of beams – Cod. Atl., fol. 152 r-*b*

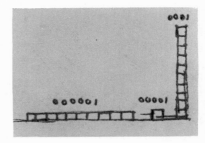

Study of strength of beams – Cod. Atl., fol. 152 v-*b*

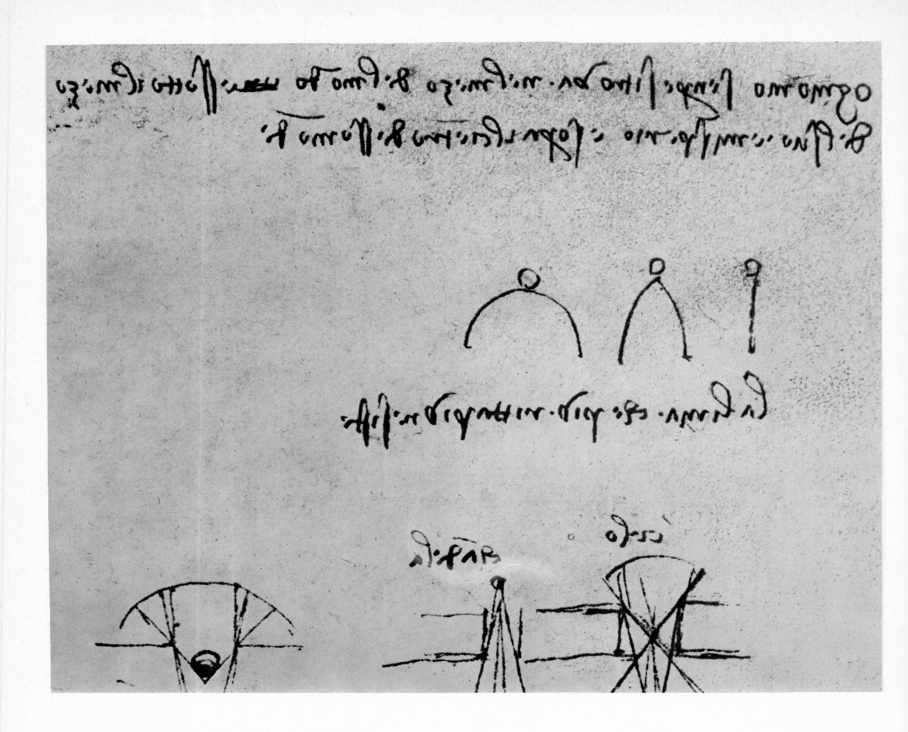

First elements of researches on arches
– Cod. Triv., fol. 29 r

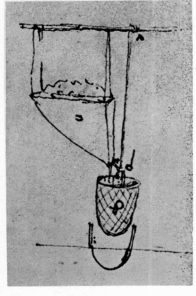

Experimental apparatus for measuring
tensile strength of wires – Cod. Atl.,
fol. 82 r-b

"Note on the way in which you should measure the capacity of an iron wire, or what weight it can bear.   In this experiment you will proceed as follows: Hang an iron wire two ells long or thereabouts from a strong point;   then hang from it a basket or a sack or what you will, into which, through a small orifice, you will pour fine sand from a hopper;   and when this iron wire can sustain no more, it will break.   Attach a little spring that will immediately close the hole of the hopper, so that no more sand may fall into the basket, which will come down upright, since it will fall from half a finger's height;   and observe what the weight was that broke the wire, and in what part the wire broke;   and always make the test over again, to see whether it always breaks in the same place. Then shorten this wire, at first by half, and see how much more weight it supports;   and then make it 1/4 of its original length, and so go on, making various lengths and noting the weight that breaks each one and the place in which it breaks.   And you will make this test for all kinds of metals and woods, stones, ropes, and anything that will support other objects;   and establish a law for each thing;   and you will do the same for terrestrial supports, that is, supports with one end fast in the ground or on the ground."

This passage, as Maganzini observed in 1912, recalls in a remarkable way the Frühling-Michaelis balance used for testing cement.

As Leonardo's drawing in the manuscript, unfortunately for us, is not easily intelligible in detail, we interpret it by reference to a modern text, Arlorio's *Metodi di prova dei materiali*. Here, in figure 6 of Plate I, no. 17 and 18 show the hopper, no. 13 what Leonardo calls a "basket" (*cavagno*), using a term from the Milanese dialect, or "bag" (*sporta*) by a Tuscan word, no. 9 the test piece, and no. 15 and 16 a lever apparatus taking the place of the spring designed by Leonardo to cut off the flow of sand.

ARTURO UCCELLI

274

MILITARY ENGINEERING AND ARMS

"Leonardo received from the sun the gift of being able to give form to everything that the human mind might speculate on and imagine in the seven liberal arts, and to demonstrate practically in drawings that which others not only could not do but could not even understand" [1]: in words like this we perceive that the essential characteristic of the technical artistic activity of Leonardo da Vinci, his universality, was perfectly understood even four centuries ago. It is a universality that makes us realize his quality as citizen of the world, as an exceptional product of the genius of humanity; it transcends frontiers and nations, but nevertheless bears within it the unmistakable signs of the genius and talent of the Italian people, a talent made up of endless versatility, of rigorous, serene scientific balance, of deep poetic inspiration. Da Vinci the scientist has now come to be fully known alongside Da Vinci the artist, and study of his marvelous and enormous scientific work justifies us in evaluating it as a tremendous contribution to the progress of the human spirit. We shall dwell here on one of the infinite aspects of his unending activity, examining his work on problems of military art and architecture; and we shall find in this aspect of his labors too the universal property of all Da Vinci studies, namely, the anticipation of forms and discoveries that would come into the public domain only centuries later.

"Most Illustrious Lord: Having now sufficiently seen and considered the proofs of all those who proclaim themselves masters and inventors of instruments of war, and finding that their invention and use of the said instruments are nothing different from common practice, I am emboldened, without prejudice to any one else, to put myself in communication with Your Excellency, in order to acquaint you with my secrets, thereafter offering myself at your pleasure effectually to demonstrate at opportune times all those things which are in part briefly noted below:

1. I have sorts of bridges, very light and strong, and suitable to be carried very easily, with which to pursue and at times flee from the enemy, and of others, solid and indestructible by fire or assault, easy and convenient to transport and place in position. Also methods of burning and destroying those of the enemy.

2. When a place is besieged I know how to cut off water from the trenches, and how to construct an infinite variety of bridges, mantlets, and scaling ladders, and other instruments pertaining to the said enterprise.

3. Also, if a place cannot be reduced by the method of bombardment, because of either the height of its glacis or the strength of its position, I have methods for destroying any fortress or other stronghold, even if it be founded upon rock.

4. I have also types of mortars very convenient and easy to transport, with which to hurl small stones like a storm, with the smoke of these causing great terror to the enemy, and great loss and confusion.

Conical screw for breech-loading cannon
– Cod. Atl., fol. 34 r-*a*

---

[1] Luca Beltrami, *Documenti e memorie riguardanti la vita e le opere di Leonardo da Vinci*, p. 196.

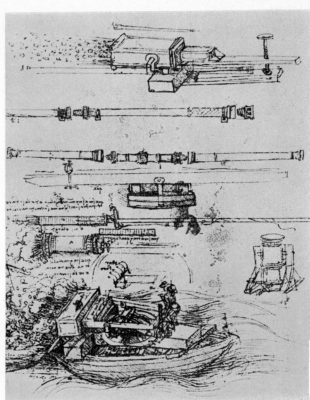

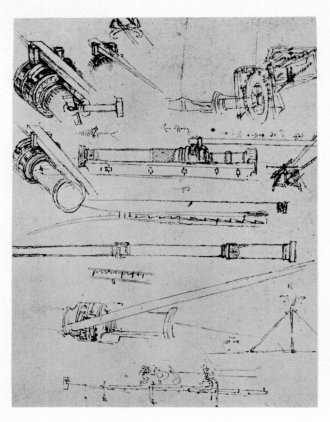

Left: Studies for screw closing of breech-loading cannon – Cod. Atl., fol. 10 v-*a*

Right: Firearms mounted on boats – Windsor, Royal Collection, no. 12652

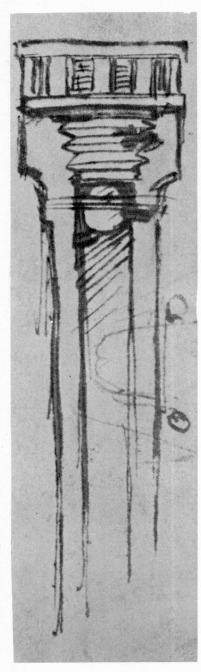

Conical screw for cannon breech – Cod. Atl., fol. 23 v-*a*

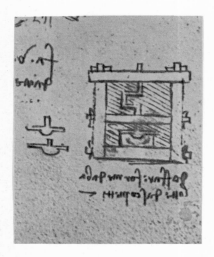

Machine for making musket balls – Ms. B., fol. 72 r

276

5. And if the engagement be at sea, I have many engines of kinds most efficient for offense and defense, and ships which will resist the fire of all the heaviest cannon, as well as powder and smoke.

6. Also, I have ways of arriving at a given spot by mines and secret winding passages, made without noise, even though it may be necessary to pass underneath trenches or a river.

7. Also, I will make covered chariots, safe and unassailable, which, when they enter among the enemy with their artillery, there is no body of men-at-arms so great but they will shatter it. And behind these, infantry will be able to follow quite unharmed and unhindered.

8. Also, if need should arise, I will make cannon, mortars, and light ordnance, of very beautiful and useful shapes, quite different from those in common use.... Moreover, I would undertake the work of the bronze horse, which is to endue with immortal glory and eternal honor the auspicious memory of the Prince your father and the illustrious house of Sforza. And if any of the aforesaid things should seem impossible or impracticable to anyone, I offer myself as ready to make trial of them in your park, or in whatever place shall please Your Excellency, to whom I commend myself with all possible humility."

With this fundamental document,[2] which is certainly authentic even if not an autograph, Leonardo enters officially into the field of military art and architecture: the letter shows him offering his services, about 1483, to Duke Ludovico Maria Sforza, known as Il Moro. Sforza, as is shown by documents of the period published some years ago,[3] had asked the Medicis for an artist able to complete the equestrian statue of the great Francesco, founder of the political and military power of the Lombard state. It was desired that this work be especially imposing, in order suitably to glorify the subject; but Da Vinci, in proposing himself for the service of Il Moro, lists an impressive series of military inventions, as we have seen, leaving for the end of his letter a single fleeting reference to the equestrian monument. This may be due in some measure to the duchy's military necessities, which were becoming more and more urgent in those years for Il Moro's government; but in my opinion the cause is to be found primarily in the preparatory studies in mechanics and technology that the young Da Vinci had made in Tuscany between 1470 and 1480, and in the self-confidence he had derived from the results that his exceptional spirit of observation, investigation, and research had enabled him to achieve in the realm of engineering and military technique. This explains why he was so sure of gaining advancement through his new military inventions, and so completely assured of victory over any competitors, "be they who they may," as appears so strikingly from the whole tenor of the document; certainly this arose from no empty self-glorification.

And this interpretation is fully confirmed by the early sheets of the pre-Sforza period, those pages of the Codex Atlanticus in which we have some samples of his preparation in the subject, and can see the typical forms that may also be found in the first treatises and notebooks of the two Sienese

[2] Cod. Atl., fol. 391 r-*a*.
[3] Calvi, *Contributi alla biografia vinciana (periodo Sforzesco)*, in *Archivio storico lombardo*.

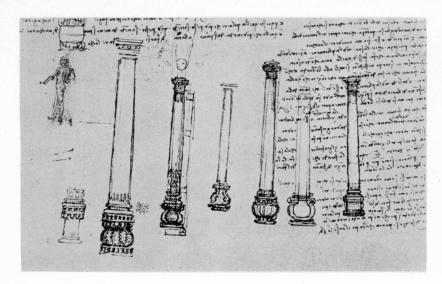

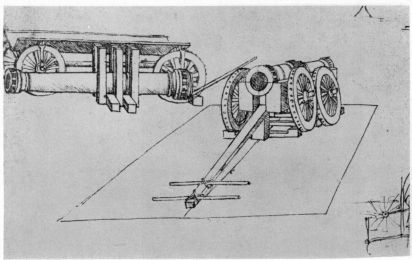

writers, Mariano di Jacopo and Francesco di Giorgio Martini. We are at the initial stages of that development which started from the basic notions of popular and craft technology in Florence and Siena in the first half of the fifteenth century, as we see in the numerous treatises entitled *De ponderibus*, *Delle leve e tirarii*, etc. A systematic examination of these youthful pages of Leonardo's in their sequence, down to the time of his arrival in Lombardy, enables us to estimate the ground he had already covered, so that he could list for Il Moro an important series of achievements in the art of war, as the result of his own original work.[4]

Left: Designs for cannon – Cod. Atl., fol. 28 v-*a*

Right: Moving cannons on inclined wheels – Cod. Atl., fol. 55 v-*a*

Advance toward modern ideas thus came much earlier (Leonardo was about thirty at the time) in the domain of mobile and operational offensive and defensive arms than in that of military architecture proper; in this field it was only later that the studies of the Lombard period were to lead, by way of remarkable innovations during the years immediately following the date of the letter to Il Moro (1483-1488), to the perfect schemes of the sheets originating in the Romagna period (1502-1503). We have seen that the reason for the priority thus given to studies on field artillery is to be sought in the nature of the Florentine and Sienese technical milieu of the fifteenth century, from which Leonardo, eager to learn and study the "infinite reasons that were never in experience," took his inspiration and first impetus, absorbing its scientific atmosphere, as it were. The result was original achievements, and indeed of a kind that warranted an attitude of triumph, in military technology —mining galleries, armored and assault cars, machine guns, emergency bridges, underwater apparatus for naval attack and defense, and the like. Knowledge of the precise tactical employment of those means naturally follows upon their invention: it is very interesting to note, for example, that in telling us of the assault car, Leonardo states its function in combat as it has remained down to the present day: "Also, I will make covered chariots, safe and unassailable, which, when they enter among the enemy with their artillery, there is no body of men-at-arms so great but they will shatter it. And behind, infantry will be able to follow quite unharmed and unhindered." Here we have the tank breakthrough of the present day, followed by the infantry exploiting it.

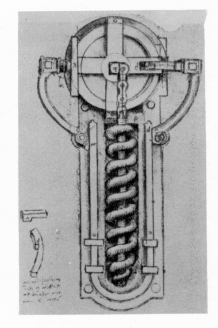

Automatic device for elevating cannons – Cod. Atl., fol. 56 v-*b*

During the Lombard period (1483-1499), which with the succeeding Romagna period (1502-1503), constitutes the time in which Da Vinci went deepest into military matters, we see him not only inventing military machines and devices but also studying defensive structures. Before going into detail regarding these two aspects, it will be well to establish a general orientation. We may say that up to roughly the first half of the fifteenth century, the technique of fortification had not changed in essentials from the practice of the late Middle Ages. The characteristics of medieval fortification were: a high ratio between vertical and horizontal dimensions; high and relatively thin curtain walls; deficient and unorganized outworks or lists and barbicans, whose sole function was protection of the entrances and exits of the stronghold; an almost absolute lack of organization of fire power, both offensive and defensive fire being based on high trajectories and thought of primarily as "plunging" fire (that is, falling by force of gravity from corbelled apertures, the machicolations) rather having a more or less rapid and extended horizontal range, and being consequently confined to the neighborhood of their base. All this went to make up a technical form for defensive structures, such as fortified enceintes and castle-palaces.

This form had come down to the engineers of the early fifteenth century in an unbroken tradition going back to Roman antiquity, the treatise writers of the empire—Vegetius, Vitruvius, Frontinus— and such later figures as Cornazzano and others. Archaeology and the accounts of historians, from Caesar on, show us that this technical tradition of military architecture can be traced down through

Systems of cannon manufacture – Cod. Atl., fol. 19 r-*b*

---

[4] See, among others, fol. 61 r of Ms. B (reference to the theme *De ponderibus*).

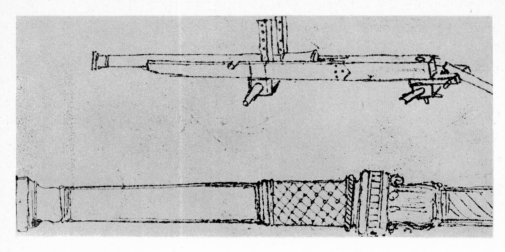

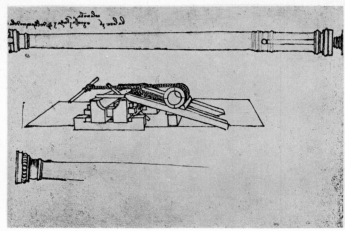

Left: Drawing of cannon and of mount for firearms – Cod. Atl., fol. 340 v-*b*

Right: Apparatus for lifting cannon – Cod. Atl., fol. 28 v-*b*

Study for cannon manufacture – Cod. Atl., fol. 19 r-*a*

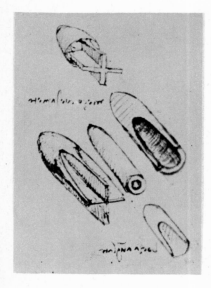

Pointed projectiles with directional fins – Cod. Arund., fol. 54 r

the centuries, and that the Italian engineers of the early Middle Ages were faithful to it, as we can see, for instance, from the treatise of Egidio Colonna entitled *De regimine principum* (thought to have been written before 1285) and the *Dei fatti d'arme e della cavalleria*, written by Cristina da Pizzano about a century later. The splendid Visigoth enceinte of Carcassonne may be regarded as a perfect fifth-century source for later medieval architecture, based on ideas of Vegetius taken up in large part by subsequent writers, such as Antonio Averulino (known as Filarete), Alberti, Giulio Ferretti of Ravenna, Roberto Valturio of Rimini, and Aristotile Fioravanti of Bologna. In some of the treatises of the mid-fifteenth century that came directly before the development of the new technique, the drawings remind us of the Roman iconography and go with the fifteenth-century editions of Caesar's *Commentaries* inspired by classical models; between these and the drawings of Roberto Valturio's *De re militari* there is but little development, and sometimes none at all.

All of these writings, including the *Commentaries*, are the distant sources of Da Vinci's technology. Valturio in particular is the proximate source, in his first two editions (Verona, 1462, Latin; 1483, vernacular) in which the resemblances to the Tuscan and Lombard studies soon to come are so evident—especially if we compare Ms. B with the vernacular edition—that we become certain that Da Vinci copied entire sections and paragraphs; many drawings of machines and weapons likewise recall the models in Valturio. This brings us to what is improperly called the transition period, which is marked by a revision of forms at first only as a tendency, and then, once we are fully in the sixteenth century, more decided and radical, following new canons born of a basic concern of the architects. This turned on the problem of making the structures of fortifications capable of resisting the enormously increased power of artillery by making the works ever lower and thicker, and, further, on the necessity of perfecting horizontal fire so as to make possible effective offensive action, adequately protected and defiladed at its bases, and economical in its expenditure of matériel. This is the natural evolution that leads to the perfect sixteenth-century examples of bastioned fortresses—Civitavecchia, Anzio, Nettuno, Pisa—and finally to that glory of Italy, the "bastioned trace."

The bastioned trace was the definitive radial organization of a certain number of "modern bulwarks," that is, pentagonally salient elements with a low ratio between height and thickness, with a higher ratio between faces and flanks, and with the latter "retired," that is, drawn in from the open field to facilitate effective flanking fire and protected by adjacent orillions, with a direct external vulnerability of something like 15º to 18º instead of the 90º angle made by the capital of the salient itself with the axis of the curtain. The technique of the greatest architects, those who made the most significant contributions toward the advent of this new style, gradually formed the essential traits of this type of salient, which is foreshadowed in their early studies as in those of Da Vinci's Lombard period. Francesco di Giorgio Martini, Michele San Micheli, Giuliano da San Gallo, and Mariano di Jacopo da Siena are the greatest names in this field. These inventors of the modern bastion left the impress of their genius for centuries, so that we see their ideas still in use during wars of the Napoleonic era, with changes due to progress in the art of war; but in the case of Leonardo we can say that his technique comes much closer to us, to the structural ideas and military requirements of our times, with their constant need to face up to the tremendously powerful means of attack of modern warfare.

We see this not only in the field of war machines but also with respect to permanent constructions. The structural forms devised by Da Vinci were not too far removed from the technique of a period antedating by only a few years the wars of the end of the nineteenth century, just before subsequent progress in the chemistry of explosives and the increased destructive power of cannon cut down still further the vertical elevations of structures, made them still more massive, and began the era of total casemating, bringing the works below the level of the ground, as in the Maginot, Siegfried, and Schröder lines. It should be remarked that in the domain of fieldworks some of Da Vinci's formulations, in their main outlines, remain valid even in contemporary technique, especially the way in which Da Vinci used and integrated into the structures themselves the principles that

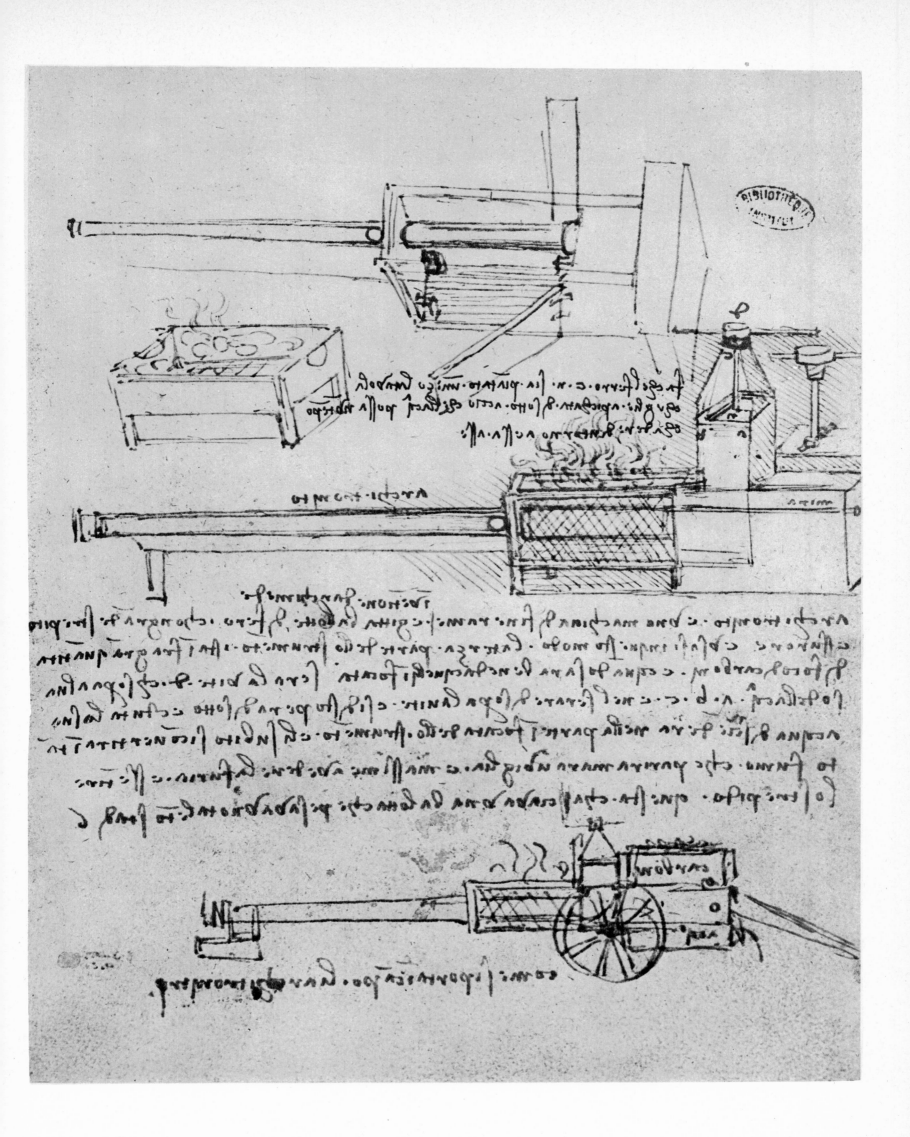

Study of *architronito* (steam cannon) – Ms. B, fol. 33 r

Left: Study of breech-loading bombard – Ms. B, fol. 31 r

Right: Studies of screw closing for cannons – Ms. B, fol. 32 r

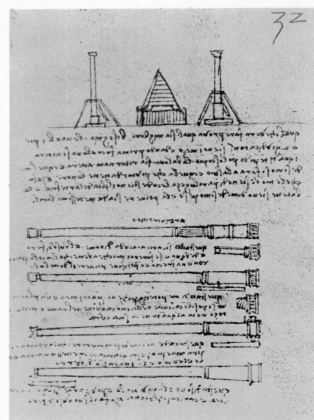

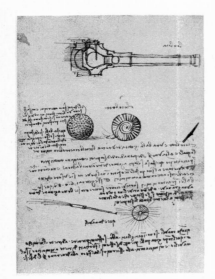

Study of breech-loading bombard and explosive bombs – Ms. B, fol. 41 v

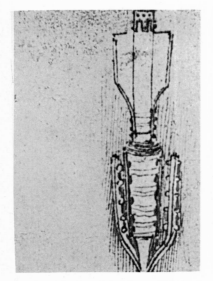

Bomb with directional fins – Windsor, Royal Collection, no. 12651

Explosive bombs – Ms. B, fol. 4 r

had found wide application in the period of transition, namely, those of cross fire and flanking fire, a subject on which present-day automatic arms (themselves descended from Vincian ancestors) speak with extreme authority.

To conclude this summary historical sketch, it seems in order to touch on a lack. As Luca Beltrami [5] has pointed out, no Da Vinci student has yet brought out the scientific and technological links between the work of the master and that of his predecessors, simultaneously showing the derivation of his ideas and separating the original contribution from the elements furnished by the tradition, and highlighting the extremely important innovations that were to serve later scientists and engineers in the advance on the long and difficult road of scientific development. A work of the nature suggested would have the great merit of outlining the scope of Da Vinci's immense production and indicating its position in history as a fountainhead, to the greater glory of his work on the one hand and in the interest of better historical knowledge on the other. For example, I have seen in many reputedly original drawings of Sangallo, and especially in later manuscripts, structural ideas for fortifications that are probably derived from Leonardian elements, in so far as we may judge from the iconographic elements and technical characteristics presented by the various authors.

Unfortunately, of the splendid studies and projects in military architecture undertaken by Leonardo, there is none of which we can say that it found embodiment in reality. He encountered enormous difficulty in carrying out the ideas his mind worked out, and especially in carrying them out promptly. The enormous labor he went through before completing a work to his satisfaction and allowing himself to sanction it, so to speak, attests this. It is also possible, on the other hand, that the buried papers of the many archives (like those of the state of Milan) still largely unexplored may bring to light a document on the basis of which we may hold Leonardo to be the creator of a work of this kind. This would seem conceivable if we consider the whole series of studies, observations, and remarks referring to definite localities of military importance visited by the master that can be recovered, *inter alia*, from Mss. B, L, and H. It is true that his inward artistic travail and his spirit of merciless, insatiable self-criticism, indices of his desire for perfection and his infinite penetration into every theme he took up, were a great obstacle to his completing works, labors, monuments, in this as in other fields; on the other hand, circumstances and practical contingencies almost always constituted the situations or motives that urged him to study a given problem of design, construction, or statics, the resistance to cannon fire of a scarp with a given section and inclination, the "best opening" to give to a parapet or battery walk.

It is therefore a timely practical question that suggests study of a given subject to the master, and in the course of this study theoretical or purely abstract considerations often intervene to post-

[5] Luca Beltrami, *Aristotile da Bologna al servizio del duca di Milano*, Milan, Allegretti, p. 9.

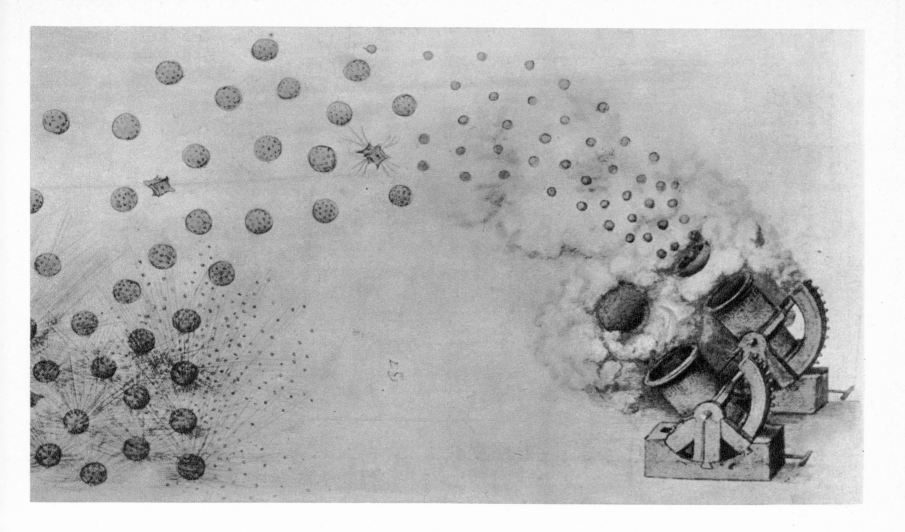

Bombard with explosive projectiles –
Cod. Atl., fol. 9 v-a

pone its conclusion. In the field of military architecture we see that his activity as scientist, designer, and engineer in relation to offensive and defensive works and operations occurs almost exclusively at those moments of his life in which he is in the service of a prince who is involved in wars or the defense of his state or the fortification of his borders, and, finally, on the occasion of a foreign war which raises pressing problems of permanent or temporary fortification. The manuscripts enable us to distinguish two periods of military studies in Da Vinci's life: first, as has been indicated, the years spent in Lombardy in the pay of Il Moro (1483-1499), and, second, those spent in Romagna as general engineer to the Duke of Valentinois, Cesare Borgia (1502-1503). Manuscript B and the famous letter to the Duke of Milan set the framework for the first period, and Ms. L and the diploma in which Borgia conferred on him the title of engineer general (August 18, 1502) mark the importance of the second. As ducal engineer to Sforza and engineer general to Cesare Borgia, the master travels through their respective dominions, observing, studying, designing, working out schemes of construction, proposing new solutions, concerned with offensive and defensive requirements, seeking to put into practice those new ideas which are being proved increasingly necessary by the increased efficiency of artillery.

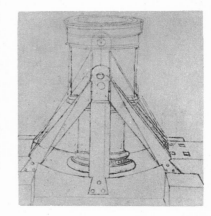

Bombard in vertical position – Cod.
Atl., fol. 18 v-b

And so about 1483 we find Leonardo in Milan, at the Sforza court, in the role of *ingeniarius et pinctor*, as he is listed in ducal documents. It had become something of a tradition to have Florentine or Tuscan artists in the service of the Sforzas. Various masters had taken part in the huge work of reconstruction and ornamentation of the castle of Porta Giovia started under Francesco Sforza in 1454 and continued under his successor, Galeazzo Maria, and now under his brother, Ludovico Maria; among these masters were Benedetto Ferrini, Fiorentino da Firenze, Domenico and Basilio da Firenze, and Filarete (Antonio Averulino), who collaborated in the erection of the central tower facing the city. In this respect I can say that examination of the still unpublished documents in the series *Autografi-Architetti* in the archives of the state of Milan reveals many notable and interesting names.

In Ms. B, which, as we have said, is typical, together with the Codex Trivulzianus, for Leonardo's military studies from 1483 on, we see his attention focussed intensively on all the military means and devices enumerated in detail in his letter. We shall run rapidly over the most important topics.

First of all there are the "sorts of bridges, very light and strong"—types of emergency bridges easily, safely, and rapidly employed during the advance and retreat of troops. In Ms. B (fol. 23 r) and other codices we find the schemes of some of the bridges worked out with original and novel solutions of great simplicity. One is the "parabolic" bridge, which solves the problem of providing

Bombard – Cod. Atl., fol. 9 r-a

Cannon in position – Cod. Atl., fol. 24 r-b

Bombard in firing position – Cod. Atl., fol. 31 r-b

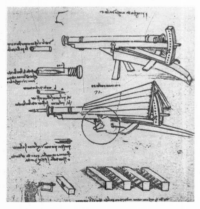

Cannons mounted – Cod. Atl., fol. 26 v-b

a span of considerable length with rapidity and ease of erection when the ends are at different levels (Cod. Atl., fol. 312 r-a). Another is the rotating bridge, for use under certain topographic conditions, with support pontoons and the requisite auxiliary equipment for moving it and securing it in place. Then there are the famous zigzag mines, mentioned at various points in the studies of the Codex Atlanticus. Leonardo devoted attention to the tortuous courses of these underground paths with the aim of evading the enemy's countermines and taking him unawares by choosing the final objective in such a way that it would be most difficult to discover. Arms of various calibers, forms, and ranges, comprising a very large number of types, appear in studies in Ms. B (e.g., fol. 31 r and v, 33 r); these range from light or heavy portable arms to medium-sized field and siege guns and up to large-caliber models, the celebrated Sforza bombards, so heavy that handling and moving them required the use of winches and cranes and a large number of artillerymen. Da Vinci also left studies of these bombards in numerous pages of the Codex Atlanticus.

The principal difficulties about these firearms lay in the problems of casting them, and in the details of loading chamber and breech. There are some models designed for breech loading (Ms. B, fol. 24 v). Although Da Vinci's letter deals with traditional arms which have been in the public domain since time immemorial, and does not speak of the innumerable types of mobile and fixed weapons for hurling missiles, there are many drawings and studies, especially in Ms. B (fol. 9 r and v, 42 r and v, et seq.), listing the various forms, with instructions for their use in practice. In this field too Leonardo made a new contribution through his projects for machines of colossal dimensions, like the famous "great crossbow" shown in pages probably of just about this period (Cod. Atl., fol. 53 r-b).

The originality thus to be seen in Da Vinci's arms is even more apparent in his designs for the ancestors of today's machine guns (Cod. Atl., fol. 51 v-a). In order to attain more effective intensity of fire with small arms, Leonardo envisages operating them successively in rapid series by skillfully mounting on a carriage the compound gun thus formed. He likewise proposes charging a single piece of higher bore-length ratio with small projectiles that will scatter upon being fired; and he even anticipates the idea of our present-day shrapnel, designing "ballots" filled with gunpowder and having holes in their surfaces (Ms. B, fol. 42 r, 30 v, 31 v, 37 r, 80 v), so that they will explode or rebound when they reach their mark, scattering the fragments or small shot around by the force of the gases evolved, thus "causing great terror to the enemy, and great loss and confusion." Manuscript B and several others (especially Cod. Atl., fol. 333 v) also have studies relating to underwater attack and defense in naval warfare. There are types of diving suits for divers manipulating powerful drills or levers for pulling out the nails holding together the shells of enemy ships, and combustible mixtures that will burn even in contact with water, to be applied to the hulls; and on the defensive side, there are types of armor that could successfully have withstood the discharge of bombards, even of large caliber.

We have already mentioned the armored car. The British Museum drawings contain prototypes of this novel means of waging war, which was not entirely new in the history of military technique but was given a new and effective conception and design by Leonardo. The covering is made of heavy wooden beams set close together, and light enters through the gap between the lower portion of the vehicle and the upper portion or roof, the gap being used as well for operating light cannon. In particular, we are shown the plan of the drive mechanism, which was either manual or horse-powered.

In all this we occasionally see dependence on tradition and on Valturio's work in particular. Valturio too gives a list of arms with descriptions of them, as Leonardo does, and a comparison gives us reason to believe that Leonardo was directly following the inspiration of the De re militari.

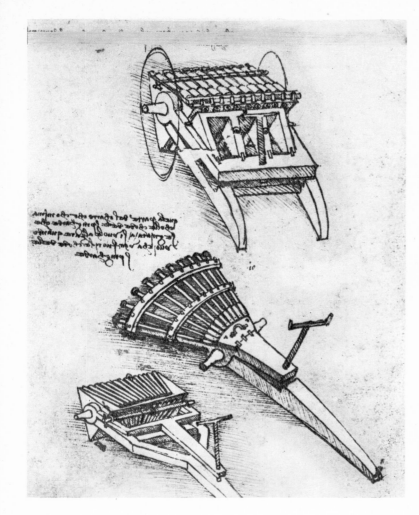

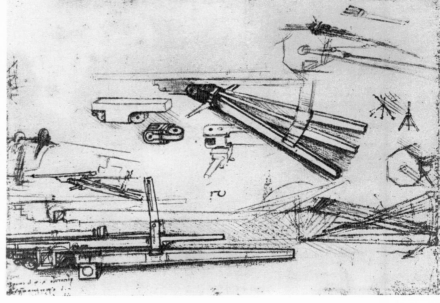

An example of this filiation is the type of the *romphaea*, as Valturio also calls it, a sort of crossbow using a twisting movement of an elastic rod as the source of its power, the percussion upon release striking against a missile or short arrow on a raised frame. Valturio's *De re militari* gives an almost identical picture of this machine, with a similar explanation. The original element due to Leonardo is always at least a modernization, even when (as in many cases) it does not amount to absolute innovation. Leonardo is more independent in the purely architectural aspect.

The studies in Ms. B and some pages in the Codex Trivulzianus would seem to lead up to a proposed treatise on the art of war, as is indicated by some words found in Ms. ex-Ashburnham (consisting of pages torn out of Ms. B when stolen by Guglielmo Libri). The passage runs (fol. 10 r): "To preserve nature's chiefest boon, that is, freedom, I can find means of offense and defense, when it is assailed by ambitious tyrants, and first I shall speak of the situation of the wall." If, as is likely, the fragment is original and not transcribed, it is of interest to note that Leonardo had the intention of especially developing the architectural element, dealing with permanent fortifications.

With respect to the projects for military construction, the Lombard period represents an intermediate phase between the early Tuscan essays we have spoken of and the mature work of Ms. L and especially of the Codex Atlanticus, which was done during or shortly after the Romagna period. Leonardo's technique begins to advance in the path dictated by the progress of artillery science, a path that was becoming inevitable of the twofold basis of structural changes and improvements in organization of the lines of fire. The two factors evolved parallel to each other, with the constructive designs showing a certain lag, which may be attributed to obvious economic factors as well as to tradition and inertia. It is this field of architectural forms that best brings out the character of the studies of the Lombard period, which aimed at "adapting" or "modernizing" the traditional forms to meet the new requirements. Wherever he can, Leonardo introduces into the thinking of the past new rational criteria for solving the problem of defense—reduction of the height-thickness ratio (or, roughly, making the form lower and sturdier), working out of the lines and dimensions of outworks, use of the possibilities of defilade, command, flanking fire and cross fire, and mutual defensive support supplied by independent elements.

This stage in the development of his technique fits well into the general picture of the technique of fortification in Italy at that time (which was in advance of that in the rest of Europe, except for some parts of France). The new ideas have not yet done away with the old altogether. Furthermore, we get the impression that these Lombard studies date from a more practical or less speculative period in the master's activity. Definite references are made to specific localities.

This preface will make it easier for us to conduct our examination of the most notable pages.

Left: Multiple-barreled cannon and machine gun – Cod. Atl., fol. 56 v-*a*

Right, above: Cannon mounts with universal joints – Cod. Atl., fol. 399 v-*a*

Right, below: Musket lock – Cod. Atl., fol. 59 v-*b*

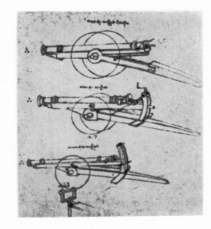

Small guns on mounts – Cod. Atl., fol. 9 r-*b*

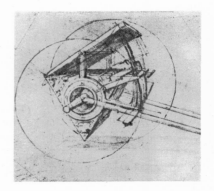

Mount for multiple-barreled cannon – Cod. Atl., fol. 21 r-*b*

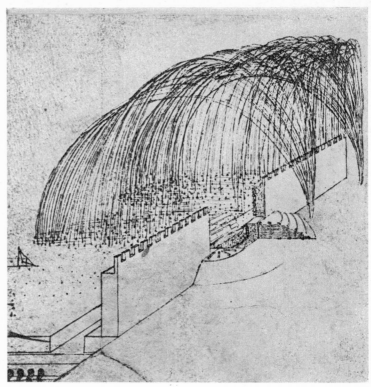

Defense of bastion by means of mortars – Left: Windsor, Royal Collection, no. 12337 – Right: Cod. Atl., fol. 24 r-a

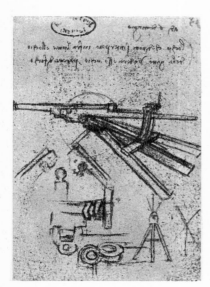

Semiportable firearm on mount – Ms. H, fol. 109

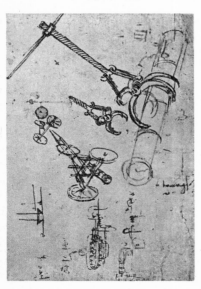

Cannon hoist and carriage – Cod. Atl., fol. 4 r-b

We begin with folios 57 verso, details *a* and *b*, and 5 recto of Ms. B, which remind us of folio 281 verso-*b* of the Codex Atlanticus. They bring out the fact that the problem that dominated Leonardo's work was that of making the advanced defenses capable of resisting attack, especially attack by long-range artillery. In detail *a* of folio 57 verso the ravelin, which originally had merely the function of defending the weak point of the perimeter of the castle, its main gate, has become a salient of very large dimensions, covering more than half of the curtain wall behind it, which has a central square tower and two round towers at the corners. The connection with the modern bastion, the direct descendant of this outwork, is obvious, if we consider first its low and massive form and then the flanking fire function of the bastion, which here is sketched out by indication of the lateral embrasures (detail *C*, section). After that it is not such a long step to the more explicit idea of "retired flanks" with their embrasures, a typical element in the bastions of the late sixteenth century that received still further development in later periods. The figure below this one shows a further enlargement of triangular outworks of this sort, and a generalization of the principle in application to all the sides of the stronghold, thereby forming a new perimeter, still rectangular but with its diagonals rotated through an angle of 45° with respect to the first one. This represents the tradition of the ravelin, while the powerful external protection at the angles, with their forms adapted for massive resistance, proclaims the need of modernizing it for defensive purposes. Thus in folio 5 recto we have a second ravelin of the same sort, and Leonardo makes the annotation, "Kind of ravelin for a fortress," however, we see that this "kind" or "type" has assumed such importance that it is effecting profound change in what Leonardo, in accordance with tradition, still calls a ravelin, though it is now much more like a bastion than the original structure covering the entry to the enceinte of the castle. In order to leave its inner portion as solid as possible, Da Vinci provides for ways of access and service to batteries, guards, and garrison, at its rear or laterally on its faces.

A further systematic development in this direction is indicated, it seems to me, on a page, probably of the Lombard period, in the Codex Atlanticus fol. 281 v-*b*. Here Leonardo, starting with the idea of a central quadrilateral defended by four large ravelins, doubles the number by adding another triangular outwork at each face of the ravelins, thereby multiplying the number of salients facing into the field and breaking the defensive enceinte into numerous segments. The trend is toward the sixteenth-century bastioned trace; the basic concept of Sangallo's bastioned curtains and of the sixteenth-century technique in general, in which the perimeter is often interrupted by salients with the purpose not only of passively breaking up the attack but also of making possible systematic organization of the lines of fire, starts from these very premises of Da Vinci.

In detail *B* the front of a fortress is strengthened in the center, but not with an impressive and artistic high tower with machicolations and battlements, as it would have been according to the technique of the early fifteenth century, but by a strong and massive rhomboidal bastion with double escarp, between two flanking towers covering attacks on the curtain, and a turret (probably a watchtower) located at the rear. Attention should be called to the close relationship between the outwork, which as a ravelin was almost always detached or at best weakly linked with the body of the structure, and the curtain it is based on; this marks a noteworthy contribution to progress toward the modern bastion and its firing functions. It is possible that in these series of studies Leonardo intended to refer to Porta Giovia and suggest rational alterations in it to the Duke, in the interest of

Defense of bastion by means of bombard fire – Windsor, Royal Collection, no. 12275

defending it effectively from attacks by heavy artillery coupled with maneuvers of infantry with small cannon at close quarters. This theme of close defense is dealt with by Leonardo in still other pages, such as Ms. B, folio 24 verso, Codex Atlanticus, fol. 43 recto-*b*, and Ms. B, folios 12 recto and 18 verso, where he is concerned with the effort to solve precisely the problem that dominates in this field, the problem of organizing the lines of cannon fire.

Folio 24 verso of Ms. B shows us in plan a stout curtain front with two large round corner towers and a square tower in the middle with a free-standing ravelin defending it, less developed than in the preceding drawings; here all these elements are considered as bases for mutually supporting defensive fire, as is shown by the clearly indicated embrasures and the lines of fire from them. The fire from the corner towers crosses in the field, grazing the outwork, while the central tower likewise flanks the half curtains and their towers; in addition, the ravelin makes it possible to flank the castle front by means of cannon at the rear of the ravelin.

The technical problems raised by the requirements of mutual defense and organization of fire between the body of the place and the independent elements are illuminated even more precisely by the sketches and appendices of folio 43 recto-*b* of the Codex Atlanticus. In the details he labels *G* and *H*, Da Vinci draws two plans showing quadrilateral forts with ravelins, and gives an exact account of the varying value of their reciprocal defilades depending on the varying positions of the ravelins with respect to their curtains, while there is a corresponding variation in the dead angle ahead in which the defenders are free of the danger of being fired at by their own artillery flanking the ravelin itself, or where, conversely, the attackers may take shelter, which must be avoided. On the same sheet he says in appendix detail *H*, "Point *A* is never touched by any artillery shot," and on folio 19 recto of Ms. B, we find a study of an original type of ravelin with total command and with no dead angle for the attackers to exploit (attacks based on the ravelin itself).

An appendix on folio 48 recto-*b* of the Codex Atlanticus says, "The ravelin, shield of the fortress, should be defended by the fortress, as the fortress is by it." Folio 43 recto-*b* of the Codex Atlan-

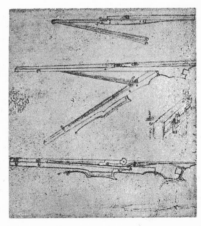

Musket on mount – Cod. Atl., fol. 51 r-c

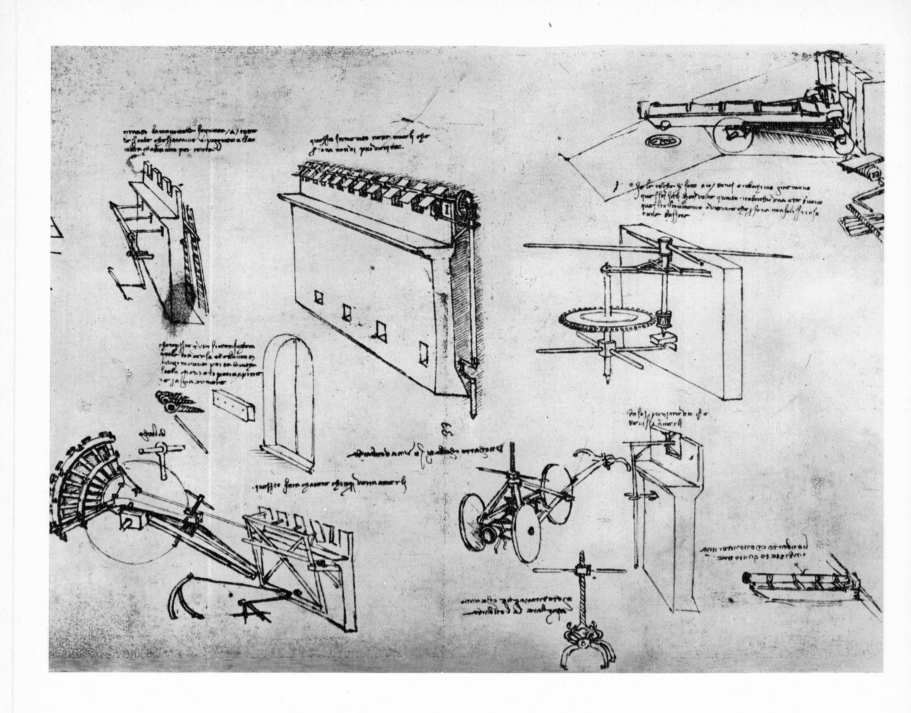

ticus shows in detail *G* how attackers who have assumed positions not visible from the castle front, that is, in a position to take advantage of the poor defilade of the outwork to hammer it with cannon located in trenches made in the glacis beyond the ditch, can obtain results that will be disastrous for the defenders, especially if they are able to make skillful use of the element of surprise. Leonardo indicates the attacking trajectories, and adds: "The two guns *HK* and the two guns *LB* break down the entire ravelin, these cannon being set in pits dug in the ramparts of the ditch," concluding logically that "the further the ravelin is from its fortress, the harder it will be hit by crossfire, and, conversely, it will be less severely hit the nearer it is to that fortress."

Summing up, the interest of these studies derives from this original conception of the interdependence of outwork and main fortification and of the organization of fire integrally connected with this, quite apart from the importance that the new proportions specified for external defense had for the safety of all the structures taken together. For the same reason it is of interest to recall the drawing of folio 11 verso of Ms. B, which gives studies of "two bastions" (as Leonardo calls them, although actually they have little in common with the classic bastion), "one of which can defend the other by means of its artillery." They are two round towerlike structures, much smaller in height than in diameter, provided with numerous embrasures in superposed rows around the entire circumference, and with Da Vinci's well-known wall-sweeping wheels, the details of which are given in such sheets of the Codex Atlanticus as folios 32 verso-*a* and 34 verso-*a*. The ditch surrounding them is flooded in the part between the two structures in order to isolate them completely. Here the idea of reciprocal organization of fire in detached elements is brought out distinctly.

This theme of organization of fire is taken up again in folios 12 recto and 18 verso of Ms. B. There is an evident process of progressive improvement in the special treatment of defense by means of reciprocal grazing fire. Some difficulties arise from the fact that flanking defenses are here applied to forms that are almost completely traditional and not adapted to the purpose, as they were soon to be in the perfect examples of the sixteenth century. The sketch on folio 18 verso portrays a square fortress with two strong, low towers at opposite corners designed to flank the four half cur-

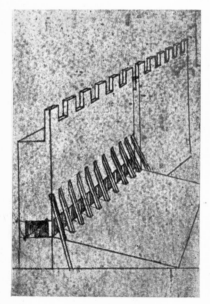

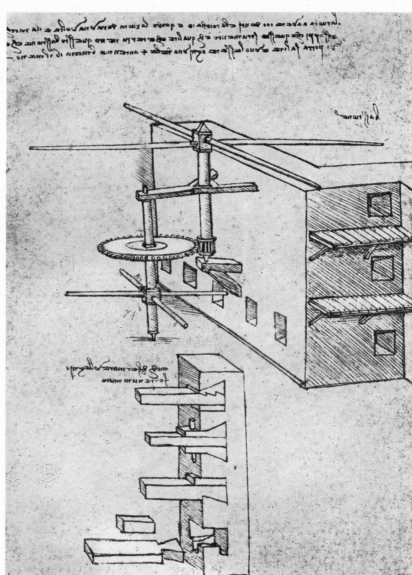

Left: Device for knocking over assault ladders – Cod. Atl., fol. 49 v-b

Right: Device for defending casemate – Cod. Atl., fol. 32 v-a

tains lying between, as we are told in the autograph note: "This square fort is given only two towers, so that they will not damage each other, as they have to fire laterally"; since the shots come from embrasures at the angles between the towers and the curtains, the line of fire must be clear. In this drawing the measurements of the towers and internal diagonals are also given— eighteen meters and sixty meters respectively—and indicate, in view of the general idea of the sketch, an ensemble of great bulk and power, in definite contrast to the traditional style, especially since it would appear to be an isolated or auxiliary structure.

"Fortress raking the ditches and the glacis outside the ditches," is Leonardo's note under another interesting drawing on the same folio 18 verso of Ms. B. This double flanking emerges clearly when we observe the arrangement of the low batteries of the bastion or angular salient, which enfilade the glacis and the inner ditch. In the right upper corner of the same page Da Vinci designs another type of angle for a fortification; the draftsmanship here is more precise, but the idea of the flanking fire less well developed. However, there are elements that are interesting from the formal point of view, such as the section given to the opposite parapet, with its relatively numerous frontal embrasures and grazing defensive fire from the gorge of the corner tower. Likewise, the tower built into the center of the front of the curtain, like its counterfort and cornerstone, constitutes an exception, or at least presents an unorthodox idea, as compared with the conventional Lombard model, and perhaps is derived from classical Roman defensive peripheries (watchtower in urban or semipermanent enceintes). If we now examine the drawing on folio 69 recto of Ms. B, we find the defilade of a fortress curtain provided by superposed batteries in the gorge of the corner tower, with additional batteries trained on the crown of the parapet, enfilading it. The formal features of this study are impressive by reason of the solidity of the works, as well as of its solution of the problem of locating the batteries in the tower; these are arranged in three series of two, one being for external flanking fire and one for the top of the curtain. This is also one of the few sketches drawn in a finished manner.

It would take too long, especially in a hasty review like this, to discuss the few pages of the Lombard period that refer explicitly to Milan. We shall recall only folio 99 recto-b of the Codex Atlanticus, folios 15 recto and 23 verso of Ms. B, a drawing in the former Vallardi collection, now in the Louvre, and folios 32 and 38 verso of Ms. I; and we shall dwell especially on the most important page of the series, folio 36 verso of Ms. B. This last is one of the very few that make unques-

Study of missile-throwing machine for defending wall – Cod. Atl., fol. 57 v-a, b

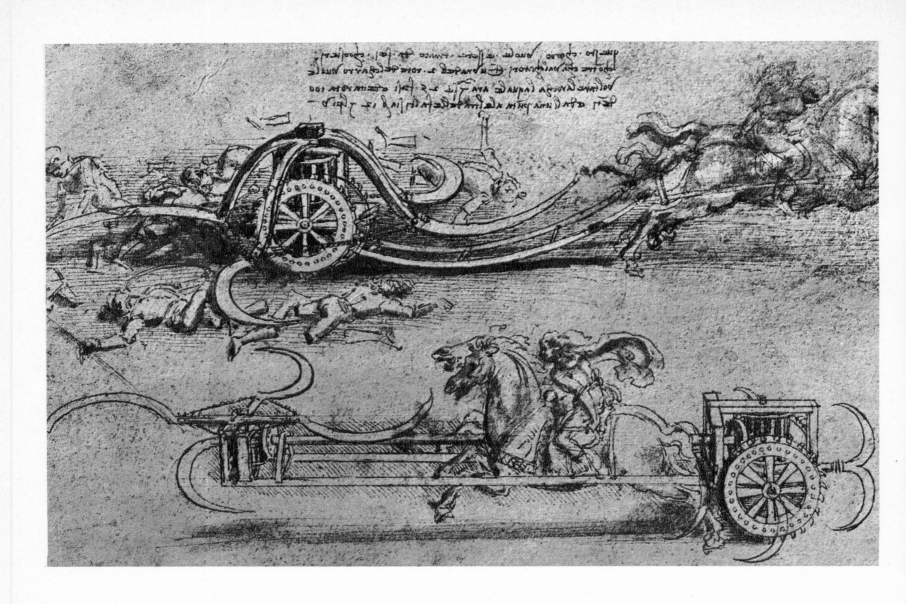

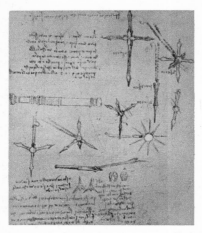

Scythed cars – Turin, former Royal Libr.

Caltrops and various arms – Cod. Atl., fol. 21 v-*b*

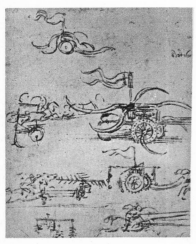

Details of scythed car – Cod. Atl., fol. 40 v-*a*

tionable reference to the castle at Porta Giovia: it shows an angle of the external enceinte of this stronghold, the *Ghirlanda*, with one of the round towers, and an angle of the internal perimeter with one of the square towers. The drawing is annotated in the hand of the master, giving the measurements of the moats and the ramparts within and without the two concentric curtains—"all of which pleases me," he says. But he goes on to suggest a change in the internal arrangements, to make it as difficult as possible for any attackers who may have gained control of the lower line of batteries in the *Ghirlanda* (*m*) to continue their advance toward its inner face by using the existing way of access (not shown in the sketch), which led to a covered gallery (*s*). This passage to the rear must have been a vital means of communication in the general system of internal organization; and Leonardo was concerned with the danger it created, since it gave too easy access from the battery emplacements. His proposal was to eliminate this access, replacing it with a vertical way, evidently provided with portable ladders that could be drawn up, and leading to a covered upper passage (*f*), from which obviously the defenders, after being forced to retreat from the battery because of a breach, could drive the invaders back and out by means of dense plunging fire prepared in advance.

This would obviate the dangerous possibility that from the enclosed passage (*m*) the attackers might open a safe pathway to commanding all the sectors of the *Ghirlanda*, from which they might even pass into the central stronghold by means of underground mines. This page is of great interest not only historically but also from the strictly technical point of view, especially so since it concerns the Milan castle; and this interest is heightened by the account that Leonardo gives of the measurements of the walls and moats as they were at that time. We may recall the width of the curtain, greater than that of the inner ditch: the former was 40 ells (22-23 m.), the latter 30 ells (about 17 m.). The height was 16 ells (9 m.). The "outer walls" (upper part of the *Ghirlanda*) were 40 ells high and 8 ells thick (23 m. and 4.5 m.), the inner castle walls were over 20 ells (about 12 m.) in height and battered outward one third. We can visualize the strength this ensemble must have shown—an elevation not excessive, a perimeter of great power of resistance in depth.

If we compute the proportion between the internal height of the *Ghirlanda* and its measurement [in the sketch], the scale of the drawing comes out as 1:350, while it is 1:500 if we consider the outside height. Another interesting point is the technical kinship between this internal arrangement of Leonardo's and the "covered way" that is a characteristic feauture in the art of Francesco di Giorgio Martini, the military engineer. In essence, these are two related solutions to the problem of how most effectively to defend an exposed outwork. We transcribe Da Vinci's text, which is perfectly clear even without the commentary we have prefixed to it: "The ditch of the castle of

Milan within the *Ghirlanda* is 30 ells and its rampart is 16 ells and 40 wide and this is the *Ghirlanda*. The outer walls are 8 ells thick and 40 high and the walls within the castle are 60 ells, all of which pleases me: except that I should like to see the casemates in the walls of the *Ghirlanda* not open onto the secret way within, that is, at *s*, but instead they should each be reached from above, as is seen at *mf*; because good bombardiers always aim at the casemates of fortresses, and if they broke open only a single one of the casemates in the said *Ghirlanda* they could then get in through the said breach by means of battering rams and then become masters of all the towers, walls, and secret rooms of the said *Ghirlanda*, whereas if the casemates were arranged as at *mf* and a bombard happened to break open one of the said casemates and the enemy entered at *p*, they would not be able to go from there, but by plunging fire from above would be driven back and out." If Leonardo's scheme for improving the defense had been put into effect, it could not have failed, as an extremely practical and original idea, to be highly successful in military use.

Another explicit reference to the castle of Milan on the part of Leonardo as ducal engineer, once more suggesting changes to be made in the internal defensive arrangements, is found in folios 18 verso and 19 recto of Ms. B (cf. Cod. Atl., fol. 79 v-*b* and 281 r-*b*). Here too a project is sketched out for eliminating defects in relation to the problem of passages between curtain and corner tower; this project brings out the fact that just as pressing a problem as defense against an external enemy was reflected in the constant search for a mode of organization that would so far as possible exclude surprises set on foot by traitors among the garrison, so that no such conspirators should be able suddenly to block off any part of the castle. There are many studies with this aim dating from the same period as this and other manuscripts; examples are the splendid projects for double staircases intended, among other things, to make it possible for the governor of the fortress to be completely independent of the *provisionati*, that is, the permanent garrison.

During this Lombard period, which ends in 1500 with the final fall and exile of Ludovico Maria Sforza, Leonardo, an untiring observer and thoughtful traveler through the duchy, put down everything he thought worthy of remark in his little notebooks—pocket-size we should call them—such as Ms. H or Ms. L. So far as military matters were concerned, he was interested in problems of permanent and field fortifications in relation to the war with Ferrara in 1482, and to the Venetian war two years later, to which the studies for harbor defenses probably refer (Cod. Atl., fol. 346 r and v, 234 r-*b*). He also studied a defense formed by a sort of river block or "moving lock," that is, a movable dike, with the purpose of flooding and drowning the attackers at a favorable moment;

Scythed car and covered armored car – London, British Museum

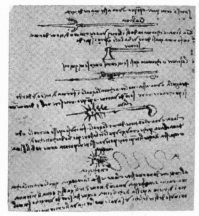

Nomenclature of various arms – Ms. B, fol. 43 v

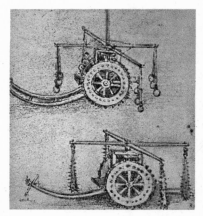

Types of armored cars – Windsor, Royal Collection, no. 12653

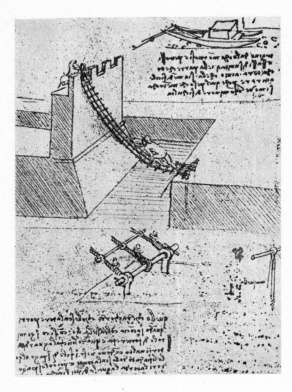
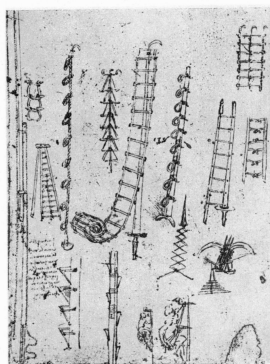

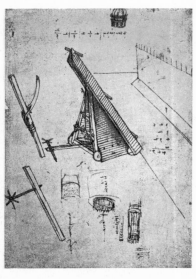

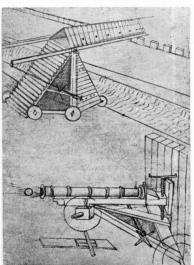

this may have been on the occasion of a threatened Turkish landing on Venetian territory in the valley of the Isonzo.[6]

It may be interesting in this connection that it is not out of the question that some of these studies, especially those dealing with projected methods of underwater attack and air-filled garments for underwater assailants of enemy ships, refer instead to the Sforza domains in Genoese territory. Leonardo had gone to Genoa with the Duke and his suite in 1498 [7] to visit the breakwater after it was ruined by storms and to study methods for its repair. And we should say the like for folio 64 recto of Ms. B—perhaps the only sheet in the codex that is not of Lombard inspiration—in which Da Vinci draws and describes (as another sort of "mobile lock") "a method of letting a flood of water loose on an army, and bridges and walls of cities." Elsewhere in Ms. B, moreover, there are studies of dikes (in convex form, the better to resist the pressure of the mass of water, as they are built today, and reinforced with towers to increase the strength of the structure) and field fortifications, the latter relating to directly military aims (see fol. 22 v). But the direction "for Lucca" (*per allucha*) leads us to suspect that this river dam of folio 64 recto may be associated with a field defense of the Genoese territory then under the rule of the Sforzas, on the border of Lunigiana. A possible hypothesis is that in 1487 (the year in which the Genoese territory was annexed), or in one of the following years, Leonardo was commissioned by the Duke to study a possible defensible plan for the Lunigian front facing Lucca, or that as a student of military problems he turned to consideration of a subject that was of interest at the time because of this application of hydraulics. The military importance that the government of Il Moro attached to Spezia and its surroundings as an outpost of his dominions is attested by that same series *Autografi-Architetti 106-109* in the archives of the state of Milan [8] in which we see the documentation of the military and fortifying activity in connection with all of the ducal castles on the northern borders and the strategic castles in the interior of the state.

There are frequent mentions, especially in Mss. B and H, of work on the Sforza cities of Pavia and Vigevano, and in the country around the latter, but we find very few points of military interest. It is probable that Leonardo worked there too as military engineer to the Duke, but it is hard to trace this today. It seems likely that he took part in the grave events of the months that decided the fate of Il Moro (1499)—who lost everything in a short time after the invasion of Louis XII—as designing or direction engineer of the fortifications and military works in the Ligurian and Piedmont zones; at the very least, there are factors justifying such a supposition. Pages of the Codex Leicester probably written at Florence some time after Il Moro had left Milan contain frequent references to sojourn in northern Italy, to places beyond the Ticino belonging to the Sforzas—places that were the first to fall into the hands of the French troops. This suggests that the memory of the fateful political events that Leonardo had witnessed and probably taken part in led him to dwell again on objects and occurrences connected with that unfortunate period of his life. Some of the names of places that he mentions are Vigevano, Candia Lomellina, Monte Rosa, Monferrato, and Alessandria della Paglia; and it would seem the more warranted for us also to think of these if we

---

[6] See also Cod. Atl., fol. 234 r-b, which should be assigned to about the year 1500.
[7] Cf. *Archivio storico Lombardo*, Vol. 37, 1910.
[8] Unpublished documents.

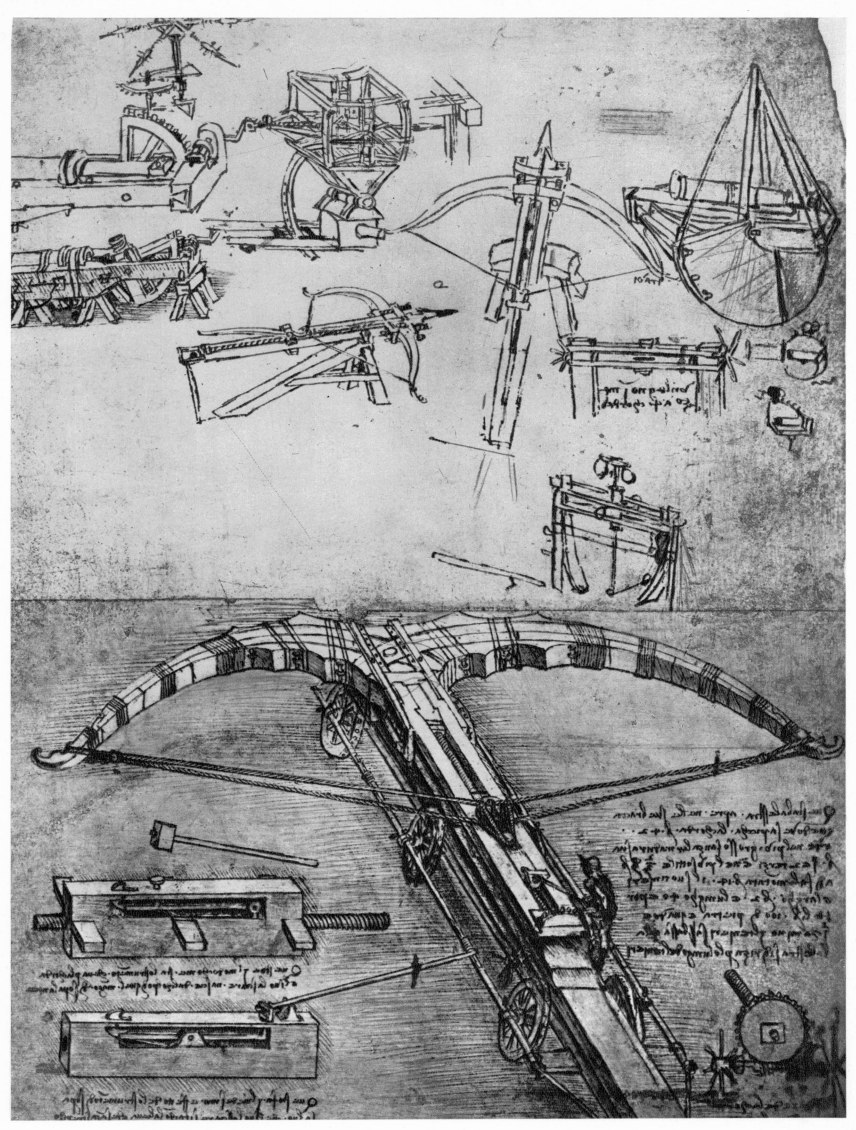

Great crossbow on carriage with inclined wheels – Other crossbow designs – Cod. Atl., fol. 53 v-*a, b*

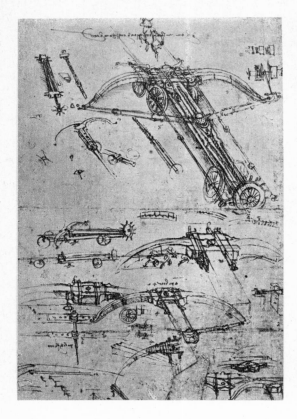

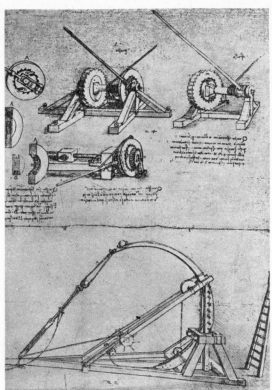

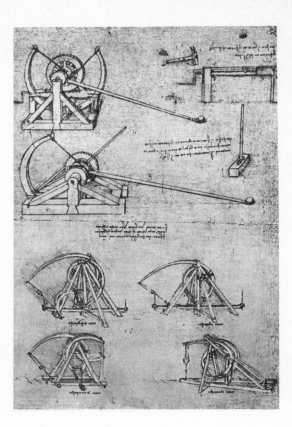

recall folio 360 verso-*a* of the Codex Atlanticus, which gives technical directions and instructions for the conquest of a fortified city that resemble the description by the Pavian chronicler Grumello of the offensive methods used by Ludovico Il Moro in his attempt to retake Novara in 1500. It should be remembered that the commander of the ducal army was that Galeazzo Sanseverino to whose service, after that of the Duke, Leonardo seems to have devoted himself particularly. It would seem that folio 24 verso of the same manuscript should also be related to this episode; the correspondence of the writing on the two pages is obvious.

It was probably at Venice, where Leonardo had gone after the first fall of Il Moro, there to learn of the latter's fate, that certain notes in Ms. L were written (cover, verso); there are some obscure hints, and then the words, "The Duke has lost his state and his goods and his liberty, and none of his works has been finished by him" come to mark the irrevocable end of that epoch.

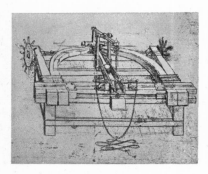

On August 18, 1502, when Cesare Borgia sent to Leonardo the diploma or letter patent that named him "architect and engineer general," the second important period of the military activity of the master begins, namely, the time passed in Romagna, from the summer of 1502 to 1503, in the service of the Duke of Valentinois.

The text of the document reads:

"*Caesar Borgia de Francia Dei Gratia Dux Romandiole Valentieque Princeps Hadrie Dominus Plumbini, etc. Ac Sancte Romane Ecclesie Confalonerius et Capitaneus Generalis*: To All our Lieutenants, Governors of Castles, Captains, *Condottieri*, Officers, Soldiers and subjects, To whom notice of these presents shall come, We Commend and Command that to our Most Distinguished and Beloved Familiar Architect and Engineer, General Leonardo Vinci, the bearer hereof, who by our Commission is to view the Places and Strongholds of our States, in order that according to their needs and his judgment we may make provision, there Be given by all passage free of all public payment for himself and his men, Friendly reception, and he be allowed to see, measure, and well estimate whatsoever he shall choose. And to this effect Command that men be requisitioned, and give him whatever aid, assistance, and Favor he shall desire, ordering that in works to be carried out in our Dominions Every Engineer be constrained to confer with him and conform to his opinion. Nor let anyone presume to do the contrary if he does not wish to incur our Indignation. Given at Pavia, the eighteenth day of August, in the Year of the Lord One Thousand Five Hundred and two, and of our Duchy in Romagna the second—CAESAR."

At the time the decree was issued, Da Vinci was already in Romagna, working in Borgia's dominions as appears from various dated notes relating to places on the Adriatic littoral or near by, such as Urbino, Cesena, Pesaro, Cesenatico, etc. Manuscript L, a kind of pocket notebook always on hand to accompany the visitor to the cities and strongholds of Romagna, shows (see cover) that he was at Pesaro on August 1 ("first day of August, 1502, at Pesaro, the library") and at Rimini a week later (fol. 78 r: "Make yourself a harmony with the various waterfalls such as you saw at the fountain of Rimini as you saw them on the 8th day of August, 1502"). Folio 7 verso shows us that his atten-

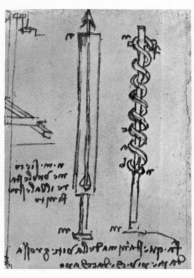

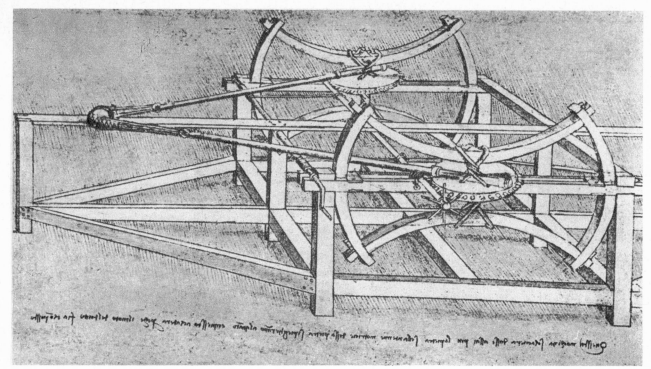

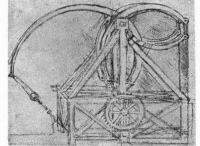

Left, above: Machine for throwing rocks and bombs – Cod. Atl., fol. 51 v-*b*

Left, below: Catapults and crossbows – Cod. Atl., fol. 54 v-*a*

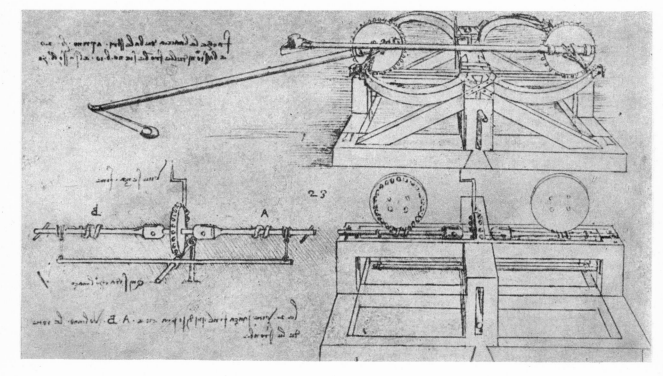

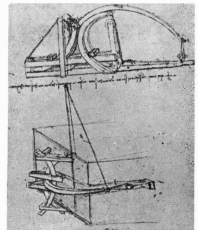

Double-spring catapult – Cod. Atl., fol. 31 r-*a*

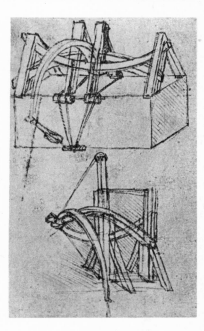

tion had been attracted to a "dovecote at Urbino" and to the spectacle of the fair of San Lorenzo at Cesena, where he passed the Assumption holiday: "The day of Santa Maria, mid-August, at Cesena 1502." A little later he studied the "port" of Cesenatico: "*Porto Cesenatico*, day of September, 1502." There is an outline drawing of a fortress with the note, "Fortress of Urbino," on folio 38 verso; and there are references to Piombino, Populonia, and other places held by Borgia, and also an interesting panoramic view of the city of Rimini showing the characteristic elements of its physiognomy. The Duke of Valentinois was trying to extend and reinforce the boundaries of the state of Romagna as he had carved it out for himself, and he relied on Da Vinci, as the best collaborator he could have in his large-scale military projects, to solve the many problems of construction and artillery that the campaign of expansion and conquest would present to him: the document cited above is proof of his great esteem.

The typical technical designs of this period, which lasted until July, 1503, are especially concerned with the problem of inventing and perfecting a type of curtain that could effectively resist the most powerful cannon, in addition ensuring the necessary properties of command and enfilade in defensive and offensive fire, and minimizing to the greatest possible extent the effects of projectile impact, by giving the exposed surfaces as much of an elliptic back slant as possible.

To begin with, some of these studies in Ms. L, which we might consider preliminary studies made by Leonardo to clarify his own ideas on structural details, deal with the problem of the "best profile" to give the reveals of embrasures, and with the resultant fields and amplitudes of vertical

Various catapults and ballistae – Cod. Atl., fol. 54 r-*a*

293

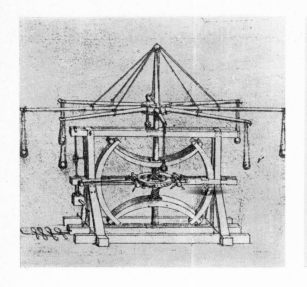
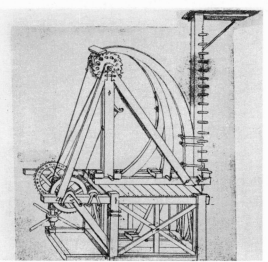
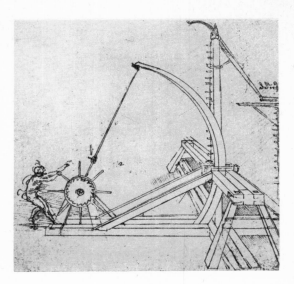

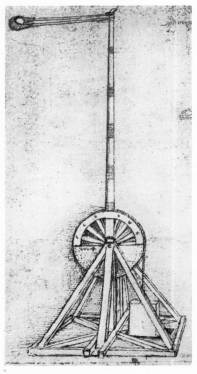

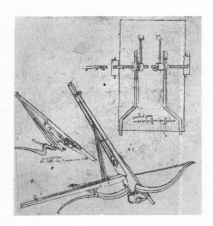

and horizontal fire; there are also researches into the effects of percussion and the ricochet of projectiles over structures, according to the various forms of projectiles and structures. Folio 43 verso says, "Ask why a ball hitting the wall obliquely does not go through as when at right angles," and the next page, folio 45 recto, states that "every reflected motion loses the more power, the closer the line it arises from is to the line of incidence, and vice versa." Folios important in relation to artillery matters are: Codex Atlanticus, 45 recto-b and 264 verso, Ms. L, 45 recto, 41 recto, 50 verso, and 43 verso. Special attention is given to the problem of the best emplacement of bombards between two salients (speroni) and of their respective fields of fire (Cod. Atl., fol. 45 r-b), followed by critical consideration of the favorable and unfavorable angles, from the points of view of defense and offense, offered by various forms of embrasure reveals (Ms. L, fol. 45 r). On folio 50 verso of Ms. L there is a study of the width of the field of fire of embrasures located in a series of semicircular salients, and, finally, of the various consequences of impact and ricochet, depending on the angle of incidence of the projectile upon the surface of the target.

There are some models of projectiles, pointed or ogival, reminiscent of present-day forms (Ms. L, fol. 43 v), and we may well say that one of the ways in which Leonardo was most notably in advance of his time in military affairs was in regard to the forms he gave these projectiles, including the pointed form. We find one with directional aerodynamic fins like those of modern aerial bombs (Cod. Arund., fig. 54 r) that seems to have been designed during World War I, rather than almost five hundred years ago. Leonardo's attention is focussed on the relationship between the aerodynamic cross section of the projectile and its velocity, and between its form and the effects on the body it strikes.

A drawing that is unique not only in Ms. L (fol. 65 r) but, if I am not mistaken, among all the known drawings of Leonardo as a military architect, shows us that although he had outstripped his contemporaries' development of the bastion with a long leap into the future, he had still laid down structural forms for a triangular salient not too different from the type of bastion proper of the sixteenth century. Since it is viewed from in front, however, we are not justified in inferring the presence of the characteristic element of the bastion, the application of "retired flanks." Instead, we may connect this formal idea with types found in the Sienese notebook and other manuscripts of Francesco di Giorgio Martini, in particular one that has an extraordinary resemblance to Da Vinci's sketch (in the collection of separate sheets in the Institutes of History and Art in the castle of Milan). We point out this connection in order to stress the fact that this drawing of Leonardo's shows that he was at least not unaware of the forms that at the end of the transition period were to lead to the introduction of the bastioned trace.

The feature that should draw our attention most of all is the analysis of the form to be considered as the best for a "typical curtain," the sections and constituent elements of which are taken up on several occasions in contemporaneous sheets of Ms. L and the Atlantic codex, notably in folios 61 recto-l, 49 verso-l, and 63 recto-l of Ms. L and folios 264 verso and 265 recto-a of the Codex Atlanticus, and further in folio 51 verso-l of Ms. L and folios 41 verso-a (detail B) and 345 verso-b (details A 1, B 1) of the Codex Atlanticus. What are the elements that Leonardo regards as requiring study and development in order to give the most satisfactory solution to the problem of a powerful defense with a considerable reserve of defensive possibilities even in face of strong attacks by heavy artillery? The fundamental idea is the low ratio between elevation and plan, leading to a massive strong section for the entire obstacle. In order to solve the problem of the top of the parapet, eliminating all the obsolete and dangerous complications of embattlement, the source of ruinous breaches, and the machicolations, which had become virtually useless, a massive cupola with a double ellipse is adopted, with the larger and major axis facing the field in such a way as to present a very slanting target, a minimum probable angle of incidence, and hence a greatly reduced chance of rupture. Finally, on the front, with the double purpose of protecting the defensive batteries without depriving

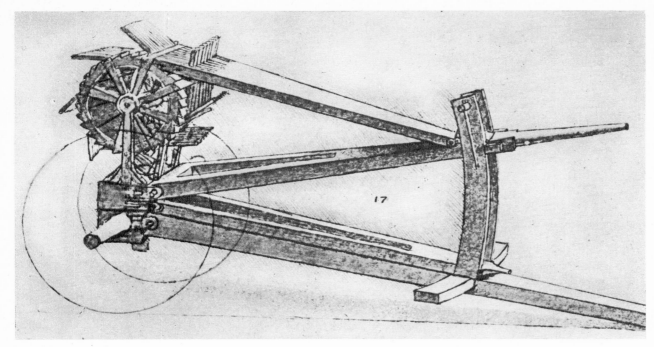

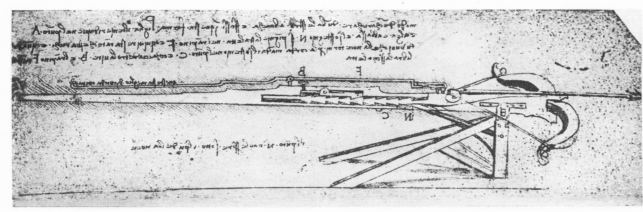

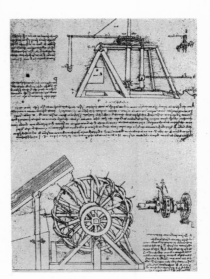

Rock-throwing machine and multiple-spring crossbow – Cod. Atl., fol. 64 v-*a, b*

them of much of their command in the vertical field of fire, and of presenting to the enemy fire a front of great strength, divided into segments, there is the use of a series of semielliptic salients, with the battery emplacements located in the intervals between them. A parapet walk, open to the internal place of arms and likewise designed to vent the smoke of the discharges, as Leonardo notes, is provided for maneuvering and serving the guns.

A construction of this nature is clearly indicated on folio 49 verso-*l* of Ms. L, which also suggests a variant profile for the salients. The escarpment is the basic element of the entire structure and is totally commanded by the upper batteries, with a view likewise to the exigencies of combat close in (where the chances of use are obviously favorable). On folio 61 recto we have, intentionally isolated along a single line, the various constituent elements of the curtain, while on the preceding page the elliptic superstructure is barely outlined. Folio 63 recto indicates the form of these casemates in plan, and slightly alters the previously considered ideas for a model derived from it. Attention should be called to the block construction of the salients, which here are almost semicircular, the superstructure also being more powerful, with a great elevation. At this point reference should be made to folio 51 verso of Ms. L, which in its turn suggests a detail of folio 41 verso-*a* of the Codex Atlanticus, which proposes, in addition to a more complex internal organization, a further increase in the bulk of the upper cupola, with an external escarp sloping sharply back and on the whole foreshadowing the models of curtains for perimeters that are dealt with in the fundamental drawings of the Codex Atlanticus. The combination of the two favorable characteristics of a glancing target facing the field and a great resistance is achieved by designing the superstructure as a quarter of a sort of elliptic spheroid. The position of the salients facing the field is given, and the outer rampart of the ditch is shown, while at the rear there is a double service gallery with smoke vents and access to the upper part. The sketch seems to indicate that the upper corridor is merely a means of communication with the lower level, to furnish access to the guns located there. The intention here was probably to make use of and to carry over into a much more modern structural ensemble the arrangement conceived of for the traditional design of the Porta Giovia castle at Milan, in order to facilitate execution of a strategic retreat from the casemates to the upper passage, from which then a downward thrusting defense might be conducted from a more favorable position.

When we reflect on the general impression derived from these architectural notions and compare them with the classic forms of the fifteenth-century tradition, many examples of which were still in active military use, we see that Leonardo departed radically from that tradition, replacing it with

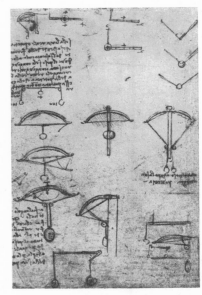

Studies on crossbows – London, Christ Church Collection

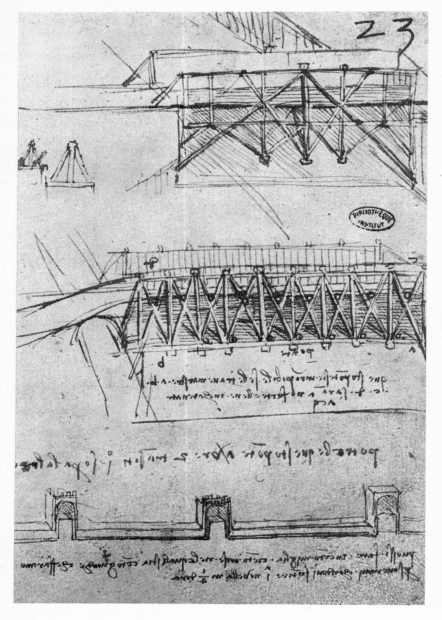

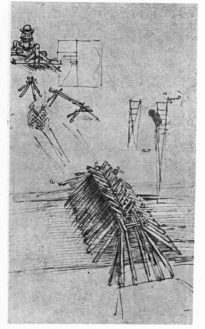

ideas that were absolutely revolutionary for their time, and born from the overriding needs of the defense. We may be fairly sure that whenever one of these ideas was carried out intelligently, the result must have proved a noteworthy military success, because of the exceptional possibilities for resisting both heavy artillery and attacks at close quarters.

What would have been the most obvious weak point in such formations? Da Vinci soon realized that it consisted in the absence of organized grazing crossfire; and to make this possible, he began to conceive of elements advanced beyond their adjacent curtains. These salients presented semiretired throats, the embryos of the retired flanks, served by superposed series of inner batteries as bases for these flanking defenses. Although the drawings are not so graphically clear as we might wish, Leonardo on folio 345 verso-b of the Codex Atlanticus works out not only a convenient arc of vertical fire—which is greater here than elsewhere because of the greater height of the typical curtain, having three superposed battery corridors (see details A 1 and B 1)—but also the first employment of effective flanking based on advanced salients (details d and c).

We should not make the mistake of thinking that Borgia's attention was focussed exclusively or almost exclusively on permanent fortifications. On the contrary, in the history of Italian and European military techniques the place of the Duke of Valentinois is that of one of those *condottieri* who put into practice ideas of tactics and field or semipermanent fortification at a time when this domain was all but forgotten, at least to any rational or systematic effect. We can confirm this by means of those notes in which Da Vinci, Borgia's military engineer, takes up the question of semipermanent or temporary defenses consisting of terrepleins held up by quickly erected walls, and using materials capable of absorbing the blows of the bombards, like today's sandbags. Leonardo's most notable sheets relating to this are found in Mss. H and L, and in the inexhaustible Codex Atlanticus—specifically folios 52 verso, 16 verso, 28 verso, and 39 verso of Ms. L and, among many others, fol. 41 verso of the Codex Atlanticus. On folio 52 verso of Ms. L we have the use of pyramidal salients, indirectly reminiscent of the outworks of permanent constructions, though they would probably have

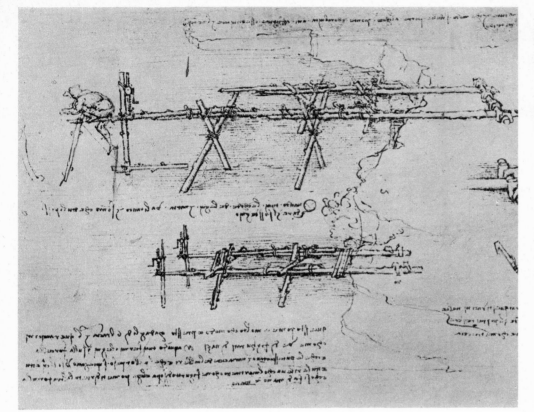

Left: Military flying bridge – Cod. Atl., fol. 16 v-*a*

Right: Temporary bridge – Cod. Atl., fol. 22 r-*a*

been built in the form of earthworks faced with bundles of pressed hay at the back, and supported by a network with central beams or connected with them externally. This device was intended to cushion the body of the structure against the bombard shots and so make it less vulnerable, just as shock-absorbing materials are provided for a bastion in a drawing on folio 75 verso of Ms. B. Types that were common even then, and are still familiar to our eyes, are also proposed, in the form of beams placed on the surface of the earthworks, like our gabions.

Folio 41 verso-*a* of the Codex Atlanticus presents by far the most important study of this style, and is basic for Leonardo's work in it. We may call this style "fieldworks," but the point of interest is that it applies the principles underlying permanent defenses, inasmuch as in it the general idea of the entrenched camp assumes huge proportions and complete development. There are two types of semipermanent obstacle, as shown, beyond the broad outer moat, by the rampart outside the first trench, composed of bundles of litter, either high grass or thick hay, which should be "wetten and muddied" before being laid down, according to the note that Da Vinci adds to detail A. Another smaller moat follows the rampart of the first trench, and then there is a higher but less massive enceinte; at the rear of this is a convenient walk with a broad escarpment, whose inclination and development are different in the two sketches. The flanking concept is very highly developed here, in keeping with those ideas of field use that were to be completely elaborated in modern war, in which our automatic arms have fully established the possibilities of flanking fire. It is applied in Leonardo's design from a double vertical set of casemates of the inner ring—which reminds one of the modern strong points, armored in steel and reinforced concrete and buried below the surface of the ground, except for the firing cupola. Here the angle of fire is higher, while from the casemates of the external ring, which are less commanding, there is a single line of embrasures.

Each casemate commands, by flanking it, the crown of its rampart; added to the potentialities of the embrasures located in the mass connecting the first and second blocks, this indicates the possibility of a third line of flanking fire, over the middle ditch, just as in the "fortress raking the ditches and the glacis outside the ditches" that we met with for a moment in our study of folio 18 verso of Ms. B.

Examination of the form would lead us to believe that Leonardo thought of the external rampart as massive and full, while the succeeding one, as the embrasures show, should be a position for defensive forces delivering a direct frontal fire, thereby fulfilling their essential function, a minimum of control of the outer enceinte, the soft covering of hay or the like being designed to absorb the impact of the cannon shot. In moments of peril, when a last-ditch defense had to be made, the function of the middle casemates was logically also that of a redoubt and point of ultimate resistance, an action for which the system in question was favorable, inasmuch as redoubts of this nature were the key to mastery of the principal line, the inner rampart, and the light guns located inside. The measurements given in the drawing itself are 10 ells (about 6 m.) for the height of the rampart of the larger ditch, 40 ells (24 m.) for its width, and 6 ells (3.60 m.) for its depth, while the width of the first rampart is 10 ells (6 m.), that of the second ditch 12 ells (7.20 m.), and that of the second rampart 4 ells (2.40 m.), with a step of 2 ells (1.20 m.) at the rear. These measurements, although they

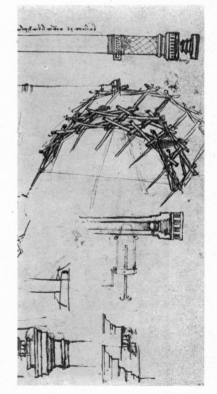

Temporary bridge and firearms – Cod. Atl., fol. 23 v-*a*

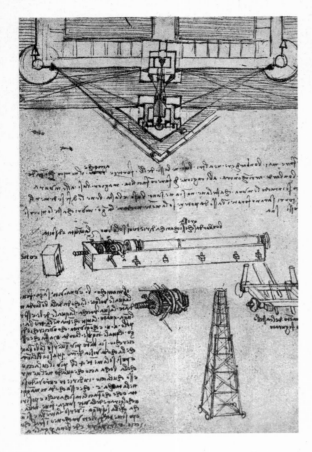

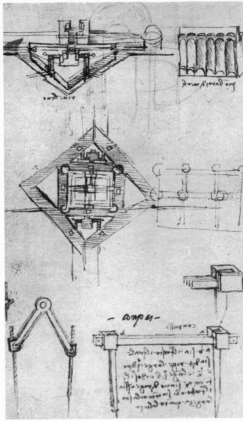

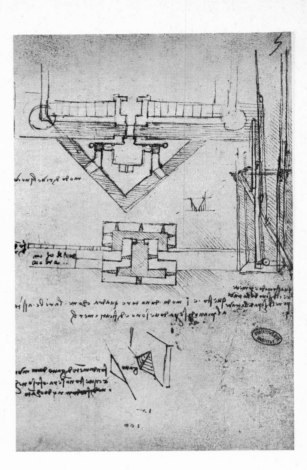

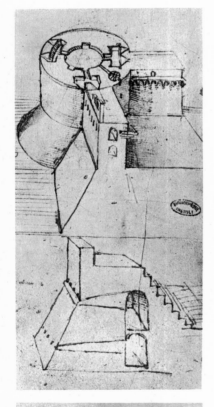

Studies of enfilading artillery fire in frontal ravelin of Sforza castle – Ms. B, fol. 24 v, 57 v, 5 r

do not always agree with the proportions of the drawing, tell us at any rate that there is here an ensemble of field or semipermanent trenches commensurate with the average dimensions of a man's body in relation to defense maneuvers and the use of arms. The supporting stockades in front lead us to believe that this and all the other vertical lines of terreplein were walled outside for support.

The power of the masses, the rational conception of the use of lines of fire, and the parallel organization and perfection of the structures, all speak of an important approach to the ideas underlying a modern line of entrenchments.

The idea of a fortification half under water is worked out in different ways in details *c* and *d* of the same sheet. In detail *c* we have the section of a circular outwork with an elliptic-cuspidate roof, a subterranean way of access from the body of the place, and a line of fire at the level of the water of the ditch; the defense was obviously designed to be carried out with nothing more than light portable firearms, as is shown likewise by the proportions of the internal arrangement (see detail *a* 1, fol. 43 v-*b*). Detail *d* (fol. v-*a*) sets forth the conception of a series of embrasures likewise placed at the level of the water of the ditch, probably in order to cut down that famous danger of their becoming disastrous breaches under accurately aimed shots from attackers' guns, as we saw was feared in connection with the castle of Milan (Ms. B, fol. 36 v). This novel treatment of the water element and the whole general idea lead up to a final study of the best treatments presented in the Codex Atlanticus, which cannot be too far removed in time from the phase here in question, and which mark one of the high points in da Vinci's technique of fortification.

The most important sheets in this connection may be said to be folios 43 recto-*a* (detail *A*), 43 verso-*b* (details *a* 2 and *b* 1), 43 verso-*a*, 345 verso-*b*, and, finally, 48 recto-*a* and 48 recto-*b* (detail *c*).

On folio 43 recto-*a* we see in vertical cross section the slanting elliptic profile characteristic of the concentric perimeters of these formations. We recognize the battery emplacements, the high line of the embrasures, dominating the enceinte in front, and in general we perceive here the progress and further development toward the modern forms of this type of curtain over the prototypes found in Ms. L; the forms are even more powerful, and their slant is also improved.

But the especially important thing to note is that in this series of models Leonardo gives us the synthesis and general organization into a definite totality of the analytical and partial elements he was thinking of for a permanent line in the studies of Ms. L; and as in Ms. L, we shall see the mind of the searcher pass through the same difficulties, and the successive phases of improvement and progress.

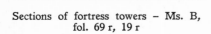

Sections of fortress towers – Ms. B, fol. 69 r, 19 r

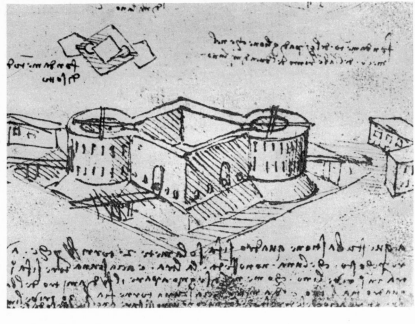

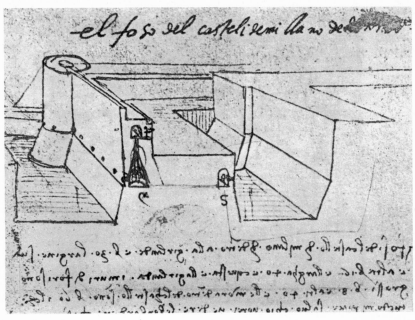

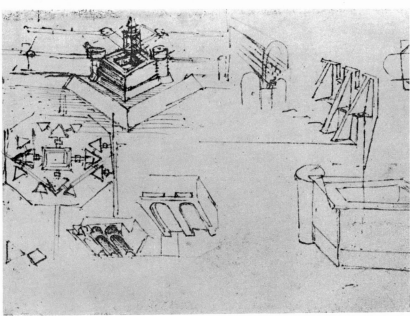

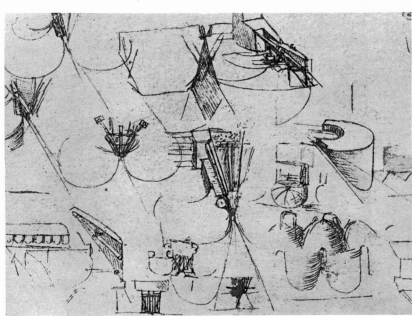

We have a first complete quadrilateral system (although in reduced proportions) in details *b* 1 and *a* 2 of folio 43 verso-*b*. These concentric elements are three in number and with their three lines of ditches surround an internal space that can be flooded. The second detail indicates also the trajectories of the attackers' projectiles, which could only with difficulty damage the stronghold, not so much because of the passive strength of the mass of each structure in itself when designed on these or similar patterns, but especially because of the slight elevation of the walls and the slant of their profiles at the top, the upper edge of the first line covering the lower part of the roof of the second, and this principle of reciprocal cover from the outside inward applying to all the enceintes. The height of the perimeters increases moderately and gradually in this way up to the maximum height, which is that of the central nucleus.

The detail gives an approximate idea of the particular features, indicating the internal passages for serving the guns in the batteries (located in the rear in order to leave the most exposed part solid) and the outside lines of the embrasures, which command the extrados standing opposite; these in turn command the field frontally beyond the largest ditch of the perimeter. Since the communications from one enceinte to another are below water level, and one ring is therefore separated from another, it is also possible to conduct a separate defense when one ring is held by attackers, by previously blocking the intercommunicating passages. In this situation the enemy could have great difficulty in advancing from one work to the next under the dense and effective fire of the defenders, and with the ditch to cross in between, and there should be reasonable hopes of resistance.

The examples of folio 43 verso-*a* (*a* 1, *c* 1, and *d*) show that Leonardo, probably with existing castles in mind—Borgia's or those of other rulers—tried to adapt this conception to fortresses in the traditional style, first by making the structures more solid and rounding out their angles as much as possible, then by enclosing the castle enceintes in powerful perimeters of the type already observed, or the like, presenting a virtually elliptic section toward the field and the now standard low ratio between elevation and base. This would provide much higher powers of resistance than the rectilinear curtains of the original castle.

Left, above: Fortress with double tower – Ms. B, fol. 12 r

Left, below: Studies of fortifications – Cod. Atl., fol. 281 v-*b*

Right, above: Towers and moat of castle of Milan – Ms. B, fol. 36 v

Right, below: Studies of fortifications – Cod. Atl., fol. 45 r-*b*

Studies of bastions with salients – Cod. Atl., fol. 43 r-*b*

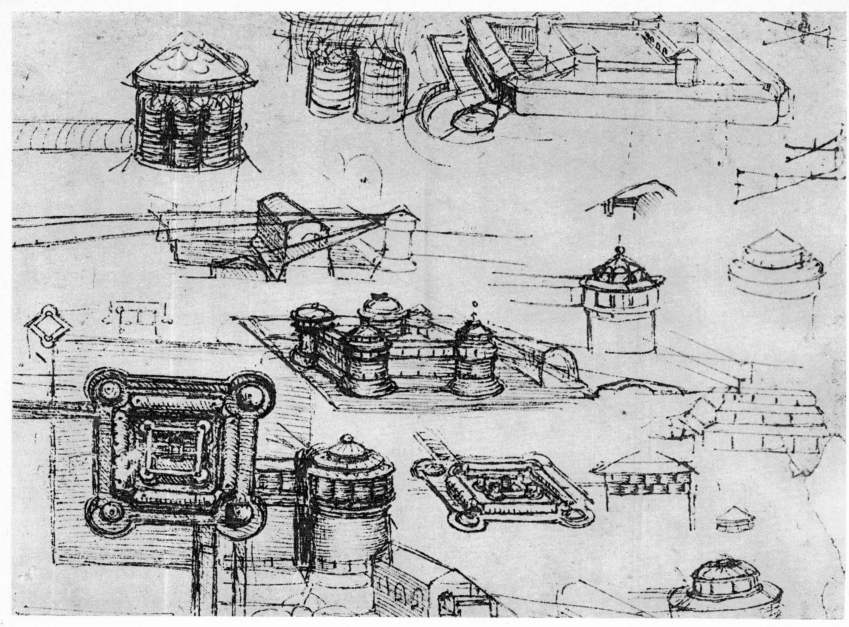

Above: Studies and designs of fortifications – Cod. Atl., fol. 43 v-a

Below, right: Plans and studies of fortifications – Cod. Atl., fol. 43 v-b

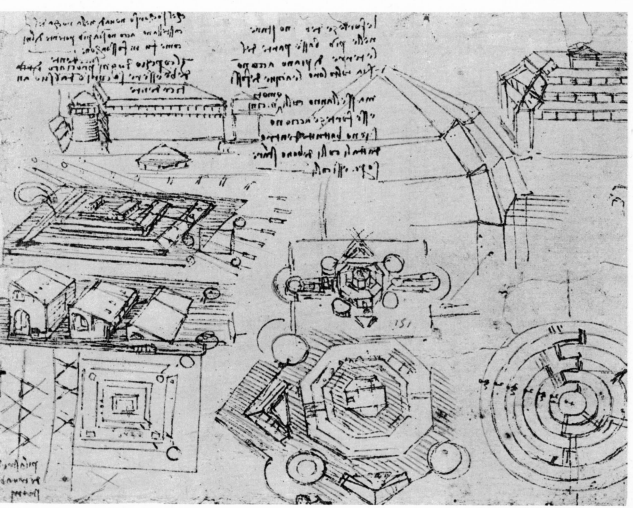

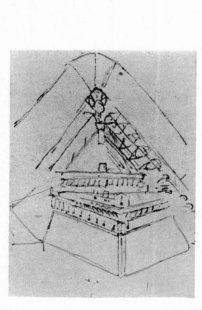

Studies of fortifications – Ms. L, fol. 65 r

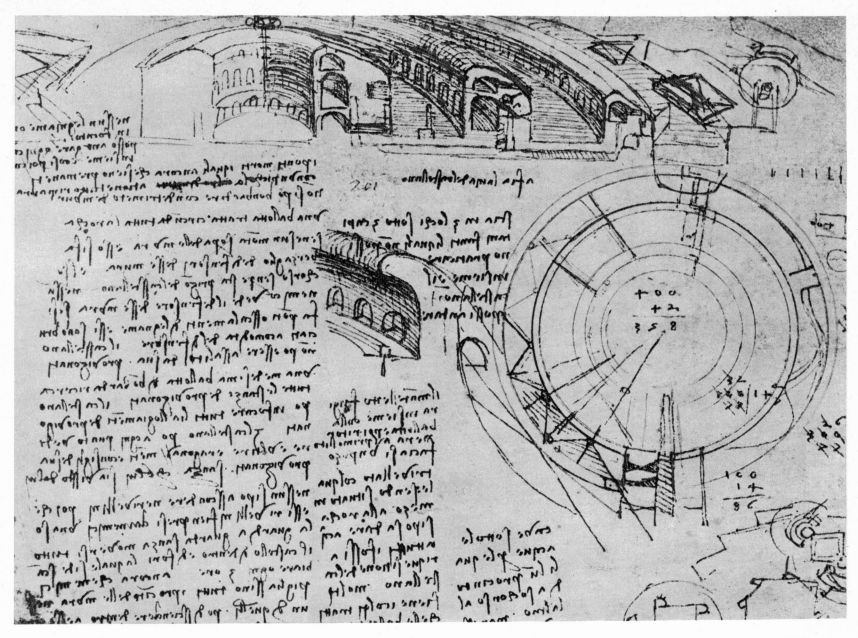

Above: Studies and designs for fortress – Cod. Atl., fol. 48 r-*a*

Below, left: Section and studies for fortress – Cod. Atl., fol. 48 r-*b*

Study of fortification of Borgia period – Ms. L, fol. 51 *b*

Above: Design of fortification with double ditch – Cod. Atl., fol. 41 v-*a*

Below: Fortifications of Borgia period

Left: Ms. L, fol. 61 r

Center: Ms. L, fol. 48 v

Right: Ms. L, fol. 52 r

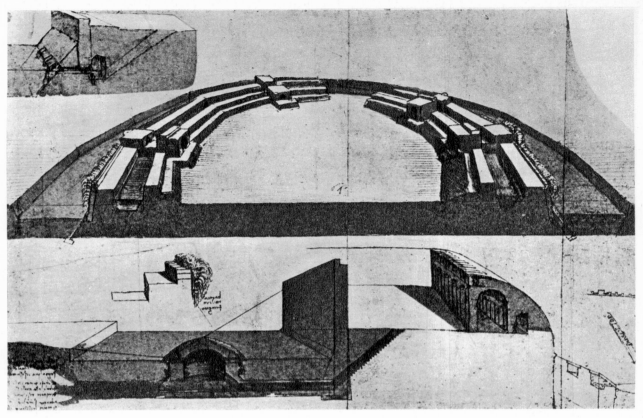

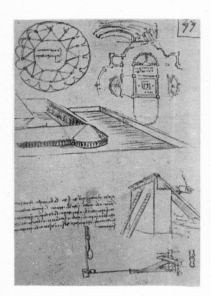

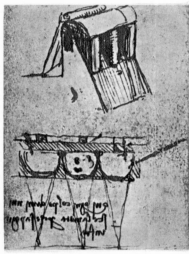

Study of fortress – Defense against escalades – Ms. B, fol. 55 r

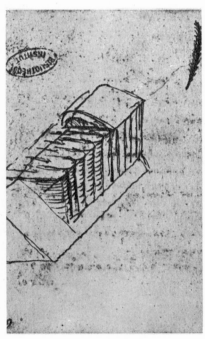

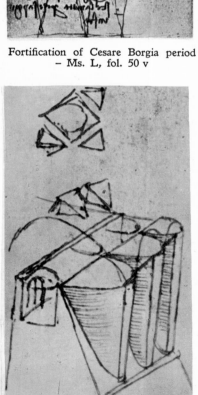

Fortification of Cesare Borgia period
– Ms. L, fol. 50 v

Study of fortification – Ms. L, fol.
49 v

The principal consequence of the continual process of smoothing out the projections and rounding out all the angles, a process that was summed up in the circular organisation of enceintes with elliptic sections, was a lack of flanking and cross fire; we have seen that the frontal defense was adequate to the requirements. Leonardo did not of course want to overlook these basic and indispensable principles. Although they could be applied in a more natural and straightforward manner in bastioned works like Sangallo's, he found that the flanking fire typical of angular structures was also possible with use of these retreating convex forms. His solution of the problem was to devise ravelins with hemispheric or elliptic cupolas, half below the level of the water and so placed as to be capable of setting up a network of lines of fire grazing the outer enceintes. This conclusion is the same as that applied, on the basis of the same presuppositions, to the permanent fortifications of the nineteenth century, down to the eve of the "total" casemate technique to producing structures that are indeed circular and of retreating section, but with outworks (likewise circular or elliptic as a rule) suitably detached for flanking purposes. Examples are sketched in detail B of folio 43 recto-*b*; these, however, also project angular forms of the bastion type. We may repeat here what has been pointed out above in connection with folio 65 recto of Ms. L. In folio 48 verso-*b* the outworks take on a semicircular or half-moon shape and are placed at intervals of 90° on the glacis of the outer ditch, with the resultant possibility of setting up eight crossing lines of fire over the field, enveloping the entire stronghold, at angles of from 55° to 60° to their capital passing through the center of the place. The same conceptions had been proposed for the flanking of the circular

302

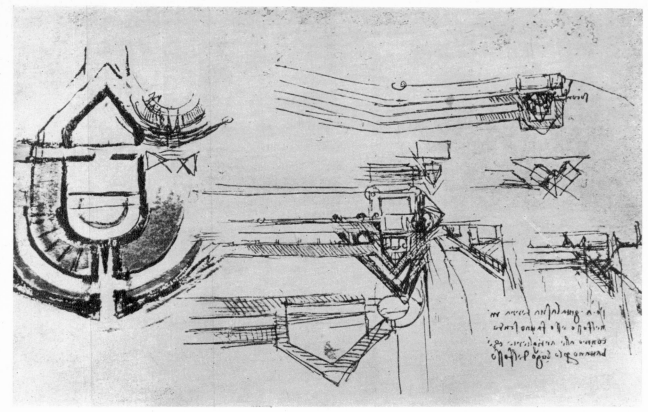

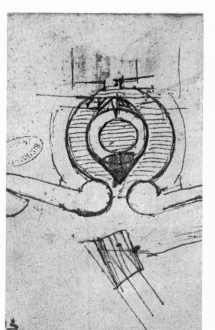

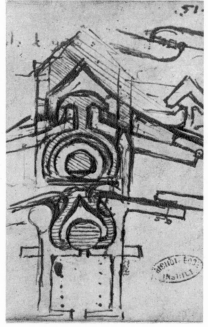

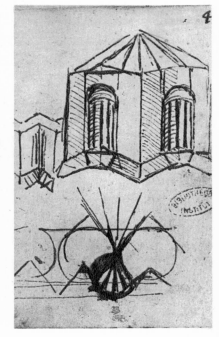

Above: Studies and plans of fortifications – Cod. Atl., fol. 45 v-*b*

Below: Designs and plans for fortifications

Left: Ms. L, fol. 50 r

Center: Ms. L, fol. 46 r

Right: Ms. L, fol. 51

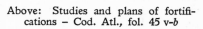

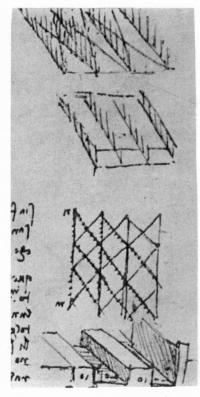

Method of planting trees to form permanent bastion – Cod. Arund., fol. 121 r

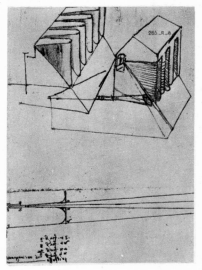

Design of fortification – Ms. L, fol. 63 r

Fortifications of Borgia period – Cod.
Atl., fol. 264 v

ravelins, also half under water, placed to defend the perimeters of quadrilateral fortresses (fol. 43 v-*a*, detail A).

Folio 48 recto-*a* offers another example, and an especially convincing one, of this type of ensemble of casemated defenses, further protected by external water barriers. This gives us a sort of Da Vincian ancestor of the modern Maginot line and its congeners, although in those great latter-day defensive lines very little was to be seen above ground, apart from the bases of the viewing means (periscopes) and firing equipment. The essential thing to keep in mind is that Leonardo, at the beginning of the sixteenth century, had come close to a fundamental conception, based on the greatest possible reduction of the exposed elevation of the structures, reciprocal protection by means of mutual defilade, extensive application of retreating profiles for exposed surfaces, and use of detached forts for flanking fire.

The differences between folios 48 recto-*b* and 48 recto-*a* relate to details by and large. Although the indications in the first example are rather sketchy, the enceintes there seem to be higher and less retreating, with a sort of tower or keep in the center. In the second example (where the outlines are clearer) the perimeters are very low, with ample elliptic covering; the inner enceinte has double rows of embrasures, with service passages; the upper batteries command the outer enceinte and the field with grazing fire, and the lower batteries are assigned to frontal close defense of the ditch they face. The outer perimeter has a high line of embrasures for long-range fire, and a second passageway below would seem to indicate a lower line of guns for use against attackers near at hand. All the

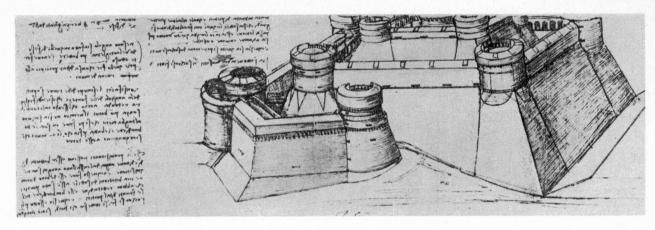

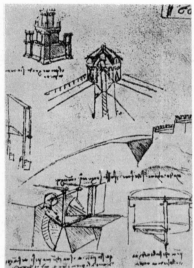

Dry ditches for mountain fortifications
– Ms. B, fol. 60 r

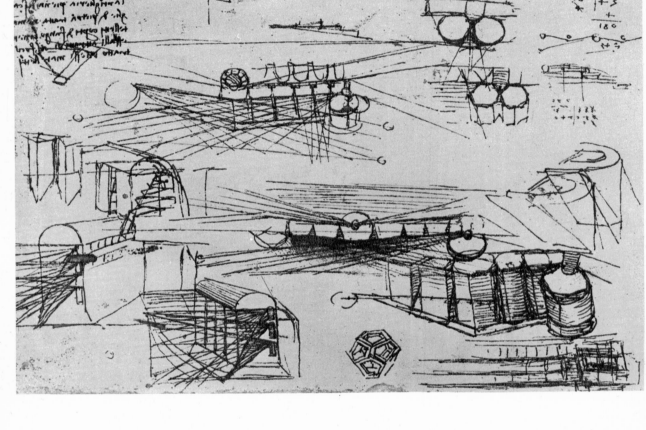

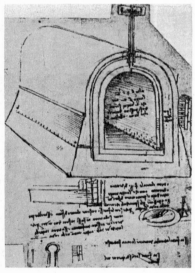

Device for flooding gallery of access
to fortress – Cod. Atl., fol. 359 v-*a*

Systems of fortification – Ms. L,
fol. 52 v

battery passages have very generous outlets for access, service of the guns, and venting of smoke: they are all located at the rear, and the same provision is made in the powerful central structure, whose profile offers the most brilliant testimony as to the progress that has been made. Here too we see the idea of leaving the part exposed to attack as solid as possible, by locating the triple row of galleries inside, with possibly the reveal of an embrasure or two opening to the outside: at any rate, it is clear that the defense of this center of resistance rests more on the strength of its walls and its isolation by water than on its fire power.

This interpretation seems to gain further support from the presence of the watchtower raised in the center of the courtyard, from which the land around over a certain radius, together with the outer curtains, can be observed by a round-the-clock guard. Underground communications between one enceinte and another are shown; undoubtedly these could be flooded in case of need to block off all access, as we see in detail studies of Leonardo's in various folios of the Codex Atlanticus, belonging perhaps to this period.

To conclude this rapid survey of the most interesting of Leonardian military constructions, we recall the splendid drawing of folio 41 verso-*b* of the Codex Atlanticus, which depicts a magnificent mountain fortress (as we see from the dry, steeply sloping ditches) already dealt with in studies of twenty years before in Ms. B. The general lines are massive and powerful, and the main characteristic is the adaptation of rather traditional forms to the new needs, that is, the "modernization" of these forms. The towers are heavy and low; and the reveals of the embrasures are cut down to a min- imum, and they are so placed as to allow of the least possible risk of being breached by enemy fire. The passive strength of the enormous escarpments at the bottom, and their dimensions as com- pared with those of the towers, testify to an almost complete reversal of the classic fourteenth-century ratio between escarp and curtains, greatly improving the defensive strength. The curtains are de- rived from those separately treated in Ms. L, although they do not have developed salients, because of the scale and importance of the escarpment. Some of the ideas of the pages in the Codex Atlanti-

304

Design of fortification – Cod. Atl.,
fol. 41 r

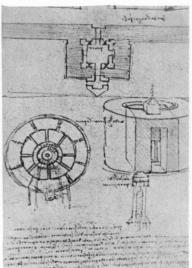
Fortifications with salients - Ms. L,
fol. 39 v

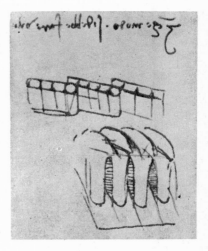
Portcullis for fortress – Ms. B, fol. 48 r

cus seem to be retained here in the forms of the two concentric quadrilateral enceintes and the central keep. The entrance is defended by a large bastioned ravelin, with a salient angle of about 125°, effectively defending the way of access, by means not only of the mass of the wall but also of the arrangement of its flanking fire (as is shown by the embrasures in its towers facing in the direction of attack). The curtains of the enceintes are defended in the same manner; the flanking embrasures are in two superposed rows. Certain features, not least among them a resemblance to some aspects of the outworks of the castle at Cesena, might lead us to think that this drawing deals with a fortress which Da Vinci saw in Romagna, or represents a study for modernizing a castle in that region which he visited in those months.

The Romagna period ends the most interesting part of Leonardo's activity in this field. But as we pointed out in reference to the Sforza period, the master's mind returns to military subjects when some martial episode in the following years raises important problems and furnishes him with the opportunity of solving them. Thus we see Leonardo, returned from his mission in Romagna, working in 1503 on the proposed deviation of the course of the Arno, which the Florentine government planned during its war with near-by Pisa, in an attempt to force the Pisans to surrender by flooding heir territory and their defenses with the waters of the river.

The Riformagioni archives in Florence (letters to the *Balia*) contain various studies and reports dealing with the "campaign against Pisa," with this end in view. During the war of 1509-1513 against the Republic of Venice conducted by the army of Louis XII of France, Leonardo is once more engaged in study of military matters, in the broad sense of the term, going through the territories of the Most Christian King, the zone of operations, and the neighboring lands—Lombardy and the Brescia-Crema region. Some topographic studies of this region, important from the standpoints not only of description and hydraulics but probably also of military strategy, tell us of the activity of those years. It is almost certain that the episode of an encounter between the opposing armies near the Castello di Trezzo on the Adda is the subject of a sketch on folio 7-*b* of Quaderno di Anatomia II (dated Jan. 13, 1513),[9] showing the tactical dispositions of the forces engaged in the battle, which four days before the date of the drawing had led to the conquest of this important place by the Spanish and Venetians.

After his stay in Rome at the papal court, and after his disappointments, Da Vinci, a wanderer now getting on in years but an unsated investigator of the infinite themes that nature and art had shown him on his path, turned toward France, where, in his last years, he cultivated his favorite studies under the protection of the King. Questions relating to hydraulics interested him in this last period as well, but it seems at best doubtful that he made any new studies of military architecture, although some investigators (especially among French scholars) have recently suggested the possibility. But this is in the realm of hypothesis, and quite unlikely.

However, he remains the great master, the farsighted anticipator of technical achievements in the field of military architecture that were to find full application only centuries later.

IGNAZIO CALVI

---

[9] Windsor, Royal Collection.

Leonardo – Drawing of cannon foundry – Windsor, Royal Collection, no. 12647

LEONARDO AS DECORATOR

Leonardo as a decorator, or, still more narrowly, as a mural decorator, within the framework of the rich ornamental painting—not always very elegant, sometimes overloaded, but straightforward and lively—that is characteristic of the architectural ornament used in the duchy of Milan in the second half of the fifteenth century, is our concern here.

To my mind there is no longer any question, in general or in particular, that Leonardo da Vinci, the painter of the *Virgin of the Rocks* and of the *Last Supper*, designed and executed decorative projects and motifs—as if we were to try to distinguish (and this distinction has always seemed futile to me, although it may be pedagogically useful) between a Leonardo or a Bramante practicing pure art and another Leonardo or Bramante practicing applied art. I have no hesistation in saying that Leonardo's decorative works show themselves to be his in that they show themselves to have been conceived and arranged by a thinker, an artist, a scientist.

Lock – Cod. Atl., fol. 292 v-*a*

We know in what manner and to what extent the architecture of the second half of the fifteenth century in the Milan region made use of the rich coloring of fresco, often altogether decoratively, with no important representation of figures, not only in the interior but also on the outside of buildings. This style reflects a love for ribbons, panels, painted imitations of marble blocks or tarsia work, repeating frets, pretended intaglios of egg-and-dart and leaf design. Actually the idea was to simulate in painting a rich carved and polychrome marble facing, such as the materials and resources of the locality could not easily and copiously supply. This, and not merely being bogged down in habit and local tradition, was the reason for the great use of plastic terra cotta, which in turn was likewise touched up with color, and was not always, and perhaps less often than is thought, left in view in the lively natural color.

The names of Montorfano, Foppa, Bernardino de Rossi, and Bramante himselft, to name only those of the first order, will serve to illustrate the point. The list could be greatly expanded by mention of buildings or parts of buildings in reference to which the names of the artists concerned are unknown or unfamiliar.

At any rate, among the favorite motifs of this kind of ornamentation are festoons and garlands —in a word, what we might call floral themes—and knotwork; these motifs, which I designedly mention as a separate unity, are those of Leonardo da Vinci as a decorator. They characterize three ornamental works executed by him or attributed to him—the decoration of the Sala delle Asse in the Sforza castle, the decoration of the vault of the sacristy of Santa Maria delle Grazie, the garlands in the lunettes over the *Last Supper*. The first two are well-known works by Da Vinci. He is less well known, perhaps, for the garlands of the *Cenacle*, as the great scene itself attracts all the attention, admiration, and fame; yet they are his, without a doubt. Description is superfluous for all three.

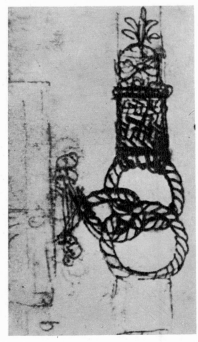

Decorated belt – Cod. Atl., fol. 292 v-*a*

As in the case of many other works of art, and of many other artists (Bramante himself, for example), there is no material historical certainty that they are from the hand of Leonardo. We may, however, make use of documentary indications and observations.

307

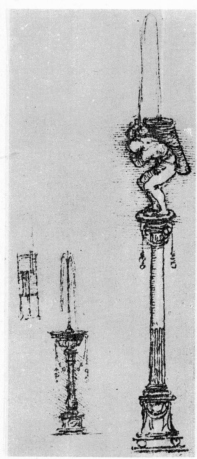

Drawings for fountains – Windsor,
Royal Collection

The solid citations and clear arguments of Luca Beltrami are a good guide to the documents that lead us to consider the decoration of the Sala delle Asse as Leonardo's. I refer in general to Beltrami's work, but feel that quoting a passage here will be helpful:

"Gualtiero, one of the Duke's courtiers, wrote to Ludovico on April 21, 1498: 'My most illustrious and most excellent Lord.... On Monday the great room of the *asse*, that is, of the tower, will be cleared. Master Leonardo promises to finish it entirely for September, and that it can be used in the meantime, because the scaffolding he will put up there will leave space for everything below...' "[1]

"In connection with this document," Beltrami continues, "which I pointed out in the first edition of my work on the castle of Milan in 1885, Gustavo Uzielli remarks in a note on page 319 of his *Ricerche intorno a Leonardo da Vinci:* 'Here Gualtiero means to say that the tower will be taken down, that is, the provisional scaffolding made of *asse*, that is, of planks—and not that there was a *Sala delle Asse*, as Beltrami interprets the passage of the letter that he cities.' To be sure, if we had no other mention than this of a Sala delle *Asse*, we might be able to agree with Uzielli's interpretation, which is: 'On Monday, the large room will be cleared of the planks, that is, of the tower or wood scaffolding.' But as we have seen, there are many references to a Sala delle *Asse* and to the reasons for this name. The Master Leonardo spoken of was Leonardo da Vinci himself, who at that same time was working on the Saletta Negra and the *camerini* in the castle. The letter of 1498 likewise shows that a framework had been up in the Sala della Torre, perhaps for reinforcing and repairing the vault of the hall, and in any case for renovating the *intonaco*, which the painter undertook to decorate in about five months, without interfering with the use and enjoyment of the hall during the work. It is really a remarkable piece of good fortune that despite the great destruction of documents, the letter above quoted has come down to us to give precious testimony that Leonardo decorated the Sala delle *Asse*, in agreement with the conclusions we are led to by study of the decoration that Ludovico il Moro caused to be carried out there, of which fortunately we can still find traces."

Unless I have overlooked some positive arguments, the only things urged against this are the weak hypotheses and vague doubts of Malaguzzi Valeri,[2] who bases his position on Uzielli's interpretation, although he cannot have been unaware of Beltrami's refutation, since he cites the latter's monograph of 1902. Malaguzzi himself is not altogether convinced, because he returns to the subject in his second volume,[3] fortifying himself with this defense: "The divergent judgments may arise in connection with the execution. But since it is no longer possible to trace out what is left of the genuine remains of the fifteenth-century decoration, although something of them can still be seen, the question of the artistic paternity of the work must be confined to the region of inductions and hypotheses." In other words, those who study and reason must proceed to examination of the work, even though, since the restoration, it is no longer possible to analyze the execution of the actual brushwork.

To be reasonable, we may grant that, as Malaguzzi says, "after the rigid though patient work of the restoring, the freedom and vigor of the art of the great master" can no longer appear; but there can be no doubt that someone like Beltrami, an extremely competent architect as regards technical matters, closely analyzed the outlines of the decoration so far as it survived and made the necessary study of the stylistic arguments relative to the historical documentation. Moreover, we have this valuable testimony reported by Malaguzzi: "An old student of Lombard art (Gustavo Frizzoni), who was able before the present restoration to examine the few intact traces of the original floral decoration of the great hall (which rose alongside the window from a big trunk, painted below and now covered over) had the impression that its spontaneity and vivacity made it truly akin to the work in the festoons surrounding the ducal shields in the refectory of Santa Maria delle Grazie." This reference to the craftsmanship of the garlands over the *Last Supper* seems to me to be decisive. I should also say that the actual execution is of importance, but is only one factor in deciding the question. We have to be guided by the conception that inspired the work.

The following consideration seems to be of importance. The conception of the highly original motif of the Sala "delle Asse" is clearly, organically architectural.[4] It is by no means mere space-filling decoration in the formal sense of the term. The distribution of the pictorial ornament is in studied spontaneous accord with the architectural structure it is designed to cover. The keen understanding with which the entire ensemble is led, in geometrical harmony, to wind its movement around the central ring of the vault; the eight spots of light, fragments of sky in the green pergola, creating regular aesthetic pauses in the octagonal development: all this is the invention of a reasoning architect and lover of accurately thought out and intended geometrical themes. It is Da Vinci's mind, his science, and even his mania.

In the branching-tree composition, of which I shall speak later, a marked characteristic is constituted by the gilded cords that bind both branches and foliage, and form among them knots and tracery of beautiful ornamental grace.

[1] Luca Beltrami. *Leonardo da Vinci e la Sala "delle Asse" nel castello di Milano,* Milan, 1902, p. 24.
[2] Francesco Malaguzzi Valeri. *La corte di Ludovico il Moro,* I, Milan, 1913, p. 315 f.
[3] *Op. cit.,* II, *Bramante e Leonardo da Vinci,* Milan, 1915, p. 562.
[4] See Ambrogio Annoni, "Considerazioni su Leonardo da Vinci architetto," in *Emporium,* Bergamo, April, 1919, p. 172.

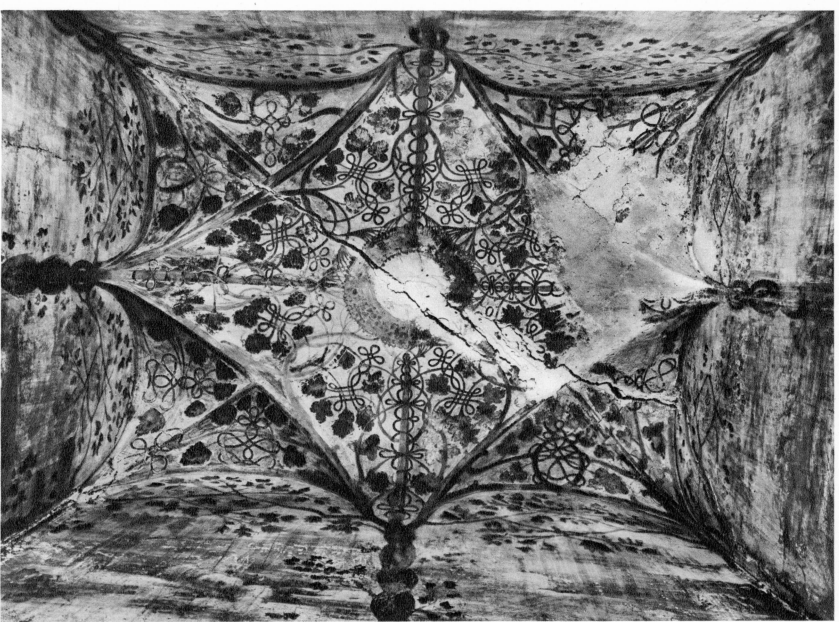

Above, left: Graffito decoration on vault of portico of Cascina Pozzobonelli. — Above, right: Decoration of vault of portico of Palazzo dal Verme, Milan. — Below: Decoration of small room in abbey of Viboldone, near Milan

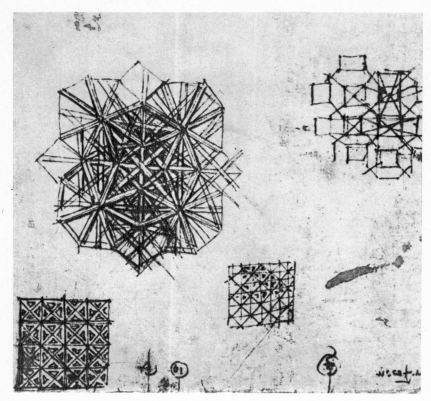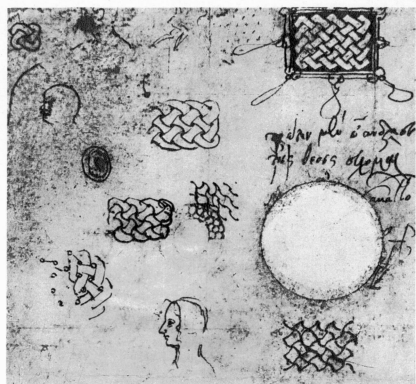

Left: Geometrical decorative drawings – Cod. Atl., fol. 178 r-*a*

Right: Decorative knotwork – Cod. Atl., fol. 342 v

As we know, even without going so far back as the chaste and elegant frets, ornamental motifs consisting of knotwork and interlace were widely used in Byzantine and Romanesque art, and in miniatures among other things. They were also used in typography, as Beltrami sagely recalls; and in the pages of his monograph dedicated to the Sala "delle Asse" he reproduces initials taken from books published between 1495 and 1519. He notes that "the interlaced designs of these initials exhibit notable affinities with the designs of the Sala delle *Asse*, so that it is possible to envisage an influence from Da Vinci, not an arbitrary influence immediately exercised by the decoration of this hall on the designers of these typographic forms, but in the sense that Leonardo had largely contributed to the vogue which this kind of ornamentation had achieved, because of the tendency and the affection for it he had shown not only in the vault of the Sala delle *Asse*, but in many other knotwork designs." [5]

Furthermore, there is geometrical knotwork in pictures, for example those of Butinone and Zenale, in the cloister arches of Santa Maria delle Grazie, in the church proper, and along the frieze of the refectory, as also elsewhere in fifteenth-century mural decoration. But these motifs are always rigidly geometrical and decorative in function, and thus sometimes reminiscent of frets. There are, however, fifteenth-century Milanese examples of decoration based on a freer use of ribbons or cords. Thus we find in the same refectory of Santa Mariá delle Grazie the ribbons holding the festoons underneath, painted by Bernardino de Rossi, and quite different in character and intention from the knotwork of the frieze. Less well-known examples of this freedom of movement in thoroughly decorative fine ribbons are the frieze painted on the arches of the cloister of the Virgin of Vettabbia [6] and that on the portico vault of the Casa dal Verme, both in Milan and of the fourteenth century.

But among all these, the interlace designs of Da Vinci stand out unmistakably by reason of two original qualities characteristic of them alone. The first is the care taken by the author never to falsify the nature of the motif—even though it is purposefully composed—as if it were really called on to perform its simulated function of binding together, supporting, combining branches or foliage or fruit. The second is the care he has taken to make use of the properties of the cords themselves in order to achieve an ornamental end along with a geometrical form, in conformity with an ever-present rationale of observation and firm intention. And this fits in perfectly with the spirit of Leonardo as an artist, and with his mental make-up as a thinker or scientist.

The outlines of strapwork, the studies for knots, the sketches of geometrical curves and closed or interlaced tracery scattered among the sheets of his writings, notes, and drawings, all indicate and testify to his tendency and to his preparation for the conception and the decorative elements of the Sala "delle Asse." The notes or sketches reach their high point, for logical completeness of pattern and patient precision of form, in the elegant and skillful knotwork that presents the emblem or finishes off the title of an *Accademia vinciana*. It is not proved that such an academy existed; it may have

Decorative shells, leaves, and fish – Institut de France – Ms. I, fol. 24 v, and 25 r

[5] *Op. cit.*, p. 39.
[6] See Reale Soprintendenza ai Monumenti della Lombardia, *Il Convento delle Dame Vergini della Vettabbia in Milano*: Ambrogio Annoni, *Note descrittive ed appunti d'arte*, Milan, 1922, p. 38 f.

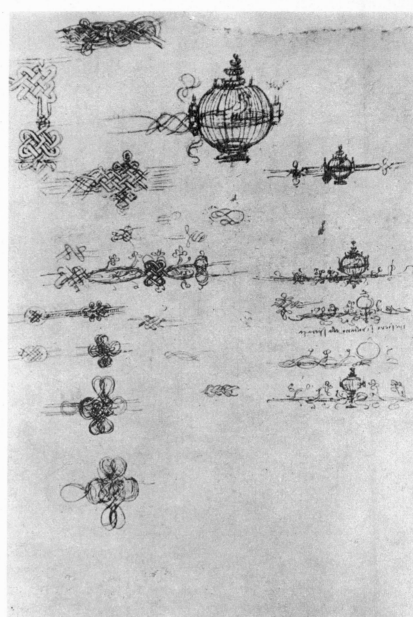

been only thought of and longed for by Leonardo. And in this sense the doubts as to attributing the allegorical and well-composed VINCI to his hand might be laid.

In addition to the Sala "delle Asse," another decorative achievement that is fully in line with Leonardo's conception, with his geometrical virtuosity combined with realistic rationalism, in the work on the vault of the sacristy of Santa Maria delle Grazie, a decoration of stout cords, laced with lovely knotwork, following and embroidering the architectural segments on a blue background. Here, lacking historical documentation, we have to trust to examination and the consideration already mentioned. But another name might come to mind, that of Bramante. Dates and circumstances would seem to favor such an attribution. These are the years between 1492 and 1499, when the apse and choir of the church were rebuilt, and this work, although there is no historical evidence, is virtually without discussion held to be due to Bramante. We know from the documents that the sacristy and the little cloister were finished in the same years, and there is no reason for not extending the same attribution to them as well. And in point of fact every aspect, for example the grace of the proportions and of the capitals of the portico in the cloister, merits reference to Bramante.

Beltrami, who well proved that the work in the Sala "delle Asse" was by Leonardo, points out the possibility of influence by Bramante or, as I should prefer to put it, an exchange of ideas between the two colleagues, because he has found a note by Da Vinci reading, "Bramante groups" (Cod. Atl., fol. 225). The word "groups" might be given a meaning other than the Milanese one of "knots," if there were not among other brief notes of Da Vinci the phrase, "I lent certain groups to Fra Filippo di Brera." These notes likewise show that Leonardo dealt with knots and knotwork, and this is confirmed by a passage of Lomazzo that Beltrami cites: "A fine idea of Leonardo's has also been found in the trees, that of having all the branches fall into various bizarre groups, interweaving them, Bramante too." [7]

[7] P. Lomazzo. *Trattato dell'arte de la pittura*, Milan, 1584, B. VI, p. 430.

Left: Decorative studies – Bayonne, Bonnat Collection

Right: Knots by Leonardo and decorative designs – Cod. Atl., fol. 68 v

Ornamental vase – Ms. B, fol. 70 v

Sala delle Asse in Castello Sforzesco, Milan – Detail of vault

Sword handles – Cod. Atl., fol. 133 r-a

Actually, Lomazzo seems to be referring merely to special tree arrangements invented by Leonardo and used by Bramante too. The word "groups" would fit very well, even without thinking of the Milanese use of the word *gruppo* to mean knot or interlacing.

I remark that the groups, in the sense of knots, mentioned by Leonardo in his quick note may perhaps have been the graffito ornaments of the lunettes and segments in the rebuilt choir of the church of Santa Maria delle Grazie. Very similar motifs, but incised with much more style and precision, adorn the little vaults in the portico of the Oratorio della Cascina Pozzobonelli, a work of such pure elegance and solid organization that it makes one think of Bramante at once.

But these are motifs that derive, although with freshened rhythm and gusto, from similar ideas in Byzantine or Romanesque or Ravenna art. They are far from having the creative character, in spirit and in detail, of the decoration of the sacristy of the church of Santa Maria delle Grazie, where the real material, diversely used in various sizes ranging from heavy cable to lace threads, is represented in painted imitation with a rationalism that goes beyond the craft of the geometrical decorator to rise to the level of an outstanding work of genius.

I know of no examples of this in Bramante's ornamentation. In his frescoes he makes use, with a constant breadth, of exquisitely classical and usually paganizing motifs. For example, there are the frescoes of the Casa Panigarola, now in the Brera museum, and the all but faded decoration of the Palazzo Fontana, now Silvestri. These and other decorations are pervaded with a classicism in form and content that absolutely excludes those other motifs. We must definitely return to Leonardo, and especially so since the tree elements is his personal characteristic.

I should not incline to give too much importance to the fact that in the portico of the *canonica* of Sant'Ambrogio, definitely a work of Bramante's, the shafts of the columns at the corners and toward

the central arcade are adorned with suggestions of branches. But this hint of plant life is not echoed in the very elegant capitals, and has classicizing overtones. Moreover, it is typical of Leonardo to use intertwined cords to bind together groups of branches and foliage, and, in the garlands of the *Cenacle,* flowers and fruits.

What I have said with respect to the specifically rational and naturally logical method of inter-twining these knots should be repeated with regard to the groups of branches or leaves, the clumps of foliage or flowers, and the bunches of fruit. The tree or plant or flower themes are always func-tionally employed and functionally represented. That is, they not only do not violate the laws of ramification that govern these elements, as Beltrami shrewdly observed,[8] but also make use, rationally and with style, of their various properties and postures.

This will be seen even more if we consider, in addition to Leonardo's botanical researches and observations, the trouble he took with and the directions he gave for some decorative arrangements of imitative architecture with plant ornamentation.

In some sketches and notes (Ms. B, fol. 28 v) Leonardo draws frameworks in the form of columns and porticoes, with instructions for covering them: "Around this column are bound four poles around which are nailed willow shoots as thick as a finger, making a base, and then go up binding clusters of juniper tops with the tops hanging down, that is, upside down";

"Let it be half an ell from one wreath to another, and the juniper alive, with the tops down, starting from below";

"Way to set the poles so as to bind the clusters of juniper over these poles, which are attached on the frame of the vault, and bind these clusters with willow shoots and cut off the superfluous tops with shears or work them in with the willow shoots";

"Way to make frameworks to make ornaments in the form of buildings."

Vault of Sala delle Asse in Castello Sforzesco, Milan

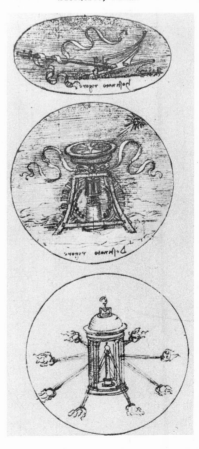

Emblems with motto *Hostinato rigore* – Windsor, Royal Collection

---

[8] *Op. cit.,* p. 41, which presents brief but precise references to Da Vinci's botanical studies. On this see Gustavo Uzielli, *Ricerche intorno a Leonardo da Vinci,* Ser. II, Rome, 1884, and A. Baldacci's section on "Da Vinci's Botany" in this volume.

Roaring lion – Paris, Louvre

Drawings of dragons – Windsor, Royal Collection

Drawings of dragons – Windsor, Royal Collection

Dragon rampant – London, British Museum, Cooper Collection

Knots – Cod. Atl., fol. 306 r-*d*

This is precious and vigorous evidence. Calvi [9] very wisely correlates it with a description by Tristano Calco dating from 1644 and an older one by Stefano Dolcino dating from 1488, relating to the marriage of Gian Galeazzo to Isabella of Aragon. He adds acutely: "These instructions by Leonardo suggest that he was commissioned to take charge of preparations for the wedding decorations, or at least followed and observed them rather closely." The likeness is especially close in the detail of shearing the juniper tops, which was so well done at the marriage of Gian Galeazzo that, in Dolcino's words, the branches were "by this means bound together and smooth with gilt between, so that there was no roughness of the foliage, no unevenness of the connected branches to diminish the artistic value of the result. You would think they had grown as they stood, or had been created by the brush of the artist."

Now, Leonardo knew well and at first hand the practical arrangements for setting up plant decoration; hence when he drew them he did not concoct fantasies in ornament but made use of his experience in the field to imitate motifs he had actually put together, or invent others that could be assembled from natural materials, as if he were actually handling "willow shoots" and "clusters."

We know that on the vaults of the portico of Casa Aliprandi, now Ponti, in the Via Bigli, Milan, there is a decoration that may be compared to those by Da Vinci; but here the plant element, ivy, is fantastic. I also mention the green foliage woven together to adorn, against a sky-blue background, the segments of the staircase vault in the sixteenth-century Simonetta palace at Milan.[10] The motif is also found, enriched with graceful *putti*, on the lunettes and small vault of a little room of the Pelluca near Monza, a work of Luini's.[11]

The last two, however, may be not even derivations but mere resonances, perhaps unconscious ones at that. Closer to the Leonardian conception of the Sala "delle Asse," and very similar in its elements, is the rather little-known decoration of a small room in the abbey of Viboldone, near Milan. In the building next to the church, sixteenth-century *cassettoni* and friezes of classical elegance, intertwined ribbons with mottoes, and architectural ornaments of terra cotta bring out the luxuriant character of architecture between the morning and high noon of our Renaissance. The decoration of a small room belongs to this period: on the walls and the segments of the vault there grow and intertwine branches and leaves held together and interwoven with loops of cord, very skillfully and rationally pointing up the architectural structure, to come together at the summit in a garland of thick green leaflets. The similarity to the decoration of the Sala "delle Asse" is so obvious as to constitute, in and of itself, a reason for giving fame and attention to this smaller edition or ingenuous imitation and timid, almost reverent reminiscence.

AMBROGIO ANNONI

[9] Gerolamo Calvi. "Contributi alla biografia di Leonardo da Vinci," in *Archivio storico Lombardo*, Milan, 1916, p. 456 f. I have followed to the letter Calvi's transcription of the passage from Leonardo.
[10] A picture of this decoration is given by Ambrogio Annoni on p. 57 of *Rassegna d'arte*, Milan, April, 1907.
[11] See Luca Beltrami, *Luini*, Milan, 1911, p. 221.

THE SCHOOL OF LEONARDO

The school of Leonardo, with the developments to which it led, was much more important than the school of any other artist at any time. The multiplicity, the universality of his intellectual work often took Leonardo away from artistic activity. "Most impatient of the brush," because entirely devoted to mathematical studies, is how he was described in April, 1501, by Fra Pietro da Novellara, who had gone to see him on behalf of the Marchioness Isabella d'Este. Fra Pietro also reported portraits being painted by two students, to which the master "puts his hand from time to time." This proves that some works took form under Leonardo's eyes and that he did part of the execution himself. These works form a first category to which we shall come back later.

A second group consists of those pictures which belong to Leonardo's art for all that his hand did not touch them, and here we are on safe ground as concerns those cases in which we have not only the paintings by the students but also the drawing of the master. Evidently there is a much larger number of paintings based on Da Vinci's ideas in regard to which direct proofs is missing, and only an indirect proof can be given, by means of our knowledge of the personalities of the students and their limitations.

Gian Antonio Boltraffio – *Youth Crowned with Vine Leaves* – Milan, collection of Prince Borromeo

Both the works carried out in collaboration and those based on the master's ideas give us essential factors toward knowing the artist. That great star fills vast spheres and affects the orbits of numberless satellites of varying size and power; in part he directs absolutely, and in part he enters into the cosmic complex, participating in the complicated play of forces while remaining a determinant factor. What other image could be found for the relationships between the supreme master and the circle of his students, some of whom were geniuses?

It is even more necessary to know Leonardo's principal pupils than to know those of other artists, for Leonardo was more prodigal than any other, and sowed the fruits of his inspiration broadcast about him. Unable to give concrete form with his hands to all the conceptions that flowed from his mind, he sometimes allowed inferior talents to translate his ideas into reality, at times insufficiently and at times excessively. This unthinking approach to their source, Leonardo's imagination, gave his Milanese scholars that homogeneity which has often been held against them, whereas we should rather be grateful to them, for to one who knows how to interpret them they tell much about their master.

Leonardo's notes often contain incidental observations regarding his pupils and aids. In 1490 he speaks of Giacomo, ten years old, and Marco, in 1491 Gian Antonio, in 1493 Giulio Tedesco and Master Tomaso, both mechanics, whom we find still in his laboratory in 1494. In 1494 Giulio finished a frame for the laboratory. In the same year mention is also made of Galeazzo, and little Giacomo appears for the first time with his additional name of Salai. Dates are lacking for the references to Joditti and Benedetto, but it is likely that they relate to the period from 1497 to 1500; both seem to have stayed with Leonardo for some years, perhaps the first years of the sixteenth century. The Maestro Benedetto named on January 5, 1511, was in all probability the sculptor Benedetto Briosco; a note of April 1, 1499, registers payments for the daily work of Bartolomeo and Arrigo; on April 14, 1505, Leonardo accepted as a student a certain Lorenzo, seventeen years old, who accompanied him to Rome in 1513. In the summer of 1505 two painters who helped Leonardo in the drawing and painting of the *Battle of Anghiari* were paid separately by the *Signoria* of Florence; they are Raffaello d'Antonio di Biagio and Fernando Spagnolo. In this period he took on Tommaso di Giovanni Masini as color grinder. This was the magic artist and eccentric Zoroastro

Boltraffio – *Madonna and Child* – New York, Howard Collection

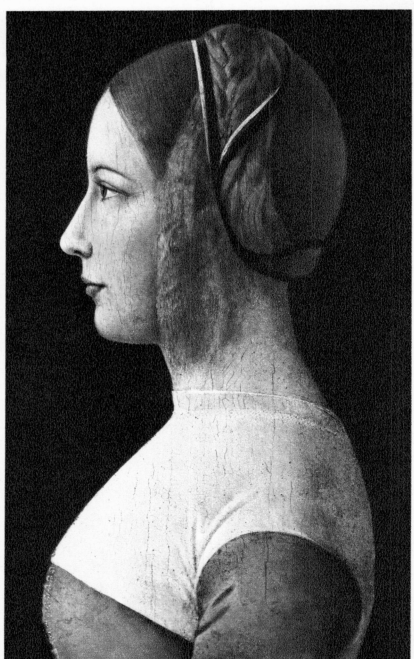

da Peretola, who was later to go to Milan with Leonardo and who appeared at Rome as well, and the Anonimo Magliabechiano names him as a disciple of Leonardo along with Salaino, Fernando Spagnolo, and Riccio Fiorentino dalla Porta della Croce. Later we find the names of Gian Maria and Gian Pietro and Gherardo together with those of Benedetto, Salai, and Bartolomeo. In 1504 Jacopo comes to Leonardo, and on October 24, 1513, Giovanni Francesco de' Melzi, Salai, Lorenzo, and Fanfoia set out for Rome with the master; the last-named must have been a servant. In Rome Leonardo had a German mechanic as an aid, Maestro Giorgio, who does not enter into the artistic picture.

Only a few of the names listed above represent concrete artistic personalities for us—Marco (d'Oggiono), Gian Antonio (Boltraffio), Fernando Spagnolo (Fernando de Llanos), Francesco Melzi, Gian Pietro (certainly this is Giampietrino): the rest is uncertain. However, in many instances a group of works of the school can be connected with the name of some artist that has come down to us.

Among his fellow workers in Verrocchio's studio during the first Florentine period, Lorenzo di Credi was the one who came closest to his slightly older fellow students; and although he was incapable of capturing Leonardo's spirit and grace, Lorenzo very often took him as a model, as for example in a fine portrait of a youth, in the former Gualino Collection at Turin. He often took over single motifs, as for example that of the Madonna kneeling, derived from Leonardo's studies for the *Nativity*. When Filippino Lippi, in 1496, painted the altarpiece of the *Adoration of the Magi* for the monks of San Donato di Scopeto, in order to finish the commission given to Leonardo sixteen years before, it was natural that he should derive the basic lines of the composition from the master's unfinished work.

The first document that attests Leonardo's presence in Milan, the contract with the Confraternita della Concezione for painting the altarpiece of the confraternity's chapel in San Francesco Grande in Milan, dated April 25, 1483, shows Leonardo collaborating with the brothers Evangelista and Giovanni Ambrogio de Predis, with whom he is also boarding. We do not know any work by

Boltraffio – Portrait of young girl – Paris, Duveen Brothers Collection

Boltraffio – *Madonna and Child* – Milan, Poldi-Pezzoli Museum

Boltraffio – *Portrait, presumably of Melzi* – Heller Foundation, Berne Museum

Evangelista, who died about 1490. Giovanni Ambrogio was an able and versatile artist, who appears in various documents from 1472 to 1506 as a miniaturist, designer of coins at the mint, portraitist, designer of cartoons for tapestries, and author of sketches for ceremonial costumes at the imperial court. The only thing that remains of all this is the portrait of the Emperor Maximilian at Vienna, dating from 1502, which has the complete signature. Something like a dozen profiles, quite homogeneous in style, although they must be distributed over several decades, have a convincing relationship to the portrait of the Emperor, and to these should be added the feminine portrait in the Ambrosiana in Milan which formely bore the name of Leonardo. The resemblance of the composition to that in the portrait of Maximilian, on the one hand, and the great difference in quality on the other, can be explained only by Leonardo's having had a hand in it. Ambrogio de Predis may well have executed the greater part of the work, but the grace of the pose and certain touches of pictorial perfection, especially in the pearls and ribbons of the headdress and in the eye, are evidently Leonardo's work.

Of the three panels of the altarpiece from San Francesco, today in the National Gallery in London, only one, the *Angel in Profile Playing the Lute*, shows the stylistic properties of Ambrogio de Predis, while the opposite panel, the *Angel Playing the Viol*, served as his model, only the pose of the head, the arm with the instrument, and the nature of the color being changed; but the viol player is much more significant, richer, and more skillful in the plastic treatment and much more interesting with respect to the colors. Local tradition, reported by C. Torre in 1674, according to which the painting passed for a work of Leonardo's, seems justified if we consider the spirit of invention and the masterly execution. The assistant in this work is the same one who executed considerable portions of the central panel, the *Virgin of the Rocks*, which is certainly from the master's hand in its essential parts. The collaborator is really skillful and comes closer to Leonardo's *sfumato* than do the other pupils. An independent work of this anonymous painter is the picture of the Madonna formerly in the Crespi Collection in Milan and later in the Gualino Collection. Many factors lead us to think that an early phase of this artist is represented by two excellent works, the *Young Man of Twenty*, dating from 1494, in London (erroneously associated with Francesco Archinto and formerly attributed to Leonardo; the monogram contains the name of the subject, not that of the artist), and the portrait with the motto, *Vita si scias uti longa est*, in the Brera. The latter was certainly sketched by Da Vinci and painted by the anonymous pupil. There is nothing to justify identification of this unknown with Ambrogio de Predis, for there is no trace of mastery of *sfumato* either in the portrait of the Emperor Maximilian or in the *Angel in Profile*.

Leonardo also influenced the creation of the "Sforza altarpiece" to some extent. The anonymous painter who takes his name from this panel began with very modest works. At the express wish of the Duke, Leonardo collaborated on the altarpiece for Sant'Ambrogio ad Nemus. The basic arrangement is in complete correspondence with the old Lombard scheme, but the head and the hands of the Madonna and of the Church Fathers, especially Ambrose, the body of the Child, and the costume of the Duke are details whose energetic modelling and pictorial delicacy are not found in previous or later works of the anonymous artist: the first look shows us that at least two artists worked on it. There is small doubt left after comparison with the little *Madonna with Donors* of the National Gallery. Some silverpoint drawings of heads seem to bear witness to attempts by the unknown painter to master Leonardo's types, and it is not possible to determine precisely how far the guidance and instruction of the great Florentine went and to what extent he actually lent his hand. It is important to observe that in the following period the anonymous painter tries variations of many compositions of the master, without ever regaining the clarity and delicacy of the Sforza altarpiece.

The genesis of the *Madonna of the Castle* is fairly mysterious, as is the case with many works of Leonardo. The technique in itself is amazing—thin tempera with glazes in oil on silk. Not only the composition, which was so often copied and varied by his pupils, but the execution of the essen-

tial portions as well belongs to Leonardo. The work of assistants is also evident in some other Madonnas executed with the same technique.

Documents and works that have come down to us tell us that Boltraffio (1467-1516) was Da Vinci's favorite collaborator: he went his own way, near the master, with the tread of a man perfectly sure of himself. His closest collaboration was in the period up to 1499, but later too he is often close to Leonardo personally. "The only pupil of Vinci Leonardo, Boltraffio," his friend from Bologna, the poet Girolamo Casio, calls him in an epigraph; this would indicate that Boltraffio had a position of exceptional distinction among the many students of Leonardo.

Two Madonnas are the joint work of the two artists; the composition and some portions of them are by Leonardo himself. In the Madonna of the Museo Poldi-Pezzoli the heads of Mary and the Child, and the coloring, have the characteristics of Boltraffio's art, while the arms of the Madonna and the clothing appear to have been executed by Leonardo. The Esterhazy Madonna of Budapest (unfinished; the flower that the Child is about to grasp is wanting) seems to be the work of Leonardo for the most part. The light-blue silk, the golden-yellow lining, and the finely painted Deruta cup determine the silvery tonality of the entire picture; nevertheless, the types retain the characteristic Boltraffio features.

Very close to these paintings in pictorial vision is the large picture, *Christ Risen between St. Lucia and St. Leonard*, in the Berlin Museum. The composition of this painting too is certainly Leonardo's, while the execution does not reveal his hand, and I believe that this was a drawing of the master's, later executed chiefly by Boltraffio.

The *Portrait of a Youth* at Chatsworth shows much more distinguished pictorial qualities; not only is Leonardo responsible for the skull on the back—the symbol of mortality—and the legend *Insigne sum Ieronimi Casii* ["I am the badge of Girolamo Casio"]; but additions due to Leonardo can be easily recognized in the boy's bust as well, which by and large keeps to Boltraffio's type. It is probable that this picture was made in the same way as the *Profile of a Woman* in the Ambrosiana. Finally, there are also two fanciful heads that seem to me to be delicate works by Boltraffio, with par-

Left: Boltraffio – Portrait of boy – Chatsworth, collection of Duke of Devonshire

Right: Boltraffio – Male portrait – Florence, Contini-Bonacossi Collection

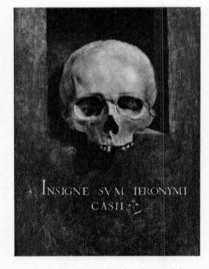

G. A. Boltraffio – Back of panel bearing portrait of boy – Chatsworth, from the collection of Duke of Devonshire

319

Andrea Solari – *Descent from the cross* – Florence, Contini-Bonacossi Collection

Solari – *Pietà* – Milan, formerly in Crespi Collection

Solari – *Virgin and Child* – Milan, Poldi-Pezzoli Museum

Solari – *Rest in Egypt* – Milan, Poldi-Pezzoli Museum

Solari – *Head of the Baptist* – Paris, Louvre

tial retouching by Leonardo—the portrait of a young girl with flowers in her hair and a richly embroidered dress, formerly in the Dreyfus Collection at Paris, and the St. Sebastian with an aureole and garments embroidered with lilies, and an arrow in his hand, which was in the Stroganoff Collection of Leningrad. I know the latter only from photographs, and Frizzoni praises it as one of Leonardo's most enchanting creations.

If Leonardo had a part in the execution of the *Belle Ferronnière*, as some believe, his finishing ouches must have been much more decisive than in other works of his student. To bring out the great qualitative differences, we may recall the *Portrait of Charles d'Amboise* in the Louvre, in which the uneven and in parts even inadequate execution does not match the splendid spirit of the invention. The picture is not by Boltraffio nor by Solario, who is usually named in this connection, but is very probably the result of the co-operation of several hands on a design that may even be by Leonardo. The works jointly painted by Leonardo and Boltraffio belong to the years around 1490 and immediately thereafter, and thus represent the very first phase of the pupil's art. In the two decades that followed, his typical characters, his coloring, and his calm and monumental composition took form, as seen in the altarpieces in London and Bergamo and the wonderful series of portraits.

The assistance that Marco d'Oggiono was able to give the master was of quite a different kind; any genuine collaboration seems to have been extremely rare. I know of only two works in which it seems possible or likely, and even there it is not as evident as in the works Leonardo executed jointly with Boltraffio—the painting of the child Jesus with the globe, giving his blessing, in the Borghese Gallery, and the Madonna Litta of the Hermitage. The two paintings were admired for centuries as works of Leonardo; both are certainly due to his inspiration and also contain pictorial touches and accents of such lofty perfection that Marco, although skillful and able, could not have achieved them. We must therefore assume that the master not only furnished the design but also partially retouched the work of his student. In other cases it would seem that Leonardo was so sat-

320

Solari – Formerly attributed to Leonardo – Portrait of Domenico Moroni – Milan, collection of Duke Gallarati-Scotti

Solari – Male portrait – Milan, Brera Gallery

Solari – Portrait of Charles d'Amboise – Paris, Louvre

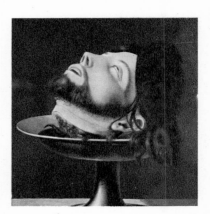

Solari – *Madonna and Child* – Paris, Gaston Duval Collection

Solari – *Head of the Baptist* – Milan, from the collection of Duke Gallarati-Scotti

isfied with the accurate interpretation Marco had given the cartoons entrusted to him that any retouching appeared unnecessary.

This seems to be the case with works like the *Madonna of the Lake* (Gentili di Giuseppe Collection, Paris), the *Virgin of the Spring* (Abbé Thuelin Collection, Paris), the *Madonna with the Two Children* (formerly in the Benson Collection, London), and the *Child Jesus and St. John Kissing* (at Hampton Court, formerly in the Mond Collection, London). This list contains only some of the most faithful work of this nature. Marco very frequently developed the ideas of the master in his own work, and made use of Leonardian elements for his own compositions.

His talent was very much different from that of Boltraffio. Born probably in 1477, he was in Leonardo's studios as early as 1490, and made such progress in the next ten years that in 1501 Cardinal Giuliano della Rovere, later Pope Julius II, commissioned him, in company with an older painter, Ambrogio de Zaffaronis, to execute a vast cycle of frescoes in the cathedral of Savona. We find him again at Milan toward 1530 as a respected artist living in modest comfort. The larger part of those works of his referred to above as based on the ideas or the collaboration of Leonardo may belong to his second sojourn in Milan (1506-1512). In the following years Marco, now an able, versatile artist,

D'Oggiono – *Madonna and Child* – Paris, R. Benson Collection

D'Oggiono – *St. Catherine* – San Remo, collection of Marquis Garbarino

D'Oggiono – *Madonna and Child* – Milan, St. Ambrose Basilica

with sensibility and temperament, strikes out a new way which meets that of Gaudenzio Ferrari. But even when he slips into baroque accents or effects, the basic elements of his artistic vision are always the Leonardian forms and motifs.

The *Madonna with the Crucifix*, once owned by Lord Battersea and now the property of Robert W. Reford of Montreal, is a very valuable documentation of the way in which Leonardo collaborated with a student. Technical research is a safe guide; Roentgen and ultraviolet rays have made it possible to establish the fact that a first sketch, with different details, was executed by two distinct hands in clearly discordant manners. Both the Child and some essential portions of the landscape are certainly by Leonardo, while the rather poverty-stricken execution of the Madonna and of the figures in the foreground is to be attributed to an anonymous transitory student who was evidently close to the master in the years at Florence from 1501 to 1506, and who developed the same compositional themes with a slightly different background in two other pictures, one of which is owned by the Duke of Buccleuch in London, while the other is in the Schlichting Collection; a copy is in the Louvre. The Battersea-Reford Madonna completes the list of what are called the "works in collaboration," so far as I know.

The number of pictures based on drawings or cartoons by Leonardo is considerable, and it is not altogether fair to consider them as copies, since the similar works by his hand never existed. Much more often the passing artist was permitted to convert an idea of the master's into a picture, the color, the details of the execution, the background, and other such matters being left to his invention. This procedure is especially evident in some Madonnas, and it is only in rare cases that we still have Leonardo's original drawing, such as the variants for the *Madonna of the Cat* in the British Museum, from which Sodoma got his inspiration for the *Madonna with the Lamb* in the Brera. In other instances we must try to extract the master's essential idea from works of various painters differing little from each other, as in the case of the *Madonna of the Lily* (replicas in the Villa Albani at Rome and at Highnam Court), the *Madonna with the Cherries* (replica by Giampietrino formerly owned by M. von Nemes; a theme often varied by the Flemish painters), the *Madonna with the Child at her Breast* (the date of this work is given by a Milanese woodcut of 1492, and there are known variants of it by Fernando de Llanos at Zurich, by Marco d'Oggiono in the Louvre and at the Ambrosiana—and others by Solario and Luini). A similar theme, particularly accenting the contrast in the movement of the Mother and the Child, is found in Giampietrino's picture in the Borghese Gallery, in Bernardino de' Conti's *Madonna in Profile with the Child at Her Breast near a Vase of Flowers*, dated 1501, at Bergamo, and, finally, in the *Madonna Hugging and Kissing the Child*; the drawing of a part of the body of this Child is at Windsor. Similar pictures are also at the Brera and at the Sforza castle in Milan, and there are variants by Quentin Matsys and Raphael.

A quick sketch by Leonardo and some paintings in the Uffizi and at Bergamo enable us to reconstruct a group of the Holy Family, while a marvelous drawing at the Metropolitan Museum of New York offers us the basis of many copies of the *Madonna Kneeling with the Two Children, Jesus and John* (Henry Harris Collection, London; Uffizi; Budapest; Melzi Collection, Milan). Further, the scheme for the composition of the *Adoration of the Shepherds* belongs with Leonardo's drawings at Bayonne and Venice, which served as the starting point for the Florentine painters Lorenzo di Credi and Piero di Cosimo, and the Milanese Marco d'Oggiono and Giampietrino. The exact description given by Pietro da Novellara in a letter enables us to establish the fact that two paintings by Andrea del Brescianino at Madrid and Berlin are copies of Leonardo's cartoon of 1501, now lost, represent-

Left: D'Oggiono – *Assumption of the Virgin* – Milan, Brera Gallery

Right: D'Oggiono – *The Archangels Michael, Gabriel, and Raphael* – Milan, Brera Gallery

ing the *Saint Anne*. We have already spoken of the group of Jesus and the infant St. John. A drapery study at Windsor proves that the half figure of *Christ Giving His Blessing with a Globe in His Hand*, which is often found in Milanese works (Vittadini Collection, Cook Gallery, etc.), also goes back to Leonardo, as is true likewise for the *Christ Bearing the Cross*, which can be reconstructed only in part from drawings at Venice, together with variants by painters of the school.

Some paintings and sculptures form a special group that can be linked to Leonardo on the basis of literary references; but it remains uncertain to what extent the tradition modified the original ideas of Leonardo, and in each particular case the artistic character of the later version seems to confirm the existence of a Leonardian content.

When the 1589 inventory states that the large picture called *Perseus Liberating Andromeda*, by Piero di Cosimo, was painted after a drawing of Leonardo's, that would be of little importance were it not for the fact that this statement is supported by the difference between this and Piero's other works, as well as by the decided Leonardian character of some of the figures. It is quite probable that there was a previous drawing by Leonardo for the central portion (without the side groups). The principal figures, the monster, the water stylized in an original manner, the weeping women, the fantastic musicians, and the girl with the olive branch give a fairly faithful representation of Leonardo's design. It is the only mythological composition with several figures that we possess today.

Another member of this group is the bust of a girl enveloped in light veils, many copies of which exist; the best, to my knowledge, are the one in the Geneva Museum, with the title *Sabina Poppea*, and that in the Lazzaroni Collection at Rome. The well-informed Lomazzo relates that Leonardo painted for Francis I a Pomona with the body showing through a fourfold thin veil. The former picture has a definite Leonardian character, and the copies we know of come from the school of Fontainebleau, that is, from Leonardo's French successors. All these facts taken together justify the conclusion that this type of picture preserves one of Leonardo's creations.

Another very difficult field of research presents itself in the horses and riders. We know the splendid Windsor drawing and the extremely complicated history of the projected monuments to Francesco Sforza and Gian Giacomo Trivulzio, with which Leonardo was busy for whole decades. We must also assume that there existed a complete series of small bronzes made after models by Leonardo, although it seems that only a few have been preserved down to the present—one of a soldier on the ground protecting himself with his shield from a horse (formerly in the Trivulzio Collection) and two horses of a later type (Budapest and England). An engraving that reproduces four such

D'Oggiono – *Madonna and Child* – Rome, Borghese Gallery

323

Vincenzo Civerchio – *The Manger* – Milan, Brera Gallery

Civerchio – *St. Rocco* – Brescia, Brunelli Collection

D'Oggiono – *The Visitation* – Strasbourg Museum

D'Oggiono – *The Redeemer and a Donor* – Milan, Sacristy of Santa Maria delle Grazie

little bronzes, as well as many representations of the figures in backgrounds of paintings, especially of the sixteenth-century Venetian school, are a valuable complement to our knowledge of Da Vinci's inventive richness in this field as well.

It should be noted that it is very probable that the front portion of the gigantic Sforza horse was later (1503) painted by Solario in his *Crucifixion*, now in the Louvre. There are also some small bronzes of horses with hide removed shown in the act of walking, in the Luthy Collection at Basel and in a private American collection, which present a connection with Leonardo, in the light of the artist's intensive studies of the anatomy of the horse. Some drawings by the master, contemporary

Above, left: Gian Pietro Rizzi, called Giampietrino – *Madonna and Child* – Milan, formerly in Crespi Collection. — Above, right: Giampietrino – *Magdalene* – Florence, Contini-Bonacossi Collection. — Below, left: Giampietrino – *Madonna and Child* – London, National Gallery. — Below, right: Giampietrino – Formerly attributed to Leonardo – *Madonna and Child* – New York, Morgan Collection

Giampietrino – *The Holy Family* –
New York, Kleinberger Collection

Giampietrino – *Madonna and Child* –
Naples, collection of Princess di Villa
Anna Acton Caraccioli

Giampietrino – *Madonna and Child
with Infant St. John* – New York,
Hurd Collection

Giampietrino – *Allegory of Abundance*
– Milan, Prince Borromeo Collection

Giampietrino – *The Nymph Egeria* –
Milan, Marquis Brivio Collection

engravings, and the copy of the model in the treatise by Bruini, the Bolognese (end of the sixteenth century), show that Leonardo's knowledge had opened the way to wider possibilities.

Vasari reports an instance of Leonardo's influence on the plastic art of the time. When in 1506 Giovanni Francesco Rustici accepted the commission to make four figures in bronze for the niche over the western door of the Baptistery in Florence, Leonardo advised him, so that some critics believe that Leonardo collaborated in the actual work as well; the statues of St. John the Baptist and of the Levite (less so that of the Pharisee) have undeniable Leonardian elements.

Because of partisan favoritism and enmity, the *Flora* remained hidden for a long time; yet it must be admitted that the wax bust in the Berlin Museum, although partially reworked, is nonetheless a sixteenth-century original and shows the Leonardo imprint. This type of female half figure was decisive for the history of painting, especially in northern Italy (Sebastiano, Palma, Titian).

The artists through whom the ideas of Leonardo were transmitted fall into three groups. The first and smallest consists of the collaborators of whom we have spoken above; they are the men who contributed toward putting the master's artistic projects into effect, alongside him and sometimes with his personal participation. I should define the second group as consisting of "means of execution," to whose hands the master appears to have entrusted drawings or cartoons on the basis of which they finished a painting. The works in the first category have full right to be considered creations of Leonardo's, but there are doubts as to the second. The descriptions given in later prints may be echoes of an older tradition; they name Leonardo as the inventor of these pictures and a student, perhaps Marco d'Oggiono, as the painter. The third group consists of copyists who, under certain circumstances and with inadequate ability, still transmit to us a precious pictorial idea of Leonardo's. While these three groups interpret the artistic intentions of the master, in a decreasing order of merit, there is a vast zone around him filled with a band of direct and indirect pupils. This field of radiation of his artistic power and counsel also is a part of the potent sphere of Da Vinci's genius. We must know the pupils to get an adequate idea of the master's capacity and force.

It is naturally very difficult to assign the individual artists of Leonardo's circle unequivocally to one or another of the above categories; the only man whom we know definitely as his collaborator is Boltraffio, while Marco d'Oggiono was primarily a "means of execution." Bernardino dei Conti (with works dated from 1496 to 1523) has transmitted some compositions of Madonnas to us through copies, the first of which, dated 1501, is at Bergamo. His figures are of archaic severity and his frank copies are interesting.

326

Francesco Melzi – Signed and dated 1525 – *Girl with Parrot* – Milan, collection of Duke Gallarati-Scotti

Of the younger generation, Giampietrino is the one who seems most frequently to take advantage of Leonardo's pictorial ideas. His name should be attached to the many paintings that, despite their range of variation from the most refined delicacy to the quality of crude studio studies, still belong to a single artist, not on the basis of documents but in accordance with a tradition that goes back to the seventeenth century. The only definite date is 1521, for an altarpiece of the cathedral of Pavia. Giampietrino—to name him pending proof to the contrary—was imbued with the types, compositional ideas, pictorial effects, and refinement of Leonardo's art, this being unfortunately joined with an undeniable but flat ability to fuse the material of others with his own. Despite the assurance with which he absorbs many of Da Vinci's inspirations in his works, it is not always possible clearly to make out the original idea of the master. This is true especially in regard to the *Madonna with the Lily*, the Borghese Madonna, and the Madonna of the Museo Poldi-Pezzoli.

In the variants of the *Nativity* made by Giampietrino we can see the way in which the theme of the kneeling Madonna is linked with freely and arbitrarily side figures. A little drawing of Leonardo's for a half figure of Mary Magdalene shows where Giampietrino got the type, but we have no outside proof that the figure of the nude holy penitent enveloped in her hair, which Titian later reproduced almost literally, is likewise one of Leonardo's ideas.

Salaino and Francesco Melzi certainly were among Da Vinci's close collaborators. We do not know with certainty any work of the first, whose actual name was Giacomo de' Caprotis (1482-1524). It is very unlikely that the copies of the *St. Anne* and the *Infant St. John* that traditionally bear his name are really his. The portrait of a girl with a parrot, in the Palazzo Melzi of Milan, seems surely, at least from the signature, to be by Francesco Melzi (1492-1570); but the arrangement of this picture is much more suggestive of the mature art of Raffaello than of that of Leonardo. Tradition assigns to Melzi a group of completely Leonardian paintings, earlier in time (the *Vertumnus and Pomona* at Berlin, the *Holy Family* formerly belonging to Sedelmayer and later to Nemes, the *Colombina* of the Hermitage, the *Pluto and Proserpina* in a private collection at Stockholm); even if the tradition is accurate, they are not very splendid testimony to his creative talent. We have no reliable documents relating to the collaboration of either of these two artists with the master.

Bernardino Luini came into close contact with Leonardo's art only toward 1512, and took over his types particularly. He copied, in passing, the *Virgin of the Rocks* (Affori church) and the London cartoon for the *St. Anne* (Ambrosiana), and left us a single inspiration of the master in the *Magdalene and Martha* (Paris, Rothschild Collection); much more frequently he varied and paraphrased in a free and personal way the motifs derived originally from Leonardo. We should not forget that the fine profile heads of young men that we know so well from Leonardo's drawings were used in many pictures formerly attributed to Boltraffio. Whether it is a St. Sebastian, an angel, or a Narcissus this pseudo-Boltraffio always succeeds in achieving a certain charm. It cannot be denied that both

Bernardino Luini – *Madonna of the Rose Garden* – Milan, Brera Gallery

Napoletano – *Madonna and Child between St. Sebastian and St. John the Baptist* – Zurich, Keller Foundation

Napoletano – *Madonna and Child* – New York, Hurd Collection

Magni – *The Holy Family* – Milan, Brera Gallery

Bernardino de' Conti – Male portrait – Genoa, Rubinacci Collection

here and in some Madonnas he achieves fine views of landscapes and a beauty of color that put him in the first rank of the Milanese painters of that epoch.

Andrea Solario (works dated from 1495 to 1524) developed his personal style on the basis of a number of sources: he knew Foppa, Antonello, the Flemish, and the Venetians, but the clarity and logic of Leonardo's composition furnished him with a sure foundation. In Cesare da Sesto (1477-1523) admiration for Da Vinci was early combined with the impressions received at Rome, first from Baldassare Peruzzi and then from Raphael. But Leonardo's *sfumato*, the infinitely accurate gradation of values in passing from darkness to full light, remains the decisive factor in his art. Our knowledge of Francesco Napoletano is limited to three very interesting pictures (at Zurich, in the Brera, at Stockholm), in which the lighting is especially notable.

Left: De' Conti – Portrait of woman
– Pavia, Municipal Museum

Right: Bartolomeo Veneto – *Woman with Lute* – Milan, Frisiani Collection

We find that the pseudo-Boccaccino of the *Washing of the Feet* of 1500, in the Academy at Venice, was as early as that date among the imitators of Leonardo; later, collaboration with Marco d'Oggiono appears to have attracted him again into this orbit.

After 1501, and the end of the Milanese period, Leonardo belonged primarily to the milieu of Florence, the renewal of which was strictly his work. Among the older men, Piero di Cosimo came especially close to him; Fra Bartolomeo received his teaching with an open mind and made it the foundation of his work, while the relations between Leonardo, Franciabigio, Bugiardini, and Granacci were more superficial; Bacchiacca made more use of Leonardian motifs in his paintings of small figures. Da Vinci's art left its mark even on Michelangelo, despite the difference in their talents and their personal antagonism; and Raphael's intelligence opened like a flower before the artistic revelations in Leonardo's teaching and works, and we find to our astonishment that almost all of his Madonnas of the years between 1505 and 1512 have their origins in types from Leonardo's compositions, as well as the figures of horsemen and the mythological representations.

This is easy to prove in the case of Raphael, and equally hard to prove in that of Correggio, who, even where he made use of Leonardian ideas, as in the Madonnas of Modena and Budapest and in the two versions of the *Betrothal of St. Catherine* at Naples and in the Louvre, or in the London *Venus*, transformed them so completely that they do not seem to be borrowings, but things inherited from previous generations.

We learn from Vasari that Giorgione, in his renewing of Venetian art, took Leonardo as his starting point, although it is not easy to demonstrate this from the types and the composition. But we can accept the assertion that in the principles of pictorial art and as regards the delicate gradation of values, the master of Castelfranco received decisive stimuli from Leonardo.

We have already spoken of the female half figures of Sebastiano and Palma, and for Titian too Leonardo was of great importance; his admiration for the great Florentine was due to a strong spiritual kinship between the two Olympian minds. Perhaps in the *Christ and the Pharisee* and the *Supper at Emmaus* Titian expressed what Leonardo left unfinished in the *Last Supper*. And it is not hard to find the trace of Da Vinci in an entire group of Madonnas by Vecelli, as in the *Repentant Magdalene* of the Pitti Palace, the *Infant Jesus and John Embracing* of the Harrach Gallery in Vienna, and, finally, in his conception of portraiture.

The influence of Leonardo extends far beyond Italy. Even taking into account only confirmed reports, his personal relationships lead to two other countries, France and Spain. When Leonardo was working on the cartoon for the *Battle of Anghiari*, a certain Fernando Spagnolo was his assistant, the same man who is named twice in the payment lists of the Florentine state for the summer of 1505. In 1506 and then in the years thereafter two painters of this name appear at Valencia—Fernando de Llanos and Fernando Yanez de la Almedina, who together created the twelve paintings of the *Life of Mary* at the sides of the silver altar of the cathedral. Both these and their other works,

De' Conti – Male portrait – Varallo Sesia, Society for the Preservation of the Fine Arts

Bernardino Luini – *Susanna* – Milan, collection of Prince Borromeo

Luini – *Madonna and Child with Infant St. John* – London, Langton Douglas Collection

Luini – *St. Catherine* – Windsor, Royal Collection

Luini – *Madonna and Child* – Milan, collection of Duke Gallarati-Scotti

Bernardino Luini – *St. Sebastian* – Florence, collection of Count Contini-Bonacossi

which are not very numerous, are full of reminiscences of Leonardo. Fernando de Llanos—there is a signed Madonna of his in the museum at Zurich—is close to his model in external forms; Fernando Yanez de la Almedina, the greatest Spanish painter of the Renaissance, soon flew toward higher goals.

There are various reports of personal relationships of French artists with Leonardo in his last years, when he was living in France. Many paintings of what is called the school of Fontainebleau show Leonardian motifs as interpreted by the French painters, especially in the female half figure.

Albrecht Dürer is the German artist who had the deepest and most manifold relationships with the art of Leonardo, whose artistic theory must have occupied him intensively; it also seems that he knew the treatises on perspective of the old Milanese. Dürer took from Leonardo, varying them, a series of compositions of Madonnas, the caricatures, the representations of horses, and the ornamental knots. By the extraordinary diffusion of his copper and wood engravings he contributed greatly to transferring the formal solutions invented by Leonardo into the public domain of European art. Lucas Cranach certainly knew something of the school of Leonardo and Lombard painting, as is seen especially in some pictures of the year 1508 to 1509; and his favorite satirical depiction of

Sodoma – *The Archangel Michael* – Milan, Sforza Castle Gallery

Luini – *St. Rocco* – Lugano, church of Santa Maria degli Angeli

an ill-matched union in the *Loving Couple* goes back to Leonardo. Hans Holbein the Younger must have been in Lombardy too between 1518 and 1519. Many elements in the composition of Leonardo's Madonnas, in representations of horsemen and single figures, and even in Lombard decorative art and rich architecture, and, finally, the surprising resemblance of the coloring in a group of Holbein's works to definite works of the Milanese school, especially of Andrea Solario, lead us irrefutably to the assumption that there were direct relations.

On the other hand, Leonardo was indebted to the Flemish for the basic elements of the art and technique of painting, as they had been developed since the times of the Van Eycks. He tried to give fresco the depth and luminous power of northern painting, an effort that failed in the *Last Supper*, the Sforza portraits, and the *Battle of Anghiari*. A Flemish landscape painter who must

Master of the Sforza altarpiece – *Madonna and Child with Saints* – Kneeling, Ludovico il Moro, Beatrice d'Este, and their children – Milan, Brera Gallery

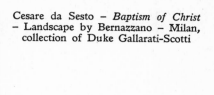

have lived in Milan for some time, where he was called Bernazzano, must even have known Leonardo personally. In the vast landscape of the *Baptism of Christ* by Cesare da Sesto, in the collection of Duke Gallarati-Scotti, Milan, the Fleming leads the spectator from the foreground, painted like a miniature, with innumerable botanically precise plants and flowers, and peopled with many animals, into fantastic, impossible rock and mountain formations outlined against the brilliant blue of the background. Did Bernazzano know Leonardo's representations of plants and animals, or did he bring these elements with him from his homeland? The first specialist in landscape painting in European art, Giachino Patenier, excited great interest in Italy in Leonardo's time; he leads the eye to the remotest distances, across land and sea, and constructs scenes of universal landscape. Albrecht Altdorfer, in his fascinating *Battle of Alexandria*, joins representation of the surface of the earth, symbolizing the infinite, with visions of light and of the colors of the firmament.

It should also be pointed out that Leonardo's landscapes in the *Mona Lisa* and the *St. Anne* opened up broad new panoramas. Echoes of Leonardo and the Milanese painters of his circle are often found in the compositions of Quentin Matsys, Joos van Cleve, and some less important painters after them, more rarely in Mabuse and Orley. The compositions of Madonnas have a preponderant part, but the *Infant Jesus and John Embracing* represents a favorite subject, and the studies of physiognomy, the so-called caricatures, raise the question once more of what Leonardo owed to the Flemish and what they owed him. Here too there is obviously a reciprocal influence that links Hieronymus Bosch with Leonardo, Quentin Matsys, Hemessen, and the Breughel of the *Peasants*.

In the sixteenth century, Peter Paul Rubens too took firm hold of the great heritage of Leonardian elements. Leonardo's bold composition in the *Battle of the Horsemen for the Standard* remained alive and known to the world through Edelinck's engraving of his design. Rubens' representations of hunting scenes and battles link up without transition to this sublime model. It is also likely that the principal themes of the lost cartoon for a painting of Adam and Eve and of another for the head of the Medusa survive thanks to Rubens; and in the Flemish master's representations of the Madonna as well it is not a rare thing to come across echoes of Leonardian views on composition, reborn to a new life through marriage with a new pictorial freedom.

With all this we have mentioned only external factors. Every generation will feel again for itself what the work and the teachings of Leonardo, the most universal of men, mean for the collective development of European culture and art; and what we have set forth has the aim of making them visible to our own time. Men who combine in themselves the highest artistic sense and the deepest wisdom (this occurred in Goethe, in relation to altogether different fields) will always be guiding stars for mankind.

GUGLIELMO SUIDA

335

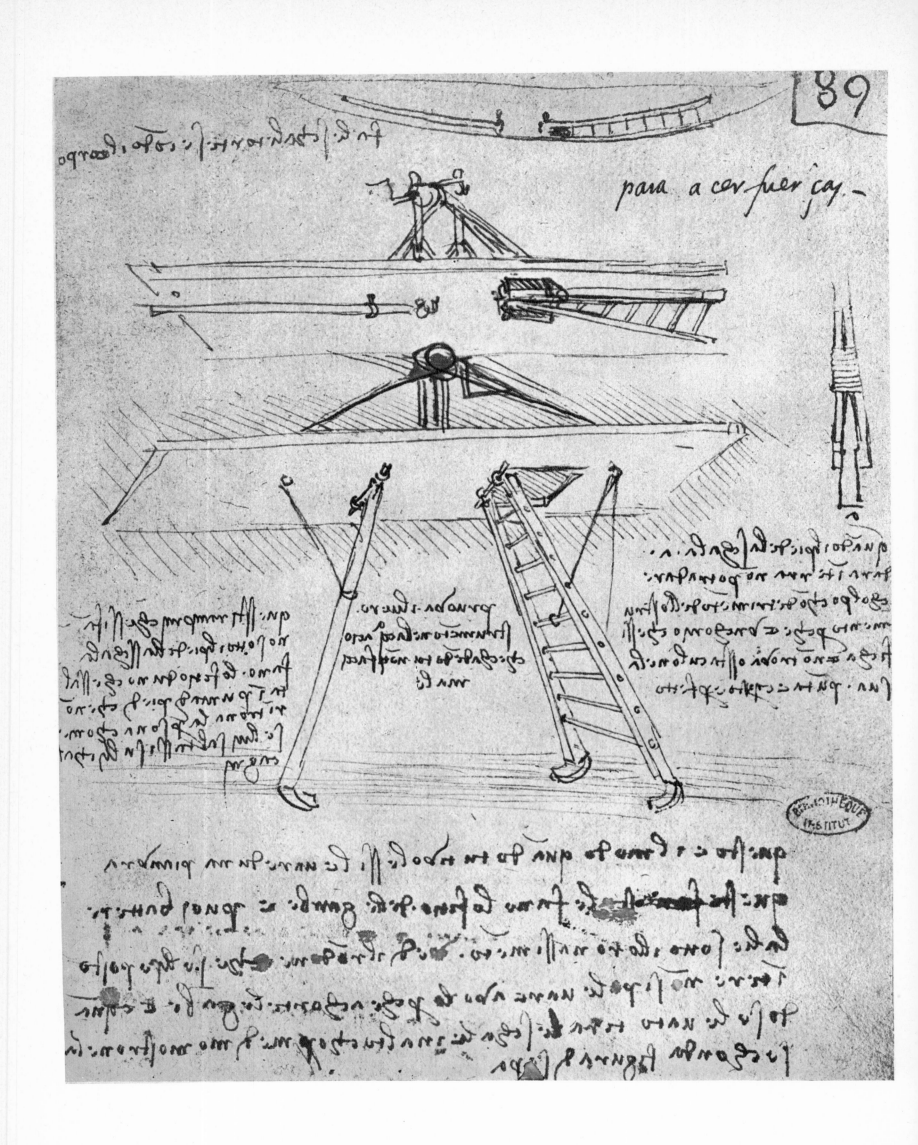

para a cer fuer cay. —

Type of apparatus to be operated by man standing, and equipped with landing steps – Ms. D, fol. 89 r

THE FLIGHT OF BIRDS

Leonardo appears to have begun his first studies of flight at Milan, where he had gone to enter the service of Ludovico il Moro in 1483.   He had recently passed his thirtieth birthday, and we can say that the problem of flight, which he studied and set down in the many drawings and notes that set the basis for the toilsome conquest of the third element, remained with him from that time down to the last years of his life, down through his voluntary exile in France.

Leonardo's work on flight, as it has reached us in various codices and manuscripts, comes to life again in the pages of the master with an amazing keenness of analysis.   The effects of the resistance of the air, the eddying motion of fluids, the physical effect of the man testing the carrying power of the wings on the scales, the sensational prowess of the birds that master and dominate the skies, and their acrobatic tricks, observations on the invisible movements of the air and the nimble movements of the wings, equilibrium, stability, steering: Leonardo has taken thought of all of these and set them down in his notes, which are very numerous and varied but sometimes have the drawback of being incomplete and occasionally fragmentary, and only the loving care of students desirous of revealing the mystery of these tightly written lefthanded characters, yellowed with time, has finally given life to the precious material, just at the time when the long and laborious development of science has reached the positions touched by the genius of Leonardo four centuries ago.

What shall we say of the problem of muscle-powered flight by human beings? Is it not today a current problem, studied assiduously by a small band of faithful men following in the footsteps of the master? What can scientists add to the knowledge of the problem over and above what Leonardo set down with such surprising acumen in developing the basic concepts of muscular flight?

The mechanical possibility of human flight is asserted by Leonardo for the first time around 1486.   On folio 381 of the Codex Atlanticus he sets down the concept of carrying power as follows: "As much pressure is exerted by the object against the air as by the air against the body.   See how the wings, striking against the air, bear up the heavy eagle in the thin air on high.   And see the air as it moves over the sea strike against the swelling sails to make the loaded heavy ship run;   so that for these demonstrative reasons that have been given you may know that man, with his great contrived wings, exerting effort against the resisting air, may conquer and subject it, and rise above it."

In any case, it seems to us that the studies on the flight of birds were to Leonardo a necessary prelude to the solution of human flight, as throughout the ages the great hope of being able to move freely through the sky, like the birds, has always haunted the human mind.

This is why, in this rapid bird's-eye view, aimed at getting a better understanding of the development of Leonardo's principles as to muscular and mechanical flight, it is necessary to refer first and foremost to his studies of the flight of birds.   It is not for mere novelty's sake that we do not follow the classification of the subject-matter hitherto adopted by the most devoted and competent students of the Leonardo manuscripts, which has been in principle a chronological criterion, however approximate;   the reason for our not doing so is that this obscures what we might call the guiding thread of Leonardo's vast body of work, his consistent desire for deductive arrangement.

"When two clouds meet, the larger envelops the smaller and they condense and turn into rain" – Ms. G, fol. 91 v

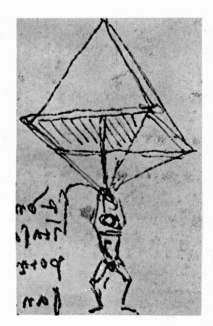

"If a man have a tent of linen without any apertures, twelve ells across and twelve in depth, he can throw himself down from any great height without injury" – Cod. Atl., fol. 381 v-a

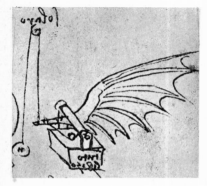

Experiment to determine human
muscle power – Ms. B, fol. 90 v

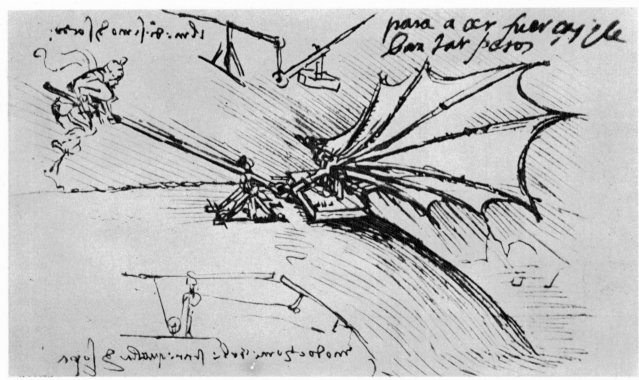

Experiments to determine the force
required to lift a man equipped with
two wings – Cod. Atl., fol. 307 r–b

"Man by his weight and body power,
with his back and his hands, will
be able to develop a force of four
hundred and twenty-five kilograms" –
Ms. B, fol. 83 r

Leonardo points out the way the researcher must follow to pose the problem of flight, and says: "First determine the motion of the wind and then describe how the birds stay poised in it, merely by the balancing of their wings and tails."

It is the physical problem of the birds maintaining themselves in flight, with all the attendant details, that attracts Leonardo's mind. Starting with consideration of the resistance of the air, by means of which a heavy body may stay up in it by reaction, he examines the various possibilities of the flight of birds, either in still air or when there is a wind.

After an anatomical study of the wing, with systematic researches, he succeeds in establishing the functions of the various parts. The wing has a double curvature, concave toward the body and convex outward; the aerodynamic function of the latter for purposes of support is that with this structure the air is compressed and exerts an equilibrating reaction (Ms. E, fol. 23 v).

Complementing the wing we find what is called the bastard wing, or alula, which has the function

338

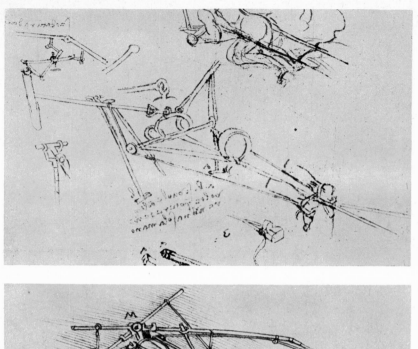

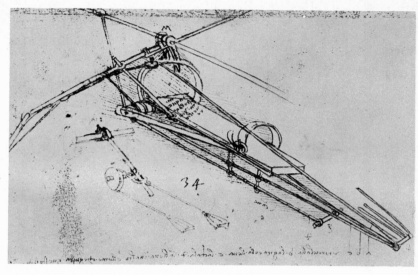

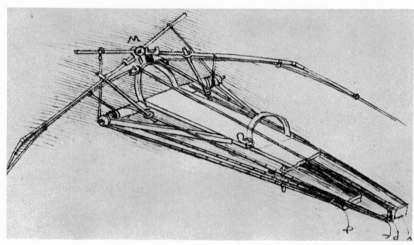

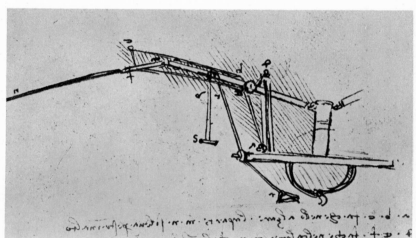

of equilibrium, according to Leonardo. We can say that it serves to increase the lifting surface, especially in the maneuver of wheeling, in which event opening one of the bastard wings has a braking effect.

Everyone will see the fundamental importance of these observations for applying and constructing the wings of modern airplanes, in which we find, for all the complex rigidity of the wing plane, all the special movable elements that are brought out by Leonardo in his detailed study of birds' wings.

After treating the functions and arrangement of wings in detail, as well as their strength and elasticity, Leonardo studies the effects of the beating of the wing—a lifting effect when the stroke is directed downward, and a propulsive effect when the stroke is directed backward; hence, when the stroke is vertical, the bird does not move forward. These requirements are satisfied separately by the two parts of the wing to which we have referred; the concave part, moving downward, gives lifting power while the convex part, moved backward, gives propulsion.

Going on to consider stability and equilibrium in flight with the wings motionless, Leonardo establishes the principle that the bird can maintain itself horizontal in the air only when its center of gravity is between equal lateral resistances. If the lever arm of one lateral resistance is reduced, that is, if one wing is drawn back, the bird slopes and descends on that side.

Finally, he lists the three principal positions of the wings in gliding (transverse axis) and the corresponding direction of the bird's movement (longitudinal axis), in order to examine the situations of disturbed equilibrium and the conditions favoring spontaneous restoration of equilibrium, namely, the lowering of the center of gravity with respect to the center of pressure on the wings and the bending of the wings upward. Here we have the concept of the transverse V position that was applied in the first designs for airplane construction as a factor greatly favoring stability.

Leonardo then observes that the bird while gliding is better assured of keeping its course and equilibrium with wings curved downward than with wings spread out wide; but this curving entails a decrease in lifting power, hence the descent is accentuated.

Leonardo makes an extremely interesting study of the positions dangerous to stability, or acrobatic positions, and arrives at the conclusion that a low position of the center of gravity of the bird (with body and legs hanging), with wings extended all the way, eliminates all danger of falling, because even if the bird should come into a position of instability, it would come out of it at once, for the following reasons, stated for the three possible situations:

1. The bird can never turn upside down by passing accidentally into a vertical position from the normal flight position, because this would be contrary to the principle of mechanics that the heavier part must precede the less heavy part;

Above, left: First flying machine designed by Leonardo – Cod. Atl., fol. 276 r-*b*

Above, right: On board on which operator is to lie full length is written: "The heart comes here" – Cod. Atl., fol. 302 v-*a*

Below, left: Fuselage of flying machine – Ms. B, fol. 74 v

Below, right: Movement of wing by means of hand and pedals – Ms. B, fol. 73 v

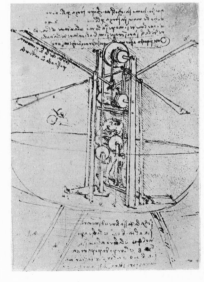

Model of four-winged flying machine with operator in lower part – Ms. B, fol. 80 r

339

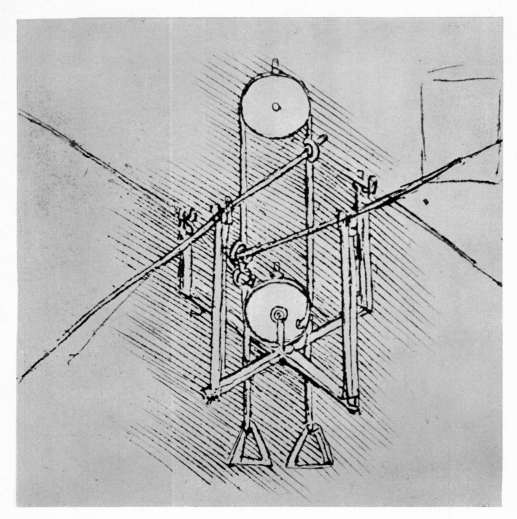

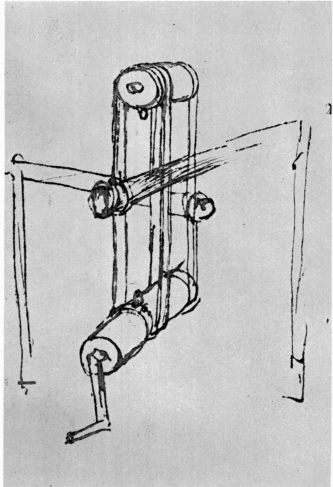

Left: Propulsive mechanism of pulleys actuated by ropes – Ms. B, fol. 76 r

Right: Propulsive mechanism of drums actuated by crank – Cod. Atl., fol. 377 r-b

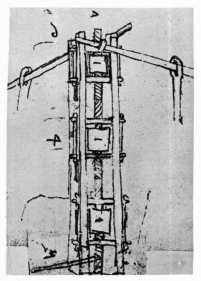

Leonardo da Vinci's study regarding propulsive mechanism based on three sections with opposite threading – Ms. B, fol. 78 r

2. The bird cannot fall backward from the normal flight position, since because of the forward position of the center of gravity, the bird can never go down backward;

3. It cannot fall sideward toward one wing from the normal flight positions with open wings, because of the principle of mechanics mentioned above.

After examining the phenomena of natural restoration of equilibrium, Leonardo goes on to study the wing and tail movements necessary to restore equilibrium mechanically, and here we come upon all the maneuvers that a plane pilot performs when he has to bring his machine out of a position of instability into which he has come either intentionally or because of an outside factor. The phenomena discussed are: recovery from lateral inclination and upside-down position; coming out of a side slip of the wings or of the tail; and, finally, recovering from a drop. The corresponding remedies are: extending the wing farther to the side toward which the inclination is occurring; lowering the wings and raising the tail; presenting the tail to the wind and moving it back; and, finally, bending the tail toward the spine.

Thus Leonardo studies the evolutions performed by birds in all their complexity, both in the vertical and the horizontal planes, examining in detail all the adaptations and corrections they may resort to in order to move in the third element under the best possible stability conditions.

Next there are very important studies of the flight of birds with the wind and against it, showing us the ways birds take advantage of the wind: either they allow themselves to be carried with motionless wings, in which case they travel at the velocity of the wind, or they make use of their own speed, which is always greater than that of the wind and enables them to go forward in every case.

Going on from horizontal flight to flight with an inclined trajectory, Leonardo establishes the fact that if the descent takes place in the same direction as that of the wind, it will be the longer, the stronger the wind; he concludes with an effort to determine the resultant of the two motions. In gliding into the wind, the slope of the trajectory determines the rapidity of the bird's descent, but, as Leonardo observes, it may happen that the action of the wind on the bird and the tendency of the bird to descend may be equal and contrary, and in that case the bird will remain stationary in the air. Here, however, Leonardo did not succeed in realizing the nature of the phenomenon, which can be explained only when we are in the presence of an ascending current. On the other hand, as Giacomelli says, "the idea that a bird can stay motionless with motionless wings merely by maintaining the inclination of the wings was long held by students of flight and has only recently been abandoned."

This rapid summary, which we have presented without going into details, brings out fundamental

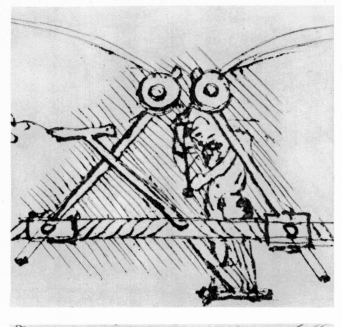

Left, above: Motive mechanism for wings – Cod. Atl., fol. 278 v-*a*

Left, below: Vertical screw effecting rise and fall of wings – Cod. Atl., fol. 278 v-*a*

Right, above: Device for propelling wings by means of wheel operated by two men – Cod. Atl., fol. 327 v-*a*

Right, below: Device for propelling wings by means of stirrups for foot action – Ms. B, fol. 77 r

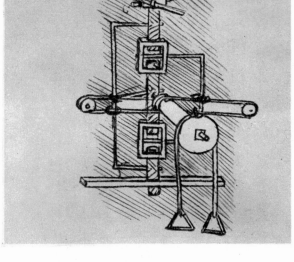

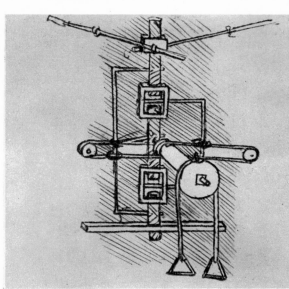

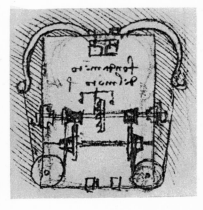

Device for flexing springs of arcs activating wings – Cod. Atl., fol. 314 r-*b*

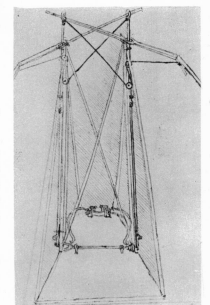

Diagram of apparatus with beating wings – Cod. Atl., fol. 314 r-*b*

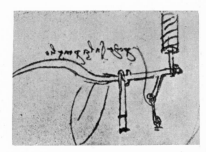

Device or rotation of wings – Cod. Atl., fol. 377 v-*b*

notions used by Leonardo for the solution of the problem of human flight on the basis of an attentive and determined examination of the mechanics of the flight of birds.

Leonardo studied birds and loved them. Vasari tells us that often, when he passed places where they were for sale, he would pay the price asked for them, take them from their cages and send them flying off into the air, giving them back their liberty. It would appear that in restoring the birds he had bought to liberty, he would send them off under the most varied conditions of weather and locality, so that he could study their flight attentively, setting down in his notebooks the conclusions and principles that he came to in each instance.

His special favorite among birds was the kite, especially because the kite may be taken to be the most perfect acrobat in flight without wing strokes and under the most difficult atmospheric conditions; he is so skillful that he can maintain himself aloft even when the wind is so gusty and irregular that it makes flight impossible for other birds.

The little codex on the flight of birds consists of eighteen tightly packed pages, whose drawings and commentary show a mastery of principle that makes us feel that they did not come solely from the short period during which they were set down on paper, but from a previous detailed mental elaboration of the observations his intellect derived from nature, and this has been our assumption.

The vicissitudes of the manuscript on the flight of birds directly after the death of Leonardo's pupil, Francesco Melzi, to whom, as we know, Da Vinci left all his manuscripts, are known in part; but with respect to the theft and recovery of some pages, facts of great interest are comprised in an unpublished article by Mario Cermenati, whom we should like to mention here in recognition of the loving care with which the eminent scholar has dealt with the question.

Cermenati proves that the thief was Guglielmo Libri, a distinguished mathematician and historian of science, a passionate collector of old books and manuscripts, who is excusable only because he was an insane bibliomaniac, eager for knowledge, and living at a time when the market of old books and holographs was overflowing with material derived from robberies of public and private libraries.

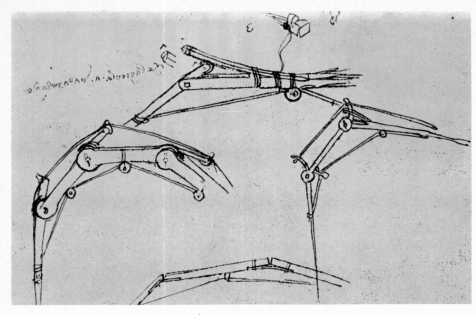

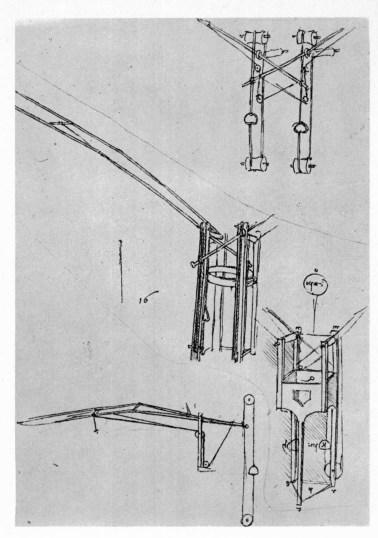

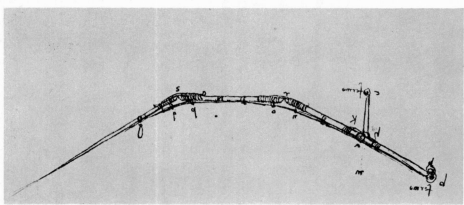

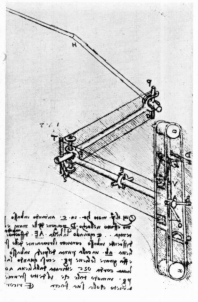

It is due to Cermenati's devoted initiative and activity that an Institute for Da Vinci Studies was formed in Rome and that a commission was set up for publishing all of Leonardo's manuscripts and drawings.

After thus rapidly setting down Leonardo's observations on the flight of birds, a necessary preliminary for achieving the technique of mechanical flight which he envisaged, we consider the rigorous theoretical preparation and patient practical solution of the least of the devices required for its realization.

It is true that at the outset he believed it would be sufficient to attach two wings to the shoulders and move them directly by muscle power, in the tradition of Icarus, but we shall see that later he studied, and tried to solve, the problem of the conquest of the third element so as triumphantly to rule over the air in the broadest sense. Leonardo's study of wings, based on the wings of birds, with the modifications made necessary because of the details of construction and the requirements of applying them to the machines he devised, is of a precision that is sometimes astonishing, especially with respect to their flexion and distension, and their rotation.

In Anatomical Ms. B (fol. 74 r) we find a complete drawing of a wing that is truly typical. The wing with its framework and covering consisted of a fir scantling forming the leading edge, from which the ribs of the wing's framework started. The coating was of fustian, with a layer of feathers glued to it to make it airtight. There were holes with flaps in the wings, which were opened in going up, to reduce the resistance, and closed in descent, to increase the lifting power.

Leonardo worked on mechanical flight during the sixteen years he was in Milan, and took up his aviation projects at Fiesole, where he had retreated to overcome the bitterness and disappointment caused by the scaling off of his fresco of the battle of Anghiari. It was during this period that he realized that man cannot achieve the speed and power of the birds in moving wings; we see the possibility of muscle-powered flight disappearing.

The projects of flying machines designed by Leonardo are many in number; we may refer here to those in which the operator lay at full length and those in which he stood erect.

In the first project the man was attached to the machine by two rings, one around the neck and one around the body, and the movement of the wings was performed by the hands in rising and by the feet in descending. In a later design the operator, instead of resting on the device, bore it on his shoulders and the wing was also capable of rotating about its own axis, thus changing its angle of incidence. A very important detail was a rudder attached to the man's neck and fixed on his head with a circlet in the shape of a wreath.

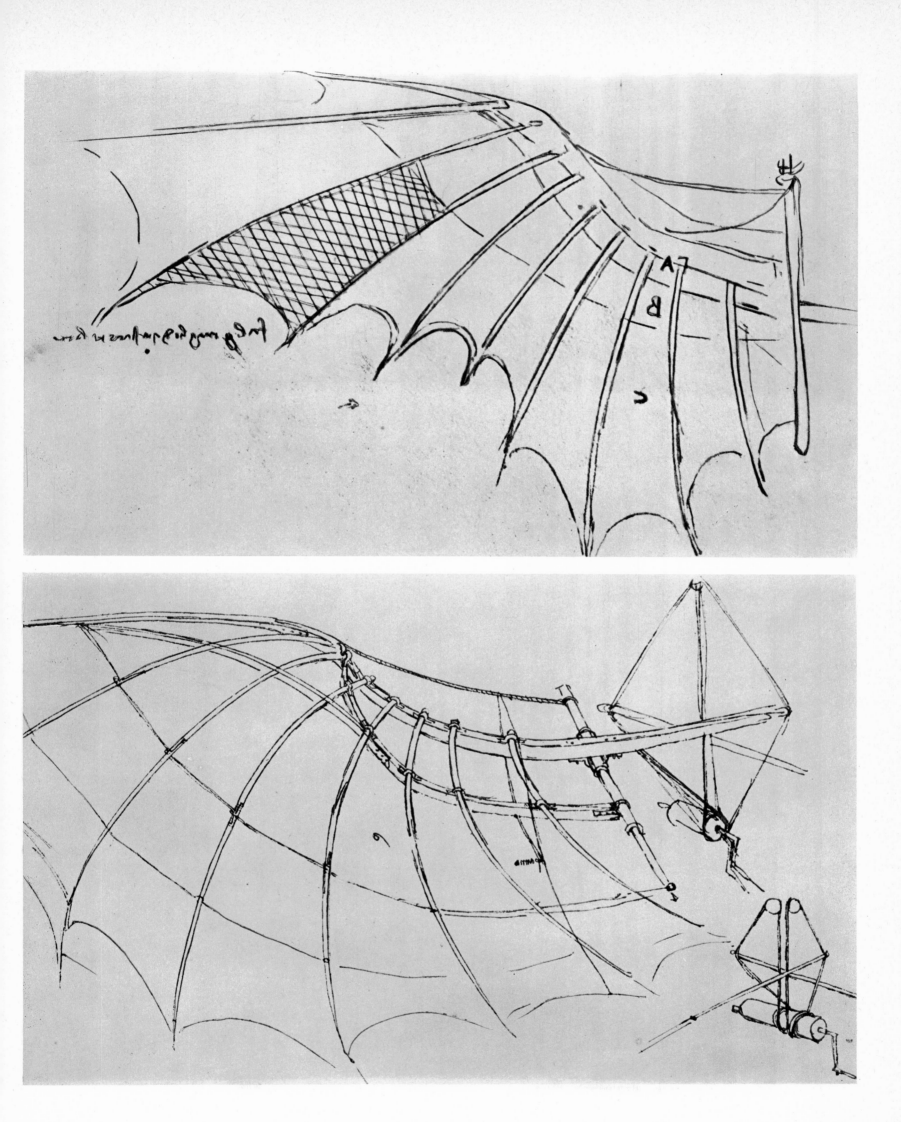

Above: Diagram of ribbed wing partly covered with silk – Ms. B, fol. 74 r. — Below: Crank device for manipulating wings – Cod. Atl., fol. 313 r-*a*

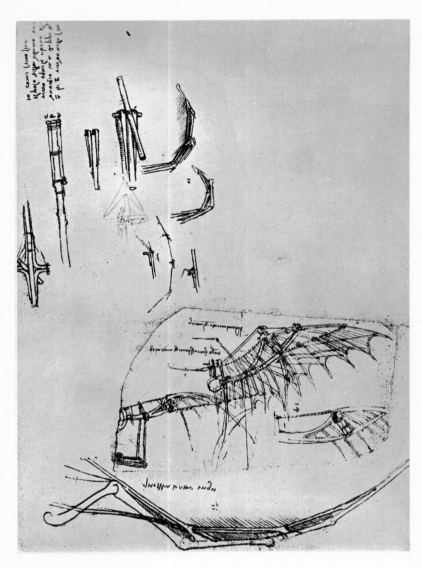

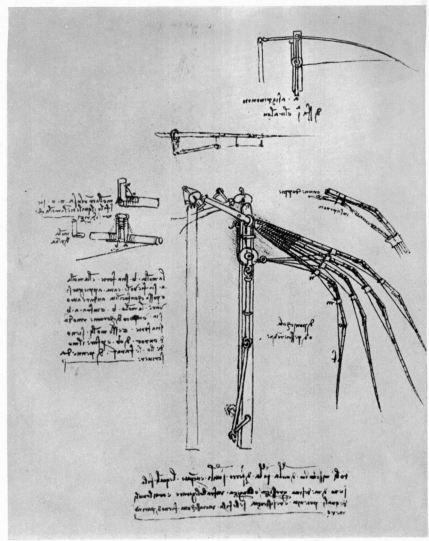

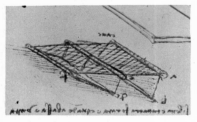

Advancing in the technique of construction, Leonardo eliminated all the joints between the pieces of wood and, where possible, substituted reeds for cords, making the ensemble more rigid and less fragile.

In the projected flying machine or ship of the air, with the operator erect, there were four wings because of the size of the apparatus. Leonardo gives us the dimensions of the various parts and the materials to be used in the construction (wood – reed – cloth). The aviator operated the wings by pushing against a pole with his head, turning two cranks with his hands and pressing down two pedals with his own weight, thus succeeding in obtaining a power of six hundred Florentine pounds, about 200 kilograms.

An interesting detail in the ship of the air were the steps to "mount and dismount." In a later machine the steps were provided with hooks and acted as a landing gear to break the shock at land-ing. The device was also to make it possible to keep a distance from the ground even on flat land, so as to give room for the downward stroke of the wings and so make the upward movement pos-sible, after which the device could be raised and arranged on the flat base of the machine, as is done today with the retractable undercarriage of modern airplanes.

Leonardo has many studies of propulsion mechanisms, all adequately embodying the beating of the wings in most brilliant ways; but illustrating them would require a treatment that would go beyond the limits of this brief survey, whose sole purpose is to give the reader a general view of the activity of Leonardo's genius with reference to the problem of flight.

Another type of machine, with the operator standing, consisted of a rectangular plane from whose longer sides there rose two uprights supporting two large wings. The wings were operated by a motor consisting of two semielliptical springs to be flexed by the man, which operated the wings through a transmission system as the tension relaxed.

The studies of lifting power made by Leonardo are of great interest. He sensed the principle of "aerodynamic reciprocity" that Newton was to enunciate two centuries later: "As much pressure is exerted by the object against the air as by the air against the body," he wrote, and in applying the principle of aerodynamic support he gives a drawing of the first parachute, in the form of a four-sided pyramid, whose dimensions and construction details he gives as follows: "If a man have a tent made of linen of which the apertures have all been stopped up, and it is twelve ells across and twelve in depth, he will be able to throw himself down from any great height without sustaining any injury."

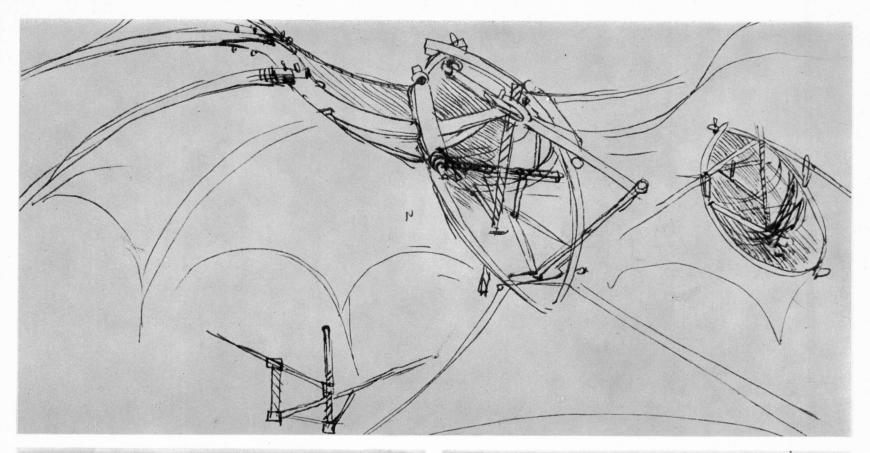

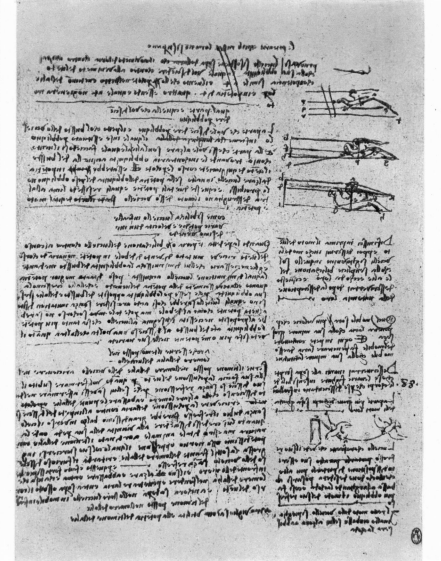

Above: Wings moved by hand by means of screws – Cod. Atl., fol. 313 v-a. — Left: Study of flight of birds in motionless air – Ms. E, fol. 23 v. — Right: Study of flight of birds with horizontal wind – Windsor, Royal Collection, no. 12657

Above: Study of flight of birds for take-off in absence of wind – Cod. Arund., fol. 166 v

Lower left: Short-tailed birds characterized by very broad wings – Ms. E, fol. 53 v

Center: Slow parachute descent – Ms. E, fol. 37 v

Right: Observations on arrangement, resistance, and elasticity of feathers – Ms. E, fol. 45 v

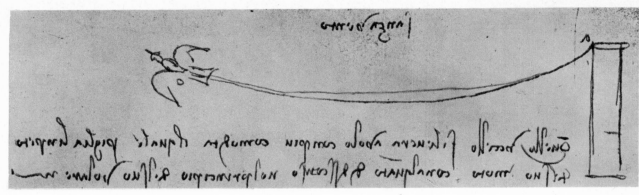

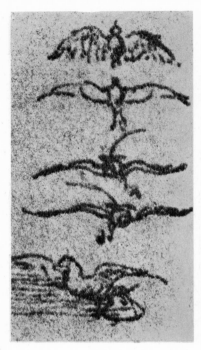

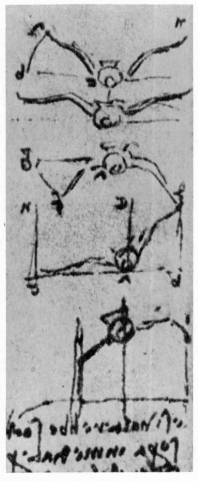

Study of equilibrium conditions of bird with outstretched wings – Ms. E, fol. 22 v

The project of the helicopter or aerial screw dates from about the same period; this asserts the aerodynamic possibilities of this machine which was to rise in the air when set in rapid rotation, and with it we have arrived at the principle on which the modern airplane propeller is based.

After 1499, the last year of his stay in Milan, Leonardo suspended his researches on flight during his wanderings to Florence and Rome, and took them up again from 1503 to 1506 at Fiesole, as we have indicated.

The attempts Leonardo is said to have made to fly would seem to date from this period, but this is all in the field of pure legend, and could not but be.

In the conclusion of the Da Vinci manuscript we read: "From Monte Ceceri [the name means "great bird"] the famous bird will take its flight, which will fill the world with its great renown." Is this prophecy, or the ardent desire of the genius to rise in the air as the reward and consummation of his studies, observations, and divinations? *Vincius tentavit* ["Da Vinci made the attempt"], says Jerome Cardan, but he failed. The old women in Fiesole still tell their grandchildren today the story of the great swan that was to rise from Monte Ceceri and disappeared, and no one saw it again.

But what is the point of inquiring further? It would seem a detail that we can ignore when we so eagerly examine the statement of the various problems of human flight traced and developed by Leonardo in his brilliant synthesis, with a keenness bordering on the marvelous and constituting the basis of the technical and scientific progress that is being made in our own time, after long years of obscurantism, as we see the wonder of the potent aerial machine victoriously ascending to the greatest heights, launched by man at a dizzying speed toward known and unknown horizons.

FRANCESCO CUTRY

346

THE CODEX ON THE FLIGHT OF BIRDS

The eventful history of the codex is well known. It was written by Leonardo at Florence, from March 14, 1505, to April 15, 1505. Seventeen years after the death of Francesco Melzi, Leonardo's heir, the manuscript was stolen from the villa of Vaprio d'Adda, together with others, by Lelio Gavardi, who gave it back to Father Giovanni Ambrogio Mazzenta to return it. The latter then received it as a gift from Orazio Melzi and left it to an heir who sold it to Pompeo Leoni. Cleodoro Calchi, heir of Leoni, sold the codex to Galeazzo Arconati, who donated it to the Ambrosiana on January 21, 1637. In 1796 Napoleon Bonaparte had all the Da Vinci manuscripts moved as war booty to the Bibliothèque Nationale of Paris, from which they later passed to the library of the Institut de France. The "Codex on the Flight of Birds" was bound together with Ms. B. The bibliomane Giacomo Libri separated it, to steal it, not long before the year 1848. It was found again by Count Giacomo Manzoni among Libri's manuscripts in 1867, and bought by him in December 1868. It already had five folios missing. In April, 1892, the learned Theodore Sabachnikoff bought it from Manzoni's heirs, and after publishing it made a gift of it to Queen Margherita. The five sheets scattered by Libri went through various vicissitudes and were finally bought in public sales, one by Sabachnikoff and four by the Genevan collector, Enrico Fatio, who presented it to the Queen. It is now in the former Royal Library in Turin.

The "Codex on the Flight of Birds" is thus designated because it deals chiefly with the flight of birds. It should be noted that Leonardo uses the words *uccello* and *volatile* to indicate both the animal and the flying machine, although the latter is sometimes designated as *strumento*. In fact, he calls human flight *volo strumentale* [mechanical flight]. Leonardo intended to write a "treatise on birds." In Ms. F, folio 41 verso, he contemplated treating the subject in four books: the first to define the nature of the resistance of the air; the second to describe the anatomy of the bird and of its feathers; the third to study the action of the feather in the movements of flight; the fourth to study the behavior of the tail and the wings in flying with the wind. Leonardo began his studies on flight in 1486, and his last writings date from 1515. The studies on flight are scattered in the sheets of Manuscripts A, B, E, F, G, I, K, L and M, and in the codices Foster I, Leicester, Trivulzianus, Arundel, and Atlanticus. The only one that has a certain unity of content, although not the organization of the treatise Leonardo himself had projected, is the "Codex on the Flight of Birds."

The codex, complete with the dispersed sheets, consists of 18 sheets (recto and verso) in addition to the cover. It measures 213 millimeters in height and 154 in width. The 40 pages contain writings on various topics, principally studies on the flight of birds; there are 174 illustrative drawings, 167 in black ink and 7 in red chalk, made previous to the composition of the codex.

S. P.

EDITORIAL NOTE

After the five folios that had been scattered and recovered were inserted in their original places in the codex, which started with thirteen sheets, they were numbered in a single sequence from one to eighteen, leaving the cover unnumbered. In our edition the margin indicates for each page Leonardo's numbering, the numbering superadded subsequently and that presumably given by Giovan Battista Venturi in 1797. Each page gives the critical transcription of the text with the orthographic and other changes necessary to make the text more easily understandable.

Words crossed out by Leonardo himself have been omitted in the transcription.

Our guide in the work of transcription has been the intelligent and diligent study of the codex made by Giovanni Piumati and the complete publication given with such profound knowledge by Monsignor Enrico Carusi.

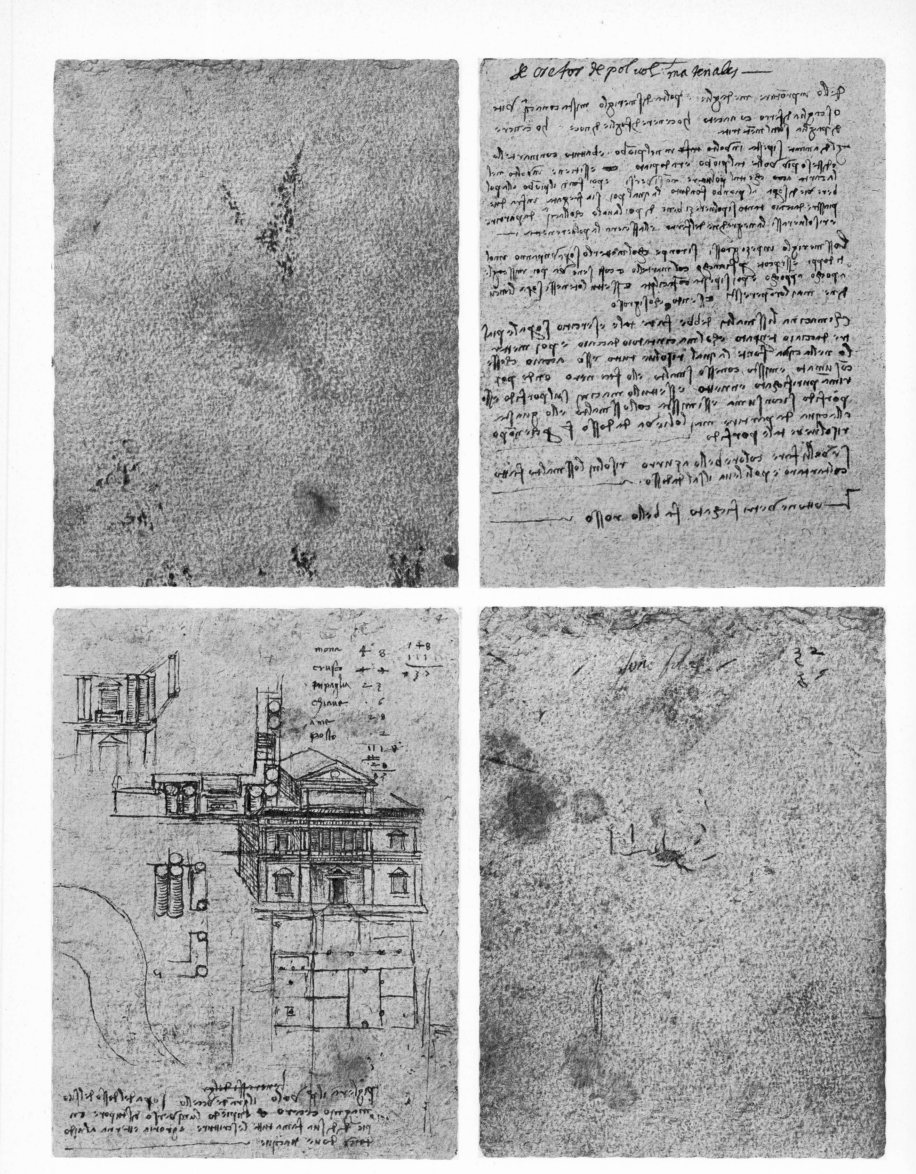

Copy of the "Codex on the Flight of Birds" – Turin, former Royal Library

348

TRANSCRIPTION OF "CODEX ON THE FLIGHT OF BIRDS"

O U T S I D E   F R O N T   C O V E R   Not numbered

Leonardo da Vinci   Written in Roman letters, not in Leonardo's hand

I N S I D E   F R O N T   C O V E R   Numbered 1, not in Leonardo's hand

Secrets of material powders   Heading in Spanish, not in Leonardo's hand

To stamp medals. Emery paste mixed with brandy, or iron-scale with vinegar, or ashes of walnut leaves, or ashes of straw finely triturated.   First paragraph

The emery is crushed enveloped in lead, and beaten with a hammer, the lead being spread out several times and refolded and kept wrapped in paper in order for the powder not to be spilled, and then melt the lead and the powder will come to the surface of the molten lead, and may then be rubbed between two steel plates to be well pulverized, and then wash it well with nitric acid and the blackness of the iron will dissolve, leaving the powder clean.   Second paragraph

Large pieces of emery are broken by placing them on a cloth folded many times and striking it from the side with a hammer, so that it will break off in flakes little by little and is then easily crushed; and if you put it on an anvil, you will never break it when it is so large.   Third paragraph

Anyone grinding enamel should do so on hardened steel plates with a steel pestle and then place it in nitric acid, which dissolves all the steel that has rubbed off and mixed with the enamel and blackens it, so that it becomes pure and clean, and if you grind it on porphyry, the porphyry rubs off and is mixed with the enamel and spoils it and nitric acid will never take it off, because it cannot dissolve the porphyry.   Fourth paragraph

If you want to make a fine color, dissolve the enamel with tartar after making it, and then remove the salt.   Fifth paragraph
Brass vitrified makes a fine red.   Sixth paragraph

I N S I D E   B A C K   C O V E R   Numbered 2, not in Leonardo's hand

At right, above, in letters not reversed

148	mona	48
111	Crusca	4
——	straw	23
037	Key	6
	to me	28
	chicken	2
		111
		28
		——
		83

The great bird will take its first flight on the back of its great swan and filling the universe with amazement, filling all writings with its fame and eternal glory to the nest where it was born.   Paragraph below

O U T S I D E   B A C K   C O V E R   Not numbered

32
35
There are 18 sheets.

At right, above, in letters not reversed

Center, above, not in Leonardo's hand

Center, illegible erased word

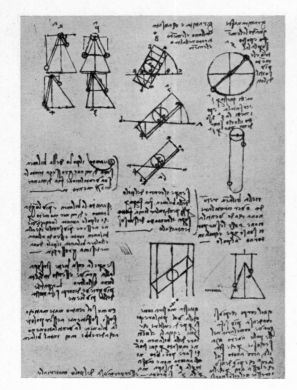

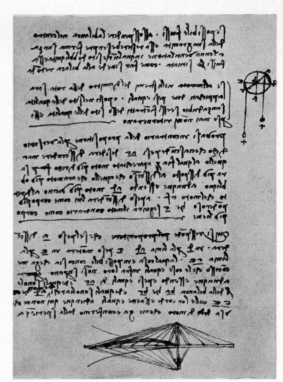

Folio 1 recto   Folio 1 verso   Folio 2 recto

FOLIO 1 RECTO

<table>
<tr><td>Detached sheet, not numbered</td><td></td></tr>
<tr><td>Upper right column</td><td>Gravity comes into being when an element is placed above another more rarefied element.</td></tr>
<tr><td>Upper center column</td><td>Gravity is caused by one element having been drawn into another element.</td></tr>
<tr><td>Right column, under circle</td><td>Set this fifth and refute it, and then set the fifth under the next place, also fifth.</td></tr>
<tr><td>Left column, first paragraph</td><td>The thinner the pivot of the balance, the less its oscillation will be.</td></tr>
<tr><td>Right column, under pulley</td><td>In the round or circular balance, there is no oscillation, because its parts are always equal around the pivot.</td></tr>
<tr><td>Center column, middle</td><td>The center of the balance pivot should always be in a vertical line above the contact of its support.</td></tr>
<tr><td>Left column, second paragraph</td><td>The longer the balance, the less important it is that the pivot being so long is thinner than in the short balance, the pivot being of the same thickness in both balances.</td></tr>
<tr><td></td><td>Antonio.</td></tr>
<tr><td>Right column, between two figures</td><td></td></tr>
<tr><td>Left column, third paragraph</td><td>A light thing is always above a heavy thing when both are at liberty. The heavier part of bodies is the guide of the lighter part.</td></tr>
<tr><td>Right column, below</td><td>The more a body is condensed, the heavier it becomes, like the air in wind balls. But if this is so, why does ice float on water, when it is heavier than the water, since it grows in melting.</td></tr>
<tr><td>Center column, below</td><td>This shows what would be the case if the vertical weights were equal to the effect of the air on the balance. It is not caused by this but rather hindered by it. Neither is it caused by the fifth above but by the seventh. It turns out to be because of the material pivot.</td></tr>
<tr><td>Left column, fourth paragraph</td><td>If the mathematical center could be the pivot of the balance, oscillation would never occur in such a balance.</td></tr>
</table>

FOLIO 1 VERSO

<table>
<tr><td>Detached sheet, not numbered</td><td></td></tr>
<tr><td>Right column, first paragraph</td><td>Velocity of the weight along the arc of the circle. That is, 8 plus 7 degrees of velocity.</td></tr>
<tr><td>Right column, second paragraph</td><td>The velocity of the weight descending along the chord is half slower, because along this chord the right angle RPV is bisected, and it is therefore half slower than along the vertical line PR, so that it will, be slower by half. We shall therefore say that the heavy body will descend along the chord in 4 plus 4 degrees of velocity and along the arc in 8 plus 7 degrees of velocity, making 15 degrees of this velocity along the arc and 8 along the chord, so that it is faster along the arc than along the chord by the excess of 15 over 8, which is 7, that is to say it is 7/8 faster.</td></tr>
<tr><td>Left text, first paragraph</td><td>Weight P will descend faster along the arc than along the chord, and the reason is that half of this arc falls from P to R along a vertical line. The rest of the path is reflex motion whose velocity is 7/8 of the incident motion as proved in the 5th, and if you allow this weight to descend along chord PN, this motion is fully a half slower than motion PR, that is 4/8, and we have already said that reflex motion RN is 7/8 of motion PR.</td></tr>
<tr><td>Left text, second paragraph</td><td>Let them say that weight P descending along PR descends at 8 degrees of velocity and has passed through half of arc PRN. Reflex motion RN is decreased 1/8 from the incident motion, which together come to 8 plus 7, 15 degrees of time in which weight P has passed along the arc and arrived at N. And if this weight descends along chord PN, it descends a half slower than along the vertical line PR because this chord bisects the right angle RPV. It is, therefore, clear that it is again half as slow. (So that if the weight has descended half the arc in 8 degrees of time, it would have descended half the chord in 16 degrees of time, and then the other half of the arc is gone through with 7 degrees of power, and the rest of the chord is also gone through in 16, so that all in all one is passed through in 32 and the other in 15.)</td></tr>
</table>

FOLIO 2 RECTO

<table>
<tr><td>Detached sheet, not numbered</td><td></td></tr>
<tr><td>First paragraph</td><td>If it were possible to suspend the balance at its center of gravity, it would always remain firm without oscillation in any oblique position whatever it was placed in. As we see in the case of the round balance.</td></tr>
<tr><td>Second paragraph</td><td>If two equal weights are placed at the ends of a diameter of a wheel and placed in a position of equilibrium, there is no doubt that if they were taken from that position of equilibrium they would never return to it of themselves.</td></tr>
<tr><td>Third paragraph</td><td>Evidence against the proposition of the adversary. I say that each of weights AC desires to descend, but the one to which more direct motion is applied will be more inclined to descend than one that will have a more oblique motion. Hence, since AD is a motion more nearly direct than motion CF, it will descend by weight like a heavier body, and C will follow the contrary motion, like a lighter body.</td></tr>
<tr><td>Fourth paragraph</td><td>Here the reply is made that if weight A descends to D along line AD, weight C will rise to E along line CE, which is impossible. Now since it has been granted me that things equal to each other do not overcome each other, then since weights A and C are equal, and the lever arms BA and BC are equal, and the arcs of their motions, AD and CE, are equal, and their chords and versed sines are equal, so that there is no cause of motion present here, as is confirmed by experience.</td></tr>
</table>

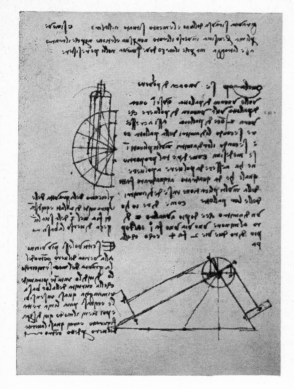

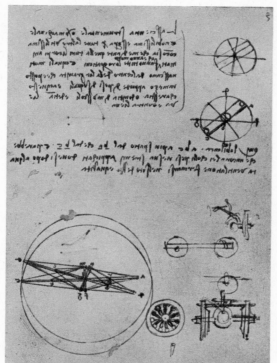

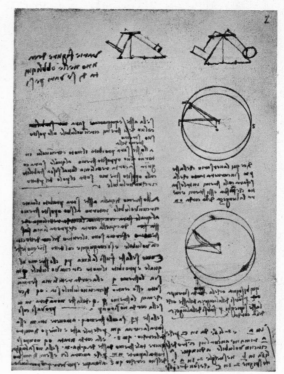

Folio 2 verso   Folio 3 recto   Folio 3 verso

FOLIO 2 VERSO   Detached sheet, not numbered

Gravity is caused by one element being situated in another; and it moves by the shortest line toward its center, not by its own choice nor because the center attracts it, but because the medium it is in cannot resist it.   First paragraph, above

If an ounce of powder requires an ounce of shot, or if an ounce of shot requires an ounce of powder, what will two ounces of shot require? It must be believed that this depends on the diameters of the shot, that is, according to their diameters multiplied by themselves, so that the proportion of powder to powder is as the square to the square, multiplying by themselves the diameters of the shot. If I have one diameter twice the other, I will say for the smaller one one times one is 1, and for the double one I will say two times two is 4, so that the...   Second paragraph, right

The center of gravity of a pyramid [triangle?] with 2 equal sides is one third of its length from the base.   Left column, first paragraph

And if you want to be closer to the true center of gravity of the semicircle, divide it into so many triangles that the curvature of their bases becomes virtually negligible and appears like a straight line, and then follow the method depicted above and you will have virtually the truth of the true center aforesaid.   Left column, second paragraph

FOLIO 3 RECTO   Folio of codex numbered 3 by Leonardo and 1 by Venturi

Instrumental or mechanical science is most noble and useful beyond all others, since by means of it all animate bodies that have motion perform all their operations; and these motions have their origin at the center of their gravity, which is placed in the middle of unequal weights at its sides, and has scarcity or abundance of muscles, and also lever and counter-lever.   First paragraph, above

Here balance ABC has more space at BA than at BC, and it would appear that, with the weights suspended at its ends, it too should after some oscillation come to rest in the position of equality.   Second paragraph, center

FOLIO 3 VERSO   Folio of codex numbered 2 by Venturi

Because of obliquity various figures give different weights.   Left column, first paragraph

   Second paragraph of left column crossed out

Here the adversary says that the rod PM will bend until the distance between its ends equals the length of cord ON.   Right column, first paragraph

The end of this rod will be prevented from rotary motion around its opposite end by the cord fastened in a straight line to the center of the said circumference, and is linked with the said rod end.   Left column, third paragraph

Thus if the rod be line PQ and the end that is prevented from moving in circumference QM is end Q, and the straight cord fastened at the center of this circumference is OQ, I say that end Q of the rod will never reach M unless the cord breaks. This is proved as follows: if rod PQ is to have its end Q move to M, it will describe the curve QM, since this rod is half the diameter of circle QMS and stretched cord OQ cannot follow this rod end Q to M, unless it stretches by the amount NM, because it too is half the diameter of its circle QNS. Hence it is true that Q cannot move.   Left column, fourth paragraph

Here it is necessary either for the cord to break so as to equal the rod in length, or for the rod to bend to equal the cord in length.   Right column, second paragraph

   Third paragraph of right column is continuation of last paragraph of folio 4 recto

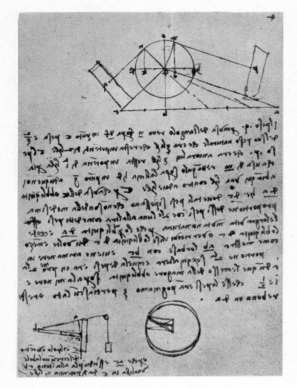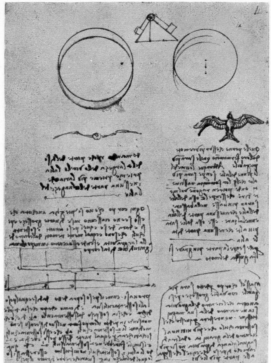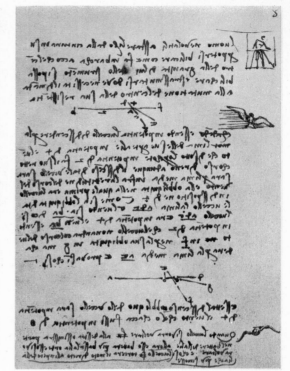

Folio 4 recto   Folio 4 verso   Folio 5 recto

Folio of codex numbered 4 by Leonardo and 3 by Venturi

FOLIO 4 RECTO

Because of right angle N on DF at point E, weight Q weighs 2/3 of its natural weight, which was 3 pounds, leaving a force of 2 pounds; and weight P, which was also 3 pounds, remains a force of 1 pound, because of right angle M on line HD at point G. Thus we have one pound against two pounds. And because of slopes DA and DC on which these weights rest, which are not in the same proportion as the weights, that is, one double the other as the said weights are, their gravities change nature, because slope DA exceeds slope DC, or contains slope DC two and a half times, as shown by their bases, AB and BC, remaining in the proportion of five to two, while the weights are in the proportion of two to one. Hence the excess of the greater inclination over the smaller is 1 and 1/2, and if the weights were say 3 on each side, they would rest at DA.

Left column, bottom
Right column, bottom, folio 3 verso

C is the pivot or center of the circumference, and since AC is half of lever CB, a pound at C gives a force of two pounds at A and gives 2 pounds at C, because A too remains center of the circumference. Hence 1 pound at B develops 2 at A and pushes 2 at C, making 4 pounds.

Folio of codex numbered 4 by Venturi

FOLIO 4 VERSO

Right column, first paragraph

Those feathers that are farthest from their points of attachment will be the most flexible. Therefore, the tips of the wing feathers will always be higher than their roots, so that we may reasonably say that the bones of the wings will always be lower than any part of the wing when the wings are lowered, and when they are raised, the bones will be higher than any part of the wing, because the heavier portion is always the guide of the movement.

Left column, first paragraph

I ask in what part of the under surface of the width of the bird the wing exerts more pressure than at any part of the length of the wings.

Left column, second paragraph

All bodies that do not bend, although each such body may be of different size and weight, will exert equal pressure on all supports that are equally removed from their centers of gravity, this center being in the center of the volume of this body.

Left column, third paragraph

The proof that the aforesaid weight exerts equal pressure on its supports: let us say that it weighs 4 pounds and is upheld by support AB. I say that since nothing prevents the body from descending but the 2 supports AB, these supports will be loaded equally by this weight, that is 2 and 2, and the same would be true of 2 other supports CD, if the other 3 supports were not there; and if only the central support E were there, it would support the entire weight.

Right column, second paragraph (continuation of left column)

But if the aforesaid body is flexible, with various thicknesses and weights, then, even though the center of gravity may be in the center of its volume, it will not remain true that the support nearer to the center of gravity, or other inequality of gravity, would not sustain a greater load than a support which is above the lighter portions.

Folio of codex numbered 6 by Leonardo (omitting number 5), later corrected to 5, and numbered 5 by Venturi

FOLIO 5 RECTO

First paragraph

A man in a flying machine must be free from the waist up to be able to balance himself as one does in a boat, in order that the center of gravity of himself and of the machine may tilt and change location when required to do so by the change of the center of the resistance to it.

Second paragraph

When the bird could fall in the line of its wings with a force of 4, and the wing striking it from below with a force of 2 makes its course straight: we shall say in that case that the descent of the bird will be in a line intermediate between the straightness of the course of the wind and the slope in which the bird was initially with the force 4. Let the inclination of the bird be line ADC and the wind BA: I say that if the bird ADC had force 4 and the wind force 2, the bird will not go to F with the course of the wind, nor to G by its own slope, but will fall by the intermediate line AE; and the proof is as follows.

Third paragraph
First paragraph of folio 5 verso (continuing third paragraph above)

And if this oblique descent of the bird has a force of 4, and the wind following it have a force of 8

and makes the reflex motion under the wind on the opposite side.

Fourth paragraph

When the bird desires to turn right or left by beating its wings, it will beat lower with the wing on the side to which it wants to turn, and thus the bird will twist its motion behind the impetus of the wing that moves most.

352

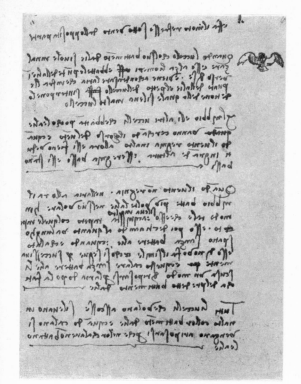

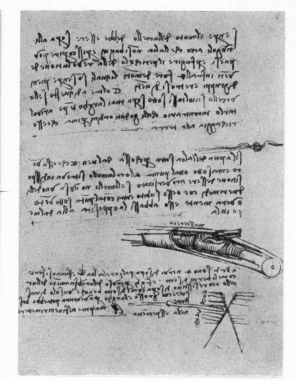

Folio 5 verso   Folio 6 recto   Folio 6 verso

Folio of codex numbered 6 by Venturi. First paragraph given on folio 5 recto

When the bird wishes to rise by beating its wings, it raises its shoulders and beats the tips of its wings toward itself and condenses the air between the points of the wings and the bird's breast, and the tension thereof lifts the bird up.

Second paragraph

When the kite and other birds that do not beat their wings much go searching for an air current and the wind is high up, they will be seen at a great height, and when the wind is low they will be low.

Third paragraph

When there is no wind stirring in the air, the kite beats its wings several times during flight and acquires impetus; it then glides down with that impetus, going down slowly without beating its wings; and when it has come down, it repeats the action, and so continues this gliding down without beating its wings as a sort of repose in the air after the action of the wings that has gone before it.

Fourth paragraph

All birds that fly in spurts rise high by beating their wings and rest during descent, because while descending they do not beat their wings.

Fifth paragraph

Folio of codex numbered 7 by Leonardo with an old correction to 6; numbered 7 by Venturi

Of the four reflex and incident motions of birds under different wind conditions.

First paragraph

The oblique descent of birds being always made into the wind, it will always be made under the wind, and their reflex motion will be made on the wind.

Second paragraph

But if this incident motion is made to the east, with the wind blowing from the north, the northern wing will remain under the wind, and will do the same in the reflex movement, so that at the end of this reflex the bird will be facing north.

Third paragraph

And if the bird descends towards the south while there is a north wind, it will make that descent on the wind, and its reflex will be below the wind; but this is a moot question, which will be discussed in its proper place, because here it would appear that such a reflex movement could not be performed.

Fourth paragraph

When the bird makes its reflex motion into and on the wind, it will rise much more than it would from its natural impetus, since it is favored by the wind, which comes up under it and acts like a wedge. But when it is at the end of its climb, it will have used up its impetus and it will have only the favoring wind left, which would upset it by striking it on the breast, except for the bird's lowering the right or the left wing, causing it to wheel to right or left, descending in a semicircle.

Fifth paragraph

Folio of codex numbered 8 by Venturi

The movement of the bird [flying machine] should always be above the clouds so as not to wet the wing, and to survey more country, and to avoid the dangers of gusts of winds within the mountain passes, which are always full of gusts and eddies of wind. And not only that, but if the bird should be turned upside down, you have plenty of time to right it according to the directions already given, before it falls to the ground.

First paragraph

If the point of the wing should be struck by the wind, and that wind should come up under the point, the bird is liable to be overturned, unless it employs one of two remedies, either immediately to force that point under the wind or to lower the opposite wing from the middle out.

Second paragraph

Masscereco

Drawing caption, "alum-tanned leather"

ABCD are four cords above for raising the wing, and are made as strong as the cords below, EFGH, because of the over-turning of the bird, so that they may offer as much resistance above as below, although a single thick and broad one of alum-tanned leather might suffice, but we shall leave the solution of this question to experience.

Third paragraph

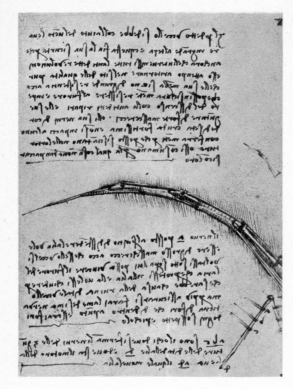 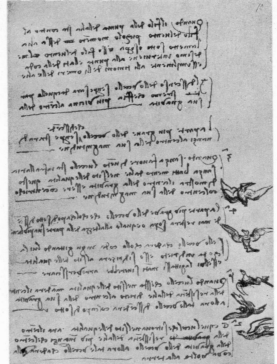 

Folio of codex numbered 8 by Leonardo, later corrected to 7; numbered 9 by Venturi

FOLIO 7 RECTO

First paragraph

The bird that has been described should be able to rise to a great height with the aid of the wind, and this will be its safety, for even if all the abovementioned rotations should befall it, it still has time to return to a position of equilibrium provided that its parts be very strong so that they may be sure to withstand the furor and violence of the descent by means of the aforesaid defenses and its joints of strong alum-tanned leather and its cords of the strongest raw silk; and let no one encumber with iron hardware, because they break very soon at the joints with twisting or wear out, so that they should not be used.

Second paragraph

Cord *A* for the purpose of extending the wing should be of thick alum-tanned leather so that, if the machine should be turned upside down, it may overcome the fury of the air striking the wing and trying to close it, which would be the destruction of the bird; but to be surer, make the cordage exactly the same outside and inside and you will avoid any suspicion of danger.

Third paragraph

ABC are the points of attachment for the cords of the three joints of the fingers of the wings. *D* is the position of the motor for lever *AD* which moves the wing.

Folio of codex numbered 10 by Venturi

FOLIO 7 VERSO

First paragraph

When the edge of the point of the wing meets the edge of the wind for an instant, I put the wing above or below the edge of the wind, and the same thing takes place at the point and sides of the tail and likewise at the helms [shafts?] of the shoulders of the wings.

Second paragraph
Third paragraph
Fourth paragraph

The descent of the bird will always be by that extremity that is nearest the center of its gravity.
The heaviest part of the bird in descent will always be in front of the center of its volume.
3) When, without the help of the wind, the bird remains in the air without beating its wings, in a position of equilibrium, this shows that the center of gravity coincides with the center of its volume.

Fifth paragraph

4) The heaviest part of the bird, as it descends head first, will never be above or on a level with the height of its lightest part.

Sixth paragraph

If the bird is falling tail down, it will return to a position of equilibrium by throwing its tail backward, and if it threw its tail forward, it would turn upside down.

Seventh paragraph

1) If the bird, being in a position of equilibrium, should put the center of resistance of its wings behind its center of gravity, that bird would descend head down.

Eighth paragraph

2) And if a bird, being in a position of equilibrium, should have this center forward of the center of gravity, then this bird will fall tail first.

Folio of codex numbered 9 by Leonardo, later corrected to 8; numbered 11 by Venturi

FOLIO 8 RECTO

First paragraph

If the wing and the tail are too much on the wind, then lower half the opposite wing and catch the impact of the wind in it, and the bird will right itself.

Second paragraph

And if the wing and the tail should be below the wind, raise the opposite wing, and it will right itself as you desire, provided that this wing that is raised slants less than the one opposite it.

Third paragraph

And if the wind and the breast are on the wind, lower half the opposite wing, which will be struck by the wind and forced upward again, righting the bird.

Fourth paragraph

But if the wing and the spine are below the wind, then the opposite wing should be raised and presented to the wind, and the bird will right itself at once.

Fifth paragraph

And if the bird should have its hinder parts on the wind, then the tail should be set below in the wind, and the forces will equalize.

Sixth paragraph

But if the bird would have its hinder parts below the wind, let it enter with the tail on the wind, and it will right itself.

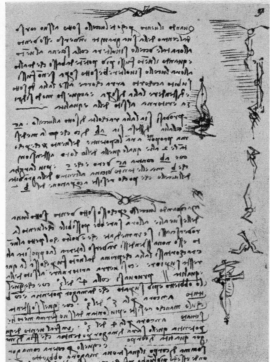

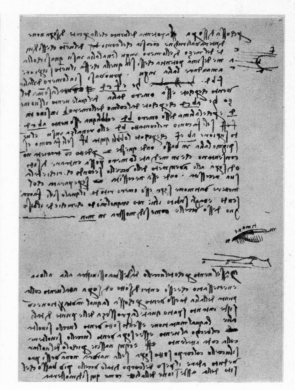

FOLIO 8 VERSO

Folio of codex numbered 12 by Venturi

When the bird is on the wind turning its beak with its bust to the wind, the bird might be turned over, if it did not lower its tail and receive therein a great volume of wind; this would make it impossible to turn it over. This is proved by the first section of the Elements of Mechanics, which shows how things in a position of equilibrium, when struck outside their center of gravity, lower the opposite parts situated this side of the aforesaid center. Let the quantity [area?] of the bird be *DEF* and its center of revolution be *E* [?] and the wind striking it be *ABDE* and *BCEF*: I say that a greater amount of wind strikes at *EF*, the tail of the bird, beyond the center of revolution, than strikes at *DE*, this side of the aforesaid center, and for this reason the aforesaid bird cannot turn upside down, especially when holding the wings into the wind edgewise.

First paragraph

And if this bird is situated with its length below the wind, it is liable to be turned upside down by the wind if it does not immediately raise its tail up. To prove this, let the length of the bird be *DNF*. *N* is the center of revolution. I say that *DN* is struck by a greater amount of wind than *NF*, and for this reason *DN* will respond to the air current, giving way to it, and will go down, raising the bird to a position of equilibrium.

Second paragraph

That the expanse of the wing is not all employed in compressing the air; and to see that this is so, note that the interstices between the primary feathers are much greater in width than the breadth of the feathers. You, therefore, who study flying creatures should not take into your calculation the entire surface of the wing and should note the different properties of the wings in all flying creatures.

Right column, and third paragraph

FOLIO 9 RECTO

Folio of codex numbered 10 by Leonardo, later corrected to 9; numbered 13 by Venturi

When the wind strikes the bird under its course from the center of its gravity toward this wind, then the bird will turn with its spine toward the wind; and if the wind were stronger from below than from above, then the bird would turn upside down, unless it were alert and immediately drew the lower wing in and extended the upper wing, and in this way it rights itself and returns to a position of equilibrium.

First paragraph

To prove this: let the wing gathered under the bird be *AC* and the extended wing be *AB*: I say that the forces of the wind striking the two wings will be in proportion to their extensions, that is *AB* to *AC*. It is true that *C* is broader than *B*, but it is so near the center of gravity of the bird that it offers little resistance as compared with *B*.

Second paragraph

But when the bird is struck under the wind beneath one of its wings, it would be possible for the wind to upset it, unless as soon as it were turned with its breast to the wind it extended the opposite wing toward the earth and shortened the wing that was previously struck by the wind and remains upmost; and in this way it will return to a position of equilibrium. This is proved by the 4th of the 3rd, according to which that object is more overcome that is assailed by greater force; and also by the 5th of the 3rd, according to which a support is weaker the further it is from its point of attachment; again according to the 4th of the 3rd, among winds of equal force that one will be of greater force that has greater volume, and that wind strikes with greater volume, that finds a larger object; hence, since *MF* is longer than *MN*, *MF* will respond to the wind.

Third paragraph

FOLIO 9 VERSO

Folio of codex numbered 14 by Venturi

If the wing is struck from above, the force of the wind striking it from above is not of full strength, inasmuch as the wedge of wind that splits off below the middle of the shoulder lifts the wind up with almost the same force as the upper wind exerts forcing the wind down. This is proved as follows: Let the shoulder of the wing be *FBD* and *EFCD* the total amount of the wind striking this shoulder of the wing; half of this wind is *ABCD* striking from the peak of the shoulder *B* down to *D*, and since the line of this shoulder *BD* is oblique, the wind *ABCD* becomes a wedge in contact with *BD* and raises it. The upper wind *ABEF* becomes a wedge upon striking obliquely *BF* and presses the wing down, and these 2 aforesaid contraries do not permit the shoulder immediately to enter below of above the arrival of the bird, as required. This requirement is met by putting a shaft on this round shoulder, acting as a shield and cutting the wind at once, in the manner required by the bird as shown at *MN*.

First paragraph

Shaft.

But if the wind strikes the bird on the right or the left wing, then it is necessary that the bird enter below or above that wind with the point of the wing struck by the wind. This change occurs in a space as great as the thickness of the points of the said wings. When this change is below the wind, the bird turns with its beak into the wind, and if it is on the wind, the bird will turn with its tail at will; and this would give rise to the danger of having the bird upset, except that nature has taken care to set the weight of the bird lower than the position of the extension of the wings, as will be shown here.

On central figure
Second paragraph

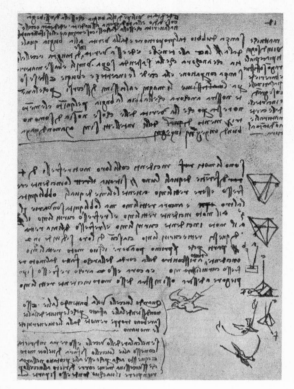 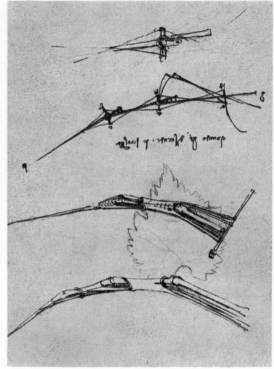 

Folio of codex numbered 11 by Leonardo and 15 by Venturi

FOLIO 10 RECTO

Note, upper left

Column in margin

First paragraph

And lying is so contemptible that if it should say fine and great things about God, it would detract from the grace of its deity; and truth is of such excellence that, if it should praise trifles, it would make them noble.

But you who live on dreams, you are better pleased with the sophistical reasoning and frauds of talkers about great and uncertain matters than those who speak of certain and natural matters, not of such lofty nature.

Undoubtedly, the truth is to falsehood as the light is to darkness, and the truth is intrinsically of such excellence that even when it deals with low and humble matters, it is higher than vagueness and lies about great and sublime discourses; for although lying may be the quintessence of our minds, it still remains true that the truth of things is the supreme nourishment of fine intellects, but not of vagabond natures.

Second paragraph

There are four different kinds of incident motions with their reflex motions. In one of them the incident and the reflex are rectilinear, the lines being of equal slope. The second is still rectilinear, but the slopes are different. The third has the incident rectilinear and the reflex curvilinear. The fourth has the incident motion curvilinear and the reflex in a straight line. Of these straight and curved lines, each is divided into two parts, for the first may have its rectilinear incident motion directly opposite to the chord of the arc made by the curvilinear reflex motion, and again the reflex arc may bend to the right or the left of that incident rectilinear motion.

Third paragraph

When the bird flies, beating its wings, it does not fully extend its wings, because the points of the wings would be too far from the lever and the sinews that move it.

Fourth paragraph

If the bird rows backward with its wings while it is descending, it will move rapidly; and this occurs because the wings strike on the air that then goes directly behind the bird to fill the vacuum that it has left.

Folio of codex numbered 16 by Venturi

FOLIO 10 VERSO

Center of sheet

When G descends, P rises.

Detached sheet, not numbered

FOLIO 11 RECTO

First paragraph

If the bird should wish to turn quickly on one of its sides and follow its circular motion, it will beat the wing on that side two times, rowing the wing backward, the other wing being motionless or beating only once to the two of the opposite wing.

Second paragraph

Since the wings are quicker to compress the air than the air is to escape, the air is condensed and resists the motion of the wind from under the wings. The motor of these wings, overcoming the resistance of the air, rises in contrary motion to the motion of the wings.

Third paragraph

This bird will descend with more rapid motion than the motion whose descent will be along a smaller obliquity.

Fourth paragraph

The descent of this bird will be along a smaller obliquity, the closer the points of the wings and their shoulders are to each other.

Fifth paragraph

The lines of the motions executed by birds in their rise are made by two lines, one of which is always curved like a screw and the other rectilinear and curvilinear.

Right column, above drawing

The bird that is rising always has its wings on the wind, without beating them.

Right column, below drawing

The motion is always in circular motion.

Right column, bottom

And if you wish to go to the west without beating the wings when a north wind is blowing, make the incident motion straight and under the wind to the west, and the reflex motion on the wind to the north.

Sixth paragraph

Thet bird will rise to a height which, by a circular screw-like motion, makes the reflex motion into the wind and against the flight of this wind, always turning on its right side or on its left side.

Seventh paragraph

Thus if the wind should be blowing from the north, and you coming above by reflex motion should run against the said wind, and if in your straight rise that wind should tend to upset you, then you are at liberty to bend by means of the right or left wing, and you will follow a curving motion with the inner wing low, with the help of the tail curving toward the lower wing, always descending and pivoting on the low sing, until you again make the reflex movement on the wind, behind the course of the wind. And when you are about to be upset, this same lower wing will curve your line of motion and you will return against the wind, and under it, until you have acquired impetus and then rise above the wind, facing its approach, and by reason of the impetus already acquired you will make the reflex motion greater than the incident motion.

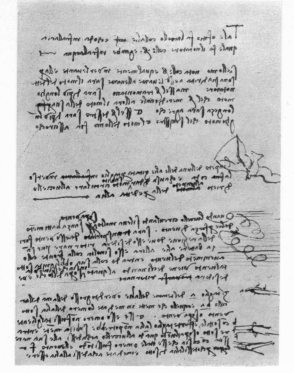

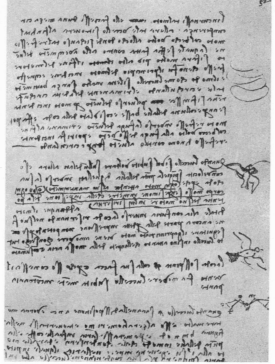

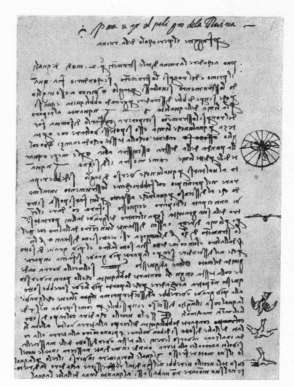

Folio 11 verso   Folio 12 recto   Folio 12 verso

FOLIO 11 VERSO

Detached sheet, not numbered

The bird makes the same use of its wings and tail in the air that a swimmer makes of his arms and legs in the water.

First paragraph

If a man swims eastward equally with his arms, and his body lies in an eastward direction, the motion of the said swimmer will be eastward; but if the north arm makes a slower stroke than the south arm, the motion of his body's length will be to the northeast. And if the right arm has a slower motion than the left arm, the motion of the man will be to the southeast.

Second paragraph

The impetus of one of the wings thrust edgewise toward the tail will be the occasion of giving the bird a sudden circular motion, following the impetus of the aforesaid wing.

Third paragraph

When by the force of the wind the bird rises circling above the wind without beating its wings, this wind will remove it away from the region to which it desires to return, also without beating its wings. It then turns so that it faces the oncoming of the wind, entering slantwise under this wind, and descending slightly until it comes to be above the spot to which it desires to return.

Fourth paragraph

The edge *A* of the shaft of the wing or thumb [*dito grosso*] of the hand of the bird, *BA*, is what sets the shoulder of the wing directly below the wind or on it. And if this shoulder were not sharp, with a thin strong edge, the wing would not be able suddenly to enter below or on the wind when the bird needed it to; for if this shoulder were deep [round?] and the wind *FE* should strike the wing from below, and the wing should immediately be...

Fifth paragraph

FOLIO 12 RECTO

Folio of sheet numbered 13 by Leonardo, later corrected to 12; numbered 17 by Venturi

... such a movement will curve it and make it a semicircle. Then the bird will be at the end of this movement with its beak turned to the place from which this reflection was caused; if the reflection is made against the oncoming of the wind, the end of the reflex motion will be much higher than the beginning of the incident motion, and this is how the bird rises without beating its wings, circling. The remainder of the said circumference would end up toward the wind by incident motion, always with one of the wings low and likewise one side of the tail; and then it makes a movement toward the going away of the wind, and at the end it remains with its beak toward the going away of the wind and then makes the incident and reflex motions again into the wind, always circling.

First paragraph

When the bird desires to turn suddenly to one of its sides, it thrusts the point of the wing on that side swiftly toward its tail, and since every motion tends to maintain itself, that is, every body that is moved always moves so long as the impression of the motive force continues in it, therefore the vigorous motion of the wing in question toward the tail, which still keeps a part of the aforesaid impression at the end of the movement, being unable of itself to continue the movement already begun, moves the entire bird with it, until the impetus of the air that has been moved is exhausted.

Second paragraph

When the surface of the tail is thrust forward and strikes the wind, it causes the bird to move suddenly in the opposite direction.

Third paragraph

If the bird is in position *ANC* and desires to rise, it will raise its shoulders *MO* and will be in position *BMNOD*, and will compress the air between its sides and the points of its wings so that it will condense the air and give it an upward movement and generate an impetus in the air, which impetus of the air will by its condensation push the bird upward.

Fourth paragraph

FOLIO 12 VERSO

Folio of codex numbered 18 by Venturi
Heading in Spanish, not in Leonardo's hand
Heading, in Leonardo's hand
Only paragraph

To escape the danger of destruction.
To escape the danger of destruction.

The destruction of these machines may occur in two ways, the first being rupture of the machine, and the second being the turning of the machine edgewise or almost edgewise; for it always should descend at a long slant and virtually along the line of equilibrium. With respect to guarding against the machine's breaking, this can be effected by making it as strong as possible in whatever direction it may turn, either falling by the edge or with the head or tail foremost or by the point of the right or left wing, or along the halves or quarters of the aforesaid lines, as the drawing shows. As for turning toward any aspect of the edge, this must be prevented beforehand by constructing the machine in such a way that in descending in any manner the remedy may be inherent, and this will occur if the center of its gravity is always in a straight line above the center of the heavy body carried by it, and one center is always sufficiently distant from the other, namely for a machine 30 ells wide, let these centers be 4 ells apart, one underneath the other, as has been said, the heavier being underneath, since in descent the heavier part is always in part the guide of the movement. In addition to this, if the bird should attempt to fall head downward at an angle that would upset it, this will be impossible because the lighter part would be below the heavier part, and the light would be descending before the heavy, which is impossible in a descent of any length, as is proved in the 4th of the Elements of Machines. And if the bird falls head downward with the body at an angle to the earth, in that case the sides of the wings underneath must be turned flat toward the earth and the tail raised toward the back, and the head or underside of the jaws likewise turned toward the earth, which will at once bring about the reflex movement of the bird. This will thrust it back toward the sky; for which reason the bird will tend to fall backward at the end of this reflex movement unless in its rise it lowers somewhat one of its wings, and ... [continued on folio 12 recto]

357

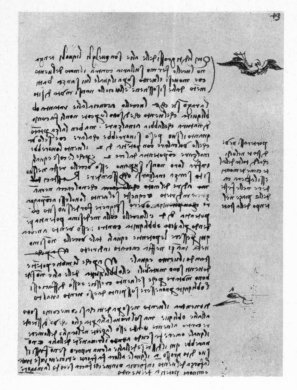 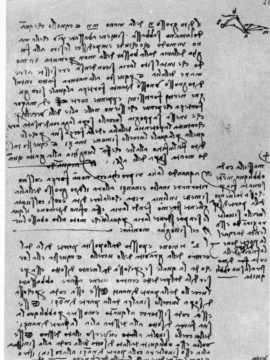 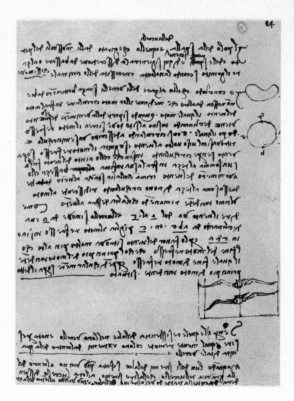

Folio 13 recto   Folio 13 verso   Folio 14 recto

Folio of codex numbered 14 by Leonardo, later corrected to 13; numbered 19 by Venturi

First paragraph

Second paragraph

FOLIO 13 RECTO

Here the big fingers of the wings are what hold the bird motionless in the air against the movement of the wind, on which it supports itself without beating its wings, and the bird does not change its location.

The reason is that the bird sets its wings at such a slope that the wind, as it strikes from below, does not make a wedge there of a kind that would tend to raise it. But it does raise it for all that by as much as its weight would tend to make it descend. Thus, if the bird tends to fall with a force of 2, the wind would tend to raise it, likewise with a force of 2, and since things equal to each other do not overcome each other, the bird remains in its place without rising or descending. It remains for us to speak of the motion that does not drive it either forward or backward, and this is when the wind would tend to carry it along or thrust it out of its location with a force of 4 and the bird is leaning into the wind at the aforesaid angle with the same force. Since the forces are equal in this case, the bird will not move forward or be driven backward, as long as the wind remains unchanged. But since the movements and forces of the winds are changeable, and the angles of the wings should not change, because if the wind changes and the bird should alter the angle in order not to be pushed up by the wind... In the cases mentioned above the wind does not come up under the slanting wings like a wedge, but only encounters the wing at the edge which tends to descend against the wind; the wind strikes the wing at the edge of the shoulder, which shoulder acts as a bulwark for all the rest of the wing, and there would be no protection against the descent of the wings if it were not for its big finger A, which in that event is to the fore and receives the entire force of the wind full face on, or less than full face, depending on the force of the wind.

Right column

Snow will be taken to hot places in the summer from the mountain summits, and will be let fall in festivals in the piazzas in the summer season.

Folio of codex numbered 20 by Venturi

First paragraph

FOLIO 13 VERSO

The big finger N of hand MN is that which, when the hand is lowered, tends to be lowered more than the hand, so that it closes and hinders the escape of the air compressed by the lowering of the hand, so that the air is condensed in that spot and resists the rowing action of the wing. Nature therefore has made a very powerful bone in that finger, to which are joined very strong sinews and short feathers with more strength than the wing feathers of birds, because by means of it the bird supports itself on the already condensed air with all the power of the wing and of its force, since it is by means of this that the bird moves forward. This finger serves the same purposes for the wing as claws do for cats when they climb trees.

Second paragraph

But when the wing regains new force with its return upward and forward, the big finger of the wing comes into a straight line with the other fingers, and with its sharp end cuts the air and serves as a rudder dividing the air for whatever movement, high or low, that the bird wishes to perform.

Third paragraph

The second rudder is placed at the opposite end, the other side of the bird's center of gravity. This is the bird's tail; if it is struck by the wind underneath, it tends to make the front part of the bird go down, since it is to the other side of the said center of gravity. And if the tail is struck from above, the bird rises in front. And if this tail is twisted somewhat and turns its under surface slanting toward the right wing, the forward part of the bird will turn to the right. And if this angle underneath to the side of the bird is to the left wing, the bird will turn to the left with its forward part, and in either of the two cases the bird will descend.

Right column

But if the tail, while in a slanting position, is struck by the wind from above, the bird will turn, revolving away from the place where the upper surface of the tail shows its slant.

Folio of codex numbered 15 by Leonardo, later corrected to 14; numbered 21 by Ventur

First paragraph

Second paragraph

FOLIO 14 RECTO

The pivot of the shoulders of birds is that which is turned by the muscles of the breast and back, and which makes it possible to lower or raise the elbow in conformity to the will and the needs of the moving animal.

My conclusion is that the rising of birds without beating their wings is due solely to their circular motion within the motion of the wind, which motion, if the starting point is the oncoming of the winds, is downward as far as the point where the reflex motion is produced, at which point, circling in this way, it will have described a semicircle. It will have its face turned to the wind, and will continue the reflex motion on the wind, still circling, until with the aid of the wind it makes its highest ascent between its lowest descent and the oncoming of the wind, and at the end has its left wing to the wind, and circling again descends from this highest point to the final incident motion, with its right wing to the wind at the end. Thus, let us say, that the wind goes from A to C and the bird moves from A and descends by ABC and at C takes the reflex motion to CDA, and because of the wind it is much higher at the end of the reflex motion than at the beginning of the incident motion, which end of the reflex motion is vertically above the said beginning of incident motion.

Third paragraph

The equal strength of bird's wings is always due to the fact that their tips are equally distant from the bird's center of gravity.

Fourth paragraph

But when one of the wing tips comes nearer to the bird's center of gravity than the other tip, then the bird will descend on the side on which the tip of the wing is nearer to the center of gravity.

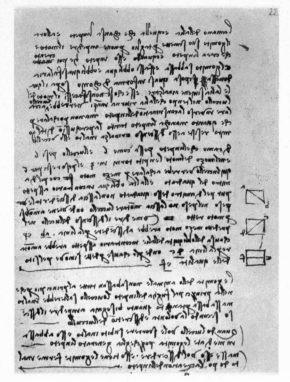

Folio 14 verso

Folio 15 recto

Folio 15 verso

FOLIO 14 VERSO

Folio of codex numbered 22 by Venturi

The hand of the bird is that which causes the impetus; and the elbow is then placed edgewise so as not to impede the motion that produces the impetus. And then when this impetus has been produced, the elbow sinks and assumes a slanting position, and the air on which it rests becomes slanting, as if in the form of a wedge on which the wing tends to rise; and if the motion of the bird did not occur in this way the bird would tend to descend toward the exhaustion of the impetus during the time when the wing is returning forward; but it cannot fall because as the impetus gives out, the percussion of the elbow resists this descent in the same proportion, and raises the bird up again.

First paragraph

Let us say that the impetus has the force 6 and the bird weighs 6, and that in the middle of the movement the impetus becomes 3 and the weight still remains 6. In this case the bird would tend to drop by half the movement, that is to say along the diagonal of the square; and the wing slanting in the opposite direction, likewise along the diagonal of the square, does not allow the weight to descend, and the weight does not allow the bird to rise, so that in the end it tends to move in a straight line. Thus, the descent of the bird in the aforesaid half-motion would have to be along line *AB*, and because of the obliquity of the wings in the contrary direction it would have to rise along line *DC*; hence, for the reasons given above, it moves in a position of equilibrium *EF*.

Second paragraph

The elbows of the animal are not completely lowered at the beginning, because in the initial flight of the impetus the bird would jerk upwards; the lowering occurs to the extent necessary to prevent descent, according to the desire and will of the bird.

Third paragraph

When the bird wishes to soar upward suddenly, it immediately lowers its elbows, once it has produced the impetus.

Fourth paragraph

But if it wishes to descend, it keeps the elbows firmly up after creating the impetus.

Fifth paragraph

FOLIO 15 RECTO

Folio of codex numbered 16 by Leonardo, later corrected to 15; numbered 23 by Venturi

Remember that your flying machine should not imitate anything but the bat, because membranes form a framework, or rather something bound to and covering the framework of the wings.

First paragraph

If you were to imitate the wings of feathered birds, those wings have more powerful bones and sinews, being pierced; that is, their feathers are separated from each other and air passes through them. But the bat is aided by the membrane which binds the whole and is not pierced.

Second paragraph

On the method of balancing oneself.

Title in center of sheet

The heaviest part of bodies is always the part that is the guide of their movement.

Third paragraph

Hence, the bird being in the position *AB*, a being lighter than *B* at which the motive power is located, *A* will always be above *B*, so that it will never happen that *A* will go before *B*, except accidentally, and this condition will not be lasting.

Fourth paragraph

A bird that has to rise without treating its wings sets itself slantingly into the wind, its wings presenting to the wind with their elbows to the fore, with the center of its gravity more toward the wind than the center of its wings. The result is that if the slant of the bird tends to make it descend with a force of 2, and the wind strikes it with a force of 3, its motion will obey the 3 and not the 2.

Fifth paragraph

FOLIO 15 VERSO

Folio of codex numbered 24 by Venturi

The purpose of this instrument is to find the center of gravity of the bird, without which instrument the machine would have little value.

First paragraph

When the bird sinks, its center of gravity is outside the center of its resistance; thus, if the center of gravity is on line *AB*, the center of the resistance will be on line *CD*.

Second paragraph

And if the bird wishes to rise, then the center of its gravity is behind the center of its resistance.

Third paragraph

Thus, let the center of the said gravity be at *FG* and the center of its resistance at *EH*.

Fourth paragraph

The bird can stay in the air without keeping its wings in the position of equilibrium, because since it does not have its center of gravity at the center of its pivot as balances have, it is not necessarily compelled to keep its wings at an equal height as the said balances do. But if the wings are outside this position of equlibrium, then the bird will descend along the line of the obliquity of the wings; and if the obliquity is compound, that is double, so that, for example, the wings slant toward the south and the head and tail slant down toward the east, then the bird will descend slanting toward the southeast. And if the obliquity of the bird is double the obliquity of its wings, the bird will descend between southeast and east, and the obliquity of its motion will be between the two aforesaid obliquities.

Fifth paragraph

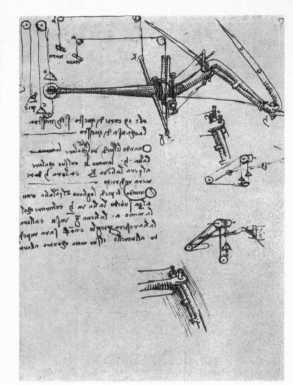

Folio 16 recto   Folio 16 verso   Folio 17 recto

Folio of codex numbered 17 by Leonardo,   **FOLIO 16 RECTO**
later corrected to 16; numbered 25 by Venturi

Headings, left   An argument to dispose of the objections.
First paragraph of right column   Bags with which a man, falling from a height of 6 ells, will not be hurt falling either into water or to earth; and these
                                                      bags, tied together like the beads of a rosary, surround each other.
Left paragraph   If you should say that the sinews and muscles of a bird are incomparably more powerful than those of man, because all the
                                                      flesh of the big muscles and fleshy parts of the breast goes to increase the power of the wings' motion, and the bone of the
                                                      breast is in one piece which affords the bird's very great power, while the wings are all compact of big sinews and other very
                                                      strong ligaments of cartilages, and the skin is very strong, with various muscles: then reply to this is that all this strength is
                                                      the purpose of enabling it, over and above the ordinary action of wings in keeping it up, to double and triple its motion in
                                                      order to escape from attackers or to pursue its prey; for this purpose it has to double or triple its power in its claws and
                                                      moreover carry as much weight through the air as it itself weighs; thus we see a falcon carry off a duck and an eagle a hare.
                                                      This sufficiently proves the purpose of such an excess of power; but they need little power to keep themselves up in the air
                                                      and balance on their wings and flap them on the currents of air and steer along their paths, a little movement of the wings
                                                      sufficing, and the larger the bird, the slower.
Second paragraph of right column   A man also has a greater amount of power in his legs than is needed for his weight; to show that this is true, have a
                                                      man stand on the shore and consider how deep his footprints are. Then put another man on his back and you will see how
                                                      much deeper his feet sink in. Then take the second man off his back and have him leap straight up into the air as high as
                                                      he can; you will find that the impressions of his feet have been sunk in deeper by the jump than with the man on his back.
                                                      Hence, we have proved in two ways that man has more than twice the power that he needs to support himself.

Folio of codex numbered 26 by Venturi   **FOLIO 16 VERSO**

Upper left   If you fall, see that you strike the earth with the double bag you have under your rump.
First paragraph   Since the wings have to row downward and backward to keep the machine up and move it forward, the movement of lever
                                                      CD is made slantwise, guided by belt *AB*.
Second paragraph   I could arrange it so that the foot that presses stirrup *G* should be the one that in addition to its usual function pulls down
                                                      lever *F*. But this would not serve our purpose, since we require that stirrup *G* move from its position before lever *F* rises or
                                                      sinks, so that the wing, as it is thrust forward and raised upward (in the phase where the impetus already acquired pushes the
                                                      bird forward by itself without its beating its wings), may enter the air edgewise, since if this were not done, the surface of the
                                                      wings would strike the air and hinder the motion, and would not allow the impetus to carry the bird forward.

Detached sheet, with an old number 17   **FOLIO 17 RECTO**

Words on drawing, upper left   Hand — Hand — Foot.

First paragraph   The 19 pages of this show the cause of this.
Second paragraph   When the feet tend to sink wing *H*, hand *B* will lift lever *K* by sinking, and then wing *H* will row backward.
Third paragraph   When the feet tend to raise the wing, and you suddenly raise the wing at *H* by pulling lever *G* up with hand *A*, then
                                                      the wing will remain edgewise, and the bird will not be impeded in its motion against the air.

360

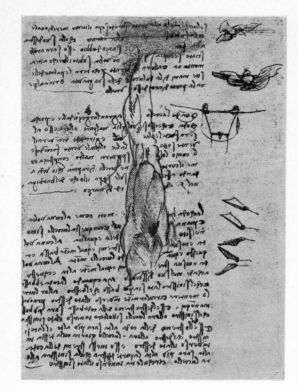

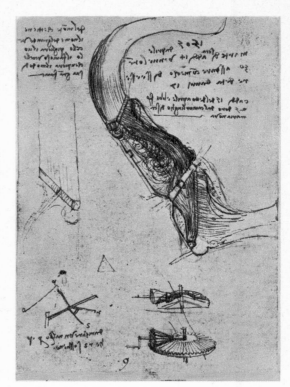

Folio 17 verso   Folio 18 recto   Folio 18 verso

FOLIO 17 VERSO Detached sheet, not numbered

If the bird sinks to the east with its right wing on the south wind, it will undoubtedly be upset unless it immediately turns its beak north, and then the wind will strike the palms of its hands beyond the center of its gravity, and will raise the forward part of the bird.
First paragraph

If the bird has great wing span and a little tail, and wishes to rise, then it will raise its wings strongly, and circling will receive the wind under its wings, which wind will become a wedge and will thrust it upward rapidly, as with the *cortone*, a bird of prey, which I saw going to Fiesole above the place of the Barbiga in 5 [the year 1505] on March 14.
Second paragraph

The tail has motions. Sometimes it is flat, and the bird moves with it in a level position, and sometimes it has its tips both low, and this is when the bird is going up. Sometimes it has its tips both high, and this occurs during descent. But when the tail is low and the left side is lower than the right, then the bird will mount in a circle toward the right side; this can be proved, but not here. And if the tail is low and the right tip is lower than the left, then the bird will turn toward the left. And if the tail is high and the left tip is higher than the right, then the bird will turn with its head toward the right, and if, with the tail high, the right tip is higher than the left, the bird will circle toward the left.
Third paragraph

FOLIO 18 RECTO Detached sheet, not numbered

In raising the hand, the elbow always drops and presses the air, and in lowering the hand the elbow rises and remains edgewise, so as not to hinder the movement by means of the air striking within them.
First paragraph, right column

Lowering the elbow at the time that the bird is putting its wings forward somewhat edgewise on the wind, guided by the impetus already acquired, is the reason why the wind strikes under that elbow and becomes a wedge, on which the bird, with the aforesaid impetus and without beating its wings, tends to rise, and if the bird be 3 pounds and its breast is a 3rd of its wing span, the wings only bear two 1/3 of the weight of the bird.
Second paragraph, right column

The hand is subjected to great effort toward the big finger, or the shaft of the wing, because it is this part that strikes the air.
Third paragraph, right column

The palm of the hand goes from A to B, always at about the same angle, pressing the air, and at B it immediately turns edgewise and turns backward, rising along line CD, and arriving at D immediately turns full face and sinks along line AB, and in turning it always turns around the center of its breadth.
First paragraph, left column

Turning the hand backward edgewise will be done with great rapidity, and pressing it backward full face will be done with a speed that will call for the utmost power of the motor.
Second paragraph, left column

The course of the finger tips is not the same in going as in returning, but is on a higher line while returning, and beneath it is the figure described by upper and lower lines, forming a long and close oval.
Third paragraph, left column

FOLIO 18 VERSO Detached sheet, not numbered

1505, Tuesday evening, April 14, Lorenzo came to stay with me; he says he is 17 years old.
First paragraph, upper right

And on the 15th of the said April, I had 25 gold florins from the treasurer of Santa Maria Novella.
Second paragraph, right

From the mountain that takes its name from the great bird, the famous bird will take its flight, which will fill the world with its great fame.
Upper left

To raise a tree by P and RS sustain...
Lower left

Saint Jerome – Vatican Gallery

ANATOMY AND THE BIOLOGICAL SCIENCES

Leonardo seems not to have devoted himself to the deeper study of human anatomy from the outset, but, like other Renaissance painters, to have cultivated it solely for the purpose of forming a solid foundation preliminary to the study of art. He appears to have devoted himself to accurate anatomical investigation only later, attracted to it by his thirst for study and knowledge.

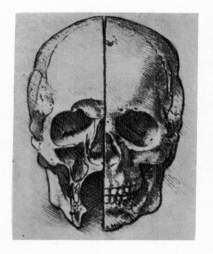

In view of this, it seems likely that the anatomical studies that according to some authors Leonardo began as early as his first Florentine period, before 1483, were the preliminary studies mentioned above, while his precise anatomical investigations began only in Milan, shortly before 1489, and continued with interruptions down to 1515, at which time Leonardo was compelled to cut them short at Rome, because of being prohibited by Pope Leo to have access to the mortuary at the Ospedale di Santo Spirito.

From the statements of contemporaries and his own declarations, Leonardo appears to have dissected more than thirty cadavers of both sexes and all ages.

He would make the anatomical preparations with his own hands, reproduce them in drawings on sheets, and often supplement the drawings with annotations; it is rare for his manuscripts to contain anatomical notes without any drawing at all. Although he speaks of one hundred and twenty books of anatomy by him, no trace remains of these books (actually, chapters), assuming that they were ever written; and the only existing document of his anatomical studies is the sheets mentioned above, or rather that part of them that survived dispersal and perhaps destruction.

For the most part these sheets are preserved, bound in codices, in the royal library at Windsor; only a few are owned by other libraries or included in manuscripts on other subjects.

The Windsor sheets were published in summary fashion by J. P. Richter in 1883, and were later published, in part accurately by G. Piumati in 1898 and 1901, under the title *Dell'Anatomia Fogli A e B*, in part incompletely and in an unauthorized edition by the French publisher Rouveyre, and later, most carefully, by the Norwegian professors Vangensten, Fonahn, and Hopstock, with the title of *Quaderni di Anatomia I-IV*, from 1911 to 1916. Among the other anatomical sheets the one of Weimar Castle should be mentioned, published by E. Möller in 1930. It can therefore be said that at present all the known anatomical work of Leonardo is accessible to students.

The importance of this anatomical work, even based as it was on direct observation of the human cadaver, is above all that it was decades in advance of the revival of anatomical studies. It was contemporaneous or virtually so with the much inferior attempts to break from the traditional anatomy of the ancients, of Galen, in particular, based principally on dissection of the monkey and the dog. Another important trait of Leonardo's anatomical studies is the richness, and more than the richness, the fine elegance of so many of the drawings that the dissecting artist either drew directly from the anatomical preparations he had made or traced later from memory.

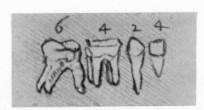

A characteristic feature of Leonardo's study of the human body is the close bond between the two branches of investigation, anatomy and physiology. Leonardo wanted "the use, the function, the purpose" of each organ or part to be studied as well. And with the aim of achieving deeper knowledge of the significance and internal rationale of the various organs and of the organism itself as a whole, Leonardo sometimes integrated the study of human anatomy and physiology with com-

Above and below: Skull and teeth – Anat. Ms. B, fol. 41 v

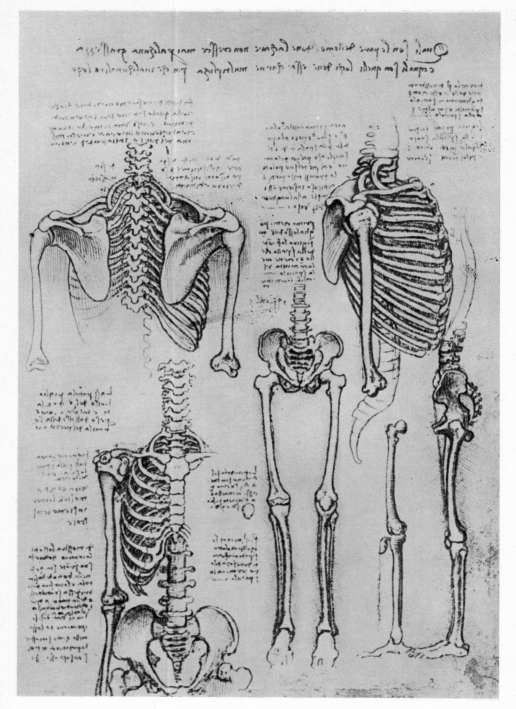

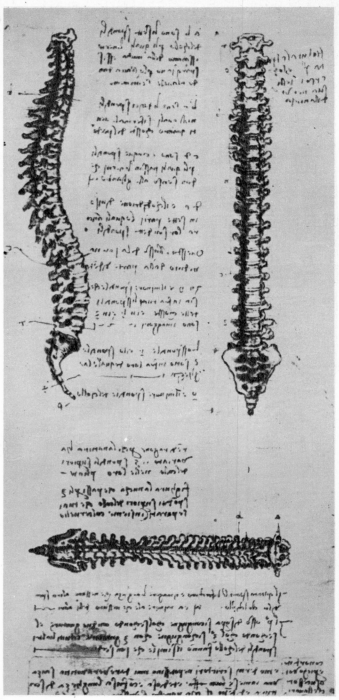

Left: Skeleton of trunk and limbs, especially lower limbs – Anat. Ms. A, fol. 13 r

Right: Vertebral column – Anat. Ms. A, fol. 8 v

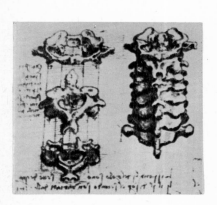

Dorsal vertebrae – Anat. Ms. A, fol. 8 v

parative study, usually of the larger mammals, thus inaugurating a method of research that is still basic for modern biology.

The organs, isolated or in groups, are often reproduced as they can be observed from several points of view, "in several aspects," and likewise for the various parts of the body, also represented in their superposed layers, or only the deeper ones, the superficial layers being omitted or drawn in as transparent, or even, in the case of muscles, being drawn as "lean and thin." Other organs, and more often entire parts of the body, are reproduced in variously oriented sections, as, for example, the head, the trunk, and pelvis in sagittal median sections, the lower limb in transverse sections made at different heights, the eye in meridian sections.

In view of the complex interweaving of the various organs, Leonardo proposed that several dissections be made for each system, and that, especially for the veins and arteries, all the organs surrounding them be extirpated so as to leave them isolated. An idea of particular importance was his demonstration of the viscera from the dorsal side of the trunk, after ablation of its posterior wall. He suggested that the bones be sawed through so as to discover their internal structure, and recognized the inadequacy of the method of maceration in "lime water," used by the ancients and even by some people today, to demonstrate the distribution of the nerves in the muscles. In order better to study the action of the single muscles, he had proposed to replace them in the skeleton with copper wires attached to the respective points of origin and termination. Although it is not impossible that others had tried something similar before him, Leonardo merits the main priority for the method of injecting solidifiable materials into hollow organs in order to reproduce the exact form of their cavities; he used this method, we shall see, to get wax casts of ventricles of the brain and the orifices and valves of the heart. He had also thought of a "plaster form" to distend the heart by means of a glass tube, and a glass form to show how the blood acts in closing the cardiac valves. Another method proposed by Leonardo, this time for the study of the eye, consisted in immersing the organ in egg

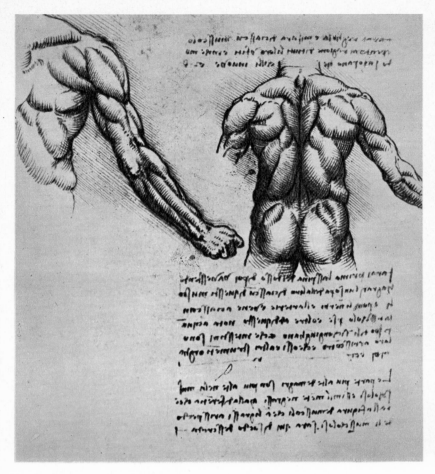

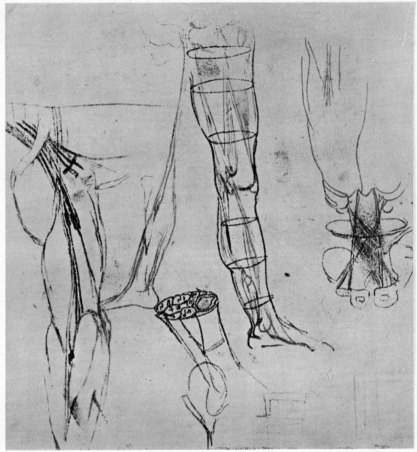

white and boiling everything so as to obtain a single coagulated block which can be cut through, eye and all; this method anticipated by centuries the method of embedding used in modern microscope technique. He also suggested boiling for the purpose of finding the structure of the kidneys.

Since Leonardo represented and studied the organs, and especially the viscera, in their positions and reciprocal relationships, sometimes including references to practical applications, he may be regarded today as a precursor in the field of topographical anatomy as well.

We proceed to set forth under main headings the principal contributions he made as regards the various systems of the human body, with occasional reference to the most important comparative data.

In general anatomy Leonardo basically followed Aristotle's conception of *partes similares* (Galen's *corpora similaria*, Avicenna's *membra simplicia* or *similia*, etc.), and recognized the presence of eleven "simple members or mechanical instruments" in the human body, namely "cartilage, bones, nerves, veins, arteries, membranes, ligaments, tendons and skin, and flesh and fat," describing their characteristics in detail. He admitted subdivisions in some of these classifications, dividing bone, for example, into "marrowy, spongy, hollow, and solid," and membranes into "tendinous, nervous, compound, and mixed."

As for the tegument, Leonardo recognized the entire "superficial skin" as the seat of the sense of touch, and also distinguished in it the *sopravesta*, that is, the epidermis and more specifically its horny layer, which flakes off under the action of the sun, and the subcutaneous tissue. He also ascribed great importance to the skin in the phenomenon of contraction of the superficial muscles, because of the compression exerted on the muscles by the tone of the skin.

In the skeletal apparatus, Leonardo draws the axial skeleton very well, from three "aspects," with few inaccuracies, both the *spina* (the vertebral column), with its various curves, and the thorax. He shows the number of "spondyles," that is, of vertebrae, comparing the dimensions of some of them. The skull is considered as a whole; masterly drawings show it either intact, or with the brainpan removed, or sawed through sagitally and open at the frontal and maxillary sinuses and the nasolacrimal duct; the sagittal sections also show the sphenoidal sinus. The skeleton of the limbs is drawn *in toto* and in its various segments, and especially studied with respect to their proportions. The acromial process of the shoulder is regarded as an autonomous bone, corresponding to Galen's *os acromiale*; it is described as a "glandular or stony bone," that is, a sesamoid bone, like the kneecap or *burella del ginocchio* and the two sesamoids of the foot. Of particular interest is the observation of the shortening of the forearm in passing from supination to pronation, because of the crossing of the radius and ulna; Leonardo thought that this shortening was considerable, but actually it comes to about 2.5 millimeters as a rule. More extensive graphic treatment is given to the skeleton of the hand, which is also dealt with in comparison with that of other mammals, especially the monkey, not to speak of the comparative data concerning the wings of bats and birds. As regards the lower limbs, the first fact to be pointed out is the precise inclination given the pelvis or "basin" of man in the various drawings in which it is represented. Here too, in the free part of the limbs, it is

Left: Muscles of back and upper limb – Anat. Ms. B, fol. 27 r

Right: Muscles of lower limb and trunk – Quad. Anat. V, fol. 19 v

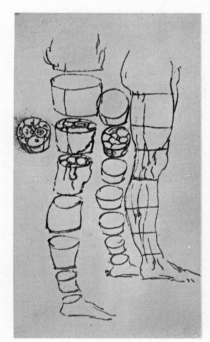

Lower limb in transverse sections – Quad. Anat. V, fol. 20 r

365

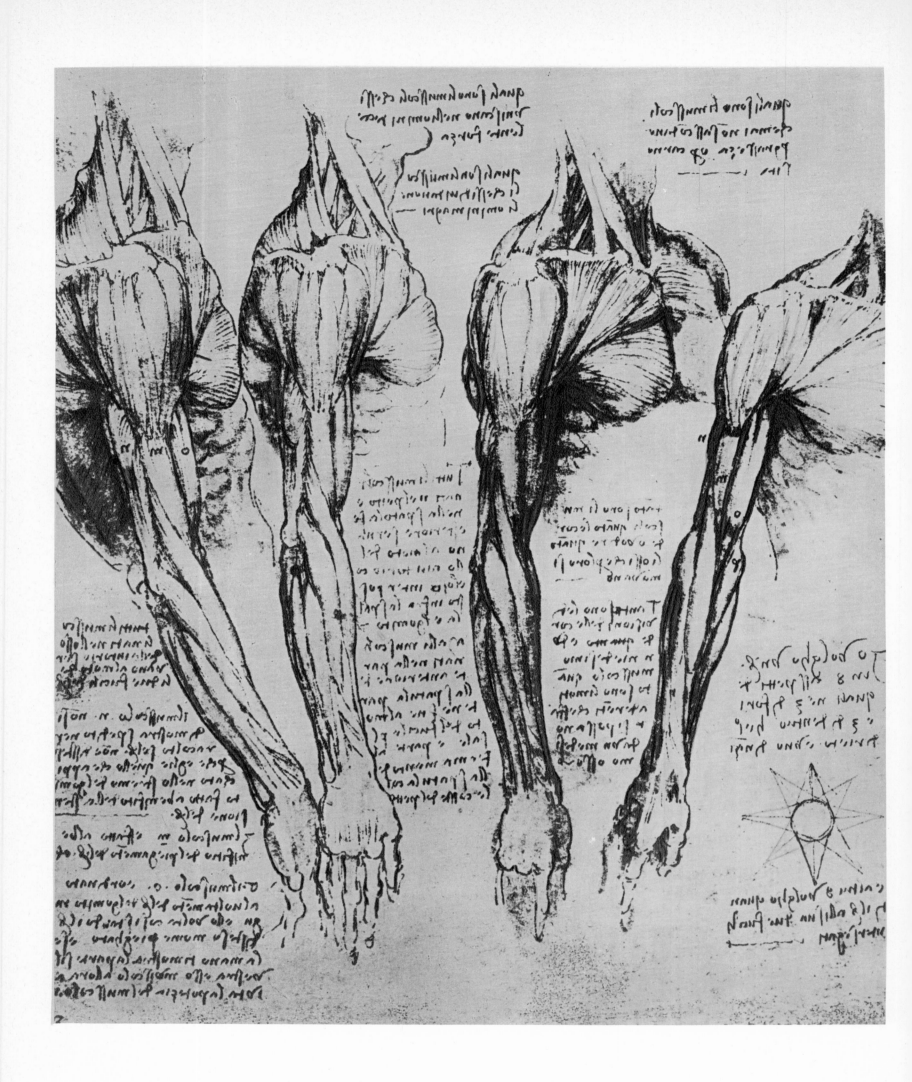

Muscles of upper limb – Anat. Ms. A, fol. 9 v

especially the foot that is drawn. Interesting data are offered for the homologies of the lower human limb (skeleton, muscles, external forms), especially lehen positioned on tiptoe, in relation to the legs of other mammals, such as the horse and the bear, for whose foot there are four splendid figures in ink, silver pencil, and white lead, reproducing the skeleton with the claws, tendons, and muscles.

With regard to the joints, apart from the drawings in which they are represented secondarily, we may say that Leonardo usually limited himself to general conceptions; he made a few particular references to the knee and to the "skins or membranous coatings" that surround it.

On the other hand, he devoted great care to the study and still more to the representation of the muscles, whose special importance in determining the external form of the body and the expression of the sentiments he fully realized. Anatomically he distinguished the muscles with respect to form, ratio between fleshy and tendinous portions, variations in volume and number (subdivision of a muscle into several, or vice versa, fusion of several muscles into a single entity), depending on the individual constitution, age, and use. He also described the perimysium. He took neither up all the groups of muscles nor all the individual muscles; the greater number are merely depicted, and only a few of them are distinguished by special names, taken for the most part from their actions. In addition, several muscles are drawn and described arbitrarily, and in a way not in conformity with the facts.

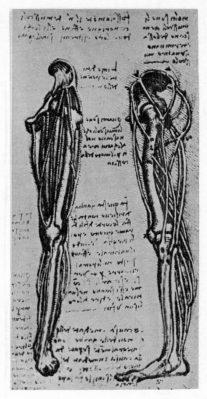

In physiology he is well aware of the general laws of muscular mechanics in relation to the bones and the articulations, and in treating the various muscular groups and single muscles he always lays particular stress on their actions; the better to study these, he proposed, as we have seen, to substitute copper wires for the muscles. The study of the facial muscles, especially in connection with mimicry, is noteworthy. With respect to the phenomenon of muscular contraction, Leonardo basically followed the theory that vital spirits flow in the lumen of the hollow nerves and bring "feeling," that is, the stimulus, to the muscle. The distension of the contracted muscle was likely to be attributed to the great accumulation of blood, and to a mechanism similar to that of the erection of the penis.

In the domain of the circulatory apparatus, the anatomy and physiology of the heart are one of the themes to which Leonardo dedicated himself with special diligence, supplementing his observations with many drawings and illustrative diagrams. In addition to his investigation of the human organ, he devoted special and perhaps even more extensive studies to the heart in large mammals, and especially in the ox. It is doubtful whether he personally experimented on the living animal; however, he made a famous observation in Tuscany of the rhythmic oscillations of the barrel opener or borer which the slaughterers drove into the hearts of living pigs through the wall of the thorax. According to Leonardo, the heart is within the mediastinum, surrounded by the pericardium or "capsule" (Mondino), and covered directly by a membrane, namely, the epicardium, which holds the coronary blood vessels against the organ. Leonardo considered the atria as integral parts of the heart, calling them "upper or extrinsic ventricles" or "ears" (a term sometimes used to indicate only auricular appendages), in contradistinction to the "lower or intrinsic ventricles." But when he came to the septum of the ventricles, even though he sometimes showed it as solid in his sections, as it actually appeared in the preparations, he could not yet liberate himself from the authority of the ancients, but continued to consider the septum, and sometimes to show it erroneously, as traversed by "pyramidal meatuses" connecting the two cavities, sometimes even using the old term of "colatorium" (sieve). He was aware of the presence of the (parietal) endocardium in the chambers of the heart, and of the intraventricular trabeculae, pointing out in particular the moderator band, the "chain," of the right ventricle, which bears the name of Leonardo today. But the valves of the heart, "gates, exits, flaps, membranes," and their way of functioning were the subjects of especially long and accurate observations—both the atrioventricular valves in connection with the "tendinous cords or fittings of the gates" and the papillary muscles, and the semilunar valves, with their arterial sinuses or "hemicycles." All these were reproduced in numbers of drawings and diagrams. He dealt with venous and arterial valves both in the right and the left side of the heart, as these relate to the "aorta" and to the "gate of the lung or arterial vein," that is, the pulmonary artery, called "arterial vein" by the ancients as opposed to the "venal artery," which is equivalent to the left atrium.

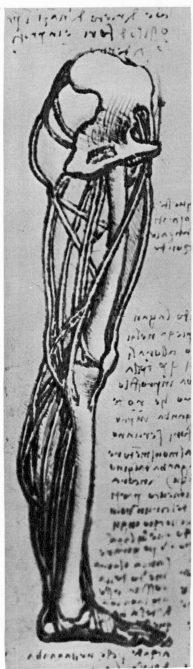

Although Leonardo makes the theoretical distinction between the major arteries "with two coats" and the veins "with only one coat," he still often gives the name of "veins" to the arteries as well, using veins as synonymous with blood vessels. Many elegant figures depict the larger and medium-sized blood vessels of the body, not always with the most faithful precision, while the vessels belonging to the individual viscera and the limbs are drawn together with them. Particular care is given to reproducing certain systems, for exemple, the superficial veins, especially those of the upper limb. It is not impossible that Leonardo at least sensed the existence of the capillaries; it is certain at any rate that he pointed out the presence of "capillary veins" in some organs, such as the skin and the liver.

The data and illustrations concerning the splanchnic apparatus are also noteworthy. In relation to the digestive apparatus, he particularly depicts and comments on the various functions of the lips, the teeth, the tongue—mentioning the special roughness of the latter in the felines and bovines—the soft palate, the pharynx, and the esophagus (under the Arabic-sounding name of *meri*), the stomach, and the various sections of the intestines or *budella*, with the *sifac* (peritoneum) and the *zirbo* or *rete*, that is, the great omentum. While there is no reference in Leonardo, not even a graphic one, to the salivary glands or the pancreas, the liver and the spleen are copiously depicted and discussed, including their functions according to the ancient conceptions. Leonardo has many important ideas on the problems of nutrition, with respect to the circulation of materials and the exchanges between the external world and the animal organism.

Two of Leonardo da Vinci's drawings regarding lower limb. Muscles have been replaced by wires, in order to show their functions – Quad. Anat. V, fol. 4 r

367

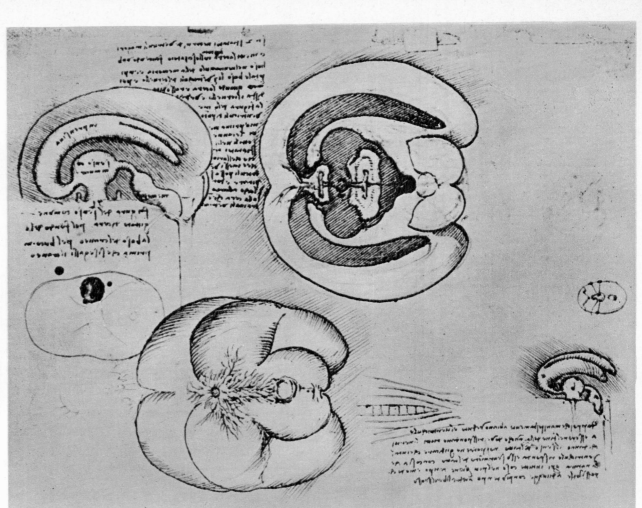

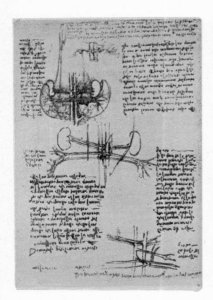

Page showing above vessels of peritoneum, in center and below, those
of liver, spleen, and kidneys – Anat.
Ms. B. fol. 11 v

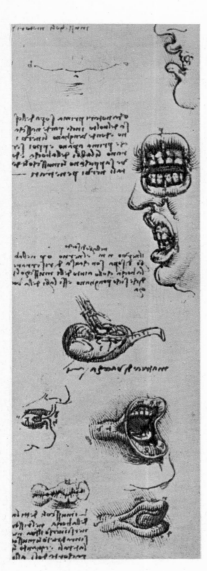

Movements of lips – Anat. Ms. B,
fol. 38 v

As regards the respiratory apparatus, Leonardo devotes special study first of all to the organs of the voice, considering them, together with the organs of the mouth, primarily from the physiological point of view. In particular, he attributes the variations in the tone of the voice to the trachea, with its variations in length and in the width of its "rings," and perhaps also to the constrictor muscles of the pharynx, the lungs behaving "in the capacity of a bellows"; he compiled a table of the elements of language, and also seems to have written a treatise *De vocie* ("On the Voice"). The thyroid gland is depicted together with the trachea, but no mention is made of the thymus. The lungs are usually considered together as a single organ comprising two virtually symmetrical parts and immediately surrounded by its "case," that is, the parietal pleura; it is depicted several times, but usually in a form suggesting the lungs in other mammals rather than in man. He studied especially the various phases of respiration, which are performed passively by the action not only of the muscles of the thorax and diaphragm but also by those of the "transverse [muscles] of the abdomen," and in order to study these motions better he proposed to substitute a bladder for the lungs. He made the very important observation that animals cannot live where flame does not live.

Coming to the genito-urinary apparatus, the first point to be noted is that Leonardo proposed to investigate the structure of the kidneys by cutting them through the middle or by boiling them, as has been pointed out, in order to make particular search for the "sieve" by means of which the urine is separated from the blood, the amount of urine being in proportion to the quantity of blood circulating in the kidneys. The organ is depicted with its "milking" vessels, in isolation and *in situ*, the right kidney being shown either at the same level as the left one, or as positioned a little higher or lower.

There is no verbal or graphic mention of the adrenal glands. The ureters (*poli* or *pori uritidi*) depicted with the kidneys and studied especially in the region where they discharge into the bladder. The bladder is shown *in situ* or in isolation, along with the other organs of the system, always in a state of distension and often surrounded by its nutrient vessels. The testicles are frequently drawn, usually within the scrotum, with the epididymes, the "spermatic ducts," that is, the vasa deferentia, and the "spermatic ventricles," the seminal vesicles (not drawn very exactly). The related blood vessels are often depicted, but the prostate is never drawn or mentioned. In contradiction to the theories of Mondino and other authors as regards the origin of the sperm, Leonardo remains basically faithful to the Aristotelian and Galenian principle, holding that "the sperm is cooked" in the testicle "after having been blood." The penis is drawn several times *in situ* or isolated, often in conjunction with the bladder, or else in transverse section, but with a structure not in conformity with actuality, on the basis of erroneous conclusions reached by Mondino. The ovaries are likewise called "testicles," and depicted, and in part discussed, as like those of the male. The feminine sperm is first blood, like the male sperm, and both, on coming in contact with the respective testicles, take on "generative virtue." The uterus is shown as single and not with two horns, as Galen held it to be, on the basis of the data acquired in regard to other mammals; it is drawn in pregnancy, sometimes

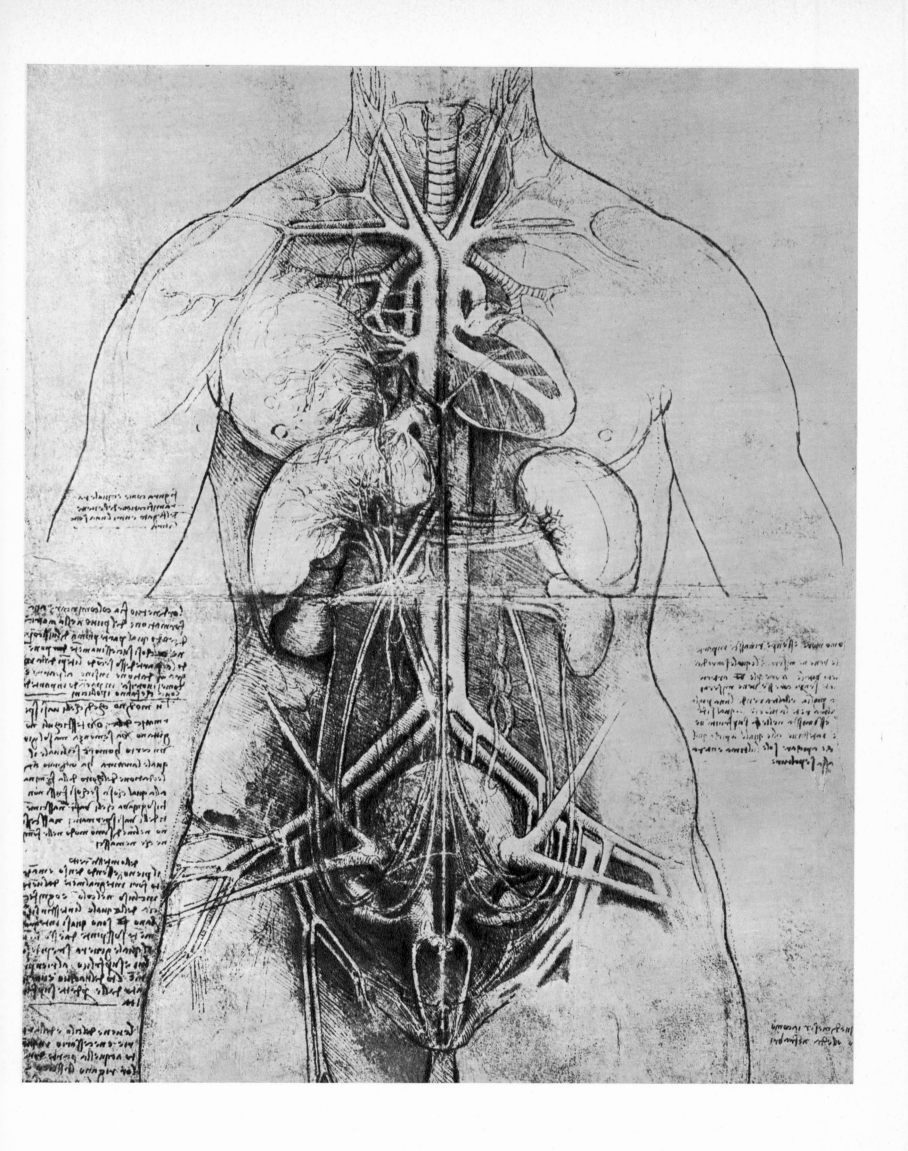

Trunk of female human body, with internal organs seen as though ventral side were transparent – Quad. Anat. I, fol. 12 r

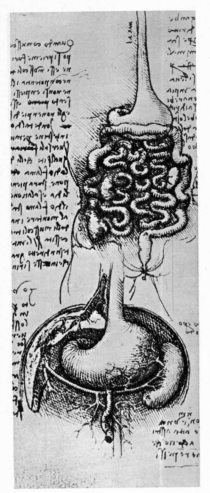

Stomach and intestines – Anat. Ms.
B, fol. 14 v

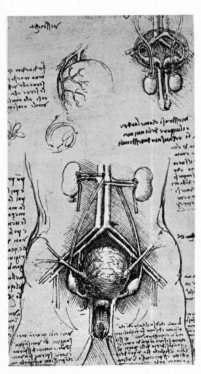

Genito-urinary system – Weimar,
Schloss Museum

closed and *in situ,* and sometimes in isolation and open, with the fetus and the membranes inside. It is shown in the abdomen with two pairs of long lateral appendages, in which the round ligaments can be discerned and also the uterine tubes, later shown by Fallopio. The clitoris, "genital member," is represented usually *in situ,* in sagittal or frontal section, and is thought to be relatively larger in its dimensions in women than in other large mammals. The vulva is drawn rather crudely; the breast is taken up particularly in studies on proportions and considered in relation to the "menstrual veins."

In the central nervous system Leonardo took up especially the encephalon, representing it in its general outlines either in the opened skull or in isolation, with the "ventricles or porosities" shown in projection or uncovered, and often some of the cranial nerves. He used two systems to perform injection of the ventricles, which we have already mentioned in connection with Leonardo's methods of investigation. He either removed the brain, making an opening into each lateral ventricle by way of a vent, into which he inserted two thin reeds to let the air escape, and then injecting melted wax with a "syringe" at the inferior angle of the fourth ventricle; or else he made the injection into the intact cranium through the foramen magnum. In both cases he then removed the substance of the brain from around the solidified cast, of which he also made a drawing; in these, as in the drawings of the encephalon, the arrangement differs somewhat from that actually found in man. Fundamentally following ancient doctrines, Leonardo localized "the memory" in the fourth ventricle, and the "*sensus communis* or concourse of all the senses and seat of the soul" in the third ventricle—to be more specific, in its floor—and set up a series of distances and levels between it and the skeleton and various superficial and deep-lying organs; finally, he situated the *imprensiva* [receptive soul] in the lateral ventricles, between the *sensus communis* and the five senses; by means of it the *sensus communis* "is moved." This "seat of the soul" is the origin of the nerves going to the muscles that move the members "at the pleasure of the will of that soul," and there the sense nerves terminate.

Leonardo, with the ancients, recognizes, and draws diagrammatically, two meninges, the dura mater and the pia mater, as well as Galen's *rete mirabile,* up against the base of the cranium, a structure that is nonexistent, at least in man. The spinal cord, which also includes the medulla oblongata, is called the "mucha" and drawn, at least in its upper portion, in diagrammatic figures together with the nerves and meninges. It originates in the brain and is of the same material; it gives rise in turn to the nerves (bulbar and spinal). On the basis of statements of Galen and experiments on frogs, Leonardo is aware that in man similarly puncture of the medulla oblongata entails immediate death. The meninges are prolonged peripherally around the nerves. Some of the nerves are motor and some sensory, and the latter "spread out in the skin with infinite ramification"; resection of the nerves sometimes causes loss of mobility, sometimes loss of sensitivity, and sometimes loss of both. Leonardo proposed study of the individual foramina from which the cranial nerves leave the base of the skull. Described and depicted together with the brain are first the *caruncole* (Mondino), the olfactory lobes, which serve the power (*virtù*) of smell and which are of cerebral material and related to the complex nasal cavities in the "leonine species," in which this sense is more highly developed; then come the "optic nerves," which serve the visual faculty, and in man are "thin, long, and weak" as compared with those of the leonine species, in which they join the eye directly to the brain. Although Leonardo refers to the "nerves moving the eye," they certainly do not appear among the nerves that are depicted, while there are without question drawings of the branches of the trigeminus and especially the maxillary nerve with some of its principal branches. It is not certain that the facial nerve was drawn, or the spinal accessory and the hypoglossal nerves, not to speak of the glossopharyngeal. The vagus nerves, especially in their thoracic and abdominal tracts, were often depicted, especially in connection with the organ of the voice, the heart, and the stomach, under Mondino's name of "reversive nerves," so called because of their collateral branch, the inferior or recurrent laryngeal nerve. As for the spinal nerves, the plexuses are often represented, especially the brachial and sacral plexuses, and described with their principal terminal branches. It is not certain that Leonardo included the cervical sympathetic trunk, not unknown as early as Galen's time, in a semidiagrammatic drawing.

Although Leonardo made more or less summary references to the sense organs, "seeing, hearing, touching, tasting, and smelling" (Aristotle), of which the *sensus communis* is the "common judge," he treated only one sense organ in a special manner, namely, the eye, which he studied not only anatomically but also physiologically, either by itself or most of all in his investigations on perspective. However, despite the above-mentioned method of embedding the eye in coagulated albumen, the true structure of the eye escaped him almost entirely, misled as he was by the old preconceptions that were still prevalent at that time. Discussing the cornea or *luce,* shown independently of the sclerotica, he ponders as to whether the visual faculty resides in the cornea, or in the lens, or in the uvea, and comments at length, with the aid of many diagrams, on numerous problems of dioptrics. However, the most important observation from the biological point of view, one which is illustrated in several passages and was known to some of the Arab physicians, is that regarding the variation of the diameter of the pupil depending on the amount of light: "The eye of man doubles its pupil in the darkness." This variation was also studied comparatively in nocturnal birds and the felines. The organs protecting the eye are taken up chiefly in the studies of proportions, while special data are given for the structure and the functioning of the eyelid apparatus of birds, especially with respect to the nictitating membrane, which Leonardo calls "second or transparent cover or membrane."

As regards embryology, we have seen, in connection with the study of the genital organs, Leonardo's theories as to the nature of the male and female sperm. Paternal and maternal characteristics are transmitted to the child equally; the soul of the mother governs the body of the fetus as well; the sense impressions of the mother may reach the fetus; the way in which copulation takes place

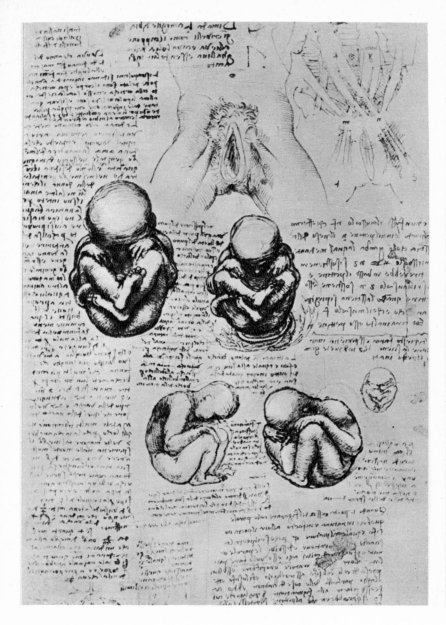

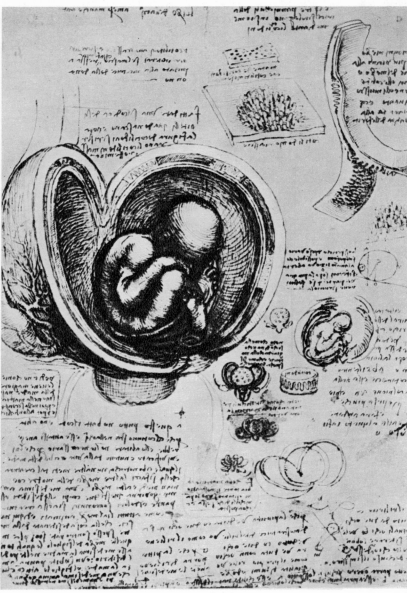

has a primary influence on the morale of the child. On the basis of Aristotelian doctrine, Leonardo asserts that the organs of the entire body have "origin in the heart as from the first creation"; but soon "the house of the intellect," the head and the brain, assumes predominant influence in development. The fetus grows at the expense of its mother's menstrual blood, which passes into its intestines through the umbilical vein, the liver, the vena porta, and the stomach; it urinates by way of the urachus through the umbilicus. At four months the fetus has reached half the length and one eighth the weight of the infant at birth, when it is one ell long. The umbilical cord in the human species has the same length as the fetus at each stage of development. There are noteworthy drawings of the human fetus in its characteristic intra-uterine position, either in isolation or within the opened uterus, together with its appendages. Fundamentally following Galen, Leonardo upholds the tenet of the presence of three membranes surrounding the fetus, which he calls "amnion, allantoid, and *secondina* or chorion"; the fetus is immersed in the amniotic fluid, which is "lemon-yellow, crystalline, in large amount," and distributes its weight equally over the inner surface of the uterus; the fetus does not breathe or speak, because it would drown at once. The fetal appendages were studied in detail in other mammals, especially in the bovines; in regard to these, descriptions and drawings are given of the "cotyledons or rosettes or *spugnole*," distinguished as having two parts, the fetal part being villous, the maternal part, sievelike; Leonardo distinguishes these by the adjectives "male" and "female." Various other embryological discussions deal with the eggs of birds.

During its autonomous life the human body grows at a constantly decreasing rate; "the amount of this growth decreases every nine months until it has reached its maximum height." At the age of three the human being has reached half its total height (Pliny). This final height is equal to three ells (1.65 meters, more likely, to 1.78 meters, according to the standard used for the ell).

Although Leonardo set up a relatively rigid canon for the proportions of the human body, as we have seen, he still was well aware of the variations due to the diverse types of individual structure —brachytype, longitype, and normotype—and showed how an individual may be well proportioned and either short and heavy, or tall and thin, or of medium build. The human body weighs 200 pounds, i.e., from 65 to 68 kilograms; women weigh less.

One of the themes that most closely show the collaboration of the anatomist and the artist is brought out in the study on the proportions of the human body, which constitutes as it were the

Left: Human fetuses in intra-uterine position – Quad. Anat. III, fol. 7 r

Right: Human fetus in opened uterus – Quad. Anat. III, fol. 8 r

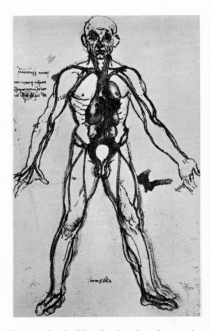

Leonardo da Vinci's drawing for study of superficial veins of limbs – Quad. Anat. V, fol. 1 r

371

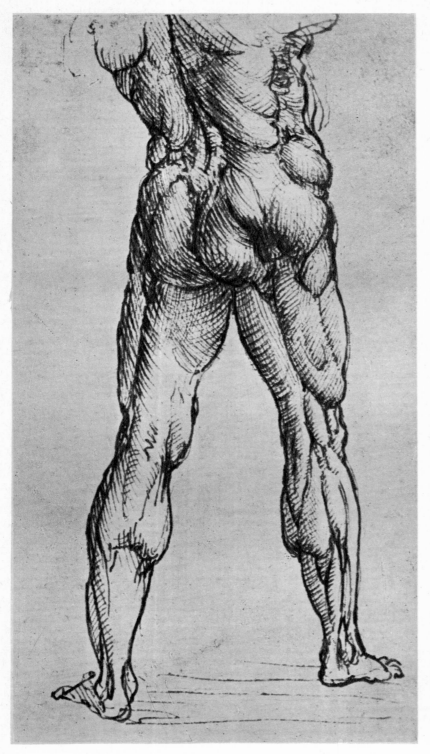

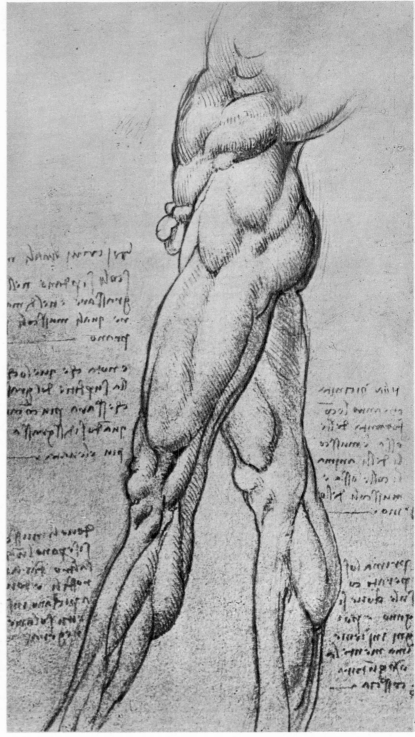

Left: Muscles of back – Turin,
former Royal Library

Right: Muscles of lower limbs – Quad.
Anat. V, fol. 22 r

complement of the basic precepts later collected in the *Treatise on Painting*. Leonardo's canon, although it has many similarities to the canons of the ancients, especially those of Varro and Vitruvius, and with some contemporary ones, still may be considered largely original, because of the richness and variety of the data, and the illustrations in the form of numerous designs or even simple sketches. Here we shall merely recall the confirmation of the ratio given by Vitruvius and Pliny between the spread of the arms and the total height, which is set, along with many other proportions, in the classic drawing of man in the square and in the circle; half the height at the level of the penis; the trunk as long as the arm down to the wrist, that is a third of the total height; the foot one seventh of it (one sixth, according to Vitruvius); the head an eighth; the face and the hand, a ninth; the lip, probably taken by Leonardo as a modulus or unit of measurement, the one hundred and twelfth part of the total height. In particular, there are many statements of proportions among the segments of the various parts of the body, especially of the various organs of the face, which is twelve lips high all in all, while the height of the scalp is from one to three.

Leonardo also gave proportions for children, horses, and dogs; those on the horse were most extensive, and probably served as a preliminary study for the equestrian statue of Francesco Sforza and the cartoon for the *Battle of Anghiari*.

GIUSEPPE FAVARO

LEONARDO AS PHYSIOLOGIST

It would be more accurate to entitle this chapter "Leonardo as Anatomical Physiologist," not in order to suggest that Leonardo was an anatomist and a physiologist at the same time, in the modern sense of the words, but because what we may take as his physiology is essentially an exposition of the functions of the parts of the human or animal body observed directly or upon dissection. De Toni felicitously expressed this idea as follows: "Leonardo did not study the structure of the human body and those of animals in order to acquire merely a knowledge of anatomy, but more especially to learn anatomy, first, in the applications it can or rather must have in art, and second, in its physiological significance.... Leonardo then tried to penetrate into the basic principles of the cold and immobile truths of anatomy with the guidance of physiology, allotting to the concept of anatomy its true importance, considering it, in the words of Lanzillotti-Buonsanti, as what it really is, the substratum and instrument of living nature and therefore inseparable from the function incumbent on the organ." [1]

Branching of elder – Ms. G, fol. 29 r

Even earlier than De Toni, Lanzillotti-Buonsanti [2] said of Leonardo's physiological work: "Arsène Houssaye [3] remarked rightly that Leonardo looked for life even in death; the words written over the door of an anatomical theater in Paris, *Hic locus est, ubi mors gaudet succurrere vitae* ("Here is where death comes to the aid of life"), which express in precise terms the importance of the anatomical study on the cadaver for understanding the phenomena of the living organism, had in him an anticipator and perfect interpreter.... This intimate cohabitation between the anatomical concept and its function constitutes the characteristic feature, the culminating point of Leonardo's thought. It is the physiological part that reveals all the power of his qualities as profound observer and modern psychologist."

Physiology as an autonomous science, independent of anatomy, had not yet been born at the time of Leonardo, and saw the light only two centuries later; even the word "physiology" in the sense in which we use it today was not yet current. During the Middle Ages a book entitled *Physiologus* was much used by naturalists. But it was nothing more than a "jumble of parallels and much more often of fables and legends about animals, serpents, and stones, considered to be the bringers of good or evil fortune to men. Its pagan kernel, considerably increased by Christian additions, had become a kind of religious natural history. The *Physiologus* was the source of the rich symbolism that was used in medieval architecture. At the time of Albertus Magnus, the assertions of this book were still accepted even by such men of learning as Vincent of Beauvais and Thomas of Chantimpré. Albert himself was not always uninfluenced by the *Physiologus*." [4]

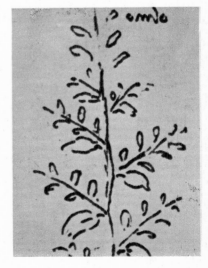

Branching of elm – Ms. G, fol. 27 r

[1] G. B. de Toni. *La biologia in Leonardo da Vinci*, Venice, 1903, p. 12 f.
[2] A. Lanzillotti-Buonsanti. *Il pensiero anatomico di Leonardo da Vinci*, Milan, 1897, p. 8 f.
[3] A. Houssaye. *Histoire de Léonard de Vinci*, Paris, 1869, p. 77.
[4] P. Girolamo Wilms, O.P. *Alberto Magno*, transl. by P. Isnardo Marega, O.P., Bologna, 1931, p. 45 f.

Origin of branches on plants – Ms. G, fol. 33 r

Light and shade on trees – Ms. I, fol. 37 v

Neither in Leonardo nor in the works of the physicians and anatomists that preceded him or immediately followed him—Leonardo was familiar with these, as is shown by Solmi's researches [5] —do we ever find the words "physiology," [6] "physiologist," "physiological," used is their modern meanings. To express the idea of function, and this word too was not current in those times, Leonardo uses the words "instrumental use of the limbs," "offices," "aids," "uses," "purposes," "benefits."

We must come down to the eighteenth century to find these words used by Albert von Haller (1708-1777) in his *Elementa physiologiae* [7] and by Lazzaro Spallanzani (1729-1799) in his works on the heart and on circulation, digestion, respiration, etc. [8] But although the words were not in use, the scientists of Leonardo's times, and Leonardo himself, were in possession of the conceptual content of the terms, as applied to the use of function of this or that organ. Their physiology was essentially a "special physiology of the organs."

At all events, Leonardo is generally much better known as an anatomist than as a physiologist; in fact, considering him as a physiologist may seem like heresy to some readers. This comes in part from imperfect acquaintance with his manuscripts, and in part from the admiration that his marvelous anatomical drawings have always aroused. And yet it is the spirit of the experimenter that is more highly developed in him, and that is the peculiar gift of the physiologist, not of the anatomist. The proof of this lies in the many valuable canons of experimental method to be found throughout his pages. If he could have experimented on animals and on man, if he had had the opportunity to make artificial models reproducing other physiological functions besides that of the operation of the semilunar valves (see below) and the mechanical action of the muscles, if he had had at his disposal even a few of the instruments and aids that are used today to investigate the activity of living organs—who knows what a harvest of physiological discoveries he would have garnered, long before the physiologists of the eighteenth and nineteenth centuries?

Several commentators on Leonardo's biological work, chief among them Favaro, [9] while giving first place to his strictly anatomical studies, also refer to his more narrowly physiological researches, and to the functional considerations he adds to his descriptions and drawings of parts of the animal or human body; but they do this almost always in such a way as to imply that physiological research was only an accessory part of his work. The truth is quite the opposite, namely, that beyond all he kept uppermost in thought the search for the phenomena in which life manifests itself, and their causes; the configurations and structures of the organs interested him as a field of knowledge indispensable for art, and thereafter primarily as the sources of information as to the locus of those phenomena. Among his topics are these:

"Of the cause of breathing, of the cause of the motion of the heart, of the cause of vomiting, of the cause of the descent of food from the stomach, of the cause of emptying of the intestines.

"Of the cause of the movement of the superfluous matter through the intestines.

"Of the cause of swallowing, of the cause of coughing, of the cause of yawning, of the cause of sneezing, of the cause of limbs going to sleep.

"Of the cause of tickling.

"Of the cause of lust and other appetites of the body, of the cause of urine and also of all the natural excretions of the body. [10]

"Which tendon causes the motion of the eye so that the motion of one eye moves the other?

"Of contracting the brows, of raising the brows, of lowering the brows, of closing the eyes, of opening the eyes, of distending the nostrils, of opening the lips with the teeth together, of pouting with the lips, of smiling, of expressing astonishment.

"Describe the beginning of man when it is caused in the womb, and why an eight months' child does not live. What sneezing is. What yawning is. Falling sickness, spasms, paralysis, shivering with cold, sweating, fatigue, hunger, sleepiness, thirst, lust.

"Of the tendon which causes the movement from the shoulder to the elbow, movement from the elbow to the hand, etc.

[5] E. Solmi. *Le fonti dei manoscritti di Leonardo da Vinci*, Turin, Loescher, 1908. With respect to anatomy and physiology, the principal sources, beyond Hippocrates, Aristotle, and Galen, are:
1. Magistri Mundini de Luccis (1270-1326), *Anathomia*, Pavia, 1478; Bologna, 1482; Padua, 1484; Venice, 1494 and 1498 (Mondino de' Liucci, *Anatomia*. Reprod. from a Bologna ms. of the fourteenth century and transl. into the vernacular in the fifteenth century; ed. by L. Sighinolfi, Bologna, Cappelli, 1930).
2. Alexandri Benedicti medici clariss. *Anatomice, sive de historia corporis humani, libri quinque*, Venice, 1498 and 1502 (Strasbourg, 1528).
We should perhaps add to these two sources the teachings of Marc'Antonio della Torre, whom Leonardo met and became friendly with in 1510 and 1511 (Solmi, *op. cit.*, p. 273). Carlo Amoretti (*Memorie storiche su la vita, gli studi e le opere di Lionardo da Vinci*, preface to an edition of Leonardo's *Trattato della pittura*, Milan, 1804) speaks of "the long and diligent study of anatomy that Leonardo made while in Pavia, having as his instructor the able professor Marc'Antonio della Torre of Genoa, whom da Vinci greatly aided by the accuracy of his drawings, while he himself drew from this an exact knowledge of human structure, and of the use of the parts of the body." On the relations of Leonardo with della Torre see G. B. de Toni, "Frammenti Vinciani, I: Intorno a Marco Antonio dalla Torre anatomico veronese del xvi secolo ed all'epoca del suo incontro con Leonardo da Vinci in Pavia," in *Atti del Regio Istituto Veneto*, etc., Ser. VII, VII, p. 190-203.
[6] The word *fisiologia* was also used by Galen. "But we shall not have read far before we discover that the term *Physiology*, as used by Galen, stands not merely for what we understand by it nowadays, but also for a large part of *Physics* as well": A. J. Brock, *Galen on the Natural Faculties, with an English Translation*, London, 1916, p. xxvii.
[7] A. von Haller. *Elementa physiologiae corporis humani*, Vol. I-VIII, Lausanne, 1757-1766.
[8] L. Spallanzani. *Le opere*, Vol. I-V, 1-2, Reale Accademia d'Italia, 1932-1936.
[9] G. Favaro. "Leonardo biologo", in *Enciclopedia italiana*, XX (1933), 887.
[10] J. P. Richter. *Literary Works of Leonardo da Vinci*, 2d ed., London, New York, and Toronto, 1939, Vol. II, no. 814, p. 93.

"Of the tendon which causes the movement of the thigh, and from the knee to the foot, etc." [11]

Now these are purely physiological problems; and it was Leonardo's burning desire to solve them, after having "figured" the organs in which the several processes took place: "And so may it please our Great Author that I may demonstrate the nature of man and his ways, as I describe his figure." [12]

If time and strength failed him, the reason was in part that his mind was attracted by too many phenomena, indeed by all the phenomena of life, which must have appeared something new and divine, the revelation of a world closed to the eyes of mortals before him. And another reason was his aversion to particularism and partial knowledge, his ardent love for the universal. For he writes: "All the love that goes to a part is taken from the whole, because all one's delight has been concentrated on that thing, abandoning the universal for the particular" (*Treatise*, ed. Ludwig, no. 58, p. 112).

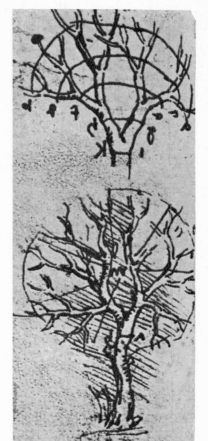

Branching of plants – Ms. G, fol. **30 v**

That Leonardo was not a gross dissector, but diligently observed the structure of the human cadaver, is shown by the fact that his manuscripts contain references to what we today call tissues and, dimly, to their functions, and hence present a sort of rudimentary physiology of the tissues, or histophysiology, as appears from the following passage:

"Definitions of the instruments.

"Discourse on the nerves, muscles, tendons, membranes, and ligaments.

"The function of the nerves is to convey sensation [and induce motion]; they are the drivers of the soul, for they have their origin from its seat and command the muscles, so that they move the members at the pleasure of the will of this soul.

"The muscles, the ministers of the nerves, draw to themselves the sinews, which are joined to these members in a similar manner.

"The tendons are mechanical instruments which have no sensation of themselves but carry out as much work as is entrusted to them.

"The *panniculi* [membranes] are joined to the flesh, being interposed between the flesh and the nerve, and most frequently they are joined to the cartilage.

"The ligaments are joined to the tendons and are of the nature of membranes which bind together the joints of the bones [capsules of the joints], and are converted into cartilage, and they are as many in number at every joint as are the tendons which move the joint and as are the tendons opposite to these which come to the same joint, and these ligaments join and merge together, helping and strengthening one another, and connecting with one another.

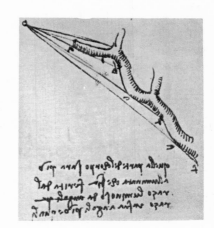

Studies of light on plants – Ms. G, fol. 22 r

"Cartilage is a hard substance, like, let us say, hardened tendon or softened bone, and its position is always between the bone and the tendon because it partakes of both substances, and it is flexible and unbreakable, the flexibility acting in it like a spring.

"Pellicles [elastic or muscular membranes?] are certain muscular parts which are made up of flesh, tendons, and nerves, the union of these forming a composition which is capable of being extended in any direction; flesh is a mixture made up of muscles, tendon, nerve, blood, and artery.

"Bone is hard matter, inflexible, adapted for resistance, and is without sensation and terminates in the cartilages which form its extremities; and its marrow is composed of sponge, blood, and soft fat, coated over with a very thin tissue. The spongelike substance is a mixture of bone, fat, and blood.

"The *panniculi* are of three kinds, that is, made up of tendons, made up of nerves, and made up of nerves and tendons; and the mixed membrane is woven (*tessuto*, "tissued": Leonardo was the first to use this word in its biological sense) of tendon, nerve, muscle, vein, and artery.

"The membranes that are between the tendons and the cartilages are so formed as to unite tendon with cartilage in a large and continuous joint, so that it may not break through excess of force; and when the muscle itself thickens it does not draw to itself the tendon or any member, but the muscle is drawn by the tendon toward the membrane and the cartilage, as happens with the muscles inside the ventricles of the heart when they shut their openings. But the muscles of the other members are drawn toward the bone where they are joined, and draw their tendon behind them together with the member that is joined to this tendon" Quad. Anat. II, fol. 18 v).

There is a remarkable definition of adipose tissue—"spongy and empty fatness that is full of minute vesicles filled with air" (*Treatise*, ed. Ludwig, p. 328); "spongy or I should say vesicular fat, with minute vesicles [one would say he was using a microscope] full of air" (Ms. G, fol. 26 r; *Treatise*, ed. Ludwig, p. 332).

Moreover, it is true that "Gabriele Zerbi of Verona examined the skin, the fat, the cartilages, the muscles, the vessels, the nerves, the bones, with such minuteness of detail in his investigations that he surpassed not only Mondino but also the celebrated Guido de Cauliaco." [13] But all this is of little moment, and can be ignored, as compared with the physiology of the organs and their apparatus, that is, with the *De usu partium*, which is what from the first attracted the attention of scientists of that time.

Growth of plants – Ms. G, fol. 32 v

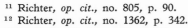

[11] Richter, *op. cit.*, no. 805, p. 90.
[12] Richter, *op. cit.*, no. 1362, p. 342.
[13] G. B. de Toni, *op. cit.*, p. 12.

Studies of light on plants – Ms. G, fol. 21 v

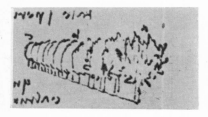

Perspective study of a row of trees – Ms. G, fol. 21 v

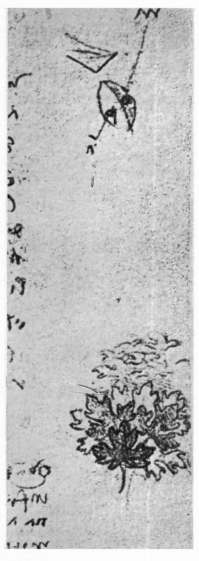

Effects of sunlight on plants – Ms. G, fol. 21 v

A problem of general nature, concerning his physiology as well, therefore, is that of the originality of Leonardo's observations. Undoubtedly he knew the ancients, and in many cases unfortunately allowed himself to be misled by their writings. He adopted the terminology[14] and many of the ideas of Galen, Mondino, and others. But as Solmi[15] says, "what the artist copied is little, as compared with what he wrote; what he received is very little, in face of what he gave, which is very much. Of all the teachers or supposed teachers... Greek and Latin and Arab and scholastic, only one remains true and authoritative for him, namely, nature. He had a right to sign himself in the Codex Atlanticus, 'Leonardo da Vinci, disciple of experiment.' "

Leonardo made observations and some experiments of strictly physiological nature on plants and animals. One refers to the ability of the epigeous organs of plants to absorb water. "The sun," he writes, "gives plants spirit and life; and the earth nourishes them with moisture. In this connection I have already tried the experiment of leaving only one very small root on a squash plant and keeping it supplied with water; and this squash brought to maturity all the fruits it could produce, which were about sixty squash of the long kind. And thinking diligently of this life [*vita*; perhaps *vite*, vine?] I realized that the night dew was what penetrated abundantly with its moisture to nourish this plant with its sons, at the joints of its great leaves" (Leonardo da Vinci, *Trattato della pittura*, Rome, 1890, p. 264). We have no way of saying whether he really made the experiment or only conceived it.

Similar observations referring to processes of nutrition are the following: "The stems of plants do not have the roundness of their thickness close to the points at which branches or roots originate. And the reason for this is that these upper and lower ramifications are the members from which the plant gets its nourishment: the parts that are above nourish it during the summer with the dew and the rains, by means of the leaves; the parts below [do so] during the winter by the contact of the earth with its roots" (Leonardo da Vinci, *Das Buch von der Malerei – Nach dem Codex Vaticanus* etc., Vienna, 1882, I, 1, n. 865, p. 272).

According to De Toni,[16] Leonardo correctly understood the way in which trees grow in thickness; he observed the effects of their annular decortications, and referred to the phenomena of negative geotropism. He points out the movement of the nutrient liquids in plants, in words that deserve to be cited: "When the bark is removed from the tree at some point, nature provides for this by sending to this wound a much larger amount of nutritive humor than elsewhere, so that because of the aforesaid deficiency the bark grows much thicker there than elsewhere. And this humor has such power of movement that, when it comes to the place being aided, part of it rises up like a bouncing ball with various pullulations and shoots, not otherwise than boiling water" (Cod. Atl., fol. 7 r). The last comparison is a fantastic exaggeration of the artist's. Elsewhere he writes: "The lower twigs of branches grow more than the upper twigs of plants, and this is because the humor that nourishes them has gravity and easier movement downward than upward" (Ms. G, fol. 34 v; Leonardo da Vinci, *Das Buch von der Malerei*, II, no. 915, p. 308).

Thus Leonardo has an inkling of the liquid flow that rises from the roots in the stems of plants, which constitutes what was only much later called "ascending" [crude] sap, and of the other current going down from the branches to the roots—"descending" [modified] sap—as well as of the physiological phenomenon that was later known as "root pressure."[17]

So far as the animals are concerned, I should like to leave aside the so-called *Bestiario leonardesco*, and the *Fior di virtù* and *Acerba* that derive from it,[18] as well as the studies on the flight of birds with which a more competent writer has dealt.[19] Instead I cite the following observations, as a sample of Leonardo's attitude toward experimentation:

"The frog retains life for some hours when the head, the heart, and all the intestines have been removed. And if you prick the said cord, it instantly twitches and dies.

"All the nerves of the animals derive from here: when this is pricked, [namely, the medulla oblongata] it instantly dies" (Quad. Anat. V, fol. 21 r).

"The frog dies at once when the spinal cord is pierced; and previous to this, it lived without head, without heart or any bowels or intestines or skin; and here [in the cerebrospinal axis], therefore, it would seem, lies the foundation of movement and life" (Quad. Anat. V, fol. 21 v).

He later notes that "the walking of man is always after the universal manner of walking in animals with four legs" (Richter, *op. cit.*, II, no. 826). He makes many observations concerning the form and changes in width of the pupils of nocturnal animals and those of the "leonine species," etc.

I cannot but give the words in which Leonardo relates the pre-eminence of the organs and the sense of smell in other animals as compared with man, as every anatomist and physiologist recognizes today. "I have found," he writes, "in the constitution of the human body that, just as among all the animal constitutions it is of more obtuse and blunt sensibilities, so it is formed as an instrument

[14] The terms *mirach* (abdominal wall), *siphach* (peritoneum), *zirbo* (omentum), *pori uritidi* (openings of the ureters into the bladder), *uscioli* (flaps or cusps of the heart valves), *porte, vena anteriore* (pulmonary artery), *arteria venale* (pulmonary veins), *meri* (oesophagus), *giovamenti* (functions), *membri spirituali e naturali, cassula del cuore* (pericardium), etc., occurring in Leonardo, are found in Mondino's *Anatomy*, for example, in the chapters on the heart, the lungs, etc.

[15] Solmi, *op. cit.*, p. 2 f.

[16] G. B. de Toni. *Le piante e gli animali in Leonardo da Vinci* (Publications of Istituto di Studi Vinciani in Rome, Vol. IV), Bologna, 1922.

[17] F. Cortesi. "Leonardo botanico," in *Sapere*, no. 95 (Dec. 15, 1938), p. 387.

[18] Cecco d'Ascoli. *L'Acerba*, Lanziano, 1916.

[19] R. Giacomelli. *Gli scritti di Leonardo sul volo*, Rome, 1936.

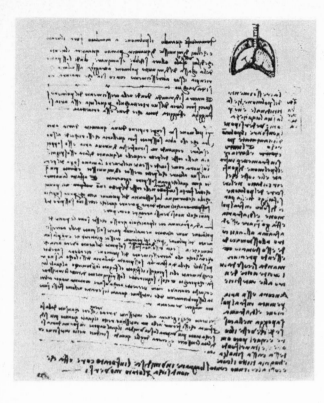

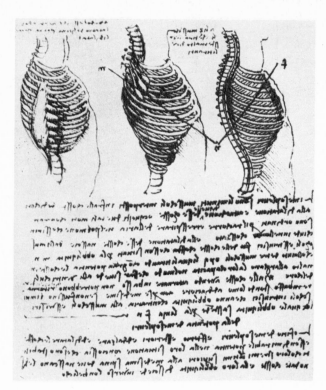

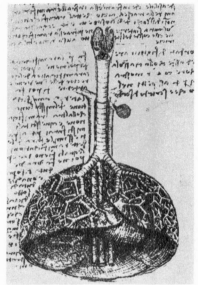

Trachea and branching of bronchi in lungs – Anat. Ms. B, fol. 37 v

less ingenious, of parts less capable of receiving the power of the senses. I have seen in the leonine species how the sense of smell, forming part of the substance of the brain, descends in a very large receptacle to meet the sense of smell, which enters among a great number of cartilaginous cells with many passages that go to meet the above-mentioned brain" (Anat. Ms. B, fol. 13 v, p. 87). This has led to the supposition that Leonardo also dissected lions' heads.

The physiology of respiration comprises two parts that may be quite clearly distinguished: the mechanical part, which studies the phenomenon of dilation and contraction of the thoracic cavity by the action of the respiratory muscles, along with the innervation of the latter, leading to the absorption of oxygen and the elimination of carbon dioxide and water vapor; and the chemical part, which deals with the oxidation processes within the tissues, in which the oxygen is consumed and the products are, in the last analysis, chiefly carbon dioxide, water, and heat.

There was no exact knowledge in antiquity of these chemical processes during respiration. According to Aristotle and Galen, the purpose of respiration was to cool the blood with the air breathed in, to recharge the vital spirits (that is, oxygen), and to expel the fuliginous matter, a term that referred loosely to what we should today call volatile products of metabolism (carbon dioxide and water vapor).

It was thought that heat was produced in the heart by the turbulent motions to which the blood is subjected by reason of its contractions, and also to some extent in the liver. Leonardo likewise adopted these errors. But Leonardo vaguely sensed the nature of the combustion process: "The element of fire continually consumes the air, which in part nourishes it, and would remain in contact with the vacuum if the surrounding air did not rush in to fill it" (Cod. Atl., fol. 237 v). And he also sensed the analogy between combustion and respiration: "Where the air is not suited to receive the flame, no flame can live there, nor any animal of the land or air.... Where flame cannot live, no animal that draws breath can live" (Cod. Atl., fol. 270 r). The long and profound study that he made of "flame" also led him to recognize that heat arises from combustion.

But it is above all in the mechanics of respiration that Leonardo made brilliant observations, studying it in himself and in animals (pig, dog, ox). He noted exactly that "the substance of the lung is expansible and extendible, and it is interposed between the ramifications of the trachea...; and this substance interposes itself between these ramifications and the ribs of the chest, after the fashion of a soft feather bed" (a most felicitous comparison) (Anat. Ms. B, fol. 37 v, p. 227 f.).

He describes the ramification of the bronchi in the lung, and reproduces it in a fine drawing. "Make first the ramification of the lung, and then make the ramification of the heart, that is, of its veins and arteries; afterward make the third ramification; ... and these mixtures you will make from four aspects, and you will do the like with the said ramifications which will be twelve; and then make a view of each from above, and one from below, and this will make in all eighteen demonstrations" (ibid. fol. 37 v).

He described the pleura (pannicolo) of the lung, both diaphragmatic and costal. He distinguished "respiratory air" from "residual air," and he was the first to do so; he observed that "the lung is always full of a quantity of air, even when it has driven out that air which is necessary for its exhalation" (ibid., fol. 17 r, p. 113).

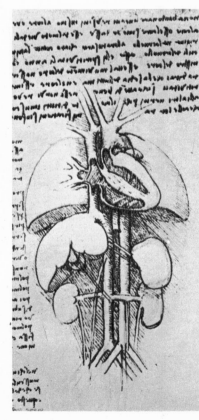

Thoracic organs, ensemble view – Quad. Anat. IV, fol. 7 r

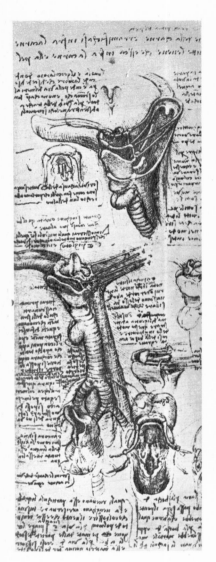

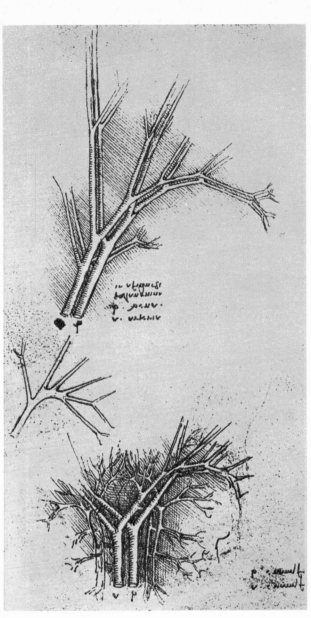

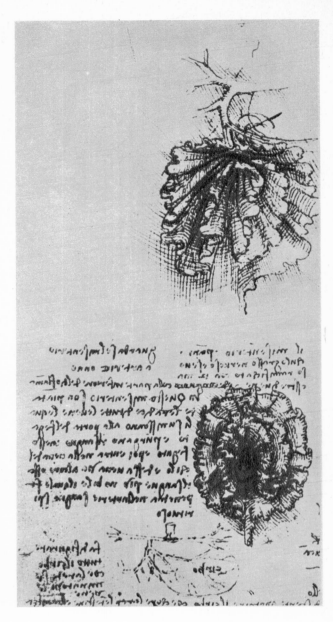

Trachea, esophagus, organs of voice
– Anat. Ms. A, fol. 3 r

But the observations for which we cannot but recognize his priority were those concerning the action of the respiratory muscles, which he in part inferred from their anatomical arrangement with the aid of the laws of mechanics, which he knew well, and in part observed himself.

He distinguished the intercostal muscles and ligaments (*mesopleuri*) from both, the muscles which are inserted only at the sides of the ribs, having their other insertion elsewhere, and from the diaphragm. "Mesopleuri are those ... that connect the ribs together. And in addition to connecting them and preventing their dilation, they hinder transverse movements" (Anat. Ms. A, fol. 7 r, p. 97; fol. 13 r, p. 143). The mesopleuri contain blood vessels and nerves, in addition to muscles and ligaments. "And through these spaces between the ribs extend the sensitive nerves for moving the muscles,[20] interposed among them for the traction and dilation of the aforesaid ribs. And between these ribs are the veins and arteries putting the nerve in the middle" (Quad. Anat. IV, fol. 9 r).

Leonardo brilliantly distinguished, for the first time, the antagonistic functions of the intercostal muscles, inspiratory for the external muscles and expiratory for the internal ones. "The threads [fasciculi] of the muscles interposed between the ribs of the chest are attached on the inner side of the ribs [internal muscles] at the angle *ab*,[21] solely for the purpose of pulling the ribs together around the lung, to drive the collected air out of it [expiratory muscles] ... and similar threads are located in the external part of the ribs (external muscles), sloping at an angle opposite to that of the internal threads along *cd*, for the purpose of dilating the contracted ribs, opening the lung, and taking in new air [inspiratory muscles]" (Quad. Anat. IV, fol. 9 r).[22]

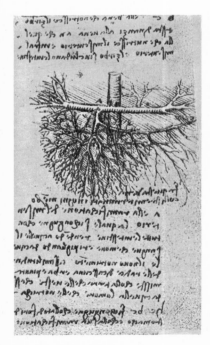

Termination of veins – Anat. Ms. B,
fol. 3 r

---

[20] If the muscles move, there must be motor nerves as well.

[21] These letters differ from those given in fig. 3 because they refer to a different but similar figure, not reproduced here.

[22] With reference to the other muscles that raise the ribs and dilate the thorax, we need only refer to the following passage, which is no less clear than the preceding one: "What function the muscles of the ribs have. The muscles of the ribs take care of dilating and raising them; the six lower [?] muscles are devoted to dilation, and in contracting move the flexible cartilages located at the points of the ribs, and for raising there are the three upper muscles, and these in contracting raise the three ribs to which they are attached, drawing with them the other lower ribs, after they are open and dilated and have gained in capacity; and this shows that dilatation of the lower ribs does not suffice for opening the lung, if they are not lifted in the direction of their convexity, that is, of the lung, which lifting is caused by the upper muscles; and it is not enough for these upper muscles to raise all the ribs, if these ribs were not spread and dilated by the lower muscles; and thus we have found what opens and raises the ribs in breathing and overcomes the power of contraction and constriction of the lateral muscles of the diaphragm, when the diaphragm straightens its convexity and the space above increases in size, and the lung in it increases in size, filling with air" (Quad. Anat. I, fol. 8 r).

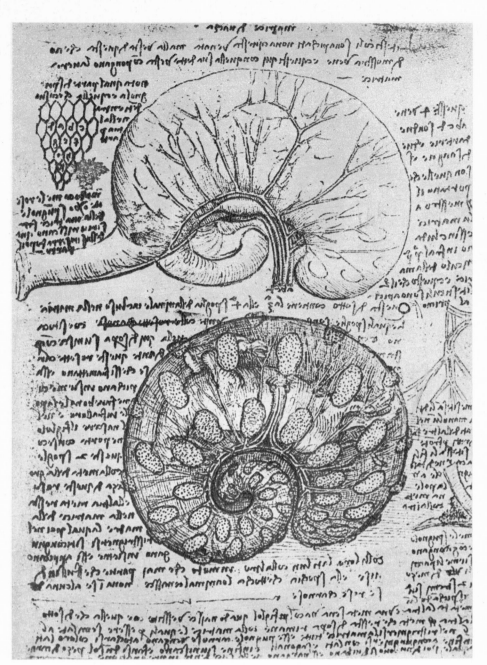

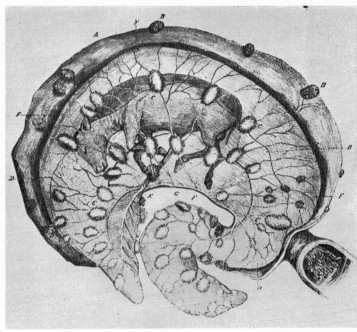

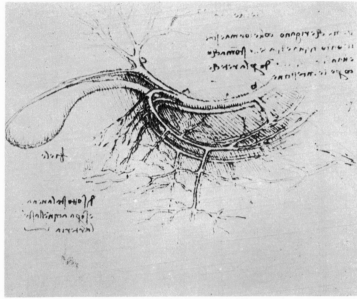

But the dilatation of the thorax is also produced by contraction of the diaphragm. In the latter Leonardo, after saying that it "has a shape resembling a fairly concave spoon" (Quad. Anat. I, fol. 5 r), distinguishes the tendinous center ("thick and nervous membrane") from the "muscles" that "surround" it; he attributes to it four *giovamenti* or *usi*,[23] that is, functions (Quad. Anat. I, fol. 5 v) when it "uncurves," i.e., "extends [flattens out] its curvature" (Quad. Anat. II, fol. 16 r; IV, fol. 1 r). Now of the *giovamenti*, "the first is that the space in the chest increases in size, in which it draws and dilates the lung and constrains it to fill with new air" (Quad. Anat. II, fol. 16 r). This effect could not take place, however, unless the lower ribs were immobilized, so that they could not be drawn inward by the contraction of the diaphragm itself. We read: "Which [dilatation of the thoracic cavity] the said diaphragm could not bring about unless the lower muscles of the chest failed to withdraw themselves [contract], together with those of the back of the neck, before the dilation and raising of these [costal] cartilages; for, if the muscle should seek to withdraw the said diaphragm from the center toward its peripheral extremities, it could not do this if these extremities were not well fixed; for if this fixation were not present, the extremities of the diaphragm would come towards its center, and thus the cartilages would be drawn back ... by which the chest would be constricted instead of dilating as is required" (Quad. Anat. I, fol. 5 r; IV, fol. 1 r). The same accurate physiological observation is expressed by Leonardo in the following words: "The extension ["uncurving"] of the diaphragm consists of a compound movement: while it is being extended by the muscles that surround it, the ribs to which these muscles are attached are being dilated" (Quad. Anat. IV, fol. 2 v). "The compound movement of the diaphragm causes the lung to collect into itself more air than is given it by the dilation of the ribs, and the dilation of the ribs to give it more air than is given it by the dilation of the diaphragm" (Quad. Anat. II, fol. 7 v).

It is not surprising that Leonardo also falls into some errors. He believes that in dilation "the increase of the lung when it is filled with air is latitudinal and not in its length" (Anat. Ms. B, fol. 17 r,

Left: Gastro-epiploic vein and coronary artery of the stomach – Anat. Ms. B, fol. 22 r

Upper right: Gravid uterus of cow: note the resemblance to Leonardo's drawing – From G. Colin, *Traité de physiologie comparée des animaux*, Vol. II, Paris, 1873, fig. 186, p. 828

Lower right: "Womb of cow" – blood vessels above, *Spugnole* below – Anat. Ms. B, fol. 38 r

---

[23] Mondino, *op. cit.*, (chap. on lung), speaks of only three *giovamenti*.

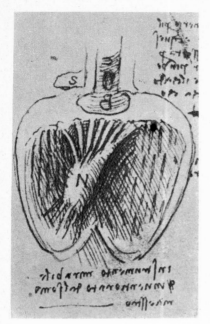

Heart cut open, showing schematically two ventricular cavities – Anat. Ms. B, fol. 12 r

p. 111-113); but he has observed this fact in a pig's lung removed from the body, and the error is corrected by what he says concerning the functioning of the diaphragm. He assumes, with the ancients, that the air "interposes itself between the deflated lung and the ribs surrounding it" (*ibid.*), and that the return of the diaphragm to a curved state in expiration is due exclusively to the upward pressure of the abdominal viscera, which have been compressed by the contraction of the *mirach* (muscles of the abdominal wall); however, the notion of the active relaxation of the striated muscles is quite recent.

As compared with these few errors, Leonardo's contribution to the mechanics of respiration is extremely important, and it should be noted that he had the accurate idea that the dilation and contraction of the lung are passive effects of the contraction of the respiratory muscles.

Leonardo depicted the muscles of the body in one hundred and forty figures; he also represented them diagrammatically in the form of threads, in order to bring out their functional relationships. He knew of the existence of synergetic and antagonistic muscles, and made minute investigations of the points at which the blood vessels and nerves penetrate into the flesh of the muscle, and of the varying ways in which they are attached to the skeleton and continued in the "cords," as he calls the tendons. The gross structure of the muscles is not unknown to him. "Every muscle," he says (Anat. Ms A, fol. 16 r, p. 167), "moves the member attached to it by the line of threads to which that muscle is coupled." The "threads" are evidently the fasciculi of muscle; and he knows that their contraction takes place in the direction of their length. He distinguishes voluntary and involuntary muscles; and of the respiratory muscles he says, with marvelous precision, that they "have voluntary and involuntary movement" (Anat. Ms. A, fol. 15 v, p. 165). Of great importance are Leonardo's researches into the musculature of face and lips, of forearm and lower extremity. "No movement of the hand and its fingers," he says correctly (Anat. Ms. A, fol. 12 v, p. 139), "is brought about by muscles located above the elbow; and thus it is also in birds, and that is why they are so powerful, because all the muscles that lower the wings have their origin on the breast, and have more weight of themselves than all the rest of the bird put together." This shows his constant concern for comparing the things he observes with the functions they have.

He describes and draws the organs of the mouth (tongue, etc.) and discovers the thyroid bodies, although without understanding their function. "These glands are made to fill the space where the muscles are wanting, and hold the trachea away from the hyoid bone" (Anat. Ms. A, fol. 37 r, p. 74). He notes that "the rings of the trachea are not joined," and "for two reasons: one is for the voice, and the other is to give space for food between it and the neckbone."

He observed the digestive canal in animals, comparing it with man's, and knew of its peristaltic motion, as well as the glands associated with it, except for the pancreas, which seems to have escaped him. He attentively studied the organs of reproduction and their functions, remarking the structure of the umbilical cord, and of the placenta of animals, together with the anatomical and nutritive relationships between mother and fetus, the latter being effected by the blood vessels and by what he calls *spugnole*, that is, the cotyledons.

The central and peripheral nervous systems and the sense organs were special subjects of his investigations, with respect to both their anatomical structure and their functions. Here his thought goes beyond the limits of pure anatomy and physiology, and enters into the domain of psychology.

Unfortunately, the limited space available here compels me to confine myself to these bare hints, since I want to go on and discuss at greater length certain masterly results obtained by Leonardo in the study of the heart.

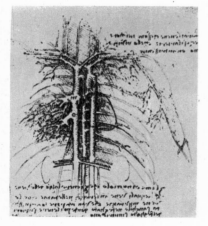

Principal blood vessels of thorax – Anat. Ms. B, fol. 11 r

A favored object of his researches and investigations was the physiology of the circulatory apparatus, and especially of the heart, which he considers an "admirable instrument invented by the highest Master" (Anat. Ms. B, fol. 12 r, p. 79), and whose functional autonomy he understands, as he points out in these words: "Of the heart. This moves by itself, and does not stop if not forever" (Anat. Ms. B, fol. 13 r, p. 83). He defines it thus: "The heart ... is a vessel made of thick muscle, kept alive and nourished by artery and vein as the other muscles are" (Anat. Ms. B, fol. 33 v). "The heart is a muscle of pre-eminent power over the other muscles" (Ms. G, fol. 1 v).

Within the heart he distinguishes the ventricles, which he calls "lower ventricles" and which according to him constitute its "substance" (Quad. Anat. I, fol. 3 r), from the other chambers, which he does not name but calls "upper ventricles," and from the auricular appendages, which he calls "ears." He is aware of the pericardial sac, which he calls the *cassula* [capsule] of the heart, and notes the liquid within it, which, to be sure, is more plentiful in the cadaver than in life (Anat. Ms. B, fol. 17 r, p. 114). He also refers to the endocardium and to the coronary arteries, "which arise in the two external openings of the left ventricle" (Quad. Anat. II, fol. 3 v).

He must also have dissected ox hearts, for he says that he found cartilaginous parts (Quad. Anat. II, fol. 23 r), and even "bone" (Quad. Anat., *ibid.*, and fol. 10 r), and saw there, and drew, the papillary muscles and the trabeculae carneae of the walls, which he describes in the following manner: "Between the cords [*cordae*] and threads of the muscles of the right ventricle there are interwoven a quantity of minute threads ...; and these wind themselves round the most minute and imperceptible nerves [tendons] and weave themselves with them. And these muscles are in themselves very capable of expansion and contraction, and they are situated within the fury of the rush of the blood,

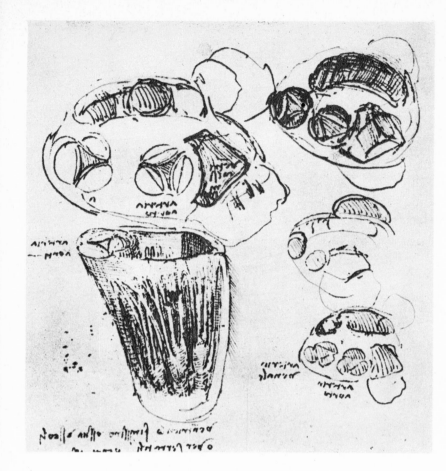

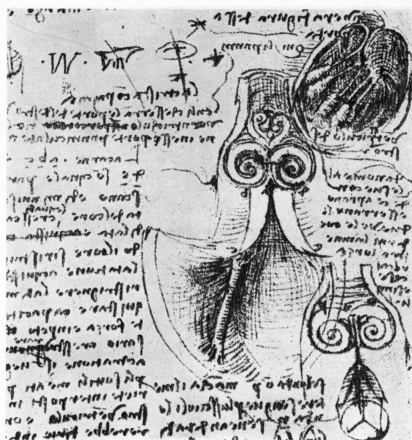

which passes in and out among the minute cords [tendinous prolongations] of the muscles before they are converted into the *panniculi* [membranes] of the *uscioli* [cusps of the valves]" (Quad. Anat. IV, fol. 13 r. See also the figure in Quad. Anat. II, fol. 23 r, depicting a large papillary muscle, *n*).

As regards the innervation of the heart, he said, in the case of only one of the two "reversive nerves," the one on the left, that it "descends to the box of the heart, and I believe that this is the nerve that enters the heart" (he does not say that it imparts movement to the heart).

At the side of a drawing of the base of a heart which has been transversely sectioned, showing the atrioventricular orifices and those of the arteries, we read: "Base of the heart. The shape of the base of the heart is somewhat like a triangle, as shown at *acf*, and at each corner it has two veins, namely, a vein outside and an artery inside, below the vein; and the veins are *acf* and the arteries *bde*; and between *c* and *f* is the right ventricle, and in the center of the base of the heart is the origin or base of the aortic artery, which is supported on the center of the base of the heart, and governs the base of the heart, as it governs the life of the animal; and the angles of the *uscioli* of this artery are turned toward the angles of the base of the heart, and the sides of the valve flaps of the heart."

We should note the importance that Leonardo assigns to the aorta, stating that it "holds dominion over the life of the animal." In connection with the *uscioli*, which are the three cusps of the tricuspid valve, he goes on to describe the "right *uscioli*," as follows: right *uscioli*. The circuit *adbfce* is the base or origin of the outer coat of the vein; the space *adbn* shows how much of the base of the heart the outer coat of the vein covers, and immediately after this origin of the vein there originates a thin membrane connected with it, which by itself covers the space *anbp*; and out of its overabundance it gives rise to one of the sides of the flap *abc*, which flap is doubled by another membrane of the same kind, which covers the capsule or right ventricle within the heart, and similarly for the other ventricle" (Quad. Anat. IV, fol. 14 v).

Leonardo made a long and profound study of the valves of the heart, especially of the semilunar valves,[24] as is proved by the many figures in which he drew them and the various original descriptions he made of their functional mechanism.

Leonardo is very well aware in what direction the valves of the heart open and close, both those of the arteries and the atrioventricular valves, and the eddies that the blood makes in the sinuses of Valsalva. He says that the valve "opens by reason of the incident motion [of the blood pushed by the contraction of the ventricle] and closes with the reflex motion. The incident motion opens the gates of the heart, and the reflex motion closes them.

---

[24] For the terminology used by Leonardo to indicate the various parts of the heart—the aortic region, the cusps of the valves, the sinuses these form with the arterial walls, later called sinuses of Valsalva, the edges of the valve flaps, etc., see G. Favaro, "La struttura del cuore nel quarto Quaderno d'Anatomia di Leonardo," in *Atti del Regio Istituto Veneto*, 1914-1915, LXXIV, 895. I am not in complete agreement with him, however, in the interpretation he gives to some terms used by Leonardo. It is true that Leonardo sometimes calls a given organ by different names.

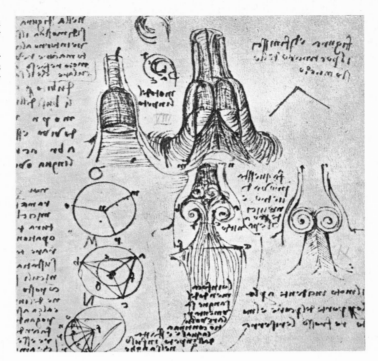

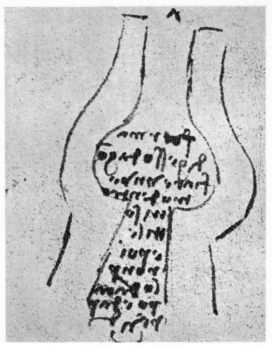

"The impetus that remains in the blood closes the outlet. When the impetus of the blood is directed by the left ventricle to the aortic artery by orifice *fg*, it strikes against the membranous cusps and dilates them and rises with the impetus from the spot of percussion, which takes place at joint *r*, and the impetus divides into constriction *r* from the spot of percussion, and turns right to one side along the curve (spiral) *en* and strikes the wall of channel *nop*, then follows the circular motion imparted to it by the wall, which yields, and strikes the membrane of the cusps with the front of impetus *b*; and upon receiving this percussion the membranous cusp immediately distends its folds and dilates, until it meets the opposite cusp, which by reason of the opposite impetus comes toward it and up against it; and the three said cusps [of the semilunar valve] behave in a similar way and close up together in close contact, until the impetus, converted into spiral motion, consumes itself; this phase is completed, in a healthy man, in about half the time of a pulse beat; and then the heart dilates [the closing of the valves is followed by the diastole of the ventricles]; and lest a vacuum be formed, the left ventricle attracts the blood of the right ventricle" (Quad. Anat. IV, fol. 12 r).

He goes on to give a better explanation of the behavior of the blood expelled during the systole: "And thus, having found the various velocities of this blood in its antechamber [vestibule of the aorta], it is necessary to find the velocity that occurs in the dilation of this blood toward the three walls of these semiventricles [sinuses of Valsalva]. Thus, when the highest velocity of this blood has developed from the constriction, and the gates have been struck and opened and dilated and lowered, giving room for the dilation of the blood, which follows the impetus of its high velocity and strikes the blood standing above it, which percussion shakes all the arteries and pulses throughout the man, and flies to the lateral percussion of the hemicycles [aortic walls of the sinuses] of the ventricles; and after this percussion has taken place, it turns downward with a rotatory motion; and another portion turns upward, the upper rotary motion dividing from the lower [rotatory motion] at the upper boundary of the hemicycle; but this rotatory motion that turns down strikes the base of the hemicycle and returns to the orifice of its first entrance, and strikes the gates with a compound motion, and distends the membrane of the gates [i.e., the valve cusp] and raises them and closes them against their opposite counterparts, which are at the same time urged to meet them in the same fashion; and immediately the rotatory motions [eddies] consume their impetus toward the center of their rotation, retarding this impetus.... The like occurs in the upper revolution, moving in the opposite direction, giving rise again to many other revolutions, one opposite to the other and one above the other, always retarding the velocity, until the impetus consumes itself.

"Having stated the method of closing of the left ventricle of the heart, there follows the way in which it reopens, which occurs immediately in two thirds of the time of a heartbeat; and since blood cannot be drawn from the closed gates, which do not close with their broad side, like other doors, but with their edges and with a great and powerful contact, the blood is removed from the right ventricle [?].

"In the phase that follows the three revolutions of the blood in the three hemicycles, and during which, by reason of this revolution, the three gates keep their positions and reinforce their closure, the heart dilates and acquires capacity" (Quad. Anat. IV, fol. 11 v).

Well before Ceradini,[25] Leonardo drew the striated figure of the commissures of the three cusps of the semilunar valves; he even tried to reproduce the valve apparatus in a model in order to be able to see what took place inside it, as is seen from the following passages: "A hollow plaster form, and a thin glass within it, and then break the form at the top and the bottom at *an*.

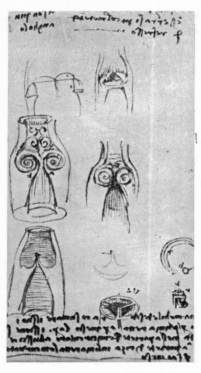

322

---

[25] G. Ceradini. *Opere*, Milan, 1906. See *Il meccanismo delle valvole semilunari del cuore*, Vol. II, drawing on p. 437.

"But first pour the wax into the gate of an ox heart, so that you may see the true shape of that gate.

"Make a form of glass, in order to see in the glass what the blood does in the heart, when it closes the flaps of the heart" (Quad. Anat. II, fol. 6 v).

"Make this glass model and inside it cause the *cise* [?] membrane to move" (Quad. Anat. IV, fol. 11 v).

Leonardo was careful to study the time relationships between heartbeats and pulse. He says that: "... the time of the heart's closing and of its beating against the ribs with its apex and of the beating of the pulse and of the entrance into the *antiporto* of the heart[26] is one and the same" (Quad. Anat. IV, fol. 11 r).

"As many times as the pulse beats, so many times does the heart dilate and contract."

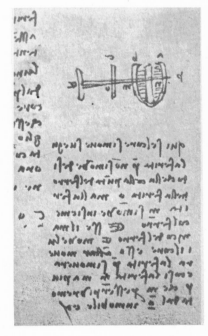

Experiment on heart of pig – Displacement of outer portion of *spillo* plunged in through thoracic wall – Anat. Ms. B, fol. 6 r

I should like now to refer to an experiment of Leonardo's on the pig, similar to the experiment that is made on the rabbit or some other animal in the physiology laboratories of schools, in order to demonstrate to the students the movements of the heart. I have already called the attention of scientists to this experiment,[27] as it constitutes such manifest proof of Leonardo's acute spirit of observation as a physiologist no less than as an artist. It is a long description, but it is worth setting down verbatim:

"Anatomy. Whether the heart at its death changes position or no.

"The change of the heart at its death is similar to the change which it undergoes during the expulsion of its blood, but it is somewhat less. This is shown when they kill pigs in Tuscany, where they pierce the hearts of the pigs by means of an instrument called a *spillo* ["borer"] which is used for drawing wine out of casks. And thus turning the pig over and tying it up, they pierce its right side and its heart at the same time with the borer, thrusting it in straight. And if this borer pierces the heart when it is distended [when it is in diastole], the heart, as it expels the blood, becomes contracted and draws the wound to the top together with the point of the borer; and the more it raises the point of the borer within, the more it lowers the handle of the borer outside; and afterward when the heart is distended [in diastole] and drives this wound downward, the part of this borer which is outside makes a movement that is opposite to that of the part within, which moves together with the movement of the heart. And this it does many times, so that at the end of life [when the heart ceases to contract, but is not yet dead] that part of the borer which is outside remains in the middle of the two extremities, where were the last contrary movements of the heart when it was alive. And when the heart becomes quite cold [in *rigor mortis*] it shrinks somewhat and contracts as much as the space occupied by the heat [?], because heat causes a body to increase or diminish in size when it enters into it or leaves it; and this I have seen many times and have observed such measurements [he measured the displacements of the borer, and from them calculated the contractions and dilations of the heart], and allowed the instrument to remain in the heart until the animal was cut up.

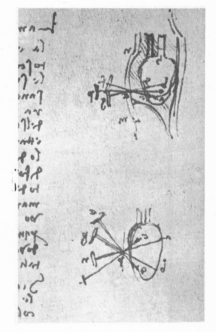

"Now let the expanded heart be *ha* and the contracted heart *ho*, and this when the animal is alive; and if the point, or borer, finds the heart distended when it enters at *fa*; when the heart contracts, the point of the borer *a* is displaced to *b*, and the part of the handle of the borer, outside, goes down from *f* to *g*. When the heart is dead, the borer remains in the middle, or thereabouts, between the extreme motions, that is at *op*.

"And from the greatest to the smallest movement of the heart of this animal is about the thickness of a finger, and at the end the heart remains with its point out of its usual position by about half the thickness of a finger; and pay attention lest you make a mistake in taking this measurement, because sometimes the handle of this borer will not make any change whether the heart is living or dead; and this occurs when the heart receives its wound halfway in the process of its contracting, in which position it remains when it is dead.

"And sometimes this handle causes a greater change. This occurs when the heart receives the wound during its period of greater or lesser length, and thus it will make as many varieties of distances as are the variations in the length or shortness of the heart when it is wounded. Moreover, this handle will make greater or lesser changes according as the point of the borer penetrates further or less into the heart; for if the point of the steel transfixes the heart, it makes a lesser movement from the center of its movement, that is, from the place, than it would if the iron had wounded the heart only in the front part of its anterior wall; and on this point I shall not dwell further, because a complete treatise on these movements has been compiled in the twentieth book on the forces of the lever. And if you should consider that, when the heart had been transfixed, the length of the borer could not follow the movement spoken of above through its being impeded by the anterior wall of the heart, you must understand that in the extension and dilation of the heart, it draws the point of this steel up or down along with its motion; and the steel, which finds itself in the anterior wall, enlarges its wound both upward and downward, or, to put it better, moves it, seeing that the roundness of the thick part of the steel does not enlarge, since it does not cut, but carries with it the front wound of the heart, compressing the part of the heart in contact with it, now from the upper part

[26] What are the *antiporti* of the heart, of which Leonardo often speaks? Probably the atria; indeed, he assumes that the ventricular systole drives blood not only into the aorta and the pulmonary artery, but also into the "upper ventricles," from which it later returns to the ventricular cavities during the diastole. But in other places it would seem that by *antiporti* he means the vestibule of the aorta and of the pulmonary artery.

[27] F. Bottazzi. "Un esperimento di Leonardo sul cuore e un passo dell'Iliade," in *Raccolta vinciana*, X (Milan, 1919), 153.

Two drawings relating to Leonardo da Vinci's experiment about motions of heart of pig – Quad. Anat. I, fol. 6 r

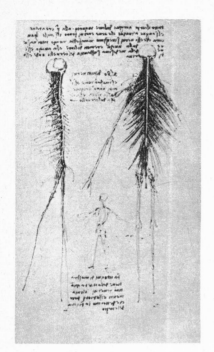

Origin of spinal nerves – Anat. Ms. B, fol. 17 v

of the wound and now from the lower part, and this rarefaction and compression is easily made by the heart when it is warm, because it is less dense" (Quad. Anat. I, fol. 6 r).

It has been said that the discovery of the circulation of the blood belongs to Leonardo, but I answer, in the words of the master, "This is not granted, but denied." Leonardo studied the arteries and the veins, and knew of the "capillary veins." He also used—once, so far as I have been able to see—the term "circulation" with reference to the concept of the circulation of the blood; he knew that the vessels that carry the blood dilate and contract, and even described in detail the pathological changes of the process, especially in the aged. But he was not aware of the physiological connection between the motor function of the heart and the circulation of the blood; his mind was put off the right track by the analogy he insisted on seeing between the circulation of the blood in animals and the conveyance of the nutrient liquids of plants, on the one hand, and the circulation of the waters in the bowels of the earth, on the other. He returns to this analogy in several places in his manuscripts, and discusses it copiously in long pages that are not free from errors. Undoubtedly he was also led astray by uncritically accepting the idea of the ancients that the interventricular septum is perforated, and that therefore blood passes from the right to the left ventricle during diastole (Quad. Anat. II, fol. 11 r; here he also speaks of a "hollow," although it is hard to say whether in the interventricular or the interatrial septum), as well as by believing that during the systole of the ventricles, blood passes into the atria (Quad. Anat. I, fol. 3 r)—a belief that is hard to reconcile with the function of the atrioventricular valves, which, as he accurately says, make a "perfect closure" when the cusps [anti] that constitute them "come to rest against one another," while "the cords originating in the [papillary] muscles of the heart" prevent their being forced back into the atrial cavities (Quad. Anat. II, fol. 8 v; fol. 11 r; fol. 12 r).

We have seen that Leonardo studied the plants and animals. But he had written, "that thing that contains more universality and variety of things in it will be of more excellence" (Treatise, ed. Ludwig, no. 27, p. 20).

This thing is man.

All organisms, present or past (e.g., "shells" or fossils [nicchi], Cod. Leices., fol. 8 v), vegetable or animal, higher or lower, are the subjects of scientific investigation, and afford Leonardo matter for philosophical speculation. But man was the primary object of the investigations of that profound and venturesome mind, who harbored the ideal, and did more than anyone else to bring that ideal to realization, of receiving everything in nature, of immersing himself in it all, not only in its external forms, but also in its internal connections, in its forms and in its essence. Leonardo had before him, as the poet says:

La nuda/ faccia del mondo immensa ["the bare/ face of the immense world"]

and saw that man, the "model of the world," is the noblest creature in it.

For Leonardo, man or any other animal is essentially a marvelously constructed machine suited to the purposes for which it was made. No other machine can be compared with it for perfection. "Though human ingenuity may make various inventions which, by the help of various machines, answer the same end, it will never devise any invention more beautiful, nor more simple, nor more to the purpose than nature does; because in her inventions nothing is wanting and nothing is superfluous, and she needs no counterpoise when she makes limbs proper for motion in the bodies of animals. But she puts into them the soul of the body which forms them, that is, the soul of the mother, which first constructs in the womb the form of the man, etc."[28]

And not to leave any doubt in our minds as regards the laws that the living machine obeys in the exercise of its functions, Leonardo says further: "Instrumental or mechanical science is of all the noblest and the most useful, seeing that by means of this all animate bodies which have movement perform all their actions; and these movements are based on the center of gravity which is placed in the middle dividing unequal weights, and it has dearth and wealth of muscles and also lever and counterlever."[29] In other words, the laws of mechanics, "the paradise of mathematical sciences—here we come to the fruits of mathematics"[30]—are those that govern living organisms. "Gravity, force, and accidental motion, together with percussion, are the four accidental potencies out of which all the manifest operations of mortal beings have their being and their death," he says elsewhere. There are no differences between animate and inanimate machines as regards the possibility of understanding their functions in conformity with the principles of mechanical determinism.

Leonardo affirms all this because he is convinced that the living organism is made in the likeness of the world and of the body of the earth; and since the laws of mechanics rule in inanimate nature, they must necessarily govern living things as well. "By the ancients, man has been called the world in miniature; and certainly this name is well bestowed, for inasmuch as man is composed of earth, water, air, and fire, his body resembles that of the earth. And just as man has in him bones, the supports and framework of his flesh, so the world has its rocks, the supports of the earth. As man has in him a pool of blood in which the lungs rise and fall in breathing, so the body of the earth has its ocean tide which likewise rises and falls every six hours, as if the world breathed; as in that

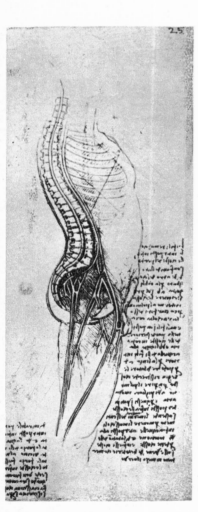

Leonardo da Vinci's study of muscles interposed between ribs – Quad. Anat. IV, fol. 9 r

384

[28] Richter, *Literary Works*, etc., Vol. II, no. 837, p. 100 f.
[29] Richter, *op. cit.*, no. 1154, p. 241.
[30] Richter, *op. cit.*, no. 1155, p. 241.

pool of blood veins have their origin, which ramify all over the human body, so likewise the ocean sea fills the body of the earth with infinite springs of water. The body of the earth lacks sinews, and this is because the sinews are made expressly for movements and, the world being perpetually stable, no movement takes place, and, no movement taking place, muscles are not necessary. But in all other respects they are much alike" (Ms. A, fol. 55 v).

To Leonardo, the world is an immense living organism, and man is the model of the world. "Nothing," he says,[31] "originates in a spot where there is no sentient, vegetable, and rational life; feathers grow upon birds and are changed every year; hairs grow upon animals and are changed every year, excepting some parts, like the hairs of the beard in lions, cats, and their like. The grass grows in the fields, and the leaves on the trees, and every year they are, in great part, renewed. So that we might say that the earth has a spirit of growth: that its flesh is the soil; its bones correspond to the arrangement and connection of the rocks of which the mountains are composed; its cartilage is the tufa, and its blood the springs of water. The pool of blood which lies round the heart is the ocean, and its breathing, and the increase and decrease of the blood in the pulses, is represented in the earth by the flow and ebb of the sea; and the heat of the spirit of the world is the fire which pervades the earth, and the seat of the vegetative soul is in the fires, which in many parts of the earth find vent in springs and mines of sulfur, and in volcanoes, and at Mount Etna in Sicily, and in many other places."

The correspondence is perfect, therefore. Both, in the macrocosm and the microcosm, "every action needs to be prompted by a motive,"[32] and "the motive power is the cause of all life,"[33] whether vegetative, or sensitive, or rational. Moreover, "where there is life there is heat, and where vital heat is, there is movement of humors. This is proved inasmuch as we see that the element of fire by its heat always draws to itself damp vapors and thick mists and opaque clouds, which it raises from seas as well as lakes and rivers, etc." (Ms. A, fol. 55 v).

"The same cause," he says elsewhere (Cod. Atl., fol. 171 r), "which moves the humors in every species of animate bodies against the natural law of gravity, also propels the water through the veins of the earth wherein it is enclosed and distributes it through small passages. And as the blood rises from below and pours out through the broken veins of the forehead, as the water rises from the lowest part of the vine to the branches that are cut, so from the lowest depth of the sea the water rises to the summits of mountains, where, finding the veins broken, it pours out and returns to the bottom of the sea. Thus the movement of the water inside and outside varies in turn; now it is compelled to rise, then it descends in natural freedom. Thus jointed together, it goes around and around in continuous rotation, hither and thither from above and from below; it never rests in quiet, owing not to its course but to its nature. It has nothing of its own but takes everything, changing into as many natures as there are different things on its course, which takes in as many images as there are things passing in front of it. So it changes continually, now as regards place, now as regards color."

This inexorable analogy between the two living beings, the great and the small, won such power over Leonardo that it sometimes interfered with the clarity of his vision. He saw the blood circulate in the vessels, and was aware of the structure and the movements of the heart; if he had kept his mind unencumbered with that analogy, inherited from the ancients, he would certainly have realized that it is not heat that makes the blood rise from the lower parts of the human body to the highest, like the "damp vapors and opaque clouds," but that the contraction of that marvelous organ generates the force opposing gravity, which unopposed would cause the blood to descend and collect in the lowest parts.

Therefore the world, or the earth, has a vegetative soul; man has a sensitive and rational soul. Several times he reminds himself: "Write what the soul is" (Anat. Ms. B, p. 134); but then he leaves this aside along with the other "unprovable things," life and God.

But it is certain that man or animals are dead things without their sensitive souls, and so is the earth without the vegetative soul. And they therefore seek each other and unite and merge, forming the living organism. "The part," says Leonardo (Cod. Atl., fol. 59 r), "always has a tendency to reunite with its whole in order to escape from its imperfection. The spirit desires to remain with its body, because without the organic instruments of that body it can neither act nor feel anything."

Body and soul, although united and fused together in a single whole, are things distinct in essence. And hence the mind of the philosopher could not but rest on the problem of how the soul enters into the new organism in the act of generation, how it passes into its new habitation. It is nature, he answers, which "in due time awakens the soul that is to inhabit it. And this at first lies dormant and under the tutelage of the soul of the mother who nourishes and vivifies it [and here the biologist reappears in the philosopher, trying to bring this high mystery back within the scope of natural phenomena] by the umbilical vein, with all its spiritual parts. This happens because this umbilicus is joined to the placenta and the cotyledons by which the child is attached to the mother."[34] What a confusion this is of disparate and incommensurable elements; and yet it is not confusion, but a vain attempt at reduction, at a naturalistic explanation of "unprovable things." Leonardo proves himself here to be the first mechanist biologist of modern times.

There is, however, one respect in which man and the world are essentially different: while "the world is perpetually stable," man, like every living organism, "continually dies and continually is re-

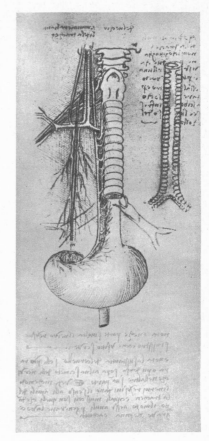

Drawing of various organs – Larynx, trachea, esophagus, stomach, nerves, and blood vessels – Anat. Ms. B, fol. 33 v

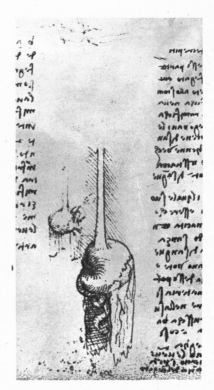

Stomach and peritoneum – Anat. Ms. B, fol. 22 r

---

[31] Richter, *op. cit.*, no. 1000, p. 178.
[32] Richter, *op. cit.*, no. 1146, p. 239.
[33] Richter, *op. cit.*, no. 1139, p. 238.
[34] Richter, *op. cit.*, II, no. 837, p. 101.

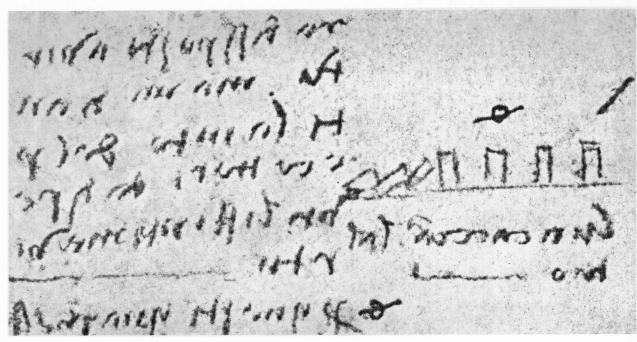

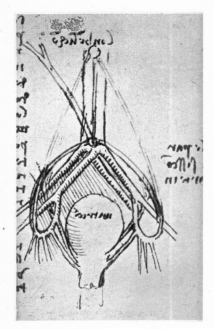

Umbilicus and womb – Anat. Ms. B, fol. 35 r

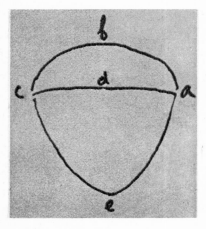

Diagram of thoracic cavity and abdomen – Anat. Ms. B, fol. 15 v

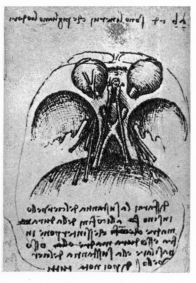

Study of olfactory and optic nerves and their interrelation – Anat. Ms. B, fol. 35 r

born." These words refer to nothing other than the material equilibrium of living beings, and I consider this intuition to be one of Leonardo's most resplendent gifts.

"Observe the light and consider its beauty. Blink your eye and look at it. That which you see was not there at first, and that which was there is no more. Who is it who makes it anew if the maker dies continually?" (Ms. F, fol. 49 v). And from consideration of light he goes on to think of living beings, and senses the analogy between these two stationary energetic systems. "The body of anything whatsoever that receives nourishment continually dies and is continually renewed. For the nourishment cannot enter except in those places where the preceding nourishment is exhausted, and if it is exhausted, it no longer has life. Unless therefore you supply nourishment equivalent to that which has departed, the life fails in its vigor; and if you deprive it of this nourishment, the life is completely destroyed. But if you supply it with just so much as is destroyed day by day, then it renews its life just as much as it is consumed; like the light of a candle formed by the nourishment given to it by the fat of this candle, which light is also continually renewed by swiftest succor from beneath, in proportion as the upper part is consumed and dies, and in dying becomes changed from radiant light to murky smoke. And this death extends for so long as the smoke continues; and the period of duration of this smoke is the same as that of what feeds it, and in an instant the whole light dies and is entirely generated by the movement of that which nourishes it" (Anat. Ms. B, fol. 28 r).

This brilliant intuition is not and could not be restricted by any doubt that a system which "continually dies and is continually renewed" might not be able to conserve its constant form. In stationary energetic systems, there is the same equilibrium of matter and energy, and this is what maintains their form. "Every figure [of powder, smoke, and water]," writes Leonardo (Cod. Atl., fol. 37 v, p. 68), "created by motion, is maintained by motion": profound words whose significance can be realized only by those who have studied the science of energetics.

Now, if our body is constantly dying and being renewed by nutrition, whence does nourishment come, and where does it go? On this subject Leonardo's views are precise. "Man and the animals," he says, "are really the passage and the conduit of food, the sepulcher of animals and the resting place of the dead, making life out of the death of another, making themselves the covering for corruption" (Cod. Atl., fol. 76 v). And in another place: "We make our life by the death of others. In dead matter there remains insensate life, which, on being united to the stomachs of living things, resumes a life of the senses and the intellect" (Ms. H, fol. 89 v). In other words, the tissues and organs of dead animals can still serve for the nourishment of living animals; and when the organic compounds of which they are composed are digested, and the digestion products are absorbed, and become part of living protoplasm by being assimilated, it is as if they were in a way resuming "a life of the senses and the intellect."

Leonardo even asks what the reasons might be for the continual succession of living beings, for such an incessant production of "lives and forms"; the reasons why, among "human conditions," "one constantly drives out the other."

"Why," he asks,[35] "did nature not ordain that one animal should not live by the death of another? Nature, being inconstant and taking pleasure in creating and making constantly new lives and forms, because she knows that her terrestrial material become thereby augmented, is more ready and more swift in her creating than time in its destruction; and so she has ordained that many animals shall be food for other. Nay, this not satisfying her desire, to the same end she frequently sends forth certain poisonous and pestilential vapors and frequent plagues upon the vast increase and congrega-

---

[35] Richter, *op. cit.*, II, no. 1219, p. 258.

386

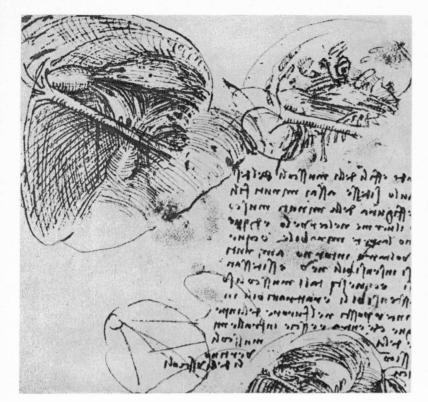

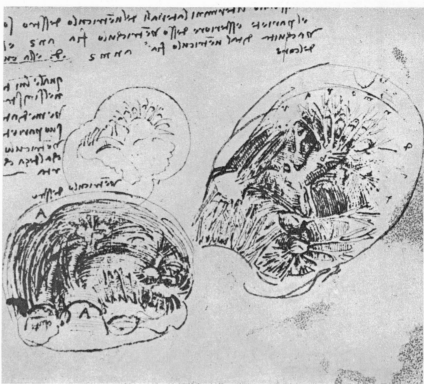

tion of animals; and most of all upon men, who increase vastly because other animals do not feed upon them; and, the causes being removed, the effects would cease. This earth therefore seeks to lose its life, desiring only continual reproduction; as you bring forward and demonstrate by argument, like effects always follow like causes; animals are a type of the life of the world."

Thus he comes upon the sought-for reason for the "augmentation of terrestrial materials" as regards living forms—and perhaps, we might be tempted to add, at the risk of being censured for recklessness, for the law of the conservation of life, which the words just cited vaguely infer, if they do not clearly formulate it; at least they recognize it as a fact, in the statement that "this earth [that is, nature] seeks to lose its life [that is, furthers rather than prevents the deaths of many beings], desiring only continual reproduction," and this desire is equivalent to the pleasure nature takes, as he says, "in creating and making constantly new lives and forms."

Left: Cross sections of heart with papillary muscles rising from cavities of ventricles – Quad. Anat. IV, fol. 13 r

Right: Transverse and longitudinal cross sections of heart – Quad. Anat. IV, fol. 13 v

It has been asked by various authors whether Leonardo was greater as an artist or as a scientist. The question is a sterile one. It would be more profitable to say that Leonardo wanted to base art on the solid foundation of science, and, where possible, make science bright with the ministry of art. In the mature years of his eventful life we see him cultivating the experimental sciences almost exclusively, "most impatient of the brush," as Fra di Novellara reported to Isabella d'Este. He sees the knowledge of natural things wrapped up in densest darkness, and feels that only science is capable of dissipating that darkness and giving man the power over nature, to which he aspires. Wherever he looks, he finds the threads of the natural sciences tangled, and in some places broken. He takes these threads in hand, one by one, and frees and disentangles them, where he can, always pointing out to later generations the right method for carrying on the titanic work he had begun.

But although in the physical sciences, and in mechanics in particular, antiquity had produced good seeds, and scholasticism had in part fertilized them—a service unjustly neglected up to our times—and although Leonardo had traced these seeds with the keenest of eyes and cleansed them from the husks that prevented them from germinating, the field of biology was deserted, or still worse, so deeply fouled that only his bold spirit could dare to undertake to reclaim it. Here Leonardo's achievements far exceed all the others with which he is credited.

Biology as an autonomous science did not exist before him. What existed was a shapeless, disconnected mass of empirical notions, rendered useless by innumerable preconceived ideas. Leonardo was the first to sense the bonds that connect all living beings with each other and with the nature that surrounds them, and to establish some of the fundamental laws of life.

Galen and his imitators had made dissections of animals exclusively. The titular anatomists of the school of Salerno, and the older ones of Bologna and Padua, had dissected a few human cadavers, but solely for limited practical purposes, to find the reason for an epidemic. But Leonardo works in anatomy with purely scientific aims, in order to discover the laws of life. This is what reveals his innovating genius. "The authors," he says, "describe the eye in one way; but I find it is otherwise." And this is what makes his strength; this is the point in which he surpasses everyone else —independence of examination, independence of judgment.

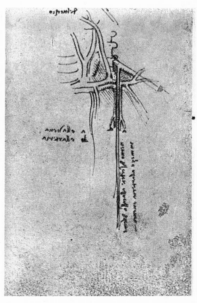

Thus in art he was supreme among the great; in the mechanical sciences, he was the first and foremost restorer. But the story of modern biology begins with him.

FILIPPO BOTTAZZI

Leonardo da Vinci's study on vagus nerve and its relationships – Anat. Ms. B, fol. 34 r

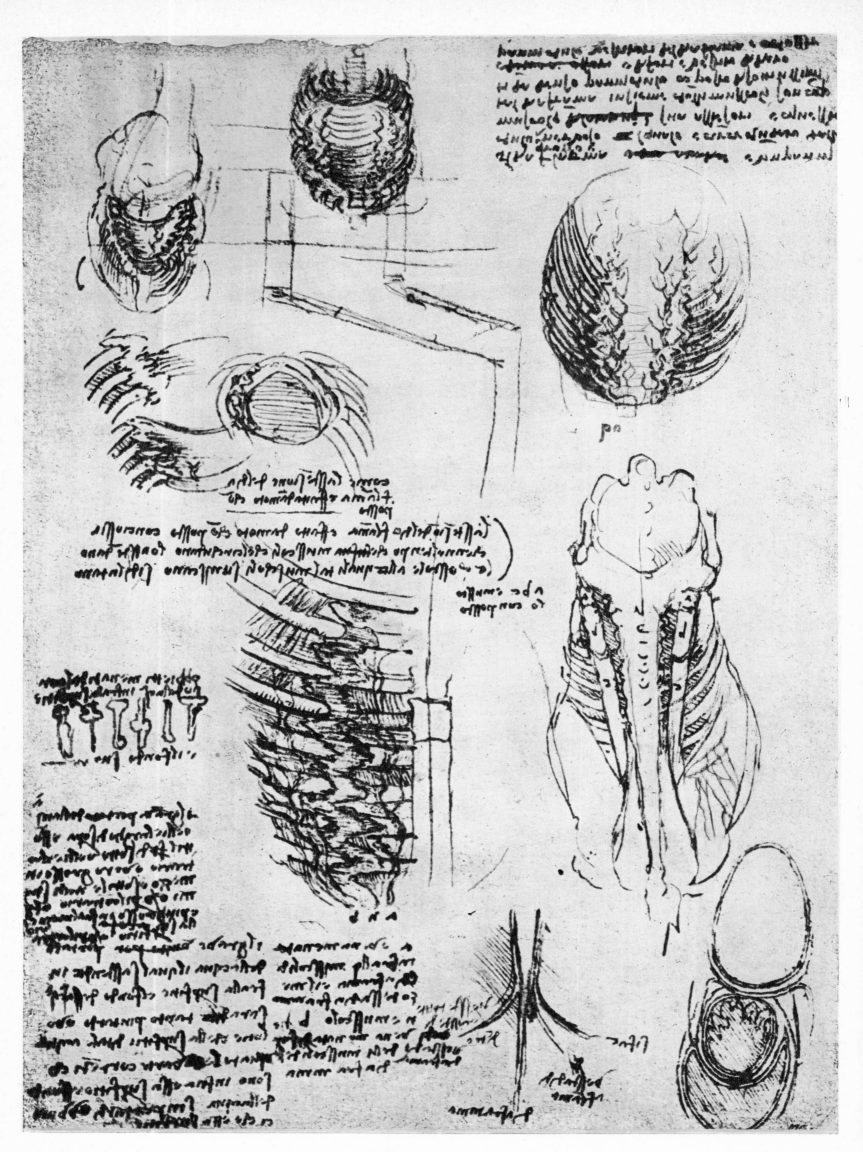

Anatomical studies on vascular system of ox – Quad. Anat. IV, fol. 2 v

COMPARATIVE ANATOMY

The anatomy of man is absolutely pre-eminent among the biological studies of Leonardo da Vinci, but the mind of the genius was also occupied with comparative anatomy, taking the term rather broadly, in his studies of the forms and positions of animals with reference to his work as painter and sculptor, in his anatomical studies of man, and in his investigations on the flight of birds; and in addition, there was his tremendous passion as investigator and researcher into everything that surrounded him.

It was precisely these reasons that led Leonardo to study the anatomy of animals, and this is why the tasks he set himself for the future, ranging in every direction, did not all remain mere wishes, even if they had as their basis an observation or insight to check or to prove, as happened so often with him. In this field his projects were frequently, even constantly, executed in researches and investigations that sometimes achieved genuinely remarkable results. This is witnessed by many scattered annotations and drawings, of which I shall try to give a brief account, illustrating the results that seem to be the most outstanding, or at least most illuminating, achieved by Leonardo as a practitioner, and perhaps in a certain sense as the founder, and certainly as the precursor of comparative anatomy.

However, although all of this material adequately demonstrates his interest in this branch of anatomy, it also is true, as we shall see, that it can only bring together mere indications of the bulk of the work that he did or wanted to do on comparative anatomy. In other words, his work on human anatomy has come down to us and is still in existence, while there are only a few traces left of his studies in comparative anatomy, and especially of the anatomy of the horse, in which Leonardo so clearly took a special interest.

This statement is based on two kinds of facts: First, testimony concerning the existence of that anatomical material, and secondly, critical examination of what has come down to us.

There were actually drawings, and perhaps explanatory notes, on the anatomy of the horse, very probably carried out in large part during the studies for the equestrian monument to Francesco Sforza; it should suffice to cite the statements made by Lomazzo, Vasari, and Rubens.

Lomazzo, speaking in his *Trattato della pittura* of the details of the members of the horse and of man, writes: "And all these details apply to the horse, which is more beautiful, freer, and agile in every member, and I intend to describe their true and just proportions, imitating Leonardo da Vinci, who was outstanding and unique in modelling and painting horses, as is seen in his anatomy." Further on he says: "After him (Michelangelo), excellent were Leonardo da Vinci, various drawings of whom are in the hands of several owners, and especially in the house of Francesco Melzi, a gentleman of Milan, his disciple, in addition to the anatomy of the horse that he made."

This was in 1584, and proves not merely that the drawings existed, but that Lomazzo had seen and perhaps consulted them at Melzi's, where we know were a large number of drawings and writings, left by Leonardo to his pupil and admirer. Lomazzo returns to the same theme, as something most natural, in his *Idea del tempio della pittura*: "But above all writers Leonardo da Vinci is worthy of note; he taught the anatomy of human bodies and of the horse which I have seen in the home of Francesco Melzi, drawn divinely by his hand," and also: "Besides that, he [Leonardo] has drawn anatomically the proportions of horses and human bodies with the skin off, with such

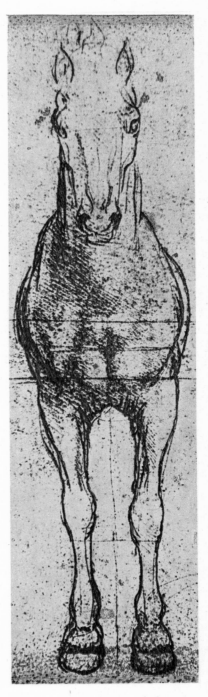

Proportions of thorax of horse –
Windsor, Royal Collection, no. 12290

389

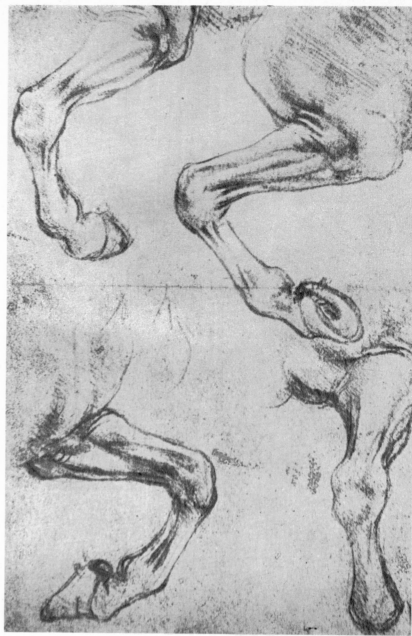

diligence and discrimination that I say for sure that no one could equal them except the great god Apollo, ruler of the sciences."

Vasari's testimony is also explicit. As regards the equestrian statue to Francesco Sforza he writes: "Also lost is a small wax model of it that he had completed, together with a book on the anatomy of the horse that he had compiled in his studies"; and later, in concluding his life of Leonardo, he says: "Of Leonardo we have the anatomy of horses and that of men, much more complete; for so many divine achievements his name and fame will never die out."

Peter Paul Rubens also assures us of the existence of the anatomy of the horse. The assurance has come down to us indirectly, however, since, as we know, Rubens' work on *Osservazioni di fisionomia* was lost in a fire in 1720. Uzielli makes reference to the fact that Rubens not only spoke at length of Leonardo's observations on physiognomy, but that he also discussed the studies of human and equine anatomy, declaring that he had been able to examine the original drawings and manuscripts at the house of Pompeo Leoni.

We may therefore consider the existence of an anatomy of the horse as proved, although not in so complete a form as the human anatomy (Vasari), and that it had been seen and in all likelihood consulted by the witnesses cited.

We now proceed to examine the other group of factors that speak in favor of my thesis; these are partly inductive and partly deductive in character.

There are scattered a large number of Leonardo's drawings, that represent various forms and positions of the horse; all of this work presupposes a thorough knowledge of the horse's anatomy on the part of the draughtsman. One need only observe a detail of the shoulder or of the front leg in these drawings in order to see the true and perfect anatomy "under the skin." All together they depict exactly the various muscles of the region as they could only be seen after a careful dissection. Of course I do not wish to deny that in some instances the drawing was not made simul-

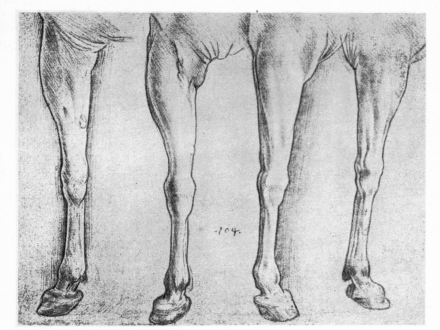

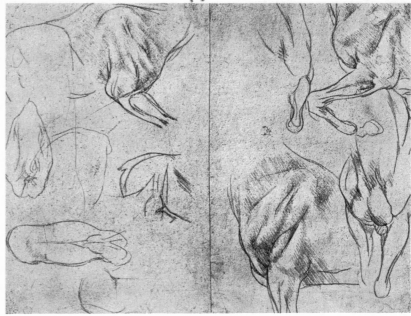

taneously with the dissection, but from memory later; besides this fact was noted, already a long time ago by Schmutzer. The question to be discussed here is the anatomical accuracy as compared with other illustrations in which that accuracy is beyond any controversy indeed.

Two small pictures from the manuscripts of the Institut de France, to be discussed later (Ms. K, fol. 109 v and 102 r), are precious studies of the osteology and myology of the pelvic limb of the horse; they not only presuppose a remarkable knowledge of the anatomy of the animal on Leonardo's part—something that might easily have been asserted—but also prove that these drawings and the others here and there represent only a few fragments of what Leonardo's work on the anatomy of the horse must have been.

For example, the fascicle or those plates that Lomazzo saw in Melzi's house and Rubens in the house of Pompeo Leoni undoubtedly existed, as is shown by their testimonies and by deduction from as much as has come down to us. And yet this material has been lost, either because it has been destroyed, or is lying unpublished and unknown in some collection or library, or has been used by others without reference to the actual author.

Here at least a question should be mentioned which Schrader raised in 1855 and which is still a source of polemics and discussions today. This is the accusation of plagiarism made against Carlo Ruini, whose treatise *Dell'anatomia del cavallo*, published in 1598, constitutes the first work on a truly scientific basis that treats exhaustively the anatomy of this animal. I will not go into the history of the matter, but merely report that Jackschath, then Bayon, and finally Léclainche attribute all or part of the marvelous drawings of the work to the hand of Leonardo da Vinci, the anatomist. Certainly anyone who will calmly and dispassionately follow the discussion that was started between Schrader and Ercolani over the accusation of plagiarism made by Schrader against Ruini, and then carried on by other disputants, cannot be surprised that many arguments have been adduced by those who would attribute the plates of *Dell'anatomia del cavallo* to Leonardo.

At any rate, if the heated discussion were decided in favor of Leonardo, it would not only restore to us the anatomy of the horse that Lomazzo and Rubens saw, but would also tell us that Vasari's judgment as to the relative merits of the two anatomies might have been revered.

The following points seem to me worth stressing to illustrate Leonardo's studies in comparative anatomy, including the descriptive anatomy of the domestic animals as well.

With reference to the anatomy of the horse, it will be useful for the purposes of the exposition to distinguish between what relates to pure descriptive anatomy and what has a more narrowly artistic aim.

A large number of drawings concerning artistic anatomy have been preserved, which partly deal with the positions of the limbs especially, and partly study the proportions of the various regions or the entire body of the animal.

Of especial importance for their evidence of anatomical study and research seem to me the following drawings: A head seen from the side (Windsor, no. 12285) which shows, even though after many thoughts and corrections, the exact anatomical structure of the bones and the muscles of the face; the drawings of the shoulder region in various positions (Budapest Museum), in which the muscles are clearly distinguishable; and finally the drawing, so close to a dissection demonstration, that depicts the right thoracic limb (Windsor, n. 12297), especially in its lateral aspect and in particular the last leg to the right; there the bellies of the various extensors are visible, the course of their tendons and

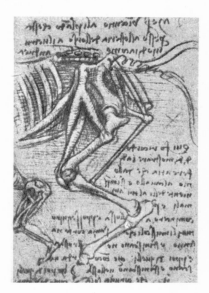

Studies of osteology and myology of pelvic limb of horse – Ms. K, fol. 109 v – From the collection of Institut de France, Paris

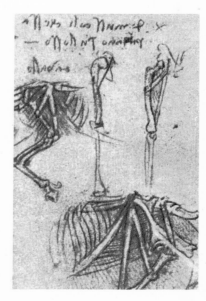

Studies of osteology and myology of pelvic limb of horse – Ms. K, fol. 102 r – From the collection of Institut de France, Paris

391

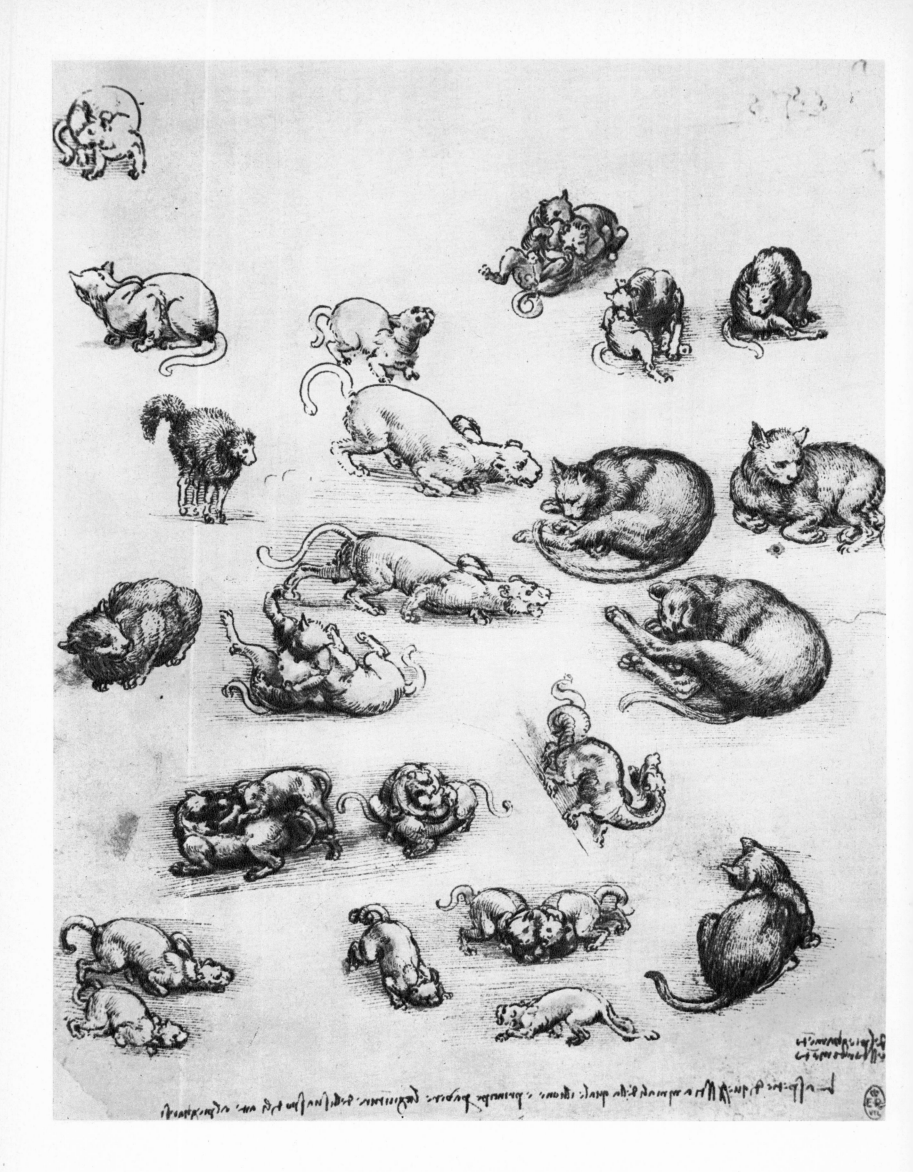

Studies and positions of cats – Windsor, Royal Collection, no. 12363

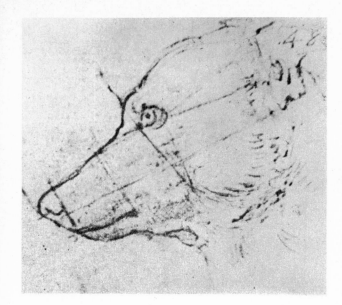

36.

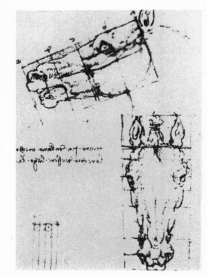

Proportions of head of horse – Ms.
F, fol. 62 v

Head of horse – Ms. G, fol. 11 r

Studies of dragon flies – Turin, former
Royal Library

those of the flexors is clearly shown, and the corresponding ligaments are almost visible. As regards the study of the proportions, which of course answers to an artistic purpose but also deals with the anatomy of the external forms, the drawing at Windsor, no. 12294, is sufficient to convey an idea of the almost pedantic precision with which the proportions are given on an anatomically conceived and drawn limb.

Conviction as to Leonardo's profound knowledge of the anatomy of the horse comes to us from a few drawings well known today, for example the two already mentioned, from manuscripts of the Institut de France, which seem to me particularly suited to the purpose. Folio 109 verso shows a drawing in sufficient detail—considering the small format of the original picture—of the osteology of the limb and pelvic girdle, with a portion of the vertebral column as far as the fifth dorsal vertebra from the last. The six lumbar vertebrae can be distinctly named, as well as the most salient features of the sacrum, the bones of the basin, and the long bones of the limb. Some muscles of the leg are also to be seen in diagrammatic form, as Leonardo often did, but still clearly and easily identifiable. Also of interest in relation to his knowledge of the horse's anatomy is the note added in his handwriting, which is one of the many projects that he set himself to execute, and which refers to a theme in pure comparative anatomy, but still shows the emphasis laid on the behavior of the voluntary muscles as regards their insertion by means of tendons or directly: "Here I make a note to show the difference that exists between man and horse and in the same way with other animals. I commence with the bones, and then go on to all the muscles which proceed from and end in the bones without tendons, then to those which proceed from and end in the bones with tendons, and then to those which have a single tendon on one side."

Folio 102 recto again presents the osteology and myology of the posterior limb, although in no great detail; but here is once more a reference to his intention of comparing the pelvic limb of the horse with that of man, an intention that will be put into effect elsewhere. On folio 22 recto of the fifth Quaderno we see the pelvic limb of a half-rearing horse compared to that of a man, with a comment: "Of the relationship that exists between the arrangement of the bones and muscles of the animals and that of the bones and muscles of man"; but having observed the different position of the long bones, especially the metatarsus, he adds: "To compare the bone structure of the horse with that of man you should show the man on tiptoe in representing the legs."

Proof of an investigation of notable anatomical value is given by folio 18 recto of Anatomical Ms. B, dealing with the genital organs of the cow and the fetal membranes in pregnancy. To be noted here are the perfect conformity of the drawing and the text to anatomical fact, apart from the position of the quiescent horn of the uterus. Leonardo points out that the ovaries are not inserted directly on the uterus, and also that the ovaries and the uterus constitute the genital organs (womb): "The testicles (ovaries) are not attached to this veined organ but to its integument, which does not show any veins; and the former together with the said integument constitute the true womb."

He brings out the way in which the villi of the cotyledons interweave in the sinuses of the uterus: "As the fingers of one hand fit into the spaces between the fingers of the other when the two hands are joined face to face, so the threads of flesh of these *spugnole* [cotyledons] interweave like burs, one against the other." He is not certain whether it is the *decidua basalis* or the *chorion frondosum* that receives the villi: "Observe which part of the *spugnole* it is that enters into the other with its teeth," and he also observes in a drawing, how the *chorion frondosum* separates from the *decidua* after birth, and points out the factors that enable the ruminants, and among them the Bovinae, to be classified as mammals with nondeciduate placentae: "As the cotyledons, which join together the two membranes between the two extremities, separate from each other, one half going off with the child when it is born cloaked, namely the lower half [referring to the drawing], and the other half,

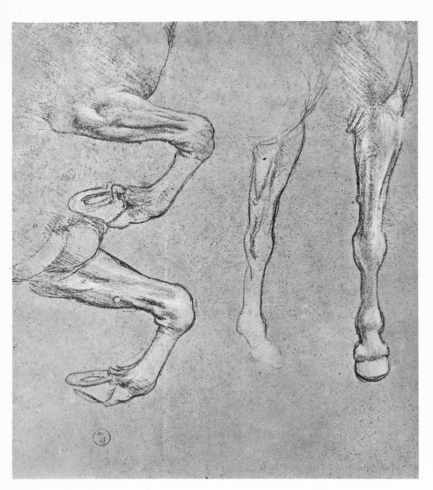

Upper Left: Foreleg of horse – Turin, former Royal Library. — Upper Right: Rump of horse – Windsor, Royal Collection, no. 12335. — Below: Drawings of horses – Windsor, Royal Collection, no. 12317

394

Left: Positions of hind legs – Windsor, Royal Collection, no. 12313

Right: Drawings of horses – Windsor, Royal Collection, no. 12321

which remains above, staying with the womb." He comes back to the same theme in another note, still on the same picture: "The lower one [figure of the integuments] contains the third and fourth skins of the animal as it lies in the womb, which skins are combined, that is they touch, and the picture above combines the uterus with it by means of these fleshy rosettes, which interpenetrate and cling together as burs would; and when the child is born, it bears with it these two skins with half of the thickness of this rose and the other half remains in the womb of the mother and then contracts there, joining, and they attach themselves to each other at their edges in such a way that they seem never to have been divided." This refers to the involution of the *endometrium* after birth, a point to which he returns: "The which [cotyledons] being distributed six by six as the womb contracts, all these cotyledons come to touch at their edges and then join with hexagonal sides and finally combine to form a single piece of flesh, out of which they divide again and spread at the next impregnation." And actually the history of the cotyledons in the cow is quite similar to Leonardo's account, although it is not precisely as it is represented in the upper left portion of the picture.

Leonardo carried his passion for anatomical research over into his study of the problems of flight. Among the many drawings referring to the flight of birds, the one at Windsor, no. 12656, is noteworthy. The anatomical dissection is reproduced with remarkable fidelity; the drawing seems to me to be flawless with respect to the osteology of the entire thoracic limbs, especially of the hand, in the central figure as well as regards the extensor and flexor muscles of the metacarpus and the phalanges. The course and the terminations of the tendons of the extensor muscles of the metacarpus and of the phalanges, visible in the next to the last dissection, are described with admirable precision: "Three tendons are attached at the joint, the first and lower one ending at *n*, and the second at *c*, and the third and last passes over the joint *S* and ends at *t* at the end of the wing, bifurcating at *a* and terminating at *o*."

Leonardo always was interested in extending his knowledge of the anatomy of the horse, and also studied other animals anatomically with various ends in view, sometimes merely for the sake of investigation; but in addition he did work in true comparative anatomy, meaning thereby the study of the various animal species in order to find the laws of the organization of living beings.

Studies of limbs – Windsor, Royal Collection, no. 12309

395

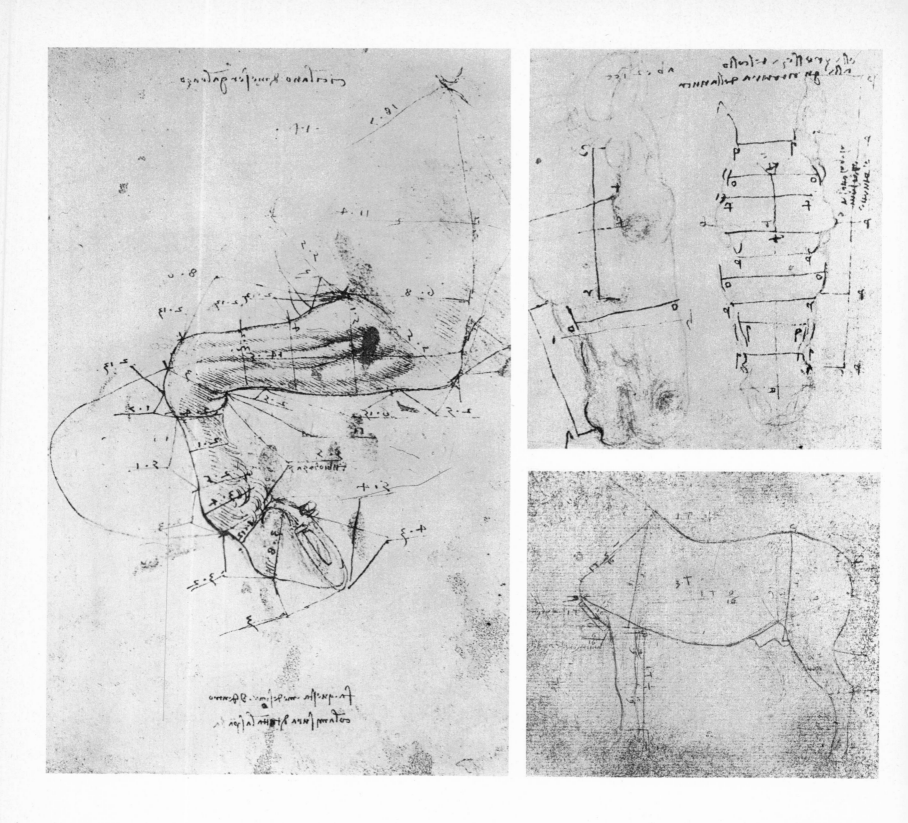

Left: Studies of proportions of foreleg of horse – Windsor, Royal Collection, no. 12294

Upper Right: Proportions of head of
horse – Windsor, Royal Collection,
no. 12286

Lower Right: Proportions of body
of horse – Paris, Louvre

The material we have in this field is scattered but rich, and for obvious reasons illustrations must be limited, enough, however, to give due honor to Leonardo as a comparative anatomist, referring to the bibliography for more complete treatments (De Toni *et al.*).

Many of Leonardo's discoveries in comparative anatomy were made with the definite aim of bringing out functional peculiarities of man and animals. In this process Leonardo rightly considered anatomy not statically but as a function of physiology, holding it to be the substratum and basis of living matter, and therefore inseparable from and at the service of the functioning of the organs and systems that constitute the animal body.

The study on the leverage of the muscles of the forearm in man and the monkey is typical in this connection (Anat. Ms. B, fol. 9 v): "In proportion as the tendon *cd* takes the gone *op* nearer to the hand, so this hand raises a greater weight; and this is the case with the monkey which is more powerful in its arms than the man is according to his proportion."

We give another passage relating to comparative anatomy, which at the same time comprises an original observation on the olfactory bulbs of the rhinencephalon of animals, which is very highly developed in the Carnivora and hence in the Felidae, as we know. Leonardo says, with reference to the sense organs in man and the animals: "I have found in the constitution of the human body that as among all the constitutions of the animals it is of more obtuse and blunt sensibilities, since it is an instrument less ingenious, and its parts are less capable of receiving the effects of the senses. I have seen in the leonine species how the sense of smell forms part of the substance of the brain

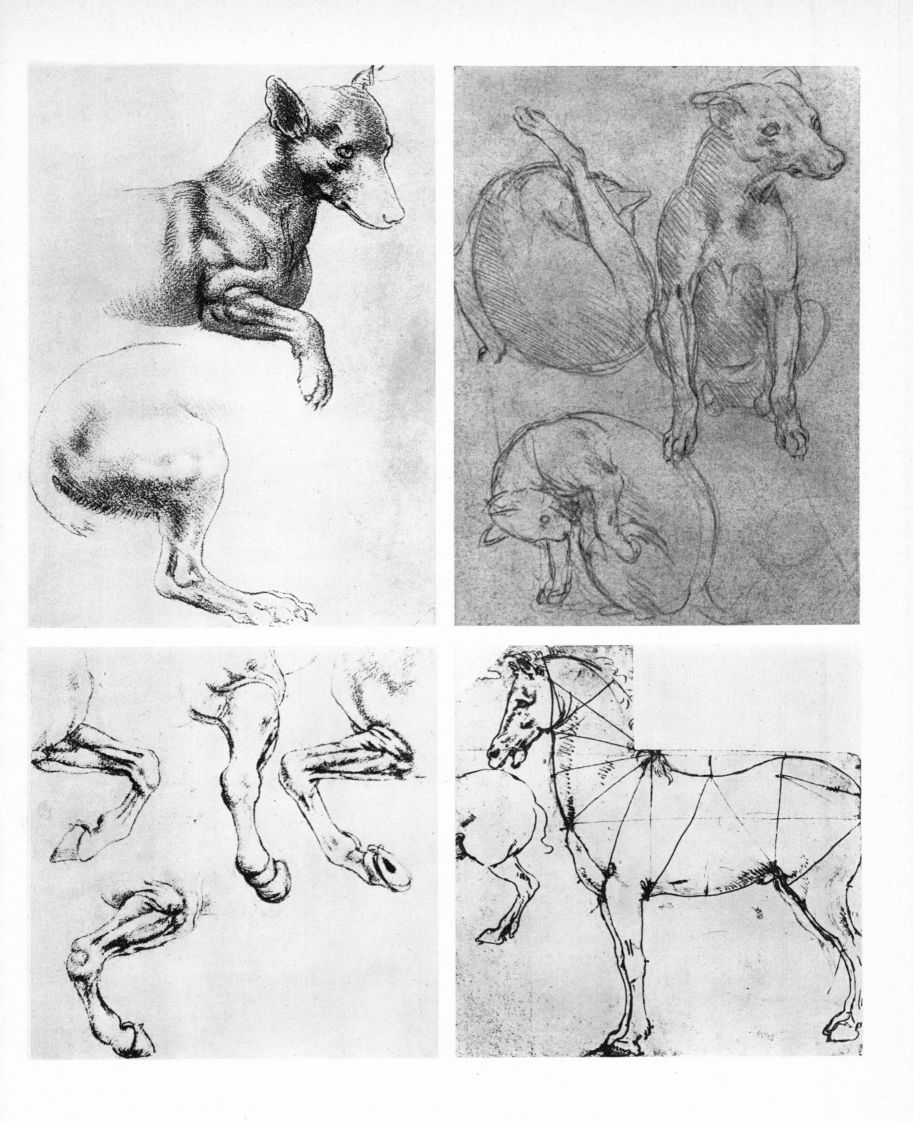

Above: Drawings of dogs – Left: Windsor, Royal Collection, no. 12361 – Right: London, British Museum. — Below Left: Shoulder muscles – Windsor, Royal Collection, no. 12299. – Below Right: Proportions of horse – Windsor, Royal Collection, no. 12318

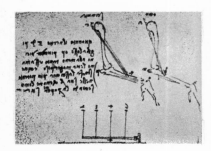

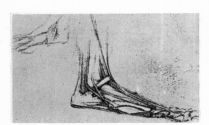

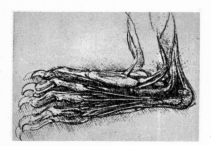

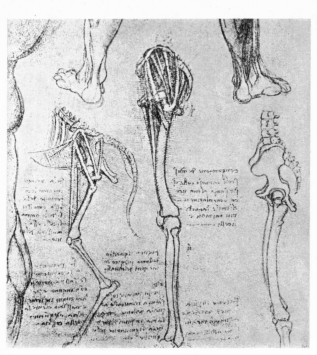

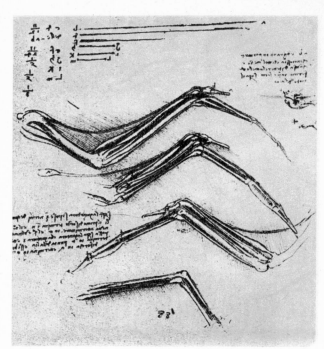

[the olfactory bulbs] and descends into a very large receptacle [the ethmoidal fossae] to meet the sense of smell which enters among a large number of cartilaginous cells [the ethmoidal labyrinth] with many passages [cribriform plate of the ethmoid] that go to meet the abovementioned brain."

Leonardo also has a remarkable knowledge of the morphological affinities among the various animal species, and on the basis of it succeeds in giving the groupings of genera and families of the modern anatomical zoological classification:

"Man. The description of man, in which is contained those that are [note well] almost of the same species, such as the baboon, the ape, and others like these, which are many."

Next comes a virtually complete listing of the Felidae:

"Lion and its kindred, such as panthers, leonze [wildcats?], tigers, leopards, lynxes, Spanish cats, *gannetti*, common cats, and the like."

The Equidae: "The horse and its kindred, such as the mule, the ass, and the like, with [incisor] teeth above and below."

The solenodont Artiodactyla or ruminants, from which the camel, which Leonardo was familiar with, is excluded, perhaps because of its dentition:

"The bull and its kindred, with horns and without upper [incisor] teeth, such as the buffalo, stag, fallow dear, roebuck, sheep, goat, wild goats, ibex, chamois, milch cattle, giraffes."

I have not tried to make a complete or even an extensive list here of all the ideas and information concerning animal and comparative anatomy that Leonardo left scattered over the pages which have come down to us. This would have been impossible in any event because of the bulk of the material, and would have been futile in view of the scope of the volume of which this article is a part. Its intention was to be a memorial of all the manifold activities to which his lofty spirit was devoted in its desire to know and to investigate, recognizing no bounds, no difficulties, no impossible tasks. The purpose of this chapter was merely to give a brief sampling of the most outstanding observations so as to show the man as a precursor, if not the founder, of scientific animal anatomy and of comparative anatomy.

I feel, however, that these few references give a fairly accurate idea of one of Leonardo's many activities, perhaps not one of the best known, but not so because of the lack of important factors, but only because overshadowed by more important or more extensive activities, such as his work on human anatomy.

In any event, I should like to voice my conviction that we have only fragmentary knowledge of his work in this field. His studies on the anatomy of the horse must have been far more comprehensive, although here too is the proof of his mighty activity as scientist and great artist, and of his versatility and outstanding ability combined with higher intuitive faculties. All these qualities, despite the ideas and discoveries of the science of that time, make Leonardo da Vinci a precursor, and perhaps the founder, of the anatomy of the domestic animals and of comparative anatomy as well as in other fields of biology.

LUIGI LEINATI

LEONARDO'S WORK IN PHONETICS AND LINGUISTICS

The value and extent of Leonardo's work in phonetics and linguistics can only be adequately appreciated after studying the condition of "linguistics" before and during Leonardo's time. Hence the following historical introduction is nothing more than a sketch; an exhaustive treatment is not yet possible because of the scarcity of the necessary texts.

The voice and its sounds, in other words the elements of language, are produced by the vocal apparatus (larynx and trachea). By means of the sounds we form words, and by means of words sentences, by which in turn we express the states of the spirit and the mind. The voice and its sounds, as well as their distortions and deformations, had been repeatedly studied by philosophers, physicians, and grammarians, long before Leonardo. I mention the most outstanding of these scientists.

What can be gleaned from the *Corpus hippocraticum* is rather meager. Hippocrates considers the voice and its sounds almost exclusively from the point of view of semeiotics [or semantics]. He expresses himself in a definitely phonetic manner in only two places. We read in the *De morbis* (ed. Cornarius, 1546, p. 242 f.): "We form the voice by means of the lung, since the latter is hollow, and there is a duct above it; the voice is articulated by the lips and the tongue .... The pulmonary duct is provided with a lid in the form of an ivy leaf, so that in swallowing, anything that might tend to enter the lung cannot pass." In the *De carnibus* (p. 59 f.) he writes: "Man speaks by virtue of the air that he introduces into the entire body and especially into its cavities. When the air is forced out of the hollow space, it produces a sound (strictly speaking, a noise), since the head is in vibration, too. The tongue articulates by means of its motions, receiving the sound in the throat and striking against the palate and the teeth, and thereby gives the sound distinct form. If the tongue did not continually articulate, man could not speak so clearly and would produce only a few primitive natural sounds. A proof of this is given by those born deaf, who form only simple sounds, since they are not able to speak." Accordingly, Hippocrates had no exact concept of the true function of the vocal apparatus.

Aristotle's ideas on the formation of the voice are as inaccurate as those of Hippocrates. It is true that he speaks more often and at greater length about various vocal phenomena; thus, for example, he discusses the different intonations of the voice in man and in animals, and the phenomena of the inanimate world of sounds (ed. Casaubon, 1590, Vol. I, *De anima*, II, 8, p. 393 f.). Along with results of direct observation we find others of evidently speculative origin (*De audibilibus*, Vol. I, p. 732-735). Of special importance are the sixty-five questions (apocryphal?) chiefly concerning the treatment of the "voice" (*ibid.*, Vol. II, *Problematum sectio*, XI, p. 422-429). Aristotle does not deal with the sounds of the voice any more than Hippocrates had done. In the field of acoustic phenomena

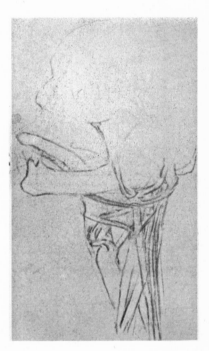

Musculation of vocal apparatus – Quad. Anat. V, fol. 17 r

Leonardo was the first to see the relationships between the larynx and adjacent muscles, and had a correct notion of the cooperation of the sternocleidomastoid muscle in the production of the voice – Quad. Anat. I, fol. 10 r

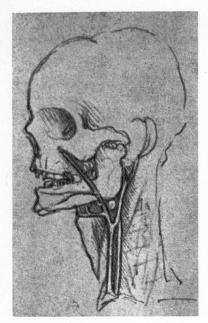

Anatomical scheme of vocal apparatus – Quad. Anat. V, fol. 17 r

We are indebted to Leonardo for the first drawing of a larynx *in situ*. However, this larynx is not human. This appears from the form of the cricoid and thyroid cartilages and the hyoid bone, as well as from the junction of the latter with the upper horn of the thyroid cartilage – Quad. Anat. V, fol. 17 r

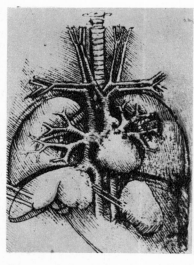

Organs of thoracic cavity – Quad. Anat. III, fol. 10 v

he distinguishes sound, voice, and articulate sounds. The latter are nothing but the product of the articulation of the voice by means of the tongue. The vowels are formed by the voice and the larynx, and the consonants by the tongue and the lips (*ibid.*, Vol. I, *Hist. animalium*, IV, 9, p. 510 c). On this subject, therefore, Aristotle simply repeats what Hippocrates had said.

Galen wrote copiously on the voice and its sounds. It is held against him that he never dissected a human cadaver. From the point of view of phonetics, however, Galen deserves the greatest attention, especially for his experiments in vivisection. In particular, he studied on the living animal the base of the tongue, the functioning of the tongue and the Vagus, as well as the effect of the contraction of the intercostal nerves on the formation of the voice, the consequences for the voice of cutting the ribs and the spinal cord, or of a lesion of the medullar canal. The wealth of Galen's knowledge is really astonishing. For example, he reports on the structure and the nature of the lungs and the trachea, the cartilages and muscles of the larynx, the form of the glottis, the innervation of the larynx, the muscles of the abdomen and thorax, etc. (ed. C. G. Kühn, 1821-1833, Vol. IV, *De usu partium*; see in particular chap. 7 and 16. Cf. Max Simon, *Sette libri di anatomia di Galeno*, 1906, Vol. II, *De voce et anhelitu* and *Vocalium instrumentorum dissertio*, which do not furnish anything more than the *De usu partium*). The ventricles ("*tasche*") of Morgagni were observed for the first time by Galen, as Morgagni himself states (*Adversaria anatomica*, 1714, p. 34). Galen also knew that the voice is formed in the larynx, to be sure, but that the palate and the uvula play an important part in its formation (ed. Kühn, III, 526).

We now leave the ancients and enter the Middle Ages with Avicenna. In phonetics this prince of physicians does not give us anything that relates to his own observations and experiences. This is no wonder; for Galen's investigations had gone so deep that for centuries there was nothing left to do but to compile, translate, and recast his works. Not even the Arab Galen escaped this fate. The references to *phonia* in his *Canon* (Bk. I, Fûnûn I, Doctr. 5, Su. II, chap. 7-14; Bk. III, Fûn. VI, chap. 1 *et seq.*; *ibid.*, Fûn. IX, chap. 1, Fûn. X, Tract. I, chap. 1 *et seq.*; *ibid.*, Tract. II, chap. 1 *et seq.*) do not contain anything that goes beyond Galen's results.

In the 13th century, at a time when Roger Bacon and Arnaldus de Villa Nova were bitterly opposing Aristotelianism and in particular the scholastic treatment of medicine, there was a pre-Renaissance of anatomy and surgery. This important revival is personified most obviously and efficaciously in the person of Mondino de' Liucci, who in 1315 undertook public dissection of cadavers. In his *Anatomia*, printed only in 1476, Mondino divides the human body into three parts: upper, middle, and lower. In the upper part (head) are the *membra animata*, in the middle part (the thoracic cavity) the *membra spiritualia* (heart, lungs, and other elements *orta ab his*), and in the lower part the *membra naturalia*.

Mondino describes several movements of the lips and also makes succinct but forceful observations on the teeth, the tongue, and on the uvula in connection with the formation of sounds. He treats of the trachea together with the esophagus; he then goes on to the anatomy of the epiglottis (by which name he means the larynx) and especially of the *nervi reversivi*, which are most important for the formation of the voice. The larynx is made up of three cartilages. The voice is formed by means of the *lingua fistulae, dicta fistula* [tongue of the pipe, called pipe]. The term *fistula* requires special explanation. The Greeks compared the larynx to the tongue (glottis)-shaped mouthpiece of a pipe. This was why they gave the name of "glottis" to the space inside the larynx in which the voice is formed. The translators of Galen into Latin rendered the word "glottis" by *lingula*, referring to instruments in which the mouth end of the pipe is the essential condition for the production of the sounds. The word "glottis" thus meant from the outset not the tongue but the sounding mouthpiece of the Pan's pipe, whose moving reeds really have the form of a tongue and are so called in acoustics. At the beginning therefore "glottis" did not mean what we call "glottis" today, but the entire internal cavity of the larynx (see J. Hyrtl, *Onomatologia anatomica*, ed. 1880, p. 244 f.). Leonardo also cites the *fistula*.

For the grammarians, the linguists of that era, the voice and articulate sounds had fundamental value, though of an altogether different nature. The concepts current among these men of learning are not in conformity with those of physicians, to be sure, and are remarkably primitive. Like with the Stoics and Varro, the starting point was the voice (*vox*), which was then distinguished as *voces articulatae et confusae*. Only the former of these (*litteralis, scriptilis vox*) can be represented by letters (*litterae*). The alphabet consists of 23 letters as a rule (including two Greek letters, *y* and *z*); these are divided into 5 vowels, 7 semivowels (*f, l, m, n, r, s, x*) and 9 mutes (*b, c, d, g, h, k, p, q, t*). A syllable equals a letter plus a vowel. From the syllable we go to the word (*dictio*) (cf. Pauly, *Real-Enzyklopädie*, 1912, XII, 1803).

Throughout the Middle Ages the grammarians limited themselves to passive imitation. The history of Romance philology shows that a certain flowering of linguistic investigations was due to Dante with his *De vulgari eloquentia*. In this work Dante treats questions that still concern linguistics, for example, the multiplicity and mutability of languages and the causes thereof, the formation of language, the transformation of language, etc. From the phonetic-linguistic point of view we may fairly say that the *De vulgari eloquentia* offers us nothing, for when mention is made of the voice and its sounds, the subject is treated from a philosophical and aesthetic point of view. Some phonetic

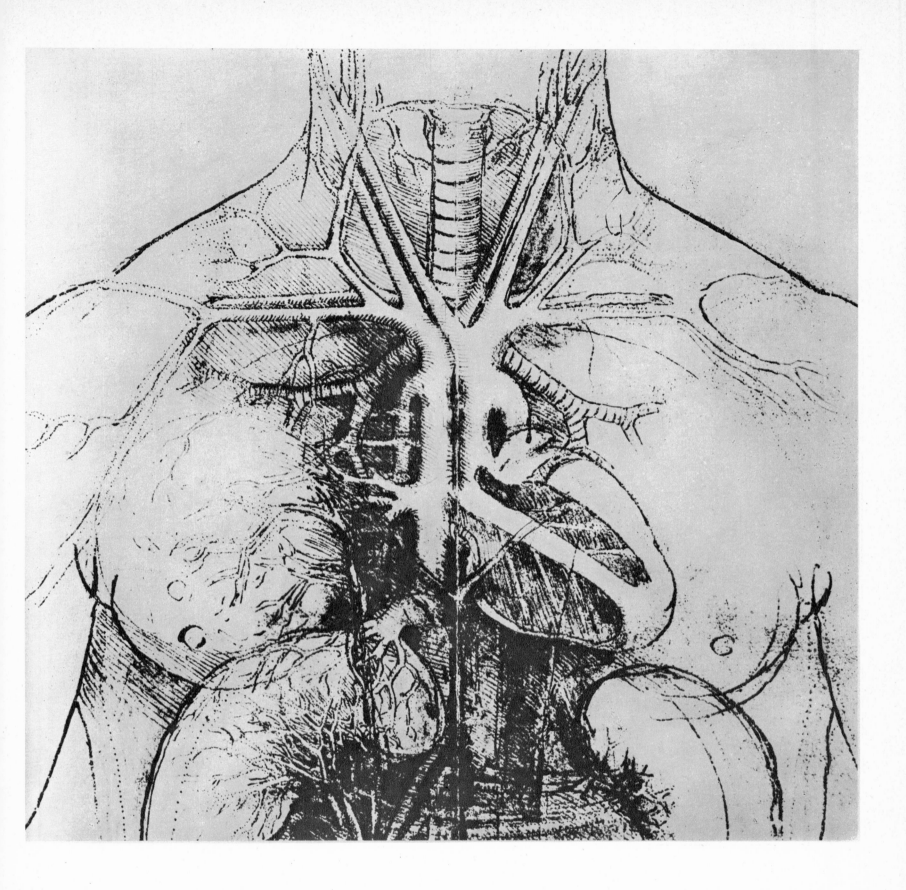

instances of orthoëpy are comprised in the examples given of various languages (Bk. I, 11 f.), but they are rare.

Organs of the thoracic cavity – Quad. Anat. I, fol. 12 r

At the time of Leonardo and even later, the "linguists" were still occupied with the struggle against Latin, trying to obtain from Dante arguments in favor of the superiority of Italian. What is said of language and sounds in the course of these efforts does not go beyond what Dante had set forth.

The state of knowledge at Leonardo's time may be summed up by saying that Galen rises above all other inquirers, for no one else had treated the voice and its sounds with so much independence and thoroughness. To what extent did Leonardo have merits despite the existence of such a precursor? To what extent was he a continuator or an initiator?

In his anatomical investigations Leonardo aimed at a very concrete goal, namely, at the composition of a compendium or treatise. He says: "The order of the book. This depicting of mine of the human body will be as clear to you as if you had the natural man before you... and in this way the natural anatomy is sufficient for your comprehension" (Quad. Anat. I, fol. 2 r). In his effort

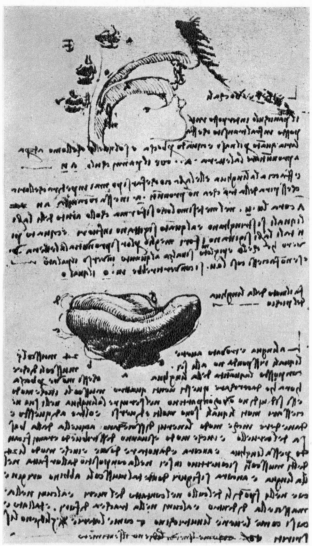

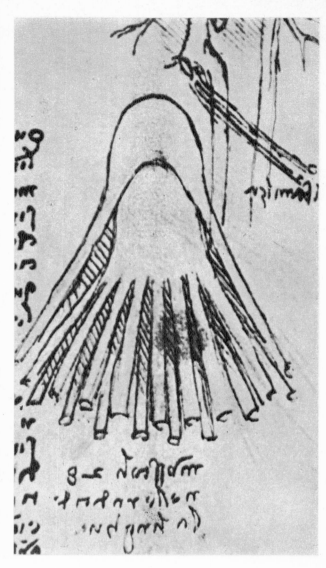

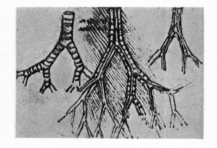

In his studies Leonardo did not neglect details on the respiratory organs, and gave us, among other things, several drawings of the trachea and its branchings – Quad. Anat. II, fol. 2 r

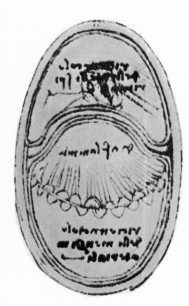

Leonardo had made many discoveries concerning the functioning of the respiratory system. In some points, notwithstanding, he remained under the influence of his predecessors in antiquity and the Middle Ages. For example, according to him the diaphragm divides the "spiritual" from the "natural" organs (Quad. Anat. I, fol. 5 v), as also appears from the figure reproduced here. Above, in mirror writing: "receptacle of the spiritual members"; in the center: "diaflamma"; and below: "receptacle of the material members" – Quad. Anat. IV, fol. 3 r

to perform this huge task, Leonardo struck out new paths and gave to his researches the imprint of his entire personality. As regards the arrangement of the treatise, he followed the classical model. "Thus, in fifteen figures, you will have set before you the microcosm on the same plan as before me was adopted by Ptolemy in his cosmography." In this way Leonardo desires to put "before your eyes a description of the whole form and substance of man, as regards his movements from place to place, by means of his different parts" (Quad. Anat. I, fol. 2 r). Later, when Leonardo calls for depiction of the branching of the trachea in the lungs, then the branching of the veins and arteries, each by itself, and finally "everything in reciprocal relationship," he gives the following advice: "But follow the method of Ptolemy in his cosmography in the reverse order. Put first the knowledge of the parts, and then you will have a better understanding of the whole put together" (Quad. Anat. III, fol. 10 v).

Leonardo gives a most accurate treatment of the anatomy of the entire respiratory apparatus (ribs and other parts of the skeleton, diaphragm, super- and intercostal musculature, innervation of the same, the entire musculature of the back and breast, lungs, trachea). Only Galen had discussed respiration as exhaustively as Leonardo, but there was a difference in that the former's discussion was based on dissection of animals and the latter's on human dissection. This point of superiority in Leonardo can never be too much emphasized.

It had been known for a long time that voice is not possible without breathing, but Leonardo was the first to stress and point out the close relationship between the respiratory movements and the formation of the voice. It is true that here too classical and medieval reminiscences crop up. According to Leonardo (Quad. Anat. I, fol. 5 v), the diaphragm has four functions; the fourth of these is to separate the spiritual parts from the natural. This recalls Mondino, who situated the spiritual parts in the thoracic cage and the natural ones in the abdomen. Leonardo even illustrates the theme with drawings. Thus, for example, when he speaks of the receptacle of the spiritual parts and of the receptacle of the material (according to Mondino, "natural") parts (Quad. Anat. IV, fol. 3 r), he refers to the *Situs spiritualis* (Quad. Anat. V, fol. 20 v). The subsequent statement: "The wind... which arises from the lung, which releases the vital spirits that command the sinews..." (Quad. Anat. I, fol. 13 v) shows us that by the expression *spiritus vitales* Leonardo means precisely those *spiritus animales* of the theory of vital and nervous spirits, a theory that goes back to the ideas of Aristotle and the Stoics.

The question of whether or not the air issuing from the trachea is condensed in its passage (Quad.

Anat. I, fol. 5 v) is answered in the affirmative by Leonardo. "The trachea contracts itself in the larynx in order to condense the air, which seems a thing of life as it comes from the lung to create the various kinds of voices, and also to press and dilate the different passages and ventricles of the brain; if the trachea were thus dilated in its upper end as it is in the throat, the air could not condense itself and perform the duties or benefits which are necessary to life and to man, that is in speaking, singing, and the like."

The idea that respiration is in direct relationship with the brain had already been stated by Hippocrates (*De carnibus*, ed. Cornarius, p. 59) and by Galen (Vol. III, p. 663). Is it possible that we today may think of the "condensation of the air" as a "compression below the glottis"?

So far as our present knowledge of the history of phonetics extends, Leonardo was the first to point out the close connections between the respiratory system and the muscles of the esophagus. To appreciate the functioning of these muscles at their true value, he holds it important above all (Quad. Anat. I, fol. 9 r) to examine the functioning of the trachea and the way it acts in producing high, middle, and low tones of the voice. Actually, the trachea can become thicker or thinner, and shorter or longer. Bass singers, for example, make it shorter, the deeper their voices become. Galen speaks in much the same way in the *De voce et anhelitu*, 5. I do not see any connection between Galen and Leonardo in this respect, however; it seems to me that the statement above is to be interpreted as meaning that the uvula moves up and down in proportion to the highness of the tone of voice. In all events, Leonardo is aware of the importance of these processes and closes the paragraph with the following counsel: "And thus you will not abandon speculating on the voice and the trachea with its muscles until you have acquired complete knowledge of all the parts around the said trachea, and of all their natural functions in the variation of the voice, and you will make particular note of this, drawing and discussing all the parts" (Quad. Anat. I, fol. 9 r).

It is strange that Leonardo thinks that it is impossible to breathe through the mouth and the nose at once (Ra-Mo [?], V; Ms. G, fol. 96 v; Sa-Piu [Anat. Ms.] A, fol. 3 r), and considers it inevitable that respiration should be through the mouth with the uvula closed (or raised) after a nasal inspiration (Anat. Ms. A, fol. 3 r).

Very probably Leonardo, in view of the enormous task he had set himself, had neither strength nor time enough to go more closely into study of the larynx, which is an extremely complex organ. It is clear that Leonardo did not arrive at definite knowledge with respect to the voice and its principal organ, the larynx, as is seen from various points in his notes, in which he attempts either to recall previous problems or to suggest investigations. Thus for example, he assigns himself the task of describing the cause of high and low voice (Anat. Ms. A, fol. 3 r). Later he suggests discovering how the modulations of the voice occur in singing; in his opinion they are a simple function of the "trachea" in which the tongue does not participate (Quad. Anat. IV, fol. 19 r).

The assertion, derived more from reasoning than from experience, that the voices of old men become feebler because all the openings of the trachea contract, as is the case for the other viscera (Anat. Ms. A, fol. 3 r), is likewise to be considered a problem he had proposed for himself. We need not be astonished, therefore, if some of Leonardo's formulations are only halfway exact, for example, the statement that the trachea does not produce any pitch in vowel sounds, but that its function is reduced merely to the formation of the voice, especially in the pronunciation of *a, o, u* (Quad. Anat. IV, fol. 10 r), and that the two ventricles ["*tasche*"] of Morgagni produce the resonance of the voice (Anat. Ms. A, fol. 3 r). Leonardo prescribes a way of demonstrating the emission of the voice: "To get an idea of how the sound of the voice is produced in the upper portion of the trachea, take the lung out of a cadaver together with the trachea and larynx; then, with the lung full of air, compress it firmly. It will be possible to see in what way the *fistula* [pipe] called the trachea produces the voice. The same phenomenon can be seen and heard using the neck of a swan or goose, which can be made to sing after it is killed" (Anat. Ms. A, fol. 3 r).

We are in Leonardo's debt for some accurate observations on the formation of articulate sounds, as for example on the structure, activity, and innervation of the lips (Sa-Piu [Anat. Ms.] B, fol. 37 v) and on the "Sinus maxcillaris" (antrum of Highmore: Anat. Ms. B, fol. 40 v). On the other hand, it is very hard to understand the expressions used by Leonardo to describe the functions of the soft palate (Quad. Anat. IV, fol. 10 r) and of the *uvula* connected with it. It is clear that he did not complete his researches on the matter, as is seen clearly from the task he set himself of splitting the upper jawbone to see the uvula and determine the function of the uvula and the spot at which it approaches the orifice of the trachea (Anat. Ms. A, fol. 3 r). The same observation applies to the tongue, since Leonardo says: "And for this reason I will resume my discourse concerning the functions of the tongue where I left it" (Quad. Anat. IV, fol. 10 r). We should also mention the subsequent injunction to examine more closely into the musculation of the tongue (*ibid.*).

The plates illustrating the vocal organs give us a good harvest of ideas. Leonardo was an outstanding initiator in this field, for before him, and for a long time after him as well, anatomical drawings were in a most primitive state and typically inaccurate and crude. Above all, we owe to him the first drawings of the uvula, of the glottis, and of other parts of the vocal apparatus. Moreover, Leonardo considered a drawing to be far better than a verbal description: "With what words, O writer, can you with a like perfection describe the whole arrangement of that of which the picture

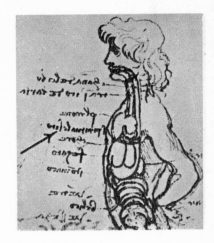

Leonardo believed in the existence of a *situs spiritualis* and situated in the thoracic cavity. The words read: "food tube – air passage – lung – seat of the spirit – heart – liver – stomach – abdomen – navel bladder – spleen – kidneys." The arrow has been added here to indicate the caption "*situs spiritualis*" – Quad. Anat. V, fol. 20 v

In this sketch it is easy to recognize the trachea, the anterior portion (?) of the cricoid cartilage, the thyroid cartilage with the upper horn, and the hyoid bone; the glottis is also visible – Quad. Anat. IV, fol. 9 v – This drawing is of historic value, since there are not drawings of the glottis, still less of the larynx, before Leonardo

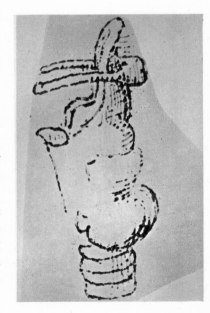

Larynx seen in profile. The drawing clearly shows the hyoid bone, between the horns of which the epiglottis rises, the other parts of the larynx, the trachea, and also the thyroid gland, which appears to be rather hypertrophic – Anat. Ms. A, fol. 3 r

403

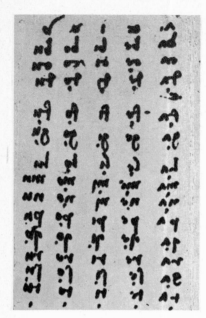

Studies of phonemes – Quad. Anat.
IV, fol. 10 r

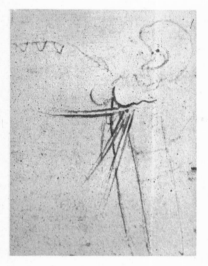

Musculature and veins of vocal apparatus – Quad. Anat. V, fol. 17 r

is here? For lack of due knowledge you describe it so confusedly as to convey but little perception of the true shapes of things, and deceiving yourself as to these you persuade yourself that you can completely satisfy the hearer when you speak of the misrepresentation of anything that possesses substance and is surrounded by surface. I counsel you not to encumber yourself with words unless you are speaking to the blind. If, however, notwithstandin you wish to demonstrate in words to the ears rather than to the eyes of men, let your speech be of things of substance or natural things, and do not busy yourself in making enter by the ears things which have to do with the eyes, for in this you will be far surpassed by the work of the painter. How in words can you describe this heart without filling an entire book? Yet the more detail you write concerning it, the more you will confuse the mind of the hearer, and you will always need commentators or have to go back to experience; and this with you is very brief, and has to do only with a few things as compared with the extent of the subject concerning which you desire complete knowledge" (Quad. Anat. II, fol. 1 r).

In fact, Leonardo's drawings are not always free of faults, and he has been reproached for having depicted parts of animal organs in drawings of human cadavers (see J. McMurrich Playfair, *Leonardo da Vinci the Anatomist*, Baltimore, 1930, p. 191-197). But in judging these anatomical drawings it should be kept in mind that the task Leonardo had set himself, that of compiling a whole treatise on anatomy, was evidently a difficult one even for a genius like Leonardo, especially in view of the size he had planned for the work. He never did finish his plan. Consequently, his manuscript notes and original drawings should not be considered as final. It should not be forgotten, in addition, that the compilation of drawings taken from the cadaver was an enterprise that had never been attempted at Leonardo's time, and he himself was fully aware of the difficulties: "And you who say that it would be better to watch an anatomist at work than to see these drawings, you would be right, if it were possible to observe all the things which are demonstrated in such drawings in a single figure, in which you, with all your cleverness, will neither see nor obtain knowledge of more than some few veins. In order to obtain a true and perfect knowledge of those, however, I have dissected more than ten human bodies, destroying all the other members, and removing the very minutest particles of the flesh by which these veins are surrounded, without causing them to bleed, excepting the insensible bleeding of the capillary veins; and as one single body would not last so long, it was necessary to proceed with several bodies by degrees, until I came to an end and had a complete knowledge; this I repeated twice, to learn the differences.

"And if you should have a love for such things you might be prevented by loathing, and if that did not prevent you, you might be deterred by the fear of living in the night hours in the company of those corpses, quartered and flayed and horrible to see. And if this did not prevent you, perhaps you might not be able to draw so well as is necessary for such a demonstration; or if you had the skill in drawing, it might not be combined with knowledge of perspective; and if it were, you might not understand the methods of geometrical demonstration and the method of the calculation of forces and the strength of the muscles; patience may also be wanting, so that you lack perseverance" (Quad. Anat. I, fol. 13 v).

It may be that Leonardo often had to be contented with a rudimentary sketch, as for example in representing the larynx (Quad. Anat. IV, fol. 9 v). I believe it is not far from the truth to attribute the presence of "animal" organs in drawings of human cadavers not so much to a preconceived idea but to consider it as a hasty notation, and hence not always faithful to the objects seen.

Voice articulated in sounds and forming language is a product of specifically human movements. Primarily, therefore, voice and articulate sounds should be thought of in a definitely physiological manner, and studied only in the human body.

Thought and comparison will be later themes. Leonardo was the first to realize this, and he therefore acted correctly when he did not concern himself with the reasons in general for man's speaking, or the origin of language, but rather dissected cadavers and observed living men. This way led him to his goal. When we are engaged in the examination of the facts, we cannot raise idle questions, lose ourselves in speculations, or pile up subtleties to defend a preconceived point of view. Instead, we must examine all the facts to recognize their true nature and only then go on to seek the primordial bond. That this was the attitude of Leonardo himself is proved among other things by this unequivocal statement: "The mental matters that have not passed through the sense are vain, and they produce no other truth than the injurious one; and as such discourses spring from poverty of genius, such discoursers are always poor, and if they are rich they will die poor in their old age ..." (Quad. Anat. I, fol. 13 v). These words apply equally to those today who eliminate from phonetics, that is, from the study of heard voices and sounds, any reference to scientific and biological principles, alleging the peril of a "mechanization of science."

Phonetics, and hence linguistics (since linguistics cannot exist without a deep basis in phonetics), honor in Leonardo the brilliant precursor of the methodologic trends that achieved their due development only three hundred years after his death.

G. PANCONCELLI-CALZIA

LEONARDO'S OPTICS

LIGHT

"That drawing has the feeling of a Da Vinci," I said to myself the first time I admired the fourth figure in Christian Huygens' *Traité de la lumière*—a candle flame all enveloped in expanding circles which intersect without breaking.

"For the circles of water do not break when they intersect," Leonardo had written (Cod. Forst., III, fol. 76 r) under one of his many drawings of waves advancing and interfering. Manuscript A at the Institut de France (fol. 61 r) has an even finer drawing, on which the theory of *transverse waves* is outlined in language that combines scientific precision and clarity of exposition. Leonardo's note here reads as follows:

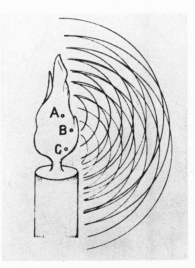

Fourth figure in *Traité de la lumière* of Christian Huygens

"I say: If you throw two small stones at the same time on a sheet of motionless water at some distance from each other, you will observe that around the two percussions numerous separate circles are formed; these will meet as they increase in size and then penetrate and intersect one another, all the while maintaining as their respective centers the spots struck by the stones. And the reason for this is that the water, although apparently moving, does not leave its original position, because the openings made by the stones close again immediately. Therefore the motion produced by the quick opening and closing of the water has caused only a shock which may be described as tremor rather than movement. In order to understand better what I mean, watch the blades of straw that because of their lightness float on the water, and observe how they do not depart from their original positions in spite of the waves underneath them caused by the occurrence of the circles. The reaction of the water being in the nature of tremor rather than movement, the circles cannot break one another on meeting, and as the water is of the same quality all through, its parts transmit the tremor to one another without change of position. Thus the water, although remaining in its position, can easily transmit the tremor to the adjacent parts, these transmitting it to other adjacent parts, while its force gradually diminishes until the end."

The blades of straw "that because of their lightness float on the water" and rise and fall without changing position longitudinally, undergoing only a *transverse* tremor, show the observant spirit and interpretative acuteness of Leonardo's genius, and many readers will remain amazed at finding in Da Vinci's writings an argument that we have been accustomed to consider as confined to modern scientific exposition. But Leonardo's great discovery, one of the greatest in all the history of science, lies in the *leap* he takes from water to *light*. Without the slightest precedent or any shadow of a precursor, the *wave theory of light* sprang up clear and precise in Leonardo's mind:

"Just as a stone thrown into water becomes the center and cause of various circles, sound spreads in circles in the air. *Thus every body placed in the luminous air spreads out in circles and fills the surrounding space with infinite likenesses of itself and appears all in all and all in every part*" (Cod. Atl., fol. 9 v).

Theory of transverse waves – Cod. Forst., III, fol. 76 r

Note the order of the progression—from water to sound, from sound to light. Leonardo begins with *water*, and analyzes the wave motion primarily in water. We have seen above that he held

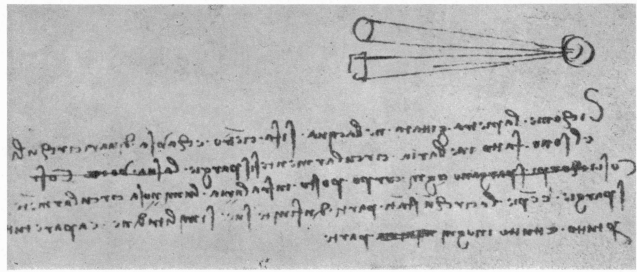

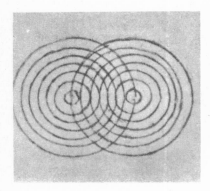

Transverse waves – Ms. A, fol. 61 r

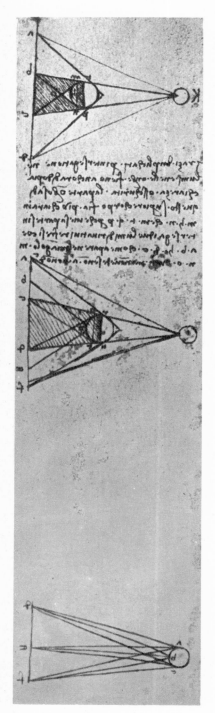

Light and shade studies – Primary
source of light and derivative or
reflected source of light – Ms. C,
fol. 16 v

it to be a *transverse* wave motion; it follows that for Leonardo all wave motions are *transverse* and not longitudinal. Hance, he holds, the wave motion of sound is transverse; and in that respect Leonardo has gone astray. Hance, he holds, the wave motion of light is transverse; and in that respect Leonardo has leaped beyond Huygens in one bound and anticipated Fresnel by three centuries.

When in 1690, almost two centuries after Leonardo, Christian Huygens set forth the wave theory of light, he did not have the slightest suspicion of the transverse nature of the movement, and did not make the slightest reference to the vibratory nature of the light waves. The concept of vibration was introduced into physical optics much later, by Thomas Young, the man who knew how to read at the age of two, the living embodiment to opposition to all specialization—physiologist, anatomist, mathematician, linguist, decipherer of hieroglyphics before Champollion, astronomer, calculator, super-intendent of the *Nautical Almanac*.

What thoughts did Leonardo have concerning vibrations?

In the first place, there is in Ms. K of the Institut de France, folio 49 recto, a sentence that by reason of its beauty of form and depth of idealism seems to come from a dialogue of Plato:

"Let proportion be found not only in numbers and measures, but also in sounds, weights, times, and positions, and whatever force there is."

Is not the *sound* that is propagated in the air a *harmonic* motion?

Is not the *weight* that gives the pendulum its motion to and fro a cause of *harmonic* motion?

Are not the periodic *times* of the seasons, the phases of the moon, and so many other natural phenomena, linked to a *harmonic* motion?

Are not the *positions* occupied by the planets, in their apparent disorder, periodically regulated, governed by a *harmonic* motion?

Sounds, weights, times, positions, and not only these, but any *force*—we should say *energy*—are governed by harmonic movements. *Proportion* is harmony.

If the reader finds this interpretation of ours a little forced, we point out that Leonardo unam-biguously and explicitly affirmed that every wave motion is necessarily and intimately connected with a *tremor*, that is, a vibration. It is precisely to this *tremor*, this *vibration*, that the propaga-tion of the wave is due. We have seen this in the passage already cited from the Codex Atlanticus (fol. 61 r):

"a shock which may be described as tremor rather than movement... its parts transmit the tremor to one another without change of position."

We know today that in the propagation of light the parts "transmit" the tremor to the adjacent parts only at the expense of, and as a consequence of the destruction of the magnetic field, thereby generating an electric field, and then by destruction in turn of the electric field, whose disappear-ance generates a new magnetic field. It is only the sequence of *electric-magnetic-eletric-magnetic* and so onward, interweaving and repeating at fantastic speed, that makes possible the advance of the light waves. This insight achieved by modern physical optics is to be credited to Maxwell, and certainly no one will dream of the possibility of finding it in Leonardo, while there can be no ex-tenuation for the author of a recent treatise entitled *Physical Optics* who ignores the very name of Maxwell.

Huygens also, two centuries after Leonardo, sought to explain the propagation of light waves. He saw that the propagation is not due to *transportation* of particles of the ether, but was content to find the cause in a slight percussion, a little shock given by the initial particles to the succeeding

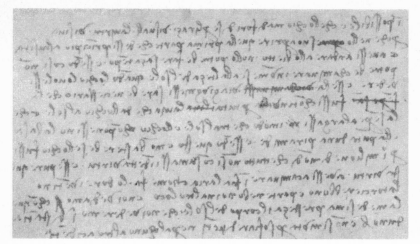
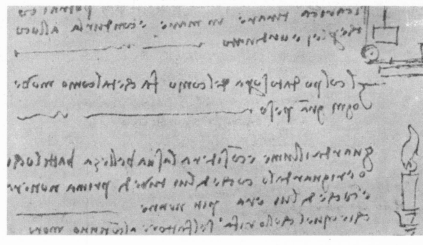

ones: "The propagation... does not consist in transportation of these particles but only in a little shock which they cannot but communicate to the particles surrounding them, despite all the movement that perturbs them and causes them to interchange places" (*Traité de la lumière*, chap. I).

The *shock* (*ébranlement*) has no necessary connection with the periodicity of the motion; in fact, this word is preferred today whenever it is desired to exclude the idea of vibration. On the other hand, the word *tremore* used by Leonardo necessarily implies a to-and-fro motion, oscillatory motion. Going more deeply into the question of the propagation of light waves, Huygens ended by expressly excluding the concept of vibration, when he said that propagation of waves through the particles of the other "consists in the very rapid motion of a subtle matter that permeates them from all sides and constrains their texture to assume such an arrangement that it gives the most open and easy passage possible to this fluid matter" (*ibid.*).

If light is propagated with a wave motion, its propagation cannot be instantaneous; rather, it must take a certain interval of time to go from one point to another. All the ancients believed in the instantaneous propagation of light; it was not until 1676 that Roemer, observing the eclipses of the satellites of Jupiter, disproved the idea, and measured the velocity of light.

Even Descartes, a century after Leonardo, was convinced that light was propagated instantaneously. I use the word "convinced" because while the ancients deduced the notion of the instantaneity of light solely from terrestrial phenomena, Descartes argued for it on the basis of astronomical phenomena, observations of lunar eclipses.

Now, when Huygens put forward the wave theory of light in 1690, he already had available Roemer's experimental results on the finite velocity of light, attained fourteen years before. As for Leonardo—genius is intuitive and precedes experience.

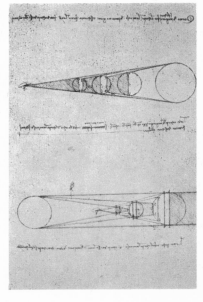

When the *cause* has been ascertained, the *experimental* observation of the effect is not indispensable. The cause is the wave nature of light, and the effect is the finite velocity of light.

"There is no effect in nature without a reason; understand the reason, and you do not need experiment" (Cod. Atl., fol. 147 v-*a*).

I think once more of Plato's dialogues when I read Leonardo's poetic words in Ms. F, folio 49 verso: "Look at light and consider its beauty. Close and open your eye and then look at it: what you see of it, was not before; and what there was of it, is no more." This is not at all an affirmation of the instantaneity of light, but evidently alludes to a high velocity of propagation.

The statement that the propagation of light takes time is explicitly made on the first folio of Ms. 2038 of the Bibliothèque Nationale, which Leonardo students call the Ashburnham codex, and which should be regarded as a complement to Ms. A of the Institut de France. The passage reads:

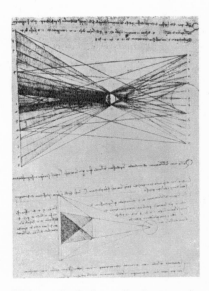

"It is impossible that the eye should project the visual power from itself, by visual rays, since, as soon as it opens, that front portion [of the eye], which would give rise to this emanation, would have to go forth to the object, and *this it could not do without time*. And this being so, it could not travel as high as the sun in a month's time when the eye wanted to see it. And if it could reach the sun it would necessarily follow that it would perpetually remain in a continuous line from the eye to the sun and would always diverge in such a way as to form between the sun and the eye the base and the apex of a pyramid. This being the case, if the eye consisted of a million worlds, that would not suffice to prevent its being consumed in the projection of its power; and if this power had to travel through the air as perfumes do, the winds would bend it and carry it into another place. But we do in fact see the mass of the sun with the same rapidity with which we see an object at the distance of an ell, and the power of sight is not disturbed by the blowing of the winds nor by any other accident."

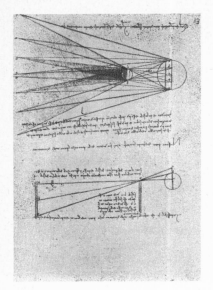

Relationship between luminous field and brightness of illuminated body – Ms. C, fol. 3 r

Observations on shadow as related to surface of illuminated object – Ms. C, fol. 12 r

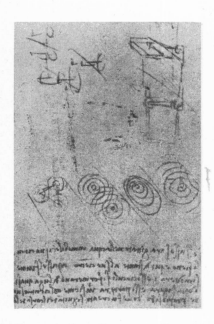

Demonstration of wave motion and propagation produced in moving water by fall of stone – Ms. I, fol. 87 r

To understand Leonardo's reasoning properly, we should think of the theory of vision that the Greek sages of antiquity upheld, and that still flourished among the learned men of Leonardo's time. This theory was that in the act of seeing the eye *sends forth* toward the object a hail of small projectiles, the *species*, and when this jet of *species* arrives at the object, there is vision of the object.

Leonardo overthrows this theory. For him the *species* still exist, although he often calls them *visual power*, but they are propagated by waves. If we consider the *species* as analogous to our photons, we shall realize that Leonardo vaguely anticipated modern wave mechanics. However, it is not the eye that sends out the *species* to the object, but the object that sends them in all directions, "circularly," by means of concentric waves that are capable of impinging on the eye, producing the phenomenon of vision: this constitutes the *overthrow* of the theory of the Greeks to which we have referred above.

If light were propagated instantaneously, the theory of the Greeks might still hold sway. But if time is required for the propagation of light, this theory must be buried forever. When we raise our heads to contemplate the sun and the stars, says Leonardo, we should not see the sun and stars at once, if the Greek theory were true, but should have to wait a long time, as much as a month, before perceiving them, to give the *species* time to reach the stars after leaving the eyes. But if we assume that the *species* leave from objects and travel "circularly" in all directions, we see sun and stars as soon as we look up, because the *species* were already on their way before we lifted our heads.

"The sun is four thousand miles from us," wrote Leonardo (Cod. Atl., fol. 260 r-*a*). In the passage cited from the Codex Ashburnham, he speaks of "a month" as the time required light to cover the distance between the sun and the earth, so that we might go on to infer that Leonardo not only held that a certain amount of time is needed for the propagation of light, but also gave a precise (though incorrect) value for the velocity of light—*four thousand miles a month*. It should be remembered, however, that the phrase "four thousand miles" appears in one manuscript, while the words "one month" occur in another. We cannot make too close a connection between two conceptions expressed at different times and places. It is very likely that when Leonardo said "one month" he meant to refer merely to a long interval of time, and that "one month" might be replaced by "one hour" or "one year."

The extent to which Leonardo studied and penetrated into the nature of wave motion is shown by the design taken from folio 87 of Ms. I—drawn in red pencil in the original—and by the writing under it:

"If the stone is flung into motionless water, its circles will be equidistant from their center. But if the stream is moving, these circles will be elongated, egg-shaped, and will travel with their center away from the spot where they were created, following the stream."

Did Leonardo, then, discover the Doppler-Fizeau principle, by which we can today measure the speed with which stars are approaching or receding?

We are too much in the habit of considering scientific principles as being intimately connected with the technical applications that made them fruitful and showed their importance. But if we get away from this mental attitude and draw a sharp distinction between the principle and its applications, there can be no doubt as to the answer: Leonardo was the first to discover the Doppler-Fizeau principle.

Genius does not bog down in innumerable experiments, often made with no further purpose than to increase their number, but uses a few well-made observations to rise to the broadest generalizations. Leonardo generalizes immediately from matter to spirit:

"The motion of earth beating against earth moves only slightly the parts struck. Water struck by water makes circles around the spot struck. For a longer distance, the voice within the air. Longer within fire. Further the mind within the universe: but as it is finite, it cannot embrace the infinite."

This is a transcription of all of page 67 in a little pocketbook of Leonardo's (Ms. H, Institut de France); it may be that Leonardo often arrived at some of his sublime ideas away from home, in the solitude of the open.

The ladder by which Leonardo's bold flight ascends has five rungs—earth, water, sound, flame, mind. He speaks expressly of the "circles," that is, the waves of water; and since he is seeking a link of analogy among the five things considered, elementary logic leads us to infer that all these entities must overcome distance by means of waves.

We may therefore paraphrase this page of the pocketbook as follows:

Everything in the cosmos is propagated by waves, coarser and finer waves, going further and further. The seismic waves generated in the hard earth below are propagated to a certain distance. The waves produced in water are propagated further than the eye can reach. The sound waves in the air travel still greater distances. The luminous waves of a flame penetrate still further. The waves of thought embrace the universe—but not the infinite, for that is forbidden to the finite, and our mind, however sublime, remains finite.

408

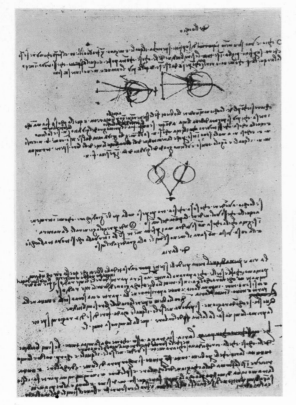

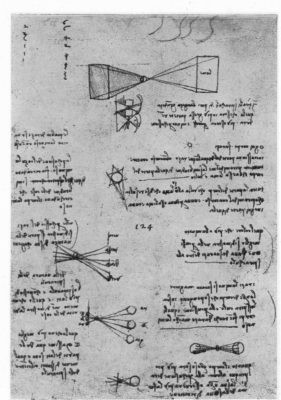

Note that the powerful generalization of this pocketbook sheet does not stand alone. Passing from waves to corpuscles, from the language of wave optics to the language of geometrical optics, Da Vinci sums up (Cod. Atl., fol. 256 r-c):

> "Every body gives off rays."

Universal radiation? Certainly. For Leonardo was convinced that in addition to visible radiations there are invisible radiations, such as those of heat and magnetism, those arising from the attraction of the planets, those of perfumes.

"This is seen in the sun, which sends out two kinds of *species*, the first luminous, the second of heat .... That the atmosphere attracts to itself, like a lodestone, all the images of the objects that exist in it, and that not their forms merely but also their nature may be clearly seen in the sun, which is a hot and luminous body. The whole atmosphere on which it acts becomes completely shot through with light and heat and takes on itself the image of the source of that heat and splendor, and does this in each minutest portion. The North Pole does the same, as the lodestone shows; and the moon and the other planets, without suffering any diminution, do the same. Among terrestrial things musk does the same, and other perfumes" (Cod. Atl., fol. 138 v-*b*).

It is astonishing to see how Leonardo, "an unlettered man," manages in simple words to give so superb a vision of the universe, from the massy earth to the thinking mind, all pervaded by waves and radiations.

In beginning this dissertation, I touched on the shadow of a suspicion—turning on the "da Vinci feeling" in a figure in Huygens' *Traité*. Could it be that Christian Huygens, whom Newton called *summus Hugenius*, may have been influenced by Leonardo's writings in his exposition of the wave theory of light?

In publishing his *Traité de la lumière* in 1690, he seems in his preface to be trying to establish an alibi, in face of whom and for what reason is not clear. He says that in 1678, that is, twelve years previously, he had communicated the substance of his treatise to the Académie Royale des Sciences, and everything would be well if the communication had been in the form of transmission of a manuscript. A few lines further on, however, he indicates clearly that he did not hand in his manuscript but only read it: *Quand j'en fis la lecture ....*

On the basis of my vague suspicions, I went eagerly through the *Oeuvres complètes* of Huygens published by the Société Hollandaise des Sciences. And I found something. On page 380 of the ninth volume (The Hague, M. Nijhoff, 1901) is a letter from Constantine Huygens to his brother Christian, dated from Kensington, March 3, 1690. It will be noted that this is the very year in which the *Traité de la lumière* was published. In the letter Constantine says that he has bought a manuscript of Leonardo da Vinci, paying three and a half guineas for it, but that he would not sell it back for four times as much. In speaking of the contents, he mentions perspective. And we students of Da Vinci know that perspective means also optics.

Even if we accept the twelve-year alibi advanced by the *summus Hugenius*, the question arises spontaneously: Could not the haste that Constantine shows in notifying Christian of his precious

Left: Statement in last paragraph of principle of invisible radiations – Cod. Atl., fol. 138 v-*b*

Center: Light and shade on body illuminated by two sources of light – Windsor, Royal Collection, no. 19149 v

Right: Statement of principle of universal radiation – Cod. Atl., fol. 256 r-c

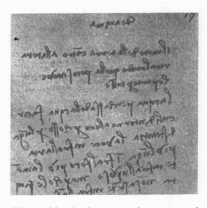

"Everything in the cosmos is propagated by means of waves" – Ms. H, fol. 67 r

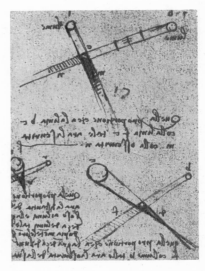

Measurement of ratio of intensity of two sources of light – Windsor, Royal Collection no. 12635 v

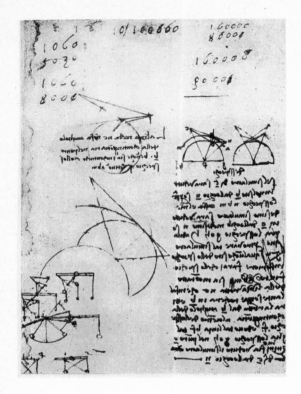
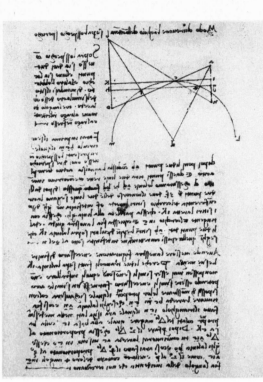
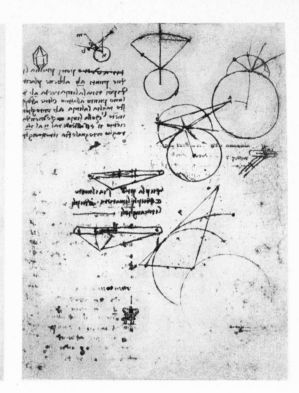

acquisition be due to the fact that Christian had even before then been interested in Da Vinci manuscripts on his own account?

I should not like to be misunderstood: I intended to touch on a mere suspicion, the shadow of a suspicion.

And so we come to Fermat's principle.

This principle had already been proposed in vague terms by Hero in the second century A.D. and by Olympiodorus in the sixth century, but it was difficult to find the correct form for enunciating it, simply because it contradicts the assumption of the instantaneity of light.

Almost two centuries before Fermat, Leonardo stated it in precise terms for the first time:

"Every action in nature takes place in the shortest way possible" (Quad. Anat. IV, fol. 16 r; cf. also Cod. Arund., fol. 85 v). The textual wording used by Fermat is, *La nature agit toujours par les voies les plus courtes* ("Nature always acts by the shortest paths").

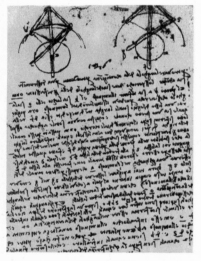

Leonardo believed in the theory of the finite velocity of light, and could therefore without contradiction calmly enunciate the famous principle. Fermat stated it first in 1657, but since he, like Descartes, believed in the notion of the instantaneity of light and wished to avoid contradiction, he put it aside for a time. It should be added, however, that he did not wait for Roemer's experiment (1676) before reconsidering the principle and advocating it. By the end of 1661 Fermat no longer doubted his principle, realizing that it led to the same law of refraction that Descartes had published shortly before.

Today Fermat's principle is the basis of geometrical optics. My distinguished friend Dr. Max Herzberger has proved, in his masterly *Strahlenoptik* (Berlin, Springer, 1931), that on the foundation of this principle alone all geometrical optics can be erected—not only Gaussian optics but also the optics of aberrations, for centered and noncentered optical systems. Carathéodory has also decisively taken the same path. Optical geometry is becoming the most interesting chapter of the calculus of variations.

It is precisely because of the ever increasing importance which this principle has been assuming in optics that I have insisted on Da Vinci's priority in enunciating it correctly.

I shall not speak of the law of the reflection of light, which Leonardo knew very well and applied with precision to spherical and parabolic mirrors. It is known that even the Greeks were aware of this law.

The problem of Alhazen attracted Leonardo greatly, and he spent much time on it without ever reaching an exact solution.

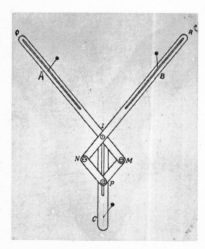

This problem (which has no importance in modern optics) consists in finding the path of the light ray that starts from a source of light with a given position, is reflected first by a spherical mirror, and then comes to the eye of an observer at a given position, fixed with respect to the mirror and the source of light. The problem had already been exactly solved geometrically by Alhazen in the fifth book of his *Opticae thesaurus*, but the exposition as the Arab author gives it is so intricate and confused that it may be considered to have been practically worthless to Leonardo. The problem is of the fourth degree. The first analytical solution is due to Kaestner (1776).

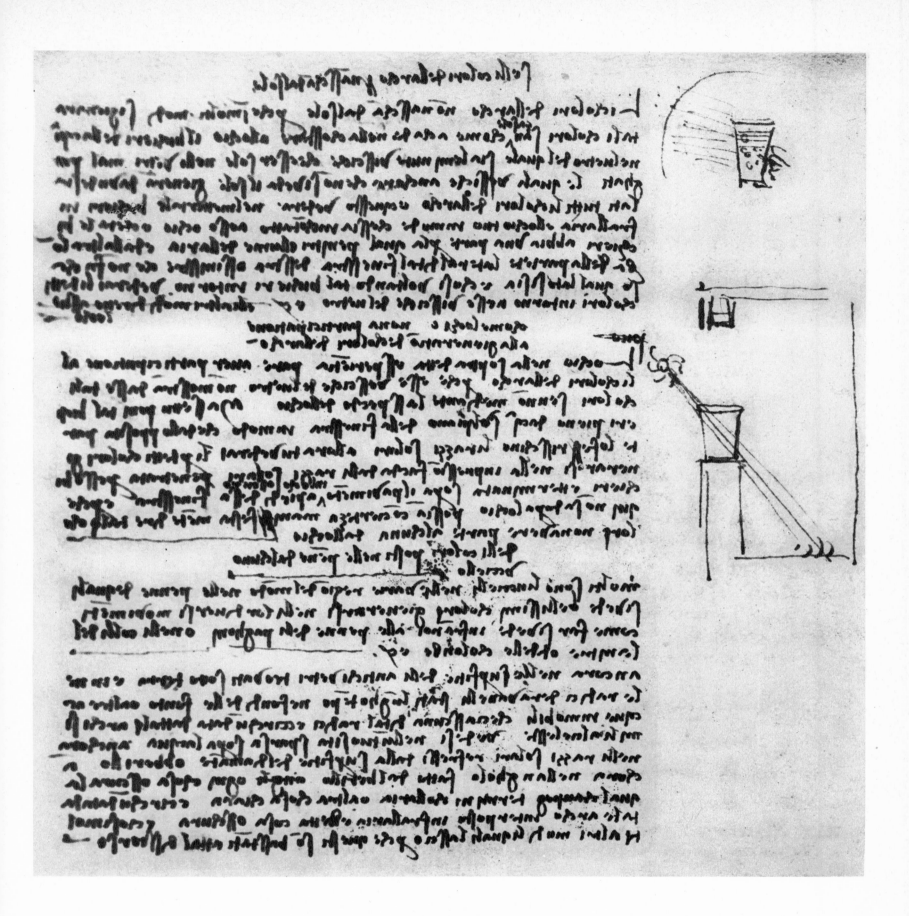

Christian Huygens (1672) gave a very elegant mixed geometrical-analytical solution. The fact that Huygens tested himself out on such a useless problem would be very easy to explain on the hypothesis we have advanced above, that he had a Da Vinci manuscript before him. Leonardo finally gave up seeking geometrical solutions and contrived a mechanical solution, constructing a special jointed instrument, described in the Codex Atlanticus (fol. 181 r-*a*). This instrument has recently been reconstructed by the distinguished mathematician and Da Vinci student, Roberto Marcolongo. It is of great interest as one of the first calculating instruments. It is also of some interest on the mechanical side, but it is of little interest for optics, as has been said.

Leonardo made many experiments to master the law of refraction.

"All light rays passing through an equal distance are straight," says Leonardo (Cod. Atl., fol. 150 r-*a*). "Through an equal distance" means through a homogeneous medium. In other words, there is no question of the *refraction* of the ray of light unless the homogeneity of the medium is changed, unless two different homogeneous media are used. To bring out the path of the light ray through the air, Leonardo hit on the ingenious expedient of sifting flour and filling the air with

Long before Newton, Leonardo decomposed light into its basic colors and collected the solar spectrum on a screen – Windsor, Royal Collection, no. 19149 r

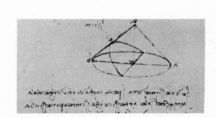

Section through cone to obtain tool for grinding parabolic mirrors – Cod. Atl., fol. 32 r-*a*

411

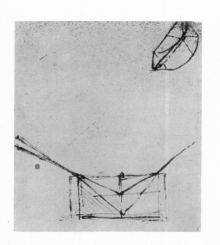

very small particles of it in suspension (Ms. C, fol. 13 v), as we today often use tobacco smoke for the same purpose: but the tobacco leaf was introduced into Europe eleven years after Leonardo's death.

In the Codex Arundel (fol. 199 v) I find, alongside a sketch, the note: "Do the club breaking in the water of the trough Sunday morning." Evidently Leonardo intended to repeat the famous experiments of the Arab Alhazen.

A veritable laboratory experiment was devised by Leonardo to study the laws of refraction between air and water, using two circular concentric glass dishes (Ms. F, fol. 33 v):

"Have two trays made, parallel to each other, and let one be 4/5 smaller than the other, and of equal height. Then enclose one in the other as you see in the drawing, and paint the outside, and leave uncovered a spot the size of a lentil, and have a ray of sunlight pass there coming from another opening or window. Then see whether or not the ray passing in the water enclosed between the two trays keeps the straightness it had outside. And form your rule from that."

A modification of this experiment was made deliberately with the purpose of studying the refraction of the earth's atmosphere, and this is worth stressing, since it has been believed hitherto that Tycho Brahe was the first to recognize the phenomenon of atmospheric refraction.

Leonardo says:

"To see how the sun's rays penetrate this curvature of the sphere of air, have two glass spheres made, one twice the size of the other, as round as can be. Then cut them in half and put one inside the other and close the fronts and fill with water and have the ray of sunlight pass as you did above. And see whether the ray is bent. And form your rule. And thus you can make an infinite number of experiments." A note in the margin says: "With your eye in the center of the sphere, look to see whether or not a candle flame keeps its size."

Probably the practical result of this "infinite number of experiments" was the preparation of numerical tables, of the sort that had been drawn up by Ptolemy and Witelo.

In the second century B.C. Ptolemy, with ingenious experiments, had measured the refraction between air and glass, water and glass, and air and water at intervals of ten degrees; these experiments had been repeated by Witelo in the thirteenth century and completed by repeating the measurements while inverting the path of the light ray, but the errors made were such that they misled many subsequent investigators, including the great Kepler.

Leonardo certainly knew the writings of Witelo; I have found his name mentioned four times in the manuscripts (Cod. Atl., fol. 225 r-*b*, 247 r-*a*; Cod. Arund., fol. 74 v; Ms. B, fol. 58).

Nonetheless, the true law of refraction escaped Leonardo. Even if his experimental measurements were more accurate than those of Witelo (and this has not been proved), it would have been hard for him to express them in a "law," in view of his complete ignorance of algebra and trigonometry —that is, of the advanced algebra of his time (we need only think of his contemporary Tartaglia, who was to solve the cubic equation) and the trigonometry that Hipparchus had already put on a solid footing and that the Arabs had developed further.

It is easy to see therefore why the discovery of the law of refraction was to be the work of a "trigonometer," Willebrord Snell, the same man who at the outset of the seventeenth century was to perform the first trigonometric triangulation, and the same who, before Pothenot, was to solve the famous problem of the vertex of the pyramid.

Later (1637), starting from a mistaken premise (namely, that light travels more quickly in a dense medium than in air), Descartes was also to discover the true law of refraction. But Snell's priority is *definite and beyond dispute.*

Refraction through a prism decomposes light into its fundamental colors, and Newton is credited with the first experiment in this field. But we shall have to reassign the credits: Leonardo was *the first to decompose a beam of sunlight, producing and receiving the solar spectrum on a screen.*

The figures reproduced here are taken from a collection of thirty small sheets of Da Vinci's, unmounted and of varying format, in the possession of the Royal Library at Windsor, which will be published by the Reale Commissione Vinciana.

Since the human eye is an integral part of the phenomenon in the experiment of the first figure, Leonardo proceeds at once to exclude the eye, devising the experiment of the second figure, in which the solar spectrum is no longer received by the eye but by a screen.

"If you place a glass full of water on the windowsill so that the sun's rays will strike it from the other side, you will see the aforesaid colors formed in the impression made by the sun's rays that have penetrated through that glass and fallen on the pavement in the dark at the foot of a window, and since the eye is not used here, we may with full certainty say that these colors are not in any way due to the eye."

Studies on law of refraction – Cod. Atl., fol. 150 r-*a*

Study on experiment of Alhazen – Cod. Arund., fol. 199 v

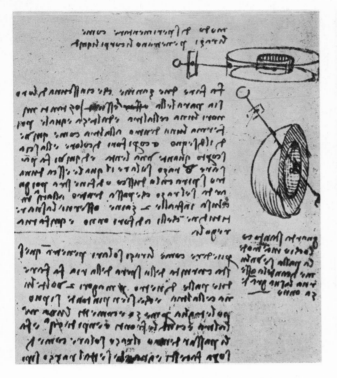

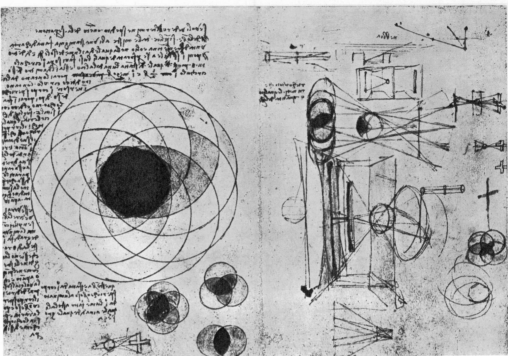

Three centuries before Fresnel, Leonardo inquired into the secret of such beautiful colors as those of butterflies or mother-of-pearl, and looked for their cause not in colored pigments but in the decomposition of light:

There are many birds in various regions of the earth in whose feathers the most beautiful colors are formed in the course of their movements, as we have seen among us in the feathers of peacocks or in the necks of ducks and pigeons, etc. Also on the surface of old glass found underground, while on radish roots that have been a long time at the bottom of springs or other still waters, each of the roots will be enveloped in rainbowlike colors; and it is seen in oil spread on water."

I have taken these words from the same folio at Windsor cited above, of which I give a photographic reproduction, and which the reader may consider as here presented for the first time.

There are innumerable passages in Leonardo referring to the meteorologic phenomenon of the rainbow. I omit them here for lack of space, but not because they do not merit attention. One of the greatest of Da Vinci scholars, P. Duhem, has made a detailed study of these passages, with references to their sources and antecedents (*Etudes sur L. de Vinci*, I, 171, 177).

Leonardo gives an explanation of the blue color of the sky that is not inconsistent with the explanation given by modern physics: it is caused by very small and imperceptible particles (we should say molecules).

"I say that the blue which is seen in the atmosphere is not its own color, but is caused by the heated moisture having evaporated into the most minute and imperceptible particles, which the beams of the solar rays attract and cause to seem luminous against the deep, intense darkness of the region of fire that forms a covering among them" (Cod. Leices., fol. 4 r).

In connection with "the deep, intense darkness" of the arch of the heavens at great heights, we note that Piccard observed this in his flights into the stratosphere. What divinatory powers of intuition Leonardo had!

Light is energy, and every form of energy is measured by its effects. We use photometry today. Who founded photometry?

When Bouguer in 1727 published his *Essai d'optique sur la gradation de la lumière*, he referred to Newton's work and added: "It might seem that after these vast speculations there would be nothing left to discover in this field; and yet optics still lacks a part, the object of which would be the force or vivacity of light." Every historian of science agrees today that Bouguer was the founder of photometry.

But there is Leonardo, who rises again, a giant of science, from the oblivion of his dusty scattered manuscripts.

Four sketches on folio 22 recto of Ms. C of the Institut de France immediately call Rumford's photometer to mind.

Under the first figure Leonardo wrote:

"If light source xv is equal to [is of the same kind as?] light source vy, the difference between the lights will be proportional to their size."

413

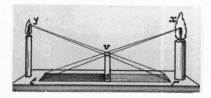

Study for spherical photometer – Ms. C, fol. 4 v

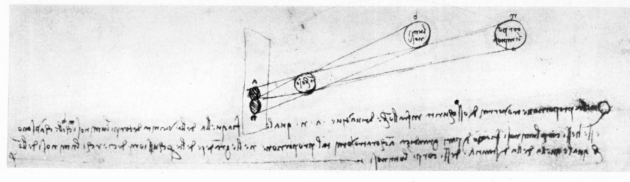

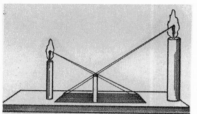

Photometry – Fig. 1

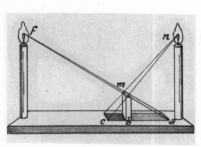

Photometry – Fig. 2

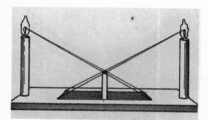

Photometry – Fig. 3

Photometry – Fig. 4

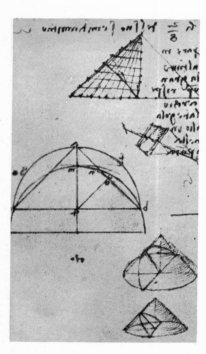

Studies on the *cientina* for grinding parabolic mirrors – Cod. Arund., fol. 73 r

Under the second figure we find:

"But if the large light is distant from the body casting the shadow, and the small light is close to it, it is certain that the shadows may be equally dark or light."

There follows this annotation:

"If a body casting a shadow be set between two sources of light, at equal distances from them, it will cast two opposite shadows, which will vary in their darkness in proportion to the strength of the two opposite sources of light causing them."

Under the third figure Leonardo points out:

"The darkness of shadow *ab* will be to that of shadow *bc* as the distances of the sources of light, that is, *nm* and *mf*.

"Region *ab* is seen to be closer to light source *n* than *bc* is to light source *f*;

"*ab* will be the brighter as it is closer to its source of light, more so than *f*, both the light sources being of equal power."

Under the fourth figure he remarks:

"This shadow-casting body will cast two shadows of equal darkness, as it will have two light sources of equal size equally distant from it."

In the Rumford photometer the body casting the shadow is a rod, while in Leonardo's photometer it is a small plaque. This entails the obvious drawback that it is not possible to juxtapose the two shadows and compare them accurately. Leonardo soon eliminates this inconvenience, devising another photometer that we might call a spherical photometer. The fifth figure exhibits it so clearly that the explanation need not be cited; it appears on another folio of Ms. C.

Paragraph 916 of the *Treatise on Painting* even presents the beginnings of chromatic photometry:

"Those who do not want to trust their judgment entirely in reproducing the true colors of leaves should take a leaf of a tree they want to paint and mix their colors on it; and when this mixture cannot be distinguished from the color of the leaf, you will be sure that your color is the true imitation of the leaf."

The foundation is also laid for the photometry of light beams that have passed through an optical system:

"Burning mirror: As many times as the point of the solar pyramid, cut in any part whatever, is contained in its base, so many times is it hotter than this base" (Ms. A, fol. 55 r).

It should be remarked that in Da Vinci's language "burning mirror" means "parabolic mirror" —a very accurate reservation, since the photometric arguments that Leonardo makes apply only in regard to an optical system that is free of spherical aberration.

In the Codex Arundel (fol. 88 r) Leonardo indicates a procedure for constructing (or at least drawing) the median section of a parabolic mirror; in the Codex Atlanticus (fol. 32 r-*a*), he shows the manner of making a tool, a "profile," for grinding parabolic mirrors. This tool is obtained by cutting a cone, which shows among other things his profound knowledge of the theory of conic sections.

Was Leonardo acquainted with diffraction?

Omitting many descriptions and some drawings of the effects he observed in the pinholes of the camera obscura—which contain obvious references to diffraction phenomena—I proceed at once to communicate a surprising discovery I made in June, 1938, in the Venturi transcription, as soon as it was shown me in galley proofs by Monsignor Carusi. The text reads:

"An eye looking at a luminous body will seem to see a circle brighter than the rest of the air around it. This circle of brightness which seems to surround luminous bodies will not change when

414

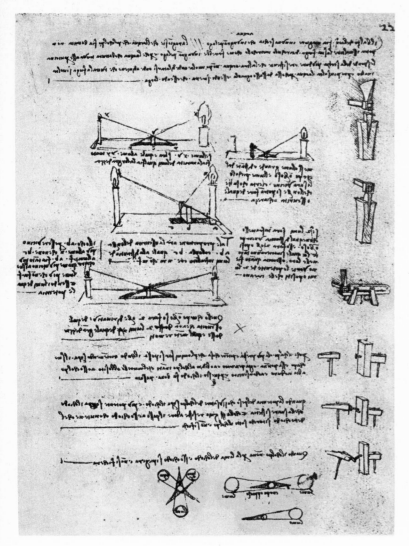

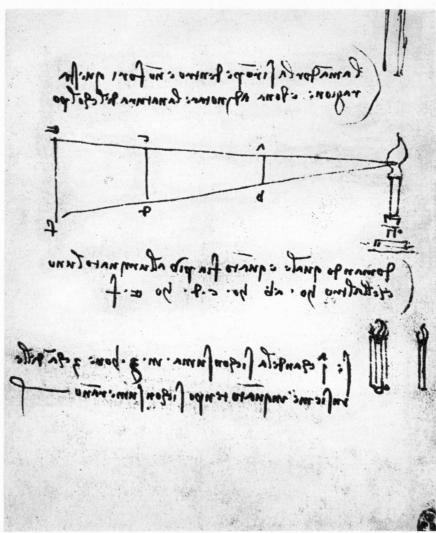

these bodies change from long to round. The reason for this is that the said brightness is in the eye, and not outside and around the source of light, as it seems to be... And the said circle will appear to have steps of various colors, like the rainbow. And as far as the edge of the light extends, there will appear a luminous ring around the source of light, brighter than the rest... And beyond this brightness you will see a dark circle... which is due to the fact that the lips of this edge are not of transparent material, so that the light does not enter; and it therefore seems dark. Behind that, there is a surrounding circle that retains a little brightness... And this is clearly seen against a dark background."

This passage was on folio 80 of Ms. A. This folio, with many others, has disappeared, but it was still in existence in 1796, and Giambattista Venturi was able to copy a large part of the manuscript in its complete state. The Venturi transcription is in the Reggio Emilia Library. Venturi designated the folio we have cited as *carta 50 recto*. We owe him gratitude for having saved at least the contents for us.

But neither in his famous *Essai* nor in another memoir on Leonardo's optics did Venturi suspect the enormous importance of this passage, which for the first time describes the diffraction rings, alternatingly light and dark, that surround the image of a luminous point. Naturally, the explanation of it that Leonardo makes bold to give is not the correct one; but the phenomena of the diffraction figure are described to perfection.

Since the luminous point he observed consisted not of a monochromatic source, but of a source of white light, he does not omit to add, most accurately, that all the colors of the rainbow are to be found between a bright ring and the adjacent dark one.

It seems to me that the actual source of this excellent observation of the diffraction figure is to be found in Leonardo's constant habit of observing the sun through a very small hole pierced in a piece of cardboard. He believed that this was the most perfect method of observation, and had no idea that it was the source of all those light and dark rings.

Thus Grimaldi was not only anticipated but surpassed.

The projector is another invention with respect to which, as in the case of so many others, Leonardo said the first word. If we examine the drawing of it he has left us in the Codex Atlanticus (fol. 10 r-*a*), we note the correct position of the plano-convex lens.

Fire is a subject that inspired Leonardo to marvelous pages. For him fire is alive:

"Where fire does not live, no animal that breathes can live" (Cod. Atl., fol. 270 r-*a*).

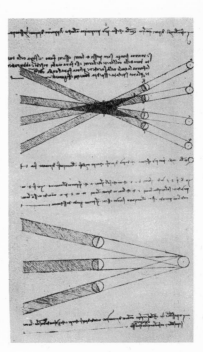

Experiments on shadows – Derivative shadows – Ms. C, fol. 13 v

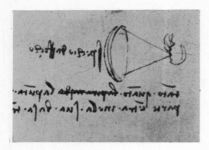

Study on photometry of pencils of light – Ms. A, fol. 55 r

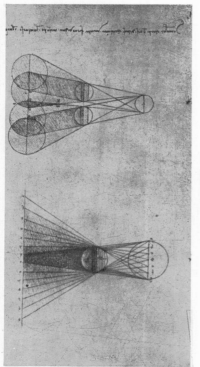

Leonardo subdivided the penumbra into an infinite number of gradations – Ms. C, fol. 14 r

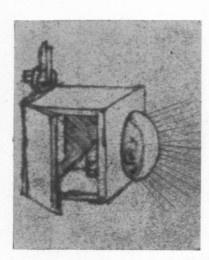

Projector designed by Leonardo – Cod. Atl., fol. 10 r-*a*

416

The other side of the same sheet in the Codex Atlanticus gives a description of the birth, life, and death of fire. At a time when the alchemists were still flourishing, Leonardo had already penetrated into what we consider a conquest of modern chemistry.

Shadows, penumbras, chiaroscuros abound in all the manuscripts of Da Vinci, and especially in the *Treatise on Painting.*

Mehr Licht! ("More light!") the dying Goethe cried. What a desperate appeal Leonardo's eye must have launched toward the light that was escaping him, there in the Château de Cloux, on that fatal May 2 of the year 1519! Surely, at that moment, a final vision must have disclosed to him all together the numberless beauties that light had revealed to him:

"What makes you, O man, abandon your home in the city and leave relatives and friends, to wander in rustic sites through mountains and valleys, if it is not the natural beauty of the world?... The harmonious beauties of an angelic face set down in painting, from whose proportions a harmonious accord arises... Giovannina, fantastic face... Among human beauties the fairest face makes the passers-by stand still."

Ah, Leonardo! Tell us, you who may know the great secret: When we close our eyes to earthly light, letting our heads fall to one side, may it not be in order to raise our heads on the other side, opening our eyes to a more splendid light?

"Man dies and always is reborn in part" (Quad. Anat. I, fol. 12 r).

THE TELESCOPE

When Galileo constructed his famous telescope in 1609, he was impelled to do so by the news that had come to Venice "that Count Maurice had been presented by a Hollander with an eyeglass with which distant things were seen as perfectly as if they were very close." This is how Galileo himself tells it in the *Saggiatore,* adding: "I say that the news helped me to rouse my will to apply thought to it, and I might otherwise never have thought of it." And again: "The Hollander that first invented the telescope was a simple maker of ordinary spectacles who, handling glasses of various kinds by chance, happened to look through two at once, one convex and one concave, placed at different distances from the eye."

Galileo himself admits that the Hollander deserves the title of original inventor of the telescope; he only repeated the Dutch experiment.

We must grant that Giambattista della Porta's fantastic mind was not entirely in the wrong when he wrote on August 29, 1609, to Cesi, president of the Accademia dei Lincei, claiming for himself the priority accorded to the Galilean invention and referring to the furore raised about the telescope as "asinine." Nor was Descartes entirely wrong when he wrote in his *Dioptrics* (1637): "To the shame of our sciences, this invention, so useful und so admirable, was first found only by empirical good fortune."

Galileo retains the imperishable glory of having been the first to scan and scrutinize the firmament with a telescope and of making the first astounding astronomical discoveries, which were to bring down the entire structure of the Ptolemaic cosmology and the Aristotelian natural philosophy, laying the foundations of a new astronomy [1] and a new philosophy. This glory is so great that it seems to me vapid sentimentality to wish to retain for Galileo the additional title of inventor of the telescope. Then who did invent the telescope?

Before Galileo there was the Hollander Lipperhey. Before Lipperhey there was Janssen. Before Janssen there was an unknown Italian who engraved the words *Anno 1590* on a telescope of his that was exported from Italy to Holland. A little earlier, about 1580, we have Della Porta's claims. Here the trace disappears, or rather, used to disappear.

[1] The inauguration of the new era in astronomy is due to Galileo's genius more than to the slight improvements he made in the Dutch telescope. Since there has been a good deal of exaggeration about this matter, I trust that I may make some observations that will not be taken as either untimely or irreverent.

The satellites of Jupiter were seen by Galileo on January 7, 1610 and one day later (January 8) by Simon Marius of Ansbach, the two being separated by many miles from each other: if the model of telescope that Galileo used was capable of showing the satellites, the model used by Marius had the same power.

The spots on the sun were seen and described for the first time in 1609 by Johann Fabricius of Osteel; hence this discovery is not due to Galileo's improvements in the telescope.

Galileo barely suspected the existence of the ring of Saturn; Huygens in 1665 was the first really to see it, and J. D. Cassini in 1675 the first to observe that it is double.

Furthermore, we know what the subsequent improvements of the Dutch type of telescope came down to, namely, gradual elongation. From 72 millimeters of Leonardo's first telescope we go to *environ un pied* in the first Dutch telescopes, and finally we come to the meter or so of the last telescopes constructed by Galileo. Are we to say that each successive stage of elongation constitutes a different invention?

Clear distinction should be drawn between the notions of *invention, improvements,* and *applications.* The telescope is being improved every day, and every day there are more astronomical discoveries made with it. But the history of science has the duty of finding out who was the first to make a tube having a convergent lens at one end and a concave lens at the other and making the objects observed appear large; today, after my researches, we are able to say that this "first" was Leonardo. Previously, this assertion could not have been made.

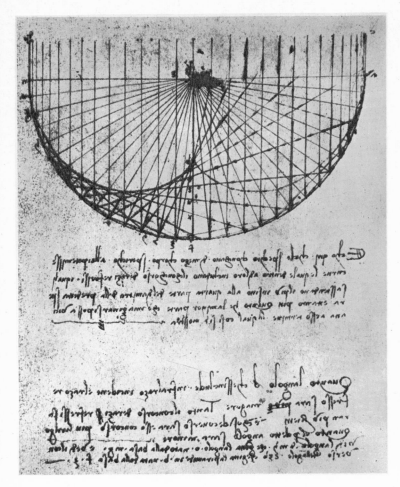

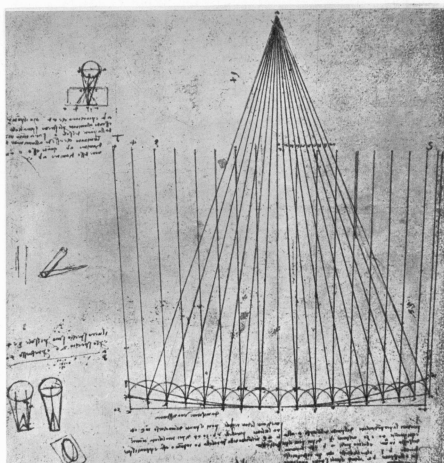

Left: Reflection of light in spherical concave mirror – Cod. Arund., fol. 87 r

Right: Paths of light rays in parabolic mirror – Cod. Atl., fol. 248 v-a

I attribute to my exceptional good luck a recent sensational discovery—the recovery of the description and the drawings of Leonardo da Vinci's telescope.

In May, 1938, while I was consulting the fine reproduction of Ms. F made by Ravaisson-Mollien (1889), my attention was attracted to folio 25 recto. Ravaisson-Mollien did not interpret the contents of this folio correctly, as I shall show later, and the initial confusion caused by the editor misled subsequent students.

I immediately identified in it a Dutch-type telescope, with a drawing of the complete mounting on a stand, and a sketch of the spherical lead shell needed to grind the negative lens of the eyepiece.

Let us soberly examine Leonardo's sheet, of which I give a reproduction. The six top lines of his writing, and the figure at the top, do not concern us: they deal with questions in hydraulics. However, the rest of the page is about the telescope.

Here there is a drawing of a short, thick tube mounted on a support.

There are no sections of convex or concave lenses to be seen at the two ends of the tube; obviously the small size of the sheet (10 × 15 cm.) prevented Leonardo from getting down to such details. But the words make up what the drawing lacks. Inside the outline of the tube, toward one of the ends, there is written in three lines:

Measurement of intensity of light rays and deformation of shadows – Ms. C, fol. 8 r

> "Eyeglass of crystal   (*Ochiale di cristallo*
> thick at the sides   *grosso da' lati*
> an ounce of an ounce"   *un'oncia d'un'oncia*)

Thick at the sides? Today we should use the word *spessa ai bordi*, if we meant to indicate a divergent lens. Leonardo, being unable to express his entire thought in the few words there was room for within the pictured section of the tube, continued the explanation in the space immediately below it:

"This glass should be free of spots and very clear, and at the sides it should be an ounce of an ounce thick, that is, 1/144 of an ell, and let it be thin in the middle."

The description is complete and unmistakable now—"thick at the edges and thin in the middle." Hence it was a negative or divergent lens that closed one of the ends of the short tube sketched by Leonardo in his notebook.

Further details are given in the third figure on this page of Leonardo's. The drawing is schematic, and to understand it—something no one has done before me—it seems necessary to refer to three tools that are widely used in optical workshops, the ball, the basin, and the shell.

The ball is a convex spherical instrument on the outside of which concave lenses are ground.

Reflection in plane mirror – Windsor, Royal Collection, no. 12587

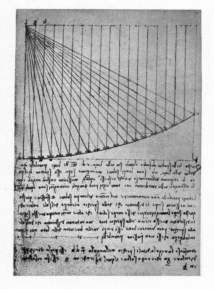

Reflection of sun's rays in mirror – Cod. Arund., fol. 88 r

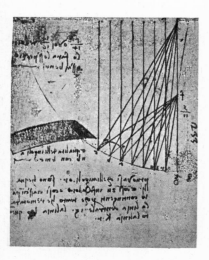

·Studies and researches effectuated by Leonardo on caustics of mirrors – Cod. Atl., fol. 88 r-*b*

The basin is a concave spherical instrument on the inside of which convex lenses are ground. The shell is a sort of spherical shape which may be used as either a ball or a basin; convex lenses can be made on one side and concave lenses on the other.

Leonardo's figure evidently represents a shell in use, with a concave lens being ground on it. It certainly cannot be a convex lens, because in that case the shell would have to be turned upside down; moreover, the lens that is being ground would have to be placed on the inner concavity of the shell.

Note that Leonardo gave movement to his figure by drawing the lens in two different positions, from which we can infer the outer limits of the path taken by the lens in its reciprocating motion on the surface of the shell.

Why does Leonardo specify the concavity of the lens so insistently? Because this was the new aspect of his invention, the part that required emphasis; the convex lens was something everyone knew, the indispensable aid of "persons advanced in years," *notus lippis et tonsoribus* ("known to the purblind and to haircutters").

Furthermore, it should be remembered that Leonardo was writing some simple notes primarily for his own use, in a little postcard-size notebook, as contrasted with the contents of his manuscripts on large paper, where he set down precepts and instructions intended for "treatises" for future readers.

Nonetheless, the following considerations will show that there can be no doubt that there was to be a convex lens at the other end of the tube. In the first place, it must be kept in mind that Leonardo's purpose was to describe an optical system capable of magnifying. This is proved by the words, "ordinary printed characters will look like the lettering on apothecaries' boxes." It is out of the question to think that any magnifying effect could be achieved with a concave lens alone. If only to avoid an absurdity, we must grant that there was to be a convex lens at the other end of the tube.

A second argument is of purely physical and optical nature. Anyone using a pair of opera glasses today knows that the tube must be lengthened for clear vision of an object near by. This phenomenon also occurs in Leonardo's instrument. He states that his instrument when set for use in the open air—"for outside," as he puts it—has a length of 1/8 of an ell, while if it is desired to have it "suitable to keep in the study," that is, for observing very close objects (at a distance of 1/3 of an ell), the entire instrument must be lengthened to 1/4 of an ell, that is, doubled in length. Shorter for observations out of doors, longer for reading books at close range. These details tell any physicist that a convex lens is indicated here.

With respect to the dioptric powers of the two lenses, the concave and the convex, Leonardo states that no rule can be laid down, since the power may vary with the ametropia of the eyes of the user of the telescope, i.e., "according to the vision of the person who is to employ it, that is, according to the strength of the eyeglasses that fit him."

Manuscript F was begun on September 12, 1508; since it is a pocket notebook, it is a reasonable presumption that Leonardo filled it with his notes and reflections in not over a year. Consequently, he was fifty-six or fifty-seven years old when he described his telescope, and at that age a normal person has at least 2 diopters of presbyopia.

This helps us to understand the road Leonardo took to arrive at the invention of the telescope: The "eyeglasses that fit" for close reading can be used for vision at a distance as well if they are neutralized by a negative lens, with the advantage that the objects seen will be magnified.

It is really strange that the now famous page of Ms. F, although published in 1889, was not understood by students of Da Vinci for so long a time.

Let us try to understand what made this failure possible.

I believe that the third figure on Da Vinci's page, which we see as representing a metal shell, was taken for a glass hemisphere. Now, the glass hemisphere was the first magnifying lens known; it was introduced by the Arab Alhazen, about the year 1000. Leonardo too, now and then, mentions the glass hemisphere as a magnifying lens, and does so in this very manuscript (fol. 53 v). Confusion could very easily arise for anyone who does not have practical experience in the preparation of lenses and hence is unaware that the shell is a lens grinder's instrument. In the figure, the four guide lines converging toward the center of the shell from the two positions of the lens that is being ground could easily be mistaken for light rays converging on a common focus. This confusion would explain the designation that Ravaisson-Mollien gives to the sheet in question—"magnifying lenses." It should be remarked that the plural used by the French writer does not refer to a plurality of lenses forming part of a single instrument, but to the fact that he thought that two distinct magnifying lenses were being described, one "for outside" and one "to keep in the study," each in the form of half of a glass sphere. Given such an interpretation, to be sure, many of Leonardo's expressions must have sounded extremely enigmatic to the distinguished student of Da Vinci. Thick at the sides? Thin in the middle? Long? Wide?

The sentence, "This glass should be used...," which we interpret as meaning, "This telescope should be used...," is interpreted by the French author as meaning, "This *lens* should be used..."

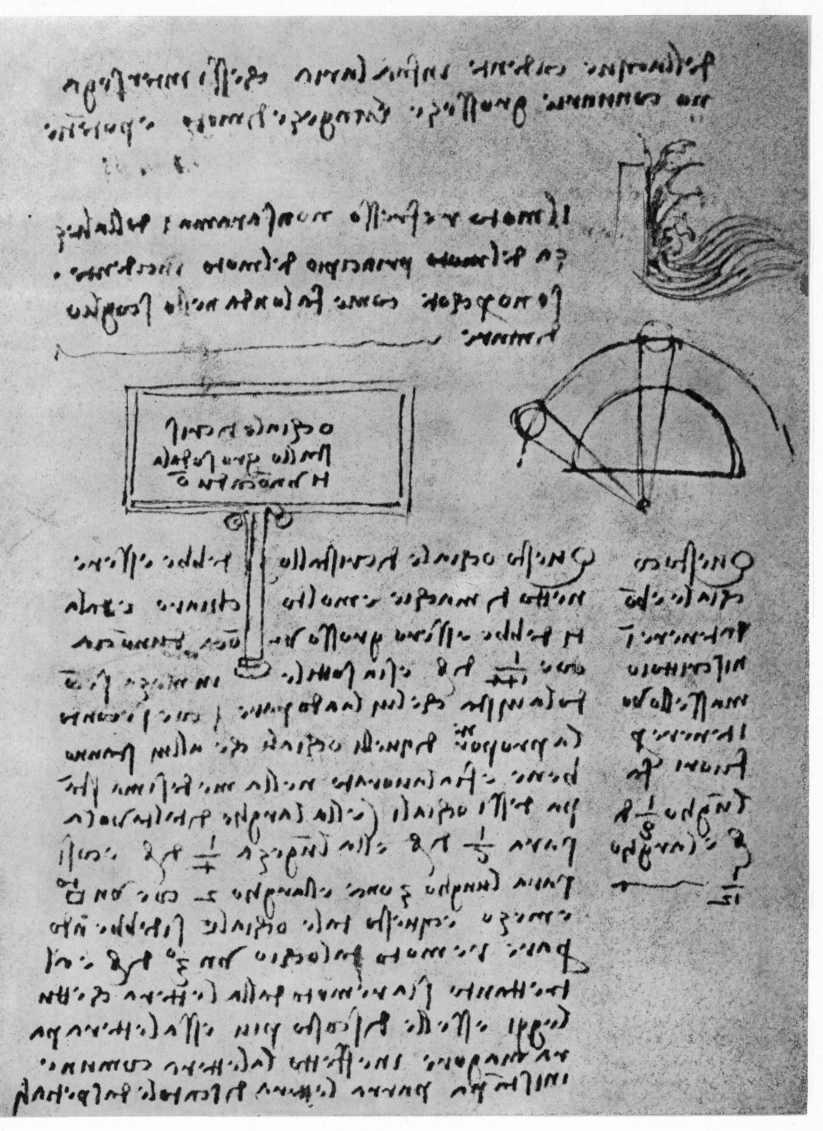

Description and diagram of telescope – Ms. F, fol. 25 r

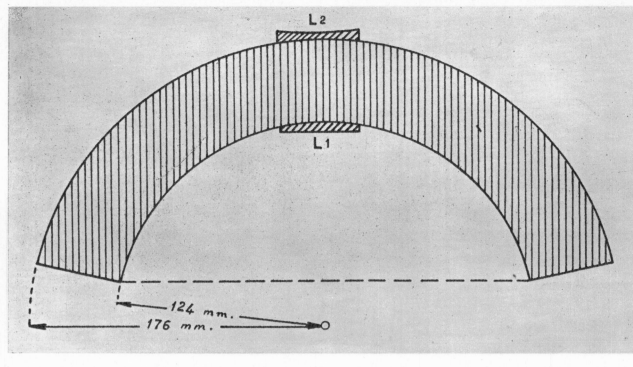

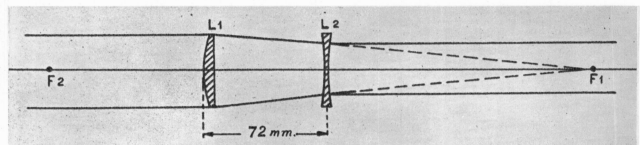

Dioptric reconstruction, with dimensions, of lead shell on which two lenses were ground which together formed telescope invented by Leonardo, and diagram of telescope

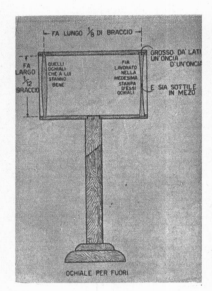

Schematic reconstruction for interpretation of phrases by Da Vinci in fol. 25 r of Ms. F referring to invention of telescope

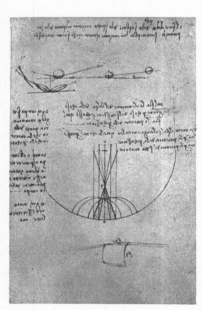

Leonardo's study of paraxial zone of concave mirror – Cod. Arund., fol. 85 r

When giving the length and diameter of the "tube" of the telescope, the word Leonardo used was not *tubo* ("tube") but *tavola* ("board"), and this is another stumbling block for Ravaisson-Mollien.

He rendered the word *tavola* by means of the French word *forme* ("form"), and thereby confused the tube of the telescope with the metal form (ball, basin, shell) used in lens grinding, the form for which Leonardo used the word *stampo* ("mold"). It is hard to understand how two dimensions, length and breadth, can be assigned to these molds, which are spherical and hence are completely identified by giving a single dimension, the radius of curvature.

However, there is every excuse for Ravaisson-Mollien's interpretating the word *tavola* as he did, since at the time neither the Codex Arundel nor the Forster notebooks had been published, and these are the only sources that have made a correct interpretation of this word of Leonardo's possible.

Now, for Leonardo *tavola* has nothing to do with wood. It is a geometrical term for him. A term in plane geometry, the reader will say; on the contrary, it is a term in solid geometry.

Leonardo gives the following definitions (Cod. Arund., fol. 154 r):

"The square figure that is higher than a cube is called a *cylinder*, the body that is less than a cube in height is called a *tavola*—as is the case with round objects as well."

A tube placed horizontally fits Leonardo's definition of a *tavola*; if it were placed vertically, it would fit his definition of a cylinder. These are peculiarities of Da Vinci's language that were unknown at the time when Ravaisson-Mollien published Ms. F; therefore, I repeat, he deserves all our indulgence.

To proceed with the reconstruction of Leonardo's telescope, we must first know the form of the objective lens; since this consisted of an ordinary eyeglass lens, what is needed is to find the form of eyeglass lenses in Leonardo's time.

In the Codex Atlanticus (fol. 83 v) Leonardo writes:

"Let there be a very thin bottle, namely, of thin glass and blown in a plaster mold which has been given the form of a lead dish for grinding eyeglasses for sixty-year-old people, and let this flask be a finger thick at the edges and 1/2 in the middle, and 1/3 long and 1/6 wide, and be full of water."

I have deduced several things from this passage of Da Vinci's.

First, this is confirmation that the lenses were made on shells, and not on balls or basins.

420

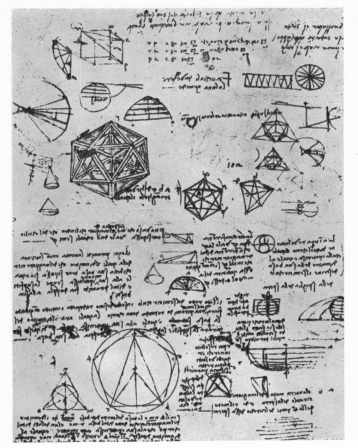

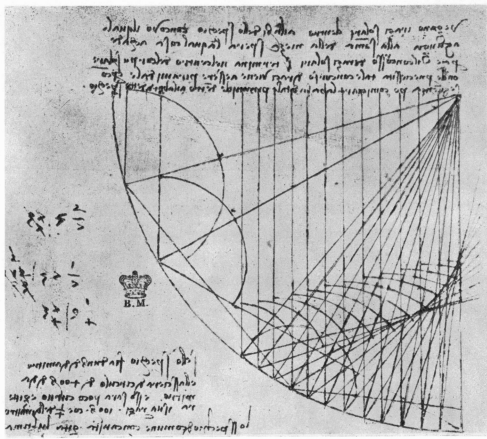

Now, the ball has only a convex spherical surface on the outside, and the basin has only a concave inner surface. However, the "lead dish for grinding eyeglasses" mentioned by Leonardo had both a convex and a concave surface—a concave surface since otherwise it could not have been used to grind lenses for the old, and a convex surface since otherwise it could not have left a concave impression in the plaster. The concave plaster mold obtained by using the convex surface of the lead shell was then used by Leonardo to give a perfectly spherical form to a glass bottle while it was being blown.

This corroborates my interpretation of the third drawing of folio 25 recto of Ms. F as a shell or calotte.

Leonardo gives the diameter of the bottle blown in the plaster mold as 1/6 ell, roughly 10 centimeters or 4 inches.

Even if we take the thickness of the shell (that described in the Atlantic codex, not that of Ms. F) as very slight, the radius of curvature of its concave surface cannot be more than 50 millimeters. The convex lenses ground on the inner side of this shell therefore had a power of not less than 10 diopters if shaped on one face (plano-convex lenses) and of over 20 diopters if shaped on both faces (biconvex lenses).

A lens of 20 diopters would be an absurdity for sixty-year-old presbyopics. Even a 10-diopter lens is very strong, but it should be remembered that old-people left free to make their own choice of corrective lenses invariably select stronger lenses than an oculist would advise; the only drawback (which may be taken for an advantage) is that it makes objects seem very close.

At any rate, there is no possible doubt as to the choice between 10 and 20 diopters, and it follows that in Leonardo's time lenses for old people were shaped on only one face, with the other left flat.

Consequently, the objective of Da Vinci's telescope was a plano-convex lens.

Since the eyepiece must be more powerful than the objective, it must of necessity be biconcave if it is to be ground on the same shell, as Leonardo wishes: "Let it be ground on the same form of these glasses."

With a plano-convex objective and a biconcave eyepiece, made of glass with a 2/3 index, the conditions for a telescope are fulfilled when the internal radius of the shell has the value

$$r = \frac{\text{distance between the lenses}}{2 - \text{ratio of the two radii}}$$

The distance between the lenses is given by Leonardo as 72 millimeters. The ratio between the two radii is obtained graphically from the drawing by Da Vinci and is about 21.4 in the vertical central portion, which is the most accurate.

Left: "Make glasses to see the moon magnified" (written in center of sheet, at top) – Cod. Atl., fol. 190 r-*a*

Right: Study on divergence of rays impinging on mirror – Cod. Arund., fol. 84 v

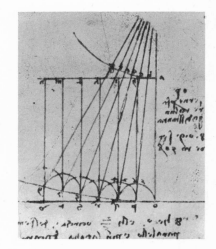

Study on divergence of rays impinging on mirror – Cod. Arund., fol. 73 r

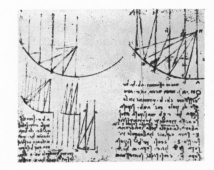

Study on incident and reflected rays impinging on mirror – Cod. Atl., fol. 88 v-*b*

421

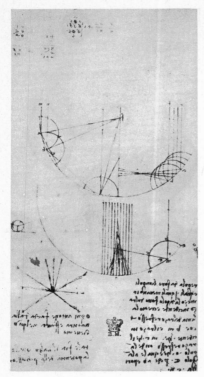

Study on incident and reflected rays in mirror – Cod. Arund., fol. 85 v

Accordingly, the inner radius of the shell will be 124 millimeters and the outer radius 176 millimeters. The thickness of the lead will be 52 millimeters, that is, about an ounce, in the measurements of that time. It should be noted too that the inner radius is about 1/5 of an ell.

With these values we have all the elements needed for constructing Da Vinci's telescope, and can write out its formula, in the manner used in optical workshops, as follows:

radii	thicknesses	indices	
+ 124			
	4	1.5	glass
∞			
	68	1.0	air
— 176			
	1	1.5	glass
+ 176			

The negative lens will be 4 millimeters thick at the edge when its diameter is 46 millimeters This is in excellent agreement with the value of 48 millimeters given by Leonardo for the diameter of the mounting tube. This is indirect confirmation of the correctness of the method used in the reconstruction.

The magnification is 1.41.

Da Vinci's telescope was in existence between 1508 and 1509, precisely a century before the Lipperhey-Galileo telescope.

The broken thread of the technological tradition is tied once more: the unknown Italian who cut the words *Anno 1590* on the telescope that Janssen copied must have learned the wonder-working secret from some old artisan who was acquainted with Leonardo's pupils.

Descartes' complaint that the discovery of the telescope was due to chance does not affect Leonardo, whose invention was the result of assiduous meditation.

A general theory of the telescope, as a modifier of perspective, is given in Ms. E (fol. 15 v): "It is possible to find means by which the eye shall not see remote objects as much diminished as in natural perspective, which diminishes them by reason of the convexity of the eye, which necessarily intersects, at its surface, the pyramid of every image conveyed to the eye at spherical right angles. But by the method I here teach in the margin, these pyramids are intersected at right angles close to the surface of the pupil."

The method taught by Leonardo consists of interposing between the object and the eye some optical system that will alter the path of what are called the principal rays. If two principal rays converge at the eye, forming a certain angle between them, the interposition of the optical system should make them converge at a much greater angle. The result will be advantageous from one point of view and harmful from another—harmful because the field of vision will be reduced, advantageous because the small field actually covered will be virtually enlarged.

Leonardo continues the passage above by saying:

"The convex pupil of the eye can take in the whole of our hemisphere, while this method will show only a single star. But where many small stars transmit their images to the surface of the pupil, those stars are extremely small; here only one star is seen, but it will be large. And so the moon will be seen larger and its spots in a more defined form."

It will be remarked that Leonardo, while thinking with reference to the telescope, never disjoined it from its possible applications in astronomy.

How could this hypothetical optical system, thought of as modifying natural perspective, be made a reality in practice?

He proposes a simple instrument, the first rudiment of his telescope.

"You must place close to the eye a glass filled with the water of which mention is made in number 4 of Book 113 on natural science; for this water makes objects which are enclosed in globes of crystalline glass appear free of the glass" (*ibid.*).

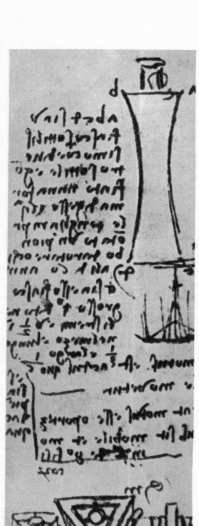

Method of constructing lenses for the old – Cod. Atl., fol. 83 v-*b*

We are not concerned here with the nature of Book 113 on natural science, cited by Leonardo, but it is important to remark that he already knows a liquid whose index of refraction is equal to that of the crystalline lens of the human eye. Excluding many liquids discovered later by chemical science, I think that bergamot oil (n = 1.465) or lavender oil (n = 1.463) could very well be the mysterious water that takes all dioptric power from the crystalline lens of the eye when immersed in it.

Accordingly, Leonardo had in mind placing before the eye a glass globe full of lavender oil or bergamot oil or the like. The magnifying effect should certainly appear, and the more so the larger the globe.

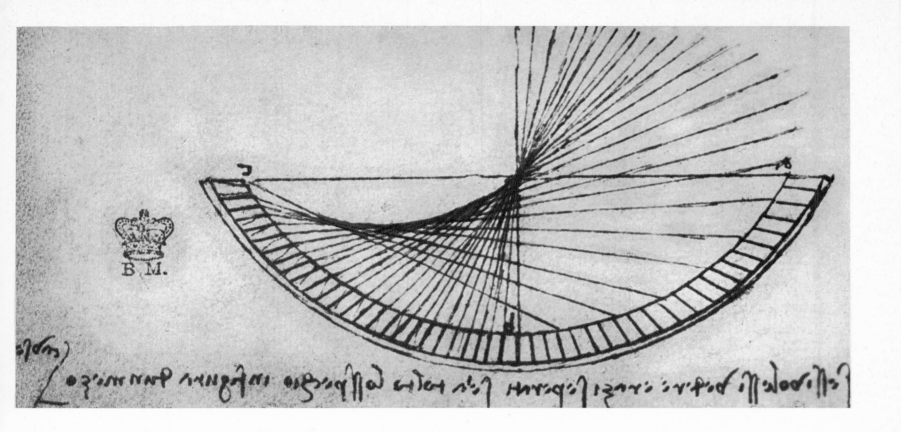

But Leonardo was able to get away from the glass globe [2] and essential oils, keeping only what constituted the essential basis of the phenomenon, a convergent lens. In this way he arrived at what we might call a telescope without eyepiece.

It is always possible to construct a perfect telescope for subjects suffering from hypermetropia or myopia, using only an objective lens without any kind of eyepiece; those with hypermetropia will see the objects erect, and those with myopia will see them inverted, with a marked magnification in both cases.

In fact, Herschel, examining one of his large mirrors without the use of any ocular whatever, was able to discern a satellite of Saturn.

The present writer has a myopia of 16 diopters and has made an astronomical telescope for himself that magnifies by 20 diameters with an achromatic objective of 120-centimeter focal length without any eyepiece.

This makes it possible to understand the importance of Leonardo's telescope without eyepiece, described in Ms. A (fol. 12 v):

"The further you place eyeglasses from the eye, the larger will objects appear in them, when they are for persons fifty years old. And if the eye sees two equal objects in comparison, one outside of the glass and the other within its field, the one in the glass will seem large and the other small. But the things seen should be 200 ells from the eye."

The figure accompanying these words is equally explicit, since it shows the lens far from the eye, as is called for by the theory of the "telescope without ocular."

In an important publication, a copy of which the distinguished author was kind enough to send me, Moritz von Rohr did not hesitate to state that these telescopes without eyepieces must have been much more effective than the first telescopes with eyepieces:

"It should be expressly pointed out that the efficacy of this sort of 'spyglass' was probably better if anything than the performance of the first telescopes and field glasses" (*Zeitschrift für Instrumentenkunde*, LVIII [No. 3, 1938], 103).

But what von Rohr did not know was that this "spyglass" had already been described by Leonardo.

Danjon too believed that telescopes without eyepieces appeared later than the Dutch telescopes:

"If the real image of a distant object given by a convex lens is examined with the naked eye... this image appears enlarged... If the use of this simple instrument had come before the use of the

To test quality of mirrors, Leonardo isolated light rays by covering surface of mirror with white lead, then partially removing it, thus anticipating Hartmann method – Cod. Arund., fol. 87 v

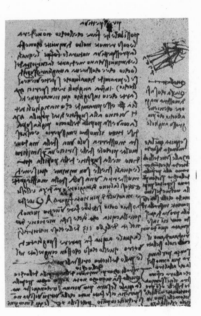

General theory of telescope – Ms. E, fol. 15 v

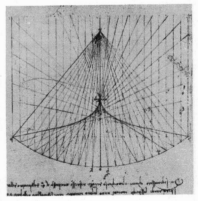

Reflection of rays in mirror – Cod. Arund., fol. 87 v

---

[2] Leonardo liked to use glass globes as substitutes for convergent lenses. The following passage should be mentioned (Cod. Atl., fol. 222 r–a): "If you put a glass globe full of water in front of your eyes, all the *species* of the objects that pass before you will seem to be upside down; and if you put two of them there, one behind the other, the species in the first one nearer to the eye will seem to be erect, in the natural orientation." The magnifying effect of a glass globe full of water was known as early as Seneca's time.

423

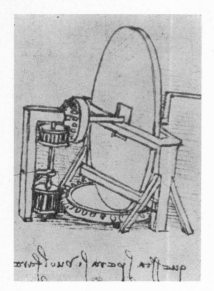

Machine for making concave mirrors
– Cod. Atl., fol. 32 r-*a*

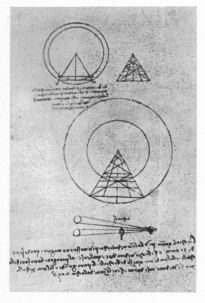

Telescope without eyepiece – Ms. A,
fol. 12 v

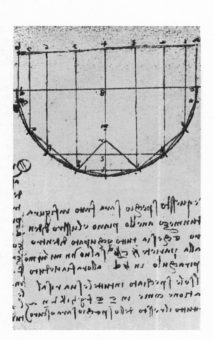

Mirror in form of half ring, flat and
polished inside, except for very small
hole, for viewing sun – Cod. Arund.,
fol. 86 r

two-lens telescope, its inventor would have deserved to be considered a precursor; but this was not the case" (Danjon and Couder, *Lunettes et télescopes*, Paris, 1935, p. 584).

Instead, it appears from Ms. A that this title of precursor belongs to none other than Leonardo; but he was the precursor of himself, for he was to be the inventor of the two-lens telescope.

Ms. A goes back to 1492, some fifteen years before Ms. F was begun. This proves that Leonardo was certainly guided not by chance but always by close study. The modest telescope without eyepiece of 1492 was replaced in 1508 by the true telescope, complete with eyepiece. Genius is protracted patience.

Many readers may wonder whether Leonardo's telescope was made only on paper—whether it was ever actually constructed. If we take into consideration the facts that the law of refraction had not yet been discovered, and that no theory of lenses had yet been born, there can be no question as to the answer: Leonardo did actually construct his telescope, because it was only by means of experiment that he could have observed the phenomena he describes, only experimentally and empirically that he could give the distances between the lenses, distances so different and yet so correct for the observation of distant and nearby objects.

Once Leonardo had invented the telescope, did he make any efforts to improve it?

On a famous page of the Codex Atlanticus (fol. 190 r-*a*) he wrote the words, "Construct glasses to see the moon magnified," along with a sketch of a concave mirror with its caustic. Does this mean that he thought of replacing the convex lens of his telescope with a concave mirror? It is very likely he did, especially when we consider that immediately after Leonardo several others used concave mirrors to magnify observed objects.

It is significant that it was in the years following 1508, that is, after inventing the telescope, that Leonardo intensified his studies and experiments on mirrors, and especially so during the three years he spent in Rome (1513-1515). There are details in Leonardo's investigations regarding mirrors that can be understood and justified only from the point of view of the formation of images.

Thus, in the Codex Arundel (fol. 86 v) he compares two mirrors with equal absolute apertures but different relative apertures. In a magnificent drawing, the two mirrors are represented with their caustics, one underneath the other, and it is shown that the mirror with the smaller relative aperture is practically free of spherical aberration, which takes on prohibitive values in the mirror with the larger relative aperture. He concludes:

"Mirror *op* is the fortieth part of the great circle of the sphere generating it, and it would be still better if it were the fiftieth, and better and more useful, the hundredth."

Hence for Leonardo a good concave spherical mirror should have a relative aperture of f: 8.

This is a really extraordinary and astonishing conclusion, when it is compared with the conclusion that modern optics has arrived at, namely, that if a concave spherical mirror with a diameter of 16 centimeters is not to go beyond the Rayleigh limit, the famous quarter-wavelength limit, its relative aperture should not exceed f: 8.

If we remember that the Rayleigh limit is the limit of absolute perfection in image formation, we can easily see that the only way in which Leonardo could have come to this conclusion was by the most attentive examination of the real image formed by the concave mirror in its focal plane.

By holding to an aperture of less than f: 8, Leonardo eliminated aberrations, but in order to obtain very high magnifications without overstraining the eyepiece (which would have brought back the aberrations, and which he could do without, being presbyopic), his only recourse was to make mirrors with very high focal length.

The Codex Atlanticus (fol. 396 v-*f*) has a drawing of a machine for grinding concave mirrors with a radius of curvature of 20 ells; this proves that Leonardo was engaged in making mirrors with a focal length of 6 meters, with which he should have obtained a considerable magnification.

This machine occupied a space at least 12 meters in length, the maximum a laboratory or shop would permit.

But the hunt for the highest magnifications haunted Leonardo's mind. He suddenly hit upon an ingenious device for making mirrors with focal lengths ten times as great, even in small and confined quarters.

The potter's wheel, that most ancient instrument, which has come down unchanged to modern potteries from biblical times and the age of Tutankhamen, was adapted by Leonardo for grinding concave mirrors. For the clay pot on the upper part of the wheel he substituted the mirror to be ground, attaching it with mastic. A kick of the horizontal wheel underneath kept the head and mirror turning.... And the tool? He found that too—a drawn copper rod [3] of uniform diameter,

---

[3] If the mirror to be ground were of bronze, it might be thought that a copper rod resting on the surface while the mirror turned would be worn down because of being softer than the bronze. This might in fact occur if the polishing were conducted by having the mirror rotate in direct contact with the copper rod. But if an abrasive powder intervenes between the rod and the mirror, it is not the rod that wears down but the mirror. The minute crystals that make up abrasive powders tend to become encrusted in the softer metal (in our case the copper), which carries them along with it and constrains them to wear down and erode the harder metal (in our case the bronze). This "copper rod" used as tool for grinding a mirror that was certainly of a harder material than copper proves clearly that Leonardo used emeries and powdered abrasives.

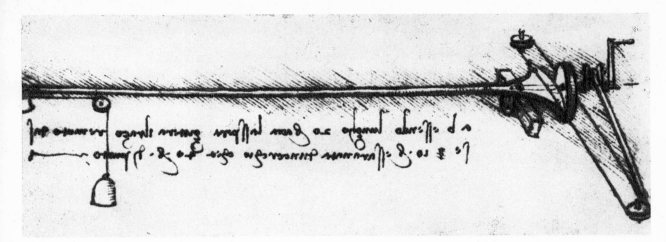

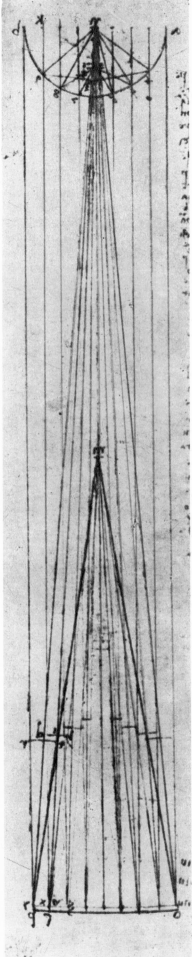

supported on either side of the head and curving slightly under the force of gravity, made a tool *sui generis*. The description of the entire device is in the Codex Arundel, and under the sketch there is the notation,

"This rod may have a curvature of 400 ells."

The result was a concave mirror with a focal length of 100 ells, that is, 60 meters.

Only Campani and Hevelins, much later, were to experiment with such enormous focal lengths.

Even as regards the material best suited for the manufacture of mirrors, Leonardo found the correct solution, two centuries before Newton—that of adding a small amount of arsenic when melting the bell metal. The addition of the arsenic made the bronze brittle and very fragile under blows or on being dropped, but it acquired a priceless property: it became so hard and close-grained that it could be polished like glass, taking on a very smooth and stable surface after polishing.

Leonardo laconically noted the miraculous formula:

"Put burnt copper into the mixture, or corrupt it with arsenic, but it will be brittle" (Cod. Atl., fol. 396 v-*f*).

Hence Leonardo lacked nothing, neither the machinery nor the arsenicated bronze, to produce a very smooth objective mirror with an enormous focal length.

Naturally such a mirror had to have a colossal mounting made for it, with all the equipment needed to move it in every direction, and before Leonardo pointed it at the starry sky in the calm nights in the gardens of the Belvedere at Rome, he must have felt a compelling need to maintain the most absolute secrecy.

Melzi and Salai had no mechanical ability, and the two German mechanics, Mastro Giorgio and Mastro Giovanni degli Specchi [Mirror John], criticized everything they did not understand and spread abroad to the four winds what little they did manage to understand:

"He [Giorgio] never did any work without discussing it every day with Giovanni, who then spread the news of it and proclaimed it everywhere, stating that he was a master of that art, and as regards the part which he did not understand he announced that I did not know what I wanted to do" (Cod. Atl., fol. 182 v-*c*).

Ah, Leonardo! Not even to us did you want to say what you wanted to do in the gardens of the Belvedere. And if I tell my fellow citizens today that you wanted to set up a machine for the heavens, they will take me in turn for a visionary, and say that I want to write science fiction.

"I cannot make anything secretly because of him... And if I should set him there to make my model, he would publish it..." (Cod. Atl., fol. 182 v-*c*).

The "model" of the machine for the heavens could not remain a secret. The wily Giovanni wanted to copy the model for himself, in order to set up one like it in his native country. Leonardo was not taken in, and refused to explain the model entirely to him, telling him that he would give him only, from time to time, partial drawings covering each separate component part:

"He wanted to have the models finished in wood, just as they were to be in iron, and wished to carry them away to his own country. But this I refused him, telling him that I would give him, in drawing, the breadth, length, height, and form of what he had to do" (Cod. Atl., fol. 247 v-*b*).

The three years of his stay in Rome passed under these sorry conditions, caught between envy and lack of understanding, and the projected machine could never be erected to scale the heavens: just

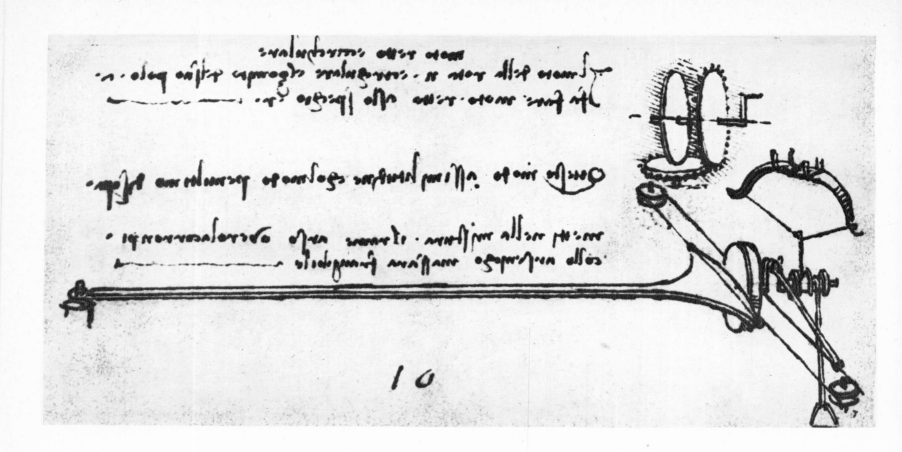

Variant of machine for grinding telescopic mirrors – Cod. Atl., fol. 396 v-*f*

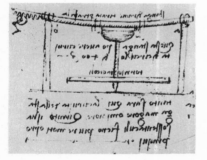

Potter's wheel for making mirrors with large focal length – Cod. Arund., fol. 84 v

Machine for grinding concave mirrors with large radius of curvature – Cod. Atl., fol. 396 v-*f*

Machine for grinding mirrors – Cod. Atl., fol. 396 v-*f*

as in the mythical dawn of time, on the plain of Babel, some god or some demon confused the languages of men when they sought to violate the virginity of the skies. And then, as in the dawn of time, dispersion and exile.

THE EYE

Leonardo had come to have a very ambitious idea as to his personal contribution to the scientific study of that masterpiece of nature, the human eye:

"The eye, whose use and operation are so clearly shown to us by experience, has been defined in one way by an infinite number of authors up to my time, and I find it is completely different" (Cod. Atl., fol. 361 v).

This proud assertion could certainly have been better supported if Leonardo had had the time and the means of measurement and investigation to put his great research plan into effect:

"Write in your anatomy what proportions the diameters of all the spheres of the eye have to each other, and what the distance of the crystalline sphere is from them" (Cod. Atl., fol. 345 v-*b*).

In other words, the model of the eye that modern ophthalmology has slowly worked out with measurements of constantly greater precision was in Leonardo's plan of work and research.

Leonardo was faced with three basic obstacles in working out his model of the eye: the absence of instruments for measuring small distances; the impossibility of studying the living eye, his researches thus being limited to anatomy; and the lack of a general law of the refraction of light.

The anatomical difficulties did not frighten him, and he was able to overcome them in a brilliant manner, as is shown by the following note (Ms. K, fol. 39):

"In the anatomy of the eye, in order to see well into it without spilling its humor, the entire eye should be put into egg white and boiled, and once it is hard, cut through the egg and the eye in such a way that nothing is spilled out of the lower half."

Unfortunately, anatomical findings are sometimes misleading.

Thus for example the crystalline, which has the form of a biconvex lens in the living eye, assumes a virtually spheroid form when it is removed from the eye.

This explains why Leonardo's diagrammatic drawings of the human eye always represent the crystalline lens as a ball.

In the living eye the iris is always attached to the crystalline; in the anatomy of the dead eye, iris and lens are almost always separate.

426

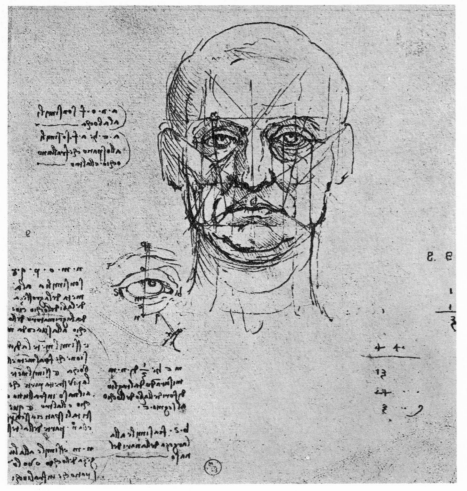

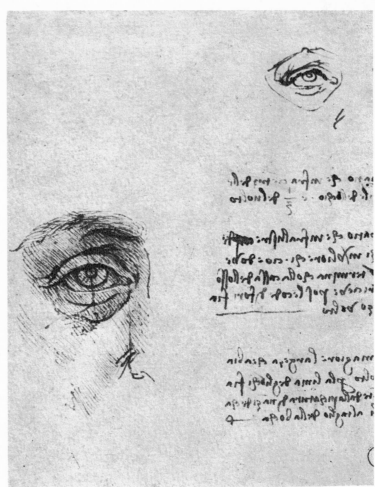

The lens in the form of a sphere and its detachment from the iris are two characteristic features of the figure shown in the Codex Atlanticus (fol. 337 r-*a*), and also characterize a model of the eye made by Leonardo in glass and metal.

The construction of this model is described in detail on folio 3 verso of Ms. D:

"A globe of glass will be made, five eighths of an ell in diameter. Let enough be cut out at one point for the face to be put into it up to the ears. And then let a box bottom of a third of an ell be set at the bottom with an aperture in the center four times the size of the pupil of the eye (or about that, it does not matter). In addition, let there be mounted a thin glass globe, one sixth of an ell in diameter. And when this is done, fill everything with tepid clear water. And put your face into this water, and look at the globe, and take note, and you will see: this instrument will send the *species* of *st* to the eye as the eye sends them to the visual faculty."

In the upper part of the figure Leonardo draws his model of the eye diagrammatically; in the lower part he describes the path of the principal rays as he understands it:

"It is assumed here that the faculty is located at the end of the optic nerves, *hm* being one of these. We shall say therefore that the visual faculty *m* cannot see *a*, an object to the left, unless the ray of the *species* of that object passes through the center of two spheres, the sphere of the pupil *dk* and the sphere of the vitreous humor *xytv*, and so the path of the ray will be *aervzx*. Hence *m*, the visual faculty, will see *a*, the object to the left, represented at *x* to the left, and thus the instrument of the eye cannot show this object at the left in its true position except by means of two intersections which pass through the axis of the eye, as has been proved."

The most serious defect of this model of the eye is the small inner globe that is to be made of thin glass, which implies that it is to be hollow inside, and remain hollow even when the entire setup is filled with water.

We know from modern optics that under these conditions the totality of this model of the eye constitutes a divergent optical system.

And yet Leonardo knew that the crystalline is denser than all the other refractive media of the eye.

It would therefore have been preferable to make the globe of solid glass, not hollow; only in that case would his eye model have afforded a convergent optical system.

Furthermore, if the small inner globe had been of solid glass, and not hollow, it should have been ground rough on the upper portion to receive the inverted image; but this inverted image is

Studies of proportions of face and eye – Turin, Royal Library

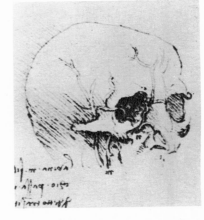

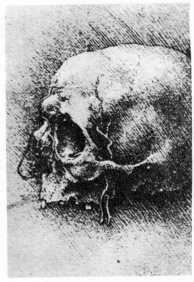

Above and below: Drawings of orbital cavities – Windsor, Royal Collection, no. 19059 r

427

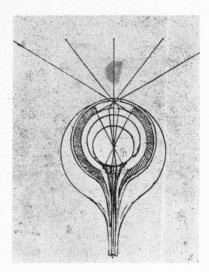

Leonardo's schematic eye – Cod. Atl., fol. 337 r-*a*

Model of eye constructed by Leonardo – Ms. D, fol. 3 v

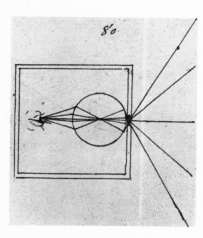

Drawing with glass sphere, as lens, placed before aperture of camera obscura – The above Leonardo's device shows the first use of lens in this position, previously credited to Daniele Barbaro of Venice – Cod. Atl., fol. 337 r-*a*

just what Leonardo did not want. All the errors in his ocular systems derive from this fundamental error—his insistence that the image on the retina be erect, at all costs.

Actually, when Leonardo initiated his study of the way in which the eye functions optically, he took the right path by comparing the eye to the camera obscura, something that no one had done before him.

The first distinct mention made of the camera obscura [4] is found in the third chapter of the work *Milchamoth Adonai* ("The Wars of the Lord"), printed at Riva di Trento in 1560, but written two centuries earlier by Leo Hebraeus (Levi ben Gerson, 1288-1344), if we ignore a vague hint offered by Alhazen and a still vaguer hint from Aristotle (*Problems*, Bk. xv).

Leonardo, however, studied the camera obscura thoroughly in its most minute details, varying the form and the size of the aperture and its distance from the screen. Moreover, he was the first to compare it with the eye. He describes:

"An experiment showing how objects transmit their images or pictures intersecting within the eye in the crystalline humor. This is shown when the *species* of illuminated objects penetrate into a very dark chamber by some small round hole. Then you will receive these species on a white paper placed within this dark room and rather near to the hole, and you will see all the objects on paper in their proper forms and colors, but much smaller; and they will be upside down by reason of that very intersection. These images, being transmitted from a place illuminated by the sun, will seem actually painted on this paper, which must be extremely thin and looked at from behind. And let the little perforation be made in a very thin piece of iron. Let *abcde* be the object illuminated by the sun and *or* the front of the dark chamber in which is the said aperture, at *nm*. Let *st* be the sheet of paper intercepting the rays of the species of these objects upside down, because the rays being straight, *a* on the right hand becomes *k* on the left, and *e* on the left becomes *f* on the right; and the same takes place inside the pupil" (Ms. D, fol. 8 r).

Leonardo adds a sketch to explain the text. This passage and sketch were published by Venturi in his famous *Essai*.

This basically correct assimilation of the eye to the camera obscura was never completely followed by Leonardo to the logical conclusion that the image is inverted on the surface of the retina.

A hundred years later Kepler (1604) was better advised and assumed this inversion, which was later brilliantly confirmed experimentally by Scheiner, who removed a part of the sclerotic and choroid from an actual eye and was able to observe a really inverted image on the fundus of the eye.

I do not believe that it was psychological factors that diverted Leonardo from the right path. It seems to me that Leonardo fell into his error solely because of his desire to give a plausible explanation of the presence and function of the crystalline lens. We know today that the principal function of the lens is accommodation, since the corneal diopter acts as a convergent lens. But Leonardo had not the slightest suspicion of the phenomenon of accommodation; and convinced as he was that nature does not make superfluous organs, he finally assumed that the chief function of the crystalline lens was to re-erect the inverted images of the cornea-pupil system.

There are many passages in which Leonardo asserts this. I cite two that seem to me the clearest and most expressive:

"The vitreous sphere is placed in the middle of the eye to rectify the *species* that intersect within the aperture of the pupil, so that the right may become right again and the left become left again at the second intersection, which takes place at the center of this vitreous sphere" (Ms. D, fol. 3 v).

"The pupil of the eye, which receives through a very small round hole the *species* of bodies situated beyond this hole, always receives them upside down, and the visual faculty always sees them upright as they are.

"And this proceeds from the fact that the said images direct themselves according to the object that has caused them, and from thence they are taken by the impression (*impensiva*) and transmitted to the common sense, where they are judged" (Ms. D, fol. 2 v).

According to Leonardo, therefore, there is a twofold crossing of the principal rays—a first crossing in the center of the pupil (which is correct), and a second crossing in the center of the crystalline lens (and this is incorrect).

We have spoken up to now of the principal or central rays, that is, of those rays that intersect the optical axis in the center of the iris of an optical system. But although the principal rays are sufficient to define the image in perspective, they do not of themselves suffice to establish the posi-

---

[4] A popular-science writer on optics, not too well informed and not up to date, has written (*Bollettino Associazione Ottica Italiana*, No. 1 [1939], p. 13) that Della Porta was the first to apply a convergent lens to the aperture of the camera obscura. This is not so. The first to apply a lens to the camera obscura was Daniele Barbaro of Venice (*La practica della prospettiva*, Venice, 1568, p. 192). It was only in the revised edition (1589) that Della Porta mentioned the lens, regarding which there is no trace of mention in the first edition.

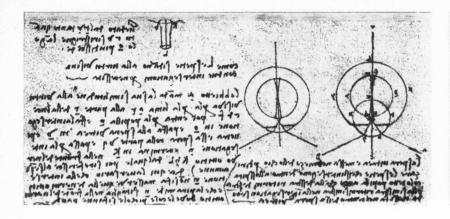

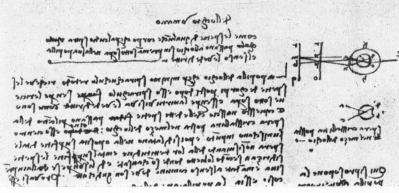

tion and sharpness of the image. They must always be supplemented by the divergent oblique or aperture rays, that is, those rays that go from the object and pass through the peripheral regions of the iris, and then come together again in the image. It is only the aperture rays that make it possible to have a focal point and a focal length.

Now, Leonardo always considered only the principal rays in his treatment of the eye, completely excluding the aperture rays. It is curious that in his treatment of spherical and parabolic mirrors he used the opposite procedure, and considered the aperture rays exclusively.

What is the explanation of this difference of method?

Here too the key of the explanation is to be found in the camera obscura. The more the pinhole of the camera obscura is cut down in size, the less important are the aperture rays, and the more indefinite the conceptions of focus and focal length.

Actually, if the pupil of the eye is small, the focal length is small as well, and the oblique rays converging to a focus cannot be ignored as they are ignored in the camera obscura.

The fact that the visual field embraced by the eye is very large, taking in over 180⁰, was observed by Leonardo long before Kepler noted it. We need only consider the figure taken from Ms. D, folio 8 verso. According to Leonardo, the wide-angle effect is due to the *luce*, that is, the cornea. To demonstrate this hypothesis he resorted to experiments.

"In order to see what function the *luce* serves in the pupil, cause a thing resembling the *luce* to be made of glass" (Ms. K, fol. 118 v).

Perhaps it was not easy for him to obtain a glass plano-convex lens, and he used a water lens in its place. He poured a little water into the lower part of a glass globe, and upon bringing the eye so close that it touched the water, he saw that it covered a very large visual field, even receiving objects located behind his shoulders:

"If you take a hemisphere of glass and put your face into it, and close it well around the edge of the face, and fill it with clear water, you will see all the things that are seen from the surface of this globe, so that you will all but see behind your back" (Cod. Atl., fol. 222 r-a).

But not all of this enormous visual field is seen by the eye with equal precision and sharpness. The maximum of precision and sharpness is obtained along what we call the optical axis and Leonardo called the central line. On either side of the optical axis the precision and sharpness fall off rapidly.

"The eye has a single central line, and all the things that come to the eye along this line are seen well. There are an infinite number of other lines around this one as their center, which are of less value the further they are removed from the central line" (Quad. Anat. IV, fol. 12 v).

This concept is repeated often in practically all of Da Vinci's manuscripts.

The phenomenon of the dilation and contraction of the pupil was long and attentively observed and analyzed by Leonardo. He says:

"The pupil of the eye changes to as many different sizes as there are differences in the degrees of brightness and obscurity of the objects which present themselves before it.

"In this case nature has provided for the visual faculty, when it has been irritated by excessive light, by contracting the pupil of the eye, and by enlarging this pupil after the manner of the mouth of a purse when it has had to endure various degrees of darkness.

"And here nature works as one who, having too much light in his habitation, blocks up the window halfway or more or less according to the necessity, and who when night comes throws open the whole of this window in order to see better within this habitation.

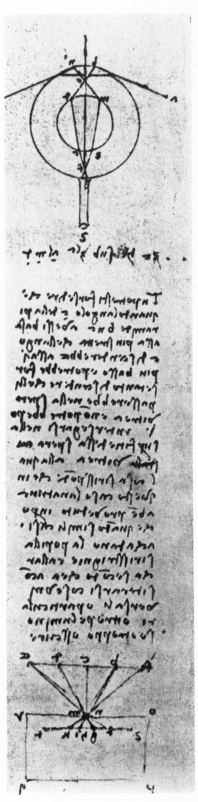

Da Vinci's System of the Vitreous Sphere – Left: Ms. D, fol. 3 v. – Right: Ms. D, fol. 2 v

Leonardo was first to compare eye to camera obscura – Above: Eye. – Below: Camera Obscura – Ms. D, fol. 8 r

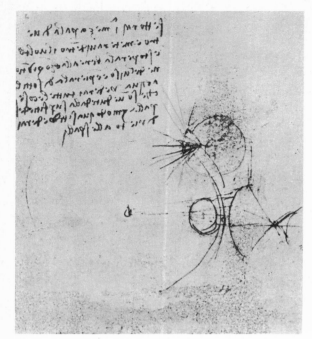
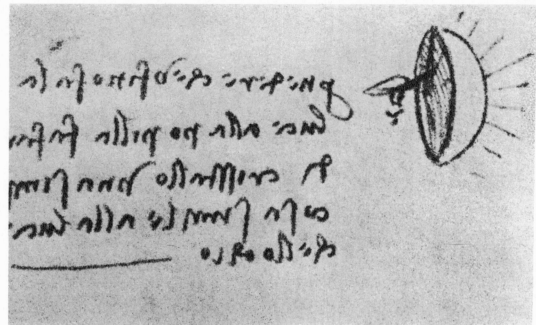

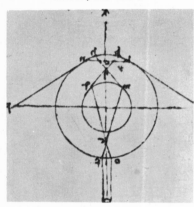

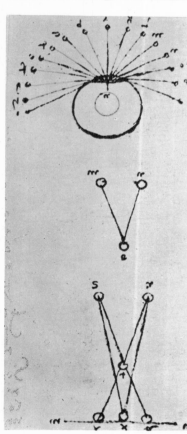

"Nature is here establishing a continual equilibrium, perpetually adjusting and equalizing by making the pupil dilate or contract in proportion to the aforesaid obscurity or brightness which continually presents itself before it.

"You will see the process in the case of the nocturnal animals, such as cats, screech owls, long-eared owls, and the like, which have the pupil small at midday and very large at night. And it is the same with all land animals and those of the air and of the water, but more, beyond any comparison, with the nocturnal animals.

"And if you wish to make the experiment with a man, look intently at the pupil of his eye while you hold a lighted candle at a little distance away, and have him look at this light as you bring it nearer to him little by little, and you will then see that the nearer the light approaches to it, the more the pupil will contract" (Ms. D, fol. 5 v).

In the second of the Forster manuscripts in the Victoria and Albert Museum, Leonardo tells us (fol. 158 v) how he learned of the dilatability of the pupil:

"This pupil of ours dilates or contracts according to the brightness or obscurity of its object, and since it takes some time to dilate or contract, it does not see at once when it comes out from the light into the dark, and likewise from the dark into the light; and this has deceived me in the past in my painting of the eye, and that is how I learned of it."

A very large pupil introduces serious spherical aberration, with the result of making a blurred spot out of the image of a luminous point, for example a star. With his usual marvelous spirit of observation Leonardo did not fail to study this phenomenon. From it he deduced a law that (at least in its verbal formulation) is not quite correct: the larger the pupil of the eye, the larger it sees the images. We know that opening or closing the diaphragm of a photographic camera changes the exposure time needed but will not alter the geometrical size of the photographic image.

The following observations are substantially correct:

"If you will make as small a hole as possible in a sheet of paper and then bring it as near as possible to the eye, and if then you look at a star through this hole, you are making use of only a small part of the pupil, which sees this star with a wide space of sky round it and sees it so small that hardly anything could be smaller. And if you make the hole near to the edge of the said paper, you will be able to see the same star with the other eye at the same time, and it will appear to you to be large, and thus in the said time with your two eyes you will see the one star twice, and once it will be very small and the other time very large" (Ms. D, fol. 5 r).

The following deductions are substantially incorrect:

"The eye sees and knows objects of vision with greater intensity when the pupil is more dilated" (Ms. E, fol. 17 v);

"All things seen will appear larger at midnight than at midday, and larger in the morning than at midday. This takes place because the pupil of the eye is considerably smaller at midday than at any other time" (Ms. H, fol. 86 r);

"As the light diminishes, so the pupil of the eye that beholds this light expands. Therefore the eye which looks through a blowgun has a larger pupil than the other, and sees the object larger and clearer than the other eye does" (Ms. L, 14 r).

One of Leonardo's great merits is to have seen clearly that the specific organ of the sensation of light is the retina.

In the Codex Arundel (fol. 172 r) he expresses himself as follows:

"The receptive faculty (*imprensiva*) must have its seat in the eye. The nerve that goes from the eye to the brain is like the hollow cords that interweave the skin of bodies with infinite branchings and by their hollow spaces lead to the sensus communis."

Is not this picture of the retina as made up of a tissue of the infinite ramifications of the optic nerve an astounding anticipation?

The existence of a *punctum proximum* for distant vision is clearly affirmed by Leonardo:

"If the eye is required to look at an object placed too near to it, it cannot judge of it well—as happens to a man who tries to see the tip of his nose. Hence, as a general rule, nature teaches us that an object can never be seen perfectly unless the space between it and the eye is equal at least to the length of the face" (Cod. Atl., fol. 138 v-*b*).

The distance of distant vision, given approximately as of the same order of magnitude as the length of the face, is more precisely stated in another place (Cod. Atl., fol. 250 v-*a*) as equal to four times the interpupillary distance. We have no corrections to make in this connection.

Leonardo nowhere refers to myopia in speaking of the ametropies of the eye, although he speaks several times of presbyopia and of the glasses suited to correcting it.

In the Codex Atlanticus (fol. 244 r-*a*) he presents several diagrams and explains:

"A proof of the manner in which glasses aid the sight: Let *ab* be the glasses and *cd* the eyes, and suppose these to have grown old. Whereas they used to see an object at *e* with great ease by turning their position very considerably from the line of the optic nerves, now by reason of age the power of bending has become weakened, and consequently it cannot be twisted without causing great pain to the eyes, so that they are constrained of necessity to move the object farther away, that is, from *e* to *f*, and so see it better but not in detail. But through the interposition of the spectacles the object is clearly discerned at the same distance as when the eyes were young, that is, at *e*, and this comes about because the object *e* passes to the eye through various media, namely, thin and thick, the thin being the air that is between the spectacles and the object, and the thick being the thickness of the glass of the spectacles; the line of direction consequently bends in the thickness

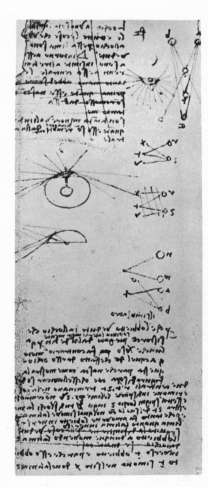

Only drawing by Leonardo showing faces with spectacles – Quad. Anat. V, fol. 6 r

Study made by Leonardo da Vinci on visual field of eye – Quad. Anat. IV, fol. 12 v

431

Objects appear larger at night than
by day – Ms. H, fol. 86 r

Dilation of pupil as function of amount
of light – Ms. L, fol. 14 r

Description of eyeglasses for the old
– Cod. Atl., fol. 244 r-a

of the glass, and the line *ad* is twisted in such a way that seeing the object at *e* the eye sees it as though it were at *f*, with the advantage that the position of the eye in relation to its optic nerves is not strained, and it sees the object near at hand and discerns it better at *e* than at *f*, and especially the minute portions."

Leonardo was right in attributing the cause of presbyopia to a lack of freshness, elasticity, and pliability in the sluggish nerves and muscles of the old; but he was wrong in blaming the nerves and muscles that control and regulate binocular convergence rather than those that compress the crystalline lens.

In his time eyeglasses seem to have been classified according to the average ages of the old persons who were to use them. Thus in Ms. A (fol. 12 v) Leonardo mentions "fifty-year-old glasses," and in the Codex Atlanticus (fol. 83 v) he speaks of a lead for grinding "sixty-year-old glasses." Figures of heads with spectacles are drawn in Quaderno V (fol. 6 r).

The famous experiments of Czermak, Scheiner, and Mile were all anticipated by Leonardo's inventive genius. In relation to one of his experiments he writes:

"Let *an* be the pupil of the eye *kh*, and let *p* be a small round hole made in the paper with the fine point of a style, and let *mb* be the object placed beyond this opening. I maintain that the upper part of this object cannot come to the upper part of the pupil of the eye via the straight line *ma*, because at *v* its passage is impeded by the interposition of the paper. But this upper extremity *m* passes in a straight course through the hole to *n*, the lower part of the pupil, or you would say of the crystalline sphere, and from there it directs its course to the center of this sphere, then rises to the upper part of the opposite side and from there, as has been said, it runs to the common sense.

"Below is shown the experiment which gives rise to the certainty of this new intersection (*intersegazione*).[5] Let *gd* be the eye whose pupil *ap* sees object *tc* through the hole *q* made in the paper *rs*. I say that if you move the style *lq* from the top to the bottom of the pupil and close to it, along the line *kh* that will lie outside of this hole *q*, that this motion of the style is contrary to its true motion. And the reason for this is that when the style touches the line *ac* it touches the highest line within the hole *q* and the lowest line outside that hole, and as the style descends it touches the line *ny*, which is the highest line within the hole and the lowest outside of that hole, and going on in this way to continue the descent of your style within the hole before the eye, you follow along the line of contrary motion outside of that hole" (Ms. D, fol. 2 v).

Five pages of Ms. K (a pocket notebook about 10×7 cm. in size) are also devoted to this curious phenomenon.

In order to understand these folios, they must be rearranged in a logical order, as follows: 127 verso, 127 recto, 126 verso, 125 verso, 126 recto. We shall not reproduce them here, since it is not our intention to offer a complete collection of Da Vinci's writings on optics, but rather a critical synthesis intended to orient and guide the student of optics and of the history of science.

Before ending our discussion of monocular vision, we refer briefly to irradiation and the persistence of images on the retina.

In the *Treatise on Painting* (par. 440) Leonardo gives due emphasis to the phenomenon of irradiation, which cannot be ignored even in practising the art of painting:

"Things seen from afar are out of proportion, and this is so because the clearer portion sends its image to the eye with a more powerful ray than the darker portion. And I saw a woman dressed in black with a white shawl on her head, who showed two of these bigger than the width of her shoulders, which were clothed in black."

In Ms. C of the Institut de France (fol. 6 r) he is even more precise, and suggests an experiment to prove that irradiation is due primarily to the eye:

"If the eye looks at the light of a candle at a distance of 400 ells, this light will appear to this eye looking at it increased to a hundred times its true quantity; but if you place in front of it a stick somewhat larger than this light, this stick which would appear 2 ells wide would hide it. This error therefore comes from the eye."

A stick to hide a luminous point? In 1659 Christian Huygens made a substantially identical proposal; to measure the apparent diameter of a planet he suggested [6] hiding its disk with a sheet of metal in the form of a rod or cone. Once more the question is suggested: Had Huygens read some manuscript of Leonardo's?

---

[5] Ravaisson-Mollien transcribes *investighazione*, which does not fit the context.
[6] *Oeuvres complètes*, The Hague, 1925, XV, 348.

432

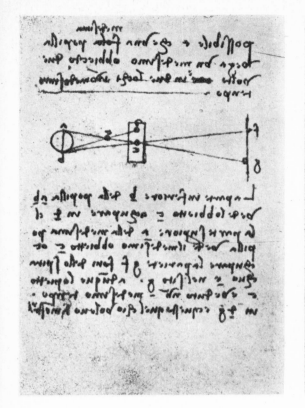
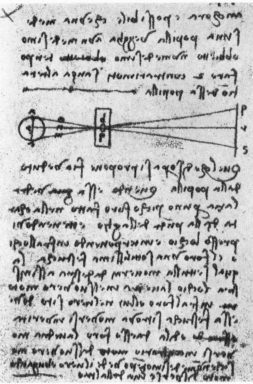
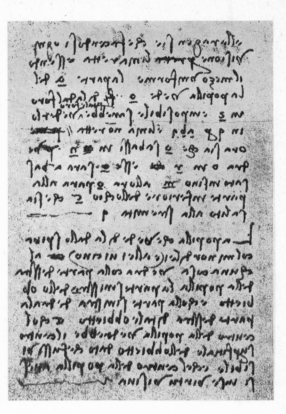

In paragraph 254 of the *Treatise on Painting*, Leonardo gives a truly modern definition of irradiation: *Bright objects increase in size in a dark field.*

The Da Vinci manuscripts are full of observations on the phenomenon of the persistence of images on the retina. These observations are much fuller than those made by Roger Bacon in the fifth part of the *Opus maius*. Leonardo writes:

"If the eye that looks at the star turns swiftly in an opposite direction, it will appear to it that this star forms itself into a curving line of fire..."

"And this occurs because the eye preserves for a certain space of time the image of the thing that shines, and because this impression of the radiance of the star is more enduring in the pupil than was the time of its movement..." (Ms. K, fol. 120 r).

The phenomenon is described at even greater length on folio 352 of the Codex Atlanticus and elsewhere. This is very well known, I should almost say too well known, so much so that some naïve commentators and popularizers have felt that they have in these passages relating to the persistence of images the certain proof that Leonardo anticipated motion pictures.

We proceed to binocular vision. A problem that interested Leonardo a great deal was that of:

"whence the turning of the eyes when one draws the other after it" (Anat. Ms. B, fol. 21 r).

In the Codex Atlanticus (fol. 305 v-*b*) he seems to have sought the source of this in the intersection of the optic nerves:

"Saw a head in two between the eyebrows in order to find out by anatomy the cause of the equal movement of the eyes, and this virtually confirms that the cause is the intersection of the optic nerves."

Quaderno V has two fine plates (fol. 6 v, 8 r) containing admirable drawings of the two eyes with the intersection of the nerves and the position of the eyeballs in their respective orbits.

The possession of two eyes gives man the perception of stereoscopie relief; Leonardo was the precursor of Kepler and Wheatstone in the study of stereoscopic vision.

In paragraph 115 of the *Treatise on Painting* (Cod. Ashb., I, fol. 10 r), Leonardo begins by asking "why things painted can never appear detached as do natural thing," and says:

"Painters oftentimes despair of their power to imitate nature, on perceiving how their pictures lack that relief and vividness which objects possess when seen in a mirror, though, as they allege, they have colors that for clearness and depth far surpass the quality of the lights and shadows of the object seen in the mirror, arraigning herein not reason but their own ignorance, in that they fail to recognize that it is impossible for a painted object to appear in such relief as to be comparable to the objects in the mirror, although both are on flat surfaces, unless they are seen by a single eye.

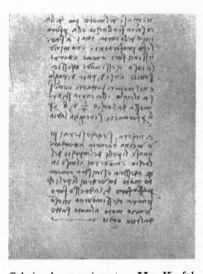

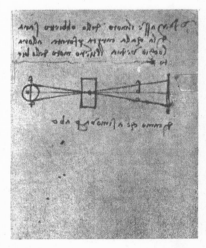

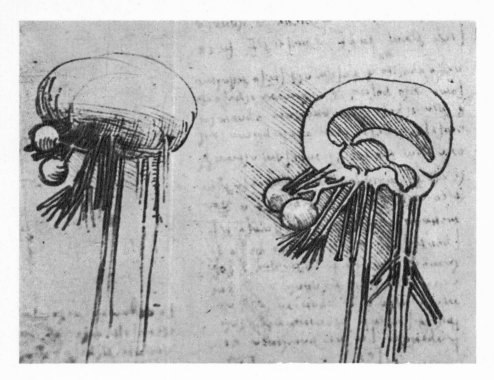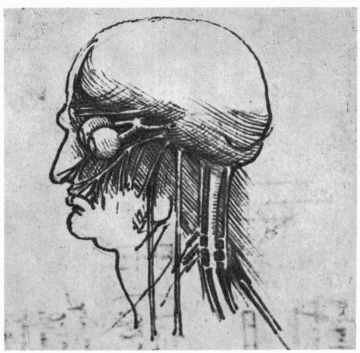

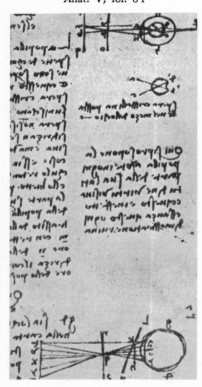

And the reason for this is that when two eyes see one thing behind another, as in the case of *ab* seeing *mn*, *n* cannot entirely cover *m*, because the base of the visual lines is so broad as to cause one to see the second object beyond the first. If, however, you close one eye, as *s* (keeping the other eye open), the object *f* will cover up *k*, because the visual line starts in a single point and makes its base in the first object, with the consequence that the second, being of equal size, is never seen."

The same conception is further illustrated and elucidated in paragraph 482; compare also paragraphs 484 and 811.

The ability to see objects in relief by means of binocular vision is not unlimited, but decreases as the distance from the objects increases:

"That opaque body will be in higher relief which is closer to the eye; and consequently the more distant object will be in lower relief, that is, will stand out less from its background" (*Treatise*, par. 483).

The loss of relief may be accentuated by the absorption of light into the air interposed between the eye and the object:

"The air interposed between the eye and that opaque body, since it is brighter than the shadow of that body, undermines that shadow, and illuminates it, and takes away the force of its obscurity, which is the reason for its losing its relief" (*ibid.*, par. 474).

The two eyes considered as a system may also be compared to a small monostatic range finder with a base of 65 millimeters (very much like the little range finders used in Leica and Contax cameras for perfect focussing); it should therefore be possible to observe, in binocular vision, the phenomenon observed in range finders, namely, the doubling of all the objects except the one voluntarily selected for defining with the range finder.

Leonardo's inexhaustible curiosity takes up these phenomena of doubling in folio 12 verso of Quaderno IV:

"The many objects placed one behind the other before the two eyes, at known distances, all appear double, except the one that is seen best, and the distance between these doublets will seem larger, the nearer these objects are to the eye when it is looking at the last one; but if you look at the first one, the aforesaid distances will appear smaller, the nearer the object is to the eye."

Leonardo uses a series of figures to give a purely physical and geometrical explanation of the phenomenon.

We cannot close this study without referring briefly to perspective.

Perspective was unknown to the ancient Egyptians and to the Assyrians and Babylonians; could it have been known to the Greeks?

No answer can be given to this question, since virtually nothing is left of Greek painting. To judge by certain passages in Vitruvius, the Greeks seem to have known at least the fundamental

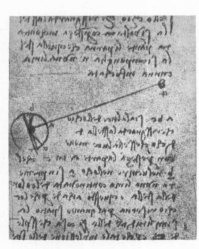

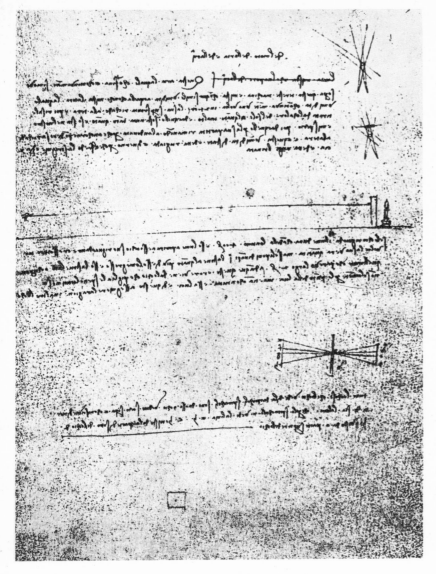

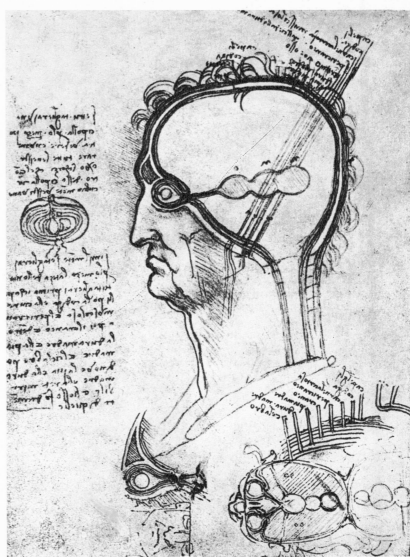

Left: Demonstration of phenomenon of irradiation due to eye – Ms. C, fol. 6 r

Right: Anatomical study of eye – Quad. Anat. V, fol. 6 v

principles of perspective. But these seeds, if they were actually present, were not collected and fecundated; the frescoes of Pompeii and the Byzantine paintings openly violate the most elementary rules of perspective. These open offenses with respect to perspective also dominate the peintings of Giotto.

It may be said that perspective was born suddenly in Italy, in the dawn of the Renaissance, producing a sort of collective intoxication, a certain naïve passionate enthusiasm.

Leon Battista Alberti, in his *De pictura*, gives early indication of acquaintance with the point of sight and the point of distance. The geometrical laws of perspective were precisely stated by Pietro del Borgo (Piero della Francesca) before Leonardo dealt with them, and a century after Leonardo's time carried to a peak of perfection by Ubaldo del Monte (1600).

What position does Leonardo occupy, between Del Borgo and Del Monte, in the creation of perspective?

Leonardo distinguishes three kinds of perspective (Ms. A, fol. 98; Cod. Ashb., I, 18 r):

"There are three branches of perspective. The first deals with the reasons for the [apparent] diminution of objects as they recede. The second contains the way in which colors vary as they recede from the eye. The third and last is concerned with the explanation of how the abjects [in a picture] ought to be less finished in proportion as they are remote. And the names are as follows: linear perspective; perspective of color; perspective of disappearance."

The same threefold division is made by Leonardo in the *Treatise on Painting* (par. 479).

Leonardo was an incomparable master in the perspective of colors and the perspective of indistinctness, while in purely geometrical perspective he is not as perfect as Piero della Francesca.

He knows the general and basic principle of perspective projection, and states it perfectly:

"Of the plane of glass: Perspective is nothing more than seeing a place [or objects] behind a pane of glass, quite transparent, on the surface of which the objects behind that glass are to be drawn. These can be traced in pyramids to the point in the eye, and these pyramids are intersected on the glass plane" (Ms. A, fol. 1 v).

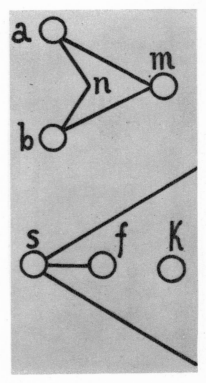

Figure for paragraph 115 of the *Treatise on Painting*

435

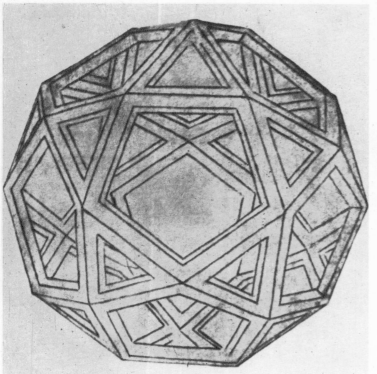
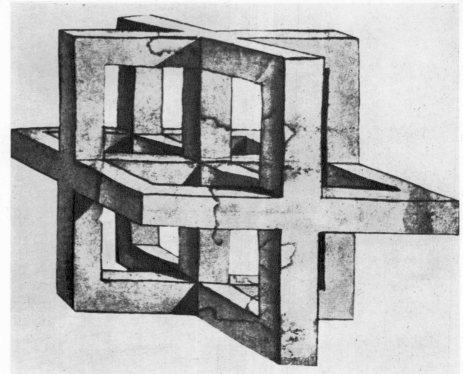

Figures in geometrical perspective –
Cod. Atl., fol. 263 r

It does not appear, however, that Leonardo deduced from this basic principle the rules for passing from geometrical considerations to those of perspective, once the point of sight and the point of distance are given, rules already enunciated by Piero della Francesca.

Here the artist gets the upper hand of the scientist, and Leonardo replaces geometrical construction with the rather empirical procedures of the glass plate and the grid or net.

In paragraph 87 of the *Treatise on Painting* (Cod. Ashb., I, fol. 24 r) he writes:

"Of a mode of drawing a place accurately: Have a piece of glass as large as a half sheet of royal folio paper and set this firmly in front of your eyes, that is, between your eye and the thing you want to draw; then place yourself at a distance of two thirds of an ell from the glass, fixing your head with a mechanism in such a way that you cannot move it at all. Then shut or cover one eye and with a brush or drawing chalk draw upon the glass that which you see beyond it; then trace it on paper from the glass, afterward transfer it onto good paper, and paint it if you like, carefully attending to the aerial perspective."

Statement of principle of perspective
– Ms. A, fol. 1 v

The device of the grid or net is the more deserving of our attention because in this respect Leonardo anticipated the great Dürer. It is described in paragraph 94 of the *Treatise on Painting* (Cod. Ashb., I, fol. 24 r):

"Set a frame with a network of thread in it between your eye and the nude model you are drawing, and draw these same squares on the paper... Then place a pellet of wax on a spot of the net which will serve as a fixed point... Afterward, remember when drawing figures to use the rule of the corresponding proportions of the limbs as you have learned it from the frame and net. This should be 3 1/2 ells high and 3 ells wide, 7 ells distant from you, and one ell from the nude model."

It is obvious that with these two devices the point of sight could not stay too well defined and constant.

I have observed that the lines in the *Last Supper* do not converge to a single point, but some to the right eye of Christ, some to his right shoulder, and some to points between the shoulder and the eye. The statement of Sirèn (*Léonard de Vinci, l'artiste et l'homme*, Paris, 1928, I, 84) that "the lines converge exactly at a point behind the right eye of Christ" seems somewhat exaggerated to me.

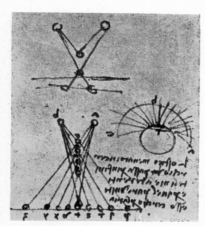

Study of doubling of images – Quad.
Anat. IV, fol. 12 v

I have found the same uncertainty as to the point of sight in the tables designed by Leonardo for Luca Pacioli's *Trattato de divina proportione*; the parallel lines placed obliquely do not all converge to a point.

Fortunately, these slight scientific inaccuracies have not entailed the slightest artistic damage for Leonardo's masterpieces, which will always be the focus of attraction for the eyes of aspiring mankind.

DOMENICO ARGENTIERI

436

ANATOMY IN ART

The rebirth of the plastic arts in Italy coincides not only with the rise of special favoring social, political, and cultural conditions, but also with the inception of the first scientific studies of the body for artistic purposes.

The fact that in classical antiquity plastic representation of the human body attained a matchless perfection is due in large part to the particular conditions of the life and environment of the great masters of that time. Those conditions made possible continual observation and study of the body, not only free of any impediments of clothing but in constant varied movement, so that the eye and the mind of the artist were led as it were unconscioulsy to know and evaluate the various morphological elements that characterize a given body and its varied attitudes and actions, which eventually become basic expressive elements of it.

The different political, social, and religious conditions of the succeeding period in history led to an abandonment of the cult of physical beauty and asked of art that it exalt above all the new mystical and religious sensibility. The result was a decline in the power to represent the human body plastically or pictorially.

With the coming of the Renaissance, artists felt the need of finding new ways for expressing their thoughts and feelings, and were urged to study nature and truth more directly, for the infinite variety of these sources was capable of supplying the artist with far more effective representational elements than he could obtain from the repetition of idioms and modes that could easily become conventional.

In the Codex Atlanticus (fol. 199 v-*a*) we read: "The adversary says that in order to acquire practice and do a great deal of work, it is better that the first period of study should be employed in drawing various compositions executed on paper or on walls by divers masters, and that in this way practice is rapidly gained, and good methods; to which I reply that the method will be good if it is based on works of good composition from the hands of skilled masters. But since such masters are so rare that there are but few of them to be found, it is a surer way to go to natural objects than to those which are imitated from nature with great deterioration, and so produce bad methods; for he who can go to the fountain does not go to the water jar."

As for the human figure, however, artists were no longer accustomed to seeing the nude form in action, as were the ancient sculptors. The old "practice" could no longer be acquired under such favorable conditions, and therefore had to be replaced by "science" to help the artist in his creative work. This tendency was also favored by the fact that just at that time there came into being the first timid and impeded anatomical researches for scientific and medical purposes.

It was at this moment that Leonardo da Vinci the "artist" appeared and launched his scientific studies on the human body, which he later pursued for purposes far exceeding his initial artistic goal, extending them to themes unconnected with art in any way, with the aim solely of quenching his inexhaustible thirst for knowledge.

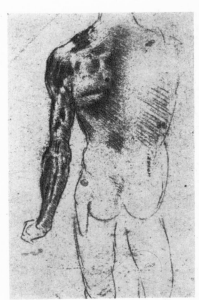

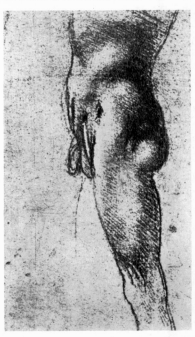

Above and below: Anatomical drawings of the nude – Quad. Anat. VI, fol. 23 r

437

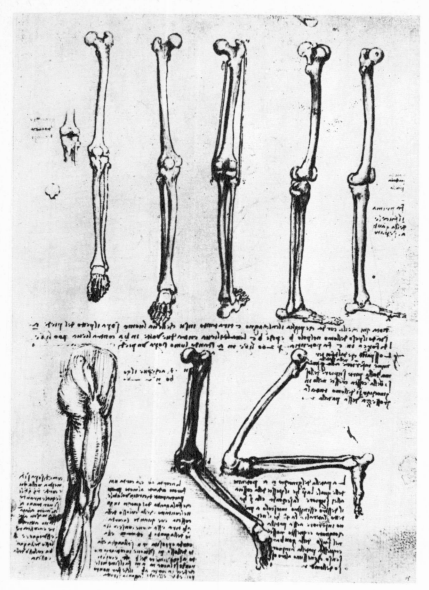

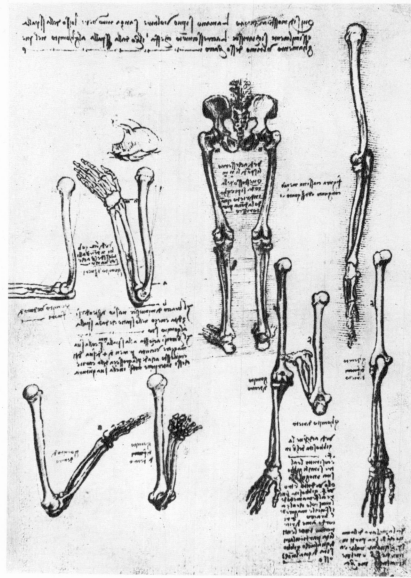

The first anatomical drawings for artistic purposes that we know of are several studies of the nude from the anatomical point of view attributed to Antonio Pollaiolo, together with some others attributed to Andrea del Verrocchio. In relation to both, Vasari mentions the anatomical knowledge they had acquired, he says, from direct study of the cadaver. But the first systematic studies in the field, and the most numerous, complete, diverse, and valuable anatomical drawings are those of Leonardo da Vinci, whom we must therefore regard as beyond question the pioneer in studies of this nature.

Leonardo was not only the first genuine adept but also the creator of that discipline which we today inaccurately call "artistic or plastic anatomy" but should rather define as "artistic morphology of man and the animals," to be faithful to the systematic conception and practical development that Leonardo himself gave it.

This conception is shown clearly in the writings and drawings that have come down to us. It is not too difficult a task, therefore, to reconstruct Leonardo's thought out of the scattered, fragmentary, and sometimes contradictory notations appearing in the various codices of his writings.

Some basic statements are frequently repeated, while others are so logically linked to one another that it is not a matter of arbitrary caprice to bring them together and unite them as would be done with the various figures of a single pictorial composition.

The general statement that "the good painter has two chief things to paint, man and the content of his mind" (*Treatise*, fol. 176) is reinforced by many similar affirmations (*ibid.*, fol. 299, 63; Cod. Atl., fol. 199 v-*a*) and leads logically to proving that the artist must work to acquire knowledge of the morphological, expressive, and mimetic elements of the human body. Hence it is necessary to distinguish between the designations, "On the Human Body" and "On the Human Figure," as probably titles for one or more books (Quad. Anat. V, fol. 3 r), as confirmed by the notation, "Book entitled 'On the Human Figure'" (Anat. Ms. B, fol. 42 r).

This distinction is developed more fully and systematically on folio 20 verso of Anatomical Ms. B and folio 2 recto of Quaderno I (Anat. Ms. C). In the first passage Leonardo says that "this *work*" should comprise an exposition of the conception and development of the infant, with its measure-

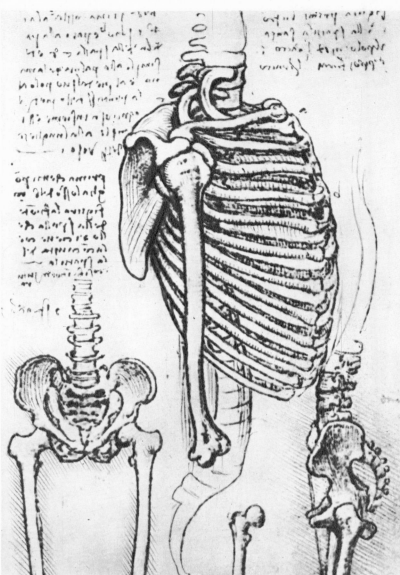

ments; a description of the adult human being of both sexes, with their proportions and their various characteristic differences in "constitution, color, and physiognomy"; a description of the anatomical structure; and, finally, an indication of the fundamental expressions, attitudes, and movements.

On the other hand, folio 2 recto of Quaderno I enunciates in detail "the order of the *book*," which deals with the anatomical structure of the human body. If in the same sheet we go on to read the other side, which explains how to study the hand (setting forth a method that "should be carried out in the same way for every member"), we find the injunction, "You should make a discourse concerning the hands of each of the animals, in order to show in what way they vary"; and we find this precept repeated even more explicitly in other notes (*Treatise*, fol. 122; Quad. Anat. V, fol. 22 r; Ms. K, fol. 109 v; Cod. Atl., fol. 297 r-*b*).

Even if these explicit statements were not adequate to bring out the general conception, together with the systematic distinction between the various sections of this discipline that Leonardo had created without even naming it (i.e., the science devoted to study of the structure and expression of the figure for artistic purposes), examination of folio 22 recto of Quaderno V would furnish ample evidence. In it we have a study of the human lower limb, in the skeleton, with the muscles diagrammatically shown as cords, and in comparison with the hind leg of the horse, as well as, finally, a presentation of the various aspects of the nude thigh and leg, in a drawing that has been consciously distorted in order to bring out the various anatomical components.

What has been said here appears to me to justify the conclusion that Leonardo had recognized that it is necessary for the painter to understand the figure in its structure in order to give expression to its spirit, and therefore intended to compile, and perhaps compiled in part, a *work* to meet this didactic need, comprising *books* on the following fundamental subjects: anatomy, morphology from life, compared in the two sexes at various ages and in various types of constitution; relationships and proportions; attitudes and movements; expression and mimicry, in man and in the animals.

These are precisely the basic headings of the discipline that guides artists in their study of the figure.

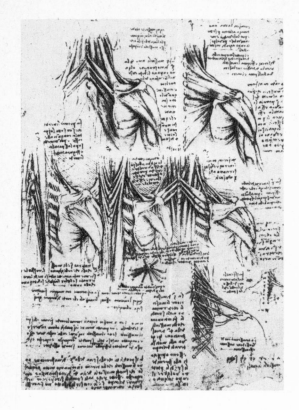

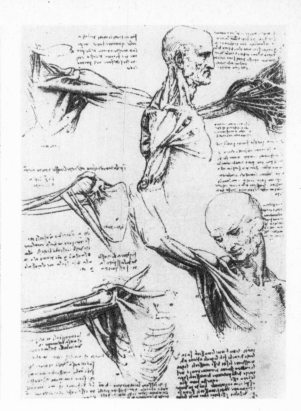

But we can arrive at still a further conclusion, namely, that strictly anatomical study is only a part, no matter how important, of the study of the figure. It does not seem to me too farfetched to imagine that Leonardo succeeded in formulating such a systematic pattern of studies only after personal experience of its usefulness, that is, after going ahead by this method in his practical work in art and dealing successively with the various subjects he indicates, or at least realizing the value of this logical order.

It is only natural that in the course of these studies, which presented him with such interesting problems—problems that had up to that time been so little studied—he should have been led to dwell on various topics that no longer had any direct connection with artistic practice; and thus the artist, with his profound spirit of observation, is replaced by the methodical researcher, the scientist.

The fact still remains that the initial orientation of his research was not altogether forgotten even in his investigations of special problems of purely scientific research.

This gives us one line of distinction to be observed in analyzing Leonardo's anatomical drawings—the determination as to which of them were made for artistic purposes, and which for purposes of pure research. And a further distinction must be drawn as to which drawings are documentary, or represent notes on personal inquiries or studies, and which were made for definitely didactic purposes, one might almost say with the aim of popularization. The same differentiation may be made with respect to the textual portions.

Obviously the sheets that deal with topics relating to the anatomy of the internal organs, the circulation of the blood, respiration, the nervous system, or embryology should be considered as purely anatomical, while those concerned with bones, joints, and muscles belong to artistic anatomy strictly so called. It is also noteworthy that the latter designs are almost all on paper and bear very similar lettering, which makes it seem likely that they originally formed part of a single copybook and were made in approximately the same period of time. These are the designs, published by Sabachnikoff, that form Fogli A and B of the treatise on anatomy (Anat. Mss. A and B).

Now, to these sheets were added many other drawings scattered through the six Windsor notebooks (Quaderni) published by Vangensten and his collaborators, among which are a large number dealing with the proportions and measurements of the human body. Nor should we lose sight of the many drawings to be found in other codices or collections, and in particular the studies of the nude form and those of the anatomy of the horse. If we undertake to state the nature of the drawings and writings, deciding whether they represent merely notes taken at a given moment to preserve an image or a thought, or whether they are sketches for a complete didactic work to be prepared in the future, we can see that many of the pictures are definitely of such a nature that they may have been put together in order to illustrate a given topic, while others treat of unrelated subjects in a confused manner.

I shall mention among the first class the osteological plates, Anatomical Ms. A, folios 5 recto, 9 recto, 13 recto, etc.; the plates on the muscles, in the same A manuscript, folios 2 verso, 4 recto, 4

440

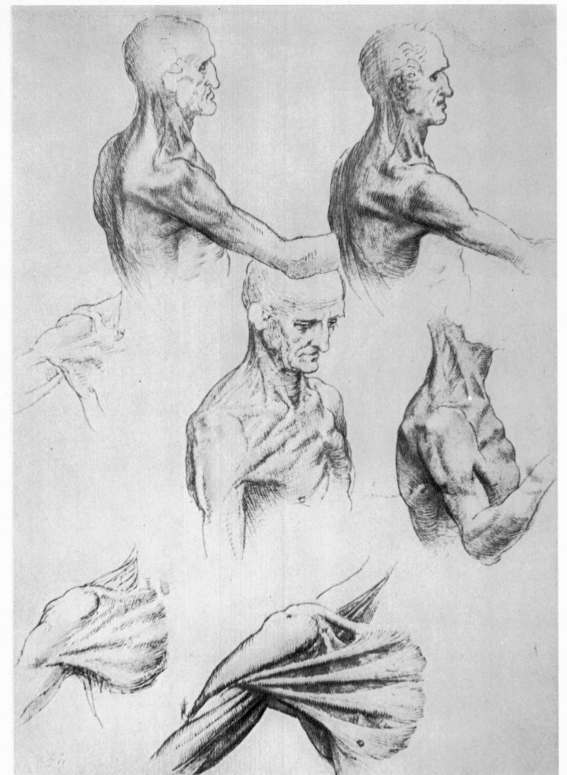

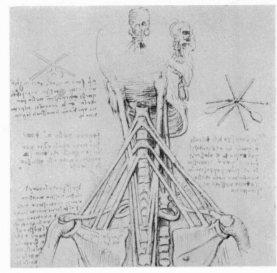

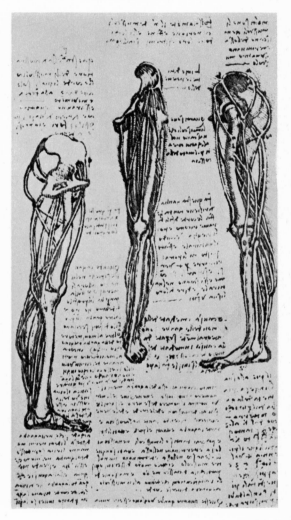

verso, 16 recto; those on drawing the nude, Quaderno VI, folios 15 verso, 16 recto, etc.; and, finally, some tables on the horse. It is obviously impossible that all the figures of these various plates should have been taken directly from nature, that is, from anatomical preparations, within a single period of time; they are the result of choosing and rearranging previously prepared material.

The didactic purpose appears even more patently in some plates in which Leonardo draws schematic figures in order to show the muscles, and even advises making models of them, using copper wires to represent the individual fascicles of muscle (Anat. Ms. A, fol. 4 v; Quad. V, fol. 4 r). In these cases Leonardo exhibits a precise didactic method, in the same way in which on other occasions he explains how to proceed in making anatomical preparations that will afford maximum clarity and visibility in demonstration.

The way in which the drawings are collected in certain plates indicates that they should be considered as a first draft for a prospective didactic work, but the annotations accompanying them are less precise in nature and are most often commentaries on the plates for the author's use rather than for the benefit of the future reader. In fact, they are frequently reminders of how a given plate should be completed or a figure changed. A good instance is found in Anatomical Ms. A, folio 4 verso, where Leonardo ends an annotation by saying, "Comment on these words, as they are confused."

Left: Muscles of chest, from life – Anat. Ms. A, fol. 2 v

Upper right: Pattern of trapezius muscle – Quad. Anat. II, fol. 5 v

Lower right: Pattern of muscles of lower limb – Quad. Anat. V, fol. 4 r

Expression and mimicry – Windsor, Royal Collection

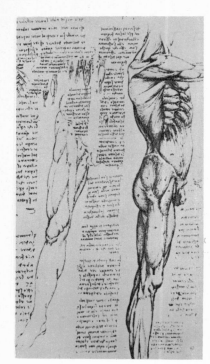

Myological study – Anat. Ms. A,
fol. 15 v

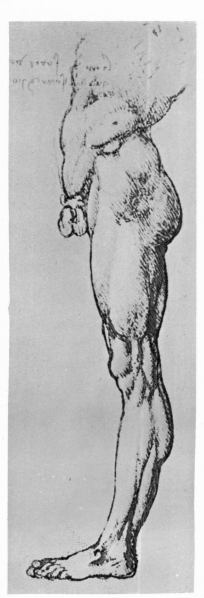

Myological study of lower part of the
body, from life – Quaderni di Anatomia VI, fol. 14 r

The fact that the verbal commentaries on the figures are so fragmentary, and the lack of genuine descriptions designed to point out to others rather than to remind himself, are quite understandable when we read paragraph IV of folio 2 recto of Quaderno II: "With what words, O writer, can you with a like perfection describe [this] as does the drawing?... And do not busy yourself with introducing by way of the ears things which have to do with the eyes, for in this you will be far surpassed by the work of the painter."

This is not to say, however, that the demonstration should be exclusively graphic, but rather that the descriptive portion should be limited: "Hence it is necessary to depict and to describe" (Anat. Ms. A, fol. 14 v).

This predominantly graphic approach that the author set for himself in his didactic work entailed need of the greatest care in executing and choosing the designs. Here too Leonardo's scrupulousness is admirable. First of all he established a "typical" position of the human figure, to which to refer every point in his description; and in Anatomical Ms. A (fol. 10 r) he points out that he has to give a certain angle to a drawing of a hand because "I was constrained thereto by the initial universal representation of the human being, in which I had to draw him with the hands turned down." Starting with this posture as his basis, he depicts separately the four principal aspects of each member or part, adding the longitudinal section for bones; he notes that all these representations should be collected "on a single sheet" (Quad. Anat. V, fol. 4 r), so that any one observing them can get as complete an understanding of the part as if he had it in his hands "and were turning it from side to side" (Quad. Anat. I, fol. 2 r). Accordingly, the drawings not only have a precision that avoids foreshortening effects and studied aesthetic refinements but are deliberately executed (see note, Quad. Anat. III, fol. 7 v) to demonstrate, without the possibility of mistake, the object illustrated. This is particularly evident in some drawings of the nude, in which the accentuated relief of the muscular masses proves that in the particular case an actual anatomical study of a definite part was intended, rather than a simple drawing of the nude; thus Leonardo sometimes represented human forms with precisely that appearance of "a sack of walnuts" or "bunch of radishes" which he cautioned the painter to avoid in representing the nude.

When we analyze the material that would have had to be dealt with in the books that were to make up his didactic work, we see that although Leonardo carried the strictly anatomical part much further toward completion than the others, he has at the same time left us enough graphic material and annotations concerning the other portions to enable us to evaluate his observations and intentions.

In the anatomical study, Leonardo proceeds methodically, as is his custom; that is, he analyzes one system at a time, stressing especially the interrelationships among the various systems, both from the point of view of function (movement) and with respect to outer form. But he is guided by both a systematic and a topographic conception in distinguishing the several parts of the body: "Draw every member joined and apart" (Anat. Ms. A, fol. 5 r). And for every member he proceeds from levels on the plane of the skeleton and gradually arrives at the plane of the skin: "Put down every member that is next to the surface of the member—the nerves, or the cords, or the veins, or the muscles" (Quad. Anat. III, fol. 8 r). Thus, in a "delineation of the hand" he concludes the description of seven successive demonstrations by saying: "The eighth and last will be the hand clothed with skin, and this will be shown for an old man, a young man, and a child, and for each there should be given the measurement of the length, thickness, and breadth of each of its parts" (Anat. Ms. A, fol. 10 v). We see how the morphological conception always dominated and inspired the anatomical research.

We possess an almost complete collection of drawings relating to the description of the skeleton. Leonardo was convinced of the importance, for the painter, of the study of osteology (Treatise, 267), and in drawing bones followed the method of picturing each bone, viewed in four aspects, either separately or together with adjoining bones (Quad. Anat. V, fol. 22 r [VI]; Anat. Ms. A, fol. 4 v). He also found it necessary to establish the relationships between the skeletal portion and the outer surface of the body (Anat. Ms. B, fol. 10 r; Quad. Anat. V, fol. 21 r). The study of osteology was thus aimed to describe the skeleton with reference to the movements of the joints, the action of the muscles, and the outer form. The research was therefore oriented not only to anatomy (structure), but also to physiology (movement) and morphology (outer form).

Neither the drawings nor the writings give us any great wealth of data concerning the joints. Beyond the reference, already cited, to the description of the surface of the joints, and other references to "membranes which are interposed between the bones" (Anat. Ms. A, fol. 18 r), we have only one or two drawings dealing particularly with the elbow joint, and references to the knee joint. All in all we do not get the impression that Leonardo considered arthrology to be an independent chapter of anatomy, but rather that he tried to account for the manner and causes of body movements solely on the basis of knowledge of the bones and muscles (ibid., fol. 9 v).

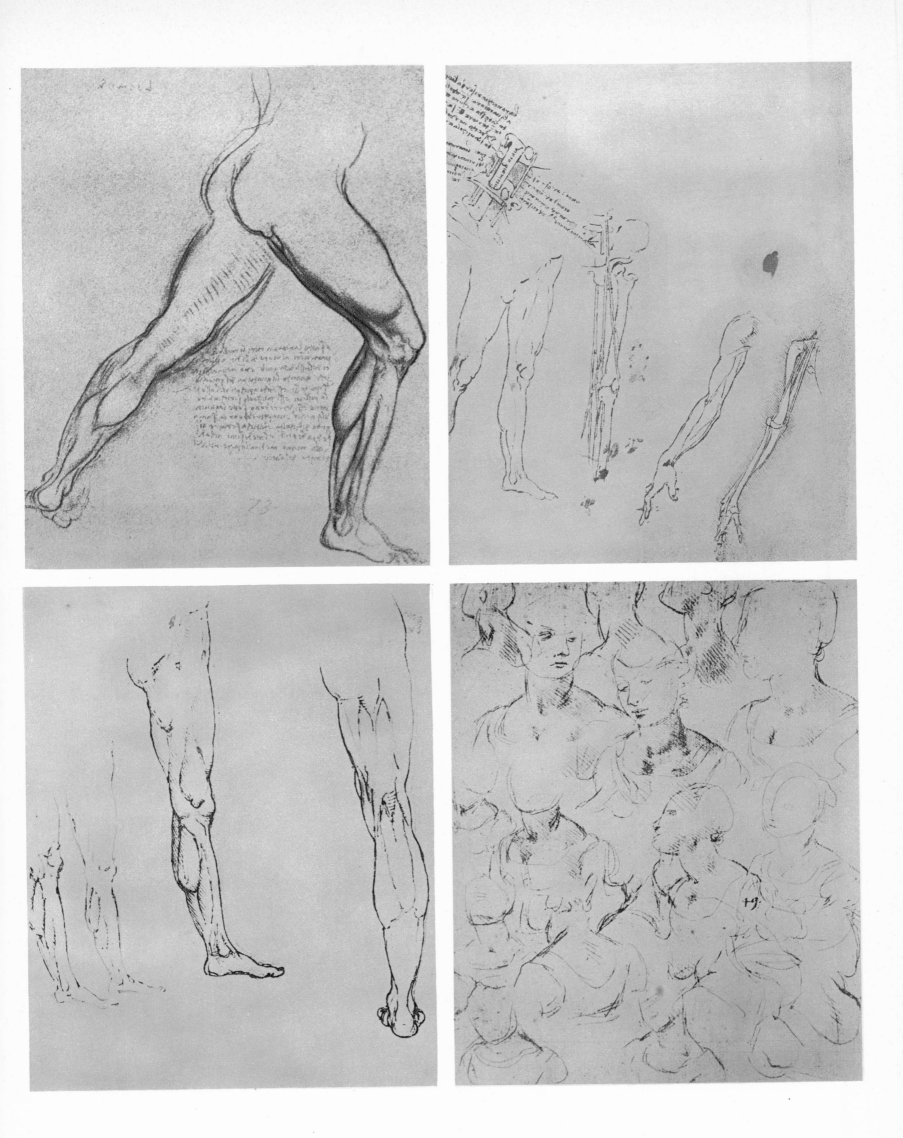

Upper left: Study of muscles of the legs, from life – Quaderni di Anatomia VI, fol. 17 r. — Lower left: Myological study, from life – Quaderni di Anatomia V, fol. 21 r

Upper right: Myological study, from life – Quad. Anat. VI, fol. 15 v. — Lower right: Morphological study, from life – Studies of women's necks – Windsor, Royal Collection

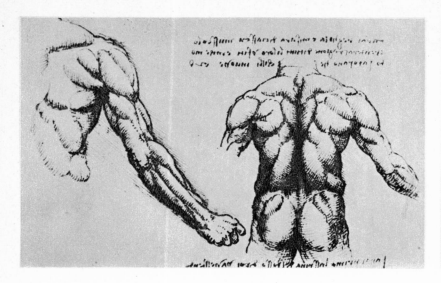
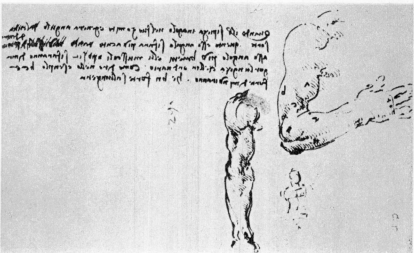

Postures and movements – Quad. Anat.
VI, fol. 18 r

Postures and movements – Anat. Ms.
B, fol. 21 v

On the other hand, he laid great stress on the muscles—with many precious investigations, drawings, and observations—either describing them in isolation with their insertions into the bones or representing them in the schematic drawings I have already referred to, in which the axis of each muscle or of the principal muscular bundle is represented by a wire. He correctly thought of the muscle (*Treatise*, 337) as the basic element in every movement or change of outer form; after declaring that "force is produced by the swelling and shortening of muscles" (Ms. B, fol. 4 v) he deduces the rule that "the muscle that is most used is most evident, and one less used is less prompt to act; and one that does nothing stays slow and soft and inconspicuous" (*Treatise*, 299).

As we see, a large part of the material of Leonardo's book on anatomy has come down to us, especially the illustrative matter, which, although not complete in every part, and not evolved to what would probably have been its definitive form, still suffices to give us a clear idea of the author's intention. But unfortunately, so far as the other putative books on the "human figure" are concerned, we have neither patterns, nor notes, nor systematically collected and interrelated figures.

On morphology, however, there are a very large number of annotations that shed light on Leonardo's interpretative and didactic conceptions with regard to the representation of the figure.

Knowledge of the structure of the body is only a preparation for knowledge of the form. Even though a given structure, apart from the organic differences between the sexes, is roughly the same in every individual, individuals nonetheless always differ from one another. This disparity of form is the result of variation above or below the norm, with respect to the bulk and amount and hence to the relationships and proportions of the various tissues and parts of the body. We shall have more or less fat according to sex, age, and individual constitution (Ms. E, fol. 20 r). These variations will bring about an increased or decreased prominence of the other organs or tissues (bones, muscles). Furthermore, the muscles will be more or less bulky according to their development, which in turn depends on the work that has been required of them, and according to the functional state in which a given muscle may happen to be in any of its various movements or actions (*Treatise*, 33).

The superficial venous system will stand out to a different extent in young and in old men, in a person exerting effort, and in one at rest (Cod. Atl., fol. 345 v). The skin itself will be smooth or wrinkled, firm or slack, and of different color in different persons, again according to sex, age, and individual constitution.

All these possible differences were noted by Leonardo, and as he preserved them for memory in his numerous notes, he studied their causes and weighed their expressive value, arriving at the conclusion that the painter should mention the various characteristic features and make notes on them for his use, and by means of these notes go on to create his figures—that is, figures corresponding to the idea that the painter himself contemplates representing (*Treatise*, 299, 266, 55). The representation of the figure should not be an objective copy of a model, but a harmonious fusion of several objectively true elements into a new ideal creation which will still retain verisimilitude (*ibid.*, 405, 280, 389).

Hence objective study of the structure and morphological elements of the figure should yield the norm of a subjective creation of the figure itself. It is only in this way that the *notomista* painter will be a "varied and universal demonstrator," and avoid becoming "wooden" and making "his figures printed, so that they will all look like sisters" (*ibid.*, 103, 122, 75).

"Then describe the attitudes and movements" (Anat. Ms. B, fol. 20 v): this is the most explicit formulation possible of another theme that was to have entered into Leonardo's work on the human figure; and it is repeated several times in other places, as in Ms. E, folio 46 recto, and *Anatomical*

Ms. A, folio 11 verso, where he says: "After the demonstration of all the parts of the limbs of man and of the other animals, you will represent the proper method of action of these limbs."

The enormous extent of the subject matter that would have gone into this book is shown by the list of all the problems referred to by Leonardo in his notes in this connection. This includes all the questions relating to the partial movements of the various joints (*Treatise*, 319; Quad. Anat. II, fol. 24 r; Cod. Ashb., II, fol. 9 v) and the factors of the various attitudes or postures, such as standing on both feet or on only one, or stepping up (*Treatise*, 291, 391, 307; Anat. Ms. B, fol. 21 v).

In the field of the general movements of the body we have, in addition to discussions of mimetic factors, descriptions of the mechanics of some actions, such as going up or down stairs (Ms. H, fol. 75 r; Anat. Ms. B, fol. 21 v), going up or down a ramp (Pl. v: Quad. Anat. VI, fol. 18 r [III]), walking, leaping, getting up from a sitting or kneeling position (*Treatise*, 303-305; Quad. Anat. I, fol. 13 r; Cod. Atl., fol. 297 b). In this connection Leonardo describes the successive partial movements, the nature of the laws of weight, and what displacements the various parts of the body undergo by virtue of these laws (*Treatise*, 316; Cod. Atl., fol. 349 b; Ms. E, fol. 15 r). All in all, he takes up the entire gamut of important movements, with all the static and dynamic factors that enter into them.

From this study it is an easy transition to the study of mimicry and expression (*Treatise*, 175). These are extremely important elements in pictorial composition; and to understand them precisely, the artist must resort not only to attentive observation but beyond that to a methodical process of accumulating sketches and notes taken on the spot (*ibid.*, 112, 189, 169). Here indeed the morphological datum is markedly subject to variations brought about by the pyschological factor in the subject under study and in the painter observing him (Cod. Atl., fol. 349 r, 345 b; *Treatise*, 141, 142). But mimicry and expression are not confined merely to the movements of the face, whose muscles are in point of fact distinguished by Leonardo according to their mimetic action (Anat. Ms. A, fol. 13 v), but extend to the entire body, and he considers the way in which the mimetic movements of the body are performed. Nor can this study be limited to man; it should be extended also to the various animals, comparing them with man where possible.

Left: Mimicry and nudes – Windsor, Royal Collection

Right: Studies of expression – Windsor, Royal Collection

Mimicry and movements – Windsor, Royal Collection, no. 12717

445

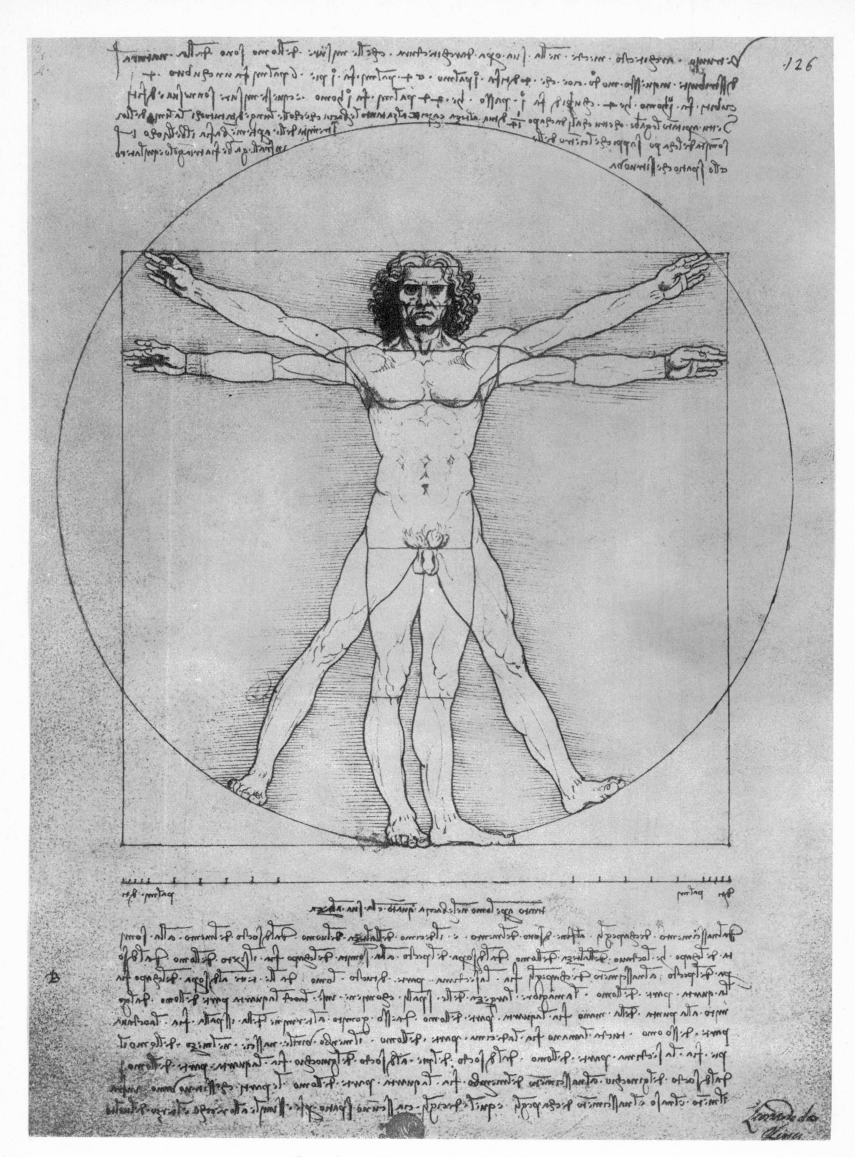

Canon of proportions – Venice, Academy of Fine Arts

446

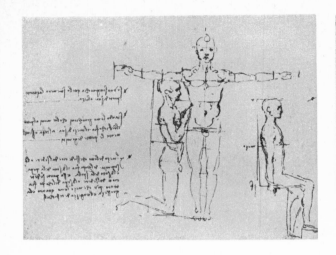

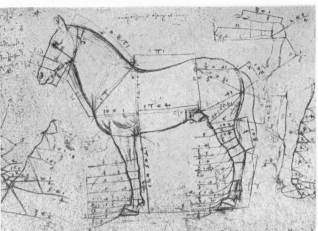

Left: Relationships and proportions
– Quad. Anat. VI, fol. 8 r

Right: Studies in proportions of horse
– Windsor, Royal Collection

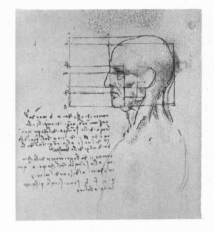

Relationships and proportions – Quad.
Anat. VI, fol. 1 r

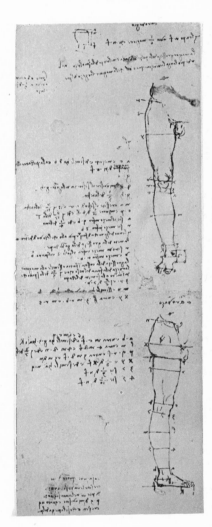

The numerous and diversified caricatures drawn by Leonardo are only experiments in representing expression, in which the exaggerated accentuation of a given single element had the purpose of isolating it in order to reveal its importance as a mimetic and expressive factor.

In all the foregoing books we have found frequent comparative references to animals. These references are not incidental but intentional. There are two notes that constitute indubitable evidence of this intention—one in Ms. K (fol. 109 v), where Leonardo says: "Here make a note to demonstrate the difference there is between man and the horse, and in the same way with other animals," the other in Quaderno V (fol. 22 r [v]): "Of how close the arrangement of the bones and muscles of animals is to the bones and muscles of man." I have already cited the plates of Quaderno V, folio 22 recto; I must also mention another plate of the Windsor collection, in which we see in close proximity similar expressions on a human face and on the muzzles of a horse and of a lion.

There are more studies of horses, of course, and this once again confirms the fact that Leonardo always began a study primarily with the goal of an artist in mind. But these studies are conducted with the same methodical procedure as those on man, and it is easy to distinguish the anatomical drawings of equine subjects from the drawings of horses made as preliminary studies for equestrian statues or pictorial compositions. This is true despite the one or two drawings which show us that Leonardo made genuine anatomical preparations of animals (Cod. K, fol. 102 r; Cod. G, fol. 11 r; Cod. K, fol. 109 v).

There is one final topic to deal with, that of ratios and proportions. The material on this subject left by Leonardo is surely copious, as regards both drawings and annotations. The data that we can read are, however, so contradictory that they cannot be used as a basis for setting up a Leonardian canon of proportions. Indeed, Leonardo himself cannot be said to have had any such purpose, if we correctly interprets his statement: "And even if you should wish to make your figures according to one and the same measure, know that one will not be distinguishable from the other, and this is not seen in nature." It was not a canon that he wished to set up, therefore; after measuring various subjects, he sought to establish their differential characteristics with respect to proportions. This would be the explanation of the study of the proportions of the so-called *trezzo* (perhaps "man of Trezzo") on folio 10 recto of Quaderno VI, or of the leg of the "Sicilian" mentioned in the Atlantic codex (fol. 291 v). He sets up various types in this way and leaves it to the artist to choose the "most graceful" type to take his measurements from (Cod. Atl., fol. 160 r [A]).

Relationships and proportions – Quad.
Anat. VI, fol. 11 v

When we have thus examined Leonardo's didactic work in the field of figure study, we tend spontaneously to inquire what use he himself made as an artist of all these ideas so carefully investigated and set forth in such detail. How does it happen that an artist who has such profound knowledge of the figure does not in his work (with the possible exception of the *St. Jerome*) exhibit his precise knowledge of anatomical details nor seek to display some sign of his deep wisdom? And yet each of his figures went through a detailed and accurate research on the score of structure and expression before he gave it its final form, and we see, in fact, that many figures in his paintings reproduce the poses of antecedent studies of the nude.

There is only one justification for these apparent contradictions, and it is a basic one. Leonardo, like anyone who has attained a high degree of wisdom, has learned that the supreme sign of sublimity in a creation is harmony; this is the end toward which he tends, as his supreme goal, in fusing lines and concepts, in molding the figurative expression to the spirit of the work—drawing on science for only so much as will give his work foundation and support, and not making anatomy an end in itself.

CARLO FELICE BIAGGI

447

Above: *Ornithogalum umbellatum.* — Below: *Euphorbia* – Windsor, Royal Collection, no. 12424

DA VINCI'S BOTANY

The Babylonians, Egyptians, and Greeks studied growing things only in so far as plants had some relationship to man and were useful or harmful to him. The first observations we have along these lines come from Aristotle, Theophrastus, and Dioscorides, but it cannot be said that any of them was a precursor in botany as the science of plant life is understood today.

In Pliny the Elder, in the first century A.D., we have the man who coordinated the canons of the doctrine of the ancient world, but his *Natural History* has no scientific value for us, even though it comprises sixteen books on botany. The reason lies not solely in the chaotic arrangement of this monumental work, which is not too uncommon for writings of that time, but also in the numberless errors to be found at every step in his material, which was uncritically compiled from earlier sources.

We must go forward many centuries to the Renaissance to find the first observers of the organography of plants. In this sense, Leonardo was the first, after a lapse of almost fifteen hundred years, to break with the system followed from the distant past, and to establish the primary scientific laws governing the organisms that constitute the world of growing things. No one before him had ever looked at matters in this way.

In the light of his times, Leonardo's work, in the texts that have come down to us, although fragmentary and feeble, inelegant in terminology and uneven in style, is still supreme for its intuitions and for its reflections, which express thoughts and conclusions of extraordinary scientific interest concerning the facts he has noted. His marvelous mind must have been the first to make fundamental observations in botany that are still accepted today, but that have been regarded as the discoveries of scientists who came long after him; however, Leonardo's priority is beyond dispute, and it is simple justice to establish it.

Leonardo's work on plants began to be known about ninety years ago, as the result of the efforts of Uzielli; [1] as exploration of his amazing manuscripts went forward, the splendor of his achievement became increasingly evident, and we can say with complete certainty that it is at least half a century ahead of that of Andreas Caesalpinus (1519-1603). The great botanist of Arezzo has hitherto been considered the founder of modern botany; his reputation was enhanced with the establishment of the botanical gardens that appeared in the sixteenth and seventeenth centuries, but precedence must be given to Leonardo da Vinci. Considered apart from the limitations of the time, Caesalpinus remains a mere describer of plants, a little superior to Pliny, while Da Vinci is the innovator and precursor in the interpretation of laws never before present to the mind of man. And since deep awareness of the necessity of truth culminates in art, Leonardo is led all the more naturally to the study of plants, as was the way of his approach in all the sciences. The study of landscape leads him to consider geological phenomena, about which he has very precise ideas, and within the silence of the countryside the world of growing things fascinates him and drives him to formulate the laws of form and development in plants. Thus the supreme artist arrives at pure science.

Inflorescence of *Liliacea* (*Asphodelus*?) – Cod. Atl., fol. 244 r-*a*

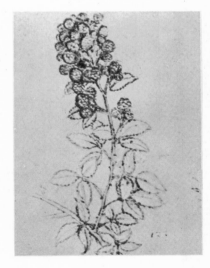

Leonardo da Vinci's drawing of cluster of fruit – Windsor, Royal Collection, no. 12420 v

---

[1] G. Uzielli, "Some Botanical Observations of Leonardo da Vinci," in *Nuovo giornale botanico italiano*, I, 1869.

Anemone nemorosa – Windsor, Royal Collection, no. 12423

Robinia (?) – Windsor, Royal Collection, no. 12431 v

As is the case in other fields, Leonardo's observations in botany do not constitute a scientific manual, but an autonomous fragmentary body of facts derived from rigorous use of the eye and the mind. A large part of this mass of observations is collected in Book VI of the *Treatise on Painting*, but much still remains to be brought together from the codices in which it is dispersed.

Leonardo's knowledge of botany goes back to his early youth and the sketches of plants he gathered for examination. His drawings even at the age of twenty are superb, of incomparable precision, softness, and elegance in every part. The minutely detailed, mist-touched representation of the leafing stalks of the Madonna lily (*Lilium candidum*), in the *Venus and Cupid* of the Uffizi is an initial essay that becomes masterful in the flowering stalks of the same plant shown in the Windsor drawing and appearing in a reduced form in the paintings of the Annunciations in the Louvre and at Florence.

From his twentieth year on, the most diversified species of plants and their parts fascinate Leonardo's mind (he does not know the cryptogams). His only interest is in depicting the chosen species whose charm he has felt in the open country, which is his infallible school. From the drawings of complete specimens he passes to representation of the forms of their organs and establishes the laws of their behavior and development, with reference to both their external characteristics and their internal structure. The organography was derived from the work of illustration; it was very minor in scope at first, but constantly expanded as a greater number of elements were mastered. The drawings of complete specimens made in his youth, from which he obtained his knowledge of the habit of various species chosen for artistic purposes at that time, were followed by splendid examples in which art is combined with scientific aims, depicting special organs (sepals, petals, stamens, pistils) and splendidly embodying the curiosity that drew him to present them as directly as a modern botanist would. In this way he analyzed the outstanding characteristics of various species (*Aquilegia, Pyrus, Viola, Euphorbia*, etc.).

In this work Da Vinci does not confine himself solely to conspicuous flowers, but comes down to the tiniest herbs and plants with the most modest external forms, including such aquatic growths as *Scirpus, Cyperus, Sparganium, Typha*, etc.

450

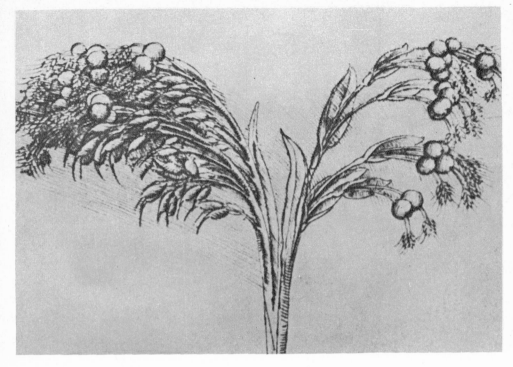

Tireless in his exploration of the tremendous range of vegetable life, he seems to have sensed the affinities that exist among certain species and to have sought to connect the elements of a single order (*Ranunculaceae, Rosaceae, Cyperaceae,* etc.), as well as to find the affinities among types of genera, as in the case of *Caltha* and *Anemone*. His unerring eye observes and divines these affinities as if to find a classification, something never thought of before.

Mespilus germanica – Cod. Atl., fol. 252 v-a

In addition to the drawing in the Academy at Venice depicting many flowers repetitively in various aspects of development and position (*Pyrus, Viola*), mention should be made of the "many flowers after nature" that he speaks of in the Codex Atlanticus; these are lost today but were undoubtedly drawn in his youth. All these added together constitute a considerable number of species, but there is more—a wonderful series of drawings in the royal collection at Windsor, the examples in the manuscripts, and finally the paintings; the *Virgin of the Rocks*, for example, offers a whole book of flora. Da Vinci had such a passion for plants that he not only drew them from life but collected species after species and kept them all in a separate room, together with animals and various sorts of natural curiosities that he found. This was certainly an inchoate museum of natural history, but it may be supposed that his desire was to have available as many species as possible, especially when the season did not allow him to find what he needed. This supposition leads us to suspect that Da Vinci came to depict some species of plants by impressing their forms on paper with lampblack, which in the case of leaves would also give him the venation. Although a contrary opinion is held by some, I believe that the desire of forming a herbarium had arisen in his mind; this can be inferred from the reference to the "*bello erbolaro*" that he saw in the Marliano house. Such a wish would have been only natural, for his school was all of creation, and he felt the infinite power of creation in all things. Plants had a prominent place in this, and from his early youth to his death they were one of his predominant passions. He began with enjoyment of the flowers of the fields while still an adolescent; and later, in the school of Verrocchio, his great teacher and his only one, his activity in botany blossomed out, for Verrocchio too was very fond of plants. Even in Leonardo's adolescence there was a struggle between art and science in his mind; in his desire to serve art he turned to nature and entered, without realizing it, into the sanctuary of science; and thus art and science merge into a single world.

From that time on Leonardo is like an eagle soaring to heights from which the uttermost horizons of human knowledge can be scanned. He has already left Verrocchio's school. His illustrations of plants have already reached a remarkable stage of perfection. Now he begins to study the arrangement of leaves on the stalk, in so many remarkable observations that they might be collected to form a veritable chapter on phyllotaxy, anticipating the development of science by a century and a half. The laws governing the unknown power present in the development of silent organisms in the wonderful harmony of the universe have been traced back to Brown (1658), Malpighi (1675), Grew (1682), and Bonnet (1754), and were accorded their due importance in the fundamental observations of Goethe on the identical origin of leaves and flower elements; [2] but priority in the great discovery belongs to Leonardo.

[2] Goethe, *Versuch die Metamorphose der Pflanzen zu erklären*, Gotha, 1790.

Salvia – Cod. Atl., fol. 72 v-a

Another important observation relates to the way in which the age of exogenous stems can be determined from their structure. In the discovery of this relationship too, of which the ancients were unaware, priority has been attributed to Malpighi and Grew, although, in any case, they were anticipated by Montaigne, who noted the fact as he passed through Pisa in 1581—having obtained it from a goldsmith of the city—in terms reminiscent of those used by Leonardo and possibly disseminated by Pacioli, Leonardo's friend, who was reader in mathematics at Pisa (1500-1505).[3] Likewise, it is to Leonardo and not to Malpighi that we must go for the first knowledge concerning the eccentricity of trunks.

Da Vinci accurately observed the way in which the bark of trees grows annually. As we know, the theory regarding this, presented at the same time by Malpighi and Grew independently of each other, was first stated by Leonardo.

There are interesting observations on the structure and development of plants, the symmetry of their secondary axes, the influence of external agents on them, and the action of poisons on plants. The discussions of ramification, the series of brilliant notes on heliotropism and geotropism, the cambium (which he calls *camicia*, or shirt), the arrangement of all types of buds in the axils of the leaves, the sexes of higher plants (which he hinted at if he did not completely understand), the structure of the ovaries, etc., are always lucid expositions (I have collected and illustrated them in a special volume); they show not so much preparation (which is out of the question, since Da Vinci had no predecessors, but was himself the creator), as intuition, perception, the characteristic ability of genius to understand things previously unintelligible to the human mind.

After laying down the foundations of a theory of the organs, Da Vinci also succeeds in formulating biological, ecological, phytogeographical, and physiological observations that, despite their rudimentary character, manifest an evident effort to account for the system that underlies the organs.

The exposition in all these matters takes the form of notes. The style is always involved and sometimes so complicated that it is very hard to interpret. It is astonishing how a man who had never studied language was able to cope with absolutely new themes of such depth and scope, even though his phraseology is sometimes such as to defy the interpreter. The notes always afford complete and obvious proof that the conclusions set forth are the result of direct observation of facts, and never fanciful or merely empirical. Leonardo wants to account for every fact, and he repeats

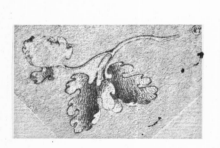

[3] *Journal du voyage de Michel Montaigne en Italie*, Rome and Paris, 1774, III, 205. Cf. Uzielli, *op. cit.*, p. 10.

452

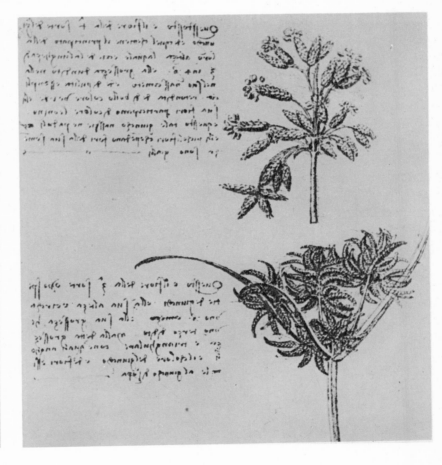

Above, left: *Lilium candidum* – Windsor, Royal Collection, no. 12418. — Above, right: *Rubus idaeus* [?] – Windsor, Royal Collection, no. 12419. — Below, left: *Genista tinctoria* – Windsor, Royal Collection, no. 12422. — Below, right: *Scirpus lacustris* (above) – *Cyperus monti* (below) – Windsor, Royal Collection, no. 12427

Rubus fructicosus – Windsor, Royal Collection, no. 12426

Typha latifolia – Windsor, Royal Collection, no. 12430 v

Sparganium erectum – Windsor, Royal Collection, no. 12430 r

Fruiting branch of *Morus nigra* – Cod. Atl., fol. 264 r-*b*

and checks and compares; in the torrent of all the things he takes up and notes, he often forgets whether an observation has already been recorded, and his manuscripts will show parallel notes, sometimes to the extent of dozens of instances, that had been put down many years before in different words. His mind in observation is like that of a modern scientist, but his eye is infallible: it always hits its mark. His lynx eye never leads his mind astray into conjectures or hypotheses that lack the sure verification of genius in the form of facts seen and noted in many detailed investigations under the control of rigorous positive thought. He is the undaunted and original precursor, who never loses complete confidence in himself; he always holds to the experimental method as his absolute guide in every subject he touches. When we consider the difference of centuries between us and the means at his disposal, we can only recognize this self-taught profound innovator as incomparable. The "child of love" remains not only one of the greatest artists of the Renaissance; he is at the same time the thinker who was able to harmonize the powers of analysis with the powers of synthesis, and thus to range through the most varied fields of human knowledge. For us botanists too he is supreme.

Applied botany is the second part of Leonardo's botanical work. It forms the converse of the first portion, and constitutes a rich and diversified receipt book comprising all the divisions of the applied botany of his time—medical botany, artistic botany, horticultural botany, and industrial botany. The section on medical botany is the one offering the smallest number of data. His artistic botany deals with the preparation of panels for paintings and of oils and colors; the horticultural botany gives counsel on the construction of gardens. The most developed aspect is that of industrial botany; it takes up the vegetable ingredients to be employed in instruments of war, fireworks, deodorants, or evil-smelling substances, in the performance of various tasks in the open with special woods, and in the manufacture of glass ornaments, especially the *mistioni* that were so popular in the Middle Ages.

To conclude this brief survey of Da Vinci's botany, we should not overlook the way in which plants abound in the matchless fables and allegories in which the immortal Florentine glorified them as protagonists.

All in all, Leonardo was the first to bridge, in those distant times, the previously insuperable chasms that had barred the way to the great miracle of modern thought. He glimpsed in the archives of our planet all that it bore on its surface and in its bowels, pointing out there the outcome of his study of sedimentary and organic deposits: "What was once the bottom of the sea has become the top of the mountains." He approaches plants with the same experimental method that has always guided him in all the sciences he has cultivated. Here too he calls a halt when it seems to him that natural explanations are wanting and the ground feels uncertain under his feet; but he never despairs of success and trusts in his infallible method, leaving it to time and conditions to make the explanations attainable.

His formidable encyclopedic intellect goes far beyond even the principles of Bacon. In botany too, therefore, he leaves antiquity behind and entrusts himself to experience, which to him is the only unfailing means of interpreting the causes of things, and the only condition under which knowledge can be reached. In every field he worked in, and therefore in the world of plants as well, he sought to introduce the precision and certainty of the mathematical sciences.

ANTONIO BALDACCI

454

DA VINCI'S GEOLOGY AND GEOGRAPHY

Of all the various and varied aspects of Leonardo's genius, not the least important is his work in geology, cosmography, and geography. This is natural. Being a deep and keen observer and investigator of all natural phenomena, and devoting a part of his many-sided and laborious life to the art that in modern terminology might be called hydraulic engineering, he often had to deal with the earth in cutting roads and canals and in carrying out various projects involving water; and he also had roamed the hills of Tuscany, observing the many fossils (*nichi*, "shells") to be found there. This enabled him, free as he was of Aristotelian or other preconceived ideas, to discover by dint of his unaided intelligence many important geological truths till then masked by false ideas, and to rise to lofty cosmographic ideas on the one hand and come down to precise geographic and cartographic drawings on the other.

The importance that Leonardo attached to geology is clearly indicated by his saying, "The knowledge of past times and of the places on the earth is both ornament and nutriment to the human mind" (Cod. Atl., fol. 373 v-*a*). In the few summary pages that follow I shall try to let Leonardo's ideas on various geological topics emerge from his own words, which I feel should give his thoughts more clarity and force.

It should be pointed out first of all that Leonardo, although he lived in a time of preponderant geocentrism (Galileo later knew something on this subject), held "that the earth is a star" (Cod. Atl., fol. 112 v)—in other words, a star "much like the moon" (Ms. F, fol. 56 r)—and that it "is not in the center of the circle of the sun, nor in the center of the universe... And if one were to be upon the moon... this earth of ours with the element of the water would appear to him in the same relationship as the moon has to us" (Ms. F, fol. 41 v).

As for the "roundness of the earth," which he postulated in the Codex Trivulzianus (fol. 29), at a time when it was not yet accepted by everyone, he proves it by pointing out in his *Treatise on Painting* "what is the true position of the horizon," adducing the experimental demonstration that the higher an observer near the sea climbs, the more his horizon expands; and he gives other proofs based on the curvature of the sea (Ms. F, fol. 52 v) and the fact "that the watery sphere is everywhere perfectly round" (Ms. F, fol. 82 v), also combatting the idea prevalent at that time that there are great differences of level among the oceans.

Thus, although Leonardo lived in a period when the Aristotelian-Ptolemaic view of the universe was still dominant, his ideas were sound in the main. Although he considered the sun as immobile, he spoke in clear terms of the diurnal rotation of the earth about its own axis, pointing out that "the days do not begin at the same time throughout the universe, so that when it is noon in our hemisphere, it is midnight in the opposite hemisphere" (Ms. Leices., fol. 6 v); and he supported the same idea in discussing "the heavy substance descending through the air, the elements that revolve making their entire revolution in twenty-four hours" (Ms. G, fol. 55 r).

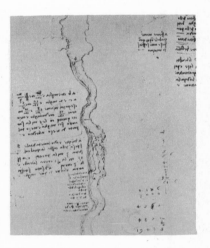

Topographic map of stretch of river Adda from Molino di Brivio to mill of Travaglia – Cod. Atl., fol. 335 r-*a*

River basin   Windsor, no. 12676

455

Tempest over Alpine village – Windsor, Royal Collection, no. 12409

As regards the size of the earth, "considering the size of 7000 miles that the earth has (Cod. Leices., fol. 35 v), that is, a diameter (in Milan units) of about 12,500,000 meters, Leonardo is not far from the figure now taken as closest to the truth (a little more than 12,700,000 m.).

With respect to the method of accounting for terrestrial phenomena, Leonardo was what could be called a neptunian geologist, as was natural because of the environment in which he lived and the nature of his studies; that is, he reasonably gave greatest importance to the influence of water, in all its forms and positions, on the life of the earth, and all the more so in view of his tendency to set up an analogy between the earth and the human body. This comparison may be valid in some respects, but in other ways it is overdrawn or even mistaken.

Leonardo states this analogy paralleling the organism of the earth with the human organism in Ms. A, folio 55 verso, and returns elsewhere to the same conception, writing: "So that we might say that the earth has a spirit of growth; that its flesh is the soil, its bones the arrangement and connection of the rocks of which the mountains are composed, its cartilage the tufa, and its blood the springs of water. The pool of blood which lies around the heart is the ocean, and its breathing, and the increase and decrease of the blood in the pulses, is represented in the earth by the flow and ebb of the sea; and the heat of the spirit of the world is the fire which pervades the earth, and the seat of the vegetative soul is in the fires, which in many parts of the earth find vent in baths and mines of sulphur, and in volcanoes" (Cod. Leices., fol. 34 r).

Leonardo had a clear idea of the circulation of the earth's waters, regarding which the ideas then current were so strange and mistaken. After various arguments he writes, "Whence we may conclude that the water goes from the rivers to the sea, and from the sea to the rivers, thus constantly circulating and returning" (Ms. A, fol. 56 v).

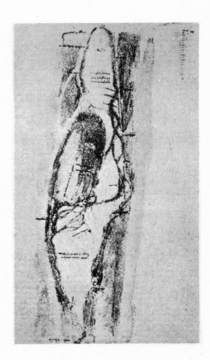

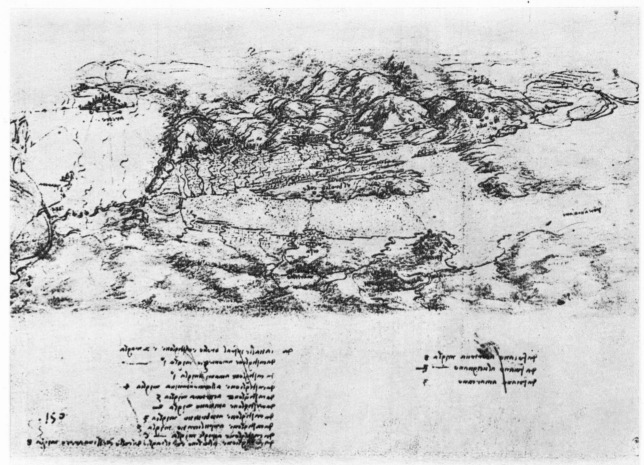

Plain of river Arno and Val di Chiana
– Windsor, Royal Collection, no. 12682

Snow-covered mountain chain – Windsor, Royal Collection, no. 12410

458

Bird's-eye view of Tuscany – Windsor,
Royal Collection, no. 12683

Mountain chain – Windsor, Royal Collection, no. 12414

459

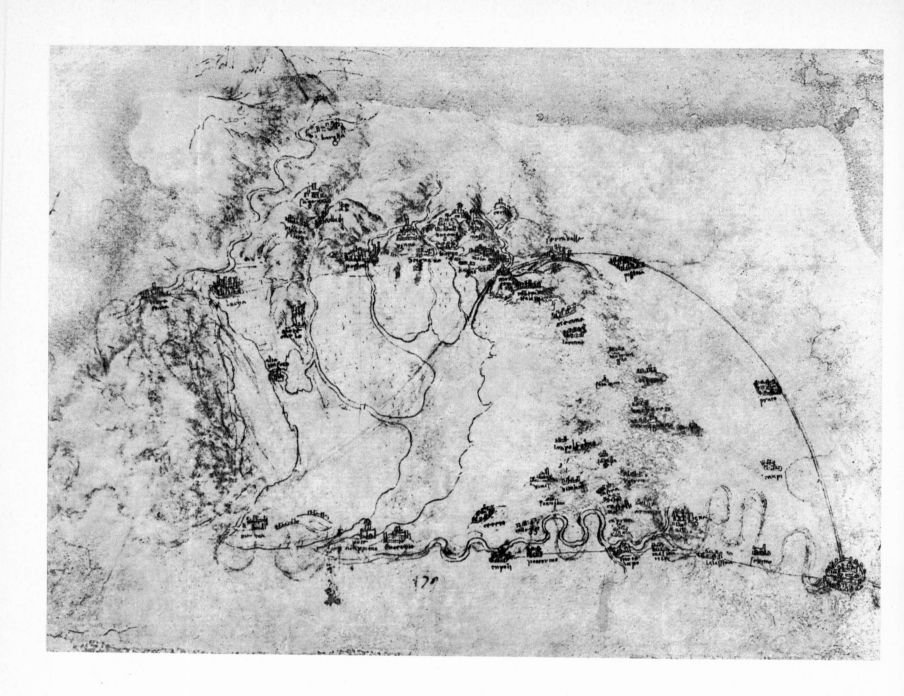

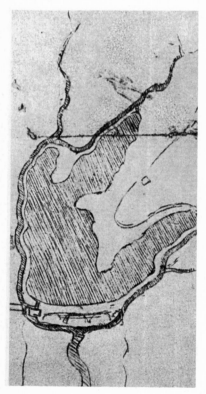

Valley of river Arno – Windsor, Royal
Collection, no. 12685

Drawing of river basin forming lake
– Windsor, Royal Collection, number
12675 r

Starting with the atmosphere, Leonardo speaks at length and quite correctly "of the consumption or evaporation of the water of the Mediterranean Sea," which he describes as "a vast river interposed between Africa, Asia, and Europe [which] gathers within itself three hundred rivers" (Cod. Atl., fol. 263 v-*b*).

Leonardo dealt with the atmosphere in many of his writings (Ms. E, fol. 47; Ms. F, fol. 61; Ms. I, fol. 69; Ms. G, fol. 10; Cod. Atl., fol. 169, 171, 212) and invented an anemometer "to know better the direction of the winds" (Ms. H, 100 r). He attributed great importance to the air currents and the deposits made by the wind, forming the dunes, so that he says, "Describe the mountains of shifting deserts; that is to say, the formation of waves of sand borne by the wind, and of its mountains and hills, such as occur in Libya" (Ms. F, fol. 61 r).

On the subject of atmospheric precipitation Leonardo wrote a "Book of Rains," in which he discussed at length and with wisdom (and it would be desirable to cite the numerous pages in full, because of their interest) the clouds "which are mists drawn up by the heat of the sun, and their ascension [ceases] at the point at which the weight they have acquired becomes equal in power to its motor power" (*Treatise*, II, par. 926, p. 320). Again, he writes: "The clouds are formed by the humidity pervading the air; this collects because of the cold, which is brought by the air with various winds" (*ibid.*, par. 928, p. 322). He repeats the idea on folio 162 recto-*a* of the Codex Atlanticus, speaking of the rain "that is produced by the accumulation of moist vapor" until it falls as rain.

In order to have better and more accurate knowledge of such phenomena he invented and gave a drawing of a special instrument, today called a hygrometer (Cod. Atl., fol. 241, 242), "to know the qualities and thicknesses of the air, and when it is going to rain."

Here mention should be made of that wonderful drawing of Leonardo's which might be defined as a very effective meteorologic diagram, since it shows us an interesting meteorologic phenomenon,

460

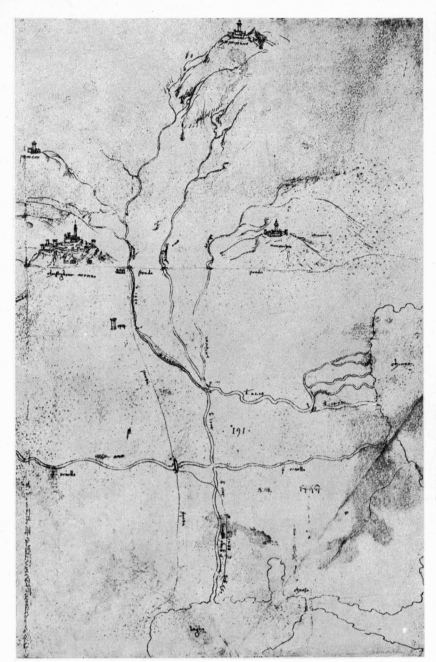

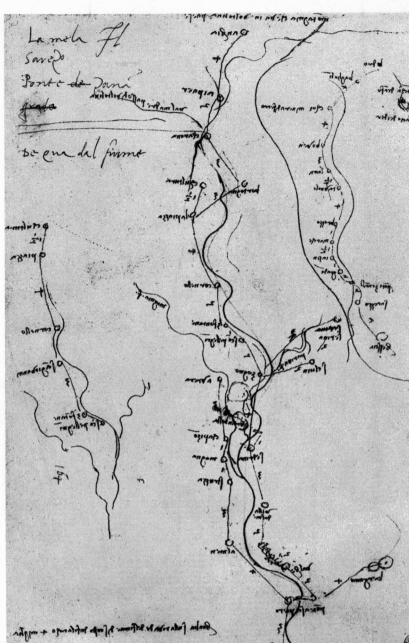

Left: Geographical map of region of
Arezzo – Cod. Atl., fol. 336 r

Right: Val Brembana and Val Trompia – Windsor, Royal Collection, no.
12673 r

certainly taken from life.[1]   It depicts the clouds heavy with water vapor, at about 2000 meters, changing partially into rain falling on the plain, while higher up, at about 3000 meters, Monte Rosa appears in bright sunlight.   Leonardo alludes to this when he says, "And I saw the sky above me quite dark and the sun as it fell on the mountain was far brighter there than in the plains below" (Cod. Leices., fol. 4 r).

Leonardo saw and described very well (see, in particular, Cod. Atl., fol. 160 v) the extremely important role of torrential rains in eroding and removing material, thereby forming the relief of the earth.   He says, for example, that "mountains are destroyed by rains and rivers," and remarks correctly, as has only recently been realized, that "a larger quantity of water descends from the middle of the mountain to its base than from the summit of the same mountain to the said middle" (Cod. Atl., fol. 160 v), and that "those mountains are more enduring and more permanent in their heights that are covered with snow throughout the winter," etc.

Leonardo was very much interested in the transformation or evolution of the surface of the earth (Cod. Atl., fol. 71, 126, etc.;   Ms. Leices., fol. 20), and gave great importance to "time, the consumer of things" (Cod. Atl., fol. 71) and "destroyer of created things" (Ms. B, fol. 156).

Consequently, Leonardo was able to rise to paleogeographic visions, as when he explained how "the summits of the Apennines stood up out of this sea like islands, surrounded by the salt waters. Africa again, behind its Atlas Mountains, did not expose uncovered to the sky the surface of its vast plains about 3000 miles in length, and Memphis was on the shores of this sea, and above the

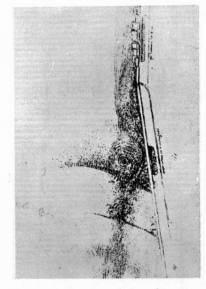

Proposed diversion of river Arno near
Florence – Windsor, Royal Collection,
no. 12680

---

[1] Although Leonardo (Cod. Leices., fol. 9) speaks of Momboso, which has led some to believe that he climbed Monte Rosa (which I cannot by any means believe), this scene was taken from some region in the foothills of the Alps. See F. Sacco, *Le Alpi*, p. 145, fig. 210.

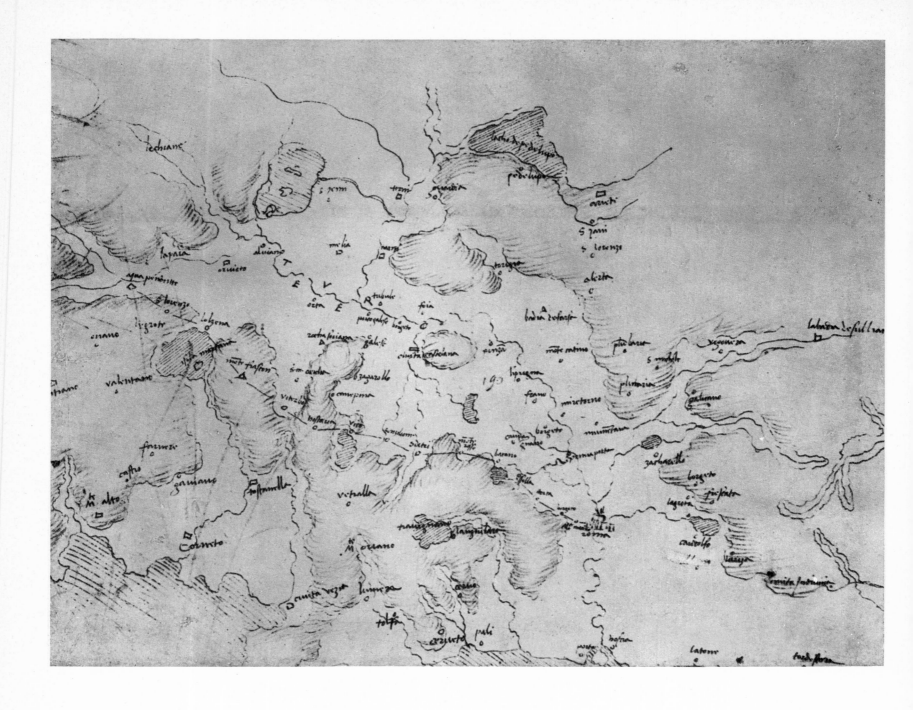

Geographical map of Latium – Cod.
Atl., fol. 336 v-*a*

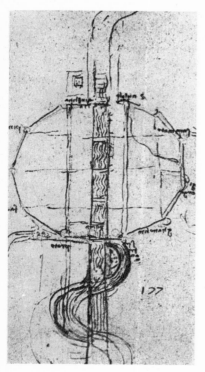

Topographic plan of Florence traversed
by river Arno – Windsor, Royal Collection, no. 12681

plains of Italy, where now birds fly in flocks, fish were wont to roam in large shoals" (Ms. Leices., fol. 10 v).

In like manner he explains how the great plain of the Po was formed, and "how within a short time the river Po will cause the Adriatic Sea to dry up in the same way as it has dried up a great part of Lombardy" (Cod. Leices., fol. 27 v), and then "how the rivers fill the sea and force it from its place" (Cod. Atl., fol. 74). Thus he prophesies the silting up of the Mediterranean, "wich will have an outlet through the Strait of Gibraltar" (Cod. Atl., fol. 84), so that the earth "will become spherical and entirely covered with water and will be uninhabitable" (Ms. F, fol. 52).

Finally, Leonardo winds up with the terrible prophecy that as the waters gradually sink deeper into the crust of the earth, it "will be abandoned and remain dry and sterile... Then its surface will remain burnt ashes, and this will be the end of terrestrial nature" (Ms. B, fol. 155 [?]).

These cogitations of Leonardo's even contain hints of the doctrine of isostasy. In speaking of the erosion, transportation, and deposition of materials by water, with the resultant tendency toward equilibrium and displacement of the center of gravity of the globe, he discusses "the earth that is constantly taken from the slopes or sides of the mountains and carried to the seas, and the more it takes from there the lighter it makes that place, and hence the heavier it makes the place to which it is delivered by the waves of the sea, from which it follows necessarily that the said center must change its place" (Ms. L, fol. 13). He develops the same idea in speaking "of the sea, which changes the weight of the earth" (Ms. E, fol. 4).

As for underground waters, "the blood of the earth," as he calls them, the ideas prevailing at that time were the incorrect views of Pliny, but Leonardo, after some hesitations, adopted the correct position of Vitruvius, saying that "the water of rivers comes not from the sea but from the clouds" (Cod. Atl., fol. 160).

462

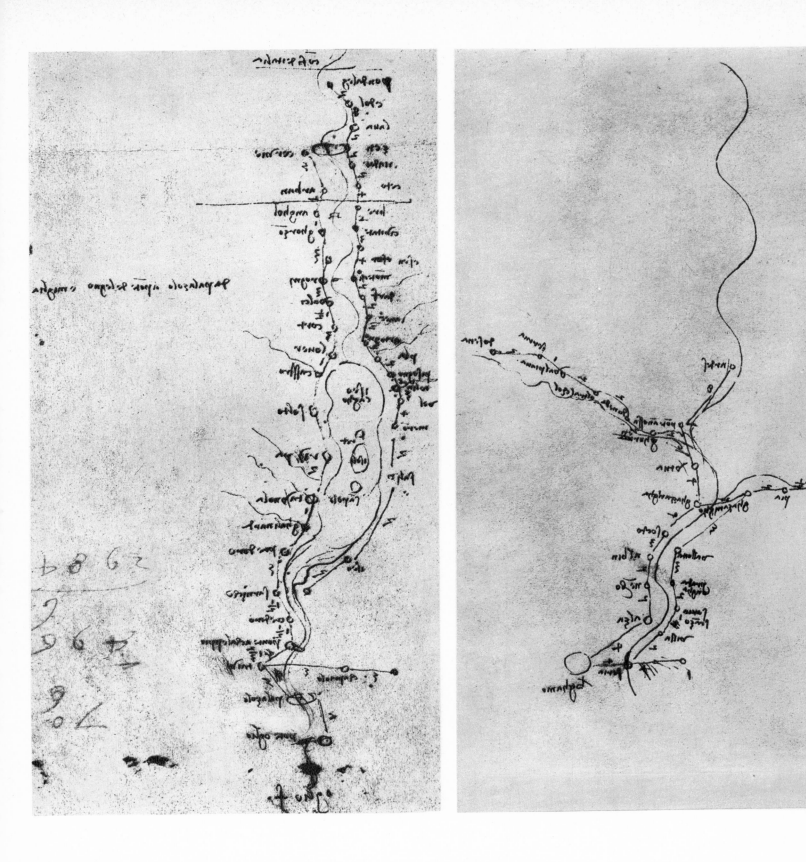

But when we come to the topic of surface water we are in the profound and vast science of hydraulics, in which Leonardo has absolute priority both in the theoretical aspect and in practice, where he presents the most varied and brilliant inventions. On this subject he intended to write a veritable treatise after having written "On the Motion and Measurement of Waters"; but he did not have time to write the treatise, although it might be constructed by collecting and setting in due order all of his deliberations, ideas, experiments, proposals, inventions, etc. Indeed, Leonardo had already outlined the book in his "Beginning of the Treatise on Water" (Ms. A, fol. 55 v), with the following "Divisions of the book: Of water in itself, of the sea, of subterranean streams, of rivers, of the nature of the depths, of obstacles, of gravels, of the surface of the water, of the things moved therein, of the repairing of rivers, of conduits, of canals, of machines turned by water, of raising water, of matter worn away by water" (Cod. Leices., fol. 15 v).

Thus, to cite an example, Leonardo describes the phenomenon that, as regards water in its normal course, "that portion is swifter which is nearest the surface; and this occurs because the water that is uppermost is contiguous to the air, which offers but little resistance because of its being lighter than the water; and the water that is below is contiguous to the earth, which offers great resistance" (Cod. Atl., fol. 153 r-a). He also notes that "rivers that are straight run with a much greater impetus

Bird's-eye view of province of Arezzo – Windsor, Royal Collection, no. 12278

Watercourse of northern Italy – Windsor, Royal Collection, no. 12277

in the center of their width than they do at their edges" (Ms. I, fol. 106; Ms. H, fol. 84). Further, "the sharp bends in the embankments of rivers are destroyed in great floods because the force of the current drives the water in a straight course; but as this diminishes, it resumes its winding, course" (Cod. Atl., fol. 185 r-*b*). Then, still in simple and incisive language, he discusses the transportation of alluvial materials, their rounding, comminution, deposition, etc. (see Cod. Atl., fol. 160), and naturally speaks in this connection of various practical corrective measures, such as "eliminating swamps by having flood waters bring earth down to them, etc." (Cod. Atl., fol. 74; Ms. F, fol. 14, etc.). But here we are invading the field of hydraulics, and hence shall go no further.

Of great importance are Leonardo's studies on the movements of the sea, collected in the book "On the Motion and Measurement of Water" (Bk. III, chap. VIII, XXXI). He concludes (Cod. Atl., fol. 84) that "a wave is a reflected impression of percussion... The May wind moves like a wave in the grain, and the wave is seen to travel over the field, and the stalks of grain do not move from their place" ("On the Motion," etc., Bk. III, chap. III), setting forth a brilliant theory of wave motion (Ms. A, fol. 9, 61, etc.).

But Leonardo goes astray in describing the ebb and flow of the tide, being misled by the idea of the "breathing of this terrestrial machine" (Ms. Leices., fol. 17, 35, etc.) relating the phenomenon to a lung of the earth; and yet he had made accurate researches on the tides.

We proceed with a brief reference to Leonardo's ideas on stratigraphy, the origin of relief features, etc. Like the neptunist that he was, for whom "water is nature's carter" (Ms. K, fol. 2 r), he assumes that all land is of sedimentary origin and correctly observes that mountains are composed of strata; as he puts it, "mountains are made up of folds... or of layers, according to the deposition of the detritus carried down by the current of rivers," adding that "there are no mountains where there has been no sea or lake" (Cod. Atl., fol. 160) and that "mountains are formed in the great

464

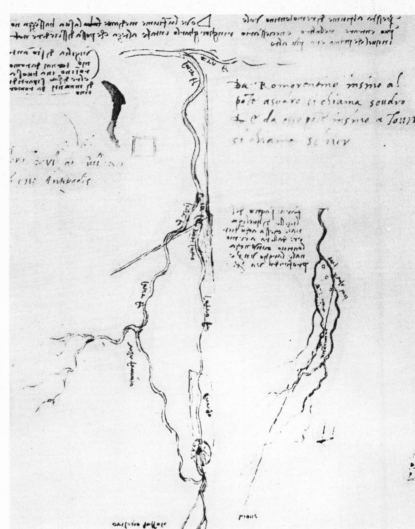

depths of the seas" ("Of the Nature, Motion, and Weight of Waters," fol. 134). His sharp eye could have observed some examples of these "folded mountains" in the formations, especially the Eocene, of the Tuscan Apennines, preceding Steno's observations by virtually two centuries.

Leonardo says that "mountains are made by the currents of rivers; mountains are destroyed by rains and rivers" (Cod. Atl., fol. 160 v); this applies to what are called negative reliefs and to the fact that the formations (especially valley forms) are due to erosion by water, as in Leonardo's time there could be no idea of mountain formation from endogenous causes.

However, Leonardo observed the corrugations of the strata, since he says that "in every hollow of the summits of mountains there are always found the bends of the folds of stone" (Ms. B, fol. 30). He attempted to explain by reference to gigantic collapses "of the earth into itself," that is, into enormous hollows inside the earth, as he shows by a drawing (Cod. Leices., fol. 36); for he thought, correctly, that "caverns are made by currents of subterranean water" (Cod. Atl., fol. 172).

It is a fact of the utmost importance that at a time when the question of the origin of fossils was disposed of by use of such meaningless terms as *lusus naturae, vis plastica lapidificata, vis vegetativa*, etc., or when they were accounted for as having been deposited by the universal deluge, Leonardo, on the basis of his penetrating observations, especially those made in Tuscany and Lombardy, resolutely opposed ideas of this kind (Cod. Atl., fol. 155). After asking, "Why are the bones of large fish and oysters, and corals and other shells and mollusks, found on the high summits of mountains" (Cod. Atl., fol. 20), he answers "that the fossils were not carried to a height of a thousand ells by the Flood," explaining why (Cod. Leices., fol. 3, 8, 9, 10), and recalling "the fossils of Monte Mario" (Cod. Atl., fol. 92) and "in the mountains of Parma and Piacenza, the multitude of fossils and corals... among which a good number were preserved in their original condition" (Cod. Leices., fol. 9). He adds an important fact that must have been very significant for him—that "in the mountains of Verona, their red stone is found all mixed with shells converted into that stone" (*ibid.*, fol. 9).

Elsewhere Leonardo observes that "the conches, oysters, and other similar animals that are born in the sea oozes are witnesses to us of the changing of the earth... These depths are now so high that they have become hills, or high mountains, and the rivers that wear away the sides of those mountains lay bare the layers of these fossils" (Ms. E, fol. 4).

Left: Navigation canal between Lago di Lecco and river Lambro – Cod. Atl., fol. 275 r-*a*

Right: Project for merging channels of river Loire – Cod. Atl., fol. 336 v-*b*

Volcanic crater – Windsor, Royal Collection, no. 12388

Course of river with dividing canal –
Windsor, Royal Collection, no. 12398

Furthermore, in obvious reference to the fossil tracks that often appear in the faces of strata, he observes acutely "how in the folds, between the one and the other, there are still found the tracks of earthworms that made their way between them when they were not yet dry" (Cod. Leices., fol. 10).

Finally, it should be pointed out that Leonardo, following his profound observations of the facts such as the example referred to above of the fossils embedded in the calcareous Veronese rock, writes further "that the fossils of Lombardy have four levels, and likewise all those that have been made in several stages" (Cod. Leices., fol. 36). This leads us to think that Leonardo anticipated Arduino by three centuries and saw four different great fossiliferous planes, which later came to be explained as geological epochs.

The preceding pages, restricted as they are to mere hints, because of the limited space available to me, but so far as possible giving the words of Da Vinci himself, show clearly that he was a keen-visioned precursor in the various branches of geology in the broad sense, from cosmography to meteorology, hydrology, stratigraphy, and paleontology, with a broad view of geological evolution.

Leonardo was superb as geographer and cartographer as well, coupling artistic genius with geometrical precision. This is true whether he is giving views of an entire region—of which we have beautiful examples in the drawings for central and southern Tuscany (Windsor, no. 12278) and coastal Tuscany (Windsor, no. 12683) and in the admirable plan of Imola (Windsor, no. 12284)—or indicating the evolution of certain valleys or particular watercourses, as in the topographic maps of Val Trompia and Val Brembana (Windsor, no. 12673), of Valle dell'Oglio and Val Seriana (Windsor, no. 12674), of a stretch of the Adda from Molino di Brivio to the mill of Travaglia (Cod. Atl., fol. 335 r-a) and in so many other instances in the Codex Atlanticus, as on folios 334, 336 (Castiglione Aretino-Monterchi), folio 346 (San Piero), etc.

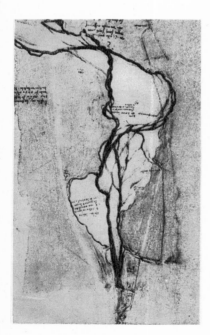

Arno and Mugnone rivers west of
Florence – Windsor, Royal Collection
no. 12678

Most of these maps were to be used in connection with hydraulic projects, as for example the maps of the course of the Arno (Windsor, no. 12678) and of the canalization of the Arno (Windsor, no. 12679), and of the navigation canal between the Lambro and the Lago di Lecco (Cod. Atl., fol. 275 r-a); we should also mention the fine map concerning the drainage of the Pontine marshes (Windsor, no. 12684), etc.

These interesting experiments in cartography are often practical examples of Leonardo's precept, "When you write of the motions of water, remember to put under each proposition its uses, that this science may not be useless" (Ms. F, fol. 2).

FEDERICO SACCO

HYDRAULIC AND NAUTICAL ENGINEERING

When we have spoken of the work of a great man and listed and described his achievements, both those things that have changed the form of the matter he deals with and so been transmitted to posterity and the more numerous ones that have remained only projects or even mere hints, we have not therewith completed our task. We must fit the man's work into the framework of its time, inquiring how much of its content had been handed down by predecessors and was common knowledge at the time, and finding out the new ideas and original themes were from which his contemporaries and later generations profited. It is always hard to determine the contribution of an individual in this way, when dealing with an epoch as distant in time as that in which Leonardo lived. It is especially difficult with respect to activity in hydraulic engineering, since no text has come down to us that tells us the extent of technical and practical knowledge in the period, and no treatise on applied hydraulics was written until some time afterward, in fact not until the development of mathematical analysis in the eighteenth century furnished the basis for working out the solutions to problems in this field. All that remains of the attainments of that period are the works themselves, and they are almost always anonymous. Accordingly, we can only infer what Leonardo could have learned if he had had available to him all of the technological resources accumulated by humanity up to that time. We shall never know how much he was able to learn from others as compared with what observation suggested and his prodigious mind worked out.

Leonardo was a son of the Tuscan land, sprung from a stock of builders of waterworks who were the teachers of the Romans and masters of an incomparable technique that they had brought with them from the Minoan east. He obtained the first elements of his knowledge of hydraulics from seeing the physical phenomena, as if by a sort of atavistic heritage. For there was no tradition of waterworks in Tuscany during his youth, and since the collapse of the central power of Rome in the fifth century no work of any importance had been done in this field. Elsewhere new projects had been started, and the attempts, failures, and recommencings were giving form to a new body of experience, but this was all unknown in the milieu frequented by the young man. In northern Italy, in the region of the Lombard lakes, *comacini* [builders from Como] and *campionesi* [builders from Campione d'Italia] had revived the knowledge of some of the basic rules of the statics of structures and built up a school which handed down the craft from master to apprentice, perfecting it in day-to-day work. Out of the workshops between the Dora Baltea and the Laguna arose a second school, likewise formed of many nameless workers who forged the basis of the new science in constant contact with practical difficulties. It is here that Leonardo was to become the first and boldest of hydraulic planners.

The art was in full flower there. Many great works had been completed, and much solid and often sorrowful experience had been accumulated. Under the Julian emperors irrigation was in current use, as would appear from the verse of Virgil, *Claudite jam rivos pueri: sat prata biberunt* ("Dam up the brooklets, slaves; the meadows have drunk enough"), which speaks of the operation of gates and sluices, an essential element of any canal. This technique, perfected under the empire, certainly cannot have been lost during the barbarian invasions and migrations. It was preserved in the region north of the Po and west of Mantua, which, because of its fertility, was chosen to be the

Study of liquid filaments of jets discharging from orifice – Ms. F, fol. 47 v

467

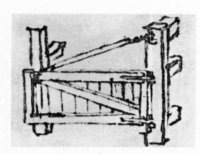

Lock gate – Cod. Atl., fol. 7 v-b

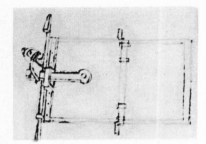

Lock gate – Cod. Atl., fol. 214 v-d

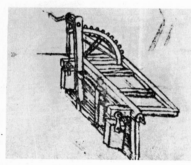

Disappearing lock gate – Cod. Atl.,
fol. 7 v-b

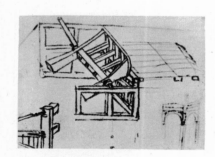

Disappearing lock gate – Cod. Atl.,
fol. 7 v-b

center of the rule of one of the invading peoples; ordinances regulated irrigation carefully. None of the Roman nomenclature has come down to us, but the expression *piede liprando* or *aliprando* is of Lombard origin, and is still used today to indicate the width of the canal at water level, to be kept free of encumbrance under any circumstances. Such terms as *diversivi* [diversion channels], *scoli* [drainage channels], *bocchelli* [outlet valves], *ponti-canale* [canals carried on aqueducts), *tombe* [siphons], and *botti* [culverts] must go back to a technology of ancient origin, to a time much earlier than the twelfth century, the era of the first works that have come down to us. These works present a structural technique that reflects full confidence on the part of its practitioners in their capacity to formulate and solve the most intricate problems. In other words, it was an adult science that had not succumbed to barbarism to such a point that it had painfully to win back forgotten laws and systems, as was the case with other branches of technology, such as building construction in general and the science of arches in particular.

The Po valley had thus been the scene of large-scale hydraulic engineering centuries before Leonardo came there; indeed, huge projects of this kind had been carried to completion. At the height of the struggles between the communes and the emperor, hardly two years after the battle of Legnano, the great canal named the Ticinello, intended at first for irrigation, was begun. It started at the bridge of Tornavento over the Ticino, led to Castelletto di Abbiategrasso, dividing there into two branches, one going to Pavia and the other, which only later received the name of Naviglio Grande [Grand Canal], to Milan. Works of this kind may have been attempted previously without success, and such beginnings are to be seen in the form of old driven piles and submerged gabions; and throughout the thirteenth century the name of Naviglio Vecchio [Old Canal], or Cavo [Canal] del Panperduto, keeps cropping up. How long it took before the work was complete can be seen from the fact that in 1272 an ordinance of the Council of Eight Hundred under Napo Torriani prescribed as the chief project of every succeeding *podestà* the prolongation of the "Naviglio di Gaggiano" up to the city, to facilitate use of its waterway; the canal had indeed been linked up with the inner moat and the *Redefossi* by an overflow channel that discharged into the Vetrabbia at Sant'Apollinare, but was evidently of too small section to permit the passage of canal boats.

This was the largest member of the Lombard system of canals, but not the only one. Water was taken from the Adda by means of the Muzza, an old trench dating from the beginning of the twelfth century and belonging to the Ospedale del Broglio near Santo Stefano in Milan; it at first intended to serve for collecting the surface waters of the region of Lavagna, Muzzano, Zelobuonpersico, Mulinazzo, Mignate, and Villa Pompeiana, and then enlarged and extended as far as Monte di Cassano, below Vaprio, where, about 1220, works for drawing the water from the stream were constructed. From the Adda likewise—under Francesco Sforza and in the short period of only thirteen years—the Martesana was led off near Brivio, and in 1457, under Bertola da Novate, the Bereguardo canal was begun.

In the second half of the fifteenth century there was a burst of hydraulic works all over upper Italy. In Piedmont, at the initiative of Yolande of France, the widow of Amedeo IX, the Naviglio d'Ivrea was carried toward completion, the greatest difficulties apparently being overcome in 1468, while its completion, under the superintendence of Bianca of Montferrat, between 1485 and 1499, came during Da Vinci's stay in Lombardy. This is a work of the greatest importance, seventy-two kilometers long from the point where it taps the Dora Baltea, immediately under the walls of Ivrea, to where it discharges at Vercelli. Together with other smaller works, it formed a network of canals taking the waters of the Ticino and the Sesia: the Roggia Gattinara, opened by the marquesses

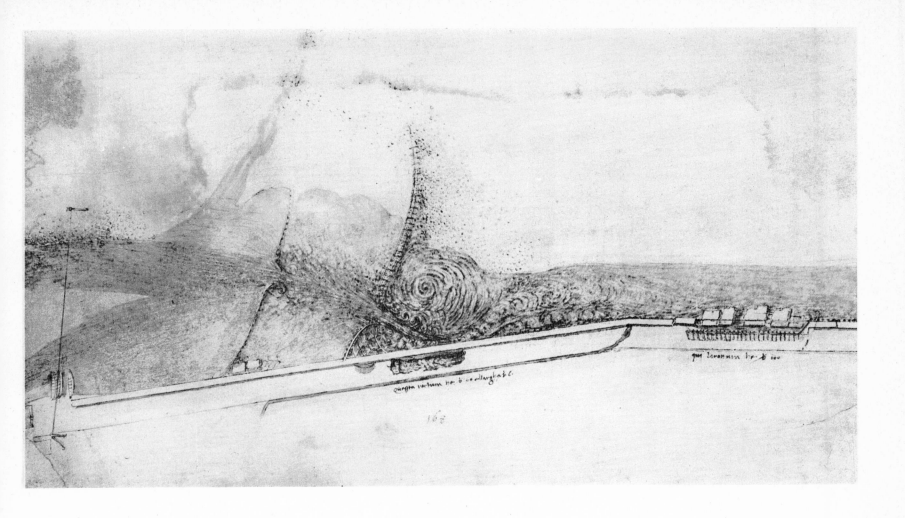

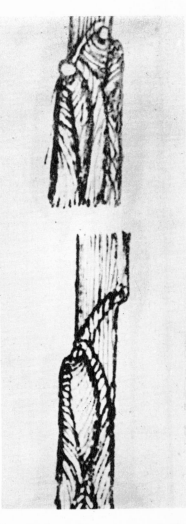

of that name in the thirteenth century; the Roggia Sartirana, which goes back to 1378; the Naviglio del Rottò, opened in the fifteenth century under Gian Giacomo of Montferrat; the Roggia Crotta (today the Roggia Busca), which Crotta Tettoni caused to be built in 1381. And for their part the *Signori* of Milan complemented Yolande's canal with the Roggia Mora, the Naviglio Sforzesco, and the Roggia Rizza Biraga, extending the irrigation of the territory from the point where the Naviglio d'Ivrea ends at the Sesia, half a kilometer below Vercelli.

Such was the setting; but in order to give the picture of the formation and development of Leonardo's thought, which is of far greater interest for us than the results actually achieved, we should have to be able to reconstruct the data and arrange them in chronological order. As others have said, this can be done to only a very slight extent, and we must confine ourselves to reviewing those passages in Da Vinci's manuscripts that relate to our topic, dwelling on those that seem most important.

In this field, as always, Leonardo appears in a double role, as theoretician and as practical man: his was the spirit of the doer complemented by the synthesizing mind. On the one hand his papers are covered with drawings of locks, sluice gates, reinforcements for banks, weirs, sections of canals, perspective views of works, and topographic surveys for dam projects; on the other, there is an enormous set of documented cases, the no less than nine hundred and three cases listed in the Leicester codex, a mass of problems with explanatory drawings that could not have been developed in full even if he had given it all his inexhaustible activity, but that contains in embryo the most complete of treatises on practical hydraulic engineering. It has been transcribed by a distinguished Da Vinci student, who sets the date of its composition in the years from 1505 to 1506, the years of Leonardo's full maturity.

The manuscript is a rearranged collection from other codices, with some illustrations, of Leonardo's many ideas on hydraulics. The problems refer to concrete cases that can occur in the work of the hydraulic engineer, but in substance they always deal with the laws governing the runoff of surface waters in their course to the sea. In his notes Leonardo employs all his experience and the fruit of his observations to make the reader master of these wild forces, so that by working along with them the technician may control them as far as possible and subject them to his will. This was the condensation of extensive preparatory work, innumerable remnants of which have come down to us chiefly in the Mazarin codices of the Institut de France.

Leonardo was much concerned with the bends in rivers and the causes for their formation, as well as with the laws under which the central filament of the current is displaced in the bed of a stream, the points at which and the force with which the banks are eroded, and the way in which the water moves around the obstacles encountered in its path or passes over them giving rise to further erosion downstream from the object. All these questions are discussed at length and supported by mechanical analogies and comparisons with other physical phenomena and similar proc-

469

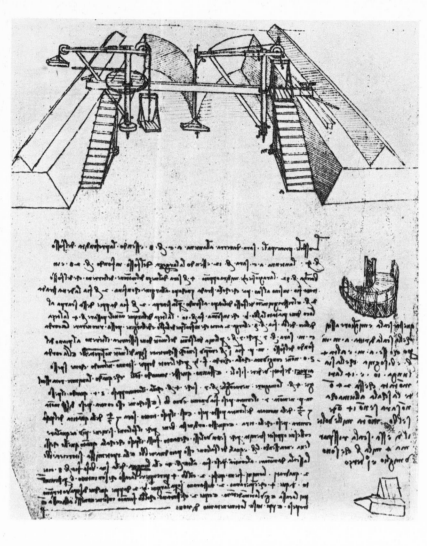

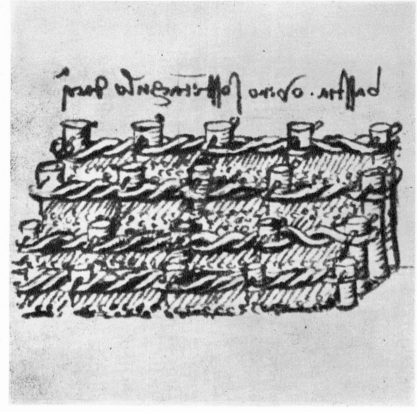

Above, left: Machines for lifting and transporting excavated materials from trench of canal under construction – Cod. Atl., fol. 363 v-*b*

Above, right: Gabion arrangement for reinforcing walls and foundations of dike – Ms. L, fol. 19 r

Below: Machine for lifting and transporting excavated materials in construction of canal – Presumably project for canal from Florence to sea – Cod. Atl., fol. 1 v-*b*

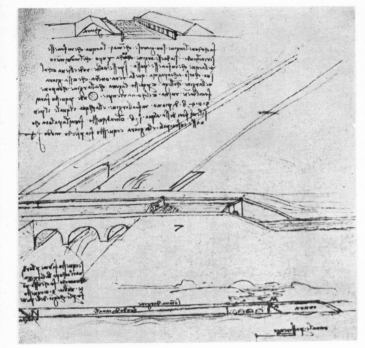

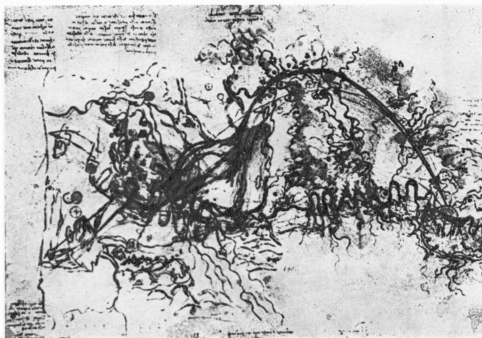

esses touching on a more abstract domain, such as the systematic study of the eddies and back-waters around the piers of bridges, considered as obstacles to the flow of a vein of constant velocity in the presence of sharp variations in section, such as might be formed by bodies located along the walls and in the center of a channel of uniform slope. Leonardo succeeds in referring the phenomenon of deviation of the central filament in river bends to the formation of the systems of standing waves derived from it, and correctly gives the method of predicting its behavior. These preparatory studies carry us back to the years before the two years in which the Codex Leicester was compiled, to his youth, his stay in the Lombard capital, his wanderings from Piombino to the Romagnas with a view to the achievement of his greater project, the navigation canal from Florence to the sea.

We know very little of his first period and of his activity as hydraulic engineer during his stay at the court of Il Moro, culminating in the position of *ingegnere camerale* or *inzenarius ducalis*. No document has come down to us that enables us to attribute to him any of the works or commissions undertaken during the years 1498 and 1499 with reference to the water system of the duchy, but the manuscripts that we have, and above all what remains of the Codex Atlanticus, give us a glimpse of what his activity may have been. He was responsible for the maintenance of the structures and equipment as well as the efficient operation of the waterways. He had to supervise the studies of the canals on the right bank of the Ticino that were the core of the Sforza system, still unfinished, which was dear to the heart of Duke Ludovico because of the wealth of the lands surrounding the castle in Milan that gave the canals their name. Leonardo's mind reworked the solutions that tradition had already established. In his sketches he examined these customary forms minutely, and new possibilities emerged.

Comparison of the standards for water supply brought him to the heart of the old question of the method of determining the amount distributed by a discharge orifice in a wall. This amount had never been defined because of insufficient knowledge. Thereby he was led to go to the root of the question, and thus began his measurements of the discharge velocities and trajectory of the stream flowing over the top of a weir, either open at the top or under a bar. The gates and locks led him to devise new solutions that were more practical, quicker, and more reliable; because of his many studies of these questions, these mechanisms came erroneously to be attributed to him.

We do not know to whom to ascribe their paternity, but the names have been handed down to us in an ordinance of the *Vicario*, assisted by the "Twelve of Provision," set up by statutes and regulations relating to the superficial waters of the commune of Milan going back to 1216; this ordinance, dated August 3, 1447, threatens serious penalties for anyone who should venture to break the locks on the canals and the stockade of Cusago. This must have been the first use of movable gates on a reach of a steeply sloping canal to raise or lower the water level by suitable changes of position, thus controlling a drop that could otherwise not have been managed without having rapids. The same gates, when applied laterally to a weir, make it possible to regulate the discharge of a reservoir, and are the essential part of a lock. We find one mentioned as early as 1165—the *chiusa al ponte dell'archetto* ("lock at the arched bridge"), in which the waters of the Nirone were caught and brought to the outer moat of the walls, which had been enlarged in 1155 and rebuilt after the destruction of the city by Barbarossa in 1162. The ditch had been broadened to a width of forty ells, and required a large quantity of water.

Many sketches of Leonardo's refer to these locks, and undoubtedly represent the locks of the canals of Milan, now filled in. Above all, he was concerned with methods for protecting the canal

Left: Details of projected canal from Florence to sea – Cross section of canal – Canal carried on aqueduct over tributary of river Arno – Cod. Atl., fol. 46 v-*a*

Right: Hydrographic map of Arno valley and route of canal – Windsor, Royal Collection, no. 12279

Caisson structure for foundations of hydraulic works – Ms. B, fol. 6 r

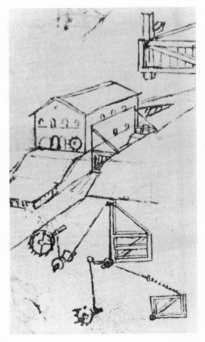

Lock on a canal used to form a waterfall – Codex Atlanticus, fol. 7 r-*b*

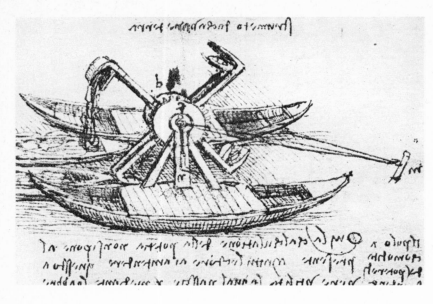

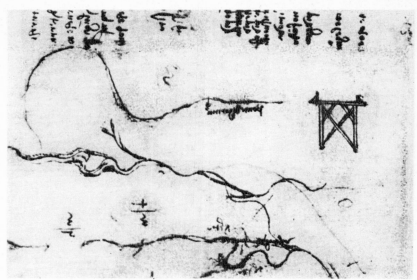

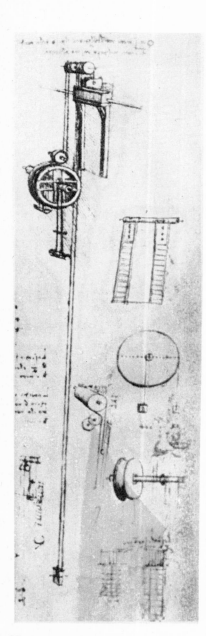

Left: Dredge on floats – Ms. E, fol. 75 v

Right: Hydrographic map of Vipacco valley – Cod. Atl., fol. 234 v-c

Machine for raising materials from pit – Cod. Atl., fol. 348 v-a

bottoms against the scouring of the water that rushes in at the moment when the gates are opened; among the systems he thought of were series of timbers linked together by stringers or anchored by rows of piles driven into the ground and connected with crosspieces. For filling the locks after the gates were closed, in such a way as to overcome the hydrostatic pressure upstream, he devised a special method of hinging the flaps controlling the intake and outlet orifices that would keep the stress on the bolts from being excessive and make it possible to actuate the flaps from above, while they would open automatically as soon as released. To make operation quicker, he devised special counterbalanced disappearing gates with a very rapid action, which the manuscripts show in several possible versions, although we do not know whether any of them was actually adopted in practice.

With preparation of this sort, it is natural that his mind went on to the boldest of conceptions, no longer based on fantasy alone but supported by a vast fund of knowledge. It must have been here at Milan, during a pause in his work as court engineer, that he came to think in concrete terms of the possibility of realizing a project he had long meditated on, that of a great navigation and irrigation canal from Florence to the sea. A diagrammatic sketch has come down to us on a sheet of the Codex Atlanticus, outlining in a few strokes the valley of the lower Arno from Florence to Pisa. The course of the projected canal is not indicated, but is stated in the words summarizing the main features of the project: his plan was to abandon the old course of the Arno below Florence and to find a new bed for it. It is evident that this was not the first idea that had occurred to him, and that he must have considered correcting the natural course of the river by means of locks, as was done elsewhere in his jurisdiction. It may be that studies turning on this alternative solution led to plans for a section of the course of the Arno, giving the details of a scheme for eliminating a rapid: the waterway runs parallel to the original bed of the stream, with a dike betwen them.

Below Florence the Arno presents a serious obstacle to corrective work, the pass of Montelupo, where the valley is broken up deeply into a series of folds running crosswise to the course of the stream. Leonardo had spent his childhood on the hills of Vinci dominating this reach of the river, and he must certainly have known the region well enough to realize that it was impossible to make a passage there, as the cost of excavation in the rocks would have been prohibitive. There was another factor favoring the choice of a different route, namely, the financing of the enterprise. Here the practice gained in his position helped him. The canal was designed primarily from the point of view of an irrigation expert, being designed to pass through arable land and near centers of industry that would be able to use the water and the power and willing to share the costs. The principal problem from the point of view of hydraulic engineering was uniformity of flow, so that consumers could be guaranteed a constant supply the year round; a storage reservoir was required, and the decision was to locate it in the valley of the Chiana.

In Roman times this broad valley, which runs parallel to the Apennine chain, had been a lake without an outlet, like Lake Trasimeno. It must have been more or less a puddle, if the ancients felt it desirable to raise its level artificially with permanent works, of which large-scale remains were found at the end of the seventeenth century, especially on the Tiber slope, when it was planned to dry and finally reclaim the region. These early works had fallen into ruin during barbarian times, the era of universal oblivion, and remained forgotten and neglected. The water level had declined again, and the detritus carried down by the floods had gradually filled the small ponds, changing the valley into a swamp which presumably looked like a lake only during the rainy season.

Leonardo knew the site well and realized that without much trouble, works could be erected there that would permit large volumes of water to enter the valley. The position of these proposed works is indicated in a study of the Valle di Chiana near Arezzo, on another sheet of the Codex Atlanticus. The project, perfectly stated in all its terms, with an admirable faithfulness to reality, is outlined as follows: "At the Chiane d'Arezzo let there be such falls made that when there is a shortage of water in the Arno during summertime, the canal will not be dry, and let the canal be 20 ells (11.70

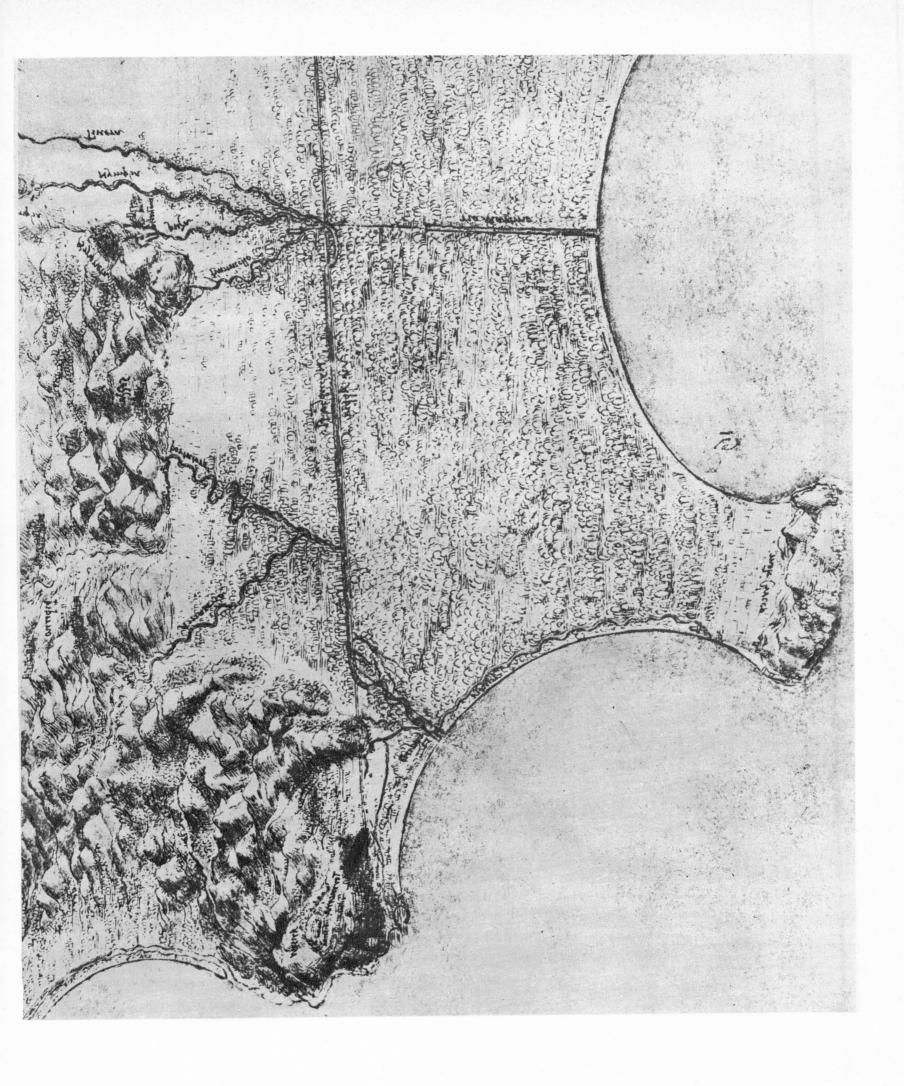

PROJECT FOR RECLAIMING PONTINE MARSHES — The project is based on reactivizing an old Roman canal paralleling the Appian Way, and called by Leonardo *Nympha fl.* It collected the waters coming down the Volscian mountains from Sermoneta to Sezze. In order to discharge the waters more rapidly from the canal, which has a slight slope, Leonardo brings into it the Portatore (now the Ufente) and the Amaseno, which come down from the mountains of Piperno. These two rivers, united in the Livoli (the present Levola), made their way to the sea by a slow winding course. Leonardo proposes a course in a straight line, emptying into the sea near the Torre di Badino. A variant of the project is also contemplated, prolonging the Roman trench of the Rio Martino as far as the junction of the streams from Sermoneta and Sezze; in any case, the Rio Martino discharges into the sea the stagnant waters below the Appian Way – Windsor, Royal Collection, no. 12684

473

Left: Rotating bridge on pontoons – Cod. Atl., fol. 312 v-*b*

Right: *Serraglio mobile* – Retaining dike with movable gates – Ms. B, fol. 64 r

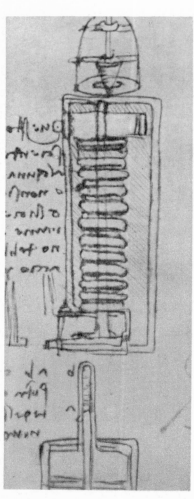

Well pump – Ms. E, fol. 75 r

m.) wide at the bottom and 30 (16.55 m.) at the top, and always two ells of water [in it] or four; because two of those ells go to the mills and fields. This will improve the country, and Prato, Pistoia, and Pisa together with Florence can contribute better than two hundred thousand ducats per year to meet the expense of this work, and the people of Lucca likewise, because the lake of Sesto will be navigable. Have it go by way of Prato and Pistoia and by-pass Serravalle and come out on the lake, because there will be no need of locks or abutments, which are not eternal but need always to be kept up."

The project was thought out down to the details of construction and preliminary estimates of cost; the other side of the folio gives a series of calculations of the cost of excavation per unit of length, and a project for a canal carried on an aqueduct manifestly inspired by a similar work on the Ivrea canal, drawn from the banks of the Dora Baltea. It is an interesting fact that Leonardo makes the calculation in Milanese money, "at four soldi for a day's work, four Milanese denari for a square ell," which proves, we think, that he was at Milan then and had the costs at his fingertips because of his position as court engineer. Two pictures at Windsor likewise represent the valley of the Arno and indicate the route, which describes a huge arc and empties into the lake north of Fucecchi. Other plates show us the Valle di Chiana flooded, with the dams quite recognizable. Many other sheets show studies of sections and parts of the canal, and a bird's-eye view of a long stretch of it with a series of locks and inclined spillways along the route to increase the volume of the lamina going over the weir; this was probably a reach beyond Serravalle, where the levels fall quite sharply down to the lake of Sesto, which has practically disappeared today.

The work was actually started after Leonardo had settled in Florence after the end of the meteoric career of Cesare Borgia. One ardent supporter of the scheme was Machiavelli, who had come into connection with Da Vinci at the time the two had met in the suite of Borgia in Romagna. But the purposes of the project had changed by now. It was no longer an irrigation and reclamation program in which the great cities at the foot of the Apennines would participate; now the work was to serve Florence alone, and make it a great commercial center with a direct outlet to the sea, indirectly dealing a mortal blow to Pisa. In order to do so more effectively, the canal was not to go back to the old bed of the Arno; it once had left the lake of Sesto at about Pontedera but now came out on the opposite bank, emptying into the sea in the lagoons of the ancient Portus Pisanus, which would be dragged for the purpose, between Pisa and Leghorn. Naturally, the project encountered the most furios opposition. The *Signoria* had to cope with a difficult and expensive engineering task and at the same time carry on an armed struggle with Pisa, which tried to interfere with the work as best it could, by raids, forays, and acts of war. It is no wonder that under these conditions the undertaking was finally abandoned after about two years, in the autumn of 1504. However, the manuscripts preserve for us the body of studies made by Leonardo to devise machines that would make labor more productive and save as much muscle power as possible—the

only power available to him. These show not only dazzling ingenuity but above all the practical common sense of an expert works manager.

Records of other works of equal interest to us are preserved in his papers. Leaving Milan after the flight of Il Moro, he stayed at Venice for a time, and while there visited the eastern frontiers of the republic—whether in an official capacity or not we do not know—and had the idea of flooding a part of the Isonzo valley between Gorizia and Gradisca in order to cut down to a relatively narrow strip of land the terrain to be defended against the incursions of the Turks, who were invading Friuli more and more frequently, and whom Venice, engaged as she was on other fronts, had difficulty in containing. This too was a bold project, of which nothing remains but the revised draft of the letter that was to have gone with the plan to the authorities in charge of arms and munitions, and a sketch of the valley of the Vipacco, which Leonardo calls the "Vilpago" in which the northern bank of the Carso, which comes in from the south, is labeled only "high—high." For flooding the Gorizia plain he advised the erection of a movable retaining wall, probably like the one whose design, made for a different purpose, is preserved in Ms. B of the Institut de France, and similar in all respects to our retaining works with movable gates. Much later, when he was living in France at the court of Francis I, he worked on new hydraulic projects and recalled it: "And let the movable retaining wall be made that I designed in Friuli."

What would be the site Leonardo had in mind? His draft, after the preamble, is a memorandum of technical questions and points in river hydraulics to be explained to the Venetian stewards (*Provveditori*) in order to prove that such a permanent work—movable only at the top to provide for the greatest floods—was possible, despite all the opinions to the contrary based on the floods, which are sudden and very violent on the Isonzo, as on all the torrential streams of the Udine region; he prudently adds, "Although it has not been possible to make reinforcements along this river that have not finally been ruined and broken down by the floods." We may infer from the local geography, in wich the contours have changed but little since that time, that the one place for which such a dam might be thought of is in back of the group of heights that form a series of eminences north of Gradisca close to the small town of Farra; they force the Isonzo to embank its bed to such an extent that the land from these hills, whose highest point is Monte Fortin, to Mossa and Capriva forms a sort of ridge that makes a bank about twenty-four meters high above the gravel of the Isonzo, along a line going from Lucinico to Mainizza, at the junction of the Isonzo with the Vipacco. No historian of the time tells us whether these operations were actually carried out, or whether Leonardo's stay at Gradisca, where he also took steps in connection with the artillery, had any practical results.

Damming up watercourses continued to interest him, and we still have a sketch of a deep mountain valley in which the course of a river is dammed below its junction with a tributary. There is no indication or point of reference by which we can identify the locality. It may be in the

Perspective hydrographic map of Chiana river valley projecting its conversion into a reservoir for canal from Florence to sea – Windsor, Royal Coll., no. 12682

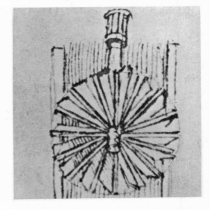

Spiral reaction wheel – Ms. F, fol. 88 v

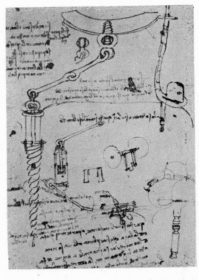

Device for secretly fastening hulls of enemy ships to sea bottom – Cod. Atl., fol. 346 v-a

475

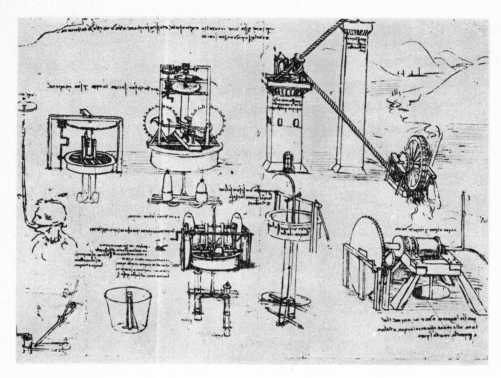

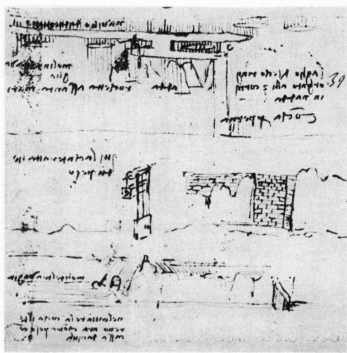

Left: Diving suit. Well and reservoir pumps operated by water wheels – Cod. Atl., fol. 386 r-b

Right: Plan and panorama of damming of river Adda from Rocchetta to Santa Maria – Cod. Atl., fol. 141 v-c

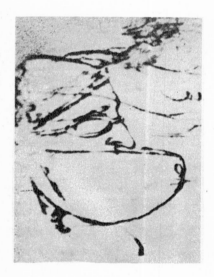

Apparatus for swimming under water – Cod. Atl., fol. 7 r-a

Method of walking on water – Cod. Atl., fol. 7 r-a

Apennines; as regards this region, we have topographic sketches by Leonardo for the Romagna-Tuscany zone; and at the period of the major operations on the canal from Florence to the sea he may have considered another site for his storage reservoir, in the event that the hostility of Arezzo to Florence made it impossible to use the Chiana. When, as it seems, he travelled through the valleys of the region of Bergamo and the Valcamonica in the suite of Louis XII during the campaign against the Venetians, he probably drew those diagrammatic plans with the place names set down in the local patois, as they would have been intelligible to a Tuscan.

The papers preserved in the royal library at Windsor include a splendid colored plate of a reclamation project for the Pontine marshes, which Pope Leo X had become very much interested in and was urging his brother Giuliano de' Medici to take part in as well. Leonardo was in Giuliano's suite at Rome. The work was begun under the direction of Fra Giovanni Scotti da Como in the summer of 1515, under definite instructions that fit in perfectly with Leonardo's plan, which has a text written in his hand from left to right, obvious evidence that the drawing was meant for others to see. The idea was to create a new short route for the lower reach of the old Ufente, now called the Levola and labelled "Livoli" by Leonardo, by which it would discharge rapidly into the sea near the Torre di Badino, which was to give its name to the new waterway; this would produce a very swift stream, bringing down with it even large rocks, which would tend to be held back. All the watercourses descending from the hills of Sezze, shown at the left of the folio, and those of Piperno shown in the center, were to be collected in a single canal running parallel to the Appian Way. The original bed of this canal went back to the end of the Roman republic or the first years of the Augustan empire; it represented a futile attempt at overcoming the increasing menace of the swamp. After being put into service again this ditch was called Fossa Giulia, after Giuliano de' Medici, who had begun the work of repairing it; similarly, the name of Portatore Giulio was given to the section of the Portatore River which comes from the vicinity of Piperno and combines with the Amaseno, and which was to be brought into a diked channel as soon as it reached the plain. To channel the springs that probably came up out of the ground between the Appian Way and the sea, as they do today, the Rio Martino was excavated in a straight line; before the recent reclamation, it ran a crooked course disappearing in the marshes of Fogliano.

Such were the principal outlines of the project; because of the correspondence between it and the descriptions of the work done by Scotti, we are justified in considering it as antedating the start of the latter undertaking, and in believing that Leonardo was a co-worker of Fra da Como, whom he may have known from other days. At any rate, this was the most serious endeavor up to that time to reclaim the vast region, whose recent condition we still can remember. The terms in which the plan was formulated show that the intention was to keep the expense within limits, and so low that it could be covered within a relatively short time by the yield of the lands reclaimed from the water. No lasting results could be expected from such a project. The only way of eliminating the sad chapter of the Pontine marshes once and for all was the method adopted recently, that of coping with the engineering difficulties at their origins and using radical solutions, regardless of the enormous investments required. One difficulty of the project of Scotti and Giuliano de' Medici was the plan for bringing all the waters coming down from the hills into a single collecting canal parallel to the Appian Way. It is clear that in view of the very slight slope of the profile along this route, it would be impossible to provide regular discharge of the water in flood periods, when the danger of its overflowing the banks and creating marshes would be greatest. The amount of

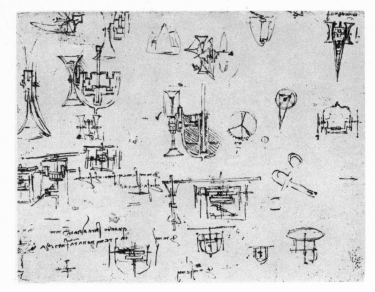

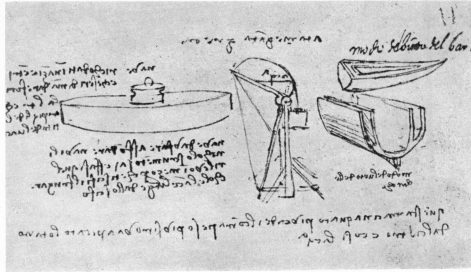

water drawn off by the accelerated course of the Portatore would not be sufficient, the Portatore being too far off. Furthermore, the Rio Martino could assure drainage of the springs below the Appian Way for only a short time, because of the advance of the beach between Anzio and the Circeo promontory by reason of the detritus constantly brought down by the Tiber; in this way the mouth of the stream would be displaced farther and farther out, and the slope of the river bed so reduced that the waters would stagnate. These points are not intended to minimize the value of Leonardo's project, which was the best that could be proposed, considering the possibilities available at the time and the probable financial limitations.

Projects on a smaller scale but of remarkable boldness are contained in some separate folios of the Codex Atlanticus. We may group them all together as a study for a navigable waterway between the Lago di Lecco and Milan. The attention is focussed chiefly on the reach of the Adda at Brivio and downstream from there toward Trezzo, a particularly difficult portion of its channel, consisting of a group of outcropping rocks which Leonardo calls the "three horns." Two panoramic views present his idea of making use of the crags in question as supports for permanent dikes that would dam up the river bed completely. These walls would form a great double lock on the right bank; the front lock would serve at the same time as a reservoir for a canal that would leave the Adda and go along the flank of the hill toward Milan, while the rear lock would dip into the solid rock like a well and come into a gallery at the level of the lower course of the river, below the dam. The entire region is depicted with care and many distances are indicated, giving positions referred to such base points as the mill of the Travaglia and the Rochetta di Santa Maria, and expressed in rods (canne, trabocchi) and miles. The term "perpetual lock" indicates that the flooding was intended to be permanent; special study is given to the gates of the well, which would have to sustain a considerable pressure, and Leonardo plans them in the form of single, counterweighted slide gates.

Judged from the view drawn in the manuscript, this project is on a level with the most modern plans for retaining dikes, although the difficulties must have been virtually unsurmountable, especially as regards the deep well in the rocks of the Rocchetta; and even if the revenues of the canal would have made the scheme profitable, the investment required must have been more than the sums available. It may be for this reason that Leonardo put forward another project designed to make use of the Brianza lakes to dam up the Lambro and reach the Lombard metropolis by way of that river. The lakes in question were to supply the water for the locks required to overcome the difference in level between the upper reaches of the Lambro and the level of the Lago di Lecco, going down to Valmadrera. The distances and differences of level are marked distinctly on the map. While several drawings of the proposed Adda project remain, so that we may think of the plan for regulating it as well advanced, we have only a hasty topographic sketch for the canal from Valmadrera to the Lambro; the latter may be a variant born out of that tireless mind but not given too much importance.

We can say little of the other hydraulic engineering projects conceived by Leonardo, since virtually nothing has come down to us. We have a small sketch relating to the Piombino marshes, which were to be drained by a peripheral canal supplemented by a rectangular network of drainage channels; there are also notes on a plan for bringing the waters of the Loire into the Romorantin brook, the sketch showing Amboise and the region of Blois. These latter studies were certainly preliminaries to a bigger plan, and the project was organized on the lines laid down years before in Lombardy, namely, looking to irrigation and transportation at the same time. It may be that Leonardo originated the first embryonic conceptions of that vast network of canals affording communication between the great rivers of France that was later to be the task of many generations. But although the assertion has been made that detailed projects of his for a navigation canal between the Loire and the Seine existed in the archives, and were brought out many years after his death and put into effect without delay, we have no surviving document of Da Vinci's to support this, and we shall not dwell on the matter in this rapid survey.

Left: Devices for mechanical propulsion of ships by means of paddle wheels – Cod. Atl., fol. 384 r-b

Right: Double hull structure and mysterious vessel for sinking enemy ships – Ms. B, fol. 11 r

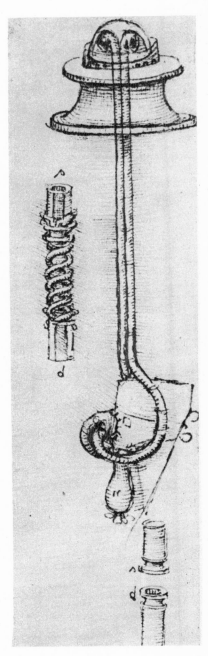

Sketch of apparatus for breathing under water (turret with openings of air ducts is on a float) – Cod. Arund., fol. 24 v

477

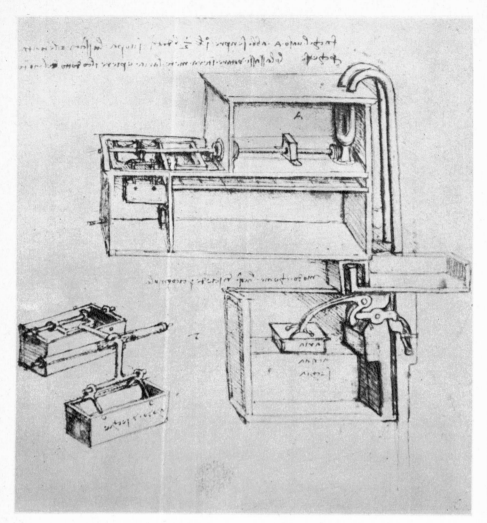

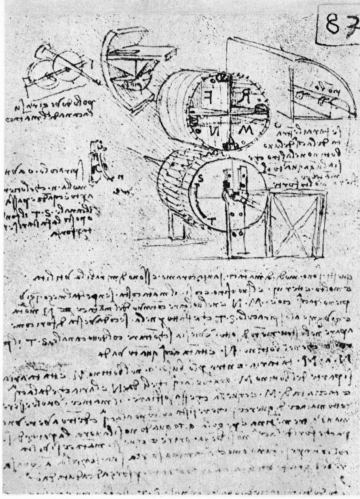

Left: Machine for raising water – Cod. Atl., fol. 401 r-*b*

Right: Hydraulic blower (drum in turning makes water pass from one sector to another, causing air to be discharged from hub) – Ms. B, fol. 82 r

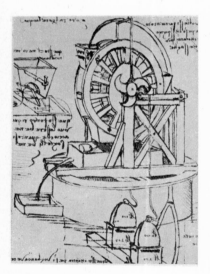

Well pump – Cod. Atl., fol. 7 v-*a*

Method of breathing under water – Cod. Atl., fol. 7 v-*a*

Leonardo also turned his inquiring and critical mind to various questions in hydraulics, including that of applying to ships the laws of the motion of fluids; but all that has come down to us of an analytic study of hull lines, which he proposed in a manuscript to discuss, is the division of the material. Likewise, he applies his inventiveness to ships, proliferating ideas of new devices and weapons to be installed on board. For one thing, he plans to meet the threat of damage from enemy ramming action, and draws a section of a ship with double planking separated by an air space, limited to the part of the hull below the water line above the knee, and to the lower part of the hull as far as the horizontal stringers; the idea is shown diagrammatically, and there is not the slightest hint of the structure of the ship. We note an apparatus for operating the tiller by means of a worm gear; it is shown as applied to a small boat, but must certainly have been designed for a large ship, in which the operation of the rudder represents a considerable expenditure of power. Just as he had thought of so many ways of producing mechanical propulsion on land, he did not neglect this problem in the nautical field, and worked out schemes for operating two paddle wheels by means of cranks from inside the boat. He speaks of these wheels as oars and gives a summary indication of their structure and that of the boat in correspondence with the mechanism; the diameters of the wheels and the number of blades are given, as well as the expected speed of a boat equipped with the apparatus.

Leonardo did not confine the exercise of his genius to problems of surface navigation, but took up again an old idea, that of enabling a man to move and act under water. Many ideas for diving bells and fantastic devices had burgeoned in the works of his predecessors, but without the slightest possibility of practical use; to this particular problem also Da Vinci applies his usual practical approach. In addition to the point of having the breath overcome the resistance of a long tube, he contemplates a diving suit with a thoroughly practicable helmet and an arrangement of intake pipes leading from a floating dome containing the air ducts. We should note the mouthpiece system with its two valves that connect the mouth alternately with the intake and exhaust tubes in rhythm with the phases of respiration. Da Vinci also has in mind the use to which this diving suit can be put, whether in cleaning the bottom of a boat without heeling it over or drawing it up on land, or in offensive actions, making it possible to approach the bottoms of enemy ships and attach ingenious devices to them for pulling off boards of the planking: the dismantling tools may be operated by the diver himself, or the mechanism may be fastened to the rudder so that it will operate when the rudder is activated.

We mention the problem of the submarine, which has given rise to so many conjectures, but we do so only to point out that the famous passage of the Codex Leicester refers merely to staying under water for as long as a man can remain without eating, and this would relate to the types of

478

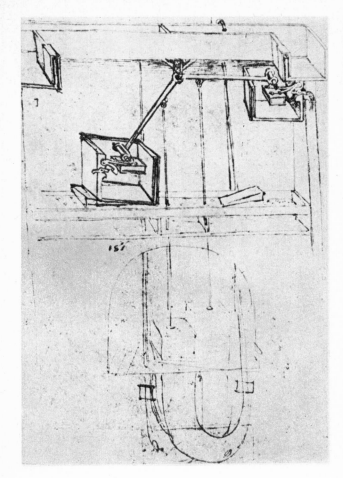

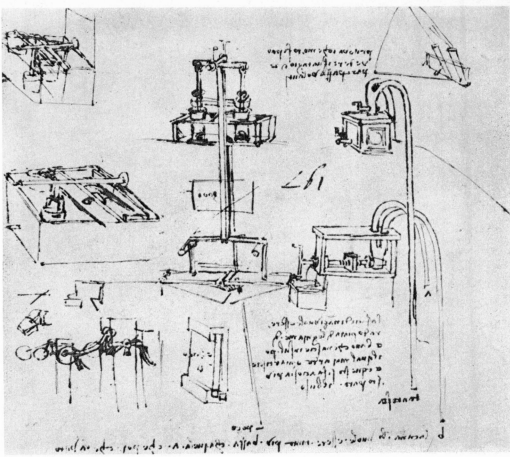

diving suits Leonardo had discussed, with a breathing apparatus on the surface and a reservoir strapped to the chest. There is no clear and unmistakable reference to submersible boats. Without doubt the problem could very well have been defined with the information that Leonardo had, for he proves in several passages that he thoroughly realizes the significance of Archimedes' law, around which the entire question centers. At two places in the Codex Atlanticus there is a summary sketch of a boat with a continuous upper deck broken only by a sort of manhole, with the admonition that the opening should be closed tight after entering, but this is not enough to allow us to consider the vessel a submarine, especially since Leonardo's practical mind would not have devised such a boat without figuring out means of performance of the function for which he destined it; for in addition to being able to make it sink at will, he would have had to provide for its propulsion when submerged.

As we have said, there is no trace of this in the known manuscripts. Accordingly, without risking a negation, which is always easy and useless when there is no basis for it, we shall say rather that we have no facts on which to base the statement that Leonardo had this in mind, since the problem, which depends at bottom on accessory technical inventions, could be dealt with only within recent times, when the progress of technology in very different fields had reached the necessary stage, the modern submarine being only an indirect consequence.

We have emphasized the constant references to theoretical investigations when Leonardo has to give an explanation of a concrete case. In the Codex Leicester itself it is hard to draw a sharp distinction between the theoretical portion and the examination of problems relating more specifically to structural technique. But Leonardo's researches led him onward to investigate the fundamental laws of hydrostatics, and in the process to observe new phenomena which in turn were a spur to his creative imagination.

We know how persistently he tried to get hold of the works of Archimedes, although we do not know whether he could have read them in the Greek. Likewise, there was no translation as yet of the surviving works attributed to Hero. It is hard for us, therefore, to decide how much he could have assimilated of the thought of the ancients outside of the Aristotelian traditions as supplemented by the later scholastics.

We cannot classify as new all of Da Vinci's notes on communicating vessels, which deal with laws that were well known to all the commentators on the Stagirite. However, Leonardo, in experimenting on these vessels, was the first to observe the phenomenon of capillary action, using tubes of different diameters communicating with each other; he noted it for liquids and for "quicksilver," remarking the opposite signs for the two. More than a century and a half was to pass before the phenomenon was mentioned again, in the work of Torricelli. Similarly, we must recognize Da Vinci's priority with respect to the principle to which we have given the name of Pascal's law, namely,

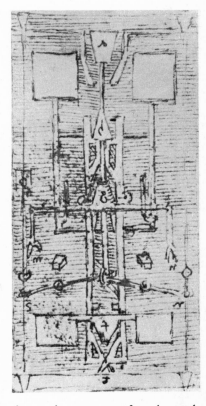

Automatic apparatus for alternately filling and emptying vessel – Cod. Atl., fol. 22 r-*b*

479

Chain pump and spirals for raising water – Cod. Atl., fol. 386 v-*b*

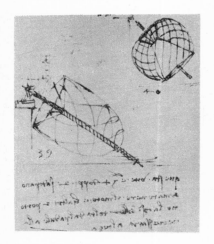

Study of life preserver for keeping wearer afloat – Cod. Atl., fol. 276 v-*a*

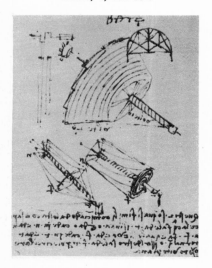

Method of raising water with moving spirals and action wheels – Cod. Forst., I, fol. 53 r

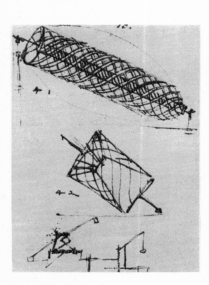

Various forms of moving spirals – Cod. Forst., I, fol. 54 v

Moving spirals for raising water – Cod. Forst., I, fol. 52 v

480

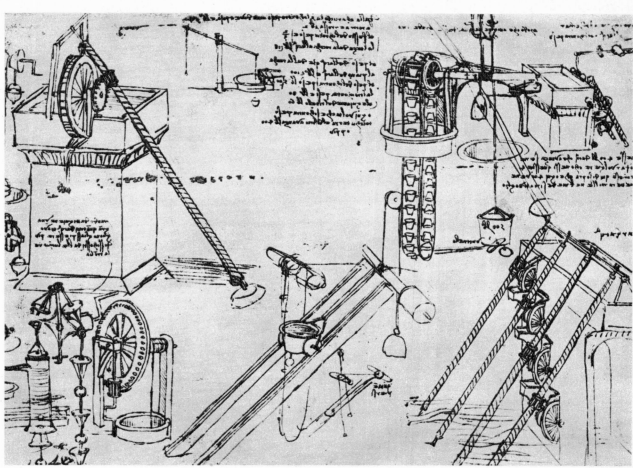

that a fluid in a vessel exerts the same pressure at every point of the vessel's surface. Some of Leonardo's notes on communicating vessels, which refer explicitly to this law, would seem to justify the hypothesis that he had thought of constructing a hydraulic press.

Four full centuries before Froude, Leonardo thought of dealing with the theoretical analysis of the lines of a ship's hull; unfortunately, all that has come down to us is the mention of the subject and of the "book of the curvature of ships' sides." This must be the material referred to in the beautiful drawings of the Windsor collection which present a rectangular surface immersed in a fluid that surrounds it and to which it is oriented in different ways. This is a clear instance of the method of Da Vinci's investigations: the "environment" is reduced to an element so simple that it can be subjected to analysis but can still express all the characteristic features of the problem. The drawing of the eddies produced by this surface is so clear that it does not suffer by comparison with any mechanical reproduction whatsoever, especially since it indicates the successive positions of the individual particles of fluid, while our systems of reproduction are necessarily limited to recording a single instant. Few of these drawings have come down to us, and we are unable to say what conclusions the researcher arrived at.

The studies referred to above, on the discharge of liquids from orifices, led him to a general study of the laws governing the outflow of a liquid from an orifice in a thin wall. He often draws the trajectory of the filament, whose pressure he observes to be greater, the greater its vertical distance from the surface of the reservoir. In this way he finds rules for deducing from the outside how full a reservoir is, but he does not appear to have identified the curve of the trajectory in question. He was the first to observe the contraction of the jet at a certain distance from the orifice, and to describe it precisely, correctly attributing it to the fact that the directions from which the individual elements going to make up the jet approach the orifice are not quite parallel. He observes a similar phenomenon in the outflow of water from under a wide low gate in a canal, and seeks in it the cause for the formation of bends in rivers.

Many observations refer to wave motion, in connection with which he observes, by means of small floats and sawdust, again for the first time, that there is no translation of the individual portions of the liquid beyond the orbital motion, if we abstract the dragging action of the wind; in a happy image, he compares wave motion to the motion of the stalks in a field of grain and calls it "as it were, a tremor."

His researches also extend to the motion of water in pipes. He comes to realize that the capacity of a straight pipe is greater than that of a pipe of equal cross section with bends; likewise, a branch at right angles to another pipe of equal cross section has a smaller capacity than the latter. Working with pipes, Leonardo was the first to observe that under certain conditions the enclosed space through which the water flows may exhibit a pressure lower than the external pressure, and he raises the questions of "why air enters water pipes," being unable to explain this by the Aristotelian doctrine of *gravitas secundum situm* ("weight depending on position"). The special behavior of air mixed

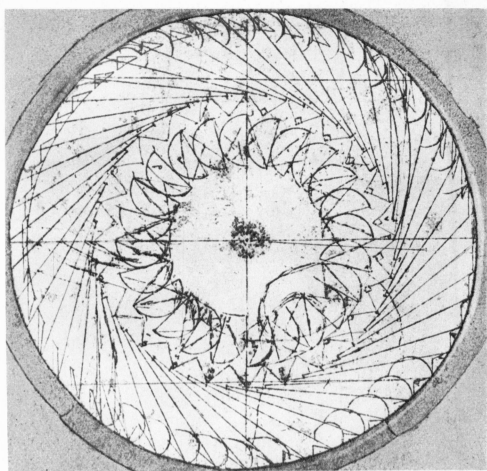

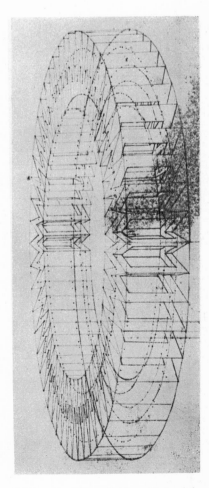

with water in pipes suggests to him the use of the violent upward motion of the bubbles to raise the water from a well, an anticipation of what we call the Mammouth pump or American well. Leonardo contemplates pumping air by means of a powerful bellows into a bell provided with a foot valve and lowered into the water of a well, while the water lifted by the air bubbles leaves by a column leading upward and is collected in a reservoir outside the well.

The many cases and studies dealing with vortex motions in water—"back currents," as Leonardo calls them—in connection either with obstacles variously placed and oriented with respect to the current of the fluid, or with the variation of the direction and cross section of the channel in which the current runs, or the coming together of two veins, constitute a study into the causes of the production and nature of a phenomenon that in Leonardo's eyes presents the greatest difficulty in the work of the hydraulic engineer. The power inherent in vortex motions, or their capacity to do harm, because of their rotatory action, suggests the idea of making use of them to operate water wheels and obtain mechanical work.

The diagrammatic notes referring to this topic are in the Codex Arundel and should be attributed to the last period of Leonardo's life. These diagrams show a small horizontal orifice for the discharge of the water, placed tangential to a hollow in the form of a pit, into which the water spurts with a vortex motion, as is clearly shown by the track of the filaments; below, at a certain distance from the upper orifice, is a wheel with blades arranged by twos at opposite ends of diameters, with their concavities turned toward the motion of the water. Above this drawing may be seen various efforts to obtain the trace of the curve of these blades by means of points. The vertical axis of the wheel shows at its upper end a pinion for transmission of the power. This is clearly different from other projects to be found in the Marciano codex and in the work of Taccola, in which the blades of the wheel, while still on a vertical axis, receive the jet directly as it falls from the orifice, while Leonardo's drawing clearly shows the formation of a vortex above the plane of the wheel and throughout the cylindrical volume of the pit. The scheme is completely identical with that of our spiral reaction turbine, named the Kaplan turbine after its inventor.

The rotatory motion of a liquid in a containing vessel gives rise to a special equilibrium configuration of its free surface, such that its upper portion rises above the original level. The depth of the hollow formed in the liquid because of the motion depends on the velocity of rotation, and it is possible to insert into the hollow, by means of a siphon, a liquid brought to the same level as the liquid contained in the vessel when at rest; a volume of water equal to the volume inserted will overflow from the vessel. In Da Vinci's drawing the vessel has the form of an inverted frustum of a cone, and the motion of the liquid is produced by a form actuated by a crank mechanism; this apparatus, when dipped into a pond, can dry it out if it is in the neighborhood of a large lake or the sea, into which the water thus raised can flow.

Among the machines for raising water that are dealt with so frequently in the manuscripts of Da

Left: Study of machine for removing water – Cod. Atl., fol. 278 r-*b*

Right: Study of water wheel – Cod. Atl., fol. 258 r-*b*

Study of water wheel – Cod. Atl., fol. 263 r-*a*

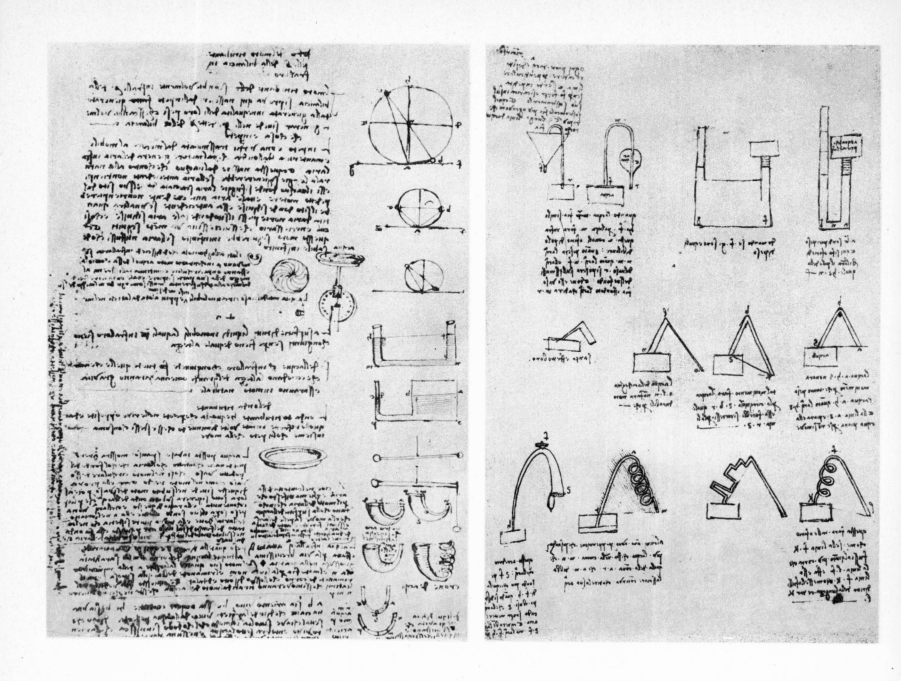

Vinci—piston pumps had been in use from the time of classical antiquity, and it does not appear that Leonardo made any personal contribution on this score—particular mention should be made of the spiral water screw, apparently known to the Egyptians of the XXIInd Dynasty, and later described and studied in detail by Archimedes. It has no practical interest for us today, but was of some importance in antiquity, since it afforded the possibility, in theory, of raising water as high as was desired without having to overcome the entire resistance, and hence with small use of power; in addition, the pressure did not strain the materials of which the tubes were made. The spiral as a means of raising water occurs frequently in Leonardo's youthful drawings—just as the works of Francesco di Giorgio Martini and Taccola are full of such models—but later it gives way to more efficient machines. Subsequently Da Vinci studied the spiral from a theoretical point of view, seeking to evaluate the resistance that the mass of water caught in the bend offers to the lifting action; this study was connected with another phenomenon that led him to consider the possibility of a new hydraulic motor. He must have observed that a spiral full of water, if set at an angle greater than the angle of slope of the spiral and left to itself, will begin to rotate as the water discharges from the lower orifice. Although he succeeded in formulating the principle of action and reaction in several cases, he was unable to realize that this is due to the reaction of the walls of the spiral to the rotary acceleration of the liquid, and sought for the explanation in purely static postulates. It is not of any importance that Leonardo, misled by a seeming hydromechanical paradox, tried to employ the fortuitously discovered principle in machines for proving the possibility of perpetual motion. The fact that remains is that he was the first to observe a property of the motion of fluids and to realize its importance, to the point of envisaging, if only schematically, its application to machines for producing energy. It had already been noted in ancient Greece, and "Hero's mill" preserves the tradition of it; but it remained a mere mechanical curiosity. It was only the middle of the nineteenth century, three hundred and fifty years after Leonardo's time, that saw the principle resumed and developed in modern reaction turbines; the individual tubes of the moving spiral of Da Vinci are the unit element, and can be identified with the course of the fluid filaments in their accelerated motion.

CARLO ZAMMATTIO

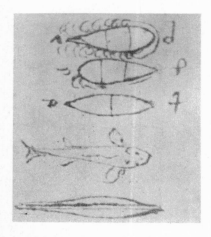

Studies on forms of fishes and hulls adapted to moving through water – Ms. G, fol. 50 v

DA VINCI'S MECHANICS

The first studies containing an authentic revelation of Leonardo as artist-scientist were initiated by A. B. Venturi in 1796, and continued by G. Libri, G. Govi, and R. Caverni, whose old essays, still incomplete, are precise and concrete syntheses that are of inestimable value even today. These studies reached their culmination in the profound work of P. Duhem at the beginning of the present century, and have definitely established the place of Leonardo in the revival of mechanics in the fifteenth century.

Taking all the previous researches into consideration, and making large use of the publications, now almost complete, of the unpublished or little-known portions of Leonardo's manuscripts, I dealt with this theme as long ago as 1934 in an extensive memoir published in my *Studi vinciani*.

The nature of the present collection of essays and the limited space available do not permit of a minute technical analysis. The student can find such an analysis in the works cited. It seems more appropriate to limit myself to general consideration that can and indeed should be of interest to every educated person who would like to fit the great figure of Leonardo as a scientist into the traditionally known and more familiar picture of Leonardo as an artist ranking among the most celebrated.

When seen in those two aspects, the figure of Leonardo is not only immense: it is all but unique in the history of the development of scientific thought, the two sides being linked by closer and deeper ties than can be perceived at first sight, although the second of them, namely, Leonardo as an artist, has been studied in extensive works far more than the first aspect, and this has been true in all times and in all countries. There are few treatments that show us a complete Leonardo, Leonardo as a true and supreme artist-scientist, with a few exceptions such as the article in the *Enciclopedia italiana*.

When we come to speak specifically of Leonardo as the reviver of mechanics in the fifteenth century, it is impossible to make a rigorous distinction between the profound theoretical researcher and the brilliant technologist. On the contrary, I believe that Leonardo, forced by events, by the circumstances of his life, by his competition with other artists, to engage in works involving all the branches of Renaissance engineering, realized, with the intuition of genius, the need for the preliminary theoretical research that he compared to the captain, practice and applications being the soldiers.

He felt the need of rising from experience, however crude and imperfect, to the cause: "No effect in nature is without a reason; understand the reason and you have no need of experience." Theory is thus the reliable guide of practice; it must give the inventor and the technician their directives and methods. It must be the dependable guide of experience; and this may well be the sense in which we should take the statement just cited, which is too gross as it stands, and incompatible with all of Leonardo's experimental activity, the activity of an individual who proclaimed himself an "unlettered man" but even more a "son and disciple of experience." But what means of studying, penetrating into, and founding theory were offered to Leonardo by medieval science? The engineer and technologist have to be able to make experiments and subject their

Researches in statics – Cod. Atl., fol. 288 r-*f*

Studies of fall of heavy bodies in air – Ms. M, fol. 59 v

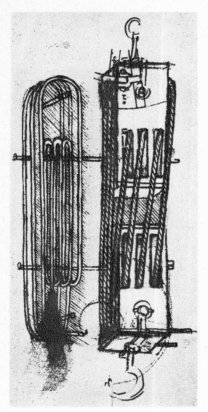

Drawing of tackle for study of tension
in ropes – Cod. Atl., fol. 396 r-*d*

Study of pulleys – Cod. Atl., fol. 149 v-*a*

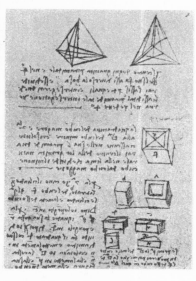

Leonardo's studies to determine the
center of gravity of a pyramid – Ms.
F, fol. 51 r

investigations to calculations; and Leonardo wrote that "mechanics is the paradise of the mathematical sciences, because in it we come to the fruits of mathematics."

But Leonardo was never a professional mathematician. What could be called his geometrical researches, inspired by artistic themes or practical problems and certainly not negligible, belong to his last years, the stormy period of his wandering life, as Solmi says; but despite their genuine interest, they certainly do not consitute a fundamental part of Leonardo's scientific activity.

We know little about the studies he must surely have begun at Florence in his first stay there, in the marvellous Italian Athens of the Renaissance, where a notable school of abacists flourished—studies continued at Milan under the influence of Luca Pacioli. Leonardo realized the importance of calculation and geometry for the science of mechanics, and made ingenious use of his meager knowledge in many problems of statics, as in the study of the strength of materials and the resistance of beams. For him, mathematics was not an end in itself, but the most reliable means for penetrating into the great temple of theoretical and practical mechanics.

"Let him who is not a mathematician not read me in my principles." And in doubtful cases, it is to mathematics that we must turn: "O mathematicians, throw light on this error." And he spoke well in saying: "There is no certainty where one cannot apply one of the mathematical sciences or else one of those based on the mathematical sciences."

In the studies and notes, long, incomplete or erroneous, and always in disorder, that occupy hundreds and hundreds of the many pages of all his manuscripts, and especially those of the two biggest codices, the Atlanticus and the Arundel, the dominant thought of Leonardo is mechanics, the paradise of mathematics.

The disorder may be due in part to whatever person it was that collected, arranged, and bound the precious folios without any great knowledge of mechanics, and in large part to the nature of Leonardo's mind; never satisfied with himself, he was always going over his researches, reworking them, certain that he would never have said the last word on them and that his successors would take them up again, as he himself had worked on the basis of his predecessors' researches and tradition. His investigations were incomplete and sometimes mistaken until the light, the true light, burst on the mind of the patient searcher; and still they are so instructive and precious for the critic and historian, who at such a remove in time have at least a little guiding thread to lead them into the mystery and the labors of that great man's research and meditation, enabling them to see once more with how much effort and toil the truth is reached. Man's way, Carlyle has said, is like a series of falls. And so it is in science. And here and there we find the names of Leonardo's inspirers, and of the books he knew, and looked up, even if he did not study them all, and did not take from them all, for it is in every way true that what he gave is infinitely more than what he took.

We come upon some of the names of the most celebrated Italian humanists, Leonardo's contemporaries—L. B. Alberti, Pelacane. However, his principal inspiration came from the books of Aristotle and Jordanus Nemorarius. The humanist environment of Florentine Neoplatonism must inveitably have led him to know Aristotle and then the less philosophical but still imposing writer of Milan. And this without having any sure and direct knowledge of the original books, for with the Aristotelian theories explained and commented on in the schools *ad nauseam*, he could learn them from the discussions of the learned men he met, and from the encyclopedias of the time. In regard to the most important part of dynamics, although he has correct and original ideas and general intuitions, he is unable to free himself from the tyranny of Aristotle, whose *Physics*, *De coelo*, and *Meteorologica* he cites. The theory of impetus came down to him through the works of Albert of Saxony and our humanists, while he may not have been acquainted with Buridan's work; he clarified those works and freed them of obscurity and of some of their useless superstructure.

Jordanus was his chief source of inspiration. The works of this writer on mechanics undoubtedly were the starting point of his researches and discoveries, and Leonardo several times more or less explicitly makes reference to Jordanus' science, which is the science *de ponderibus*. Who was Jordanus, and what were his works? The most probable hypothesis yet advanced, due to B. Buoncompagni, is that he was Jordanus of Saxony, general of the Dominicans in the first quarter of the thirteenth century. Many of his works on arithmetic, geometry, and optics had recently been exhumed and published; others were available in manuscript form, in numerous codices. These prove that Jordanus was a mature and acute mathematician; but what interests us most are his works on mechanics, which exerted a powerful intellectual influence throughout the Middle Ages, and on Leonardo as well. The *De Ponderibus* was famous in all the medieval schools. A curious question was raised by Duhem with respect to Jordanus. The *Elementa Jordani super demonstrationem ponderis*, transcribed by ignorant copyists, was the source of two quite different treatises. One of these is designated as the Peripatetic commentary on the *Elementa*. The other is the *Liber Jordani de ratione ponderositatis*; it differs substantially from the first and other similar works, and was known to N. Tartaglia. It is here that we find exact study of the conditions for equilibrium on an inclined plane and of the equilibrium of a bent lever, and the explicit references to the concept of moments. The first part was reproduced, without citing the author, by Tartaglia in his *Quesiti et inventioni diverse* (1546) and republished in 1565, after his death.

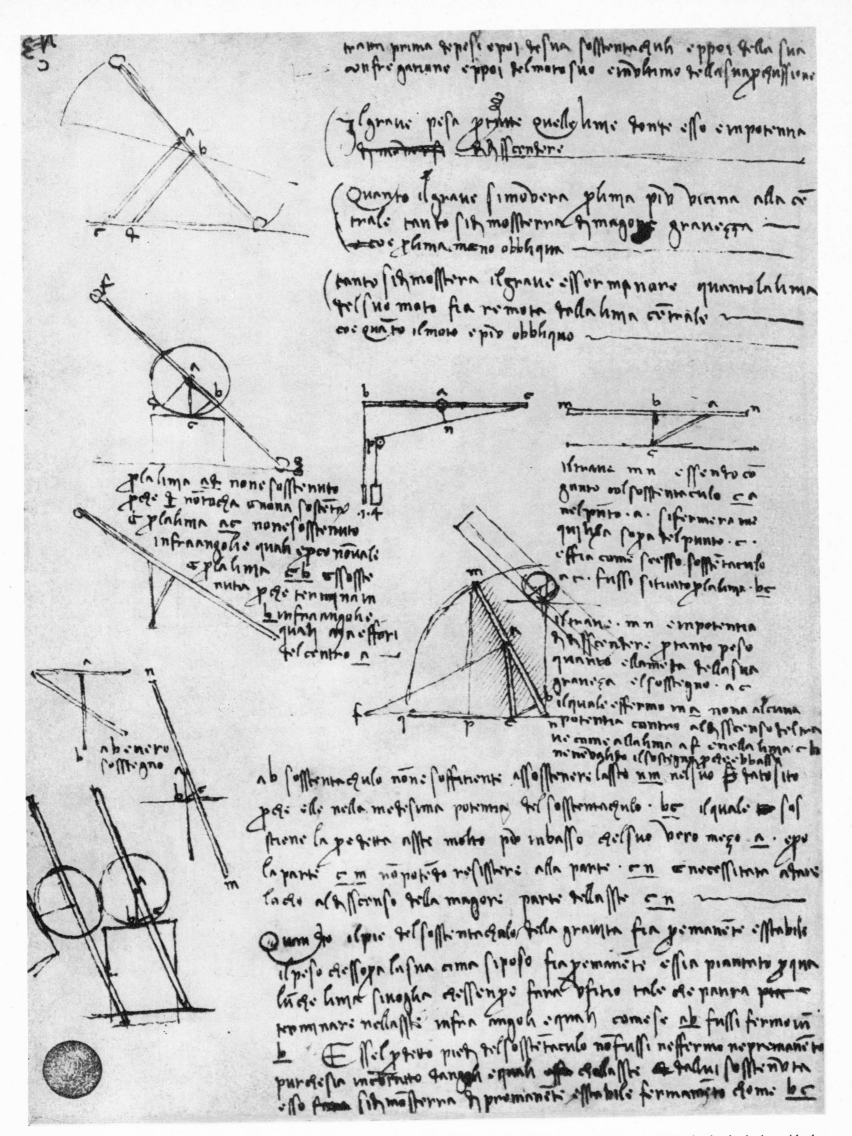

On this page, which is fundamental for Da Vinci's mechanics, Leonardo has subdivided the materials of his treatise into various books, beginning with the book on weights and ending with the book on percussion (theory of impact) – Folio in Academy of Fine Arts, Venice (reproduced in reverse to facilitate reading)

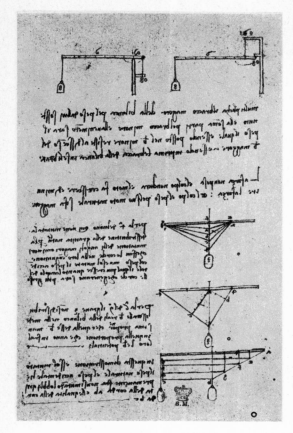

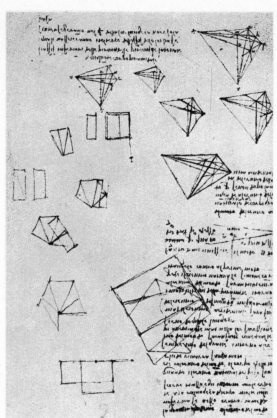

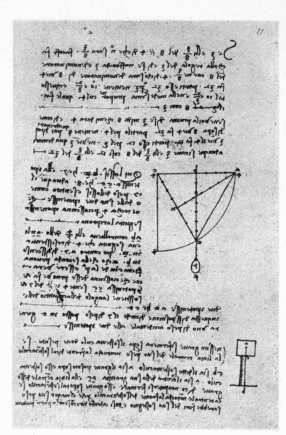

Left: Studies on static moments and composition of forces – Cod. Arund., fol. 1 v

Center: Determination of center of gravity of pyramid – Cod. Arund., fol. 65 r

Right: Enunciation of static principle for equilibrium of solid on horizontal plane support – Cod. Arund., fol. 11 r

Duhem formulated a new hypothesis, attributing this work not to the traditional Jordanus but to an unknown mathematician of the thirteenth century, whom the great historian of mechanics called the "precursor of Leonardo"; this assumption later gave rise to another hypothesis concerning a "precursor of Stevin."

But in view of the extreme liberties notoriously taken by copyists, and their arbitrary interpolations, encouraged by publishers, I believe that the question of Jordanus the writer on mechanics should not and cannot be separated from the entire question of Jordanus the algebraist and geometrician, who was able, if not very original. The author of the splendid treatise *De triangolis* was certainly capable of having worked out the acute demonstration of equilibrium on an inclined plane. Substantially, without resorting to hypotheses concerning predecessors and thereby still further complicating the mystery of Jordanus, the simplest hypothesis is the following: The original book of Jordanus, *De ratione*, etc., is the standard book that was famous throughout the Middle Ages, and from it copyists and expositors ignorant of mechanics and not even in possession of sound geometrical knowledge drew the Peripatetic text or commentary, composed of the most disparate elements, and more in conformity with the entire Aristotelian mechanics.

There is no doubt that Leonardo was acquainted with the book *De ratione*, even though he does not cite it explicitly, for he takes the best things in it, almost in identical words, namely, the discussion of the conditions for equilibrium on an inclined plane and of the equilibrium of a bent lever, and (although not explicitly) the basic concept of moments. It is from this book that he takes off for his new discoveries. He reproduces and translates Jordanus' statements almost literally, often however, giving them a perspicuous form of his own, and never reproducing Jordanus' demonstrations, despite their clarity. He is content to illustrate them with numerical examples and seek for experimental verifications, including the remarkable experiments devised in regard to equilibrium on the inclined plane and the concept of moments. The explanation for this may be that these were very familiar matters whose value, correctness, and utility he had daily occasion to realize in his work as an engineer.

This absence of theoretical proofs in the modern sense, and their frequent replacement by unclear and sometimes incorrect explanations of truths intuited by genius, is virtually the rule in Da Vinci's mechanics, in which the aim is primarily that of application and numerical examples, which are very numerous and most always exact.

The first step in advance over Jordanus' work achieved by Leonardo relates to two special cases of the theorem of moments. Leonardo was the first of the writers on mechanics of his period to rise to a full and penetrating idea of the concept of force; the definition of the concept in its final and definitive form occurs on a page of Ms. A and is reproduced in all the Italian and foreign anthologies of the writings of that artist and scientist who loved to call himself an "unlettered man"; in its profundity and vigor of expression it constitutes one of the finest productions of Italian literature.

The idea of the tension in ropes hanging from a support or drawn through a fixed or movable pulley and supporting a weight is clear and distinct in Leonardo, as it must have been to technicians

Studies of free fall of heavy bodies – Ms. C, fol. 28 v

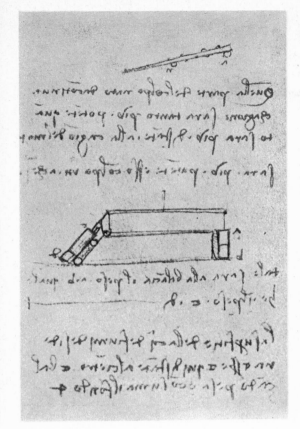

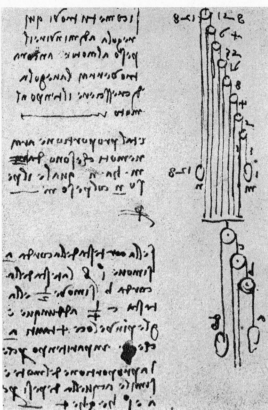

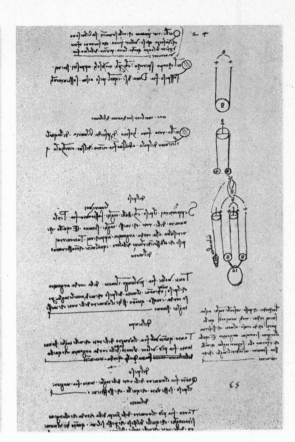

from time out of mind. But Leonardo was the first to set himself the problem of finding the tensions in a piece of cord supporting a weight or, as we should express it, the problem of the decomposition of a force (weight) along two given lines of direction. He solves the problems with two theorems, to which we have referred, in the first pages of the Codex Arundel, which were composed, or recopied from earlier notes, at Florence in March, 1508. Expressed in modern terminology, they state that with respect to a point on the resultant, the two components have equal moments; with respect to a point on one of the components, the moment of the resultant is equal to the moment of the other component. These theorems make it possible to give a numerical solution of the problem which Leonardo poses and of which he makes various numerical applications. If we translate them into geometrical terms—which Leonardo does not do, however—they coincide with the familiar rule of the parallelogram of forces.

How did Leonardo derive his theorems, or link them with the principle of the bent lever? Little or nothing on this point can be obtained from the manuscripts that have come down to us. The statements in the Codex Arundel were nothing but notes, a collection of many sheets that he later transcribed, whose purpose was probably to set down the basic points, which were then to be developed, with all the necessary calculations, in the book on the elements of machines for which we have the list of chapters or theorems, and which has been lost or (more likely) was never written. After this step forward, the greatest taken since the work of Jordanus, it may be said in brief that there is no problem of statics that Leonardo did not consider, with a fullness and depth unknown to all his predecessors and successors, at least up to the time of Stevin and Galileo. His genius and deep knowledge of practical and theoretical questions were turned to deal with the inclined plane with problems of the stability of equilibrium—not new but brilliantly elucidated—and with that of centers of gravity. There is an original treatment of pulleys and multiple tackles, with a first view of the principle of virtual work. He concerns himself with the problem of constrained reactions, with the principle of the polygon of support, with researches into the strength of materials and the theory of the arch, and with friction.

In the theory of the centers of gravity of plane and solid figures, Leonardo goes back directly or indirectly to Archimedes and then to Albert of Saxony. After his attempt to find the center of gravity of a semicircle by approximate methods translatable into easy graphic constructions, which he was in a position to make rapidly and elegantly, his greatest contribution is the discovery of the centers of gravity of the tetrahedron and of pyramidal and conical bodies. For the tetrahedron, he sets down, in the Codex Arundel, the geometrical theorem of the common point of intersection of the "axes" (assis), that is, of the straight lines connecting the vertices with the centers of gravity of the opposite faces; the geometrical method of demonstration is vividly referred to in three simple figures. Later, in other manuscripts, he states that this point is the center of gravity of the tetrahedron, and again in the Arundel codex he points out that the segments joining the mid-points of the opposite sides bisect each other at that point. The demonstrations of these two new and accurate theorems in mechanics are not given. It is possible to make an assumption as to how they were arrived at; but this interpretative method is dangerous and likely to lead to reckless or incorrect conclusions.

Left: Ratio of force to load on inclined plane – Ms. H, fol. 81 v

Center and right: Theory of fixed and movable pulleys – Cod. Atl., fol. 120 v-c, 321 r-a

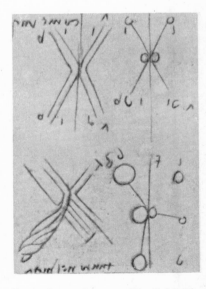

Researches on impact – Ms. I, fol. 76 r

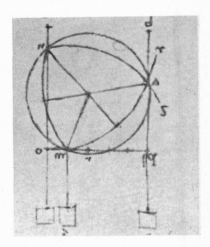

Study of triangular balance – Cod. Atl., fol. 58 v-c

487

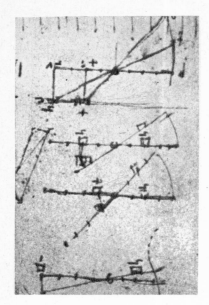

Researches in statics – Cod. Arund., fol. 63 v

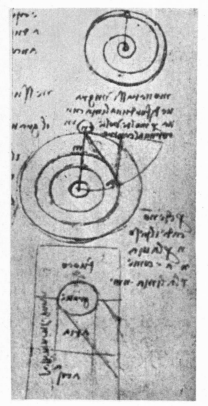

Researches on gravity – Cod. Arund., fol. 175 v

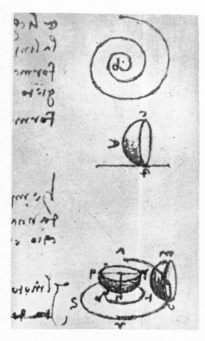

Researches on rotary motion – Ms. E, fol. 34 v

Examining leaning towers, earth over caverns, and paradoxical cases of equilibrium that are still today the theme of ingenious toys, Leonardo made the acute observation that a heavy solid on a plane is in equilibrium if its center of gravity falls within the outline of the base (polygon of support), and gives a sensible reason for this, by and large; but here too a genuine demonstration is wanting. Leonardo had no predecessors in his investigations on friction, the first ever conducted experimentally, with an apparatus similar to that which Coulomb was to use, in more perfected form, more than three centuries later. He have the coefficient of friction for all substances as 1/4, later, however, perhaps as the result of more extensive and repeated experiments, he came to suspect that the coefficient depends on the nature of the substances. Still more remarkable, he made use of this principle to solve problems of statics arising in actual work, with splendid examples, contradicting not only the "science" of the *De ponderibus* but also customary practice, in which levers were considered as geometrical (linear) elements, and no account was taken either of their weight or of the friction that limits the efficiency of any mechanical contrivance.

He treated at length both sliding and rolling friction, chiefly with practical purposes in mind, such as that of diminishing the wear on the bearings of wheels and the resistance to the traction of vehicles, devising an easy-rolling wagon with axle supported at the intersection of two wheels, and provision for cooling journals overheated by the friction.

Some problems in Aristotle's mechanical questions, repeated in Jordanus' work, and, even more, Leonardo's own practice as an engineer, led him to deal with the strength and bending of rectangular or cylindrical beams, supported at one end and loaded at the other. He was a century and a half ahead of Galileo, using the same method that his great successor was to follow, with more accurate results. In dealing with this kind of strength Leonardo, although he showed at various points of the theory of impact that he had clear and correct theoretical ideas as to the elasticity of bodies, could not take advantage of elements that were introduced into science only three centuries later. He was ignorant of Hooke's law and of the concepts of the modulus of elasticity and the moment of inertia. Here too he followed a crude and intuitive method, which could apply merely as a first approximation and led to results only partially confirmed by experiment.

It would be an exaggeration to apply to all this the high-sounding name of a theory. Leonardo's great merit is to have posed the problem distinctly for the first time and to have attempted an approximate solution with the meager means that the science of his times, plus his own discoveries, could offer. Here too the theoretical researcher is not divorced from the technician, who often towers above the theoretician: an example is his experiment on the rupture of metal wires, in connection with which he invented an automatic device for stopping, at the breaking point, the fall of the weights that bring the rupture about. Although it is virtually certain that he made the experiments and noted the results, these results have unfortunately not come down to us.

The same characteristics occur in his studies on the theory of the arch, which he inimitably defined as a stronghold built of two weaknesses. He was well aware of the thrust against the abutments, and investigated some causes of failure; but the sketch does not go beyond this, and remains a first marvellous attempt, a small ray of light in the midst of so many shadows.

All these researches into the statics of rigid and deformable bodies and into the conditions of their equilibrium, accompanied by a complete vision of their applications in the most diverse fields, reflect truths confirmed by the more developed science of Leonardo's successors, despite the habitual disorder with which they are strewn through all his manuscripts and despite the gaps that have been noted.

When pruned, ordered, and freed of unnecessary constructions, this work constitutes a complete treatise on statics in the most modern sense of the word. Although for the basic points there are no proofs strictly so called, as we understand them, this does not mean that Leonardo did not have such proofs; we can even conceive or imagine the ways in which he might have arrived at them with the scientific knowledge available at the time, but we cannot say more than that. Here too the nature of all Leonardo's scientific activity reveals itself—so like indeed to his artistic activity. Never satisfied with himself, always in search of perfection, he did not have the strength and the time and the will to create the final integrating work.

One of his first biographers had good reason to say that "his knowing his errors too much did not allow him to get much done." But Leonardo, in his rebellion against writers taken as authorities, always went back to experience as the supreme judge: "Many will believe they can fairly reprove me by stating that my demonstrations go against the authority of some men whom their inexperienced judgments hold in great reverence, not conceding that what I have done is the fruit of simple experience, which is the true teacher."

The same observations can be made in relation to all his researches and studies in hydrostatics, hydrodynamics, and aerodynamics. Leonardo was a marvelous observer, almost miraculously precise, whether he was describing the motion of water current, some of whose fundamental laws he intuited, or the wave motion of the sea, or the flight of birds, whose anatomy he studied directly. His power of observation is all the more surprising and admirable since he had nothing at his disposal but his own senses, guided though they were by the mightiest of minds, yet unaided by the most modest of the apparatus used by modern science. The observations he made were the solid founda-

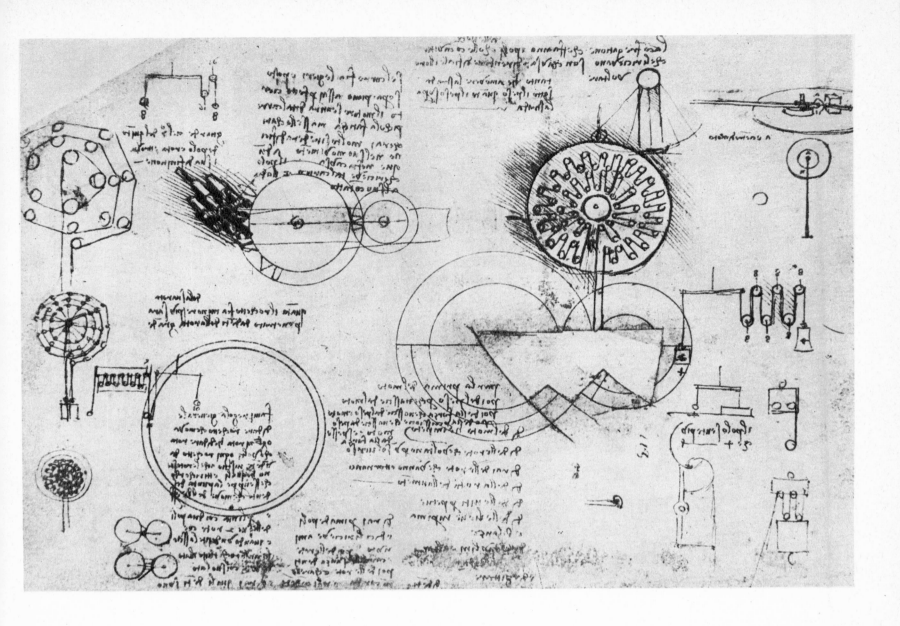

Studies on tackle – Cod. Atl., fol. 155 v-b

tion on which every subsequent rational theory was to rest; they were the indispensable preliminary research; they were certainly not theory, at least as we understand it today. The merit of having considered all these problems for the first time, problems on which modern science is still engaged, is immense, and constitutes a true title of glory for Leonardo. It would be absurd, in researches of such difficulty and complexity, to ask for the further theoretical completion, and sometimes the rectification, of laws whose existence crude observation could lead him only partly to suspect.

This was to be the task of his successors, and two more centuries were to elapse before analysis could complete—and even then not in final form—the edifice whose first stones Leonardo began to lay, small perhaps as compared to later developments, but solid and secure.

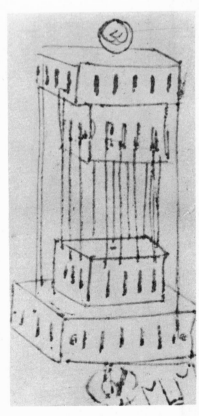

The science of motion claimed his attention virtually at the same time as his researches in statics. He tells us this in a note dated August, 1499: "Here I have written concerning motion and weight." It could not be otherwise. How was it possible for the engineer not to be interested in questions of dynamics? How could Leonardo, either in the environment of Florence, brimming with humanism and science, or in that of Milan, escape the more or less direct influence of the abundant production of our humanists, who were spreading the theories of Buridan, Albert of Saxony, Oresme, and the English school, although Leonardo certainly had neither the time nor the patience to read their undigested volumes in barbarous medieval Latin? He cites some of these authours, but, I believe, merely from memory, and what he knew of them he got either from other sources (such as encyclopedias) or from such third parties as Luca Pacioli, Marliani, and others.

His researches in dynamics, which are linked directly with the Aristotelian mechanics, are even more fragmentary than those in statics, and contain greater elements of uncertainty. All too often the errors, largely derived from Aristotelian mechanics, alternate with and are not cancelled by truths and brilliant intuitions; hints at demonstration are scarcer and more incomplete, when not entirely lacking, and the experimental tests are less lucid and not always conclusive.

The tremendous concept of force shines like a lighthouse, as has been said. After mastering the theory of impetus, Leonardo rises to a clear notion of the law of inertia, although certainly not so complete a conception as ours today or that of G. Ballo or Descartes, who were familiar with

Four-sided tackle – Cod. Atl., fol. 32 r-b

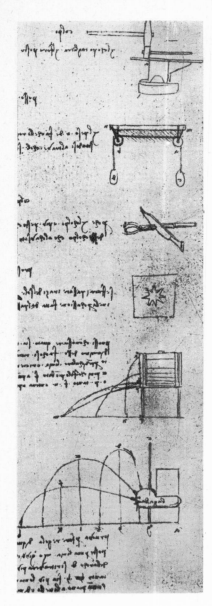

Varied studies of pulleys and on motion of discharge of jet of fluid – Ms. C, fol. 7 r

Leonardo's design of a circular tackle – Cod. Atl., fol. 225 r-g

the idea of the abstraction of a body not subject to forces, isolated as it were in the cosmos. The mind of Leonardo as a physicist and engineer was repelled by such a conception, as was Galileo's; impetus, that power or energy which the mover impresses on the moved and which is the cause of the motion, in conformity with the ideas of Philoponus, Buridan, and Albert of Saxony, in contrast to the Aristotelian theories, is consumed by external forces which the practical engineer can never abstract from nor neglect; and the idea that it is conserved if these causes can be completely eliminated made no sense to Leonardo. In the applications, however, and this is the real root of the matter, his insight was as true and correct as ours could have been, so that in the history of this principle, the first law of motion according to the Newtonian scheme, the most severe hypercritic cannot but give a place of honor to Leonardo. His applications of it to pendulum motion and flight were correct.

With respect to the relationships between force and the motion it induces, namely, velocity and acceleration, Leonardo, like all his contemporaries and successors down almost to Galileo, followed Aristotle and his incorrect dynamic law. In this field experience, limited to simple qualitative observation of the most common phenomena, could not tell him much to put him back on the right track.

One of the consequences of this law refers to the fall of heavy bodies. According to Aristotle, the more a body weighs, the faster it falls, and this seems in fact to agree with ordinary observation, when the resistance of the air is not taken into account; it was contradicted only by the atomistic theories. But if, as Galileo did experimentally and, even before Galileo, G. G. Benedetto did theoretically, Leonardo had considered two spheres of equal size and different materials falling from a suitable height, he would certainly have realized his error. Even in the midst of the disorder that prevails in his manuscripts relating to this topic, Leonardo's hesitation is apparent; although most of the times he states what Aristotle teaches, at some other times he says decidedly that velocity is independent of weight.

What was Leonardo's final opinion? We cannot say anything definite. But here too his intuition led him, in opposition to Albert of Saxony, to state a law correctly, to make another step toward the truth, asserting that in the free fall of a heavy body the velocity increases proportionally to the time and not to the distance, as Albert states. He tried a crude and inconclusive experiment, measuring the penetration into soft earth of balls dropped from different heights; it is inconclusive because, if I am not mistaken, it might lead to confusion as to the proportionality between velocity and distance, as well as between velocity and time. At any rate, the statement of the law is correct, as we know; and likewise correct is the statement of the law governing the times of fall of a heavy body on two inclined planes; thus Leonardo formulated two beautiful and fundamental dynamic laws. There was one step more to be made to reach the relationship between space and time, and Leonardo could well have made it if he had gone more deeply into Oresme's graphic methods, which I believe he was acquainted with; but this glory was reserved for Galileo. The way of science, as we see, is slow and arduous, and the dispelling of the mists that conceal the truth requires the gigantic efforts of the greatest mind for centuries.

The fall of a weight in such a way as to produce motion automatically (for example, in clocks driven by weights), the principle of which was known from ancient times and applied by Leonardo himself to various contrivances (file-cutting machines, rotating cranes, pulleys), may well have drawn Leonardo's attention to this subject, and we need only recall his motto: "Understand the reason and you have no need of experience." Machines employing the motion of a pendulum (and these too were known) must have suggested to him the study of the laws of the pendulun and of the motion of heavy bodies along arcs of circumferences. This is a serious and difficult problem in dynamics, the solution of which was not to be given until more than a century and a half after Leonardo's time, and was not even attempted by Galileo himself, to whom we owe the experimental laws of small oscillations.

Yet here too, although he was unable to penetrate into this mystery of dynamics, Leonardo made a brilliant observation. He observed that the motion of heavy bodies along arcs of circles is more rapid than that along the subtending chords. How could he have been sure of this, if he did not have the relationship between space and time? There is nothing to tell us how, and it cannot be said whether this is a result of direct experimental observation; the demonstration that he sketches is really so obscure—while perhaps also incorrect—that it presents one more confirmation of the predominant characteristics of Leonardo's dynamic researches.

There is no doubt that a great sage of the fifteenth century, Cardinal Nicholas of Cusa, had a great influence on Leonardo through his geometrical researches and ideas on cosmogony. Did Leonardo completely accept the heliocentric system in regard to which the Cusan was a precursor? It is probable, although there are no explicit references in the manuscripts. He makes clear reference to the rotation of the earth around its axis in twenty-four hours, and it is surprising that he posed the problem of the influence of this rotation on the fall of a heavy body from a great height; this is yet another difficult problem in dynamics of which Leonardo could give only a sketch, a very simple scheme, a crude first approximation, but still it led him to guess the deviation of the heavy body from the vertical (this is the well-known deviation toward the east). I use the word "guess" because this deviation, which was theoretically established by A. Borelli and then by Newton, is so

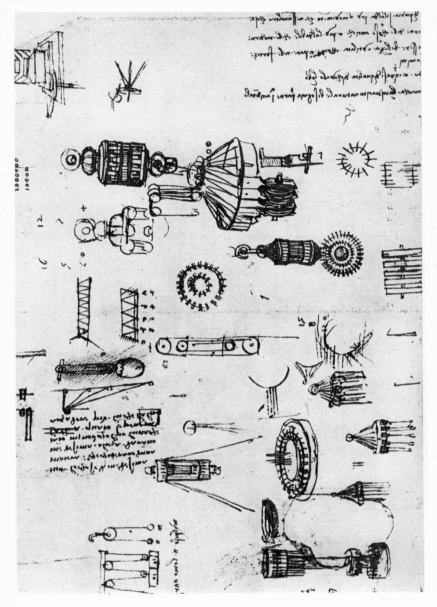

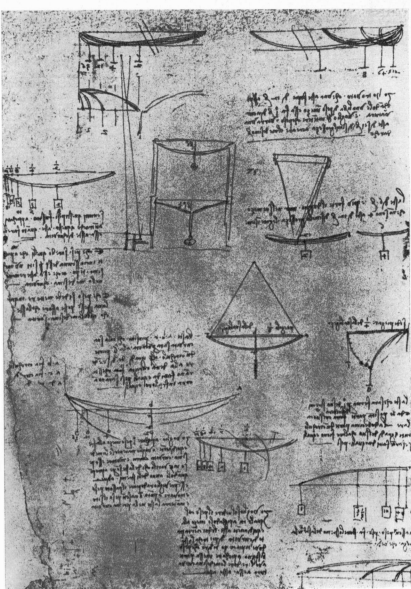

small that it seems almost impossible that Leonardo could have observed it experimentally. This is another of the great mysteries of Leonardo's mechanics. Is this statement of Leonardo's merely a theoretical conclusion arising out of the geometrical pattern of the composition of a uniform rectilinear motion with a circular motion, or does it record the observation of an experimental fact? I could not say; the first historically known observation was that made by Renieri from the tower of Pisa in 1640.

Proceeding from the case of the natural motion of heavy bodies to that of violent motion, it is well known that Leonardo was concerned with internal and external ballistics, with the forms of cannon shells and their automatic ascent, with bombards, crossbows, and machine guns—in other words, with investigations in a field in which he had famous precursors, such as Kyeser and Marino. But here too he is a vassal to Aristotle and his commentators. How did it happen that Leonardo, who posed so many weighty dynamic problems, and began on the solution of them, never posed the question of the trajectory of projectiles, even approximately and apart from research on air resistance? It may be that the practical engineer objected to such an abstraction for the practical purposes of gunfire; but the problem then was full of difficulties that have just been solved in our own times, and incompletely at that. The ideal case, of zero resistance, was to be one more of Galileo's triumphs, marking a new stage in researches in dynamics. Nonetheless, some drawings that Leonardo has left us in the Codex Arundel demonstrate his exquisitely keen spirit of observation, and the trajectories he drew are quite close to the parabolic form, but the drawings are among those that bear no legend. He also made exact observations on the recoil of cannons, perhaps the first of which there is written record.

Leonardo's studies on the flight of birds, with the consequent application to mechanical human flight, one of his most stupendous dreams, are classic; and it was in this connection that he was led to formulate two fundamental principles of mechanics—the law of the relativity of motion and the principle of action as equal and contrary to the reaction.

Limiting himself first to the merely kinematic aspect, he observed that "the movement of the air against the stationary thing is as great as the motion of the moving thing against the motionless air." So likewise for the motion of water against water, and of the air against the bird—a principle

Left: Studies and researches on tackle – Cod. Atl., fol. 147 r-*b*

Right: Researches on bending – Cod. Atl., fol. 211 r-*b*

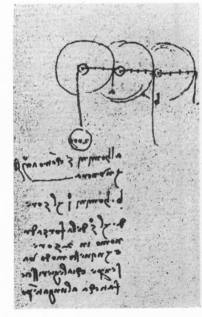

Researches on weights – Quad. Anat. VI, fol. 11 v

491

Studies of equilibrium on inclined plane – Ms. E, fol. 75 r

of constant application in all modern hydrodynamic and aerodynamic researches. From this kinematic aspect he rose immediately to the dynamic aspect, observing again: "The force of the object against the air is as great as that of the air against the object." Passing rapidly to the applications, he added in his robust, incisive prose: "See how the wings striking against the air hold up the heavy eagle in the thin upper air, near to the element of fire. And likewise see how the air moving over the sea strikes against the bellying sails, making the loaded, heavy ship run; so that by these demonstrative and definite reasons you may know that man with his great contrived wings, battling the resistant air and conquering it, can subject it and rise above it."

Thus, of the three fundamental principles on which classic Newtonian mechanics is based, Leonardo had distinct theoretical and practical ideas with respect to two; and although in regard to the most fundamental of them, the second, he adhered to the Aristotelian law of dynamics, he was able to discover a part of the truth in some views concerning the fall of heavy bodies. Possibly the times did not permit anything more, even to his genius; and the error of having followed Aristotle is much more than compensated for by all that his inventive genius contrived in the most diverse and unexpected applications; here, even taking into consideration what he must certainly have borrowed from his distant and immediate precursors, he appears like a magician, a technician to whom no artifice of mechanics is unknown. He stands out from and above all others, because in him the technician was not separated from the theoretician, who saw in theory the source, method, and *raison d'être* of the applications, who was able to conquer and discipline the forces of nature, who preached the complete adoption of machines to reduce or abolish the labor of man by means of the few sources of energy known at his time, saving time and hardship, and who demanded of mechanical tools their greatest mechanical contribution. In this sense, Leonardo was a modern man in the heart of the fifteenth century, and the only one.

Other topics in dynamics attracted his attention; we must limit ourselves to referring to his discussion of the impact of spherical bodies (central and oblique impact), which strikingly exhibits the characteristics we have tried to bring out, and of perpetual motion.

The concepts of work and energy that dominate all of modern science never appear explicitly in Leonardo; but in a sense not too different from the modern concept of work, he uses the word *fatica* ("labor"), and we get from his writings the feeling that he was aware of the physical meaning of energy as something that is transformed and consumed in machines by friction and in water by internal friction or viscosity, which makes the speculations of the seekers of perpetual motion futile.

Govi remarked, however, that there is serious doubt that Leonardo always held fast to this idea; this, to be sure, is not strange. Certainly, in various studies of his on the water screw as a means for raising water, he makes clear reference to perpetual motion. But this perhaps goes back to the days of his youth. Several extremely interesting drawings in the Codex Atlanticus are devoted to refuting this error, precisely in considering the motion of water. He says: "This motion cannot take place, because the water in the pit, which causes the first motion, must always weigh more than the water that is raised and poured into it." And he writes several times "against perpetual motion."

In one of the Forster codices he says: "Whatever weight is hung on a wheel, which weight will cause the motion of that wheel, there is no doubt that the center of that weight will come to rest under the center of that axis. And no instrument that human ingenuity can make, causing that axis to turn, will have power to do away with that effect." He ends with the famous invective which is at the same time a shot at the alchemists: "O speculators about continuous motion, how many vain plans have you created in that search! Go to join the seekers for gold!"

We do not know whether or not Leonardo's researches, at least the theoretical ones, were known to his contemporaries or remained buried with his manuscripts in the castle of Vaprio and were later disseminated more or less at random. His manuscripts have for the most part attracted the attention of artists because of the incomparable beauty of their drawings. All this does not in any way detract from their importance and from the position they should hold in the history of the development of mechanics. It is certainly not the only case in which discoveries have remained unknown or passed unnoticed. If the manuscripts had been more widely known, as almost certainly some of his inventions and ingenious mechanical devices were, they would surely have made the progress of theoretical mechanics and technology more rapid.

Reading them and meditating on them more than four centuries later, the reader cannot miss the deep poetic feeling that pervades them; for Leonardo was a tremendous poet without ever having written a verse. Whether he is defining force, or is enraptured by the divine harmony of the human body; whether he is ridiculing an adversary or describing the marvels of the ear, or finding a vigorous realistic phrase to describe the swift rise of the helicopter into the air, Leonardo shows himself as the artist-scientist, the sublime and exquisite poet. Examining the phenomenon of the camera obscura, which, if he did not invent it, he certainly studied and perfected as none of his contemporaries did, he is inspired to say; "O magic vision, what mind can penetrate such an essence? What tongue can explain such a marvel? This raises human discourse to divine contemplation."

ROBERTO MARCOLONGO

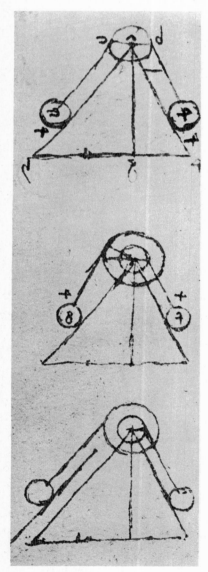

Static researches on suspended and constrained heavy bodies – Cod. Atl., fol. 365 v-*a*

LEONARDO'S MACHINES

Far from the milieux of the *università* and from the cultural coteries of his time, a stranger to the strident polemical challenges on the most abstruse and often useless topics that were fashionable then, Leonardo, who was self-taught, was able, in full liberty of spirit and discourse, to develop his scientific thought and follow that marvelous instinct of observation which underlies all of his work as engineer, scientist, and artist.

In applied mechanics he surpassed all his predecessors and contemporaries, not only because of his inventions, but because he was the first to analyze machines and study them in their details— the first who sought to understand their mechanisms and elements and, in sum, realized their actual functioning. It was precisely from this understanding of machines and their parts that he could go on to conceive new applications and new mechanisms.

For the mechanicians who preceded him, on the other hand, machines remained, as the Aristotelian definition puts it, products of a particular craft, of an artisan, hence constructs apart, formed of parts peculiar to them that could not be separated and analyzed, still less drawn, studied, or subjected to distinct calculations. And even among Leonardo's successors each machine was still considered by itself, and described all over again each time, as in Ramelli, Lorini, and Besson, for example, who repeated descriptions of contrivances that were alike, and had been used over and over again, as if they were new.

With Leonardo the graphic representation of the machine took on a character that was a prelude to the modern procedures of machine designing. Most often it is on the details of the apparatus that he dwells, and one would be tempted to say that some of the folios of his codices are shop drawings that he handed to the workmen engaged in constructing the mechanisms he was devising.

He almost always entrusted his ideas to the expressive power of drawing and did not lose himself in detailed descriptions, unless calculations or statements summarizing his experiments were involved. Even when he was reproducing machines already well known, or returning to mechanical applications that had already been employed, Leonardo gave the project and the drawing the imprint of his artist's personality and many-sided genius. If we compare the drawings of his machines with those of Kyeser or Taccola, of his anonymous predecessors, or of Valturio, his contemporary, we see at once the enormous distance between these mechanicians of the decadence and the man who must be considered the true inaugurator of the scientific method and the precursor of machine technology.

It would be hard to determine the principal sources from which he drew in the field of machine construction, especially since there was a veritable historical desert between Hero and him; it is certain an any rate that he took up again, drew, modified, and perfected some machines that belong to the work of some of the great mechanicians who preceded him. In truth, it is his study of ancient mechanics that reveals the critical and inquiring spirit which was the basis of all his work in technical mechanics; it is precisely in his systematic effort at understanding existing machines, and perfecting them, that his mechanical genius and positive creative spirit shine forth.

On these solid foundations Leonardo built the imposing structure of his mechanical constructions and of that "instrumental or mechanical science" which he defined as "most noble and useful beyond all others, since by means of it all animated bodies that have motion perform all their operations," clearly delimiting the scope and function of machines, which serve to channel available forces in such

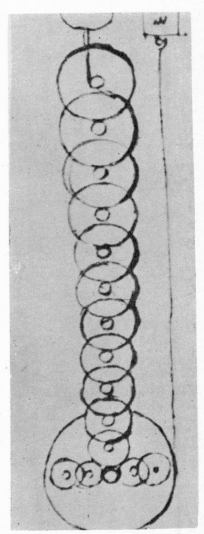

Above and below: Leonardo's studies of antifriction devices – Manuscript I, fol. 58 r

Bell and harness mounted on rollers

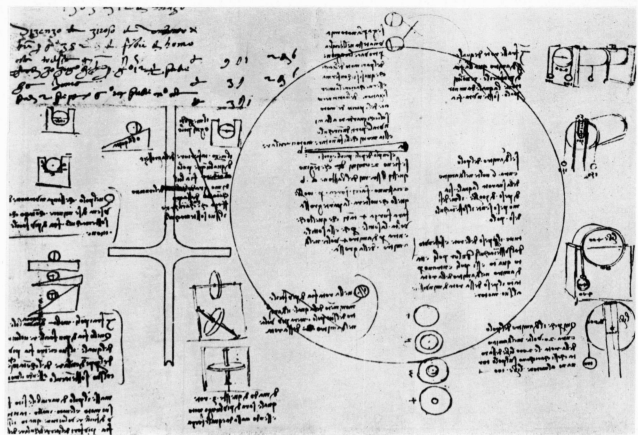

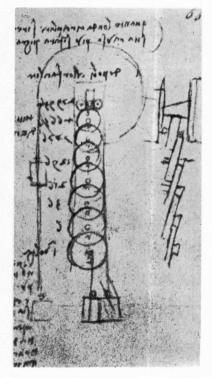

Another system of drive wheel with journal on sloping rollers – Ms. I, fol. 114 r

Journals rotating on rollers – Cod. Atl., fol. 9 r

Details of a small experimental apparatus for study of friction of *poli* [axles] – Cod. Ashb. II, fol. 9 r

a way as to obtain a determinate amount of work with the greatest possible accuracy and the smallest use of man's direct labor.

Now, in all Leonardo's work as a designer and constructor of machines, there is this obvious tendency to reduce man's labor, to make use of the sources of energy in his possession, to obtain the greatest precision of movement and the greatest mechanical advantage from his mechanisms, and to achieve his great dream of "making instruments by which this force could be generated, since by it infinite worlds would be moved."

Leonardo has been blamed for designing machines and contrivances that could not be constructed; it has also been said that most of these drawings of his are but the offspring of an artist's heated imagination. But although it is true that Da Vinci's notes are not always clear or complete, and that some of the mechanisms are incomprehensible, because not perfected, it is also true that some of the many machines drawn by that miraculous "left hand" are easy to build, rationally conceived, and perfectly functional.

Furthermore, Leonardo himself, when he writes that "every instrument must be made with experiments," tells us that his constant concern in planning machines was precisely to build and to test the mechanisms he had devised. But his writings also contain the direct proofs of this activity of his as a constructor of machines; they show that alongside his painter's studio there was a mechanical workshop in which craftsmen and specialists worked.

He writes in a note of 1493: "We made a reckoning on the first day of November. There were four months to pay Giulio and nine months due to Maestro Tomaso. Then Maestro Tomaso made six candlesticks: 10 days. Giulio, on some springs, 15 days. Then he worked for himself until May 27, and worked for me on a winch from July 18 till August 17, and out of that a half day for a woman, and then for me on two locks until August 20." The Maestro Tomaso in question was Masini, known as Zoroastro, a skilled woodworker, and Giulio was a German mechanic who did precision work.

At Rome, in the Belvedere, the studio of Leonardo, which was composed of several rooms or sections, was frequented by students working with him and for him, and by specialized German artisans working with him in building mechanisms and machines. Leonardo had some trouble with one of these mechanics, a certain Giorgio, who seems among other things to have attempted to appropriate his inventions and discoveries.

But in addition to these precise data on his activity as a mechanical engineer, there is all the work of his followers in this field to prove that Leonardo's drawings were not mere artist's fantasies, but projects that were the product of research, experiments, and calculation. The influence of the work of Da Vinci is evident, or at least indisputable, in Ramelli, Cardan, Zonca, and Besson, to cite only the best known. Even though this work was not published in print, and his manuscripts and notes, before their dispersal, were known only to a few who were close to him, it cannot be assumed

494

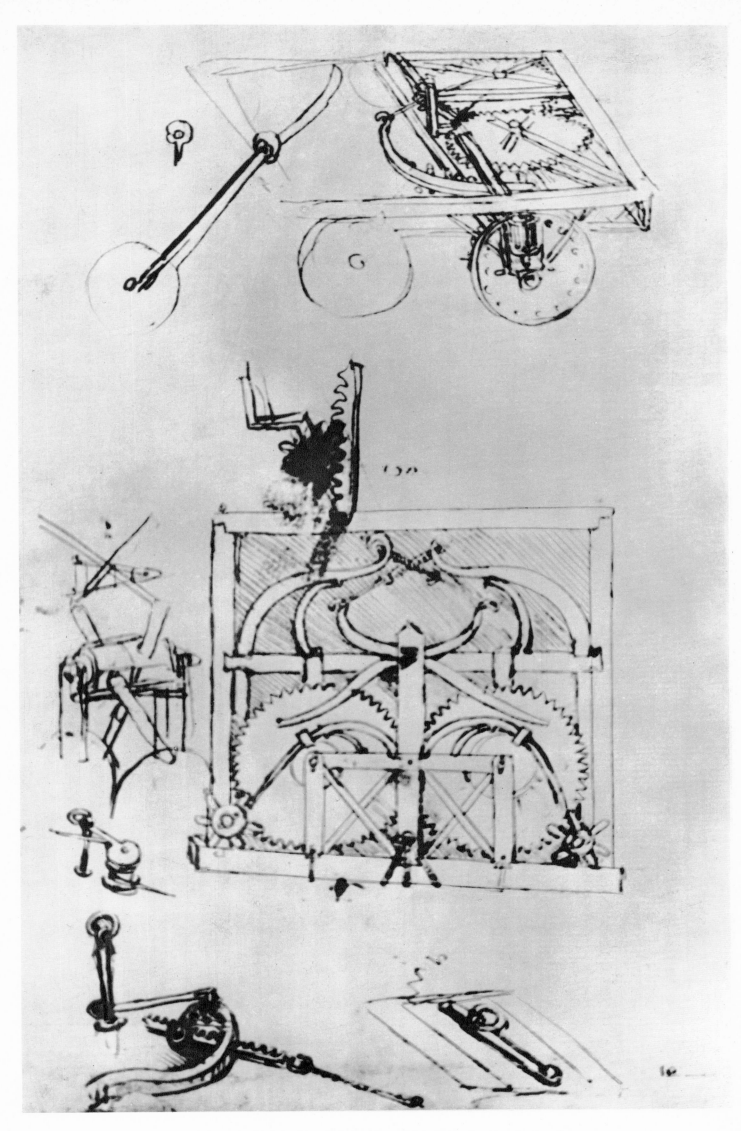

Perspective and plan drawings of automotive wagon, moved by system of springs
and equipped with differential transmission – Cod. Atl., fol. 296 v-*a*

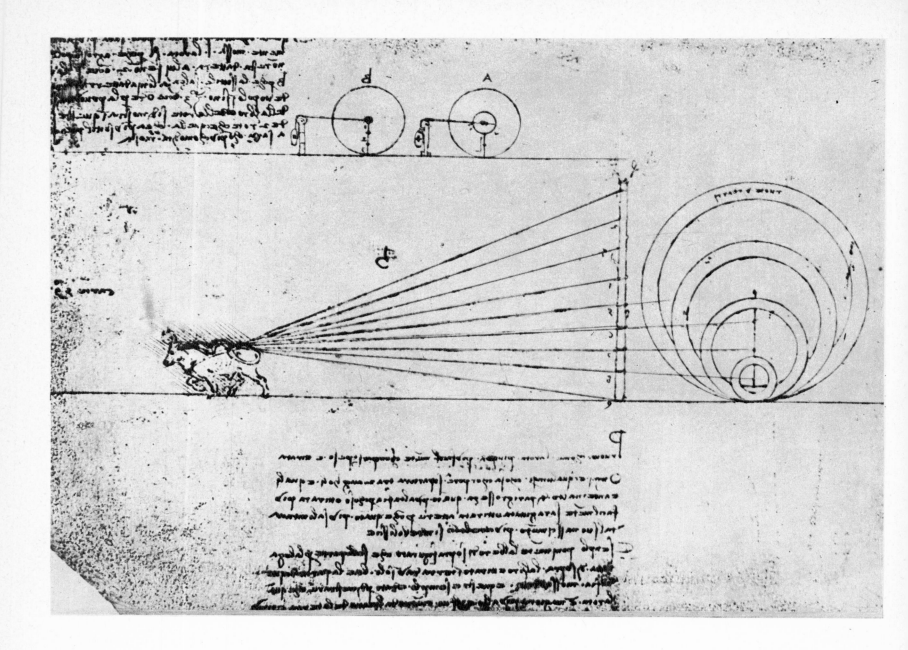

that his contemporaries were not aware of Leonardo's activities as a mechanician. When we see the drawings of the most famous mechanicians of the sixteenth and seventeenth centuries, we are continually and naturally led to correlate them with Da Vinci's schemes and inventions, to which they are technically inferior in many cases.

For example, Ramelli's *currolotti* are nothing but Leonardo's *curi o bilichi*, or rollers; Ramelli also copies from Leonardo the *sopate* of his pumps, which are nothing but the conical valves drawn in the manuscripts now at the Institut de France, and gets the "eccentric wheels within the coverings," or diaphragms, of his pumps from Leonardo's "bellows without leather."

Is it not possible that Fausto Zonca's blowers, crank mechanisms, machine tools, and presses, Cardan's fan for smoke and his jack wheel, Verantio's parabolic-frame bridges, life belt, and ropemaking wheel, and Besson's lathes were all more or less directly derived from Da Vinci's constructions?

Even apart from any influence that the thought and work of Leonardo in mechanics may have had on his contemporaries and successors, there is no doubt that he stands above them all by reason of the scope and variety of his activity as an engineer, and especially because he is the first to have penetrated to the essence of machines and evaluated their true functions.

When he denied the possibility of perpetual motion, as the result of experiments he had made on a device suggested by Tàccola, he implicitly recognized the great principle of the conservation of energy. And when he wrote, "Gravity and force, together with percussion, are the generators of motion, which cannot exist without these creatures. But each of these powers cannot in similar motion generate a power similar to itself," he anticipated Galileo's limpid preface to his *Meccaniche*: "The belief that these workmen have had, and continue to have, that with a little power they can move and raise the greatest weights, outwitting nature with their machines, as it were—whose essence it is, and most stable constitution, that no resistance can be overcome by a power that is not more powerful than it."

Research into the causes of friction began with Leonardo; with him the conception of mechanical advantage was introduced into the science of machines, which began, to use Mach's terms, to assume that feature of economy which is characteristic of modern mechanics.

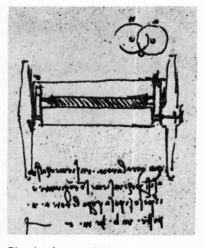

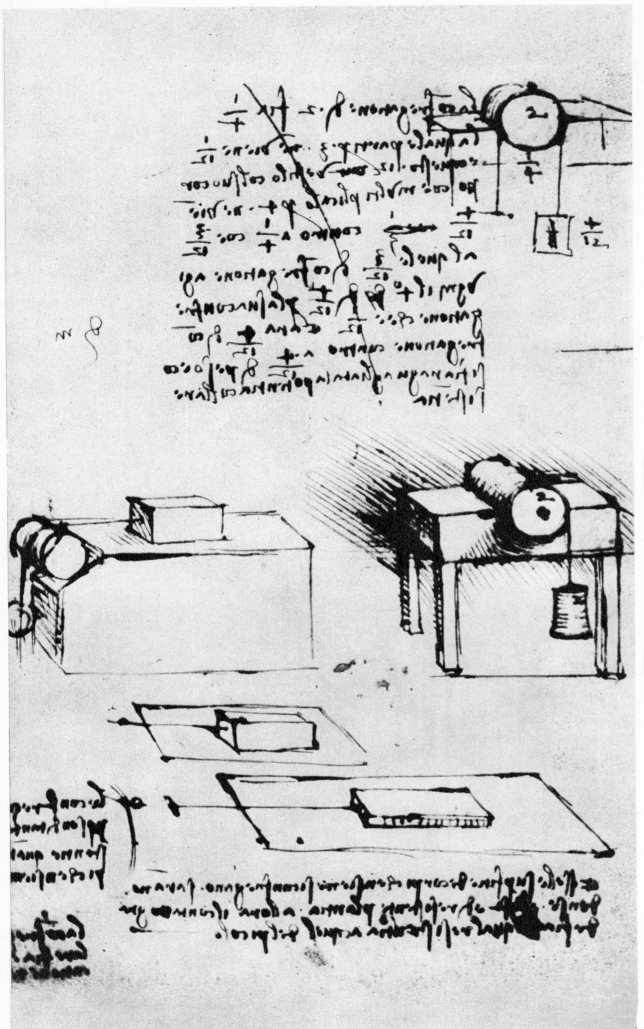

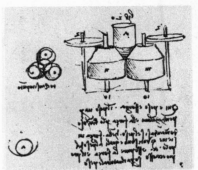

System of rotating cylinders with thrust rollers for journals – Cod. Atl., fol. 390 v-*b*

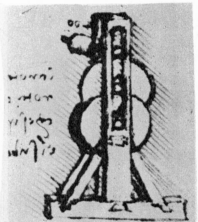

Frame with roller supports for winch – Cod. Atl., fol. 348 v-*a*

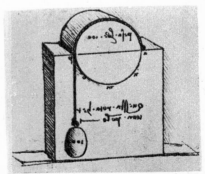

Apparatus for practical determination of frictional resistance in journal – Cod. Atl., fol. 363 v-*c*

Leonardo was the first to conduct systematic study of the causes of friction, either on plane surfaces or in bearings, preceding Amontons (1699) and Coulomb (1781) by two centuries; the latter was to construct for his experiments the apparatus shown in the drawing above, which appears on folio 41 recto of the Codex Arundel

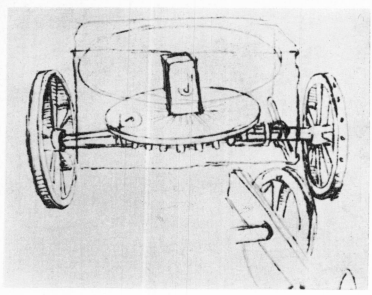

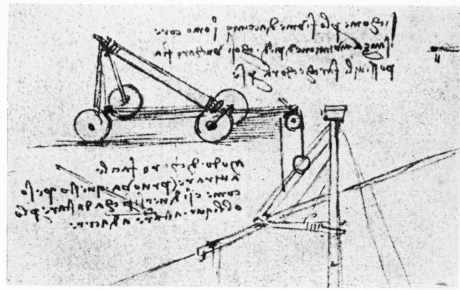

Above, left: Transmission with multiplying ratio for wagon axle – Cod. Atl., fol. 4 v-*a*

Above, right: Wagon moving itself by means of falling weight – Cod. Ashb. II, fol. 2 v

Below, left: Millstone transmission with band brake – Ms. L, fol. 34 v

Below, right: One of the finest plates of mechanical drawings, in which Leonardo draws details of articulated chains, anticipating Vaucanson and Balle, and cylindrical and accordeon-shaped springs – Cod. Atl., fol. 357 r-*a*

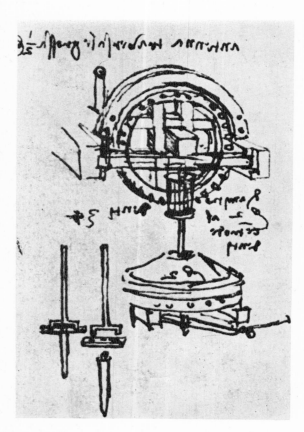

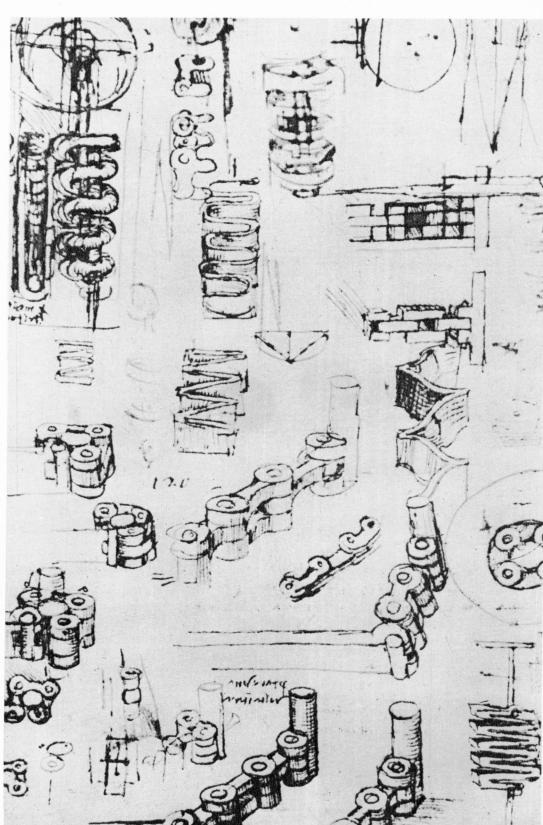

Leonardo realized at once the great importance of passive resistances in machines, and in view of the dates assigned to the various codices, he must have begun his studies of friction, which he calls *confregazione*, by 1487, continuing them beyond 1505. For we find notes, citations, and statements referring to friction in the Codex Atlanticus, in the Forster codices, in the manuscripts at the Institut de France, and in the Codex Arundel. We believe that the sum total of these studies, along with the experiments on tractive force, constitute one of the most complete and original sections of Da Vinci's mechanics. In fact, the fundamental conclusions of Amontons (1699), Musschenbroek (1729), De Camus (1722), Désaguillers (1751), and Coulomb himself (1781), the men to whom, with Morin, the most important studies on friction are due, do not go beyond the general laws already found and stated by Leonardo.

Da Vinci not only studied friction in solids, explicitly and fully distinguishing rubbing or sliding friction from rolling friction and friction in bearings or journals, but also experimented with the various kinds of friction as functions of the nature of the materials in contact, and of the possible interposition of lubricants or rollers between the surfaces. Of particular importance is the fact that in a note on folio 209 verso-*a* of the Codex Atlanticus Leonardo speaks just as explicitly of the friction between "liquid and liquid," sensing the existence of a resistance to motion in fluids.

On the basis of all of Leonardo's experiments, many evidences of which still remain in the drawings of experimental apparatus employed, as found in various codices, it may be stated definitely that Leonardo perceived the following principles:

1. Frictional resistance depends on the nature of the materials in contact;

2. Frictional resistance depends on the degree of finish or "slipperiness' of the surfaces in contact;

3. Frictional resistance depends on the possible presence of a fluid or other material interposed between the surfaces;

4. Frictional resistance increases with the pressure urging one body against the other;

5. Frictional resistance is independent of the area of the surfaces in contact.

From the reference on folio 132 verso of the second Forster codex to "the friction of a weight at the beginning of its motion," it also follows that Leonardo correctly stated all the principal laws of friction, sensing the law of static friction as well.

In his calculations, he usually assumes the uniform value of 1/4 for the coefficient of friction, but it is quite clear that he adopts this value only in the case of smooth, flat surfaces in contact, as folio 198 verso-*a* of the Codex Atlanticus confirms: "Experience shows that a polished object drawn across a polished plane resists being moved by its mover with a force equal to the fourth part of its weight." It is probable that he adopted the value of 1/4 for simplicity in calculation, and in consideration of the fact that actually this figure was very near the actual values of the coefficients relating to the materials he usually employed.

Normally, at any rate, in solving problems of equilibrium on inclined planes, in pulleys, or in balances, Leonardo took the frictional resistance into account, with particular reference to the friction in the hubs of wagon wheels. The problems of locomotion attracted his attention particularly, as is shown by the very large number of drawings and sketches of vehicles to be found everywhere in his manuscripts. It can be said that no one prior to Leonardo gave such extensive and complete study to the most varied kinds of vehicles, and especially to war cars and wagons for transporting heavy loads; he proposed new systems of propulsion and ways of reducing passive resistance. Several times he writes under his pictures of vehicles, "Easy-moving wagons," or "Easy wagon," showing his constant concern with reducing tractive force, either by applying rollers (*bilichi*) to the pins of the wheels, or by devising special original transmissions, or by determining, through research and experiment, the most favorable conditions of draft for the vehicle, or the most logical methods of construction. And even though his proofs in this field are not always precisely formulated, especially as regards the angle of traction, the fact that he was able to establish experimentally that resistance to traction decreases as the diameter of the wheels increases, and as the ratio between the diameter of the journal and that of the wheel decreases, undoubtedly represents one of the most notable conquests of Da Vinci's genius.

It is beyond question that, as he thought of flight, he also thought of the possibility of an automotive vehicle. He may or may not have been aware of Giovanni Fontana's projects for mechanical vehicles, but he certainly knew those of Valturio, which suggested to him the idea of the "covered chariots, safe and unassailable," of which he speaks in his letter to Ludovico Sforza. In following up this idea of constructing war vehicles that would do away with the horse, so vulnerable in combat, he designed the most diversified types of transmission, searching for the system that would best enable him to make use of man's energy or the potential energy of weights, and deliberated—probably as the first to do so—the possibility of developing and accumulating in the vehicle itself the energy necessary for motion.

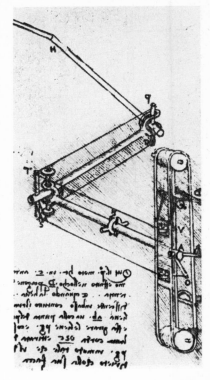

Detail of articulated joint of wing – Cod. Atl., fol. 341 r-*c*

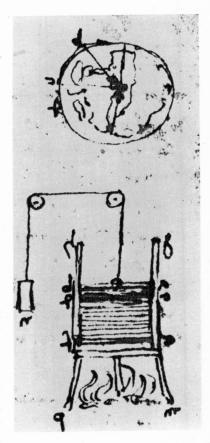

A device for testing the expansion of water vapor – Papin was to adopt this arrangement of Leonardo da Vinci's in his first engine – Codex Leicester, fol. 10 r

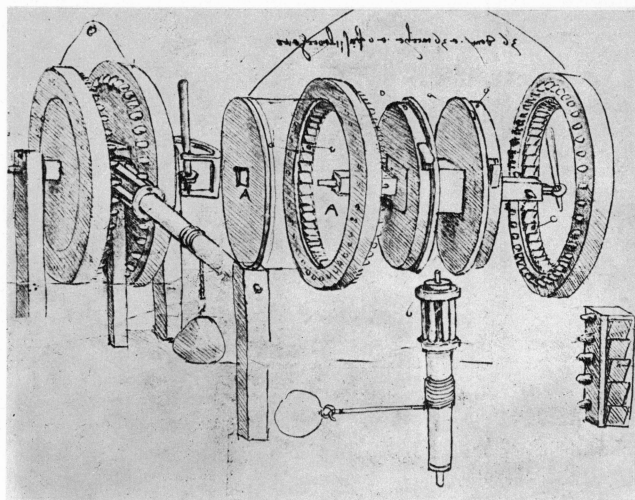

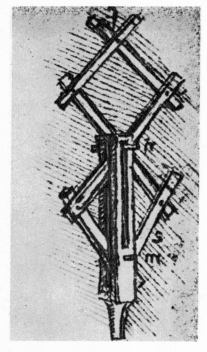

Even if, as seems likely, Leonardo did not build his automotive wagon, which Calvi pointed out and Semenza described and studied, it is his merit in any case that he tried to make use of the energy stored in a system of springs to move a vehicle, an idea that still tempts the minds of technicians today. This wagon, which is considered the forefather of the modern automobile, probably represents the final stage of a process of development which can be traced through the designs and projects for other vehicles. Leonardo devised and drew a wagon transmission with a multiplying transmission ratio and steering wheel, obviously actuated by manpower; in his "tortoise" he adopted four driving and steering wheels, operated by eight men by means of cranks and reduction gearing; finally, in his automotive wagon, he arrived at independent transmission for each wheel, with an epicyclic wheel arrangement that is a forerunner of the modern differential. But the clarity of this part of the vehicle in the drawing is matched by the lack of clarity in the portion referring to the system of springs that was to supply the energy needed for the motion of the wagon. Leonardo left this incomplete, and it is likely that he had to abandon the attempt to perfect this vehicle when faced with the difficulties of linking the springs with the driving wheels.

In trying to reconstruct this vehicle, I made a further interesting observation which is of some importance in interpreting drawings by Da Vinci. If the arrangement of the wagon wheels and lantern transmission gears drawn by Leonardo were adopted, the width of the tread would be not more than forty centimeters, making the stability of the vehicle very precarious. However, more attentive examination of the drawing in a photographic enlargement showed that actually the gear teeth of the driving wheels of the wagon are turned inward and not outward; it is clear, therefore, that Leonardo consciously changed the planes about in his graphic representation of the mechanism. Since this transposition is to be found in other machine drawings of his, we may infer that he followed this practice in order to make some details of his mechanical devices more comprehensible.

Construction of some of Da Vinci's machines has also brought out the fact that the arrangement of some kinematic elements is not always correct, but it should not be forgotten that the drawings we know of are usually nothing more than sketches, in which the general idea is given rather than the method of constructing the machine or mechanism. Indeed, in Leonardo's drawings of machines the studies of details are more interesting than the projects as a whole, of which, as a rule, only a few parts are completed. His manuscripts constitute an enormously rich mine of notes and drawings of machines, a genuine treatise on applied kinematics and the art of mechanical drawing.

As we have pointed out, what distinguishes Da Vinci's mechanics from that of his predecessors is the fact that he was the first, it seems, to consider machines as complexes of kinematic elements, which he analyzed, described, calculated, and drew, within the limits of his knowledge, abandoning

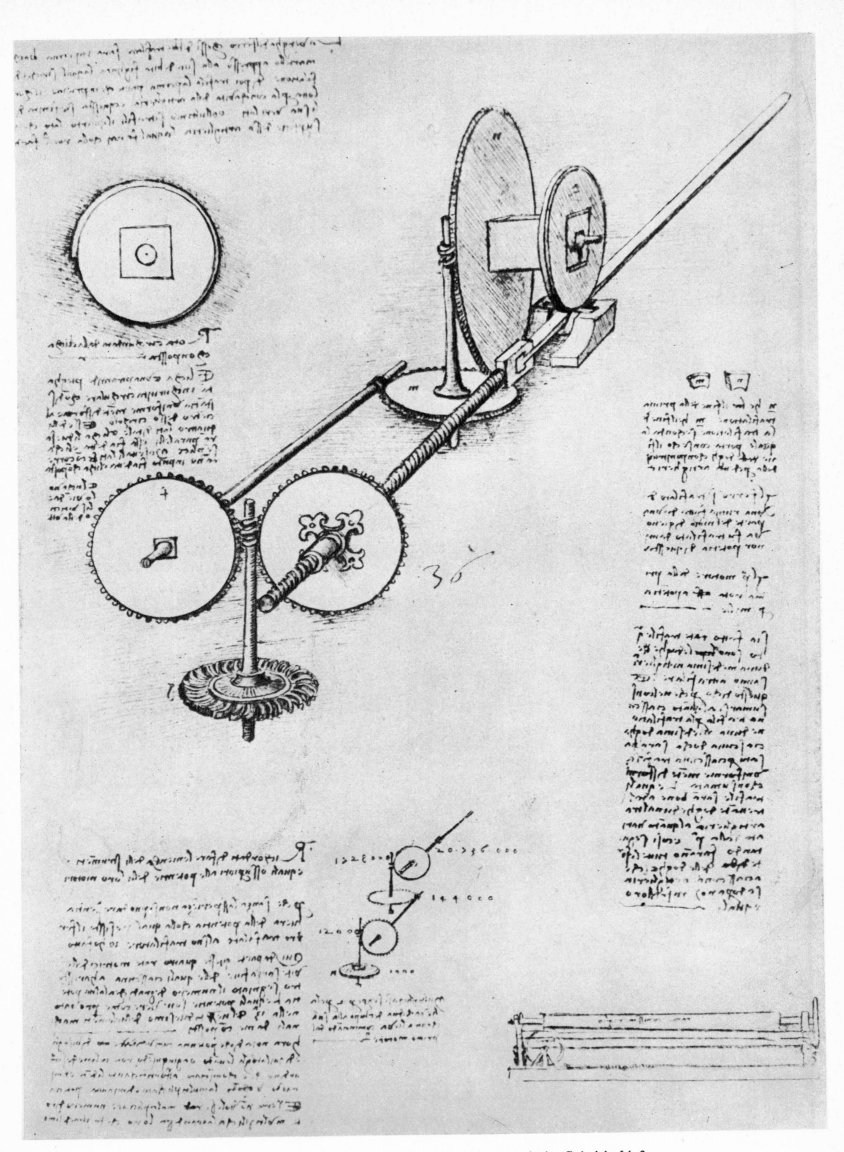

Machine for drawing cannon staves, actuated by horizontal water wheel – Cod. Atl., fol. 2 r-a

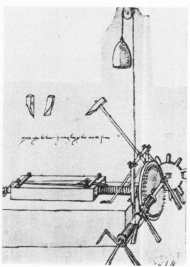

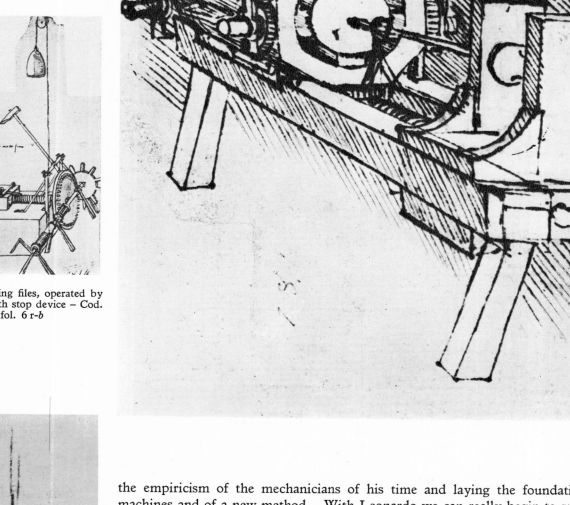

Machine for cutting files, operated by falling weight, with stop device – Cod. Atl., fol. 6 r-*b*

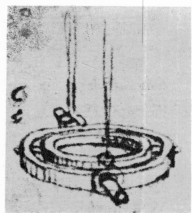

Gimbal ring suspension – Cod. Atl., fol. 288 r-*b*

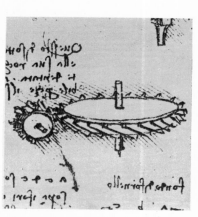

Gears with helicoidal teeth - Cod. Atl., fol. 396 r

502

the empiricism of the mechanicians of his time and laying the foundations of a new conception of machines and of a new method. With Leonardo we can really begin to speak of progress in machines, in the modern sense, and of new horizons opening in technology with the introduction of the most ingenious machine tools and operating machines, found in his drawings in great numbers.

The limited sources of energy available to him naturally led him to concern himself more with operating machines than with motors, but he thought of "instruments where this force might be generated," thinking among other things of the power of expansion of steam, sketching a rudimentary motor with an arrangement that closely recalls the first steam engine of Papin.

Leonardo did not succeed, and could not have succeeded, in making use of steam as motive power, but it is true nonetheless that in the two devices that he drew and described on folios 10 and 15 of the Codex Leicester he was actually making two rudimentary steam engines, imagining an arrangement that was to be reproduced exactly by Huygens and Papin. In these two apparatus devised by Leonardo to "measure how much water increases on turning into air," he anticipated the experiments of Giovanni Battista della Porta and Salomon de Caus.

The sources of energy he usually has recourse to are the muscles, water, the potential energy of suitably placed weights, sometimes the wind, often the stored energy in springs; but in his fan-operated roasting jack he has also given us an example of the use of hot air for moving a spiral fan, which may be considered the first of the kind. In making use of these limited sources of energy, Leonardo's ingenuity appears in the most highly original arrangements, the most diverse kinematic linkages, the most varied and sometimes surprising of applications.

Among the moving parts, the gear trains naturally occupy a pre-eminent place in da Vinci's machines. He often used crown gears with pegs and lantern wheels, or gears with triangular teeth, known also to the ancients, and evidently in common use and construction in his time; but the numerous drawings of toothed wheels and of details of gearing that he has left us show clearly that he was concerned with and gave exhaustive study to the problems of the resistance and mechanical advantage of these kinematic couples, so necessary to his machines.

For example, on folio 61 verso of the Codex Atlanticus he takes up the problem of the contact profiles of cylindrical toothed wheels, and writes: "The wheels that are desired to have teeth always

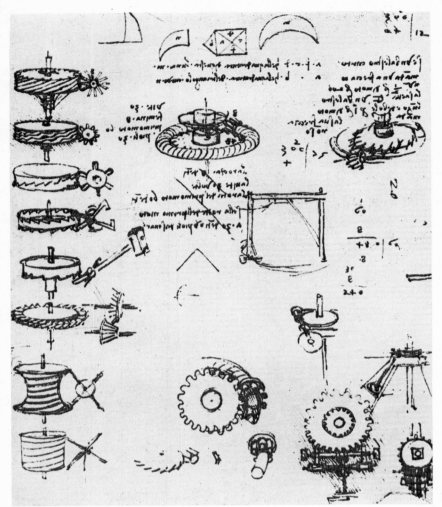

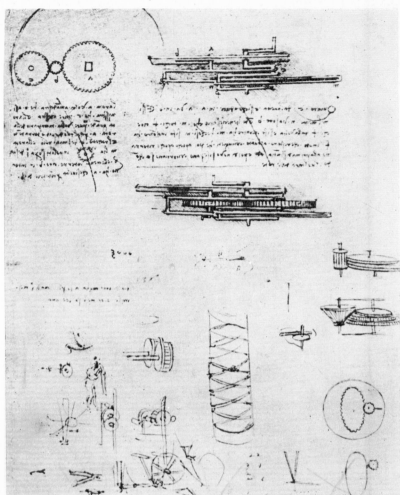

engage and disengage by those teeth; but as for those that are enmeshed, the line of their contacts should always be straight to the axis of each wheel; and this occurs in the case of teeth the end points of whose thicknesses are directed toward the center of their wheels." He depicts a remarkable variety of tooth forms; among them are beautiful examples of helicoidal teeth for gears and shafts at angles to each other, teeth of trapezoidal cross section, and teeth for bevel gears.

In his machines he likewise makes frequent use of worm-rack and worm-worm-gear couples, as well as of the helicoidal couple, in which he appears to have preferred, probably for constructive reasons, a rectangular thread, with single or multiple pitch. When speaking of the worm as a means of transmission, he writes in one of the Forster codices: "Among screws of equal thickness, that one will be most difficult for its mover which has the largest number of paths. And among those of equal length, thickness, and [number of] paths, you will find that one more easily moved which has in it the largest number of turns of its path."

We find a very interesting set of gear trains, among them a pair of bevel gears, on folio 372 recto of the Codex Atlanticus, so clearly represented that it needs no detailed explanation. We cannot help being surprised at the study, on folio 27 verso of the same codex, of a crank and linkage mechanism, with a sketch of epicycloid gears, which we find also in folio 205 recto. In other instances he draws rapid-return gears, gear systems comprising a pinion and an elliptic wheel, pairs of wheels with primitive curves of various sorts, complex gear systems including one with three gears having parallel axes actuated by a single cylindrical gear, and another system, with three coaxial gears driven by a single conical gear, which embodies the principle of a three-speed gear shift.

From toothed wheels Leonardo passes easily and with equal originality to ratchet-and-pawl devices and detent mechanisms, which he uses especially in his machines operated by the fall of weights, and to various means of transforming motion; in connection with the latter, especial interest attaches to the drawing on folio 113 of Ms. G, which shows a mechanical system for converting oscillatory motion into rotary motion, and to another drawing in which a cylindrical guide is used to obtain the alternating motion of a pump piston.

Other moving elements used and studied by Leonardo are: bearing shafts and thrust shafts, such as he adopted in the rotating couple of a mill or of water screws; systems with linkages in parallelogram form; various crank mechanisms, rectilinear and cylindrical guides; the articulated joint that forms part of the wing of the flying machine; numerous rope, belt, and chain drives. For the last-

Left: Various types of gearing and ratchets – Cod. Atl., fol. 372 r-b

Right: Studies of planetary motion and speed changes – Cod. Atl., fol. 27 v-a

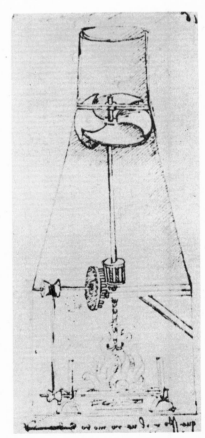

Leonardo's design of a mechanical roasting jack operated by a hot-air fan – Cod. Atl., fol. 5 v-a

503

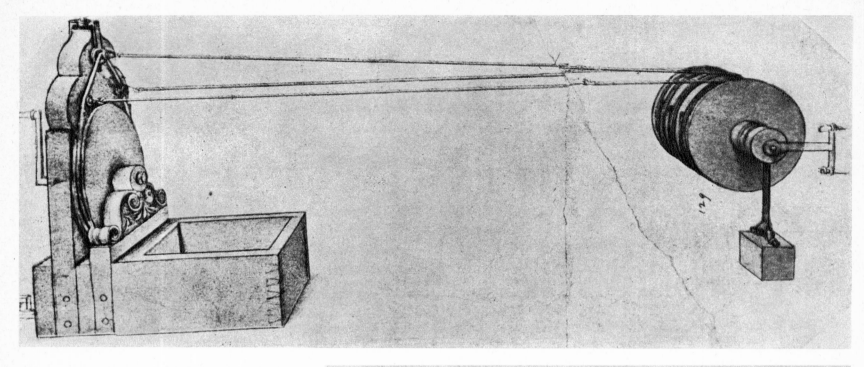

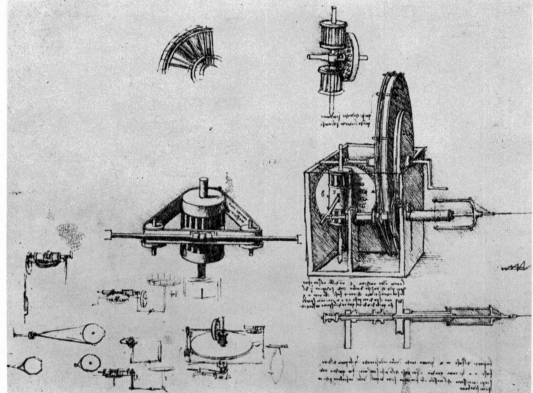

Leonardo's contribution to textile machinery was fundamental. He anticipated Johann Jürgen (1530), by at least thirty years, drawing on folio 393 of the Codex Atlanticus a machine for spinning with a flyer, for which he gives a detailed cross section on the same folio

In this machine Leonardo was already using the flyer as winding means and a device for automatically distributing the thread which was not to be invented and applied in England till 1794 (center figure)

Also among the drawings of the Codex Atlanticus we find on folio 2 verso-*b* a cord machine with three spindles (upper figure), and on folio 2 verso-*a* a cord machine with fifteen spindles (lower figure)

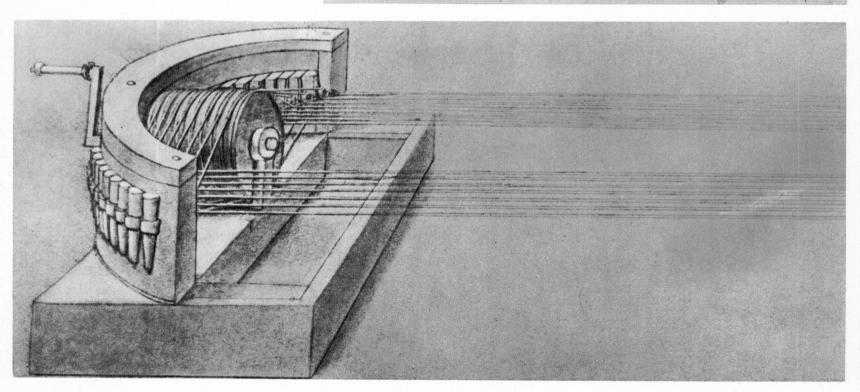

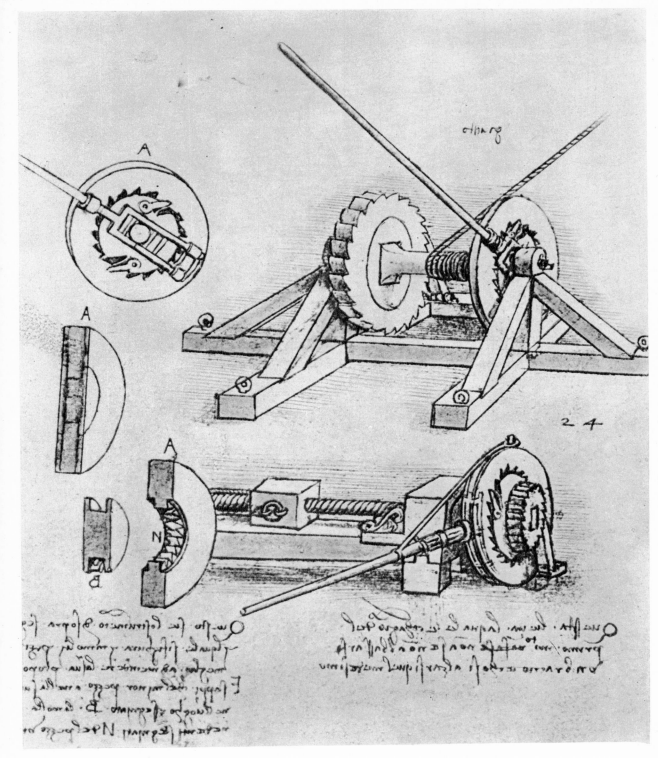

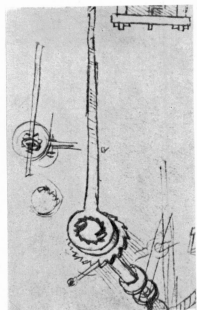

Shaft with stopping device and ratchet
crank – Ms. B, fol. 72 r

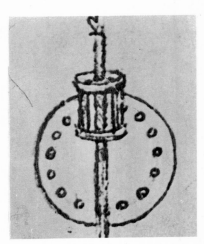

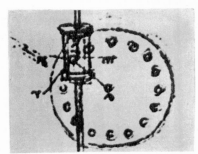

Study of wear of teeth in gearing with
crown and lantern wheels – Ms. H,
fol. 86 v

named, Leonardo gives us a masterly drawing of articulated chains on folio 357 recto of the Codex Atlanticus, which proves irrefutably that he anticipated Vaucanson and Galle, who have been considered as the inventors of this type of chain.

Reduction of the frictional resistance at bearings attracted his special attention as a constructor of machines, and he makes any number of applications of rollers, in vehicles, in moving carriages on machines, in various types of oscillating or rotating mechanisms, and in bell-suspension systems. In this connection he also speaks of "marvelous motions" and of marvels of the art of mechanics, possibly deceiving himself as to the excellence of the roller systems he had devised, but at any rate showing by these applications that he had a surmise of the importance that roller and ball bearings were to have in modern machines. He also gave some thought to brakes, and on folio 37 verso of Ms. L drew a band brake that was later taken up again by Ramelli.

All these studies and projects on kinematic elements, mechanisms, and contrivances constitute the basic material of his applications of them to machines. It was precisely by perfecting these elements that he intended to arrive at reduction of the power employed and at elimination, where possible, of man's labor and interference.

In the field of lifting machines, such mechanisms as pulleys, windlasses, tackle, water screws, and jacks were of course widely used in Leonardo's time, but he took up and solved, either by calculation or by means of many ingenious devices, the problems involved in the lifting of heavy

505

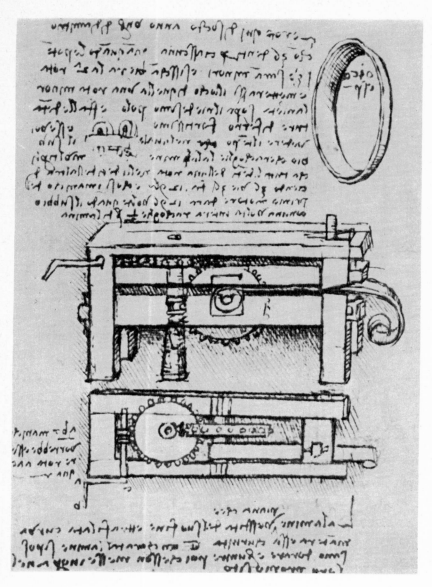

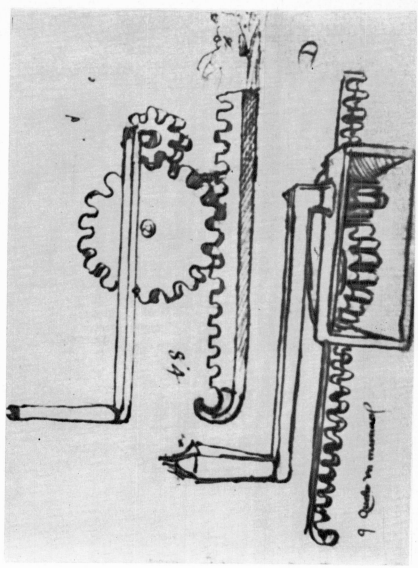

weights, in particular artillery and bells. Leaving aside the machines for raising liquids, which come under the heading of hydraulics, we note an interesting wagon, the forefather of present-day trucks; here a winch and a three-legged derrick are mounted on the wagon itself and operated by the draft horses through a transmission by way of the wheels, for lifting the heavy objects to be transported, in particular heavy bells.

In the construction of machine tools, Leonardo can be designated immediately as a precursor of genius. Unfortunately not all his drawings are complete or understandable, and although some of these machines can be easily reconstructed, and it is likely that he himself built them, other remain obscure in design and cannot be built. It must be considered that in some cases he tried to express certain ideas in his drawings but did not succeed, lacking the materials and means, as offered by technology today, for translating them into reality. This mental toil of his is also evident from the drawings and sketches of some details. Among the most characteristic and perspicuously designed of Da Vinci's machine tools, some of which were reconstructed on the occasion of the Leonardo Exposition at Milan in 1939, faithfully following the indications of the manuscripts, is the file-cutting machine, completely automatic, with a controlled sliding carriage and intermittent motion of the striking hammer and automatic stop. In this instance the motive force is furnished by a falling weight; the tool, which is a cutting hammer, is interchangeable. The system applied to this file cutter was also used by Leonardo in various other machines with striking hammers, designed for other mechanical operations.

Drawn with equal clarity, and with a sense for art that is unknown to modern mechanical draftsmen, are the two splendid drawing machines for profiled bars, operating by traction, which can be admired in the first pages of the Codex Atlanticus. These drawing machines are actuated by a water wheel which through a worm meshing with two gears sets in motion both the wheel of the pressure cylinder [roll] and the traction wheel for the bar. Of similar design are other types of rolling mills for sheets and strips of lead or copper.

The pages of the Codex Atlanticus showing these machines for drawing cannon staves may be cited as extremely interesting examples of Da Vinci's technology, and constitute one more proof that he built and used these machines. He gives advice as to the material that is to be drawn, lists the

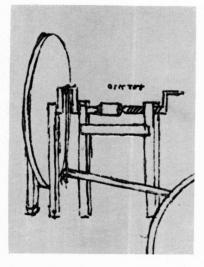

506

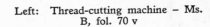

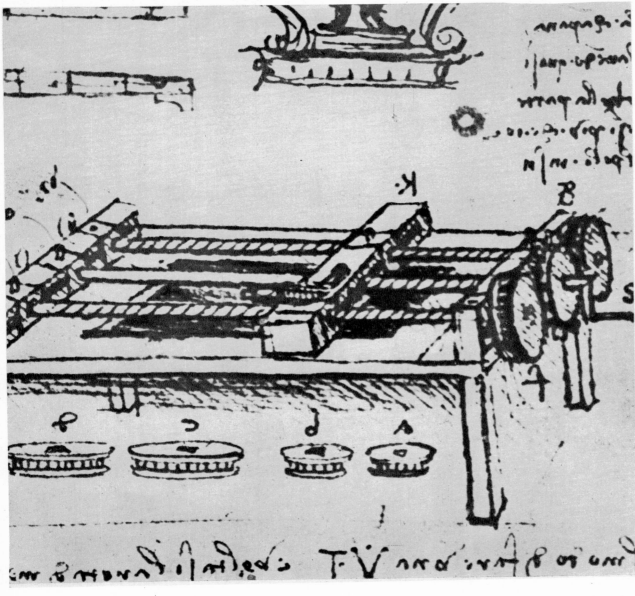

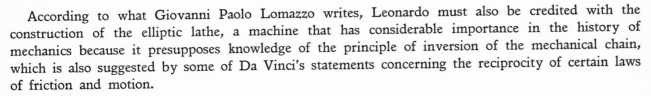

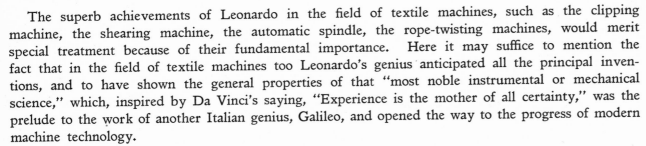

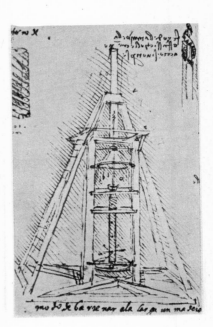

Well-drilling machine – Ms. B, fol. 47 v

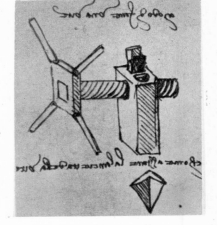

Block drawing machine – Cod. Atl., fol. 56 v

Ratchet mechanism for converting oscilatory motion into rotary motion – Ms. H, fol. 113 v

successive operations that have to be performed, explains the functioning of the machine, calculates the power necessary for that functioning, and advises the builder to "make the members of the machines equal or superior to the powers of their motors," speaking from experience, "for without experience it is impossible to give true knowledge of the power with which the drawn iron resists being drawn." He delineates the "machine elements" and the profiles of the bars, and, finally, gives the diagram of a grinding machine for finishing the drawn bars.

With equal clarity he explains the operation of the screw-threading machine, one of the most interesting of his machine tools, as well as of punching machines, drills of various types, and the beautiful machine for boring wooden pipes, containing a most ingenious self-centering device; he does this also for threading taps, pipe holders, various kinds of presses, printing presses, big vertical well-drilling machines, and various types of flywheel lathes.

According to what Giovanni Paolo Lomazzo writes, Leonardo must also be credited with the construction of the elliptic lathe, a machine that has considerable importance in the history of mechanics because it presupposes knowledge of the principle of inversion of the mechanical chain, which is also suggested by some of Da Vinci's statements concerning the reciprocity of certain laws of friction and motion.

The superb achievements of Leonardo in the field of textile machines, such as the clipping machine, the shearing machine, the automatic spindle, the rope-twisting machines, would merit special treatment because of their fundamental importance. Here it may suffice to mention the fact that in the field of textile machines too Leonardo's genius anticipated all the principal inventions, and to have shown the general properties of that "most noble instrumental or mechanical science," which, inspired by Da Vinci's saying, "Experience is the mother of all certainty," was the prelude to the work of another Italian genius, Galileo, and opened the way to the progress of modern machine technology.

GIOVANNI CANESTRINI

507

Head of combatant – Study by Leonardo for *Battle of Anghiari* – Budapest, Museum of Fine Arts

BIBLIOGRAPHICAL NOTE

It is difficult, even impossible, to sum up in a few pages the vast amount of study and criticism that has been devoted to the work of Leonardo. Ettore Verga, who was for many years director of the *Raccolta Vinciana* and maintained a correspondence (not always cordial, it is true) with that fortunate generation of Da Vinci scholars who were the first nucleus of its membership, undertook to publish a *Bibliografia Vinciana*.[1] The result was two thick volumes, but it cannot be said that Verga succeeded in achieving the completeness that he evidently intended. Still earlier, in 1905, Gerolamo Calvi, presenting to the Istituto Lombardo di Scienze e Lettere the materials relating to writings on Leonardo with which he competed for the Tomasoni prize, had attached thereto a solid bibliography of about 1500 entries, systematically arranged. And from that time to the present, during this period of intense resumption of Da Vinci studies, what a harvest we have had of notes and observations, of judgments often original and objective!

It has therefore seemed useful, at the end of this volume, to outline so far as possible a kind of rapid guide for orienting the reader toward those essays among the body of writings on Leonardo that may best help him in finding information on individual topics or avenues of study, or on the most general problems of organization and method. I shall try, to the best of my ability, to sketch out the principal lines of what this enormous interest in Da Vinci's genius on the part of scholars of every country has produced; and I feel it my duty to invite those who wish to go further to study this mind—as splendidly fertile as any man ever possessed—directly in the various codices, the printed works here summarily mentioned, and the thousands preserved in the *Raccolta Vinciana* and in other institutions.

Attention was aroused by Leonardo's work during the very course of his life, which he loved to envelop in a cloud of mystery. The first mention of his work as a painter is found in the *Rime* of Bellincioni (1493); one of its sonnets alludes to a portrait of Cecilia Gallerani, the same portrait that is referred to in a well-known letter of Isabella d'Este, and other sonnets speak of the festival called "Paradise" prepared in honor of the Duchess of Milan. In his *Epistolae*, Piattino Piatti (1504) announces the sending of a Latin tetrastich composed for Il Moro in honor of the great equestrian statue of Francesco Sforza, which is also referred to in one of the twenty-three epigrams of Francesco Arrigoni preserved in Ms. 1592 of the Bibliothèque Nationale in Paris.

Fra Luca Pacioli's *Divina proportione*, for which Leonardo himself seems to have furnished the illustrative drawings, is of interest because of its documentary evidence regarding the life at the Sforza court, where Da Vinci's sovereign genius shone among humanists and artists. When Il Moro fell, the celebrated mathematician journeyed with Leonardo from Milan to Florence, in those wanderings we know so well. In the same year in which that work appeared at Brescia (1509), the poet Jean Lemaire de Belges, in his elegy entitled *La plainte du désiré*, includes Leonardo among the great men whom painting summons to mourn the death of the Duke of Ligny, and in the next year Alberto Albertini, in his *Memoriale di molte statue et picture della città di Firenze*, mentions

Poem by Baldassarre Taccone – Frontispiece and page with two stanzas in ottava rima honoring equestrian monument to Francesco Sforza – Milan, Pachel, 1493

---

[1] Bologna, Zanichelli, 1931.

509

Le rime of Bernardo Bellincioni – Frontispiece and pages in preise of Leonardo – Milan, Mantegazzi, 1493

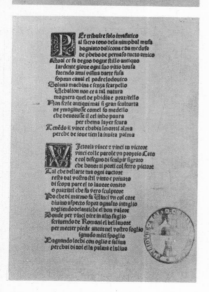

Prospettivo milanese – Small volume of 1500 – Page dealing with Da Vinci's art – Rome, Biblioteca Casanatense

Da Vinci drawings in the cloister of Santa Maria Novella and "the horses of Leonardo da Vinci." There is a reference concerning the monument to Francesco Sforza in the *De cardinalatu* of Paolo Cortese.

When Leonardo went to live in France, Antonio de Beatis, secretary to Cardinal Louis of Aragon, had occasion to meet him; in the interesting diary he kept of the long journey he undertook in the suite of the Cardinal, the manuscript of which is preserved in the Biblioteca Nazionale of Naples, he refers to the visit made to the Château de Cloux and to the solitary artist, and notes that "one can no longer expect good work from him because of a certain paralysis in his right arm." In Milan he observes that the *Last Supper* "is beginning to deteriorate; I do not know whether because of the moisture in the wall or through some other inadvertency." Vague testimony by other contemporaries of Da Vinci is contained in Giambattista Taccone's *Coronazione e sposalizio della serenissima regina Bianca Maria Sforza* (Milan, 1492) and in the *Sivarum* of L. Curzio (Milan 1521).

Thus far, our references have been fragmentary items, of the nature of chronicle entries. It was only later that an attempt was made to bring data together in monograph form. In a series of biographies beginning with the *Libro* of Antonio Billi (Cod. Magliabechiano CLXXV. 636 of the Laurenziana) and continuing with Paolo Giovio's *Vite*, we have the special example of Vasari, whose references, unfortunately derived from unevaluated historical sources, were precisely and exhaustively edited and commentated by Giovanni Poggi (Florence, 1919); this edition is packed with notes and data that amount to research material of the very first rank. Of much higher critical value are the notes on Da Vinci's art left by G. P. Lomazzo in his *Trattato*. Lomazzo was personally acquainted with Melzi and gathered reminiscences from those of Leonardo's disciples who had lived closest to the creative milieu of the master. In this way he was able to get the fruit of that work of loving care and interpretation of the wonderful heritage which on the one hand determined the further trends of the school of painting and on the other led, by way of the first collectors and commentators of Da Vinci's texts, to the formation, even though unconscious and often mistaken, of a method of studying the great master's art and science. An example is Francesco Melzi, who inherited a large fraction of the manuscripts; he intended in his way to follow the precepts of Leonardo himself by putting everything in its place, and at the same time followed his own taste in a *Trattato della pittura* which was later systematically assembled and now constitutes Codex Urbinatus 1270 of the Vatican Library.

It is evidently to this treatise that Lomazzo refers when he speaks of a book "that he wrote with his left hand, to decide the question whether painting or sculpture is the nobler." Some copies of the *Trattato* circulated in manuscript, and it may be that Cellini bought one. The first edition was prepared by Cassiano del Pozzo and completed by Du Fresne (Paris, 1651), very nearly at the same time that Arconati in Milan was putting together the materials for the *Trattato del moto e della misura dell'acque* contained in the Barberini codex; it was from a copy of the latter in the possession of the Grand Duke of Tuscany that Francesco Cardinali was to prepare an edition in 1828. Giovanni Ambrogio Mazenta, the Barnabite, studying the manuscripts he had succeeded in recovering from Lelio Gavardi, had already drawn from them his *Memorie de' fatti di Leonardo da Vinci e de' suoi libri*, which remained for a long time unpublished, until Uzielli saw it through the press. In this way there came to be in increasing tendency toward critical re-examination of Da Vinci's work. The various manuscripts were traced in public and private collections, and in 1690 at London Constantine Huygens indicated the existence of a "book in quarto written and drawn by Leonardo da Vinci. It deals with drawings of nude figures of men, women, and children, there is also something about horses and perspective. For the most part the figures are only in outline, with the muscles shaded lightly... The purpose of the author is to describe all the proportions of the members and the parts of the body." This is the very book purchased by the Morgan Library and prepared for publication by Erwin Panofsky; as for the other miscellany put together by Pompeo Leoni and later broken up into the present collection of drawings in Windsor Castle, parts of the caricatures were engraved in Paris in 1730 and in London in 1786. Just at that time, along with the production of selections of drawings of this sort, the most interesting one being that published in Paris in 1793 by Carlo Giuseppe Gerli, there began the keen researches of eminent students like Baldassare Oltrocchi, who compiled a valuable work entitled *Memorie storiche su la vita di Leonardo da Vinci* (published by S. Ritter at Rome in 1935), and Giambattista Venturi, who in 1797 in Paris, where the manuscripts now at the Institut de France had been taken, made that systematic and accurate critical inspection of them set forth in his *Essai sur les ouvrages physico-mathématiques de Leonardo da Vinci* and paving the way for those better-organized investigations which have led to our present knowledge of the great Italian.

Costantino Baroni

Leonardo da Vinci – *Del moto dell'acqua* – Cover of Codex Barberinianus – Rome, Vatican

Pomponio Gaurico – *De sculptura* – Page praising Leonardo's art and mind – Florence, 1504

BIOGRAPHIES

Amoretti, C. *Notizie storiche su la vita, gli studi e le opere di Leonardo da Vinci*, Milan: *Classici Italiani*, 1804, p. 256.

Brown, G. W. *The Life of Leonardo da Vinci*, London: Pickering, 1828, p. 256.

Campori, G. "New Documents on the Life of Leonardo da Vinci," in *Atti e Memorie della R. Deputazione di Storia Patria di Modena*, 1865, p. 43-51.

Milanese, G. "Unpublished Documents Relating to Leonardo da Vinci," in *Archivio Storico Italiano*, 1872, p. 16.

Mazenta, P. G. "Some Memories of the Deeds of Leonardo da Vinci at Milan and of His Books," in *Buonarroti*, 187, p. 342-350.

Guasti, G. "Concerning the House Occupied by Leonardo da Vinci in Florence," *ibid.*, 1884, p. 405-409.

Uzielli, G. *Ricerche intorno a Leonardo da Vinci*, II, Rome: Salviucci, 1884, p. 486.

Luzio, A. "More concerning Leonardo da Vinci and Isabella d'Este," in *Archivio Storico dell'Arte*, 1888, No. 1, p. 181.

Yriarte, C. "The Relations of Isabella d'Este with Leonardo da Vinci," in *Gazette des Beaux-Arts*, XXXVII, p. 118-131.

Uzielli, G. "Leonardo da Vinci and Three Milanese Ladies in the Fifteenth Century," in *La Letteratura*, 1890, p. 46.

Bosseboeuf, L. A. *Clos-lucé, séjour et mort de Léonard de Vinci*, Tours: Tourangelle, 1893, p. 124.

Smiraglia Scognamiglio, N. *Ricerche e documenti sulla giovinezza di Leonardo da Vinci*, Naples: Marghieri, 1900, p. 159.

Horn, P. *The Life of Leonardo da Vinci*, London: Bell, 1904, p. 125.

Solmi, E. *Ricordi della vita e delle opere di Leonardo da Vinci raccolti dagli scritti di G. B. Lomazzo*, Milan: Cogliati, 1907, p. 46.

Calvi, G. "Leonardo da Vinci and the Comte de Ligny, and Other Notes on Personalities Connected with Da Vinci," in *Raccolta Vinciana*, 1907, p. 99-100.

Seidlitz, C. von. "Some Data on the Life of Leonardo da Vinci," in *Repertorium für Kunstwissenschaft*, An. XXXIV, p. 448-458.

Wizewa, T. de. "An Italian Tourist in France in the Reign of Francis I," in *Revue des Deux Mondes*, 1908, p. 457-468.

Biscaro, G. "Leonardo da Vinci's Vineyard outside the Porta Vercellina," in *Archivio Storico Lombardo*, 1909, p. 36.

Solmi, E. "Leonardo da Vinci and Nicola Spinelli," in *Raccolta Vinciana*, 1912, No. VII.

Solmi, E. "Leonardo da Vinci and the Arezzo Uprising," *ibid.*, p. 133-137.

Brun, C. "The Sources for Leonardo's Biography and his Relationship to God and Man," in *Festausgabe für Hugo Blümmer*, Zurich, 1914, p. 374-398.

Calvi, G. "Contributions to the Biography of Leonardo da Vinci" (Sforza period), in *Archivio Storico Lombardo*, 1916, p. 417-508.

Verga, G. "Da Vinci Records," Ser. 4, in *Raccolta Vinciana*, 1919, No. X, p. 301-322.

Dorez, L. "Leonardo da Vinci in the Service of Louis XII and Francis I," in *Per il quarto centenario della morte di Leonardo da Vinci*, Rome, 1919, p. 350-376.

Toni, G. B. de. Da Vinci Fragments, in *Raccolta Vinciana*, 1919, No. X, p. 127-139.

Bottazzi, F. *La vie et l'œuvre de Léonard de Vinci*, Paris: Doin, 1919, p. 46.

Beltrami, L. "The Life of Leonardo," in *Emporium*, 1919, p. 227-271.

Beltrami, L. *Documenti e memorie riguardanti la vita e le opere di Leonardo da Vinci*, Milan: Treves, 1919, p. 221.

Poggi, G. *Leonardo da Vinci: La vita di Giorgio Vasari nuovamente commentata ed illustrata*, Florence, 1919, p. 63.

Beltrami, L. "Leonardo da Vinci's Lawsuit with the Other Sons of Ser Piero da Vinci," in *Nuova Antologia*, 1921, p. 193, 207.

Beltrami, L. "The Storming of the Castle of Trezzo in January, 1515, in a Sketch by Leonardo," in *Miscellanea Vinciana*, Milan: Allegretti, 1923, p. 34.

Beltrami, L. *Ancora per la madre di Leonardo*, Milan: Allegretti, 1923, p. 34.

Ritter, S. *Baldassare Oltrocchi e le sue memorie storiche su la vita di Leonardo da Vinci*, Rome: Maglione, 1925, p. 125.

Herzfeld, M. "More about Leonardo and Ligny: A Supplement to Calvi's Essay," in *Raccolta Vinciana*, 1926-1929, No. XIII, p. 53-62.

Calvi, G. "Sketch of an Introductory Chapter for a History of the Life and Works of Leonardo da Vinci," *ibid.*, p. 3-34.

Balducci, A. "The Adolescence of Leonardo da Vinci and the Green World," *ibid.*, p. 114-129.

Calvi, G. "Da Vinci Gleanings from the State Archives of Florence," *ibid.*, p. 35-43.

Freud, S. *Un souvenir d'enfance de Léonard de Vinci*, Paris: Gallimard, 1927, p. 216.

Carusi, E. "A Unknown Manuscript (Vaticanus Lat. 3160) of the Work of A. De Beatis," in *Raccolta Vinciana*, 1930-1934, No. XIV, p. 240-243.

Coleman, M. *Amboise et Léonard de Vinci*, Tours: Arrault, 1932, p. 236.

Moeller, E. "Ser Giuliano di Ser Piero da Vinci and His Relations with Leonardo," in *Rivista d'Arte*, 1934, p. 387-399.

Pettorelli, G. *Leonardo da Vinci: Pagine scelte precedute da uno studio biografico-critico*, Turin: Paravia, 1935, p. 274.

Savorgnan di Brazzà, F. *Leonardo da Vinci in Friuli ed il suo progetto di fortificazione dell'Isonzo*, Udine: Arti Grafiche Friulane, 1935, p. 19.

Varela Aldemira, L. *A arte e psicoanalise* (lecture), Lisbon: *Società Industrie Tipografiche*, 1935, p. 115.

Calvi, G. *Vita di Leonardo*, Brescia: Morcelliana, 1936.

Baroni, C. "A Correction concerning Da Vinci's Biography: Leonardo da Vinci Was Ducal Engineer of Milan," in *Rendiconti R. Istituto Lombardo di Scienze e Lettere*, 1937, No. III, p. 9.

Carusi, E. "The Life of Leonardo," in *Sapere*, 1937, p. 362-365.

EDITIONS

Variæ figuræ et probæ artis picturæ incipiendæ juventuti utiles a Venceslao Hollar collectæ et acquæ forti ære incisæ, Antwerp, 1645.

Diversæ effigies a Venceslao Hollar aqua forti ære insculptæ, Antwerp, 1648.

Leonardo da Vinci: Il trattato della pittura, con la vita dello stesso autore scritta da R. du Fresne, Paris: Langlois, 1651.

Caylus (Comte de): *Recueil de textes de caractère et de charge dessinés par Léonard de Vinci florentin*. Paris: Mariette, 1730.

Disegni di Leonardo da Vinci. Engravings from the originals, by C. G. Gerly. Milan: Galeazzi, 1784.

Chamberleine, F. *Imitations of Original Designs by Leonardo da Vinci*, London: Bulmer, 1786.

Rigaud, J. F. *A Treatise on Painting by Leonardo da Vinci*, London: Taylor, 1802, p. 236.

Leonardo da Vinci: Traité de la peinture, Paris: Perlet, 1803.

Amoretti, C. *Leonardo da Vinci: Trattato della pittura*, Milan: Tipografia Classici Italiani, 1804, p. 256.

Manzi, G. *Trattato della Pittura di Leonardo da Vinci tratto da un codice della Biblioteca vaticana*, Rome: De Romanis, 1817.

Trattato del moto e misura dell'acqua (Raccolta d'autori italiani che trattano del moto dell'acqua, Vol. X), Bologna: Marsigli, 1826.

Piattino Piatti – *Epigrammi* – Frontispiece and page mentioning Leonardo da Vinci – Milan, Ponti Gottardo, 1508

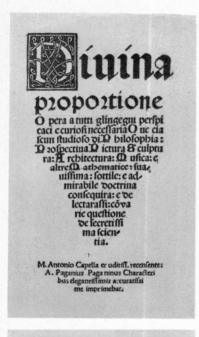

Disegni di Leonardo da Vinci. Engravings from the originals, by C. G. Gerli. With explanatory note by G. Vallardi, Milan: Ronchi, 1830.

Saggio delle opere di Leonardo da Vinci. With 24 photolithographic reproductions of writings and drawings taken from the Codex Atlanticus, Milan: T. G. Ricordi, 1872.

Les manuscrits de Leonardo da Vinci: Manuscrits de la Bibliothèque de l'Institut. Preface and index by C. Ravaisson-Mollien, Paris: Quantin, 1881-1891 (6 vol.).

Il codice di Leonardo da Vinci della Biblioteca Trivulzio in Milano. Transcribed and annotated by L. Beltrami, Milan: Pagnoni, 1891.

I manoscritti di Leonardo da Vinci: Codice sul volo degli uccelli ed altre materie. Published by T. Sabachnikoff. French translation by C. Ravaisson-Mollien, Paris: Rouveyre, 1898.

Il Codice Atlantico di Leonardo da Vinci nella Biblioteca Ambrosiana di Milano. Published by R. Accademia dei Lincei, Milan: Hoepli, 1894-1904.

I manoscritti di Leonardo da Vinci della Reale Biblioteca di Windsor: Dell'anatomia, Fogli A. Published by T. Sabachnikoff. Transcribed and annotated by G. Piumati, Paris: Rouveyre, 1898.

I manoscritti di Leonardo da Vinci della Reale Biblioteca di Windsor: Dell'anatomia, Fogli B. Published by T. Sabachnikoff. Transcribed and annotated by G. Piumati, Turin: Roux & Viarengo, 1901.

Rouveyre, E. Feuillets inédits, réproduits d'après les originaux conservés à la Bibliothèque du château de Windsor, Paris, Rouveyre, 1901, vol. 23.

Beltrami, L. Disegni di Leonardo e della sua scuola alla Biblioteca Ambrosiana. Plates by C. Fumagalli, Milan: Montabone, 1904.

Il codice di Leonardo da Vinci della biblioteca di Lord Leicester in Holkham Hall. Published by G. Calvi, Milan: Cogliati, 1909.

Leonardo da Vinci: Quaderni di anatomia. Published by C. Ove, L. Vangesten, A. Fohnan, and H. Hopstock. With English and German translations, Christiania: J. Dybwad, 1911-1916 (6 vol.).

Leonardo da Vinci: Del moto e misura dell'acqua, libri IX. Arranged by L. M. Arconati. Published from the Codex Barberinianus by E. Carusi and A. Favaro, Bologna: Zanichelli, 1923.

I manoscritti e i disegni di Leonardo da Vinci: Codice Arundel 2631. Published by R. Commissione Vinciana under the auspices of the Ministry of Public Instruction, Rome: Danesi, 1923-1927 (4 vol.).

I fogli mancanti al codice di Leonardo da Vinci sul volo degli uccelli. Edited by E. Carusi, Rome: Danesi, 1926.

I disegni di Leonardo da Vinci. Published by R. Commissione Vinciana. Edited by A. Venturi, Rome: Danesi, 1928-1939 (5 vol.).

Il Codice Forster del Victoria and Albert Museum. Edited by R. Commissione Vinciana, Rome: Danesi and Libreria dello Stato, 1930.

I manoscritti e i disegni di Leonardo da Vinci: Il Codice A 2172 dell'Institut de France. Published by R. Commissione Vinciana under the auspices of the Ministry of National Education, Rome: Libreria dello Stato, 1936 (2 vol.).

Galbiati, G. "Leonardo Speaks from Unpublished Pages," in Sapere, 1938, p. 393-397.

MONOGRAPHS

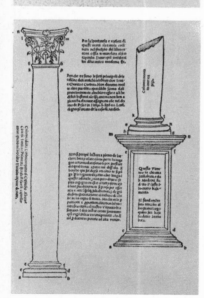

Merejkowsky, D. Le roman de Léonard de Vinci (La résurrection des dieux), Paris: Calman Levy [n. d.], p. 718.

Rocca, P. Leonardo da Vinci: Cenni storici ed artistici, Milan: Bernardoni, 1858, p. 92.

Blases, C. de. Leonardo da Vinci, Milan: 1872, p. 61.

Eaton, C. W., and Black, C. Leonardo da Vinci and His Works, London: Macmillan, 1874, p. 300.

Houssaye, A. Histoire de Léonard de Vinci, Paris: Didier, 1874, p. 487.

Koenig. F. Leonardo da Vinci. Tours: Mame, 1877, p. 190.

Richter, J. P. The Literary Works of Leonardo da Vinci, London: Sampson, Low, 1883, p. 361-399. 2d ed., London: Oxford University Press, 1939.

Tedeschi-Borbola. Leonardo da Vinci, Budapest: Lampel, 1905, p. 37.

Falcone, N. A. Leonardo da Vinci, Lanciano: Nasuti, 1907, p. 40.

Muther, R. Leonardo da Vinci, London: Siegle, Hill, 1907, p. 69.

Vaux, Carra [de]. Leonardo da Vinci, Paris: Blondel, 1910, p. 62.

Bellini, O. Leonardo da Vinci, Florence: Salesiani, 1910, p. 111.

Rosenberg, A. Leonardo da Vinci, Leipzig: Velhagen & Klasing, 1913, p. 136.

Beaume, G. Leonardo da Vinci, Paris: Michaud, 1914, p. 189.

Malaguzzi-Valeri, F. La corte di Ludovico il Moro, Milan: Hoepli, 1915, Vol. II.

Orestano, F. Leonardo da Vinci, Rome: Universelle, 1919, p. 218.

Paoli, V. Leonardo da Vinci, Naples: Giannotti, 1920, p. 126.

Haring, E. Leonardo da Vinci, sein Leben und seine Hauptwerke, Leipzig: Velhagen & Klasing, 1912, p. 78.

Pauli, G. Leonardo da Vinci, Leipzig: Seeman, 1922, p. 10.

Pfister, Kurt. Leonardo da Vinci, Munich: O. C. Recht, 1923, p. 95.

Solmi, E. Scritti vinciani, Florence: La Voce, 1924, p. 414.

Calvi, G. I manoscritti di Leonardo da Vinci, Bologna: Zanichelli, 1925, p. 321.

Lucas, E. V. Leonardo da Vinci, London: Methuen, 1926, p. 12.

Taylor, R. Annand: Leonardo the Florentine. A study in personality. London: Richard Press, 1927, p. 580.

MacCurdy, E. The Mind of Leonardo da Vinci, London: Cape, 1928, p. 360.

Oberdorfer, A. Leonardo da Vinci, Turin: Paravia, 1928, p. 182.

Klingsor, T. Leonardo da Vinci, Paris: Rieder, 1930, p. 63.

Mazzucconi, R. Leonardo da Vinci, Florence: Vallecchi, 1932, p. 432.

Basler, A. Leonardo da Vinci, Paris: Bran, 1934.

Weismantel, L. Leonardo da Vinci, Cologne: Berder, 1938, p. 427.

MacCurdy, E. Leonardo da Vinci's Notebooks, London: Cape, 1938 (2 vol.).

Fumagalli, G. Leonardo "omo sanza lettere," Florence: Sansoni, 1938, p. 376.

Vallentin, A. Leonardo da Vinci, New York: Viking Press, 1938, p. 561.

Hevesy, A. de. Pèlerinage avec Léonard de Vinci, Paris: Firmin-Didot, 1939, p. 277.

THE ARTIST

Pino, D. Storia genuina del Cenacolo insigne dipinto di Leonardo da Vinci, Milan: Oreno, 1796, p. 139.

Bossi, B. Del Cenacolo di Leonardo da Vinci, Milan, 1810.

Monteleon [Guillon de]. De quatre tableaux attribués à Léonard de Vinci, Paris: Guillon, 1836, p. 50.

Escle, V. Das Abendmahl von Leonardo da Vinci, Tübingen: Laupp, 1867, p. 20.

Riegel, F. Über die Darstellung des Abendmahles, Leipzig: Devrient, 1869, p. 94.

Calvi, G. Notizie dei principali professori di belle arti che fiorirono in Milano durante il governo dei Visconti e degli Sforza. Pt. III, "Leonardo da Vinci," Milan: Borroni, 1869, p. 111.

Jacobin, A. La Madonna dell'anello di Leonardo da Vinci, Rome: Bartoli, 1873, p. 16.

Frantz, E. Das Heilige Abendmahl des Leonardo da Vinci, Freiburg: Herder, 1885, p. 83.

Geymüller, H. de. "The Latest Works on Leonardo da Vinci," in Gazette des Beaux-Arts, 1885, p. 83.

Stangs, R. Stich des Abendmahles von Lionardo da Vinci, Lugano: Beau Séjour, 1888, p. 305-325.

Jacques, P. Notice raisonnée sur un Bacchus de Léonard de Vinci, Liège: Godenne, 1889, p. 16.

Müller-Walde, P. Leonardo da Vinci: Lebenskizze und Forschungen über sein Verhältnis zur florentiner Kunst und zu Raffael, Munich: Hirt, 1889, p. 232.

Müller-Walde, P. "Contributions to the Study of Leonardo da Vinci: Leonardo da Vinci and the Ancient Equestrian Statue of the Regisole; Some Sketches by Leonardo for the Equestrian Monument to Giacomo Trivulzio," in Jahrbuch der königlich-preussischen Kunstsammlungen, 1890, No. II, p. 81-116.

Geymüller, H. de. "The Madonna of the Carnation," in Gazette des Beaux-Arts, 1890, p. 97-104.

Séailles, G. Léonard de Vinci, l'artiste et le savant, Paris: Perrin, 1892, p. 457.

Séailles, G. Leonardo da Vinci (Les grands artistes), Paris: Renouard, p. 124.

Motta, E. "Ambrogio Preda and Leonardo da Vinci," in Archivio Storico Lombardo, No. XXI, 1894, p. 175.

Melzi d'Eril, F. La Madonna di Leonardo da Vinci e la villa Melzi a Vaprio d'Adda, Milan: Montorfano, 1895, p. 15.

Bode, E. V. "The Liechtenstein Gallery in Vienna," in Zeitschrift für bildende Kunst, 1896.

Müller-Walde, P. "A Sketch after Praxiteles and the Mercury in Milan Castle," in Jahrbuch der königlich-preussischen Kunstsammlungen, 1897, No. II and III.

Müller-Walde, P. "Contributions to the Study of Leonardo da Vinci: New Documents Relating to the History of the Equestrian Monument to Francesco Sforza; Leonardo's First Model," ibid., p. 78.

Kuno, W. Abendmahl von Leonardo da Vinci, Brunswick: Westermann, 1898, p. 19.

Müller-Walde, P. "Contributions to the Study of Leonardo da Vinci: Preparatory Study for the St. John of the Louvre among Plans for the Trivulzio Monument and Geometrical Calculations," in Jahrbuch der königlich-preussischen Kunstsammlungen, 1898, No. IV, p. 226-266.

Müller-Walde, P. "Contributions to the Study of Leonardo da Vinci: An Early Version of Leonardo's Composition of the Madonna and St. Anne with the Lamb," ibid., 1899, No. I, p. 54-80.

Brinton, S. Leonardo and His Followers, London: Simpkin, Marshall, 1900, p. 82.

Wolinsky, A. L. Leonardo da Vinci, St. Petersburg, 1900; Kiev: Kulyensk, 1909, p. 499.

Hamilton, N. Die Darstellung der Anbetung der heiligen drei Könige in der toskanischen Malerei von Giotto bis Leonardo, Strasbourg: Heitz, 1901, p. 118.

Monti, S. La Cena di Leonardo da Vinci, Como: Ostinelli, p. 14.

Gronau, G. von. Leonardo da Vinci, London: Buckworth, 1902, p. 198.

Beltrami, L. "The Sala delle Asse in Milan Castle, Decorated by Leonardo da Vinci in 1498," in Rassegna d'Arte, 1902, p. 65-90.

Beltrami, L. Leonardo da Vinci e la Sala delle Asse nel castello di Milano, Milan: Allegretti, 1902.

Bode, W. von. "Leonardo's Portrait of Ginevra de' Benci," in Zeitschrift für bildende Kunst, 1903, p. 274.

MacCurdy, E. Leonardo da Vinci, London: Bell, 1904, p. 125.

Herzfeld, M. Leonardo da Vinci, Leipzig: 1904, p. 269.

Beltrami, L. Il ritratto di Beatrice d'Este di Leonardo da Vinci, Milan: Allegretti, 1905, p. 84.

Ricci, C. "Alessandro Araldi's Copy of the Last Supper," in Raccolta Vinciana, 1906, No. II, p. 75-80.

Klaiber, H. Leonardostudien, Strasbourg: Heitz, 1907, p. 144.

Ratti, A. "The Table and the Chest in the Codex Atlanticus at the Biblioteca Ambrosiana," in Raccolta Vinciana, 1907, No. III, p. 111-126.

Hoerth, O. Das Abendmahl des Leonardo da Vinci, Leipzig: Hiersemann, 1907, p. 250.

Pisani, Bertoglio. Il Cenacolo di Leonardo da Vinci e le sue copie, Pistoia: Sinibaldiana, 1907, p. 21.

Ricci, C. "On the Virgin of the Rocks," in Raccolta Vinciana, 1908, No. IV, p. 9-11.

Beltrami, L. "Professor L. Cavenaghi's Report on the Reinforcement of the Last Supper," ibid., p. 95-102.

Ricci, C. Orate Deum, ibid., p. 115-117.

Beltrami, L. "Reconstruction of a Study by Leonardo for the Last Supper," ibid., p. 118-120.

Beltrami, L. Il Cenacolo di Leonardo, 1495-1908, Milan: Allegretti, 1908, p. 53.

Seidlitz, W. von. Leonardo da Vinci der Wendepunkt der Renaissance, Berlin: Julius Bard, 1909, Vol. 2

Biscaro, C. "Leonardo da Vinci's Commission for the Virgin of the Rocks," in Archivio Storico Lombardo, 1910, p. 125-161.

Frontispiece, page, and architectural and geometrical drawings from Luca Pacioli's Divina proportione – Venice, Pagani, 1509

Albizzi, L. *La testa del Battista*, Florence: Riga, 1910, p. 31.

Poggi, G. "Filippino Lippi's Panel for San Donato di Scopello and the *Adoration of the Magi* by Leonardo da Vinci." in *Rivista d'Arte*, 1910, No. VII, p. 93.

Sirén, O. *Leonardo da Vinci*, Stockholm: Bagges, 1911. English translation, London, 1916. French translation, Paris and Brussels: G. van Oest, 1928.

Venturi L. "Essay on the Italian Works of Art at St. Petersburg," in *L'Arte*, 1912, p. 126.

Colvin, S. "A Note on the Benois Madonna of Leonardo da Vinci," in *Burlington Magazine*, 1912, p. 30-32.

Reymond, M. "Leonardo da Vinci's *Leda*," in *Revue de l'Art Ancien et Moderne*, 1912, p. 321-334.

Cook, H. "The Portrait of Ginevra de' Benci by Leonardo da Vinci," in *Burlington Magazine*, March, 1912.

Ricci, C. "Leonardo's Benois Madonna," in *Raccolta Vinciana*, 1913-1917, No. IX, p. 153-160.

Frimmel, T. "The Leonardo in the Liechtenstein Gallery," in *Studien und Skizzen zur Gemäldekunde*, Vienna, 1913.

Ricci, C. *Note d'arte: Il "Musicista dell'Ambrosiana,"* Rome: Calzone, 1913, p. 6.

Supino, B. J. *Una copia sconosciuta della Vergine delle Roccie di Leonardo da Vinci*, Bologna: Parmeggiani, 1914, p. 5.

Coppier, L. "Is the *Gioconda* a Portrait of Mona Lisa?" in *Les Arts*, January, 1914.

Schaeffer, E. *Leonardo da Vinci: Das Abendmahl, mit einer Einleitung von Goethe*, Berlin: Bard, 1914, Pl. 46.

Eyre, J. R. *Monograph on Leonardo da Vinci's "Mona Lisa,"* London: Grevel, 1915, p. 15.

Andersen, A. J. *The Admirable Painter: A Study on Leonardo da Vinci*, London: Stanley, 1915, p. 310.

Bode, W. von. "Leonardo's Portrait of the Young 'Lady with an Ermine' from the Czartorysky Museum in Cracow, and the Pictures of the Artist's Youth," in *Jahrbuch der königlich-preussischen Kunstsammlungen*, 1915, p. 189-207.

Beltrami, L. "The *Virgin of the Rocks* in London Is an Original Painting by Leonardo da Vinci" (*Nuovi documenti vinciani*, 1506-1508), in *Rassegna d'Arte*, 1915, p. 97.

Malaguzzi-Valeri, F. *Un nuovo documento sulla Vergine delle Roccie di Leonardo da Vinci*, Milan: Hoepli, 1915, p. 390.

Berenson, B. *The Study and Criticism of Italian Art*, London: Bell, 1916, III, 155.

Seidlitz, W. von. "Leonardo da Vinci and the *Lady with an Ermine*," in *Preussische Jahrbücher*, 1916, p. 501-513.

Moeller, E. "Leonardo's Portrait of Cecilia Gallerani in the Gallery of Prince Czartorysky in Cracow," in *Monatsschrift für Kunstwissenschaft*, 1916, p. 313-315.

Sarasin, P. *Der Verkündigungsengel des Leonardo da Vinci*, Basel: Frobenius, 1917, p. 67.

Beltrami, L. *Documenti inediti per la storia della Vergine delle Roccie*, Milan: Allegretti, 1918, p. 30.

Calvi, G. "Leonardo da Vinci's *Adoration of the Magi*," in *Raccolta Vinciana*, 1919, No. X, p. 1-44.

Brun, C. "Leonardo's *Adoration of the Magi* in the Light of his *Trattato della pittura*," ibid., p. 45-60.

Reinach, S. "An Engraved Portrait with the Name of Leonardo da Vinci," ibid., p. 61-63.

Ricci, C. "The *Lady with an Ermine* Is a Composition of Leonardo da Vinci's," ibid., p. 65-116.

MacCurdy, E. "Leonardo and War," ibid., p. 117-126.

Venturi, L. *La critica e l'arte di Leonardo da Vinci*, Bologna: Zanichelli, 1919, p. 200.

Ochenkowski, H. "The *Lady with an Ermine* Is a Composition of Leonardo da Vinci's," in *Raccolta Vinciana*, 1919, No. X, p. 65-111.

Beltrami, L. *Madonna "Cecilia" di Leonardo da Vinci*, Milan: Allegretti, 1919.

Venturi, A. *Leonardo da Vinci pittore*, Bologna: Zanichelli, 1920, p. 196.

Herzfeld, M. "The Masque of *Danae* Organized by Leonardo da Vinci," in *Raccolta Vinciana*, 1920-1922, No. XI.

Carotti, G. *Leonardo da Vinci pittore, scultore e architetto*, Turin: Edizioni d'Arte, 1921, p. 136.

Venturi, A. "On Leonardo da Vinci," in *L'Arte*, 1922, p. 2-4.

Venturi, A. "Leonardiana," ibid., 1922, No. XXV.

Roger-Milles, L. *Léonard de Vinci et les Jocondes*, Paris: Fleury, 1923, p. 116.

Beltrami, L. *Franchino Gaffurio "Il musicista" di Leonardo*, Milan: Allegretti, 1923, p. 34.

Beltrami, L. *Nuovi indizi sulla provenienza del ritratto femminile dell'Ambrosiana*, Milan: Allegretti, 1923, p. 31.

Gareche, E. *Great Christian Artists: Leonardo da Vinci*, Milwaukee: Brure, 1924, p. 209.

Knapp, F. *Leonardo da Vinci*, Dresden: Reissner, 1924, p. 104.

Venturi, A. "Leonardiana," in *L'Arte*, 1924, p. 49-57, 243-246.

Venturi, A. *Grandi artisti italiani*, Bologna: Zanichelli, 1925.

Venturi, A. *Storia dell'arte in Italia: La pittura del '500*, Milan: Hoepli, 1925, Vol. IX, Pt. I, p. 1-22.

Rinaldis, A. de. *Storia dell'opera pittorica di Leonardo da Vinci*, Bologna, Zanichelli, 1926, p. 261.

Suida, W. "Additions and Clarifications on the Subject of the *Madonna with the Playing Children*," in *Raccolta Vinciana*, 1926-1929, No. XIII, p. 63-79.

Nicodemi, G. "Leonardo's Light," ibid., p. 87-98.

Hildebrandt, E. *Leonardo da Vinci*, Berlin: Grote, 1927, p. 350.

Suida, W. *Leonardo und sein Kreis*, Munich: Bruckmann, 1929, p. 327.

Valentiner, W. R. "Leonardo and Verrocchio's Co-worker," in *Art Bulletin, University of Chicago*, March, 1930, p. 43.

Horst, C. "Leonardo's *Last Supper* as Reflected in Copies and Imitations," in *Raccolta Vinciana*, 1930-1934, No. XIV, p. 118-200.

Calvi, G. "Old Reservations and New regarding the *Annunciation* of Monte Oliveto," ibid., p. 201-239.

Bodmer, H. "Leonardo's Preliminary Drawings for the *Battle of Anghiari*," in *Mitteilungen des deutschen kunsthistorischen Instituts in Florenz*, 1932, p. 463.

Degenhart, B. "Some Problems of the Development of Leonardo's and Lorenzo di Credi's Painting in Verrocchio's Studio," in *Rivista d'Arte*, 1932, p. 41.

La Tourette, G. de. *Leonardo da Vinci (Les maîtres du moyen âge de la Renaissance)*, Paris: Michel, 1932, p. 169.

Bayer, R. *Leonardo da Vinci: La grâce*, Paris: Alcan, 1933, p. 298.

MacCurdy, E. *Leonardo da Vinci the Artist*, London: Cape, 1933, p. 248.

Dromard-Mariot, M. T. *Le fond de la Joconde et l'esthétique de Léonard*, Besançon: Jacques & Demontrond, 1933, p. 163.

Lessing, M. *Die Anghiari-Schlacht des Leonardo da Vinci*, Quakenbrück: Kleinert, 1935, p. 79.

Moeller, E. "Salvestro di Jacopo Pollaiuolo dipintore," in *Old Master Drawings*, 1935, p. 17-21.

Guber, A., Givelegov, A. K., Zubov, V. P., Scileiko, V. R., Efros, A. M. *Leonardo da Vinci: Selected Works*, Moscow and Leningrad: Akademia, 1935 (2 vol.).

Lazareff, V. M. *Leonardo da Vinci*, Leningrad: Union of Soviet Artists, 1936, p. 113.

Sutter, K. F. *Das Rätse von Leonardos Schlachtenbild*, Strasbourg: Heitz, 1937, p. 91.

Moeller, E. "Leonardo's *Madonna with the Carnation* in the Old Pinakothek of Munich," in *Jahrbuch der bildenden Kunst*, 1937, No. 1-2.

Berence, F. *Leonardo da Vinci ouvrier de l'intelligence*, Paris: Payot, 1938, p. 370.

Mezzana, C. "Leonardo's Artistic Technique," in *Sapere*, 1938, p. 374-378.

Brunn, C. "Leonardo da Vinci-Bernardino Luini," in Dohme, *Kunst und Künstler des Mittelalters und der Neuzeit*, No. 61, 1879, p. 84.

Beltrami, L. "Bernardino Luini and the [Villa] Pelucca," in *Archivio Storico dell'Arte*, 1895, p. 19.

Beltrami, L. "The Church of San Maurizio in Milan and the Paintings of Bernardino Luini," in *Emporium*, 1899, p. 51-62.

Gauthier, P. "Notes on Bernardino Luini," in *Gazette des Beaux-Arts*, 1899, p. 89, 307; 1900, p. 25, 229.

Frizzoni, G. "Bernardino Luini," in *L'Arte*, 1901, p. 98.

Beltrami, L. "The Comic Series Painted for the Sforzas by Bernardino Luini," in *Rassegna d'Arte*, 1903, p. 1-32.

Gauthier, P. "New Investigations on Bernardino Luini," in *Gazette des Beaux-Arts*, 1903, p. 189.

Arsène, A. "Bernardino Luini," in *Burlington Magazine*, 1906, p. 243-258.

Carotti, G. "Bernardino Luini," in *L'Arte*, 1908, p. 140.

Frizzoni, G. "An Allegorical Picture by Bernardino Luini," in *Rassegna d'Arte*, 1910, p. 41.

Santambrogio, D. "Bernardino Luini's Fresco in the Parish Church of Capiano," ibid., p. 94.

Beltrami, L. *I dipinti di Bernardino Luini alla Villa Rabia detta "La Pelucca,"* Milan: Allegretti, 1911, p. 107.

Beltrami, L. *La tavola Torriani di Bernardino Luini già nella chiesa di S. Sisinio a Mendrisio*, Bellinzona: Colombi, 1911, p. 4.

Beltrami, L. *Luini*, Milan: Allegretti, 1911, p. 618.

Ratti, A. "More concerning Bernardino Luini's *Holy Family* in the Ambrosiana," in *Rassegna d'Arte*, 1912, p. 33-38.

Frizzoni, G. "Concerning the Altarpiece of the Musée Jacquemart-André and Luini's Youth," ibid., 1914, p. 201-206.

Beltrami, L. *La giovinezza di Bernardino Luini (a proposito della pala Jacquemart-André a Parigi)*, Milan: Allegretti, 1914, p. 38.

Frizzoni, G. "Concerning Bramantino and His Alleged Relations with Luini," in *Rassegna d'Arte*, 1915, p. 147-155.

Venturi, A. *Pittori lombardi del '500 dopo l'avvento di Leonardo (Storia dell'arte italiana)*, Milan: Hoepli, 1926, p. 1213.

Nicodemi, G. "Bernardino Luini," in *Milano*, 1933, p. 77-84.

Ansaldi, G. "The First Phase of Bernardino Luini's Art," in *Nuova Antologia*, 1933, p. 439-451.

Gauthier, P. *Luini (Les grands artistes)*, Paris: Laurens [n. d.], p. 126.

Bode, W. "A Portrait by Ambrogio de Predis of Bianca Maria Sforza, Second Wife of the Emperor Maximillian," in *Jahrbuch der königlich-preussischen Kunstsammlungen*, 1884, p. 71-79.

Raymond, M. "Cesare da Sesto," in *Gazette des Beaux-Arts*, 1892, p. 314.

Motta, E. *Ambrogio Preda e Leonardo da Vinci*, Milan: Bertolotti, 1894, p. 27.

Frizzoni, G. "List of Notable Italian Artists," in *L'Arte*, 1901, p. 91-110.

Seidlitz, W. von. *Ambrogio Preda und Leonardo da Vinci*, Vienna: Tempsky, 1906, p. 48.

Sinigaglia, G. "A Painting by Cesare da Sesto to Go to the Brera Gallery," in *Bollettino d'Arte*, 1907, No. 10, p. 32.

Philips, C. "*St. John the Baptist* by Cesare da Sesto," in *Burlington Magazine*, 1908, p. 34-38.

Malaguzzi-Valeri, F. "Cesare da Sesto and a New Acquisition of the Brera Gallery," in *Rassegna d'Arte*, 1908, p. 21.

Malaguzzi-Valeri, F. "The Female Portrait by Boltraffio Left to the Commune of Milan by Senator D'Adda," ibid., 1912, p. 9-11.

Malaguzzi-Valeri, F. *Un ritratto di A. de Predis a Brera*, Rome: Calzone, 1914, p. 7.

Badt, Kurt. *Andrea Solario, sein Leben und seine Werke*, Leipzig: Klinkhardt & Biermann, 1914, p. 221.

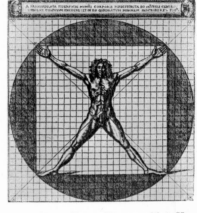

Antonio de Beatis – Diary, 1517 – Page mentioning Da Vinci's *Last Supper*

Vitruvius – *De architectura libri X* – Como, Da Ponte, 1521 (Caesariano edition)

Francesco Arrigoni – Latin epigrams, 1592 – Pages on which Leonardo is mentioned

First folio of treatise on motion of water – Codex Barberinianus 4332 – Rome, Vatican

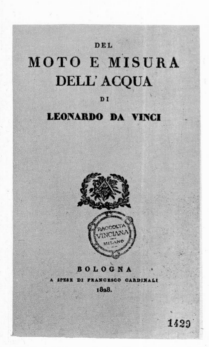

Marshal Gian Giacomo Trivulzio – Miniature in *Callimachus* – Milan, Trivulziana

DEL

MOTO E MISURA DELL' ACQUA

DI

LEONARDO DA VINCI

BOLOGNA

A SPESE DI FRANCESCO CARDINALI

1828

1429

First edition of treatise on motion and measurement of water – Bologna, 1828

Beltrami, L. "The Enigma of Salai Solved," in *Marzocco*, September, 1919.

Calvi, G. "The Real Name of a Pupil of Leonardo's: Gian Giacomo de Caprotti, Called Salai," in *Rassegna d'Arte*, 1919, p. 138-141.

Beltrami, L. *La commissione dell'ancona per la chiesa di San Rocco in Milano di Cesare da Sesto*, Milan: Allegretti, 1920, p. 22.

Liphardt, E. de. "Cesare da Sesto, a Pupil in the Studio of Lorenzo di Credi," in *Rassegna d'Arte*, 1921, p. 397.

Beltrami, L. *Nuovi documenti relativi ad Ambrogio Preda*, Milan: Allegretti, 1923, p. 31.

Moeller, E. "Salai and Leonardo da Vinci," in *Jahrbuch der kunsthistorischen Sammlungen des allerhöchsten Kaiserhauses* (Vienna), 1928, p. 139-161.

Nicodemi, G. *L'opera e l'arte di Cesare da Sesto*, Milan: Pizzi & Pizio, 1932, p. 24.

Hauvette, H. *Le Sodoma* (Les grands artistes), Paris: Laurens [n.d.], p. 125.

Faccio, C. *Giovan Antonio Bazzi (Il Sodoma)*, Vercelli: Gallardi & Ugo, 1902, p. 238.

Gielly, L. "Sodoma," in *Revue de l'Art*, 1910, p. 437-453.

Vaudoyer, J. L. "Sodoma," *ibid.*, 1912, p. 218-234.

Ravaisson, C., and Courajod, L. "A Marble Bust of Beatrice d'Este," in *Gazette des Beaux-Arts*, 1877, p. 330-354.

Courajod, L. *Léonard de Vinci et la statue de Francesco Sforza*, Paris: Champion, 1879, p. 50.

Gatti, G. "An Unpublished Document on the Equestrian Statue of Francesco Sforza Designed by Leonardo da Vinci," in *Gli studi in Italia*, 1888, p. 568-574.

Malaguzzi-Valeri, F. *Leonardo da Vinci e la scultura*, Bologna: Zanichelli, 1892, p. 112.

Bode, W. von. "On the Problem of the Bust of Flora in the Kaiser Friedrich Museum," in *Amtliche Berichte aus dem königlichen Kunstsammlungen*, 1909, p. 74-87.

Bode, W. von. "The Wax Bust of Flora in the Kaiser Friedrich Museum at Berlin," in *Jahrbuch der königlich-preussischen Kunstsammlungen*, 1909, p. 12.

Bode, W. von. "Leonardo and the Female Half Figure of the Italian Renaissance," *ibid.*, p. 61-74.

Meller, S. "Leonardo's Representations of Horsemen and the Bronze Statuette at Budapest," *ibid.*, p. 212-250.

Schmutzer-Wadheim. "Remarks on Leonardo da Vinci's Equine Anatomy," in *Archiv für die Geschichte der Naturwissenschaft*, 1910, p. 61-70.

Beltrami, L. "The Reconstruction of Leonardo da Vinci's Tomb Monument for Marshal Trivulzio in Milan," in *La Lettura*, February, 1920.

Beltrami, L. "An Excursus on the Trivulzio Monument," in *Miscellanea Vinciana*, Milan: Allegretti, 1923, p. 27.

Cook, A. T. *Leonardo da Vinci, Sculptor*, London: Humphreys, 1923, p. 108.

Popp, A. E. "Leonardo's Projects for Equestrian Statues," in *Zeitschrift für bildende Kunst*, 1926, p. 53-62.

Herzfeld, M. "On the History of the Sforza Monument," in *Raccolta Vinciana*, 1926-1929, No. XIII, p. 80-86.

Sirén, O. "A Madonna by Francesco Napoletano," in *Pantheon*, 1929, p. 382.

MacCurdy, E. "Leonardo's Statuette at Burlington House," in *Burlington Magazine*, 1930, p. 141-142.

Moeller, E. "Leonardo and Verrocchio: Four Reliefs of Ancient Captains, Made for King Matthias Corvinus," in *Raccolta Vinciana*, 1930-1934, No. XIV, p. 3-38.

Venturi, A. "Leonardo as a Sculptor in Verrochio's Studio," in *Nuova Antologia*, March, 1934, p. 34-39.

Jeannerat, P. "A Newly Discovered Statuette by Leonardo da Vinci," in *Apollo*, 1934, p. 313-316.

Meller, S. "Antonio Pollaiuolo and the Francesco Sforza Equestrian Monument," in *Különnyomat a Petrovics Elek Emlékkönyvböl*, Budapest, 1934, p. 8.

Venturi, A. "Leonardiana," in *L'Arte*, 1936, p. 234-265.

Lubke, W. "Leonardo da Vinci as Architect," in *Kunstwerke und Künstler*, Breslau: Schottländer, 1888, p. 219-230.

Beltrami, L. *Leonardo da Vinci negli studi per il tiburio della cattedrale di Milano*, Milan: Allegretti, 1903, p. 83.

Annoni, A. "On Leonardo as Architect," in *Emporium*, 1919, p. 171-180.

Heydenreich, L. H. *Die Sakralbau-Studien Leonardo da Vincis: Leonardo da Vinci als Architekt*, Leipzig: Vogel, 1929, p. 97.

Heydenreich, L. H. "Leonardo da Vinci's Archaeological Studies at Civitavecchia," in *Raccolta Vinciana*, No. XIV, 1930-1934, p. 53.

Pica, A. "Leonardo's City," in *Casabella*, September, 1935, p. 10-12.

Baroni, C. "Florentine Stylistic Elements in Da Vinci's Studies of Dome Architecture," in *Atti del I Congresso Nazionale di Storia dell'Architettura*, 1936, p. 25.

Bolis, B. "Leonardo and Streets," in *Le Strade*, 1938, p. 366-373.

Venturi, A. *Storia dell'arte italiana*, Vol. IX, Pt. I: *Architettura del cinquecento*, Milan: Hoepli, 1938, p. 1-49.

Baroni, C. "Leonardo, Master of Architecture," in *Sapere*, 1938, p. 379-382.

Calvi, I. "Leonardo da Vinci, Military Architect," *ibid.*, p. 412-416.

THE DRAWINGS

Gerli, C. G. *Disegni di Leonardo da Vinci*, Milan: Galeazzi, 1784, p. 16.

Dozio, S. *Degli scritti e disegni di Leonardo da Vinci all'Ambrosiana*, Milan: Agnelli, 1871, p. 45.

Beltrami, L. "A Drawing by Leonardo da Vinci," in *Raccolta Vinciana*, 1908, No. IV, p. 91-93.

Frizzoni, G. "A Drawing of Leonardo da Vinci's in the Royal Library of Turin," *ibid.*, p. 121-126.

Forati, A. *Il "Regisole" di Pavia e i disegni di Leonardo*, Empoli: Lambruschini, 1921, p. 10.

Demonts, L. "The Drawings of Leonardo da Vinci in the Louvre," in *Gazette des Beaux-Arts*, 1922, p. 19.

Moeller, E. "An Unpublished Leonardo Drawing," in *Burlington Magazine*, 1925, p. 175-276.

Popp, A. E. "Leonardo da Vincis Zeichnungen," Munich: Piper, 1928, p. 57.

Hind, L. *The Drawings of Leonardo da Vinci*, London: Newnes [n.d.], p. 18.

Clark, Kenneth: *A Catalogue of the Drawings of Leonardo da Vinci in the Collection of His Majesty the King at Windsor Castle*, Cambridge: Cambridge University Press, 1935 (2 vol.).

PHILOSOPHY AND PHILOLOGY

Vulliaud, T. "On Leonardo da Vinci as a Philosopher," in *Entretiens Idéalistes*, Vol. XIII, No. XLVI, p. 36-43.

Ferri, L. *Leonardo da Vinci e la filosofia dell'arte*, Turin: 1871.

Ferri, L. *Leonardo da Vinci scienziato e filosofo*, Rome: 1873, p. 294-334.

Ferri, L. "Leonardo da Vinci and the World View of the Renaissance," in *Nuova Antologia*, 1873, p. 530-570.

Prault, H. von. "Leonardo da Vinci from the Point of View of Philosophy," in *Sitzungsberichte der königlich-bayerischen Akademie der Wissenschaft*, 1885, Jan. 3.

Solmi, E. *Studi sulla filosofia naturale di Leonardo da Vinci: Gnoseologia e cosmologia*, Modena: Vincenzi, 1890, p. 117.

Séailles, G. "Aesthetics and Leonardo da Vinci," in *Revue des Deux Mondes*, 1892, p. 302-330.

Valdarini, A. *Esperienza e discorso in Leonardo da Vinci*, Rome: Balbi, 1897, p. 15.

Lombardi, E. *Due precetti di Leonardo da Vinci*, Verona: Minerva, 1898, p. 54.

D'Eufemia, A. *Studi filosofici su Leonardo da Vinci*, Naples: Giannini, 1900, p. 112.

Wolff, J. "Leonardo da Vinci as Aesthetician," in *Repertorium für Kunstwissenschaft*, 1901, p. 140.

Bottazzi, F. "Leonardo da Vinci as Philosopher, Naturalist, and Physiologist," in *Archivio per l'Antropologia e l'Etnologia*, 1902, No. II, p. 23.

Solmi, E. *Nuovi studi sulla filosofia naturale di Leonardo da Vinci*, Mantua: Mondovi, 1905, p. 223.

Faguet, E. "The Thoughts of Leonardo da Vinci," in *La Revue*, 1908, p. 318-323.

Peladan, S. "Leonardo's Philosophical Ideas," in *Nouvelle Revue*, 1910, p. 397-410.

Vulliaud, T. *La pensée ésotérique de Leonardo da Vinci*, Paris: Grasset, 1910, p. 103.

Croce, B. "Leonardo as Philosopher," in *Leonardo da Vinci: Conferenze Fiorentine*, Milan: 1910, p. 227-256.

Peladan, S. *La philosophie de Léonard de Vinci d'après ses manuscrits*, Paris: Alcan, 1910, p. 189.

Fumagalli, G. *Leonardo prosatore*, Milan: Albrighi & Segati, 1915, p. 393.

Della Seta, U. "The Moral Vision of Life in Leonardo da Vinci," in *Blychnis*, October, 1919, p. 82-94.

Credaro, L. "Some Pedagogical Ideas of Leonardo da Vinci," in *Leonardo da Vinci*, 1919, p. 27-33.

Orestano, F. "Leonardo as Philosopher," in *Leonardo da Vinci*, 1919, p. 87-116.

Losacco, M. "Leonardo as Educator," in *Rivista di Filosofia*, 1920, p. 247-270.

D'Anghiari, A. M. "The Philosophy of Leonardo da Vinci," in *Rivista di filosofia Neo-scolastica*, 1920, p. 203-444.

Lo Perfido, A. "The Philosophy of Leonardo da Vinci," in *Rassegna Italiana Illustrata*, September, 1930, p. 10-14.

Liburdi, E. "The Pedagogical Precepts of Leonardo da Vinci," in *Corriere delle Maestre*, 1935, p. 61.

Bongioanni, F. M. *Leonardo pensatore*, Piacenza, 1938.

Tauro, G. "Leonardo da Vinci and the Question of the Italian Language," in *Tribuna Scolastica*, An. V, p. 21-22.

Morandi, L. *Lorenzo il Magnifico, Leonardo da Vinci e la prima grammatica italiana*, Città di Castello: Lapi, 1908, p. 158.

Staffetti, L. "Leonardo as a Vocabulist and Grammarian," in *Rivista Ligure*, 1909, p. 54.

Salvadori, G. "The First Italian Grammar and the First Dictionaries," in *Fanfulla della Domenica*, April, 1909.

Solmi, E. "Nicolò Peretti, Luigi Pulci, and Leonardo da Vinci's Autodidactic studies," in *Rivista d'Italia*, 1910, p. 54.

SCIENCE

Frisi, P. *L'elogio di Galileo*, Livorno: Istituto dell'Enciclopedia, 1775, p. 103.

Govi, G. *Leonardo letterato e scienziato*, Milan, 1872.

Gunther, S. *Die Lehre von der Erdrundung und Erdbewegung*, Halle: Nebert, 1877, p. 56.

Padeletti, D. *Le opere scientifiche di Leonardo da Vinci* (lecture), Naples: Academia delle Scienze, 1885, p. 34.

Wagner, B. F. "Leonardo da Vinci's Knowledge, and Ability" in *Jahresbericht der technischen Staatslehranstalten*, 1894-1895, p. 48.

Krembs, G. "Leonardo da Vinci, the precursor of Galileo," in *Natur und Offenbarung*, XLVII (1901), 110.

Iacobi, M. "Cardinal Nicholas of Cusa and Leonardo da Vinci: Two Precursors of Copernicus in the Renaissance," in *Prometheus*, 1902, p. 391-492.

Baratta, M. *Leonardo da Vinci ed i problemi della terra*, Turin: Bocca, 1903, p. 318.

Schoen, E. "Leonardo da Vinci, the Forerunner of Modern Science," in *Craftman*, 1903, p. 17.

Thayer, W. "Leonardo da Vinci as a Pioneer in Science," in *The Monist*, 1904, p. 507-532.

Duhem, P. *Les origines de la statique*, Paris: Hermann, 1905-1906 (2 vol.).

Favaro, A. "Leonardo da Vinci and Galileo Galilei," in *Raccolta Vinciana*, 1906, No. II, p. 85-88.

Russel, B. "Leonardo as a Man of Science," in *The Dial*, 1906, p. 510-512.

Ratti, A. "The Application of the Pendulum to Clockwork in the Drawings of Leonardo da Vinci," in *Raccolta Vinciana*, 1908, No. IV, p. 131-133.

Favaro, A. *Amici e corrispondenti di Galileo Galilei*, Venice: Ferrari, 1909, p. 130.

Evlachow, A. "Leonardo da Vinci and Scientific Method," in *Raccolta Vinciana*, 1912, No. VIII, p. 170-174.

Duhem, P. *Etudes sur Léonard de Vinci*, Paris: Hermann, 1913, p. 605.

Schuster, F. *Zur Mechanik Leonardo da Vincis*, Erlangen: Junge & Sons, 1915, p. 153.

Favaro, A. "Whether Leonardo Influenced Galileo and the Galilean School, and in What Way," in *Scientia*, 1916, p. 417-443.

Favaro, A. "Leonardo da Vinci's Place in the History of Science," *ibid.*, 1919, p. 137-149.

Anile, A. "Leonardo da Vinci's Science," in *Rivista d'Italia*, 1919, p. 36-44.

Feldhaus, F. M. *Leonardo, der Techniker und Erfinder*, Jena: Dietrich, 1922.

Hart, I. B. *The Mechanical Investigations of Leonardo da Vinci*, London: Chapman, 1925, p. 240.

Timpanaro, S. *Leonardo: Pagine di scienza*, Milan: Mondadori, 1926, p. 467.

Marcolongo, R. "The Centers of Gravity of Bodies in the Writings of Leonardo da Vinci," in *Raccolta Vinciana*, 1926-1929, No. XIII, p. 99-113.

Bertacchi, C. "Leonardo da Vinci as Mathematician, Physicist, Natural Philosopher, and Founder of the Science of the Earth," in *Rassegna Italiana*, 1928, p. 391-406.

Blaschke, W. *Leonardo und die Naturwissenschaften*, Hamburg: Hartung, 1928, p. 15.

Baratta, M. "Leonardo da Vinci and the Pontine Marshes," in *La Geografia*, 1928, p. 21.

Marcolongo, R. *L'Euclides Danicu di Georg Mohr, Amsterdam, 1672*, Naples: Tipografia Combattenti, 1929, p. 7.

Heydenreich, L. H. "Leonardo da Vinci's Studies on Artillery," in *Die schwere Artillerie*, January, 1934.

Marcolongo, R. "Leonardo in the 'Paradise of the Mathematical Sciences' — Physicist-mathematician, Astronomer, Mechanician, and Engineer," in *Sapere*, 1938, p. 306-373.

Hart, I. B. "The Physical Science of Leonardo da Vinci: A Survey," in *The Monist*, p. 464-485.

Grothe, H. *Leonardo da Vinci als Ingenieur und Philosoph*, Berlin: Nicolaischer Verlag, 1874, p. 94.

Beck, T. "Historical Remarks: Leonardo da Vinci's Codex Atlanticus," in *Civil-Ingenieur*, 1893-1906, No. 4.

Reverchon, L. "Leonardo da Vinci's Clock," in *Revue Chronométrique*, March, 1913, p. 41-49.

Lieb, J. W. "Leonardo da Vinci, Engineer and Artist," in *Stevens Indicator*, 1914, p. 125-152.

Fermont, C. *Origine de l'horloge à poids*, Paris: Macon 1915, p. 28.

Schuster, F. *Zur Mechanik Leonardo da Vincis*, Erlangen: Junge & Sons 1915, p. 153.

Toni, G. B. de. "Leonardo and the Clock of Chiaravalle," in *Leonardo da Vinci*, Rome: 1919, p. 230-235.

Marcolongo, R. *La dinamica di Leonardo*, Milan: Tamburini, 1929, p. 20.

Marcolongo, R. *Lo strumento inventato da Leonardo da Vinci per la risoluzione del problema di Alhazen*, Naples: Tipografia Combattenti, 1929, p. 3.

Marcolongo, R. "Leonardo da Vinci's Geometrical and Mechanical Researches," in *Bollettino Società Italiana delle Scienze*, 1929, p. 53.

Marcolongo, R. "On a Recent Work of G. Boffito and on Leonardo da Vinci's Proportional Compasses," in *Rendiconti R. Accademia di Scienze Fisiche e Matematiche*, Naples, 1931, p. 8.

Marcolongo, R. *La meccanica di Leonardo da Vinci*, Naples: S.I.E.M., 1932, p. 147.

Arredi, F. "Da Vinci's Statement of the Principle of Permanent Motion," in *Annali LL. PP.*, 1932, p. 11.

Uccelli, A. "Leonardo da Vinci's Spring Automobile," in *La Lettura*, 1936, p. 261-263.

Marcolongo, R. *Studi Vinciani: Memorie sulla geometria e sulla meccanica*, Naples: S.I.E.M., 1937, p. 354.

Uccelli, A. "How some Machines of Da Vinci's Will Be Reconstructed," in *Sapere*, 1938, p. 409-411.

Venturi, G. B. *Essai sur les ouvrages physico-mathématiques de Leonardo da Vinci*, Paris, 1797; 2d ed., Milan, 1911; 3d ed., Rome, 1924.

Werner, O. *Zur Physik Leonardo da Vincis*, Berlin: International-Verlag für Kunst und Literatur, p. 184.

Libri, G. *Histoire des sciences mathématiques en Italie depuis la renaissance des lettres jusqu'à la fin du dix-septième siècle*, Paris: Renouard, 1938 (4 vol.); 2d ed., Halle: Schmidt, 1865.

Heller, A. *Geschichte der Physik*, Stuttgart: Finke, 1882, Vol. 2.

Cantor, M. "On Some Constructions of Leonardo da Vinci's," in *Festschrift der mathematischen Gesellschaft*, Hamburg: 1890, p. 8-15.

Schmidt, W. "On the History of the Text of the *Ochumena* of Archimedes," in *Bibliotheca Mathematica*, 1902, p. 176.

Favaro, A. "New Researches on the Mathematician Leonardo Cremonese," *ibid.*, 1905, p. 326-341.

Toni, G. B. de. *Frammenti Vinciani*, Pt. V, Modena: Vincenzi, 1911, p. 80.

Favaro, A. "Archimedes and Leonardo da Vinci," in *Atti R. Istituto Veneto di Scienze e Lettere*, 1912, p. 934, 975.

Marcomanno, R. *Il trattato di Leonardo da Vinci sulla trasformazione dei solidi*, Naples: S.I.E.M., 1934, p. 46.

Ferber, F. *Le progrès de l'aviation par le vol plané*, Paris: Berger-Levrault, 1906, p. 85.

MacCurdy, E. "Leonardo da Vinci and the Science of Flight," in *Nineteenth Century*, p. 126-142.

Beltrami, L. *Leonardo da Vinci e l'aviazione*, Milan: Allegretti, 1912, p. 25.

Sirén, O. *Leonardo da Vincis studier rörande flygproblemet*, Stockholm: Haeggström, 1910, p. 22.

Beltrami, L. "Where and When Leonardo da Vinci Started His Experiments in Aviation," in *Marzocco*, Oct. 3, 1920.

Boffito, G. *Il volo in Italia*, Florence: Barbera, 1921, p. 384.

Bilancioni, G. *Le leggi del volo sugli uccelli secondo Leonardo*, Pisa: Pacini, 1927, p. 31.

Giacomelli, R. "Leonardo da Vinci and Mechanical Flight," in *L'aerotecnica*, 1927.

Giacomelli, R. "Leonardo da Vinci's Flying Machines and Flight with Sails," in *Comptes Rendus du IVe Congrès de Navigation Aérienne*, Rome: 1927.

Bilancioni, G. *Svolgimento storico del concetto di aria*, Pisa: Mariotti, 1928, p. 171.

Giacomelli, R. "The Aerodynamics of Leonardo da Vinci," in *Mechanical Engineering*, October, 1930, p. 887-888.

Giacomelli, G. "Aerodynamic Study of Wind in Leonardo da Vinci," in *Atti del V Concorso di Navigazione aerea*, September, 1930.

Giacomelli, R. *Gli scritti di Leonardo da Vinci sul volo*, Rome: Bardi, 1936, p. 366.

Giacomelli, R. "Leonardo da Vinci and the Problem of Flight," in *Sapere*, 1938, p. 404-408.

Sacchetti, N. *Della misura delle acque correnti*, Bologna: Del Dolza, 1666, p. 184.

Lombardini, E. *Dell'origine e del progresso della scienza idraulica nel milanese e in altri posti d'Italia*, Milan: Saldini, 1872, p. 78.

Sirio, V. *L'acqua potabile in Milano e l'origine dell'idraulica, con cenni storici su Leonardo da Vinci*, Milan: Tipografia Sociale, 1881, p. 78.

Beltrami, L. "Leonardo da Vinci and the Naviglio," in *Strenna Istituto Rachitici*, Milan, 1886, p. 50.

Cermenati, M. "Geology and the Art of Drawing," in *Rivista d'Italia*, 1905, p. 27.

Bottazzi, F. "Leonardo da Vinci as a Naturalist," *ibid.*, 1907, p. 1048-1076.

Biglia, F. *Sulla navigazione interna in Toscana: Il canale di Leonardo da Vinci*, Florence: Tipografia Fiorentina, 1908, p. 36.

Solmi, E. *Leonardo da Vinci ed i lavori di prosciugamento delle Paludi Pontine ai tempi di Leone X (1515-1516)*, Milan: Cogliati, 1911, p. 37.

Cermenati, M. *Da Plinio a Leonardo, dallo Stenone allo Spallanzani*, Rome: Cuggiani, 1912, p. 58.

Favaro, A. "Leonardo da Vinci and Hydraulics," in *Emporium*, Emporium 1919, p. 272-279.

Lorenzo, L. di. *Leonardo da Vinci e la geologia*, Bologna: Zanichelli, 1920. p. 189.

Verga, E. "The Discovery of a Canal Lock in France Attributed to Leonardo da Vinci," in *Raccolta Vinciana*, 1920-1922, No. XI, p. 177-180.

Salomon, W. *Geologische Beobachtungen des Leonardo da Vinci*, Berlin: De Gruyter, 1928, p. 13.

Arredi, F. "Benedetto Castelli's Treatise on the Measurement of Flowing Waters," in *Annali LL. PP.*, 1933, p. 24.

Toni, N. de. *Frammenti Vinciani, II: Repertorio dei passi Leonardeschi ai quali attinse Frate Luigi Maria Arconati per la compilazione del trattato "Del moto e misura dell'acqua"*, Brescia: Morcelliana, 1934, p. 15.

Toni, N. de. *L'idraulica in Leonardo da Vinci*, Brescia: Morcelliana, 1935 (6 no.).

Marcolongo, R. "Leonardo Knew It," in *Sapere*, 1938, p. 8-10.

Arredi, F. "Leonardo as Hydraulic Engineer," *ibid.*, p. 390-392.

Lorenzo, G. de. "Leonardo as Geologist," *ibid.*, p. 401-403.

"Memoirs on a *Mappemonde* by Leonardo da Vinci," in *Archaeologia Relating to Antiquity*, London: Nichols, 1886, p. 256.

Cialdi, A. "Leonardo da Vinci, Founder of the Theory of the Wave Motion of the Sea," in *Rivista Marittima*, 1872, p. 31.

Fiorini, M. "Leonardo da Vinci's Map of the World and Other Similar Maps," in *Rivista Geografica*, 1894, No. 4, p. 213-223.

Cermenati, M. *Intorno al "mappello" di Leonardo da Vinci*, Rome: Voghera, 1907, p. 53.

Oberhummer, E. "Leonardo da Vinci and the Art of the Renaissance and Its Relations to Geography," in *Geographical Journal*, p. 540-568.

Baratta, M. *Sopra alcuni schizzi di Leonardo da Vinci riguardanti il territorio bresciano e bergamasco*, Florence: Ricci, 1910, p. 34.

Baratta, M. *Le piante d'Imola di Leonardo da Vinci*, Rome: Società Geografica, 1911, p. 25.

Frontispiece of *Vite degli uomini illustri* by Paolo Giovio, 1678

Leonardo's treatise on painting in Du Fresne edition, 1651

Frontispiece of collection of drawings published by Carlo Giuseppe Gerli — Milan, G. Galeazzi, 1784

Left: Collection of drawings and caricatures, engraved at Paris, 1730

Right: Collection of drawings and caricatures, engraved at Paris, 1767

Heading of *Trattato della pittura* in Nuremberg edition, 1724

RECUEIL.
DE CHARGES
ET
DE TÊTES
DE DIFFÉRENS CARACTERES,
Gravees à l'eau forte d'après les deſſeins de
LEONARD DE VINCI,
Précédé d'une lettre de M. MARIETTE ſur ce Peintre Florentin.
NOUVELLE ÉDITION,
Revue & augmentée par l'Auteur.

A PARIS, RUE DAUPHINE,
Chez CHARLES-ANTOINE JOMBERT, Libraire du Roi pour
l'Artillerie & le Génie, à l'Image Notre-Dame.
M. DCC. LXVII.
AVEC APPROBATION ET PRIVILEGE DU ROI.

Lomazzo's treatise in English edition of 1598

Frontispiece of *Trattato della pittura* in Nuremberg edition, 1724

Baratta, M. "The Importance of the Publication of Leonardo da Vinci's Manuscripts for Geology and Physical Geography," in *Bollettino Società Geologica Italiana*, 1911, p. 7.

Toni, G. B. de. *Frammenti vinciani: Di alcuni appunti e disegni nelle carte leonardesche*, Modena: Vincenzi, 1912, p. 13.

Maggi, A. "Sketches by Leonardo da Vinci Relating to the Territory around Bergamo," in *Bollettino Civica Biblioteca di Bergamo*, 1913, p. 38.

Baratta, M. *Sopra una antica carta del territorio bresciano*, Rome: Reale Società Geografica, 1913, p. 23.

Beltrami, L. *Un altro contributo di Leonardo da Vinci alla cartografia milanese*, Milan: Allegretti, 1918, p. 15.

Baratta, M. "Leonardo da Vinci and the Val di Chiana," in *La Geografia*, 1927, p. 26.

Bossi, G. *Delle opinioni di Leonardo da Vinci intorno alla simmetria dei corpi umani*, Milan: Stamperia Reale, 1811, p. 35.

Marx, G. H. *Über Marc'Antonio della Torre und Leonardo da Vinci, die Begründer der bildlichen Anatomie*, Göttingen: Dietrich, 1849, p. 20.

Raab, F. *Leonardo da Vinci als Naturforscher*, Berlin: Habel, 1880, p. 40.

Holl, M. *Über die bildliche Darstellung der Lage des menschlichen Beckens: Ein historisch-anatomischer Excurs*, Gratz: Leuschner-Lubenski, 1894, p. 17.

Lanzillotti, B. A. *Il pensiero anatomico di Leonardo da Vinci in rapporto all'arte*, Milan: Manini Wiget, 1897, p. 47.

Cuyer, E., and Duval, M. *Histoire de l'anatomie plastique*, Paris: Ricard & Kaan, 1898, p. 351.

Elsasser, W. "The Significance of Leonardo da Vinci for the Exact Natural Sciences," in *Preussiche Jahrbücher*, 1899, p. 272-295.

Botazzi, "Leonardo da Vinci as Philosopher, Naturalist, and Physiologist," in *Archivio per l'Antropologia e l'Etnologia*, 1902, No. II, p. 23.

Toni, G. B. de. *La biologia in Leonardo da Vinci.* Lecture given at solemn convocation of Royal Institute of Venice. Venice: Ferrari, 1903, p. 26.

Hopstock, F. *Grundtraek af anatomiens historiske abvikling*, Christiania: Steen'ske Boktrykkeri, 1904 (2 vol.).

Forster, A. "On the Relationship of Vesalius to Leonardo da Vinci and Marc'Antonio della Torre," in *Archiv für Anatomie und Physiologie*, 1904, p. 12.

Bottazzi, F. "Essays on Leonardo da Vinci," in *Anatomia e Embriologia*, 1907, p. 48.

Weindler, F. *Geschichte der gynäkologisch-anatomischen Abbildung*, Dresden: Zahn & Jensen, 1908, p. 186.

Solmi, E. *Leonardo da Vinci come precursore dell'embriologia*, Turin: Bocca, 1909, p. 60.

Böttcher, G. "Leonardo da Vinci as Natural Scientist," in *Senckenbergische naturforschende Gesellschaft*, September, 1913, p. 203-234.

Favaro, G. "The Structure of the Heart in Leonardo da Vinci's Fourth Anatomical Notebook," in *Atti R. Istituto Veneto di Scienze e Lettere*, 1914-1915, p. 4.

Favaro, G. "On Leonardo da Vinci's First Three Anatomical Notebooks," *ibid.*, 1914-1919, p. 887-942.

Castiglioni, A. *Leonardo da Vinci anatomo e fisiologo*, Milan: Unitas, 1915, p. 389.

Klebs, A. C. "Leonardo da Vinci and His Anatomical Studies," Chicago: American Medical Association, 1916, p. 18.

Favaro, G. "Measurements and Proportions of the Human Body according to Leonardo," in *Atti R. Istituto Veneto di Scienze e Lettere*, 1918-1919, p. 7.

Wright, W. "Leonardo da Vinci as an Anatomist," in *Burlington Magazine*, 1919, p. 186-194.

Carusi, E. "Leonardo and the Heart," in *Le malattie del cuore*, 1919, p. 15.

Anile, Antonio. "Leonardo da Vinci's Anatomy," in *Giornale di Medicina Militare*, November, 1919, p. 1272-1278.

Bottazzi, F. "An Experiment of Leonardo on the heart and a Passage of the *Iliad*," in *Raccolta Vinciana*, No. X, 1919, p. 153-163.

Mortet, V. *La mesure de la figure humaine et les canons des proportions*, Paris: Champion, 1919, p. 20.

Romiti, G. "Leonardo and Anatomy," in *Léonard de Vinci*, 1919, p. 221-225.

Bilancioni, G. "The Hierarchy of the Sense Organs in Leonardo's Thought," in *Giornale di Medicina Militare*, 1919, p. 30.

Favaro, G. "Leonardo da Vinci and the Dorsal Topography of the Viscera," in *Emporium*, 1919, p. 280-281.

Bilancioni, G. *L'orecchio e il naso nel sistema antropometrico di Leonardo da Vinci*, Rome: Nardecchia, 1920, p. 101.

Toni, G. B. de. *Le piante e gli animali di Leonardo da Vinci*, Bologna: Zanichelli, 1922, p. 283.

Singer, C. *The Evolution of Anatomy*, New York: Knopf, 1925, p. 209.

Bilancioni, G. "Leonardo da Vinci and the Woodpecker's Tongue," in *Rivista di Scienze Mediche e Naturali*, 1926, p. 12.

Lebengarc, J. *Die Anatomie und Physiologie des Herzens von Leonardo da Vinci*, Leipzig: Barth, 1926, p. 172-188.

Garrison, Fielding H. *The Principles of Anatomic Illustration before Vesalius*, New York: Hoeber, 1926, p. 58.

Bilancioni, G. *I nervi della voce in Leonardo da Vinci*, Rome: Casa Ed. Leonardo da Vinci, 1926, p. 42.

Castiglioni, A. *Storia della medicina*, Milan: Unitas, 1927, p. 959.

Castoldi, L. *La figura umana in Leonardo da Vinci*, Siena: S. Bernardino, 1927, p. 48.

Blaschke, W. *Leonardo und die Naturwissenschaft*, Hamburg: Hartung, 1928, p. 15.

Moeller, E. "Unknown sketches and Texts of Da Vinci Relating to Anatomy," in *Raccolta Vinciana*, 1930, No. XIII, Suppl., p. 13.

McMurrich, J. P. "Leonardo da Vinci, the Anatomist (1452-1512)," Washington: Carnegie Institution, 1930, p. 205.

Nicodemi, G. "Leonardo as Anatomist," in *Atti della Società Italiana di Anatomia*, September, 1936, p. 9.

Favaro, I. "The Anatomy of Leonardo da Vinci," *ibid.*, 1937, p. 2.

Favaro, G. "Leonardo as Anatomist," in *Sapere*, 1938, p. 383-386.

Bottazzi, F. "Leonardo and the Physiology of Respiration," *ibid.*, December, 1938, p. 397-400.

Baldacci, A. *Leonardo da Vinci botanico e fondatore del metodo sperimentale*, Bologna: Gamberini, 1914, p. 14.

Baldacci, A. *La botanica di Leonardo da Vinci desunta dai manoscritti della Biblioteca dell' Istituto di Francia*, Bologna: Gamberini, 1915, p. 20.

Baldacci, A. *La botanica nel Codice Atlantico di Leonardo da Vinci*, Bologna: Gamberini, 1916, p. 26.

Toni, G. B. de. *Le piante, gli animali in Leonardo da Vinci*, Bologna: Zanichelli, 1922, p. 283.

Baldacci, A. *Le piante di Leonardo da Vinci nei codici della Biblioteca Reale del Castello di Windsor*, Bologna: Azzoguidi, 1923, p. 8.

Baldacci, A. *Le piante e la pittura di Leonardo da Vinci*, Bologna: Azzoguidi, 1930, p. 15.

Baldacci, A. *Gli alberi e le verdure nel trattato della pittura di Leonardo da Vinci*, Bologna: Azzoguidi, 1931, p. 10.

Cortesi, F. "Leonardo as Botanist," in *Sapere*, 1938, p. 387.

BIBLIOGRAPHICAL SUPPLEMENT

To the bibliographical note of Costantino Baroni, whose recent death is a misfortune for Da Vinci studies, we add a list of titles chosen from among the approximately two thousand volumes and articles on Leonardo published from 1939 to the present.

BIBLIOGRAPHY

Steinitz, K. T. *Bibliographical Report of the Elmer Belt Library of Vinciana*, Los Angeles, 1946.
"Leonardo: Bibliografia Leonardesca," in *Enciclopedia Cattolica*, Vol. VII, 1951.
Moeller, E. "Recent Literature on Leonardo da Vinci," in *Das Münster*, 1952.
Heydenreich, L. H. *"Leonardo Bibliography, 1940-1952,"* in *Zeitschrift für Kunstgeschichte* (Munich), 1952.
Bibliografia, MCMXXXIX-MCMLIII. Edited by E. Mazzali and A. M. Raggi. In *Raccolta Vinciana*, 1954, No. XVII, p. 331-407.

EDITIONS

Il Codice Trivulziano. Transcribed by N. de Toni. Milan, 1939.
I manoscritti ed i disegni di Leonardo da Vinci pubblicati dalla R. Commissione Vinciana, Rome, No. V, 1939; No. VI, 1941; spec. no., *I disegni geografici*, 1941; No. VII, 1952.
Il Codice B (N. 2173) nell'Istituto di Francia, Rome, 1941.
Il Codice sul volo degli uccelli. Facsimile reproduction. Transcription and bibliographical annotations by Jotti da Badia Polesine. Milan, 1946.
Cento tavole del Codice Resta: Fontes Ambrosiana, XXIX. Milan, 1956. Leonardo's autograph with A. Marinoni's transcription, p. 22.
Marinoni, A. "Unedited Papers of Leonardo da Vinci in the Ambrosiana Library: The Resta Folio and the Annotated Drawings of the Gallery," in *Convivium*, 1956.

I libri di meccanica nella ricostruzione ordinata da A. Uccelli, Milan: Hoepli, 1940.
Marinoni, A. *Gli appunti grammaticali e lessicali di Leonardo da Vinci:* Vol. I, *L'educazione di Leonardo*, Milan, 1944; Vol. II, *Testo critico*, Milan, 1952.
Heydenreich, L. H. *I disegni di Leonardo da Vinci e della sua scuola conservati nella Galleria dell'Accademia di Venezia*, Florence, 1949.
Brizio, A. M. "Leonardo da Vinci: First Book on Waters," in *Scritti Vari*, Turin: Gheroni, 1951.
Leonardo da Vinci: Tutti gli scritti. Scritti letterari, edited by A. Marinoni. Milan: Rizzoli, 1952.
Uccelli, A. *I libri del volo di Leonardo da Vinci.* With analytical introduction and collaboration by C. Zammattio. Milan: Hoepli, 1952.
Marinoni, A. *I rebus di Leonardo da Vinci raccolti e interpretati*, Florence: Olschki, 1954.

ANTHOLOGIES, TRANSLATIONS, LISTS

The Notebooks of Leonardo da Vinci. Arranged and rendered into English, with introductions, by E. MacCurdy. London: Cape, 1938 (with subsequent editions).
Galbiati, G. *Dizionario leonardesco.* General list of words and subject matter contained in the Codex Atlanticus with six unpublished drawings from the codex, transcribed passages, and special indexes. Milan: Hoepli, 1939.
Semenza, G. *Indici per materie ed alfabetico del Codice Atlantico di Leonardo da Vinci*, Milan: Hoepli, 1939.
The Notebooks of Leonardo da Vinci. Edited with commentaries by I. A. Richter. London: Oxford University Press, 1939.
Leonardo da Vinci: Tagebücher und Aufzeichnungen. Translated from the Italian manuscripts and published by T. Lücke. Leipzig: P. List Verlag, 1940; Zurich, 1952.
Les carnets de Léonard de Vinci. Translated from the Italian by Louise Servicen. Paris: Gallimard, 1942.
Leonardo da Vinci: Tratado de la pintura. Spanish version by M. Pittaluga. Buenos Aires: Losada, 1943.
Leonardo da Vinci: Paragone (A Comparison of the Arts). With introduction and English translation by I. A. Richter. London: Oxford University Press, 1949.
Toni, N. de. *Saggio di repertorio dei passi leonardeschi ai quali attinse Frate Luigi Maria Arconati per la compilazione del trattato "Del moto e misura dell'acqua,"* Brescia, 1950.
Chastel, A. *Léonard de Vinci par lui-même*, Paris: Nagel, 1952.
Leonardo: *Scritti scelti.* Edited by A. M. Brizio. Turin: U.T.E.T., 1952.
Micheli, M. de. *Leonardo da Vinci: L'uomo e la natura*, Milan: Universale Economica, 1952.

HISTORY OF THE MANUSCRIPTS — STUDIES ON THE HANDWRITING

Venturi, A. "The Use of the Left Hand in the Writing and in the Drawings of Leonardo da Vinci," in *Arte*, 1939.
Venturi, L. "Leonardo da Vinci's Right Hand," in *Arte*, 1939.
Bescapè, G. *La scrittura di Leonardo: Noterelle paleografiche*, Milan: Allegretti, 1942; in *Raccolta Vinciana*, 1954, No. XVII.
Manuscripts of Leonardo da Vinci: Their History, with a Description of the Manuscript Editions in Facsimile. Catalogue by K. T. Steinitz with the assistance of M. Archer. Los Angeles, 1948.
Marinoni, A. " The Manuscripts of Leonardo da Vinci and Their Editions," in *Leonardo: Saggi e Ricerche*, Rome, 1954.

PUBLICATIONS CELEBRATING THE QUINCENTENARY IN 1952

Biblioteca Medicea Laurenziana. *Leonardo da Vinci: Quinto centenario della nascita — Mostra di disegni, manoscritti e documenti.* Catalogue published by the Exposition. Florence, 1952.
Brunetti, G. "The Leonardo Exposition at the Biblioteca Medicea Laurenziana," in *Accademia e Biblioteche d'Italia*, 1952.
Burndy Engineering Company Library. *The Works of Leonardo da Vinci.* Catalogue and invitation to the Exibit. Norwalk, Conn., 1952.
Leonardo da Vinci 500th Anniversary Exhibition, Los Angeles and Pasadena, 1952.
Ministero Pubblica Istruzione. *Mostra didattica leonardesca 1952*, Rome, 1952.
Musée du Louvre. *Hommage à Léonard de Vinci, Exposition en l'honneur du cinquième centenaire de sa naissance*, Paris, 1952.
Royal Academy of Arts. *Leonardo da Vinci: Quincentenary Exibition*, London, 1952.
Quinto Centenario della nascita di Leonardo da Vinci, 1452-1952: Scienza e tecnica di Leonardo — Artiglieria, Genio, Marina, Aeronautica. Guide to the Milan Exposition. Rome: Stab. Aeronautica Militare, 1952.
"City Exposition on Leonardo at the Ambrosiana," in *Città di Milano*, 1952.
U.N.E.S.C.O. *Exposition itinérante de reproductions: Leonardo da Vinci*, Paris, 1952.
"Homage to Leonardo da Vinci," in *Ars* (Buenos Aires), 1952, No. 59.
Les Cahiers du Sud, No. 313, October, 1952.
Leonardo da Vinci: Homenaje, Cuenca: Casa de la Cultura Ecuadoriana, 1952.
Leonardo in occasione del quinto centenario della nascita, Florence: *Marzocco*, 1952.
Leonardo da Vinci e Pavia, Pavia: Busca, 1952.
Leonardo a Milano, Turin: R.A.I., 1952.
Sapere, Apr. 15, 1952.
La Universidad de Córdoba rinde homenaje a Leonardo da Vinci, Córdoba, 1952.
Les Nouvelles Littéraires, Apr. 10, 1952.
Deutsche Akademie der Künste. *Leonardo da Vinci zur fünfhunderten Wiederkehr seines Geburtstages, 1452-1952*, Berlin, 1952.
Colloques Internationaux du Centre National de la Recherche Scientifique. *Léonard de Vinci et l'expérience scientifique au XVIe siècle*, Paris, 1952.
Nicco Fasola, G. "The Leonardo Year," in *Il Ponte*, 1952.
Frattarolo, R. "About the Centenary: Leonardo Studies," in *Accademie e Biblioteche d'Italia*, 1952.
Heydenreich, L. H. "The Leonardo Year," in *Kunstchronik*, 1952.
Atti del Convegno di Studi Vinciani indetto dalla Unione Regionale delle Province Toscane e dalle Università di Firenze, Pisa e Siena, Florence: Olschki, 1953.
Leonardo: Saggi e ricerche. Published under the auspices of the National Committee for Tribute to Leonardo da Vinci on the Fifth Centenary of His Birth (1452-1952). Rome: Libreria dello Stato, 1954.

BY OTHER EXPOSITIONS

Museum of Science and Industry. *An Exhibition of the Scientific Achievements of Leonardo da Vinci*, New York, 1940.
Dallas Museum of Fine Arts. *Leonardo and His Time: An Exhibition Arranged by Panold Masters*, Dallas, 1949.
Leonardo da Vinci. *An Exibition of His Scientific Achievements and General Survey of His Art, Arranged by Panold Masters, with an Introduction by L. H. Heydenreich*, Los Angeles, 1949.
Denver Art Museum. *Schleier Memorial Gallery: Leonardo da Vinci Exhibit*, Denver, 1949.

BIOGRAPHY — MONOGRAPHS

Marcolongo, R. *Leonardo da Vinci artista-scienziato*, Milan: Hoepli, 1939 (1943, 1950).
Moeller, E. "Leonardo's Birthday," in *Jahresbericht der preussischen Kunstsammlungen*, 1939.
Lansing, E. C. *Leonardo, Master of the Renaissance*, New York: T. H. Crowell, 1942.
Giglioli, O. *Leonardo da Vinci: Iniziazione alla conoscenza di lui e delle questioni vinciane*, Florence: Arnaud, 1944.
Langton, Douglas R. *Leonardo da Vinci: His Life and His Pictures*, Chicago, 1944.
Christensen, E. C. "Freud on Leonardo da Vinci," in *Psychoanalytical Review*, 1944.
Heydenreich, L. H. *Leonardo da Vinci*, Berlin, 1944; Basel, 1952.
Freud, S. *Leonardo da Vinci: A Study in Psychosexuality*, New York: Random House, 1947.
Singer, H. *Das Geheimnis Leonardos*, Burgdorf, 1947.
Stites, S. R. "A Criticism of Freud's *Leonardo:* More on Freud's *Leonardo*," in *College Art Journal*, 1948.
Lewis, L. *Leonardo the Inventor and Pioneer*, London: Nelson, 1949.
Dumont, H. *Léonard de Vinci*, Paris: Hyperion, 1949.
Bovi, A. *Leonardo filosofo, artista, uomo*, Milan: Hoepli, 1952.
Brion, M. *Léonard de Vinci*, Paris: Albin Michel, 1952.
Flora, F. *Leonardo*, Milan: Mondadori, 1952.
Fumagalli, G. *Eros di Leonardo*, Milan: Garzanti, 1952.
Isarlo, G. "Leonardo's Work," in *Le Combat*, May 26, 1952.
Nebbia, U. *Leonardo da Vinci*, Novara: De Agostini, 1952.
Papini, G. "Portrait of Leonardo," in *Scena Illustrata*, May, 1952.
Pedretti, C. *Leonardo da Vinci a Bologna e in Emilia*, Bologna: Fiammenghi, 1953.

THE ARTIST

Boglione, G. *L'adorazione dei Magi*, Rome: Ausonia, 1939.
Venturi, A. "The *Madonna of the Cat*," in *Arte*, 1939.
Clark, K. *Leonardo da Vinci: An Account of His Development as an Artist*, Cambridge: MacMillan, 1939, 1952.
Bottari, S. "On Leonardo's Artistic Formation," in *Emporium*, 1939.
Annoni, A. "On Leonardo da Vinci as an Architect." in *Rassegna di Architettura*, 1940.
Bertini Calosso, A. "The Nature and Limits of Leonardo's Architectural Activity," in *Atti IV Congresso Nazionale dell'Architettura*, Milan, 1940.
Panofsky, E. *The Codex Huygens and Leonardo da Vinci's Art Theory*, London: Dodd, 1940.
Heydenreich, L. H. *Intorno a un disegno di Leonardo da Vinci per l'antico altare maggiore della SS. Annunziata*, Florence: Istituto d'Arte, 1940.
Pica, A. "Dream and Reality in Leonardo's Architecture," in *Annali dei Lavori Pubblici*, 1940.
Regteren-Altena, C. V. "Leonardo's *Battle of Anghiari*," in *Burlington Magazine*, 1940.
Venturi, A. "A Bust of a Woman by Leonardo," in *Arte*, 1940.
Venturi, A. "On Leonardo da Vinci," in *Nuova Antologia*, 1940.
Moeller, E. "The *Madonna of the Cat*," in *Pantheon*, 1940.
Moeller, E. "Leonardo's *John the Baptist in the Wilderness:* Cesare da Sesto and Leonardo," in *Miscellanea G. Galbiati nella Biblioteca Ambrosiana*, Milan, 1941.
Leporini, H. *Leonardo da Vinci Handzeichnungen, mit Text*, Berlin, 1941.
Suida, W. "A Leonardo Profile and Dynamism in Portraiture," in *Art in America*, 1941.
Weismantel, L. *Lionardo da Vinci: Die Geschichte eines Malers der Gott und der Welt ins Antlitz zu schauen, wagte*, Cologne, 1941.
Heydenreich, L. H. "Regarding recent Researches on Leonardo da Vinci," in *Rinascita*, 1942.
Venturi, A. *Leonardo da Vinci and his school*, Novara: De Agostini, 1942.
Johnson, M. "Leonardo's Fantastic Drawings," in *Burlington Magazine*, 1942.
Tolnay, C. de. *History and Technique of Old Master Drawings*, New York: Bittner, 1943.
Bottari, S. *Leonardo da Vinci*, Bergamo: Istituto Italiano di Arti Grafiche, 1943.
Bottari, S. *Leonardo's "Last Supper,"* Bergamo: Istituto Italiano di Arti Grafiche, 1943.
Suida, W. "Leonardo's *Madonna of the Pomegranate*," in *Burlington Magazine*, 1943.
Victor, R. *Zur deutung der Felsgrottenmadonna: Ein Beitrag zur Ikonographie der Christus-Johannes Begegnung*, Berlin, 1943.
Benesch, O. "Leonardo da Vinci and the Beginning of Scientific Drawing," in *American Scientist*, 1943.
Benesch, O. "Leonardo da Vinci and Scientific Drawing" (abstract), in *American Journal of Archaeology*, XLVIII (1944), 195.
Coomaraswamy, A. "Iconography of Dürer's Knots and Leonardo's Concatenation," in *Art Quarterly*, 1944.
Popham, A. *The Drawings of Leonardo da Vinci*, New York, 1945; Brussels, 1950.
Dell'Acqua, A. "Leonardo and Bramante at Milan and the Fate of Leonardo's Influence in Lombardy," in *Lettere e Arti*, 1946.
Hahn, H. G. *The Rape of La Belle.* With introduction by Thomas Hart Benton. Kansas City, Mo.: Glenn, 1946.
Neufeld, G. "Drawings in the Royal Library at Windsor Castle: Scenes from the End of the World," in *Art Bulletin*, 1946.
Wilde, J. " The Great Council-Hall of Florence," in *Warburg Journal*, 1946.
Gould, C. "Leonardo da Vinci's Notes on Colour of Rivers and Mountains," in *Burlington Magazine*, 1947.
Davies, M. *Leonardo: The "Virgin of the Rocks" in the National Gallery.* With an account of documentary evidence concerning the picture. London, 1947.
Suida, W. "La bella Simonetta," in *Art Quarterly*, 1948.
Venturi, L. *Léonard de Vinci*, Geneva and Paris: Mazenod, 1948.
Neufeld, G. "Leonardo da Vinci's *Battle of Anghiari:* A Genetic Reconstruction," in *Art Bulletin*, 1949.
Suida, W. "Again the Simonetta Bust," in *Art Quarterly*, 1949.
Matejcek, A. *Leonardo and the Baroque*, Prague, 1949.
Bertini, A. *Prima mostra dei disegni italiani della Biblioteca di Torino*, Turin, 1950.
Popham, A., and Pouncy, P. *Italian Drawings in the Department of Prints and Drawings in the British Museum*, London, 1950.
Aronberg, M. "A New Facet of Leonardo's Working Procedure," in *Art Bulletin*, 1951.
Heydenreich, L. H. "Investigation of the Sources of Leonardo's Treatise on Painting," in *Kunstchronik*, 1951.
Moeller, E. *La gentildonna dalle belle mani di Leonardo da Vinci*, Bologna: Pedretti, 1951.
Venturi, L. *Lezioni di storia dell'arte: Leonardo da Vinci*, Rome: Edizioni dell'Ateneo, 1951-1952.
Boglione, G. *Leonardo dalle opere sue: Tre finzioni rivelate*, Milan: Alfieri, 1952.
Clark, K. "Leonardo: A Note on the Relation between His Science and His Art," in *History of Today*. London: *Financial Times*, 1952.
Gould, C. "Leonardo's 'Neptune' Drawing," in *Burlington Magazine*, 1952.
Tolnay, C. de. "Mona Lisa," in *Revue des Arts*, 1952.
Tolnay, C. de. "Remarks on *La Gioconda*," *ibid.*, 1952.
Goldscheider, L. *Leonardo da Vinci: Landscapes and Plants*, London: Phaidon Press, 1952.
Hours, M. *Radiographies des tableaux de Unesco, exposition itinérant de reproductions: Leonardo da Vinci série A*, Paris, 1952.
Popham, A. "The *Virgin of the Rocks*," in *Burlington Magazine*, 1952.
Popham, A. "The Reappearance of Some Leonardo Drawings," *ibid.*
Popham, A. *Les dessins de Léonard de Vinci*, Brussels, 1952.
Heydenreich, L. H. "Leonardo da Vinci, Architect of Francis I," in *Burlington Magazine*, 1952.
Heydenreich, L. H. "An Ashmolean Drawing Here Attributed to Leonardo," *ibid.*
Heydenreich, L. H. "Leonardo da Vinci: Art and Science in Leonardo's Drawings," in *Graphis*, 1952.
Babinger, F., and Heydenreich, L. H. "Four buildings Proposed by Leonardo da Vinci to Sultan Bajezid II," in *Nachrichten der Akademie der Wissenschaften in Göttingen*, 1952.
Longhi, R. "The *Virgin of the Rocks*," in *Paragone*, 1952.
Longhi, R. "Difficulties of Leonardo," in *Paragone*, 1952.
Stcerbaceva, M. "Works of Leonardo da Vinci at the Hermitage in Leningrad," in *Notizie Sovietiche*, Apr. 30, 1952.
Wolters, C. "On the State of Preservation of Leonardo Pictures in the Louvre," in *Kunstchronik*, 1952.
Venturi, L. "The *Adoration of the Magi* and the *Virgin of the Rocks*," in *Nouvelles Littéraires*, Apr. 10, 1952.
Venturi, L. "Thought and Fancy in the Art of Leonardo da Vinci," in *Atti dell'Accademia Nazionale dei Lincei*," 1952.
Venturi, L. "Leonardo's Light," in *Vie d'Italia*, 1952.

Weismantel, L. *Leonardo da Vinci Frauen und Madonnen*, Munich, 1952.
Baroni, C. *Tutta la pittura di Leonardo*, Milan: Rizzoli, 1952.
Sartoris, A. *Léonard architecte*, Paris: Tallone, 1952.
Brizio, A. M. "Leonardo's Drawings," in *Lo Smeraldo*, May 30, 1952.
Castelfranco, G. *Leonardo*, Milan: Martello, 1952.
Castelfranco, G. *Il paesaggio di Leonardo*, Milan: Amici di Brera, 1953.

IN *ATTI DEL CONVEGNO DI STUDI VINCIANI*, FLORENCE, 1953

Annoni, A. "On an Unknown Version of the *Virgin of the Rocks*."
Bottari, S. "An Unknown Lombard *Last Supper*."
Wittgens, F. "The Current Restoration of Leonardo's *Last Supper*."
Fazzari, I. "On Leonardo's Biology and His Artistic Canon."
Blum, A. "Leonardo da Vinci's Engraved Work."
Popham, A. E. "Leonardo's Drawings at Windsor."

IN *LEONARDO: SAGGI E RICERCHE*, ROME, 1954

Wittgens, F. "Restoration of the *Last Supper*."
Hours, M. "Analytical Studies of the Paintings of Leonardo da Vinci at the Laboratory of the Musée du Louvre."
Sanpaolesi, P. "Leonardo's paintings at the Uffizi."
Gould, C. "On the Critique of Leonardo's Drawings."
Gombrich, E. "Leonardo's Grotesque Heads: Prolegomena to Their Study."
Popham, A. E. "The Dragon-Fight."
Nicco Fasola, G. "The New Doctrine of Space."
Suida, W. "Leonardo's Activity as a Painter: A. Sketch."
Maltese, C. "Leonardo's Thought in Architecture and City Planning."
Brugnoli, M. V. "Documents, Notes, and Hypotheses on Leonardo's Sculpture."
Castelfranco, G. "Aspects of Recent da Vinci Criticism."
"Copyings and Derivations from Leonardo in the Huygens Codex."
"On Leonardo's Geological Thinking and His Landscape."

IN *RACCOLTA VINCIANA*, MILAN, 1954

Venturi, L. "Leonardo's Unfinished Projects."
Hinzelmann, A. "The Controversial Female Portraits of Leonardo da Vinci."
Brizio, A. M. "Correlations and Correspondences between Folios of the Codex Atlanticus and Folios of Anatomical Ms. B and Mss. A and C on the Eye, Perspective, the Pyramid of Light Rays, and Shadows."
Bottari, S. "Followers of Leonardo in Sicily: Cesare da Sesto and his Circle."
Bovi, A. "The Vision of Color and Light in the *Last Supper*."

PHILOLOGY — LINGUISTICS — LITERARY CRITICISM

Bolelli, T. "Notes on the Language of Leonardo da Vinci," in *Cultura Neolatina*, 1941.
Robertis, G. de. "Leonardo's Difficult Art," in *Studi*, Florence: Le Monnier, 1944.
Marinoni, A. *Gli appunti grammaticali e lessicali di Leonardo da Vinci*, Milan, 1944-1952.
Momigliano, A. "Leonardo's Prose," in *Cinque Saggi*, Florence: Sansoni, 1945.
Croce, B. *Poeti e scrittori del pieno e tardo Rinascimento*, Bari, 1945-1952.
Bolelli, T. "Linguistic Observations on Leonardo da Vinci's *Treatise on Painting*," in *Lingua Nostra*, 1952.
Olivieri, D. "Leonardo da Vinci and the First Attempts at Italian Dictionaries," in *Nuova Antologia*. 1952.
Marinoni, A. "For a New Edition af All the Writings of Leonardo," in *Atti del Convegno di Studi Vinciani*, 1953.
Flora, F. "Leonardo's Humanism," *ibid*.
Fumagalli, G. "The 'Unlettered Man' and Poetry," *ibid*.
Fumagalli, G. "Beauty and Utility: Notes on Da Vinci's Aesthetics," *ibid*.
Sapegno, N. "Leonardo as a Writer," *ibid*.

MUSIC — THEATER

Becherini, B. "Leonardo and Music," in *Sapere*, 1952.
Confalonieri, L. "Leonardo as a Musician," in *Lo Smeraldo*, 1952.

Steinitz, K. T. "A Reconstruction of Leonardo da Vinci's Revolving Stage," in *Art Quaterly*, 1949.
Becherini, E. "Stage Management and Stage Machinery in Leonardo da Vinci," in *La Scala*, 1951.
Pedretti, C. "Leonardo's Stage Machinery for Politian's *Orfeo*," *ibid.*, 1956.
Marinoni, A. "The 'Reign' and the 'Seat' of Venus," in *Convivium*, 1956.

PHILOSOPHY

Passarella, L. "Leonardo as a Naturalist Philosopher," in *Sophia*, 1942.
Orestano, F. *Leonardo, Galileo, Tasso*, Milan, 1943.
Péladan, I. *La filosofia de Leonardo da Vinci*, Buenos Aires: *Biblioteca Humanista*, 1945.
Corsano, A. "Philosophy, Science, and Technique in the Crisis of Renaissance Thought," in *Rivista di filosofia*, 1949.
Saitta, G. *Il pensiero italiano nell'umanesimo e nel Rinascimento*, Bologna, 1949-1950, Vol. II, cap. I.
Abbagnano, N. "Leonardo as Philosopher," in *Lo Smeraldo*, 1952.
Castelfranco, G. "An Introduction to Leonardo," in *Nuova Antologia*, 1952.
Cassier, E. *Storia della filosofia moderna*, Vol. I, Turin: Einaudi, 1952.
Rassegna Sovietica, No. 17, June, 1952. Articles by Givelegov, Lazarev, Nedoscivin, Guber, Arkin, Alpatov.
Estiú, E. "Leonardo's Treatise on Painting and Renaissance Philosophy," in *Notas y estudios de filosofia*, Tucumán, 1952.
Cortesi, E., and Lombardo Radice, L. "The Philosophy of Nature and Science in the Thought of Leonardo da Vinci," in *Rinascita*, 1952.
Garin, E. *L'umanesimo italiano: filosofia e vita civile nel Rinascimento*, Bari: Laterza, 1952.
Garin, E. "Florentine Culture in the Age of Leonardo," in *Belfagor*, 1952.
Garin, E. "Leonardo's Philosophy," in *Scientia*, 1952.
Garin, E. "The Problem of the Origin of Leonardo's Thought," in *Atti del Convegno di Studi Vinciani*, 1953.
Luporini, C. *La mente di Leonardo*, Florence: Sansoni, 1953.
Maritano, L. "The Conception of the Real in Leonardo," in *Rivista di Filosofia neo-scolastica*, 1953.
Saitta, G. "The *Amor Vitae* in Leonardo da Vinci," in *Atti del Convegno di Studi Vinciani*, 1953.
Banfi, A. "Leonardo and Modern Man," *ibid*.
Jaspers, K. *Leonardo als Philosoph*, Berne: Francke, 1953.
Johnson, M. "Why Did Leonardo Look for the Manuscripts of Archimedes and How did He Find Them?" in *Léonard de Vinci et l'expérience scientifique au seizième siècle*, Paris, 1953.
Michel, P. H. "Leonardo da Vinci and the Problem of the Plurality of Worlds," *ibid*.
Santillana, G. de. "Leonardo and the Authors That He Did Not Read," *ibid*.
Klibansky, R. "Copernicus and Nicholas of Cusa," *ibid*.
Chastel, A. "Leonardo and Culture," *ibid*.
Chastel, A. *Marsile Ficin de l'art*, Geneva: Droz, 1954.
Troilo, E. *Ricostruzione e interpretazione del pensiero filosofico di Leonardo da Vinci*, Venice, Istituto Veneto di Scienze, Lettere ed Arti, 1954.
Marinoni, A. *I rebus di Leonardo da Vinci raccolti e interpretati con un saggio su "Una virtù spirituale,"* Florence: Olschki, 1954.
Garroni, E. "Leonardo and His Times," in *Rassegna di Filosofia*, Rome, 1955.

SCIENCE AND TECHNOLOGY

Marcolongo, R. *Leonardo da Vinci artista-scienziato*, Milan: Hoepli, 1939.
Maier, A. *An der Grenze von Scholastik, und Naturwissenschaft*, Essen, 1943.
Maier, A. *Vorläufer Galileis*, Rome, 1948.
Annovati, A. "Leonardo da Vinci: More Artist or Scientist?" in *Viator*, 1949.
Gemelli, A. "Leonardo's Scientific Works," in *Vita e Pensiero*, 1952.
Randall, J. H. "Leonardo da Vinci and Modern Science," in *Journal of the History of Ideas*, 1953.
Lilley, S. "Leonardo da Vinci and the Experimental Method," in *Atti del Convegno di Studi Vinciani*, 1953.
Infeld, L. "Leonardo da Vinci and the Fundamental Laws of Nature," *ibid*.

Canestrini, G. *Leonardo costruttore di macchine e veicoli*, Milan: Tuminelli, 1939.
Marcolongo, R. "Leonardo's Mechanical Studies," in *Atti del Ministero dei Lavori Pubblici*, 1939.
Caversazzi, C. "A Geometrical Invention by Leonardo," in *Emporium*, 1939.
Marcolongo, R. "Leonardo in the Paradise of the Mathematical Sciences," in *Sapere*, 1952.
Castelfranco, G. "The Concept of Force in Leonardo," in *Nuova Antologia*, 1952.
Signorini, A. "Leonardo and Mechanics," in *Archimede*, 1952.
Signorini, A. "Leonardo and Mechanics," in *Atti del Convegno di Studi Vinciani*, 1953.
Dugas, R. "Leonardo da Vinci in the History of Mechanics," in *Léonard de Vinci et l'expérience scientifique au seizième siècle*, Paris, 1953.
Francastel, P. "Leonardo da Vinci's Perspective and Scientific Experiment in the Sixteenth Century," *ibid*.
Sergescu, P. "Leonardo da Vinci and Mathematics," *ibid*.
Daumas, M. "Instruments of Observation in the Fifteenth and Sixteenth Centuries," *ibid*.
Gille, B. "Leonardo da Vinci and the Technology of His Times," *ibid*.
Hooykaas, R. "Leonardo da Vinci's Corpuscular Theory," *ibid*.
Pedretti, C. "Unpublished Pages by Leonardo da Vinci concerning Mechanics," in *Sapere*, 1953.
Somenzi, V. "Leonardo and the Principles of Dynamics," in *Leonardo: Saggi e Ricerche*, 1954.

Argentieri, D. *Ritrovamento delle curvature delle lenti del canocchiale vinciano*, Milan: Macciachini, 1939.
Schneider, W. *Das chemische Wissen Leonardo da Vincis und seine Bedeutung für die Geschichte der Chemie*, 1949.
Reti, L. "Chemical Substances, Drugs, and Minerals in Leonardo da Vinci's Manuscripts; Other Interesting Technological Anticipations by Leonardo; the Problem of Combustion; Leonardo and Alchemy; Leonardo's Chemical Skills," in *La Chimica e l'Industria*, 1952.
Ronchi, V. "Leonardo and Optics," in *Leonardo: Saggi e Ricerche*, Rome, 1954.

Lorenzo, G. de. "Leonardo's Geology and Physical Geography," in *Annali dei Lavori Pubblici*, 1939.
Weyl, R. "Actualism and History of the Earth in Leonardo da Vinci's Geological World Picture," in *Forschungen und Fortschritte*, 1949.
Weyl, R. "The Geological Studies of Leonardo da Vinci and Their Position in the History of Geology," in *Philosophia naturalis*, 1950.
Pedretti, C. "Leonardo da Vinci and the Astronomers of His Time," in *Coelum*, 1952.
Pedretti, C. "The Topographical Reliefs of Imola on an Unpublished Page of Leonardo's," in *Sapere*, 1952.
Gianotti, A. "Geography and Geology in the Writings of Leonardo da Vinci," Milan: *Mostra della Scienza e Tecnica di Leonardo*, 1953.
Abetti, G. "Optics and Astronomy in Leonardo," in *Atti del Convegno di Studi Vinciani*, 1953.
Almagià, R. "Leonardo da Vinci as Geographer and Cartographer," *ibid*.

Baillie, G. H. *Clocks and Watches: An Historical Bibliography*, London: Jones, 1951.
Pedretti, C. "Unknown Inventions of Leonardo da Vinci in Two Unpublished Manuscripts of the Sixteenth Century," in *Sapere*, 1951.
Bassoli, F. S. "The 'Uriolo' of Leonardo da Vinci for the Convent of San Donato at Scopello: A Perspectograph by Leonardo," *ibid.*, 1952.
Rimediotti, U. "Automatic Weighing Machines in the Manuscripts of Leonardo da Vinci," in *Rivista di Meccanica*, 1952.
Giacomelli, R. "Leonardo da Vinci in Aerodynamics, Aerology, Aerotechnicology, and as an Observer of the Flight of Birds," in *Atti del Convegno di Studi Vinciani*, 1953.
Giacomelli, R. "Leonardo da Vinci's Science of the Winds," *ibid*.
Grifone, N. "Criteria Used by the Istituto Storico e di Cultura dell'Arma del Genio in Reconstructing Models of Bridges and Fortifications for the Milan Exposition of the Science and Technology of Leonardo," in *Bollettino dell'Istituto Storico e di Cultura del Genio*, 1953.
Somenzi, V. "Reconstructions of Flying Machines," in *Leonardo: Saggi e Ricerche*, 1954.
Pedretti, C. "Aeronautical da Vinci Gleanings," in *Raccolta Vinciana*, 1954.
Pedretti, C. "Flying-Machine Projects on an Unpublished Page of Leonardo's," in *Sapere*, 1954.
Marinoni, A. " 'Harmonic' or 'Musical' Time in Leonardo da Vinci," in *Lingua Nostra*, 1955.

Calvi, I. *L'architettura militare di Leonardo da Vinci*, Milan: Libreria Lombarda, 1943.
Dibner, B. *Leonardo da Vinci, Military Engineer*, New York, 1946.
Grosso, L. "Leonardo's Military Machines; Leonardo da Vinci as Military Architect," in *Rivista Aeronautica*, 1952.
Calvi, I. *L'ingegneria militare di Leonardo*, Milan: Mostra della Scienza e Tecnica di Leonardo, 1953.

Tursini, L. "Leonardo and the Problems of Nautical and Naval Technology," in *Annali dei Lavori Pubblici*, 1939.
Tursini, L. "Underwater Navigation in Leonardo," in *Atti del Convegno di Studi Vinciani*, 1953.
Tursini, L. "Ships and Diving Suits in Leonardo's Studies," in *Leonardo: Saggi e Ricerche*, 1954.

Arredi, F. "Leonardo's Studies on the Motions of Water," in *Atti del Ministero dei Lavori Pubblici*, 1939.
D'Arrigo, A. "Leonardo da Vinci and Control of the beach at Cesenatico: Researches on the Origins of Canal Ports in the Renaissance," *ibid.*, 1939.
Bellincioni, G. *Leonardo da Vinci, fondatore della scienza idraulica*, Florence: C.O.S.P.I.T., 1952.
Bellincioni, G. "Leonardo and the Treatise *On the Motion and Measurement of Waters*," in *Atti del Convegno di Studi Vinciani*, 1953.
Pedretti, C. "The Hydraulic Machine Constructed by Leonardo for the Account of B. Rucellai, and the First Water Meters," in *Raccolta Vinciana*, 1954.

Chiodi, C. "The City Streets of Leonardo da Vinci," in *Le Strade*, 1952.
Arata, G. U. *Leonardo architetto e urbanista*, Milan: Mostra della Scienza e Tecnica di Leonardo, 1953.
Sisi, E. *L'urbanistica negli studi di Leonardo da Vinci*, Florence: Cencetti, 1953.

Colombo, G., and Gallese, G. "Leonardo as Inventor of Silk-working Machines," in *Bollettino Ufficiale della Stazione Sperimentale per la Seta*, 1939.
Born, W. "Leonardo da Vinci's Ideas in the Mechanization of Spinning," in *Ciba Symposia*, 1947.
Strobino, G. *Leonardo da Vinci e la meccanica tessile*, Milan: Mostra della Scienza e Tecnica di Leonardo, 1953.

Bertieri, R. "Leonardo's Printing Presses in the Codex Atlanticus," in *Risorgimento Grafico*, 1939.
Pedretti, C. "The Art of Printing in Leonardo da Vinci," in *Linea Grafica*, 1952.

Maestro, T. "On a New Priority of Da Vinci—the Diploscope," in *Annali di Oftalmologia e Clinica Oculistica*, 1941.
Favaro, G. "The Intrinsic Muscles of the Hand as Pointed Out by Leonardo," in *Atti e Memorie R. Accademia di Scienze, Lettere, Arti di Modena*, 1942.
Esche-Braunfels, S. *Die Anatomiezeichnungen Leonardos*, Berlin, 1943; Basel, 1953.
Bilancioni, G. "The Representations of the Thyroid Gland in Leonardo," in *Archivio di Storia della Scienza*, An. IV, No. 1.
Bucher, O. "The Embryological Views and Investigations of Leonardo da Vinci," in *Vierteljahrsschrift der naturforschenden Gesellschaft in Zurich*, 1946.
Arcieri, G. "Leonardo da Vinci and Andrea Vesalius," in *Rivista di Storia delle scienze mediche e Naturali*, 1949.
Niesert, H. W. "The Gynecological-anatomical Studies of Leonardo da Vinci and Their Significance for the Development of Descriptive Anatomy," in *Zentralblatt für Gynäkologie*, 1949.
Castiglioni, A. "Leonardo da Vinci and Renaissance Medicine," in *Castalla*, 1950.
Castiglioni, A. "Leonardo da Vinci's *Trattato d'Anatomia*," in *Il Policlinico*, 1950.
Ferrero, N. "Leonardo da Vinci on the Eye," in *American Journal of Ophthalmology*, 1952.
Keele, K. D. *Leonardo da Vinci on Movement of the Heart and Blood*, London, 1952.
O'Malley, C. D., and Saunders, J. B. *Leonardo da Vinci on the Human Body*. The anatomical, physiological, and embryological drawings, with translations, emendations, and a biographical introduction. New York, 1952.
Casotti, L. "Leonardo da Vinci and Stomatology," in *Clinica Odontoiatrica*, 1952.
Belt, E. "Leonardo da Vinci's Studies on the Aging Process," in *Geriatrics*, 1952; in *Raccolta Vinciana*, 1954.
Bodenheimer, F. S. "Leonardo da Vinci as Biologist," in *Léonard de Vinci et l'expérience scientifique au seizième Siècle*, Paris, 1953.
Benedicenti, A. "Leonardo da Vinci and the Medicine of His Time," in *Atti del Convegno di Studi Vinciani*, 1953.
Pazzini, A. "The Biological Thought of Leonardo da Vinci," *ibid*.
Keele, K. D. "Leonardo da Vinci's Anatomical Drawings at Windsor," *ibid*.
Djalma Vitali, E. "Anatomy and Physiology," in *Leonardo: Saggi e Ricerche*, 1954.
Belloni, L. "On Leonardo's Thoracoparasite," in *Rendiconti dell'Istituto Lombardo di Scienze e Lettere*, 1954.
Belt, E. *Leonardo the Anatomist*, Lawrence, Kan.: *University of Kansas Press*, 1955.

Bazardi, A. *La botanica nel pensiero di Leonardo*, Milan: Mostra della Scienza e Tecnica di Leonardo, 1953.
Corti, R. "Intuitions regarding Biology and Plant Ecology in the Botanical Observations and Experiments of Leonardo da Vinci," in *Atti del Convegno di Studi Vinciani*, 1953.

I N D E X E S

CONTENTS

BIOGRAPHICAL DOCUMENTS

PLATES

* For plates bearing no page numbers, figures in italics indicate the pages between which they are to be found

DA VINCI PAINTINGS

SCULPTURE BY AND CONNECTED WITH LEONARDO

SCHOOL AND DISCIPLES OF LEONARDO

DRAWINGS BY LEONARDO

ACKNOWLEDGMENTS

The photographs illustrating the volume have been kindly furnished by the following studios:

A. C. Cooper, London – Anderson, Rome – Boissarmas, Geneva – Edizioni Brogi, Rome – F. Bruckmann A. G., Munich – F. Kleinberger & C., New York – Foto Spada, Naples – Photographic Cabinet of Windsor Castle – British Museum, London – Palazzo dell'Arte, Milan – Art Museums, Geneva – Brooklyn Museum – Gottfried Keller Cabinet, Zurich – Castello Sforzesco, Milan – Günther Beyer, Weimar – Istituto Geografico De Agostini, Novara – J. E. Bulloz, Paris – Archives Photographiques, Paris – M. Danesi, Rome – R. Gasparini, Genoa – S. A. Crimella, Milan – S. A. Dotti & Bernini, Milan – S. A. Fratelli Alinari, Florence – S. A. Lanzani & Gemelli, Milan – Savastano, New York – Silvio Pezzi, Milan – Studio A. Reali, Florence – Studio Bombelli, Milan – Studio Braun, Paris – Studio Giraudon, Paris – Studio Miccinesi, Vinci

Stampato in Italia – Istituto Geografico De Agostini S. p. A. - Novara - 1964
Printed in Italy